THE
ENCYCLOPEDIA
OF
HUMAN BEHAVIOR

Psychology, Psychiatry, and Mental Health

ROBERT M. GOLDENSON, Ph.D

Volume Two

Garden City, New York

DOUBLEDAY & COMPANY, INC.

1970

Library of Congress Catalog Card Number 68–18077
Copyright © 1970 by Robert M. Goldenson
All Rights Reserved. Printed in the United States of America

Anatomical drawings by Howard S. Friedman.

Grateful acknowledgment is made to the authors and publishers for permission to reprint excerpts from the following material:

"Emotional Deprivation in Infants," H. Bakwin, *Journal of Pediatrics*, 35:512–21, 1949, The C. V. Mosby Company.

"Criminal Genesis and the Degrees of Responsibility in Epilepsies," R. S. Banay, *American Journal of Psychiatry*, Vol. 117, pages 875–76, 1961.

The Neglected/Battered Child Syndrome, G. J. Barbero et al., Child Welfare League of America, 1963.

A Mind That Found Itself, C. W. Beers. Copyright 1907, 1917, 1921, 1923, 1931, 1932, 1934, 1935, 1937, 1939, 1940, 1942, 1944, 1948, 1953, by the American Foundation for Mental Hygiene, Inc. Reprinted by permission of Doubleday & Company, Inc.

Clinical Psychology, L. E. Bisch, The Williams & Wilkins Company, 1925.

The Psychology of Behavior Disorders, N. Cameron, Houghton Mifflin Company, 1947.

Behavior Pathology, N. Cameron and A. Magaret, Houghton Mifflin Company, 1951.

Abnormal Psychology and Modern Life, J. C. Coleman. Copyright © 1964 by Scott, Foresman & Company.

Adapted from *The Great Imposter*. Copyright © 1959 by Robert Crichton. Reprinted by permission of Random House, Inc.

Textbook of Abnormal Psychology, R. M. Dorcus and G. W. Shaffer. Copyright © 1945, Williams and Wilkins Company.

Introduction to Psychiatry, O. Spurgeon English and Stuart M. Finch. Copyright 1964 by W. W. Norton & Company, Inc.

"Experimental Demonstrations of the Psychopathology of Everyday Life," M. H. Erickson, *The Psychoanalytic Quarterly*, VIII, 1939, pages 338–53.

"The Permanent Relief of an Obsessional Phobia by Means of Communications with an Unsuspected Dual Personality," M. H. Erickson and L. S. Kubie, *The Psychoanalytic Quarterly*, VIII, 1939, pages 471–509.

"The Use of Automatic Drawing in the Interpretation and Relief of a State of Acute Obsessional Depression," M. H. Erickson and L. S. Kubie. *The Psychoanalytic Quarterly*, VII, 1938, pages 449–50.

Practical Clinical Psychology, J. Ewalt, E. A. Strecker, and F. G. Ebaugh, McGraw-Hill Book Company, 1957.

"Developmental Evaluation and the Institution of Remedial Programs for Children with Learning Difficulties," M. Frostig, The Marianne Frostig Center of Educational Therapy, 1965.

"Exploring the World of the Insane," R. M. Goldenson, *Look* magazine, September 21, 1954, pages 30–32. By permission of the editors of *Look* magazine. Copyright © 1954, Cowles Communications, Inc.

"A Case Study of Fetishism," V. M. Grant, *Journal of Abnormal and Social Psychology*, 1953, 48, 142–49. Reprinted by permission of the American Psychological Association.

The Patient in the Mental Hospital, M. Greenblatt, The Macmillan Company, 1957.

Men Under Stress, R. R. Grinker and J. P. Spiegel, McGraw-Hill Book Company, Blakiston Division, 1945.

Condensed and adapted selection from *How to Increase Reading Ability*, A. J. Harris. 4th edition,

1961. By permission of David McKay Company, Inc.

"A Psychiatrist Listens to Dysphonia Syndromes," L. Heaver, *Talk* magazine, September–October 1957, Vol. 31, No. 3. Reprinted by permission of the Speech Rehabilitation Institute.

Henderson and Gillespie's Textbook of Psychiatry edited by D. Henderson and I. R. C. Batchelor, 9th edition, London, Oxford University Press, 1962.

"The Homosexual Community," Evelyn Hooker. From *Proceedings of the XIV International Congress of Applied Psychology*. Munksgaard Press, 1962.

The Lost Weekend by Charles Jackson. Copyright © 1944, 1960 by Charles R. Jackson. Reprinted by permission of Farrar, Straus & Giroux, Inc., and Brandt & Brandt.

Handbook of Psychiatry, L. J. Karnosh and E. M. Zucker. The C. V. Mosby Company, 1945.

Mental Hygiene in Modern Living, B. Katz and G. Lehner. Copyright 1953, The Ronald Press Company.

"My Twelve Hours As a Madman," S. Katz, *Maclean's* magazine, October 1, 1953.

"Concepts of Normality and Abnormality in Sexual Behavior," by A. C. Kinsey, W. B. Pomeroy, C. E. Martin and P. H. Gebhard. From *Psychosexual Development in Health and Disease*, edited by P. H. Hoch and J. Zubin. Grune and Stratton, 1949. Used by permission.

The Disorganized Personality, G. W. Kisker. Copyright © 1964 by McGraw-Hill Book Company, Inc. Used by permission.

"The Character Structure of Sex Offenders," S. B. Kopp, *American Journal of Psychotherapy*, 1962, 16.

The Therapy of the Neuroses and Psychoses, S. H. Kraines, Lea & Febiger, 1948.

Mental Depressions and Their Treatment, S. H. Kraines. Copyright © 1957 by The Macmillan Company. Reprinted with permission.

Textbook of Abnormal Psychiatry, C. Landis and M. M. Bolles. Copyright 1946 by The Macmillan Company. Reprinted with permission.

"Narcolepsy as a Type of Response to Emotional Conflict," O. R. Langworthy and B. J. Betz. *Psychosomatic Medicine*, 6, 1944, 222–26.

"Primary Affect Hunger," D. M. Levy, *American Journal of Psychiatry*, Vol. 94, pages 644–45, 1937.

"Maternal Overprotection," D. M. Levy, *Psychiatry* (1938), 561–82. Reprinted by permission of the William Alanson White Psychiatric Foundation, Inc.

Research in Dementia Praecox, N. D. C. Lewis, 1936. Reprinted by permission of the Supreme Council, 33°, Ancient Accepted Scottish Rite of Freemasonry for the Northern Masonic Jurisdiction, U.S.A.

"Dissociated Personality: A Case Report," S. Lipton, *The Psychiatric Quarterly*, 17, 1943, pages 41–44.

Cases from *Principles of Abnormal Psychology*, revised edition by A. H. Maslow and B. Mittelmann. Copyright 1941, 1951 by Harper & Row, Publishers, Inc. Reprinted by permission of Harper & Row, Publishers.

The Practice of Dynamic Psychiatry, J. N. Masserman, W. B. Saunders Company, 1955.

Principles of Dynamic Psychiatry, J. N. Masserman, W. B. Saunders Company, 1946.

The Human Mind, K. Menninger, Alfred A. Knopf, Inc., 1945.

Case from *Psychoanalysis and Culture*, K. Menninger, International Universities Press, Inc., 1951.

Psychiatry in a Troubled World, W. Menninger. Copyright 1948 by The Macmillan Company. Reprinted with permission.

"Schizophrenic Reaction, Childhood Type," and "School Phobia," S. Mink. From *Abnormal Psychology* edited by E. Rosen and I. Gregory. W. B. Saunders Company, 1965.

"Remarks on the Effects of Anhelonium Lewinii," S. Mitchell, *British Medical Journal*, Vol. 2, page 1625, 1896.

Foundations of Psychopathology, J. C. Nemiah. Copyright © 1961 by the Oxford University Press. Reprinted by permission.

Cases from *Modern Clinical Psychiatry*, A. P. Noyes and L. C. Kolb. W. B. Saunders Company, 1963.

"Some Observations on the Functional Organization of the Human Brain," W. Penfield, *Proceedings* of the American Philosophical Society, Vol. 98, No. 5, 1954.

Psychotherapy: A Modern Theory and Practice, E. L. Phillips. Copyright © 1956. Reprinted by permission of Prentice-Hall, Inc.

Case from *Encyclopedia of Aberrations* edited by E. Podolsky. Philosophical Library, 1953.

Manual of Psychiatry and Mental Hygiene, A. J. Rosanoff, John Wiley & Sons, Inc., 1938.

Abnormal Psychology edited by E. Rosen and I. Gregory. W. B. Saunders Company, 1965.

"Group Psychotherapy in a Child Guidance Clinic," Leslie Rosenthal, *Social Casework*, Vol. XXXII, No. 8 (October 1951). Reprinted by permission of the Jewish Board of Guardians and the Family Service Association of America.

Psychology and Life by Floyd L. Ruch, Scott,

Foresman & Company. Quoted material originally appeared in *The Biology of Human Starvation*, A. Keys. J. Brozek, A. Henschel, and H. L. Taylor. Copyright 1950 by the University of Minnesota.

"A Mixture of Madness," R. Shaw, *Harvard Medical Alumni Bulletin*, October 1959, Vol. 34, No. 1, pages 38–42.

The Jack-Roller, C. R. Shaw. Reprinted by permission of the University of Chicago Press. Copyright 1930.

Mental Conflicts and Personality, M. Sherman, pages 226–27. Longmans, Green & Company, Inc., 1938. Reprinted by permission of David McKay Company, Inc.

Civilization and Disease, H. E. Sigerist. Copyright 1943 by Cornell University. Used by permission of Cornell University Press.

"The Importance of the Mother-Child Relationship During the First Year of Life," R. A. Spitz, *Mental Health Today*, 7, 1948.

Practical Clinical Psychiatry, E. A. Strecker and F. G. Ebaugh. McGraw-Hill Book Company, 1940.

Psychosomatic Medicine, 2nd edition. E. Weiss and O. S. English. W. B. Saunders Company, 1949.

The Psychology of Abnormal Behavior, 2nd edition, L. P. Thorpe, B. Katz and R. T. Lewis. Copyright © 1961 by The Ronald Press Company.

The Abnormal Personality, 3rd edition, R. White. Copyright © 1964 by The Ronald Press Company.

"Schizophrenia Associated with Addison's Disease," H. D. Wolff and P. E. Huston, *American Journal of Psychiatry*, 1959, No. 116, pages 365–67. Copyright 1959 by the American Psychiatric Association.

"Personality Features and Reactions of Subject with Migraine," H. G. Wolff, *Archives of Neurology and Psychiatry*, 37, 1937, 895–921.

"The Anticriminal Society: Synanon," L. Yablonsky. *Federal Probation*, September 1962.

Patterns of Psychopathology, M. Zax and G. Stricker. Copyright © 1963 by The Macmillan Company. Reprinted by permission.

Grateful acknowledgment is made to the following for permission to reproduce their material:

TEXT ILLUSTRATIONS

1. Adapted from *Fields of Applied Psychology* by A. Anastasi. Copyright © 1964. Used by permission of McGraw-Hill Book Company.
3. Reproduced by permission. Copyright © 1961, The Psychological Corporation, New York, N.Y. All rights reserved.
4. Reproduced by permisson. Copyright © 1947, 1961, 1962, The Psychological Corporation, New York, N.Y. All rights reserved.
5. Reproduced by permission. Copyright © 1947, The Psychological Corporation, New York, N.Y. All rights reserved.
6. From Flanagan Aptitude Classification Tests, Assembly, Form A by John C. Flanagan. Copyright © 1953 by John C. Flanagan. Reprinted by permission of the publisher, Science Research Associates, Inc., Chicago, Ill.
7. Marietta Apparatus Company, Marietta, Ohio.
8. From Ainslie Meares, *The Door of Serenity*. Courtesy of Charles C. Thomas, Publisher, Springfield, Ill., and Faber & Faber Ltd., London.
9. From Ainslie Meares, *The Door of Serenity*. Courtesy of Charles C. Thomas, Publisher, Springfield, Ill., and Faber & Faber Ltd., London.
10. Adapted from "The Physiology of Fear and Anger" by D. H. Funkenstein. Copyright © 1955 by Scientific American, Inc. All rights reserved.
13. From *Progressive Matrices*, J. C. Raven. H. K. Lewis & Co., Ltd.

14. Copyright © 1949, 1960 by the Institute for Personality & Ability Testing. International Copyright in all countries under the Berne Union, Buenos Aires, Bilateral, and Universal Copyright Conventions. All property rights reserved by The Institute for Personality & Ability Testing, 1602–4 Coronado Drive, Champaign, Ill., U.S.A.
15. Copyright by the American Orthopsychiatric Association, Inc., reproduced by permission. In part from the *American Journal of Psychiatry*, Vol. 124. pages 682–87, 1967.
16. Reprinted from the *American Journal of Psychiatry*, Vol. 124, pages 682–87, 1967.
22. After L. Carmichael, H. F. Hogan, and A. A. Walter, *Journal of Experimental Psychology*, American Psychological Association, 15, pages 73–86, 1932.
23. Adapted from *Remembering* by F. C. Bartlett. Cambridge University Press, 1932.
29. C. H. Stoelting Co.
34. C. H. Stoelting Co.
39. Adapted from The Physiology of Fear and Anger by D. H. Funkenstein. Copyright © 1955 by Scientific American, Inc. All rights reserved.
40. Adapted from *Psychology, The Fundamentals of Human Adjustment* by N. L. Munn. Boston: Houghton Mifflin Company, 1966.
43. Copyright © 1949 by Harcourt, Brace & World, Inc. Reproduced by special permission of the publisher.

44. Copyright © 1946 by Harcourt, Brace & World, Inc. Reproduced by special permission of the publisher.
45. Adapted in part from *Psychology, the Fundamentals of Human Adjustment* by N. L. Munn. Boston: Houghton Mifflin Company, 1966.
47. Adapted from "The Pathology of Boredom" by Woodburn Heron. Copyright © 1957 by Scientific American, Inc. All rights reserved.
48. Adapted from figs. 6.3, 6.4 and 6.5 ("Sociograms of three groups") from *Industrial Psy-*

chology and Its Social Foundations, revised edition, by Milton L. Blum, Ph.D. Copyright © 1949, 1956 by Harper & Row, Publishers, Inc. Used by permission of the publishers.
49. Adapted from *Psychology, the Fundamentals of Human Adjustment* by N. L. Munn. Boston: Houghton Mifflin Company.
51. Tomkins-Horn Picture Arrangement Experiment by Silvan S. Tomkins and Daniel Horn, Springer Publishing Company, Inc.

BLACK AND WHITE PLATES

1. Photo by Sponholz for the Wisconsin Primate Research Center.
2. Photo by Sponholz for the Wisconsin Primate Research Center.
3. Medical Audio Visual Department, Walter Reed Army Institute of Research, Washington, D.C.
4. Nicholas Pastore, Queens College, City University of New York.
5. By permission of Yerkes Regional Primate Research Center, Emory University, Atlanta, Georgia.
6, 7. Photos by Sponholz for the Wisconsin Primate Research Center.
8. The Psychological Corporation.
9. By permission of Norman C. Meier and the Bureau of Educational Research of the University of Iowa.
10, 11, 12, 13. Modern Clinical Psychiatry by Noyes and Kolb, courtesy of E. S. Goldensohn.
14. C. H. Stoelting Co.
15. C. H. Stoelting Co.
16. Courtesy of Philip H. Gray.
17. Photo courtesy of Bausch & Lomb, Inc.
18. Courtesy Ralph Gerbrand, by permission of Houghton Mifflin Company and George C. Harrap & Company, Ltd.

19. Photo by National Institute of Mental Health.
20. Lawrence Radiation Laboratory, Livermore.
21. William Vendivert.
22, 23, 24. "Annotations—The History of LSD-25," *Triangle*, The Sandoz Journal of Medical Science, 2, (No. 2) 117 (October) 1955.
25. Courtesy Hadley Cantril, Institute for Social Research.
26, 27. Myron Davis, *Life* magazine, © 1962 Time, Inc.
28. Stanford University.
29. By permission of Edward Adamson, Director of Art Department, Netherne & Fairdene Psychiatric Hospitals, Coulsdon, Surrey, England.
30, 31. From Ainslie Meares, *The Door of Serenity*. Courtesy of Charles C. Thomas, Publisher, Springfield, Ill., and Faber & Faber, Ltd., London.
32. National Association for Mental Health.
33. Bernard Hoffman, *Life* magazine, © Time, Inc.
34. National Association for Mental Health.
35. National Association for Mental Health. Photo by Byron Filkins.
36. National Association for Mental Health.
37. National Association for Mental Health.
38. National Association for Mental Health.
39. National Association for Mental Health.

COLOR PLATES

1. Reproduced by permission of the Dorvine-Pseudo-Isochromatic Plates, published by the Scientific Publishing Co., Baltimore, Md.
2, 3. From *Introduction to Psychology*, 3rd edition,

by Ernest R. Hilgard, © 1962 by Harcourt, Brace & World, Inc. (after Evans, 1948). Reproduced by permission of the publisher, Methuen & Company, Ltd., publisher of the British edition.

To Irene with love and gratitude

ACKNOWLEDGMENTS

The author gratefully acknowledges the invaluable contributions of Donald P. Kenefick, M.D., Director of Research and Professional Affairs, National Association for Mental Health, who reviewed the psychiatric and mental health articles; and of Sherman Ross, Ph.D., Executive Secretary, Education and Training Board, American Psychological Association, who reviewed the psychological topics. The author is deeply indebted to Robert Fudin, Ph.D., Assistant Professor of Psychology, Long Island University, for his careful and thorough research assistance. Philip S. Bergman, M.D., was kind enough to review the anatomical drawings skillfully executed by Howard S. Friedman. Special thanks are due Irene Goldenson, wife of the author, for her many helpful suggestions and her patience and fortitude in typing over 3000 pages of manuscript. Finally, an encyclopedia of this kind could not come into being without drawing, directly or indirectly, upon a vast number of sources—but here it is only possible to express blanket appreciation to the hundreds of authors listed in the References at the end of the book.

ROBERT M. GOLDENSON

HOW TO USE THIS BOOK

THE ENCYCLOPEDIA OF HUMAN BEHAVIOR is based on the need for a convenient yet comprehensive reference book covering all major phases of psychology, psychiatry, and mental health. Its purpose is to present essential information on what is surely the most important subject of all: man's knowledge of himself. There has probably never been a period when interest in human behavior was greater, nor a time when increased understanding was more urgently needed.

The book has been written with three principal objectives in mind. First, to offer a maximum amount of information within the scope of its two volumes. Second, to draw that information only from the most authoritative sources. And third, to present it in a form that will be readily understood by the student and the interested layman, yet useful to the professional worker.

The ENCYCLOPEDIA has been designed from the reader's point of view. Its over one thousand entries are arranged in alphabetical order for ready reference. Each article starts with a concise definition to establish an immediate frame of reference. All obscure or highly technical terms are briefly defined at the point of use. Illustrative cases, drawn from recognized sources, have been included in 165 articles on psychiatric disorders, to give them a personal as well as a clinical dimension. Nearly 100 other articles are illustrated with photographs and drawings.

The following suggestions are offered to enhance the usefulness of the book:

If a term or subject cannot be found among the alphabetical articles, consult the Index, which contains over 5000 entries.

If a fuller account of any topic is desired, follow the cross references from article to article.

If a comprehensive view of a major area or field is desired, make use of the Category Index, in which all topics are listed under broad headings.

CATEGORY INDEX

The following is a listing of all articles in the *Encyclopedia* grouped into related subject-matter categories.

FIELDS OF PSYCHOLOGY AND PSYCHIATRY

HISTORY OF PSYCHOLOGY

HISTORY OF PSYCHIATRY

THEORIES, SYSTEMS, SCHOOLS*

AREAS OF PSYCHOLOGY

CHILD DEVELOPMENT

* *See History of Psychology and History of Psychiatry for other Theories.*

EMOTIONS

INTELLIGENCE, MEMORY, THINKING

LEARNING

MOTIVATION

PERSONALITY AND INDIVIDUAL DIFFERENCES

PHYSICAL BASIS OF BEHAVIOR

PSYCHOLOGICAL TESTING

SENSATION AND PERCEPTION

SOCIAL BEHAVIOR

WORK AND EVERYDAY LIFE

MENTAL DISORDERS AND MENTAL HEALTH*

ORGANIC BRAIN DISORDERS

FUNCTIONAL DISORDERS

PSYCHOTIC DISORDERS

* Classification of mental disorders based on *Diagnostic and Statistical Manual: Mental Disorders,* American Psychiatric Association, 1952.

Psychophysiologic Autonomic and Visceral Disorders

Psychoneurotic Disorders

SYMPTOMS AND REACTIONS

TREATMENT TECHNIQUES AND FACILITIES

MENTAL HEALTH

MISCELLANEOUS TERMS

ILLUSTRATIVE CASES

Cases will be found at the end of each of the following articles

LIST OF PLATES

THE ENCYCLOPEDIA OF
HUMAN BEHAVIOR

M

MACROCEPHALY (**Megalocephaly**). Gross enlargement of the head due to abnormal growth of the supporting tissue of the brain.

Macrocephaly is an extremely rare congenital defect resulting in moderate or severe retardation, often with impairment of vision and severe epilepsy. The cause is not known, though it may be related to defective genes. No treatment has been found. *See* MENTAL RETARDATION (CAUSES).

MAGICAL THINKING. The tendency to believe that thought can bring about changes in reality, that "thinking makes it so."

Magical thinking stems from the tendency of young children to believe that they can create an object or bring about what they want merely through the process of thought: "If I close my eyes and think real hard, I will get that toy." The term "omnipotence of thought" is sometimes applied to this tendency. Some psychoanalysts believe the infant derives his first or "primordial" belief in his omnipotence from the elation he experiences in successfully moving his limbs.

Magical thinking often manifests itself in the dreams and daydreams of both normal and disturbed individuals. In these fantasies wishes are fulfilled and astonishing events are brought about simply through the process of imagination. Dreams are believed to be one of the most important sources of the magical practices of primitive men, many of which are preserved in our own society in the forms of superstitions. Curse words are also the result of magical thinking, and are thought to arise from the primitive belief that cursing an enemy will bring him bad luck.

Magical thinking is a feature of many psychiatric disorders, but is especially prominent in obsessive-compulsive and schizophrenic reactions. Residues of such thinking are found in the obsessive individual's preoccupation with repetitious thoughts and ritual acts. The compulsion to repeat certain prayers, for example, arises from the belief that words can be used to atone for sins, appease fate, or ward off evil. Compulsive acts frequently reflect magical thoughts, although on an unconscious level. The need to arrange one's clothes in a certain order before going to bed is an example. The rather common urge to spit when angry is believed to serve the unconscious purpose not only of showing contempt for enemies, but of annihilating or contaminating them with one's own excretions. This act can also be traced to primitive societies, although many psychoanalysts would find its ultimate origin in the anal sadistic stage of infantile development.

One of the more common symptoms in catatonic schizophrenia is a tendency to strike queer postures and make mysterious gestures. It is often difficult or impossible to tell what this behavior means, but we do know that some patients believe they can correct the ills of the world simply by standing erect, while others are convinced they can "think" an enemy to death. Even in a state of stupor, when he is completely immobile and shows no signs of thinking, a patient may still be utilizing his thoughts and wishes in a magical way. He may believe, for example, that he is involved in a life-and-death struggle on behalf of all mankind, and that his thoughts will determine the outcome. The obsessive individual's thoughts and rituals are sensible and prosaic in comparison with such psychotic magical thinking. *See* AUTISM, DEREISTIC THINKING, DAYDREAMING, OBSESSIVE-COMPULSIVE REACTION, RITUAL, SCHIZOPHRENIA (CATATONIC TYPE).

MAKE - A - PICTURE - STORY TEST (MAPS). A projective test in which the subject tells stories about cardboard figures which he selects and places against a background.

The MAPS Test, which was created by E. S. Shneidman, combines features of psychodrama, the Thematic Apperception Test, and the World Test (a play test in which the child uses miniature representations of common objects such as houses, cars, animals, fences, and people). Different forms of the test are administered to children and adults. The test materials consist of sixty-seven cardboard figures and twenty-one backdrops or stages. The figures include (in order of decreasing number) males, females, children, members of minority groups, legendary and fictitious characters, silhouettes, figures with blank faces, animal figures, and figures of indeterminate sex. The backdrops include highly structured scenes such as a living room, bedroom, cemetery, stage, nursery, schoolroom, and clinic, as well as unstructured backdrops such as clouds or a blank card.

The examiner shows the materials to the subject and usually says, "Now let's see how imaginative (or creative) you are." He then presents the backgrounds, one at a time, and asks the subject to select and place figures against one of them just as they would be in real life. When a scene has been set up, the subject is instructed to tell a story that shows who the characters are, what they are doing and feeling and thinking, and how the incident depicted was resolved. After each story the examiner asks a series of questions about the sex, age, and personality of any characters he feels the subject has identified with. He also inquires about the title of the story, any portion of it that appears unclear, or any other aspect of the instructions that have not been carried out, such as failure to resolve the story. The materials are usually intriguing to the subjects, and they enjoy the freedom of selecting their figures and backgrounds.

The examiner records the stories and marks off the placement of the figures on a special recording device so that each scene can be reconstructed later on. He also notes down the initial reaction time before placement of the first picture, as well as any figures which were first chosen and then rejected. Two types of interpretation are used. The stories are subjected to qualitative analysis of the same general type as with the TAT, and are also objectively scored according to the choice of figures, placement of figures, use of figures, backgrounds, and reaction times. These factors are then closely examined as a means of interpreting the subject's goals, desires, conflicts, values, and ego ideal, as well as his characteristic modes of behavior. Many considerations play a part in this analysis: excessive number or variety of figures, perseveration (same figure always used), crowding and bizarre placement, use of blank side of figure, superimposition of figures, excessive reaction time, and so on.

The MAPS Test has a number of applications. First, it is useful in revealing personality dynamics in both normal and abnormal subjects, and has therefore been applied in making differential diagnoses. In this connection Shneidman (1948) applied it to schizophrenic patients and found that they differed from normals in a number of objective ways—for example, isolation of figures from each other, inappropriate use of materials, and a high incidence of religious themes. Second, it has been effectively applied to the study of minority tensions (ten of the figures represent minority groups). Third, estimates of a subject's capacity for abstract thinking can be made by asking him to assort the figures into categories. Fourth, the test has proved to be a useful research instrument not only for revealing normal personality differences, but in studying hostility among mental patients (Walker, 1951), as well as the dynamics of neurotics, disturbed adolescents, homosexuals, asthmatic children, and suicidal mental patients.

MALINGERING. Deliberate feigning of an illness or disability for financial gain or to avoid hazardous or distasteful responsibilities.

Many types of disorders are simulated by malingerers. A psychosis is sometimes feigned to establish a defense in a criminal trial. Mental defect or disorder may be faked to get out of military service. Physical illness may be simulated following an accident in order to obtain compensation. It is interesting that many of these physical conditions are hard to prove on objective examination. "Back trouble" is a notable example.

Psychiatric investigations have shown that malingering may sometimes be a symptom of emotional disturbance rather than simply a calculated fraud. The man who pretends he is mentally unbalanced or incompetent is likely to be at least a warped personality, and is probably suffering from severe anxiety. Although such a person may be intentionally faking, he is also motivated by unconscious factors of which he is not aware. On the other hand, many malingerers are completely cynical and use this form of deception for gain. A substantial number are afflicted with a character disorder and may be classed as antisocial or psychopathic personalities. Such individuals show a total disregard for truth and honesty, with a complete absence of anxiety.

The problem of identifying a malingerer may not be so difficult as it first appears. Experienced observers find that he usually gives himself away through his defensive manner and inconsistent behavior. He also reveals himself through his performance on psychological tests—for example, in attempting to simulate mental retardation, he usually performs far below the level indicated by his speech and behavior during the interview. In faking a psychosis, he betrays himself by adopting behavior that is overly bizarre, or inconsistent with the usual patterns of the abnormality.

It is often hard to distinguish malingering from conversion (hysterical) reactions, yet there are a number of differentiating characteristics. The hysteric has an air of naïve, rather extraverted belief as he talks about his symptoms; in contrast, the malingerer presents his case in an aggressive, evasive, and suspicious manner. If inconsistencies in behavior are pointed out—for example, the individual may be able to drive a car even though his leg is "paralyzed" —the hysteric is blandly unconcerned ("belle indifférence"), while the malingerer becomes defensive and argumentative. The malingerer is eager to avoid examination and loath to talk about his symptoms for fear of giving himself away; the hysteric, on the other hand, likes nothing better than to dwell on his complaints, and readily submits to examinations. In doubtful cases surprise examinations or secret observations will often expose the malingerer. *See* COMPENSATION NEUROSIS, CONVERSION REACTION, BELLE INDIFFERENCE.

MANAGEMENT DEVELOPMENT (Executive Development).

In recent years the scope of industrial training has widened to include supervisory and managerial personnel, and the term "development" has been adopted to indicate that this training includes broader goals than the improvement of specific work skills. Among these goals are: a thorough knowledge of company policies, practices, and long-range objectives; ability to handle interpersonal relationships with company personnel; knowledge of the scientific principles involved in planning and organization; acquaintance with new processes and concepts in the company's field; and the development of imagination, creativity, and leadership ability. The following techniques are being used—some widely, some less widely—in attempting to reach these goals.

Conferences and Group Discussions. Applied both in supervisory and management training, the conference technique is best suited for developing the ability to solve problems and make decisions, to present new and complex material, and to modify attitudes. The conference leader plays his role according to the objectives in view. He is more active when the purpose is to give information than when the object is to improve decision-making or to bring about a change of attitude. In any case, the members of the group are encouraged to participate and interact with each other so that they can gain practice in expressing themselves, reaching decisions, and developing leadership qualities. At the same time the interchange with their peers gives them an opportunity to become aware of other people's feelings and attitudes, and to observe not only effective approaches used by others, but also to recognize faulty tendencies such as the habit of making snap judgments or the use of stereotypes.

Problem-solving Interviews. Many supervisors hold problem-solving interviews on a regular basis, or initiate them when an employee is having difficulty on the job. They usually deal with issues of a human relations nature. The employee is encouraged to develop his own ability to handle such problems by discussing them freely in a permissive atmosphere and by attempting to work out his own solutions. A similar approach is now being applied to the training of supervisors and executives, except that a consulting psychologist usually does the interviewing. In the process of facing their own difficulties, they become more sensitive to the feelings and attitudes of others, and more responsive to cues that indicate the reasons underlying their behavior. The experience also teaches these supervisors how they themselves can use the interview as an instrument in dealing with subordinates.

Case Study. In this procedure, an actual or theoretical problem is presented for group discussion. Pigors and Pigors (1955) give many representative examples—for example, a problem involving a clerical error in the hiring date of an employee, which affects his seniority status. In a case of this kind, the discussion leader encourages the group to study the incident, assemble all the facts, and determine what needs to be decided. They then make the decision and evaluate it in the light of its consequences and in relation to similar cases. In the process the participants gain valuable training in the use of discussion methods for dealing with realistic problems. They also correct some of their faulty attitudes and habits, such as resorting to smug generalizations or looking for the single "right" answer. *See* GROUP DYNAMICS.

Sensitivity Training (also called Laboratory Training, T-Group Training, Human Relations Training, Group Dynamics Training, Action Research). This technique is based on the realization that industrial leadership requires not only technical competence but skill and insight in human relations. It can be traced to Kurt Lewin's discovery of the value of group discussion in changing attitudes, and to the effectiveness of group therapy in increasing self-awareness and "sensitivity" to others. In its industrial application, a small group of high-level employees, usually executives, meet in relative isolation for several days. Although some specialists feel that participants should come from different companies, on the theory that there would be greater freedom of expression, the more common practice today is to bring together a "family group" from the same company, since they are more likely to deal with existing issues and carry their new approaches over to the job itself. In any case, the group meets under the general direction of a trained leader, whose role is primarily to set the stage for the process by providing a psychologically safe laboratory in which the participants will feel completely free to express themselves and to experiment with different ways of dealing with interpersonal problems. While the discussions are in progress, the leader usually remains on the sidelines as an observer, and the group is therefore basically on its own. Issues are suggested by the T-group itself, and as the discussion proceeds, the participants interact with each other, bringing a wide variety of feelings—anger, jealousy, admiration, irritation, overconfidence, insecurity—into play. As in group therapy, they are encouraged to examine their own reactions as well as those of the other members.

Laboratory training is a relatively unstructured affair in which the emphasis is more on the process than on solutions or decisions. Recently, A. J. Marrow (1964) has outlined a three-step procedure in which about one week is devoted to increasing the participants' self-awareness and understanding of the feelings of others; a second week focuses on the development of the group

and group participation; and a final week deals with methods of improving the effectiveness of the industrial organization through better leadership and a collaborative approach. The methods include not only discussions within the small T-groups, but lectures, demonstrations, and role-playing as well.

The object of sensitivity training is not only to develop greater insight into one's self and other people, but to improve interpersonal relationships in work and other areas of life. So far, it is difficult to assess the effectiveness of this technique. There is evidence that the group process brings forth some remarkable insights and solutions to problems, and it would seem likely that some of this would carry over to actual situations. On the other hand, there is little or no *objective* evidence of modified behavior, since the available studies have been limited to surveying the opinions of the participants.

In an investigation made by the Foundation for Research on Human Behavior in 1960, a number of employees of a large petroleum-refining company were given a "perceptionnaire" both before and after a three-day sensitivity training session. Their self-ratings indicated a significant though not large improvement in "problem-solving" and "problem diagnosis," and slight improvement in "consideration." When questioned about the effect of the training on their work and relationships, the mean rating was "quite helpful" though they felt it was only "slightly more helpful than useless" in its effects on the organization.

Marrow reports that about 70 per cent of participants in American Management Association training sessions "find it has greatly improved their managerial competence," and many of them refer to the experience as "the most important three weeks of my adult life." He also reports that subordinates and associates find the participants more confident, easier to work with, more interested in people, more concerned about group problem-solving, and better able to delegate responsibility.

Role-playing. This technique, originated by J. L. Moreno, has been applied to management development by Maier and others. The goals are similar to those of sensitivity training, and the problems presented are of the same type as in the case study method. Typically, a situation involving, say, allocation of overtime or an assembly-line bottleneck is presented in oral or written form, on film or in dramatic dialogue, and from there on the trainees assume assigned roles and attempt to resolve the problem. Each person, however, is instructed to act as he would if he were actually the supervisor or employee involved in the situation. After the role-playing, the entire group, including the observers, discusses the action. This may be followed by another enactment in which the trainees reverse their roles. The theory is that when a person puts himself in another individual's place, he sees things from his point of view and acquires a new understanding of his behavior. The technique also enables him to become aware of attitudes and behavior of his own which irritate other people or interfere with the solution of everyday problems.

Maier and his associates have also developed a multiple role-playing technique (MRP) for use with large groups. In this process, groups of six persons each are formed by having every three persons in alternate roles turn around and meet with the three persons directly behind them. Then each group is given the same problem in written form, and the members are assigned roles to play in a decision-making discussion. Finally, the solutions reached by each group are tabulated, compared, and reported to the entire body. The differences in the solutions are often highly provocative. *See* ROLE PLAYING.

Management Games. The training procedures just described are primarily devoted to the solution of personal problems. In contrast, management games are designed to give top-level executives practice in handling business problems of a complex nature. The technique has long been used as a training procedure in the armed services, and was first applied to executive training by the American Management Association in 1957. Today management games are widely used in business schools and company training programs, and there are special directories which contain complete instructions for putting them into operation. (Greene and Sisson, 1959; Kibbee, Craft and Nanus, 1961)

In management games a group of executives is divided into two or more "companies" which compete with each other in solving simulated business problems. These problems involve the same types of decision-making that are required in real life—for example, industrial sales, production scheduling, personnel assignment, and market negotiation. In the course of the game decisions must be made on such questions as issuing debentures or common stock, applying funds to research and development, or building a new plant. In any case, the terms are supplied with appropriate information covering such matters as assets, inventories, labor costs, and interest charges. They may also request further information as needed.

The teams organize themselves by selecting officials, and start their activities by making a thorough study of the problem presented. Each step in the game involves a decision which controls the operations of the firm for a specified time. This simulated period may vary from a week to a year, and the moves themselves may require as little as fifteen minutes or as much as two to three hours to make, depending on the complexity of the game. Each of the decisions involves specific effects that can be calculated manually or in some cases by the use of computers. This provides an immediate "feedback" for the players, and at the end of the game it is possible to determine which team has won. When the game is over, the various decisions are analyzed and appraised.

The players generally feel that they have greatly benefited in many ways, such as increased awareness of the interdependence of company decisions, the importance of long-range planning, the value of systematic analysis, and the need for making full use of such tools as financial statements and inventory statistics. It is reasonable to suppose that some of the experience would transfer to actual job situations, but, as Tiffin and McCormick point out, "There is as yet little factual evidence of the long-range effectiveness of management games as a training experience" (1965).

Creativity Training. In the highly competitive world of modern industry it is not enough for the managerial group to carry on the traditions of the enterprise. They must also be aware of constantly changing conditions, and be capable of originating new and imaginative ideas. There is therefore an increasing recognition of the need not only to select executives who are creative, but to develop their potential through training procedures. Only a few actual attempts at creativity training have been made, however. One recent approach, called "brainstorming", is particularly worthy of comment.

Brainstorming is a technique for stimulating the production of fresh ideas through uninhibited imagination. It may be used by individuals working alone or in groups, but the group method has been given more attention. In a typical session, a number of people gather in a room and a problem is presented. In the first, or "green light" stage, they are instructed to suggest any solution that comes to mind, no matter how far-fetched or impractical it may appear.

To avoid the inhibiting effect of criticism, no one is allowed to comment on any idea that is suggested. The object is to create a "wild and free" atmosphere in which minds will operate at a peak of creativity. The entire session is recorded and in a later meeting, known as the "red light" stage, the material is sorted out and evaluated.

The brainstorming technique was first proposed by A. F. Osborn in 1953, and has been put to use in business and industry. Typical problems are finding a name for a new product, new applications for an established product, or slogans to be used in advertising. The sessions frequently generate a rapid flow of ideas, and imaginative solutions are sometimes achieved. As a result, the procedure has been hailed as a new triumph of "free association" and as a significant contribution to creative thinking.

These dramatic claims have been somewhat dampened by laboratory tests. Although some experiments have yielded positive results, Taylor and others (1958) found that the group technique did not produce any more original ideas than did individual thinking. Nevertheless, many people still regard brainstorming as a useful method and worthy of trial.

MANGANESE POISONING. A toxic disorder produced by inhalation of volatile manganese; classified by the American Psychiatric Association (1952) under brain syndromes resulting from drug or poison intoxication.

Manganese workers occasionally suffer from permanent neurological and psychological symptoms of a serious nature. The neurological symptoms include gait and speech disturbances, tremors, and muscle weakness. About one out of five cases also exhibit such mental symptoms as restlessness, euphoria, and uncontrollable laughing and crying. No specific therapy is available. *See* BRAIN DISORDERS.

MANIA. This term has three principal meanings. First, in popular usage it refers to a violent, frenzied, deranged state of mind; secondary forms of the term are usually used: "a maniacal killer," or "the ravings of a maniac." Maniac is a sensational, inaccurate, misleading term often applied to all seriously disturbed individuals, giving the false impression that they are likely to be dangerous to others.

Second, mania is a technical term for a state of hyperactivity and excitement. In manic-depressive reactions there are three major levels of mania: hypomania, acute mania, and, most extreme, delirious mania.

Third, the term is also applied technically to denote a morbid preoccupation with a certain activity, idea, or desire; or an uncontrollable impulse to perform a certain kind of act. Here the term is used either as a suffix or in combination with other terms. A person who has a pathological urge to collect various articles is often said to have a collecting mania; one who is morbidly interested in himself suffers from egomania; an irresistible impulse to steal is called kleptomania. Other examples are: doubting mania (obsessive doubting even when the truth is obvious), nosomania (the delusion of being diseased), oniomania (the compulsion to spend money), arithmomania (the compulsion to count), onomatomania (preoccupation with words or a particular word), graphomania (a compulsive urge to write), erotographomania (to write love letters), choreomania (to dance, as in the medieval dancing mania), phanermania (to touch a part of one's body, such as the nose, which may represent the penis), poriomania (to wander, with or without amnesia, as in certain epileptic and senile patients), tomomania (to be operated on), and pharmacomania (to take medicines).

Some authors seem to have an uncontrollable urge to devise special names for the many kinds of manias.

One example is "trichorrhexomania," which simply means the compulsion to break off one's hair with the fingernails. The creator of this term was probably suffering from "nominomania," a mania for naming. *See* KLEPTO-MANIA, NYMPHOMANIA, NECROMANIA, PYROMANIA, EGOMANIA, GRANDIOSE DELUSIONS, MONOMANIA, HYPOMANIC PERSONALITY, MANIC-DEPRESSIVE REACTION (MANIC PHASE), PATHOLOGICAL INTOXICATION, HOARDING, OBSESSIVE COMPULSIVE REACTION, MASS HYSTERIA.

MANIC-DEPRESSIVE REACTION (CIRCULAR AND MIXED TYPES). Manic-depressive psychosis was long known as a *cyclic or circular illness,* but actually only 15 to 25 per cent of patients have been found to alternate between manic and depressive phases. When alternation does take place, the change-over is usually direct, although sometimes there is an interval in which the patient is free of symptoms for weeks, months, or even years.

The different phases of the disorder may vary considerably in intensity and duration—for example, a long period of severe depression may be followed immediately by a short hypomanic reaction, or acute mania may be followed by a mild depression. The sequence may also be irregular, some patients experiencing more than one depressive or manic phase before the opposite state takes over.

In mixed reactions, manic and depressive reactions occur in combination. There are many varieties, and some authorities question the value of classifying them as separate disorders, since they are all manifestations of the same disease process. These combinations include agitated depression, unproductive mania, inhibited mania, depressive mania, depression with flight, and manic stupor. In manic stupor the patient is elated but practically inactive and unproductive of ideas. In agitated depression, which is the most common combination, the patient feels extremely depressed, anxious, and threatened, and reacts to his uneasiness with restlessness and excitement. He assails himself with self-accusations while pacing the floor, wringing his hands, and bewailing his fate. *See* AGITATION.

Illustrative Case: MANIC-DEPRESSIVE REACTION (CIRCULAR TYPE)

J.M., female, forty-four, married, housewife. Diagnosis: Manic-depressive psychosis, circular type. Family history negative.

Personal History: Was healthy, active child, described as bright and quick-tempered. Outgoing, fond of social affairs, much interested in sports, put a great deal of zest into everything she did. Married at twenty; for several years was happy and well adjusted. At twenty-eight gave birth to a child after going through serious and prolonged labor. One year later developed thyroid difficulty; although operation was successful, was depressed for several months. Several years later husband suffered financial reverses and patient was greatly upset for two months. Husband's business recovered and became better than ever, and patient seemed again happy and satisfied. Two years later became excessively "blue" at monthly period, cried and said she wished she were dead. Following this became excited, overactive, and expansive. Spent money recklessly, gave parties, and indulged in several flirtations.

Finally brought to hospital and since that time has gone through two depressions and two periods of excitement. During depressed periods she is sad, dejected, engages in no activity, and speaks almost entirely in monosyllables. Frequently takes a minute or two to answer a simple question and then replies in a dismal tone with a single word. Gives the appearance of one who has the weight of the world on her shoulders. Usually sits with head bowed, brow wrinkled, hands clasped in lap. Even simplest request appears to require too much activity; when she does speak, it is only to say that she is very sick.

In manic phase we would not recognize her as the same individual. Impossible for her to remain still for an instant. She is all over the ward, dancing, singing, slapping patients and nurses on the back, pulling off her clothes, and throwing things about with absolute abandon. She writes poetry and insists on reciting it to everyone near her, monopolizes the conversation, and has a flippant reply for every remark that is made by anyone else. In these phases she becomes unusually demanding; when repulsed is abusive both in language and activity. A good bit of her behavior at this time is erotic. She tears off her clothing, talks of her sex appeal and of men trying to seduce her, and throws her arms about any man who happens to appear. (Dorcus and Shaffer, 1945)

Illustrative Case: MANIC-DEPRESSIVE REACTION (MIXED TYPE, MANIC STUPOR)

F.D., twenty-three, male, single. Admitted to hospital with diagnosis of manic-depressive psychosis, manic stupor. Behavior first noted by family to be unusual about fifteen months ago. Was exceedingly hilarious, overactive, and silly. Continued in this fashion about two months, after which he became less active and talkative but still acted childish in many respects. During past four months has become practically immobile (confines himself to his home, and more often to his room), rarely says anything, and appears to be in a fog. Expression is one of elation. (Thorpe, Katz, and Lewis, 1961)

Illustrative Case: MANIC-DEPRESSIVE REACTION (MIXED TYPE, AGITATED DEPRESSION)

Expression is one of apprehension and sadness. Is restless and agitated. Unable to sit still or go to bed. Wrings hands, runs hands through hair, paces floor. Utters phrases of despair: "Oh my God, Oh my God." and "Let me die, let me die." In three weeks lost twenty-three pounds (from 164 to 141). Although he appears to be oriented (realizes he is in a mental hospital), he fails to recognize his children. Whenever he sees his wife he cries, "Don't come near me, I am saturated with disease." He evidenced no hallucinations. (Thorpe, Katz, and Lewis, 1961)

MANIC-DEPRESSIVE REACTION (DEPRESSIVE PHASE). Depressive reactions frequently occur in persons who have a history of manic episodes, but are even more often the sole expression of manic-depressive psychosis. There are three degrees of depression: mild or simple, acute, and stuporous. These divisions, however, merge into each other. The mild type may arise imperceptibly from normal moods and may therefore go unrecognized for some time.

The major features of *simple depression* are inertia, loss of interest and enthusiasm, and physical complaints without organic basis. The patient becomes dejected, thinks of suicide, and finds that speech, work, and eating require more effort than he can manage. He avoids people and sits by himself, obsessed by ruminations about unworthiness, failure, sin, and hopelessness. He usually sleeps poorly, loses weight, suffers from digestive difficulties and constipation, and becomes preoccupied with vague aches and pains. He is likely to believe that his real disorder is physical, and to insist that his feelings of discouragement are merely due to ill health. At the same time he may attribute his ailments to punishment for misdeeds committed in the past. Although he finds thinking and speech difficult, and confines himself to few topics, he does not show any impairment of memory, disorientation, or clouding of consciousness. There is, however, a distinct retardation in thought, speech, and general activity. *See* DEPRESSION.

The retardation is greatly increased in *acute depression*. Response to questions is slow and hesitant, physical activity is almost at a standstill, and contacts with other people are rarely initiated. The patient is a picture of dejection: his body is stooped, his forehead furrowed, his face troubled, his gaze fixed downward. The vague feelings of guilt and worthlessness of the mild depressive state are now transformed into self-accusations, and he holds himself responsible for floods, depressions, droughts, and wars. Similarly, his hypochondriacal tendencies now become outright delusions, and he feels that his brain is being eaten away, his innards putrefying, and his bowels stopped up. These delusions may be accompanied by hallucinations, and he usually blames his imaginary ailments on equally imaginary sexual transgressions or other sins. Some patients develop ideas of persecution, and become sullen, morose, and hostile.

Patients in an acute depressive state lose all interest in life and, though rarely disoriented, are frequently beset with feelings of unreality. They have an air of resignation, see no hope for the future, and have no confidence in treatment. Many of them try to starve themselves because they feel unworthy of food or simply want to die. They must be constantly watched to prevent suicide.

This phase of manic-depressive psychosis reaches its most intense form in *depressive stupor*. Motor retardation is so complete that there is practically no spontaneous activity or response to external stimuli. The patient is usually mute, confused about time, place, and person, and has either an anxious or masklike expression on his face. At the same time he is preoccupied with delusions, hallucinations, and weird fantasies involving sin, death, and rebirth. He usually has to be bedridden, cannot control elimination, refuses food, and must be tube-fed. He becomes constipated, his breath is foul, and his general health is clearly on the decline.

Illustrative Case: MANIC-DEPRESSIVE REACTION (SIMPLE DEPRESSION)

A.B., eighteen years old, is a good example of a simple retarded depression. She had had a former attack one year previously, which had lasted only for about one week, and from which she made, apparently, a good recovery. The family history indicated suicidal tendencies, because a paternal grandmother had taken her life when she was sixty-two years old, and a maternal uncle had committed suicide at the age of forty-five. This family history seemed to have a definite bearing on the case.

She had always been a strong, healthy child. She was not nervous, but was quiet, shy, reserved, and not inclined to make friends easily.

She did quite well at school, but was described as being more practical than intellectual, and was especially interested in housewifery tasks. It was while she was attending a course of instruction at a School of Domestic Science that she broke down. The illness developed acutely, and three days before her admission she suddenly told her parents that she had drunk a bottle of eye lotion that had been in the house. On the night following this she got out of bed and attempted to leave the house. It is of interest that preceding the onset of her previous attack she had overheard talk about suicide. This reminded her of similar incidents in her own family, and she was depressed for about a week afterward.

At the time of her admission she was in a dull, depressed state, feeling hopeless and that she had not been learning and concentrating as she should have done. She feared in consequence that she would become a burden on her friends. Suicide had therefore seemed the simplest solution of her difficulties. She was slow in answering questions, replied for the most part in monosyllables, readily admitted that she was melancholy and that her mind was not at peace, but was occupied with morbid feelings and thoughts. As a result she had not been sleeping well. She said, "I seem just to have been slipping along, and doing my duty. I feel as if I had got everybody into a mess. I thought I was not so efficient as others, and that I could not hold my own with them." Her answers to questions were always quite coherent and relevant. She denied ever having suffered from ideas of reference, from hallucinations or delusions. Her memory, her grasp on school knowledge, and her intellectual faculties generally were not impaired. She realized that she was ill and in need of treatment in a mental hospital, so much so that she came as a voluntary patient. Her general physical state showed that she was in good condition, and there was no evidence of physical disease. She had an erosion of her lower lip, due to the eye solution which she had swallowed.

After a short period in bed she was allowed up; an attempt was made to cultivate her interest in the occupational department and this she readily took to. She found that she was able to do certain simple pieces of work comparatively well, and in consequence her self-confidence rapidly returned, and in the course of two months she made a good recovery. She put on weight, her sleep improved, she realized more clearly than heretofore what her actual difficulties had been and was able to return home.

A case such as the above illustrates very clearly a simple depressed, retarded state, occurring in a somewhat shy, sensitive girl. There is no reason to suppose that she will not be able to carry on satisfactorily in the future. (Henderson, Gillespie and Batchelor, 1962)

MANIC-DEPRESSIVE REACTION (ETIOLOGY).

Most investigators agree that biological factors of one kind or another play at least a contributory role in manic-depressive reactions. They do not, however, agree on the relative weight to be assigned to heredity, constitution, and organic pathology.

Statistical studies by Slater (1944) and Kallmann (1952, 1953) indicate that between 15 and 25 per cent of manic-depressives have close relatives who are affected with the same disorder. In addition, Kallmann (1958) has found a concordance rate (if one has it the other gets it) of 26.5 per cent between fraternal twins and 95.7 per cent between identical twins. All these figures may be compared with an expectancy of .5 per cent for the general population. He also noted that schizophrenic and manic-depressive reactions do not both occur in the same twin pair, and concluded that the manic-depressive condition is due to a genetic defect in the neuro-hormonal mechanisms that control emotion. These studies are strong evidence for hereditary predisposition, but they do not rule out environmental factors such as disturbing experiences and parental attitudes operating early in life.

Other investigators have found strong

evidence of extreme mood swings during childhood, and have concluded that they arise out of a "cyclothymic" constitution. This tendency has not been traced to any specific physiological make-up, and it is not known whether it is a hereditary predisposition, a constitutional tendency acquired in the course of early growth, or a learned behavior pattern. There is also a possibility that the mood swings are related to specific physiques. Kretschmer (1925) found that manic-depressives tend to be short, stocky, and vigorous, while Sheldon et al. (1954) observed that they may be either mesomorphic (muscular, energetic) or endomorphic (plump, extroversive) individuals. Other studies have shown that manic-depressive reactions are not confined to these personality types. Moreover, it is not known whether the physique fosters the temperamental patterns or the other way around. There may well be an interaction between the two factors. See CONSTITUTIONAL TYPES.

The question of organic pathology in manic-depressive reactions is under active investigation. So far no underlying structural or toxic condition has been demonstrated, and no clear-cut brain wave abnormalities have been found in recovered patients. On the other hand, there are indications that the reaction patterns themselves produce, or at least are associated with, abnormal brain functions. Different investigators have found hypoactivity of certain motor areas in depressed patients. Some have noted excessive excitation, overloading, and weakened inhibition of higher centers in manic states, and inhibition of lower centers in depressive states. Others have found distinctive biochemical changes in brain functioning in each state. All these phenomena may be the result rather than the cause of this disorder, although they may also feed back into it.

Psychological factors have been receiving increasing attention in recent years. Even where hereditary and constitutional tendencies exist, family background, life situation, and precipitating stresses may play an essential role in producing the actual illness. There is some evidence that both manics and depressives come from "oversocialized" homes where competitiveness, envy, and the search for social approval set the pattern. In one extensive investigation, disturbing life situations were found in at least 80 per cent of patients. Another study revealed typical precipitating stresses of three kinds: death of a cherished significant person; failure in an important personal relationship; and a severe disappointment or setback in work life. All three have the common denominator of great personal loss, and represent loss of meaning and emotional security.

Specific factors have been found to be operative in predominantly manic and predominantly depressive patients. Prior to their illness, manic patients have usually been ambitious, energetic, outgoing individuals who place a high value on achievement and conformity. Although they appear confident, they are basically overdependent; and in spite of their sociability they are often envious and hostile. They react to stress by a "flight into reality"—that is, restless activity rather than withdrawal. In the fully developed psychosis, they unconsciously attempt to deny their failures or inadequacies, and allay their anxiety and bolster their ego by proposing important projects, meddling in other people's affairs, and keeping themselves occupied every minute of the day. This process may develop to a point where both the sensory and motor systems become so overloaded that the patient becomes incoherent, wild, and finally exhausted. Many authorities believe these activities are primarily a means of warding off depression, and analytically oriented therapists suggest that in the manic stage the patient is identifying with the dominant, aggressive parent, usually the father. *See* FLIGHT INTO REALITY.

Depressed patients share the manic's conventionality and concern for the opinions of others, but tend to be meticulous, perfectionistic, anxious people who frequently belittle and reproach themselves. They have a rigid, overdeveloped conscience which makes them susceptible to strong guilt feelings and unable to express hostile impulses. As a result of these tendencies they react to disappointment, failure, or loss of loved ones by turning their anger and resentment inward. They proceed to blame themselves for their difficulties, discover that they have committed or wanted to commit a "sin" (usually trivial or irrelevant) in the past, and feel increasingly worthless.

Psychoanalysts and others have put particular emphasis on the death of a parent as a precipitating factor in this disorder, and believe that repressed hostility toward that person is the major cause of the feelings of guilt and depression. The hostility may in some cases be due to the fact that the parent placed the burden of maintaining the family's prestige on the patient. The guilt feeling may be so strong that the patient may come to believe that his own hostile feelings were responsible for the parent's death.

Recent studies have emphasized the idea that the loss of a loved one, or some other drastic change, may produce depression by depriving life of meaning. This may happen to a wife who has been discarded in favor of a younger woman, to a man who has lost or been retired from an occupation on which his whole existence has been centered, or to individuals who lose a friend on whom they have long been dependent. These cases, too, are usually aggravated by feelings of failure or guilt, and the patient may unconsciously seek to relieve his suffering by slowing down painful thought processes or by denying himself every satisfaction

of life as a means of atoning for fancied shortcomings. In some cases, the patient becomes not only depressed but agitated, and in others he tries to put an end to a life that seems bereft of all meaning and hope.

MANIC-DEPRESSIVE REACTION (GENERAL). A group of affective psychotic reactions characterized by a predominant mood of elation or depression, accompanied by related disturbances of thought and activity. The behavioral changes that occur range from relatively mild to extremely severe and uncontrolled reactions, but in most cases they appear to be exaggerations of normal tendencies rather than bizarre distortions.

Manic-depressive reactions were observed by the Egyptians, Hebrews, and Greeks. Hippocrates' descriptions of "melancholia" and "mania" were remarkably similar to our own. As early as the sixth century, Trallianus recognized that the two reactions may alternate in the same person. Théophile Bonet used the term *"folie maniaco-mélancolique"* in 1684, and Jean Pierre Falret called the disorder *"folie circulaire"* in 1854. Emil Kraepelin introduced the term "manic-depressive psychosis" in 1899, and gave a clear clinical picture of both elation and depression. Recent studies have shown that recurrent manic or depressive episodes are more prevalent than an alternation between the two, and sometimes the two states are found in combined form.

The clinical pictures of the various types will be given separately. In general, the manic patient is elated, boisterous, uninhibited, distractible, and hyperactive. He constantly proposes wild schemes, and may have delusions of grandeur. The depressed patient, on the other hand, is despondent, lonely, listless, slow-thinking, hypochondriacal, and often accuses himself of unpardonable sins. About 75 per cent of depressed cases entertain suicidal thoughts, and about 10 to 15 per cent make the attempt. Manic patients sometimes become hostile and assaultive if they are interfered with, but rarely kill anyone. Both episodes tend to be shorter than other psychotic reactions. On the average, the untreated depressive phase runs its course in nine months, and the manic phase in about three months— but the range is from a few days to a year. The episodes are briefest among adolescents and young adults. Therapy will shorten their duration in practically all cases, but there is a distinct tendency for them to recur; only 25 per cent have one attack. After an episode, the patient returns to normality and shows no evidence of mental deterioration.

Due largely to successful treatment in clinics, the rate of first admissions to public mental hospitals has dropped from 6 to 2 per cent within the past fifteen years. The rate for private clinics and hospitals, particularly for depressive cases, appears to be much higher. Most cases occur between the ages of twenty-five and sixty-five, and the median age of first admissions is forty-four. Manic episodes generally start earlier in life than depressive episodes, but are less likely to become chronic. In either case, the earlier the onset, the poorer the prognosis. Female patients outnumber male by about four to three.

Reports on the socioeconomic distribution of the disease are conflicting; some studies in this country indicate that it is most common on the lower, others on the higher occupational levels. The incidence is considerably higher in urban than in rural areas. Forty-five per cent of the hospital cases are depressed, 30 per cent manic, and 25 per cent mixed and circular—that is, alternating. For details on these types, as well as on etiology, therapy, and prognosis, see entries that follow.

MANIC-DEPRESSIVE REACTION (MANIC PHASE). Manic reactions are characterized by elation and hyperactivity, and range in degree from the mild through the acute to the delirious form. The manic state is often preceded by a brief simple depression, and there is frequent evidence of sadness and brooding lurking beneath the episode. For these reasons some authorities consider manic attacks as defenses against depression.

In the mild manic form, termed *hypomania*, the patient is highly euphoric, exhilarated, and optimistic, declaring that he never felt better in his life. He thinks rapidly, talks incessantly, and engages in tireless activity in spite of little sleep. He is effervescent, often witty, and constantly suggests ambitious but unrealistic solutions to problems with complete assurance. He is likely to telephone or telegraph other people because he finds writing too slow. The hypomanic's jokes tend to be crude and risqué, his actions uninhibited, his verbiage extravagantly phrased. He spends money recklessly and may be sexually promiscuous and drink to excess. Most of the time he displays an air of infectious good humor, but he is also dominating and meddlesome, intolerant of criticism, and becomes argumentative, irritable, and angry when opposed.

The stage of *acute mania* may develop out of hypomania or suddenly appear after a brief period of restlessness and insomnia. Euphoria increases to elation or even exaltation, and the entire tempo of life is speeded up. The patient sings, dances, laughs, and gesticulates with a total lack of self-consciousness and restraint. The "pressure of speech" is so great that he constantly declaims in theatrical tones, or orders other people about with a dictatorial manner. His "flight of ideas" may increase to a point where associations appear nonsensical and speech becomes incoherent. The thought pressure or "pressure of ideas," is ascribed by the patient to an irresistible force within his own mind, in contrast to the patient with paranoid schizophrenia, whose thoughts appear to be due to pressure from others. *See* EUPHORIA, ELATION, FLIGHT OF IDEAS, CLANG ASSOCIATION.

There is a similar increase in "pressure of activity." The patient exhibits a violent motor excitement during which he constantly interferes with other people, decorates himself with badges and medals, makes indiscriminate sexual advances, and may break up furniture or tear his clothes to pieces. His attention shifts so rapidly that he is likely to misidentify people, become momentarily confused about time and place, deliver a sermon one moment and tell an obscene joke the next. In some cases transient delusions of an expansive type may develop, usually centering around grandiose ideas of wealth or ability. He may also carry on conversations with people he imagines to be present. These periods of irrational thought and ceaseless activity may be interrupted by short intervals of insight.

The most severe type of manic reaction, *delirious mania,* sometimes develops directly out of acute mania but more often appears suddenly and without warning. In this state, the patient becomes totally disoriented and incoherent, develops vivid auditory and visual hallucinations, and engages in constant overactivity that includes screaming, shouting, gesticulating, and pacing up and down. His eyes have a peculiar glare, his features are contorted, and it is impossible to reach him. At one time he may refuse to eat and require tube feeding; at another, he may voraciously wolf down huge quantities of food. He pays no regard to his appearance, is utterly shameless and may smear his excreta on himself or the walls. If he is not given tranquilizing drugs, he is likely to become extremely destructive, dangerous, and "maniacal." Loss of sleep, poor eating habits, and violent activity put such a strain on him that he loses weight, becomes exhausted and

dehydrated, and is an easy prey to acute infections such as pneumonia and nephritis.

Illustrative Case: MANIC-DEPRESSIVE REACTION (HYPOMANIA)

More than once, letters twenty or thirty feet long were written, and on one occasion the accumulation of two or three days of excessive productivity, when spread upon the floor, reached from one end of the corridor to the other—a distance of about one hundred feet. My hourly output was something like twelve feet. . . . Under the pressure of elation one takes pride in doing everything in record time. Despite my speed my letters were not incoherent. They were simply digressive, which was to be expected, as elation befogs one's "goal idea."

[The writing of colossal letters soon proved an insufficient means of using up his energy.] I proceeded to assume entire charge of that portion of the hospital in which I happened at the moment to be confined. What I eventually issued as imperative orders were often presented at first as polite suggestions. But, if my suggestions were not accorded a respectful hearing, and my demands acted upon at once, I invariably supplemented them with vituperative ultimatums. (Beers, 1908)

Illustrative Case: MANIC-DEPRESSIVE REACTION (ACUTE MANIA)

When his wife had left, the patient soon demonstrated what he meant by "high gear." He bounded down the hall, threw his medication on the floor, leaped up on a window ledge and dared any one to get him down. When he was put in a room alone where he could be free, he promptly dismantled the bed, pounded on the walls, yelled and sang. He made a sudden sally into the hall and did a kind of hula-hula dance before he could be returned to his room. His shouting continued throughout the night, and betrayed in its content the ambivalent attitudes which the patient maintained toward his hospitalization: "What the hell kind of a place is this? A swell place? I'm not staying here. I'm having a hell of a good time. Oh, I'm so happy. I have to get going. My gray suit please, my gray coat please, my gray socks, all gray on their way, going to be gay. I'm going out as fast as I came in, only faster. I'm happier than I have ever been in my life. I'm one hundred per cent better than normal."

The following morning, after almost no sleep, the patient was more noisy and energetic than ever. He smashed the overhead light with his shoes and ripped off the window guard. He tore up several hospital gowns, draped himself in a loincloth made of their fragments, said he was Tarzan, and gave wild jungle cries to prove it. "I've tasted tiger's blood!" he roared. "I'm a success and I'm the man for the boss's job. I've made a killing and this time I will keep on going." He made amorous remarks to the nurses, accused them of flirting with him, and announced loudly, "At the present time I am not married; but my body is not for sale, regardless of the price." (Cameron and Magaret, 1951)

Illustrative Case: MANIC-DEPRESSIVE REACTION (DELIRIOUS MANIA)

M.A., an unmarried woman, twenty-six years old, was admitted to hospital in a state of great excitement. She would not cooperate in an examination, answered questions at random, talked in a fragmentary, almost incoherent way, and had no appreciation of time or place, or people around her. She tore her clothes, refused her food, jumped in and out of bed, spat on the bedclothes, and often would run up and down the ward in an aimless way. It was impossible to gain her attention. Her excitement was so intense and her co-operation so poor, that it was necessary to tube-feed her. Her mouth was in a foul condition, her tongue was thickly coated, she was careless and inattentive to bladder and bowels, and she had bruises on her arms and legs. There was no evidence of any organic disease, but physical examination on account of her great restlessness was very difficult. Her weight was 6 st. 3 lb. After a few days her mouth became much cleaner, she looked better, but she was sleeping very poorly at night, was still very restless, tended to be flighty and flippant in her talk, and was tremendously elated. She talked in a low, hoarse voice, and was difficult to follow. During any examination she would shift about in her bed, attempt to get out, play with her hair, tuck the sheets round her arms, and so on.

When asked how she was, she said, "Just daft, dearie. Knife and fork—no, they would not do it." She paid very little attention to questions, and answered more or less at random. She said she wanted "One, two, three sugars: Aunty Jinty filled her pockets —dickey birds—it's the highest—you can roll round as much as you like."

Six weeks after admission she was still restless and inaccessible, and her temperature now rose in the evenings often as high as 103° F. Two weeks later it was found that she had a swelling of her left leg, which seemed to be caused by thrombophlebitis, which reacted to treatment. This condition was accompanied by an irregular but gradually declining temperature. At this time she was constantly wetting, and a catheter specimen of her urine showed a considerable bacilluria. Gradually she became less restless, her temperature came down to normal, she began to take her food well, and slept from seven to eight hours every night. She was still flippant in her answers, and when asked what place this was, she replied, "I suppose it is a blooming hospital." What is my name? "Walter." What is my business? "Nothing at all." She then laughed uproariously, and said, "Excuse me for laughing." When asked what had caused her illness, she said, "An explosion in San Francisco," and enjoyed this reply very much. Her whole attitude was still one of great elation; her laughter was of a merry, infectious character, and there was a great deal of restless energy about her conduct.

After a period of two and a half months she was able to give a comprehensive account of the onset and development of her illness. She stated that she had no recollection of having been excessively energetic or excited. She remembered having been taken to a nursing home, but of events following this she had no remembrance until several weeks after her admission to this hospital. She also recalled that when her family doctor had come to see her she had misidentified him. (Henderson, Gillespie, and Batchelor, 1962)

MANIC-DEPRESSIVE REACTION (THERAPY AND PROGNOSIS). The first aim in the treatment of manic reactions is to control hyperactivity, and this can often be accomplished through the use of tranquilizing drugs, particularly chlorpromazine. Mild cases can sometimes be treated in day or night hospitals and some patients can even live at home, although it is important for the family to recognize that the condition is a genuine disorder and to watch the patient lest he invest his money unwisely or engage in sexual improprieties. Electroshock treatment or prolonged narcosis are used in refractory cases. These forms of treatment do not always shorten the duration of the episodes or prevent recurrence, but they do reduce the intensity of the symptoms to a point where the patient becomes accessible to psychotherapy, and where his energies can be directed into constructive channels. In addition, lithium has recently been administered to acutely manic patients, and results have been promising.

Patients who suffer from prolonged delirious mania may become so debilitated that they develop severe infectious diseases. In such cases treatment is primarily directed at the infection, but the delirium itself can often be controlled by ice packs, continuous baths or packs, and tranquilizing drugs. These treatments are most effective when they are accompanied by such psychological measures as reassurance, a quiet and unstimulating environment, and the presence of the patient's family. Disorientation for time, place, and person clears up before the hallucinations disappear, and ordinarily the patient returns to normal a short time after the fever subsides. There is no damage to the brain except in rare cases where the illness has been both severe and prolonged.

Mild depressions are sometimes treated on an outpatient basis with antidepressants, such as imipramine (Tofranil) or with one of the MAO inhibitors. The patient should not be cared for at home, however, if there is any danger of suicide. If these drugs prove insufficiently effective, electroshock therapy is administered.

In severe cases antidepressants and electroshock are often combined, and chlorpromazine is usually added in agitated depressions. Hospitalization is always required in severe depressions, not only to assure adequate nursing and frequent nourishment, but to relieve the patient of burdens and to guard against suicide.

When the patient's symptoms subside, he is given reassurance, emotional support, and psychotherapy directed at relief of guilt feelings and an understanding of the forces that precipitated the depression. Neither the depressed nor the manic patient is amenable to a deeper analytic approach. Social therapy is particularly valuable in helping patients reorganize their lives and return to usefulness.

Despite the fact that only one in four patients remains completely free from a recurrence of attacks, the general prognosis in manic-depressive reactions is favorable. The great majority of patients recover within a year without special treatment and active therapy increases the recovery rate to well over 90 per cent. Response to treatment may be slower or less complete where aggravating factors are present, such as schizoid trends, old age, or unfavorable life situations—but the presence of manic-depressive reactions in the family has been found to have little or no effect on the prognosis. See ENERGIZER, TRANQUILIZER, ELECTROSHOCK THERAPY, NARCOTHERAPY.

MANIPULATIVE DRIVE. A general drive to handle and examine objects, not clearly distinguishable from the curiosity or exploratory drive.

Early in this century many psychologists subscribed to the theory that the organism is motivated to act only by physiological needs such as hunger or sex. More recently, most investigators have come to believe that human beings, and animals as well, are also motivated by innate drives which are not dependent on physical deprivation. One of the most important of these drives is the need to investigate the environment by manipulating novel objects of all kinds, a need that may be almost as strong as the urge to seek food. While some psychologists still insist that this impulse can be tied to physical needs if it is analyzed down to its basic core, others believe it is a drive in its own right.

The manipulation drive was first reported at the end of the nineteenth century, when observers noted that monkeys handled any new objects placed in their cages. One monkey, for example, worked unsuccessfully for two hours trying to unlock an empty trunk (Romanes, 1881), and more recently Harlow and Meyers (1950) found that monkeys would repeatedly unlock hasps on a door even though they received no reward of any kind (PLATE 2). Similarly, young children who are placed in a strange room with a set of toys will almost immediately start to examine and manipulate them. Piaget (1952) found that infants of four or five months of age will learn to pull a string to set a hanging rattle in motion; by five to seven months they will enjoy removing a cloth that covers their face; and between eight and ten months they will look for objects placed beneath or behind other things. In addition, ten-month-old infants will examine the shape, texture, weight, and size of objects by pounding, banging, and biting them. Brighter children usually do more exploring and manipulating than duller children.

These and other observations are frequently cited in support of the idea that manipulation is an independent drive which brings its own satisfactions. While some psychologists attribute the drive to a need for stimulation—as in playing solitaire to prevent boredom—others believe it satisfies an inner urge to become acquainted with the environment. It is therefore difficult if not impossible to differentiate the manipulative drive from the curiosity drive and the exploratory drive, although attempts have been made to do so. It may well be that the three are different aspects of the same fundamental drive.

But whatever the basic status of manipulation, there is no doubt that the child who is limited in his activities and kept from expressing this tendency will feel acutely frustrated and unhappy. Moreover, if he is persistently restricted he will not only fail to learn about the world, but will feel uncomfortable if not threatened by novel situations of any kind. But the child who is given ample opportunity to investigate his surroundings and play with a variety of stimulating toys will be almost certain to develop his skills and attain a sense of competence and self-confidence in dealing with both things and people. See CURIOSITY DRIVE, EXPLORATORY DRIVE.

MAPLE SUGAR URINE DISEASE. A rare disorder affecting amino acid metabolism shortly after birth, and leading to mental retardation. It is believed to be due to a single recessive gene.

The name was suggested by the characteristic maple-syrup odor of the urine, which shows excessive secretion of some amino acids (valine, leucine, isoleucine) and deficiency of others. Within the first few weeks of life the infant appears spastic, loses the Moro reflex (a massive "embracing" reaction to a sudden stimulus), and suffers progressive deterioration of the brain. Until recently it was taken for granted that the child would die within a few months, but some promising experiments with diets low in certain keto and amino acids have been conducted. See MENTAL RETARDATION (CAUSES).

MARASMUS. A gradual wasting or withering of tissues. The term is used in psychology to denote the physical effects of emotional deprivation.

Infants raised in cold, impersonal institutions and in homes ridden with tension and anxiety tend to become withdrawn and lethargic, and in extreme cases literally waste away. As late as 1919, about one half of the mortality among institutionalized infants under one year was attributed to marasmus. These children usually received adequate physical care, but were deprived of "mothering" and failed to receive warm, personal attention. They were also deprived of the psychological and physical stimulation which children receive in normal family life. As a result they became apathetic and depressed, had little interest in food, and showed diminished muscle tonus and reflex responses. Some of these children developed severe cases of marasmus.

In recent years efforts have been made to introduce more personal and individual care into institutions so that all the children would be provided with the affection and stimulation they need. Although the emotional and psychological climate varies greatly from institution to institution even today, the extreme reaction known as marasmus is believed to occur only rarely. *See* MATERNAL DEPRIVATION, MOTHERING.

Illustrative Case: MARASMUS

Alan Scott weighed nearly eight pounds at birth. On admission, at five and a half months, he weighed ten pounds. At three months, Alan had developed loose, foul stools, continuing for ten weeks and accompanied by vomiting. During this time, he lost two pounds, and he was urgently referred to us by the local pediatrician. Alan was a severely marasmic infant who showed no overt reaction to external stimulation, mouthed his fingers, and made chewing motions with his mouth. He did not make eye contact with persons or objects; when he was too weak to move his head, he rolled his eyes away.

Intensive tests for intestinal or other abnormalities that might be causing his diarrhea did not yield any explanation for Alan's symptoms. No pattern could be found in Alan's feeding, vomiting, or comfort responses, and his life was severely threatened. He was initially maintained by intensive intravenous, caloric, and nutritional supplementation as well as oral feeding. During the first three weeks of hospitalization, his weight remained the same. In the next three weeks, though, there was a slow but definite growth to eleven pounds four ounces.

On Alan's admission, Mr. Scott was and had been away for some weeks serving in the National Guard. Mrs. Scott had been entirely unprepared for the bereavement she felt when her husband left. She cried as she had when her childhood home dissolved because her father developed tuberculosis. When she was so bereaved, Alan turned his eyes away from her, stopped smiling, and "refused" to eat and gain weight, thus defeating her plan to prove herself a good mother by fattening him up while Mr. Scott was away.

Attempts to get help from her mother had ended when her mother told her, "I have nothing to give you. They raise children differently today." Her mother-in-law had said, "I raised mine. I can't see why you can't raise yours." Even before he went away, her husband had been spending many nights with the "boys." Finally, she had depended completely on Alan for proving she was good. He, too, had failed her, and now seemed about to desert her fully—in death. When her pediatrician had said there was nothing wrong with Alan, she made the inevitable inference that *she* was Alan's trouble.

Mrs. Scott's interviews with the social worker were full of bitter, angry denunciation of all the people who could have helped and "wouldn't," and of increasing spitefulness to her husband for being undependable in the past months. She wanted to be a good wife and mother and, clearly, she had not thought that her failure was in any way her own responsibility. She had conflicting attitudes that made her want to master and to escape the tasks of motherhood.

A crisis occurred in the hospital ward when Alan vomited while Mrs. Scott was feeding him. She tried to corner and ensnare us all into criticizing and blaming her. She tried the ward nurse, the pediatrician, and the social worker, but the team held firm. We told her that none of us knew why he vomited; he also vomited when the nurse fed him. Then we asked her to help us find out when and why he did this.

One time, Mrs. Scott fed Alan while her mother-in-law was there. He vomited. She realized she had been concerned with her mother-in-law instead of Alan. For the first time, she told her mother-in-law to keep her anxious criticisms to herself, especially since her mother-in-law had refused her previous request for help.

Shortly thereafter she told us that Alan was taking her in with his eyes. Soon, the nurses could feed him the milk for a while; things were going to be all right. Her cue reading of Alan's needs appeared spontaneously. She stopped poking him and pushing him, and she moderated her over-stimulating demands for his attention. When she looked at him, she smiled.

Both Mr. and Mrs. Scott spoke of lifelong lack of confidence. Mr. Scott felt like a boy; at sixteen, he had had to assume responsibility for running the farm when his father went to a state hospital. Mr. Scott wanted to be proud of his wife and son, but things had been too tense. His main status in life came from the National Guard, but even there he feared promotion, lest his men sense his lack of confidence and, therefore, despise him. Mr. Scott refused to see anything hard or unpleasant, and he was shocked when Mrs. Scott told him how she had felt during and since her pregnancy. He was also pleased, though, because to him, her anger was a measure of his importance. (Barbero et al., 1963)

MARIJUANA. A drug, medically termed cannabis indica, derived from the hemp plant and taken primarily in cigarette form to obtain pleasurable effects.

In Eastern countries preparations of marijuana, also known as hashish, bhang, and charas, are chewed, smoked, or drunk. There has recently been a sharp increase in the number of young people in the United States and other Western countries who are smoking "reefers," or "pot," as they call it. An estimated 25 to 40 per cent of college students experiment with the drug, but the majority try it on no more than one to four occasions. Inhalation of marijuana produces a state of euphoria and exhilaration, during which the smoker talks volubly and feels increasingly self-confident. This state is usually followed by pleasurable relaxation and sensations of drifting or floating on a cloud.

Psychological tests have demonstrated that in spite of feelings of greater capability and efficiency, practically all abilities—motor, intellectual, and perceptual—are actually diminished. This combination of increased confidence with reduced competence is a dangerous one, and often leads to reckless driving, impulsive antisocial acts, and sexual misbehavior. Marijuana smoking is reputed to increase sexual adequacy, but this is based more on psychological than on physiological effects, since the smoker simply feels more self-assured and less inhibited.

In contrast to the opium addict, the marijuana user does not become physically dependent on the drug, nor does he acquire an increased tolerance which would lead to more and more smoking to get the same effect. Moreover, the habit can be given up without experiencing withdrawal symptoms. For these reasons the drug cannot be said to produce a true addiction, although it is sometimes described as addictive. The term habituation is more accurate.

Marijuana does not appear to lead to physical deterioration. Nevertheless many users react in unpredictable ways. It sometimes produces pathological intoxication and the disturbed behavior that goes with it; and it may even precipitate an acute psychotic reaction in predisposed individuals. Louria (1967) quotes a study in which "one subject smoked one cigarette and became restless, agitated, dizzy, fearful of his surroundings, afraid of death, and had three short attacks of unconsciousness." He comments, "That is not my definition of an entirely safe drug."

The social and personal effects of prolonged use may be highly injurious. It may lead to psychological dependence, retreat from normal activities, escape from reality, and association with undesirable persons who serve as smoking companions or suppliers. But probably the greatest single danger lies in the fact that marijuana smoking lowers the barrier to the use of drugs in general, and the smoker may be led to seek even greater "kicks" by trying morphine or heroin: "It does often start an individual in the morass of drug use; whether he moves on or stops depends upon him and his environment" (Louria).

Illustrative Case: MARIJUANA INTOXICATION

A classic example is that of a twenty-five-year-old single young man brought to one of us by his father. The father reported that the patient imagined people were trying to kill him, that he could see his girl friend with her throat cut, and could smell gas coming from his mattress. He also felt that he had been castrated. The patient stated that he was being tricked, that automobiles on the street jumped at him, and that somebody was giving him electric shocks as he walked down the street. Background revealed that the patient was a temperamental, unstable, fearful, and imaginative child who made few friends and had a poor school record. At the age of thirteen his right testicle was accidentally injured. Shortly after this he began to drink whisky and beer and to run around with the wrong class of youngsters, apparently attempting to compensate for his feelings of inferiority exaggerated by the above injury. During this time he would frequently get into fights and was usually beaten, further adding to his sense of inferiority. He began to take marijuana following a series of family quarrels over his behavior. At the time of admission to the hospital the patient was extremely apprehensive, hallucinating,

and fearful. He was lewd and confused. Spontaneous activity was almost entirely in reaction to his hallucinations. On withdrawal treatment in the hospital, his symptoms very rapidly cleared up, and within a week of admission he was entirely free of the psychiatric symptoms. Attempts to go further into the psychogenic background were resisted by the patient and his father, and he was removed from the hospital nineteen days after admission. This case is a rather typical example of marijuana intoxication, illustrating the instability present in most of these individuals and the fact that patients use marijuana to obtain a lift and bolster their ego. (Ewalt, Strecker, and Ebaugh, 1957)

MARITAL ADJUSTMENT. There appears to be wide agreement among specialists that while marriage is the richest and most rewarding of all human relationships, it is also the most complex and requires the greatest amount of effort. In spite of the difficulties involved, there seems to be no decline in the "popularity" of marriage as an institution. It is an interesting fact that the United States, which has one of the highest divorce rates in the world, also has one of the highest marriage rates: over 90 per cent marry, 13.5 per cent more than once.

The marriage manuals of our day tend to stress the following factors as most essential to a satisfactory adjustment: developing a core of shared experiences, interests, and especially values, with each partner respecting the individual aims and activities of the other; maintaining open lines of communication for the expression of thoughts, feelings, and differing points of view; working out effective decision-making techniques and methods for settling disagreements; attaining mutual sexual gratification, with respect for each other's individual needs; discussing expectations, both before and after marriage; clarifying roles and responsibilities of each of the partners; gradually learning to understand each other's temperament, attitudes, and shortcomings in or-der to reach a constructive adaptation of the two individual personalities to each other.

A number of large-scale investiga-tions have brought to light many of the basic factors which have made for good adjustment in marriage. The most widely quoted are Terman and his as-sociates' study of 792 representative couples in 1938, and Burgess and Cot-trell's study of 526 couples in 1939. In both instances an index of marital happiness was first established, then a marital happiness prediction scale was constructed on the basis of factors pres-ent in the backgrounds of the couples. Taking the two studies together, the factors found to be most predictive of marital happiness were: happiness of the parents' marriage, absence of in-tense or persistent conflict with par-ents, attachment to parents and siblings, parental frankness about sex, firm but not harsh discipline in childhood, ad-vanced education, and especially a happy childhood: "According to our data, no other item of information re-lating to the background is more signif-icant. It far outweighs such items as adequacy of sex instruction, religious education, adolescent 'petting,' or even premarital intercourse." (Terman et al., 1938)

Other studies tend to confirm these findings. In addition, Kelly (1939) gave 82 couples a marital happiness predic-tion test made up of background-per-sonality items during their engagement period, and gave the same couples a marital happiness test two years *after* marriage. The correlation between the two tests was .59 for husbands and .56 for wives, showing that it might be possible to predict success in marriage with some accuracy. Burgess and Wallin (1944) obtained similar results for 646 couples tested during the engagement period and after three to five years of marriage. These studies indicate that the kinds of experiences a person has

had and the kind of person he is determine whether or not he is a good marital risk. However, even though the correlations are positive, they are not high enough to warrant giving them a great deal of weight in individual guid-ance.

Fruitful studies have also been made of specific aspects of marriage, as in-dicated by the following summary:

Preparation for marriage. In the past thirty years there has been a substan-tial increase in the number of marriage and family courses offered in high schools, colleges, Y's, churches, and community centers. These courses cover a variety of topics: dating, engagement, money matters, sexual relationship, in-terests and hobbies, religion, adjustment techniques, child-rearing, etc. A study conducted at the Pennsylvania State University (Adams and Packard, 1946) has shown that students who take such courses and receive premarital counsel-ing not only feel more confident than others about their choice of a mate, but tend to achieve a substantially higher record of marital happiness. This is strong evidence that people can be ed-ucated for marriage.

Courtship and engagement. It is gen-erally agreed that this is a testing pe-riod when the couple should have a full opportunity to become acquainted, explore interests and values, discover areas of agreement and disagreement, and test their responsiveness to each other. Studies show that this process takes time, and both length of ac-quaintance and length of engagement period correlate highly with marital suc-cess. Hasty marriages have an extremely poor record—which is one reason why the divorce rate reached an all-time high just after World War II.

Age. Marriages contracted before age twenty or twenty-one are far more hazardous than those contracted in the middle twenties, due to the fact that many teen-aged couples have failed to achieve the level of emotional maturity, independence, self-knowledge, and skill in human relations that successful marriage requires. All important adjustments—in the areas of sex, in-laws, friends, finances—take longer and are more difficult in early than in later marriages. (Landis, 1946)

The fact that the average marriage age has been dropping for several decades (it was 22.8 for grooms and 20.3 for brides in 1960, 24.3 and 21.3 in 1930, 26.1 and 22 in 1890) is often cited as one of the reasons for the high rate of marital breakdown in this country (now about one in five marriages). Beyond the middle or late twenties, however, age makes little difference.

Baber (1953) has found that 75 per cent of college men wanted their wife to be about three years younger than themselves and 94 per cent of girls wanted their husband to be about four or five years older. However, age discrepancies, at least up to a difference of ten years, have been found to have little relation to marital happiness. (Locke, 1951)

Sexual experience. Results here are inconclusive. Terman et al. (1938) found a low positive correlation between premarital relations and marital happiness, but a study by Reevy (1959) indicated that sexually active students generally obtained lower than average scores on marital happiness prediction tests. At any rate, what counts most is the individual sexual relationship between the husband and wife, not their adjustment to others before marriage.

Sexual Adjustment. Marriage specialists fully recognize the need for sexual fulfillment on the part of both husband and wife, and its basic importance for successful marriage. Studies show a close relationship between sexual agreement and marital happiness, but full sexual harmony and satisfaction frequently take months, even years, to achieve—partly because sex adjustment involves the *total* relationship between the partners and partly because the sex drive reaches its peak earlier in men than in women (according to Kinsey, before twenty in men and after thirty in women). The most frequent causes of poor sexual adjustment are: fear, inhibition, and disgust instilled during childhood; misinformation and lack of sex education; haste and lack of expressed affection on the part of the husband; traumatic or anxiety-provoking sexual experiences before marriage; the belief that good adjustment "just comes naturally" and does not require time and effort. *See* SEX DRIVE, FRIGIDITY, IMPOTENCE.

Economic Factors. Money management is one of the most frequent grounds for complaint but rarely the most serious. Studies show, however, that it may be a focal point for deeper frictions. Steadiness of income and low indebtedness are generally more important than amount of income (Williamson, 1952). Couples who agree on how to spend the family income have been found to have a better than average record of happiness in marriage, but personal preference and ability should determine whether the husband or the wife takes charge of budgeting and bill-paying. Home economists urge that girls study family finance before marriage, since wives do 80 per cent of the buying in America. Women who work before marriage have been found to have a better than average chance for marital success, not only because they have learned to deal with people but because they are likely to have a realistic attitude toward money.

Children. According to Burgess and Cottrell's study, a similar desire for children augurs well for marital happiness. People who do not want children are generally poor marital risks, and those who have children without wanting them are still poorer. A generation ago about 10 per cent of American marriages were involuntarily infertile —about 35 per cent of these were due to the husband. Recent advances in treatment, including psychotherapy as well as medical techniques, are now making it possible to cure about a third of these cases. *See* INFERTILITY.

Sixty per cent of couples who get a divorce do not have children—nevertheless, counselors do not advise people to have a child to try to mend an ailing marriage. Even among reasonably happy couples, disagreements on child-rearing are quite common. The most frequent complaints are these: the husband complains that the wife pampers the baby (and neglects him!); the wife claims that the husband is too strict or does not help care for the children; and each complains that the other undermines his authority. The trend today, however, is toward sharing the responsibility and recognizing that all children need and profit from a close relationship with both parents. Landis and Landis (1963) have found that almost twice as many couples who are in basic agreement on child-rearing rate themselves "very happy," in comparison with couples who agree only half or less than half the time.

Religion. There are fewer marital breakups among people who belong to a religious institution than among those who do not, partly because religion fosters values that make for harmony, partly because religious activity is itself a cohesive force, and partly because religious institutions discourage divorce or offer marriage counseling. Terman and his associates found that far more couples rate themselves "very happy" when they agree on the expression of religion than when they disagree—and the riskiest marriage of all is the one between a deeply religious person and a completely irreligious individual.

As a whole, intermarriages have a far poorer record than marriages within a denomination when the partners are immature, but the record among mature and thoughtful couples is at least as good as average. As McGinnis (1967) points out, "The prime consideration may not be the name of the denomination to which husband and wife belong, but whether they agree on the basic values of life."

Personality. Happily married people tend to have well-matched temperaments—but "matching" does not necessarily mean they must be identical or even similar, for dissimilar people often get along well because they complement each other and meet each other's needs (Winch, 1955). The Terman studies indicate that happily married women tend to be kindly, helpful, careful about money, fairly conventional, quietly confident, and not unduly concerned about the impression they make on others; happily married men tend to be emotionally stable, well-organized, co-operative, fairly conservative, and they also like to take responsibility, show superior initiative, and treat women as equals.

Jacobson (1952) compared divorced couples with happily married people and found that among the divorced the husband often insisted on old-fashioned domination while the wife wanted an equal voice; and among the happily married couples, responsibilities tended to be shared on an equal basis. In another study, Popenoe (1950) found that only 47 per cent of well-educated couples could be rated happy when the wife dominated, 61 per cent when the husband was in full control, and 87 per cent when they were on an equal footing. Locke has concluded that when both partners are fully co-operative, they may achieve happiness under the most adverse external circumstances. But even in marriages that are basically democratic, it has been found that the wife tends to look to the husband for leadership more often than the husband looks to the wife. (Kelly, 1941)

MARRIAGE COUNSELING. Counseling devoted to the solution of problems arising in the marital relationship. In its broadest sense the term also includes premarital counseling and divorce counseling. Premarital counseling aims at deepening the understanding of all aspects of the marital relationship, so that the individual will be better prepared for the undertaking. Divorce counseling is undertaken after a couple has already decided on this final step; its purpose is to help the couple handle the emotional, practical, and, if they have children, parental problems that arise during this period.

A number of general factors have set the stage for the development of marriage counseling as a distinct specialty. First, people in general demand more from marriage than ever before —more happiness, more fulfillment, more mutuality—and are ready to seek help when it falls short of expectations. Second, ours is a psychological age which recognizes the value of professional assistance with problems of human relations. Third, these problems are especially acute at a time when the marriage relationship is not rigidly governed by custom, convention, and traditional values. Fourth, the high divorce, separation, and desertion rates of today have brought the need for marriage counseling to the fore. Fifth, there has been a growing recognition that a relationship as complex, as sensitive, and as vital as marriage should be served by a corps of specialists who are prepared by training and experience to apply sound principles of counseling.

Currently marriage counseling is provided by three types of practitioners. The largest category consists of professional people who deal with marital relationships in the course of their regular work: physicians, psychologists, psychiatrists, clergymen, social workers, lawyers, and teachers in the family life field. Some of them approach marital problems from a limited point of view, but an increasing number are receiving broad training in counseling and human relations as part of their professional preparation. The second category includes the counselors on the staff of an organization devoted specifically to marital relationships, or in family service agencies offering help with the entire range of personal and family problems. These counselors are usually qualified social workers who function under supervision and who call upon consultants from other professions when needed.

The third group comprises the small but growing number of specialists who carry on a private practice in marriage counseling, often in combination with other professional work such as psychotherapy, teaching, or medical practice. Many of these specialists are members of the American Association of Marriage Counselors in addition to their other affiliations. Since this field has been wide open to charlatans in the past, the Association has established a set of standards and qualifications for the profession. These include a minimum of a masters degree in social work; an M.D.; a Ph.D. in psychology, sociology, or a closely related field; or a B.D. or other recognized graduate degree from a theological seminary, plus an adequate clinical orientation. In addition, the candidate should have at least three years of experience in his professional practice; and, if possible, a year's clinical internship in a center that offers professional training in marriage counseling.

The process of marital counseling varies from practitioner to practitioner, but a few general principles are widely recognized. First, the counselor's responsibility is not to advise, admonish, or dictate, but to help the couple "reach" and understand each other so that they can arrive at their own solution. Second, he usually sees the partners separately during the first sessions, and encourages them to express their feelings freely by creating an atmosphere of interest and acceptance. Third, this unburdening process not only affords a sense of relief, but helps them see the issues in a clearer light. The counselor may then urge each of the partners to abandon an attitude of blame and instead to recognize how he himself might have contributed to the problem. Fourth, as he comes to understand the points of view of the individual partners, and to recognize the sources of their difficulty, the counselor begins to act as a communication link, interpreting feelings and attitudes of each partner to the other. Fifth, he encourages the partners when they make suggestions that might lead to changing their behavior or testing out a new relationship. Sixth, when he feels they are arriving at a meeting ground, he usually sees them jointly, acting as a catalyst as they work through the issues together. If, however, a break appears inevitable, he uses the joint discussions to help them face this decision together and without undue recrimination.

This entire process takes many interviews, since the problems have usually been building up over a long period of time and are often based on deep-seated personality tendencies. If it becomes necessary to trace these tendencies to their origin, the counseling process blends into psychotherapy. In that event the counselor may himself apply the psychological treatment, if he is equipped to do so, or he may refer one or both of the clients to a psychiatrist or clinical psychologist. See MARRIAGE THERAPY.

MARRIAGE THERAPY. Psychotherapy directed to improving the marital relationship, and "centered on the effort to alter the psychodynamics and behavior of two persons who are married." (Sager, 1966)

The possibilities inherent in marriage therapy have only been recognized in the 1960s, although its principles and approaches stem from a variety of sources. Among these are marriage counseling; Oberndorff's psychoanalytic treatment of a case of folie à deux in a married couple, and his treatment of married couples in succession; Mittelmann's simultaneous analysis of marriage partners in different sessions; experiments on joint treatment of couples; studies of small-group dynamics; and group therapy of families, as developed by Ackerman, Bell, and Midelfort. See FOLIE A DEUX, FAMILY THERAPY, GROUP DYNAMICS.

According to Sager, seven general methods are currently being explored; (1) successive treatment of husband and wife; (2) simultaneous treatment in separate sessions ("concurrent therapy"); (3) simultaneous treatment in joint sessions ("conjoint treatment"), sometimes with concurrent individual treatment ("combined therapy"); (4) therapy conducted by two therapists, each seeing one spouse, but conferring from time to time ("collaborative therapy"); (5) treatment of each spouse by a separate therapist, with joint or "four-way" sessions involving both analysts and both patients; (6) various types of group therapy, such as groups composed of couples with one therapist and groups with co-therapists; (7) family therapy oriented toward the parental relationship rather than the children.

In conjoint and combined therapy, treatment is directed to the "sick marriage" and dependent on the couple's awareness that they have a problem. The joint sessions are especially effective in eliciting reactions based on childhood relationships, but the greatest advantage of seeing the couple together is that their defense mechanisms and methods of dealing with each other come quickly to the fore and enrich the therapist's knowledge of the dynamics operating within and between them. Moreover, historical material is often readily available, since each spouse can fill in the other's gaps and correct distortions of memory.

Joint sessions may be conducted on different levels. They can be primarily cathartic, giving each partner an opportunity to air his grievances in order to uncover the sources of discord. They can be used to work through specific problems, such as "Who's in charge?" or to discover where the marriage is running smoothly and where clashes occur. Or the sessions can be conducted on a deeper level, and focused on free associations, dreams, unspoken communications, and the origins of defensive behavior.

Various investigators have suggested that the conjoint approach is often effective when individual therapy fails, when distorted attitudes threaten to disintegrate the family, and when the relationships can be manipulated to produce greater harmony. On the other hand, triadic sessions may be too threatening for some mates, or one mate may use the session to attempt to destroy the other. They are also contraindicated if one of the patients is strongly opposed to maintaining the marriage.

As in individual therapy, no single treatment approach can be recommended for all types of cases. Each situation must be evaluated individually and handled flexibly. Sager suggests that although individual sessions alone or joint sessions alone may often prove helpful, there are many instances where a combination of the two would be even more effective. He himself typically sees his patients in weekly conjoint sessions and also weekly individual sessions, though in some cases only the primary patient is seen individually. It usually takes three initial sessions to elicit the symptoms, evaluate the difficulties and potentialities of the relationship, and gather information on the history of the marriage. Every important aspect of the relationship is covered, including prior expectations, obligations engaged in before and during the marriage (the "marriage con-tract"), role perceptions of both spouses, how well they are filling their roles, origins of friction, extent of complementarity, relationship of each spouse to his parents and siblings, whether the marriage is repeating themes from the parents' marriages, emotional attitudes toward the spouse, and relationships of each spouse to the children. The early conjoint sessions are devoted largely to broadening and deepening communication. An impartial attitude is maintained, and suggestions aimed at modifying the couple's attitudes or behavior are avoided until communication and transference between the therapist and both parties are well established.

MASCULINE PROTEST. A term applied by Alfred Adler to an urge to escape from the feminine role in life.

The masculine protest occurs primarily in women but may also be found in men. Among women it consists of attempting to take over the supposedly superior position of the male, or at least to adopt characteristics which are associated with masculinity, such as aggressiveness, masculine dress, male mannerisms, and sexual freedom. In males it takes the form of an extreme emphasis on self-assertiveness, conquest, and power over other people.

Adler (1924) interpreted the masculine protest as an overcompensation for feelings of inferiority. In men it arises from feelings of inadequacy, insecurity, and infantile doubts as to whether they are really males. The drive is particularly significant in women, however, and the term masculine protest is usually applied to their desire to compete with men and deny their own femininity. It is a form of rebellion against the lower status accorded women in our culture, and the sense of inferiority which it generates.

Adler considered the masculine protest a prime motive in neurotic disorder, for it sets up an unrealistic and distorted goal—a "fictive" goal, to use Adler's term—that interferes with relationships to others. Instead of using the normal feelings of inferiority, which Adler believes exist in everyone, as the motivating forces for constructive behavior, the neurotic woman or man develops an excessive, insatiable drive to be masculine in the false sense of dominating others. This goal is substituted for healthy motives such as friendship, love, and social interest.

MASCULINITY-FEMININITY TESTS. A number of tests have been designed to measure the degree of masculinity and femininity. The first to be developed, and the most comprehensive, is the Attitude-Interest Analysis Test of Terman and Miles, usually called the Masculinity-Femininity Test (1938). More recent tests, such as the scales included in the Strong Vocational Interest Blank, the Minnesota Multiphasic Personality Inventory, the Guilford-Zimmerman Temperament Survey as well as the Gough Femininity Scale, are based on fewer and more limited items. These tests have some value in their specific context but do not correlate highly with each other.

All these tests are based on the common principle of comparing men and women on responses that have proved most characteristic of each sex in recent American culture. The Guilford-Zimmerman Survey presents an inventory based on questions of the yes-no variety; one of the ten personality traits tested is masculinity-femininity. Among the characteristics indicative of masculinity are: masculine activities, not easily disgusted, hard-boiled, inhibits emotional expression, and little interest in clothes and style. Femininity is judged in terms of such characteristics as interest in feminine activities and vocations, easily disgusted, fearful, romantic, and emotionally expressive. The Strong Blank includes a masculinity-femininity scale based on interest patterns found to be highly characteristic of men and women.

The Masculinity-Femininity scale of Terman and Miles was based on particularly extensive research. In seeking test items that would successfully discriminate between the sexes, they first searched the psychological literature for types of test material that yielded the most marked sex differences, then prepared a preliminary set of items which were administered to elementary, high school, and college students, as well as unselected adults, members of different occupations, and a number of special groups such as athletes, juvenile delinquents, and adult homosexuals. On the basis of this research they retained items that yielded significant differences, and constructed a seven-part test consisting of word association, inkblot association, information, emotional and ethical attitudes, interests, opinions, and introvertive response. The scale proved successful in differentiating between male and female groups at all age levels from teen-agers to octogenarians, and threw considerable light on the more prominent sex differences in our culture. Here is a portion of Terman and Miles' summary of these differences:

"From whatever angle we have examined them the males included in the standardization groups evidenced a distinctive interest in exploit and adventure, in outdoor and physically strenuous occupations, in machinery and tools, in science, physical phenomena, and inventions; and from rather occasional evidence, in business and commerce. On the other hand, the females of our groups have evidenced a distinctive interest in domestic affairs and in esthetic objects and occupations; they have distinctly preferred more sedentary and indoor occupations, and occupations more directly ministrative, particularly to the young, the helpless, the distressed. Supporting and supplementing these are the more subjective differences—those in emotional disposition and direction. The males directly or indirectly manifest the greater self-assertion and aggressiveness; they express more hardihood and fearlessness, and more roughness of manners, language, and sentiment. The females express themselves as more compassionate and sympathetic, more timid, more fastidious, and esthetically sensitive, more emotional in general (or at least more expressive of the four emotions considered), severer moralists; they admit in themselves weaknesses in emotional control, but less noticeably in physique."

In interpreting these results, it must be recognized that the scores on the Terman-Miles Masculinity-Femininity Test (and on similar scales) are based largely on the differences rather than the similarities between the sexes. Moreover, they tend to reflect the particular culture in which they were developed, and therefore emphasize social differences of the more extreme sort. They do not necessarily apply to other cultures—for instance, only a few of the items were found to differentiate between the sexes in Holland.

What is more, there is some question of their value even in our own society. In applying their test, Terman and Miles found that dressmakers, domestic employees, and women over sixty rate highest in femininity, whereas twenty-year-old women (who may be at the height of their sexual attractiveness) are only moderately feminine since they are likely to have many "masculine" interests such as sports. Similarly, a young man who would be considered highly masculine in appearance and physical strength, and would be at the peak of his interest in women and his attractiveness to women, would nevertheless rate only moderately masculine on this test if he showed a special interest in music and religion. In other words, the scale gives too much consideration to custom and culture, and

too little to sexual and physical differences.

A number of other investigators have attempted to construct more accurate and penetrating tests. The California Psychological Inventory (Gough, 1957) is based on the same approach as the Masculinity-Femininity Test, but eliminates some of the more extreme social items such as attendance at pool halls as an indication of masculinity and at beauty parlors as an indication of femininity. A completely different approach is represented by the projective test devised by Franck and Rosen (1949), which is based on the assumption that men and women differ in fantasy and imaginative productions. On this test the subject is shown a series of simple lines and geometrical forms and is asked to draw a picture incorporating them. The results are then compared to productions which have been found to be typical of representative members of the subject's sex. It is interesting that the scores do not correlate with the scores on the question and answer tests, and there is some evidence that they reveal latent aspects of masculinity and femininity that are not revealed on the social type of test. (Miller and Swanson, 1960)

MASKING. The partial or complete obscuring of one sensation by another.

The most striking form of masking occurs in the sense of hearing. It is also the most fully investigated. Some sounds are found to screen out others —for example, we find it hard to hear if we telephone in a noisy room or over a noisy circuit. Experiments show that tones which are close in frequency mask well; tones of widely different pitch, less well. Low tones mask high tones better than vice versa, and complex tones have a greater masking effect than pure tones. Noises are especially good maskers because they have a wide spread of energy throughout the audible range. This is particularly true of "white noise," which contains all the frequencies within the sound spectrum.

Masking also occurs in other senses. Smoking tends to dull the sense of taste, and excessive use of condiments such as pepper or ketchup will often completely mask the flavor of foods. The French prefer white wine with fish because red wine tends to mask its delicate flavor. One smell can also be used to mask another, since we tend to react only to the stronger of two odors. Carbolic acid is used in some soaps not merely as a disinfectant but as a means of masking body odors. Perfumes can also be used to mask odors; deodorants not only apply the masking principle (since they are perfumed) but also neutralize the odor of perspiration through chemical action. One pain can mask another. The irritant, Spanish fly, has been used for this purpose; similarly, some doctors slap their patients as they give injections in order to mask the sudden, sharp pain of the needle. See METACONTRAST.

MASOCHISM. A sexual deviation in which pleasure is derived from pain. The pain may be self-inflicted or inflicted by others, and either consciously sought or unconsciously invited.

The term is derived from the name of the Austrian novelist Leopold V. Sacher-Masoch (1836–95), whose stories frequently included scenes of sexual pleasure associated with pain. But masochism is also applied in a broader sense to the satisfaction which some persons experience from imposing extreme suffering or hardship on themselves, as in martyrdom, religious flagellation, asceticism, and needless sacrifices for others. Many psychiatrists believe there is a sexual component even in these cases, although it may be deeply hidden or disguised.

In some cases masochistic tendencies are expressed only in sexually stimulating fantasies of abuse by others. Full-

blown masochists, however, obtain sexual excitement and satisfaction from such activities as cutting themselves, sticking pins into various parts of their bodies, or being whipped, choked, tied up, bitten, trampled, or castigated verbally. In general, behavior of this kind seems to be more common in women than men, perhaps because of an association between submissiveness, sex, and suffering in our culture. The tendency occurs in mild form in normal individuals but may be extremely exaggerated in certain psychiatric disorders.

Many explanations of masochistic behavior have been offered, but no single theory seems to apply to all cases. Most of the causal factors run parallel to those for sadism, since the two deviations are frequently found in the same individual. The following are most often cited:

First, in some instances sexual masochism appears to be an expression of a general tendency to react to frustration, disappointment, and failure by feeling sorry for one's self and wallowing in one's misery. With many people, suffering yields major satisfactions in terms of self-righteousness, self-sacrifice, atonement for the sins of mankind, or general spiritual uplift. "Secondary gains" of attention and sympathy may also be involved, and in some cases of both sexual and non-sexual masochism, suffering may be accepted or invited as a means of relieving a conscious or unconscious sense of guilt.

Second, according to psychoanalytic theory, people seek out situations in which they can be injured or humiliated as a means of denying or holding in check their hostile sadistic impulses. Instead of hurting others, they crave to be hurt themselves. Sometimes this reaction carries over directly into sexual behavior. In addition, psychoanalytic theory relates masochism to castration anxiety. The individual may invite pain as a price to be paid in advance to ward off castration, or as a means of reassuring himself that he can be hurt without being castrated. *See* CASTRATION COMPLEX.

Third, women who have been taught that sex is disgusting and shameful may require the infliction of pain as a prelude to sexual relations—that is, it is the price they must pay for this guilt-laden pleasure.

Fourth, an association between sex and pain may be established early in life. Some mothers warn their daughters away from early sexual experiences by exaggerating the pain of first intercourse. Painful menstruation, masturbation, or defloration may confirm the association between sex and suffering. In some cases children actually experience sexual pleasure while they are suffering pain: the boy or girl who is put across an adult's knee to be spanked may be sexually aroused as a result of the bodily contact.

Fifth, neglected or rejected children may in some cases interpret punishment of any kind as evidence of interest or even affection. Later on, such children, usually girls, may submit to being hurt by their sex partners in order to increase their erotic response and assure themselves that they are loved and wanted. Such women may actually seek out sadistic marital partners.

Sixth, masochism may be practiced as a direct means of increasing sexual gratification, often as a result of early experiences that associate sexual pleasure with pain. Young girls and boys frequently discover that tickling and hair-pulling are stimulating and pleasurable. This may later lead to masochistic behavior that is more directly associated with sex—for example, during sexual foreplay they may find that they enjoy being playfully beaten or crushed or "smothered" with kisses. In most cases they are content with these milder forms of masochism, and the tendency does not progress further. In some instances, however, a man or woman finds that he cannot be sexually aroused or reach orgasm unless he suffers pain. From there on, masochism may progress to any conceivable proportions.

Neurotic individuals who have fundamental doubts about their sexual adequacy, or strong unconscious feelings of guilt, frequently require increasingly strenuous whippings or other forms of abuse before they can achieve sexual gratification. Male masochists sometimes visit brothels that are equipped with ingenious devices for torture. In psychotic cases, where the individual has gross delusions of sin, or where behavior is completely disorganized and irrational, masochists have been known to mutilate, castrate, and even fatally injure themselves. *See* SADISM, GAMBLING.

Illustrative Case: MASOCHISM

A woman of forty-two was brought to the emergency ward after she had attempted suicide by swallowing an ounce of tincture of iodine. The social service history as secured from various informants left a somewhat confused impression. On the one hand, the facts indicated that the patient had been living in pitiable circumstances. She was the wife of a drunkard who had deserted her several months previously. Unable to secure outside employment because of various organic illnesses, she had been reduced to knitting gloves and sweaters at home to support herself and her three children. She had lived in squalor and privation but had stoically refused help from neighbors or charitable organizations. And yet this pathetic account was somewhat altered by further data. For instance, the patient had also refused medical care that would have greatly improved her health. Again, her present marriage was the third of a series, and it seemed more than a coincidence that all three of her husbands had been irresponsible, improvident, and abusive. Finally, the patient, despite her refusal of material help, had made so obvious a spectacle of her suffering and "martyrdom" that her neighbors had almost unanimously agreed that she "just gloried in misery," and her social worker had concluded that she was a "masochist." In all instances the outcome was the same: everyone had eventually ceased trying to help her.

Physical and laboratory examinations in the hospital confirmed the presence of mild arteriosclerosis, general malnutrition with anemia, and moderate but uncontrolled diabetes with pruritus and dependent edema. More significantly, however, the psychiatric history revealed the following:

The patient's father had been an illiterate, sadistic backwoods farmer who kept his family in isolation and physical subjection and who terrorized them by excesses of cruelty during his drunken rages. However, even in this fear-torn household there was a scale of relative security, ranging from the mother down to the younger and more helpless children. In this hierarchy the patient envied her mother, the only one able to resist her father's abuse or ever to elicit from him even a transient sign of physical affection. Warped by this unconscious but deeply embedded identification with her mother, and, indeed, hardly acquainted with any other conception of marriage, she had passively "let herself be married off" at the age of sixteen to a neighboring farmer of her father's choosing. This man soon lost his farm and moved to Chicago where, after four years of neglecting or abusing the patient, he deserted her and their two children. The patient supported herself for two years and then married again—this time deliberately selecting an irresponsible drunkard for the announced purpose of "reforming him." The sequence of poverty, abuse, and desertion was repeated, and the patient three years later found herself divorced and now with a third child on her hands. And yet within a short time she was again married, again to an alcoholic, and was again mistreated and deserted. By this time she had become known to various social agencies who, after a third suicidal gesture on her part, abandoned their well-meaning attempts to help her directly and arranged for her admission to a psychiatric hospital.

Here the patient, with a characteristic air of resigned but valiant martyrdom, insisted on telling her troubles and sufferings in interminable detail to all who would listen until she was avoided by patients and nursing staff alike. Moreover, although she professed profound gratitude for everyone's care and kindness, she actually co-operated very poorly in regulating her diabetic diet and medication, or in conforming with ward routine. Similarly, she welcomed—indeed, demanded—frequent interviews with the physicians and social workers, yet progressed not an iota in acquiring any insight into her own responsibility for many of her difficulties, or any realistic reorientation as to future plans for work, care of her children, or better social adaptations. Finally, her behavior became so annoying to other patients that she had to be discharged, to return for renewed and equally futile attempts at extramural guidance and social service care. (Masserman, 1961)

MASS BEHAVIOR. This term is used to designate the characteristic actions and reactions of crowds, mobs, audiences, or the public at large, including such phenomena as rioting, lynching, panic, fads, crazes, mass hysteria, and social movements.

In a review of mass phenomena (1954), Roger Brown suggests that all "collectivities" can be classified along four major dimensions. First, *size:* groups are room-size collectivities; crowds, mobs, or audiences are large enough to fill a square or public hall; the public, electorate, class or "the masses" are too large to congregate. Second, *congregation:* collectivities may come together periodically, irregularly, temporarily, or in the case of the public, never. Third, *polarization* is the term used for the degree of simultaneous attention to an object or event called a focus. Fourth, *identification,* or the degree to which members of a collectivity regard themselves as part of it. This may never occur, or may occur temporarily, or be expressed in an intense feeling of belonging.

To illustrate, a bridge club is a group that meets temporarily, with a definitely polarized interest, and usually develops a sense of camaraderie; a lynching mob is considerably larger, usually transient, highly polarized, but shows only temporary and shallow identification. In addition, collectivities may be described in terms of other dimensions such as organized or unorganized, co-acting or individual, anonymous or named, with members in contact with each other, or separated in space.

The following are some of the major principles of collective behavior recognized by social psychologists of today.

Crowds in general. As a whole, crowds congregate and are polarized on a temporary-irregular basis, and involve little if any sense of belonging. This means, according to Brown, that "they tend to be co-acting, shoulder-to-shoulder, anonymous, casual, temporary, and unorganized collectivities." They may be further divided according to the dominant behavior pattern. Audiences, for example, may be described as relatively passive crowds brought together by a fixed intention, but on a casual basis. In contrast, mobs are active crowds which may show different patterns of behavior: aggressive, escape-motivated, acquisitive, or expressive. A milling crowd in Times Square on New Year's Eve is highly expressive, but not as aggressive as a lynching mob or as acquisitive as a crowd of customers at a department store sale.

Mobs. Three major characteristics of mobs are (a) *mental homogeneity,* or general conformity and unanimity of feeling, thought, and overt action; (b) *emotionality:* heightened emotional response that may rise to a feverish pitch; (c) *irrationality:* various investigators have described this characteristic in terms of a hypnotic state, childishness, even paranoid delusions, but the common denominator of all these characterizations is that mob behavior is on the whole less reasonable and intelligent than individual behavior.

There is considerable difference of opinion as to the mechanisms that elicit these three patterns. The homogeneity of thinking and behavior was attributed by Freud to suggestion, by Tarde to imitation, and by McDougall to "primitive sympathy" stemming from the self-preservation instinct. Some authors explain the intensified emotion of the mob in terms of taking the lid off unconscious urges which are inhibited or fail to find expression in ordinary social situations. Others hold that the emotional responses are ready-made but not unconscious—but in either case the motivation is pre-existent, and people who do not harbor these impulses, whether conscious or unconscious, do not react to crowd stimulation.

The actual release of emotional and irrational behavior is also ascribed to different factors. Le Bon (1917) attributed mob action to loss of the sense of responsibility based on the anonymity of the crowd. F. H. Allport (1924) ascribed it to the "impression of universality," the feeling that it must be the right thing to do because everyone is doing it. Freud based his view on the theory that crowds ordinarily submit to a leader as a common father substitute; but in the case of the mob, which has no leader, a common wish or impulse acts as the substitute.

The concepts of anonymity and impression of universality are used to explain the behavior of existing mobs, but they fail to explain why the mob forms in the first place. Brown believes that too little attention has been paid to the "triggers" of mob action. According to his theory, there are wide variations in the threshold for mob behavior, and the mob is started on its way by the impulsive acts of two types of individuals: the *lawless,* who show the same type of behavior in their individual private life as in the mob; and the *susceptible,* who are always ready to follow aggressive, truculent leaders. These two groups start the ball rolling, and the feelings of universality and loss of responsibility draw in some of the more *cautious* individuals, particularly those who are predisposed to violent activity but afraid of punishment. Beyond these groups are the *yielders,* who join the mob only when it is full-fledged; and the *supportive* individuals who, as onlookers rather than participants, add to the impression of universality. Finally, the group whom Brown terms *resistant* oppose mob action and frequently risk physical attack or loss of life.

Lynching. This is a form of mob aggression against one or more people in the name of a supposedly moral principle. The term itself comes from a Judge Lynch, who organized a court in Virginia to punish Tories during the Revolutionary period. Ironically, the court was considered just, and never invoked the death penalty. Actual lynchings began somewhat later, and between 1830 and the Civil War most of the victims were white abolitionists who were lynched on the grounds that freeing the slaves would upset the economic system. After the Civil War the number of Negro lynchings increased until the last decade of the century, when Negro victims far exceeded whites. During that period, the total number of lynchings rose to 1111. In this century the annual rate has tapered off and by 1950 had dropped to one or two per year. It has recently been on the increase, due to renewed activities of white supremacy groups.

Since the Civil War, lynching has been a Southern phenomenon, occurring most frequently in poor rural counties where Negroes were a minority. Most of the victims were accused of homicide, and it appears that they were usually innocent of any crime. This also applies to cases involving accusations of rape. Studies show that these accusations were often made by women who were sexually dissatisfied, and many cases suggested an element of delusion or unconscious provocation. Most of these lynchings were committed by lower-class whites who feared the competition of the Negro and sought to "keep him in his place" both socially and economically.

In 1940 Hovland and Sears found evidence for an economic interpretation by showing a relationship between the year-by-year lynchings and the price of cotton, but their correlations were later reduced by a re-analysis of their statistics made by Mintz (1946). Studies have also shown that the largest number of lynchings occur in the summer months, with the highest point in July, possibly because the greatest degree of contact between the races occurs at that time. Another consideration is the fact that in the rural South personal grievances are often avenged by the individual instead of being taken to court. There also appears to be some truth in H. L. Mencken's much-quoted statement: "Lynching often takes the place of the merry-go-round, the theater, the symphony, and other diversions common to the larger communities."

A distinction has been made between two categories of lynching. The Bourbon type usually occurs in the "black belt" where Negroes are in the majority. Here the lynching party is organized by leading citizens to punish a specific person for a specific crime, though the basic motive is to maintain white supremacy. They usually act in secret, and disperse as soon as the job is done. Newspapers and civic officials often support their activities, and this helps to dispel any qualms of conscience that might arise.

The other type, termed proletariat, occurs in communities where Negroes are in the minority. In this case the lynching is carried out by members of the poorer class who have little interest in proving the guilt of the victim or even in discovering whether it is the right person, since their object is not to punish an individual but to persecute a race. Typically the crowd is whipped into a frenzy by self-appointed leaders, many of whom have police records. In the famous Leeville, Texas, case, the lynchers dynamited the courthouse, brought out the victim, dragged him through the street behind a car, and hanged him on a tree even though he was already dead. After that, the mob descended upon the Negro community, breaking into stores and setting fires to buildings that represented social and economic advances made by the Negro.

A study of lynchings that took place in the United States between 1900 and 1930 has shown that only .8 per cent were followed by conviction (Chadbourne, 1933). Since that time a few convictions have been made, and both the press and the church have become more vigorously and openly opposed to the practice. Organizations have also been formed to combat lynching, but studies indicate that the active mob members are seldom reached by any of these social forces. Moreover, as recent events amply attest, even if there are fewer lynchings than fifty years ago, the same motives tend to express themselves in other forms of violence such as snipings and church bombings.

Aggressive mobs. The clearest example of an aggressive mob is found in race riots, which are described by Brown as "mass lynchings in which a mob aggresses against large numbers of a submissive group." Riots of this kind tend to occur in rural communities in which there is a large minority population. The term "universalistic" can be applied to this type of violence since it is directed at groups of people solely because they are members of a certain race. In many cases not even the elderly or the crippled are spared. Before the Civil Rights movement, race riots tended to cluster around world wars, when employment was high, suggesting that the primary cause was the Negro's effort to better himself and the white's determination to hold him down.

Dahlke (1952) has listed the following as elements which predispose a community to race riots: (1) a tradition of violence against a subordinate group; (2) a subgroup struggling to improve its position; (3) antagonism between law enforcement agencies and the minority; (4) organizations actively defaming the minority and advocating violence against them; (5) inability of the minority to gain access to the press and other mass media, or unfair treatment by these media; (6) an upper class that plays the role of onlookers or inciters, and younger people and lower classes who are ready to play the role of rioters.

Acquisitive mobs. This type of mob develops when the relationship between the public and its institutions tends to break down, especially when large groups of people lose faith in the ordinary social processes. Typical examples are hunger riots, food-hoarding stampedes, and bank runs. In all these cases the crowd converges on a desired object in a thoroughly emotional and irrational manner. At the start of World War II there was a rush on sugar, tires, gasoline, shoes, and coffee. It was reported that one woman purchased $75 worth of light bulbs and one family laid in a forty-year supply of canned food. Such people are influenced by the "impression of universality." They feel that everyone else will storm the stores in anticipation of shortages, and that the only practical thing to do is to get there first. They do not listen to assurances that no serious shortages are likely to occur, but in time they may actually *create* a shortage through hoarding.

Expressive mobs. Typical examples of collective expressive activity are found in orgiastic dances, revival meetings, and the Mardi Gras. One object of this "revelous behavior," as La Pière (1938) points out, is to obtain release from psychological tensions; another is to get away from the humdrum routine of everyday existence. We not only set aside official periods—New Year's eve, fiestas, etc.—for expressive behavior of this type, but many private institutions also provide opportunities for release.

Among these are the corner bar, the discothèque or night club, the burlesque show, and evangelist meetings.

Football games are vivid examples of a highly polarized expressive "mob," especially when the rooters stream onto the field to tear down the goal posts at the end of the game. Religious revival meetings frequently take on mystical overtones, but in some cases the term hysterical would be more apt. In many instances, too, the atmosphere has a distinctly sexual tinge—for example, when the audience listens to detailed confessions of promiscuity given by the "converted," or hears the pornographic object lessons of a Billy Sunday. Many revivalists use professional "confessors" and fake "miracle cures" to trigger their audiences into action. Once the process is started, the two principles of emotional contagion and impression of universality take hold, and one individual after another rises to his feet and comes forward to be converted. One positive aspect of religious revivals is that they give many people emotional support and a feeling of social solidarity when times are bad—but this usually takes place on a primitive level.

Audiences. These are polarized crowds which come together primarily to be "directed and affected," not to act. Any activity that does occur is likely to be highly formalized and overt, as in crying, "Bravo!" Audiences fall largely into two types. The "casual audience" congregates accidentally and not as a result of plan: people gather around to watch a street fight or to stare at an object floating in the sky. The "intentional scheduled audience," on the other hand, has a definite purpose and is regulated as to time and place. Some authorities feel that the total polarization of an audience is akin to hypnotism. This is believed to account for the fact that spectators may become so absorbed in a melodrama that they shout a warning to the hero when the villain is approaching.

Audiences may also be divided into recreational and information-seeking, but the line between the two is hard to draw. The average lecturegoer is probably seeking recreation, though he may convince himself that his motive is self-improvement. On the other hand, people often go to the more serious "problem" plays for intellectual stimulation rather than carefree recreation.

Mass collectivities. This term includes various groupings that are too large to congregate: nationalities, electorates, castes, classes, and publics. Psychologists have attempted to investigate these huge collectivities through public opinion surveys, studies of individual differences, and other systematic observations. Many of these observations have centered around the characteristics already mentioned: mass contagion, polarization, and impression of universality.

The fads and crazes that sweep through the public offer particularly vivid illustrations of mass contagion. Fads usually have to do with relatively superficial aspects of life such as ornaments, linguistic expressions, games, and fashions. Bogardus (1942) has shown that 80 per cent of fads last no longer than a year. There is evidence that a full cycle of dress of European women takes about a hundred years, though in America this cycle appears to be considerably shorter; the extremely short skirt, for example, was popular in the early 20s and came into fashion again in the mid-60s. It also appears that clothing fads are not so widespread today as they were at one time, probably because of the emergence of several well-accepted designers rather than a single fashion authority. On the other hand, the development of television, communication satellites, and jet transportation makes it possible for the contagion to spread more quickly than ever before.

There appear to be three basic reasons why clothing fads catch on. First, the ingenuity of the originators and especially the publicizers in making these innovations appear attractive; second, the conformity need and the satisfactions of being "in the swing"; and third, the fact that many people become bored with sameness and are constantly in need of new stimulation.

Crazes usually stem from more basic needs, emotions, and desires than fads. The "tulipomania" of the Dutch in 1635 and the Florida real estate boom of the 1920s were both motivated by economic gain. In Holland, concentration on tulips led to greatly inflated prices and neglect of other industries. Many people invested fortunes in a few rare bulbs, and when the market began to weaken, a wave of selling set in, bringing total collapse. The Florida "bubble" also burst, and many investors, who had paid exorbitant prices for inferior land, ended in bankruptcy.

An example of a craze that rose to a peak in an extremely short time is the "phantom anesthetist of Mattoon," a small town in Illinois. In this case a woman reported to the police that someone had opened her bedroom window and sprayed her with a nauseating gas that partially paralyzed her legs. Her story was published in the local paper, and almost immediately calls came in reporting similar experiences. Groups of armed citizens were then organized to apprehend the marauder. These attempts failed and the reports subsided in about two weeks.

Soon afterwards a psychologist, M. Johnson (1945), investigated the case and concluded that the woman had suffered a hysterical attack, since every one of her symptoms was typical of this disorder. He also suggested that the contagion had spread because of two primary factors: first, a generalized anxiety stemming from World War II, which was raging at the time, and second, sensational newspaper reports under headings like "Phantom Anesthetist Strikes Again." One of these accounts read in part: "Groggy as Lon-doners under protracted aerial blitzing, this town's bewildered citizens reeled today under the repeated attacks of a mad anesthetist who has sprayed a deadly nerve gas into thirteen homes and has knocked out 27 victims." *See* MASS HYSTERIA, DEMONOLOGY, SUGGESTION.

The second principle operative in mass collectivities, polarization, can readily be illustrated by the broadcast media, which reach so many millions at once. As Brown points out, all four forms of crowd behavior—acquisitive, aggressive, expressive, and escapist—may be aroused. Advertising on radio and television evokes the acquisitive drive; the violence depicted in TV dramas increases our preoccupation with aggression and in scattered cases helps to release aggressive tendencies themselves. Some of the popular programs that show uninhibited dancing of teenagers undoubtedly stimulate "expressive" activity. There is evidence, too, that the medium can arouse escape and panic reactions. The most provocative study on this point is the one carried out by Hadley Cantril on the Orson Welles broadcast of 1938 based on H. G. Wells's *War of the Worlds*. Cantril's investigation, in which public opinion survey techniques were used, indicated that over a million people were seriously disturbed by this broadcast, many of them to the point of panic (Cantril, 1940). A translation of the same program presented in Quito, Ecuador, a few years later had similar effects on the listeners.

Briefly, the story was told in the form of a newscast, but anouncements were made before, during, and after the presentation stating that it was a play based on Wells's novel about an invasion from Mars. In spite of these precautions people all over the United States telephoned their neighbors to warn them, rushed out to rescue their loved ones, prayed, wept, hid, and in a few cases even jumped out of the window. Many of these listeners had tuned in late and missed the initial announcement, but others had heard the program from the beginning. The reactions were especially intense near the "scene" of the invasion, in New Jersey.

In his analysis, Cantril divided the individuals who interpreted the program as a news broadcast into the following four groups. First, those who analyzed the internal evidence of the program and knew it could not be factual. These included people who recognized Orson Welles's voice, knew the story on which it was based, or noticed that the sequence of events was too rapid to be actually occurring. Second, those who checked by consulting the program listings in the newspaper or by dialing other stations to see if they were broadcasting this sensational "news." Most of these people concluded that it was merely a play. Third, those who attempted to check but were unsuccessful and continued to believe it was a news broadcast. Many of them looked out of the window or went outdoors, but they encountered ambiguous evidence, such as people running or the fact that few cars were on the road. They usually interpreted these observations as confirming the fact that it was actually a news broadcast. Fourth, those who made no attempt to check the authenticity of the broadcast.

Cantril's questionnaires revealed that people who could be expected to possess "critical ability" were most often found in the first two categories. He also found evidence that people who not only lacked critical ability but who were especially susceptible to suggestion were more often found in the second two categories. This indicated that personality characteristics as well as educational level play an important role in panic reactions. *See* PANIC, CIVILIAN CATASTROPHE REACTION.

MASS HYSTERIA (Collective Psychoses). These terms are applied primarily to the "psychic epidemics" which have at times swept through an entire population. The most vivid examples are the dancing manias and lycanthropies that occurred in many parts of Europe between the eleventh and seventeenth century. As Arieti and Meth (1959) point out, these disorders should not be classified as psychoses but as "psychoneuroses of a hysterical nature which were induced by the effect the crowd had on the predisposed person. The atmosphere of superstition, ignorance, and intense religiosity predisposed unstable individuals to this form of collective hypnosis." The term "mass hysteria" therefore seems more apt than collective psychosis.

The dancing mania can be traced as far back as the tenth century in Italy. People would gather near a church and sing and dance for several days and nights until many of them had convulsions and lost consciousness. The condition was named tarantism or tarantulism by Baglivi, since the participants thought they had been bitten by a spider, lycosa tarantula, and as a result danced about in great fear and excitement. They also believed that music would be an effective treatment, and the "tarantella" has remained a popular type of dance music in Italy to this day. Some authorities point out the similarity between the dancing manias and the orgiastic rites of ancient Greece, and offer the conjecture that secret gatherings kept the custom alive when it was banned by Christianity, but that in time the rites lost their original meaning and became symptoms of emotional disorder or reactions to the stresses of the period (Gloyne, 1950). Sigerist (1943) gives this description based on a report of a physician in thirteenth-century Italy:

"The disease occurred at the height of the summer heat . . . People, asleep or awake, would suddenly jump up, feeling an acute pain like the sting of a bee. Some saw the spider, others did not, but they knew that it must be the tarantula. They ran out of the house into the street, to the marketplace, dancing in great excitement. Soon they were joined by others who like them had been bitten, or by people who had been stung in previous years. . .

"Thus groups of patients would gather, dancing wildly in the queerest attire . . . Others would tear their clothes and show their nakedness, losing all sense of modesty . . . Some called for swords and acted like fencers, others for whips and beat each other . . . Some of them had still stranger fancies, liked to be tossed in the air, dug holes in the ground, and rolled themselves into the dirt like swine. They all drank wine plentifully and sang and talked like drunken people . . ."

The dancing mania spread to Germany and the Flemish countries, where it became known St. Vitus' Dance. The name is believed to have been adopted after a tragedy at Utrecht in 1278, when two hundred people danced so violently on a bridge over the Rhine that it collapsed into the river. Many of them lost their lives in the water, but some were treated in a chapel dedicated to St. Vitus—hence the name.

A second type of collective disorder, lycanthropy, occurred in isolated areas, and is still occasionally reported in mountainous villages of Italy. People afflicted with this illness imagine that they are transformed into wolves. Stone (1937) cites a case from 1541 in which a lycanthrope (literally, wolf-man) told his captors in confidence that he was actually a wolf but that his skin was smooth because his hairy coat was turned inward. In an effort to cure him of this conviction, his arms and legs were amputated, but he died unconvinced. Many other victims committed violent crimes while under this delusion, and it therefore became the custom to arrest and execute anyone afflicted with the disorder. During an epidemic in France, one judge is said to have condemned six hundred lycanthropes, or "werewolves," to death.

In their comments on this disorder, Arieti and Meth state that while some of the victims were probably schizophrenics, it is possible that the majority were affected by some form of collective hysteria. They point out that the belief that men can be transformed into animals is the basis of many ancient myths. They also recall that Nebuchadnezzar thought he was a wolf, and that St. Patrick is said to have transformed Veneticus, the King of Gallia, into a wolf. These authors suggest that the disorder may arise from a strong sense of guilt and unworthiness which makes the individual feel he does not deserve to belong to the human race. This feeling makes him afraid he will undergo a metamorphosis, and he later acts out this fear by behaving like an animal. This is especially likely to happen when he sees other people behaving in this way, so the disorder spreads from one person to another.

Other collective epidemics have been reported in convents where the nuns suddenly abandoned their religious discipline and performed some bizarre action for a short time. In the fifteenth century a German nun developed a compulsive urge to bite her associates. The mania was taken up by the other nuns and within a few months had spread to convents in Germany, Holland, and Italy (White, 1896). Another historian, Ferrio (1948), relates that in about 1700 the nuns in a convent near Paris started to mew as if they had been transformed into cats. These cases are probably another expression of lycanthropy.

In present-day psychiatry the term lycanthropy is usually reserved for those rare cases of schizophrenia or paranoia in which the patient has an outright delusion that he has been transformed into an animal. One such case was recently reported in which a boy of four labored under the delusion that he was a dog. He crawled about on all fours, barked instead of talked, and would only eat out of a bowl placed on the floor. *See* PANIC.

MASTURBATION. Self-stimulation of the genital organs for purposes of sexual pleasure. Some writers include manipulation of other erogenous zones, such as the anus, as well as such "symbolic" activities as nail-biting, handkerchief-twisting, hair plucking or twisting, playing with hangnails or buttons or the earlobe, and inserting a finger in the nose, mouth, or ear.

Genital self-stimulation is considered a normal sexual outlet and a natural phase of sexual development. Some authorities believe it serves the purpose of centering sexual interest on the genital organs during childhood and is therefore a preparation for heterosexual activity.

Masturbation is a common practice among both sexes, although more prevalent among immature males than females. Mutual masturbation is sometimes practiced by males or females with members of the same or opposite sex. The Kinsey reports (1948, 1953) have indicated that 93 per cent of males and 62 per cent of females engage in masturbation at some time in their lives. Prior to marriage it is the most common sexual outlet for men, and for women it is second only to petting. Ordinarily it is put aside after marriage, when heterosexual relations take over; but it may be revived when a couple is separated for long periods or when sexual relations are unsatisfactory or infrequent.

Masturbation, as practiced by the average individual, has no known harmful effects. Yet it has been surrounded with so many taboos and warnings that it frequently arouses intense feelings of guilt and anxiety. These attitudes may interfere with personal, social, and marital adjustment. Practically every type of physical and mental disorder has been falsely ascribed to this activity at one time or another. Young people have been told time and again that it will undermine their health, make them impotent, and even bring on insanity. It has been described as a vile habit practiced primarily by the feeble-minded or the morally degenerate, and the person who gives in to the urge has frequently been pictured as abominably weak and lacking in self-control.

As a result of these threatening ideas, young people who yield to the impulse sometimes develop severe conflicts that damage their personalities. This does not occur so frequently today as in the past, since the attitude toward masturbation is becoming more enlightened.

Although masturbation is not regarded as a sexual deviation in itself, it may be considered pathological when it is associated with certain disorders and maladjustments. Children who are rejected, lonely, or bored may resort to excessive masturbation as a substitute satisfaction. Resentful children sometimes masturbate in public as a means of getting back at their parents—and in one recorded case, a whole class of sixth-grade boys from underprivileged homes masturbated before their female teacher as a mass protest based on feelings of inadequacy, anger, and frustration. Adults who prefer masturbation to normal heterosexual behavior are usually emotionally disturbed. Some may be excessively shy and fearful of the opposite sex; others are withdrawn, schizoid individuals who cannot establish intimate relations of any kind; still others may be using masturbation as a defense against perverted impulses.

Most people have sexual fantasies during masturbation, and these fantasies are frequently a clue to the underlying motivation. A rather normal fantasy on the part of a married man is to picture a woman who attracts him more than his wife. Some fantasies, however, reveal maladjustments: a man with homosexual inclinations may picture male bodies, or a person with sadistic tendencies may imagine himself hurting others. Under these circumstances masturbatory practices indicate a need for treatment.

Illustrative Cases: MASTURBATION

Mr. D.D., aged thirty-one years, complained of having had a feeling of pressure on top of his head since the age of sixteen. This pressure was associated with the sensation of a band squeezing around his head, and with insomnia. This man had begun to practice masturbation at the age of sixteen and was discovered early in this practice by his father, who had told the boy that he would certainly go insane. Immediately upon hearing this prediction, the patient developed a pressure in his head and thought so much about his masturbation that he could not sleep. His entire interest became centered upon sex, and he could not develop the normal interest in physical, social, and recreational activities. He began to feel that people knew about his practice, and condemned him, and he grew very sensitive and was on the defensive whenever any of his nonsexual wishes failed, feeling that failure was entirely the result of his autoerotism. (Kraines, 1948)

MATERNAL DEPRIVATION. Lack of adequate affection, care, and stimulation from the mother or mother substitute, particularly during infancy.

Maternal deprivation is a recognized problem in orphanages and other institutions for young children, but it probably occurs even more frequently in disturbed family situations. It is considered one of the major factors in faulty psychological development, since early experiences in life have been found to have a potent and lasting effect. Every phase of the child's personality may be affected by a lack of maternal care and affection: his emotional reactions, attitudes toward himself, relationships to other people, intellectual development, and even his physical well-being.

A number of significant studies have been made of young children who have been treated in a cold, mechanical manner and deprived of personal care, emotional warmth, and individualized attention. The effects are particularly severe in institutions where children are also deprived of sufficient intellectual, social, and emotional stimulation and encouragement. In 1942, Bakwin pointed out that the failure of young infants to thrive in hospitals was largely due to the fact that they were isolated from human contact in order to prevent infection. These infants became apathetic and even wasted away, primarily from loneliness and lack of stimulation. Bakwin found that they began to thrive both physically and emotionally when he asked his staff at Bellevue Hospital to mother, cuddle, and play with them, and when the parents were invited to the ward and encouraged to hold and fondle their babies. Psychological care of this type is believed to play an important part in the decrease in infant mortality which has taken place in hospitals during the past twenty years.

Ribble (1944, 1945) found that children of rejecting, indifferent, or punitive mothers become tense, restless, and negativistic even in the first few months of life. Many of them refuse to nurse, and soon develop such symptoms as muscular rigidity, shallow breathing, and constipation, while others became apathetic, semi-stuporous, and depressive, with little interest in food or physical activity. Spitz (1949) compared infants reared in an impersonal foundling home with nursery infants who were visited regularly by their own mothers. Observations and tests over a two-year period showed that the foundlings fell further and further behind in practically all functions—manipulation, perception, memory, imitation, and social development—and by age two they had not learned to walk, talk, or feed themselves, and gave the impression of being apathetic or agitated mental retardates. In an earlier article (1945), Spitz applied the term "hospitalism" to this pattern of behavior.

Spitz and Wolf (1946) have reported that the child is most vulnerable during the first six months to a year, and Bakwin (1949) has given this clinical picture of institutional infants: "Infants under six months of age who have been in an institution for some time present a well-defined picture. The outstanding features are listlessness, emaciation and pallor, relative immobility, quietness, unresponsiveness to stimuli like a smile or a coo, indifferent appetite, failure to gain weight properly despite ingestion of diets which are entirely adequate, frequent stools, poor sleep and an appearance of unhappiness, proneness to febrile episodes, absence of sucking habits."

Later studies have confirmed these findings. Sears et al. (1957) and Prugh and Harlow (1962) have studied the effects of maternal deprivation within the home. They found that cold, unfeeling mothers usually complained that their children were feeding problems, bed-wetters, aggressive, poor sleepers, and irritable. Ainsworth (1962) found that children who were deprived of mother love and care were particularly affected in these areas: language development, ability to form attachments to other persons, and ability to control their momentary impulses. He also found that even a series of separations from the mother or mother figure had adverse effects. Provence and Lipton (1962) obtained similar findings in a study of institutionalized infants. These children did not form strong attachments, rarely turned to adults for help or comfort, demanded immediate gratification of their needs, and were apathetic, markedly retarded in speech and language, and unimaginative in their play activities.

The effects of severe maternal deprivation tend to be lasting. Beres and Obers (1950) examined thirty-eight adolescents who had been institutionalized between three weeks and three years of age, and found that only seven had attained a satisfactory adjustment: twenty-one had character disorders, four were psychotic, four mentally retarded, and two psychoneurotic. Goldfarb (1943, 1945) compared a similar group with a control group of foster children and found them inferior in abstract reasoning and use of language. They also exhibited more behavior problems, restlessness, anxiety, demands for attention, and difficulty in concentration. Interestingly, those who had been placed in institutions after eleven months were better developed and adjusted than those placed at six months, a confirmation of Bakwin's and Spitz's findings.

These adverse effects are not universal. Infants vary considerably in their vulnerability to the stress of deprivation. Nevertheless the effects are widespread and severe, and in some cases seem to be devastating and irreversible. As Bowlby (1951) has said, "the retrospective and follow-up studies make clear that . . . some children are gravely damaged for life. This is a somber conclusion which must now be regarded as established." See MARASMUS, MOTHERING.

MATERNAL DRIVE. The drive to protect and care for offspring. In animals this drive stems largely from hormonal changes involved in bearing and nursing the young, and is expressed in four principal activities: nest-building, retrieving, behavior at birth, and suckling. In human beings it is less dependent on hormonal changes and consists mainly of the impulse to see that the infant is well nourished, comfortable, secure, and loved.

The nature of the maternal drive can best be understood by comparing the behavior of mammalian animal mothers with human mothers. Although there is some variation from species to species, practically every female mammal engages in all four kinds of maternal activity. The studies of rats, however, provide the clearest illustration of the dependence of maternal behavior on physiological changes.

Nest-building. The female rat engages in nest-building when she is pregnant and sometimes even when not pregnant. This activity greatly increases about five days before giving birth, in response to increased secretion of progesterone. Between ten and twenty days after birth the hormonal condition again changes and the nest is broken up. Studies show that there are probably two immediate stimuli that can motivate the nest-building. First, *body temperature:* the temperature of the mother rat's body falls due to lower metabolism during pregnancy, and nest-building activities are believed to keep it warm (Kinder, 1927; Morgan, 1943; Koller, 1956). Another investigator, Richter, has shown that nonpregnant females and even males will engage in nest-building when heat regulation is disturbed by removing the thyroid gland. Second, *the presence of the young* will quickly increase nest-building activity, as shown by the fact that introducing rat pups into the nest of a nonpregnant rat will have this effect (Koller, 1952, 1956). Ordinarily the original nest-building is initiated by hormone secretion when the rat is pregnant, but apparently the presence of the young serves to continue this activity. Morgan (1965) suggests that the social stimulus of the young may itself bring about hormonal changes in the pituitary and thyroid glands. Riess (1950) showed that another factor is also involved: experience in handling objects. He raised female rats in such a way that they had no opportunity to handle food or other articles, and found that they showed little or no nest-building behavior when pregnant.

All these experiments indicate that nest-building is a complex activity governed by specific physical factors. It is not enough simply to call it an instinct and let it go at that.

Behavior during birth. Studies show that behavior during birth and behavior toward the newborn are an extension of activities which the mother directs toward her own body. During pregnancy rats and other mammals develop a salt lack, and during birth the genital region becomes highly irritable. Both these conditions are apparently alleviated by licking this region. They then go on to licking and eating the membrane surrounding the fetus, and in the process also sever the umbilical cord and eat the placenta. These activities are undoubtedly stimulated by specific physiological conditions, as indicated by the fact that mother rats do not engage in this behavior if they are delivered by Caesarean section, a procedure that does not irritate their genital region (Wiesner and Sheard, 1933). Also, if collars are placed around their necks so that they cannot lick their genitalia before parturition, they do not lick their offspring but either eat them or neglect them completely (Birch, 1956).

Higher mammals show greater variation in behavior toward the newborn, probably because their activities are not completely controlled by specific physiological changes. Most chimpanzee mothers care for their offspring in a solicitous, motherly way; but some of them seem to be terrified and run away from the infant (Nissen, 1951). The attitudes of human mothers are especially varied since they are greatly influenced by what they hear about childbirth. In some cultures where giving birth is taken as a matter of course, the mother apparently experiences little or no pain. In our own society we associate birth with "labor pains," and in consequence the suffering is greatly magnified due to anxiety and expectation. Sometimes women who have had a difficult time develop negative attitudes toward the child (Berelson and Steiner, 1964). On the other hand, women who have received instruction in the process of childbirth, or who practice some form of natural childbirth, usually feel less pain and look upon the process as a gratifying and joyous experience.

Retrieving the young. As long as the rat mother is nursing a pup she will retrieve it whenever it leaves the nest. Here, too, physical factors are critical, especially temperature and size of offspring. The pups are retrieved as long as they are small, but when they are larger they are left on their own and allowed to stray. There is evidence also that some mammalian mothers can tell the difference between their own offspring and others by differences in smell and touch.

Retrieval is less necessary among infant chimpanzees and monkeys because their grasping reflexes are present at birth and they cling to the mother by themselves. Interestingly, this close contact seems to develop a social bond between the infant ape and its mother, as shown by the fact that both the mother and the offspring become acutely distressed if the infant is taken away after they have been together for a period of time. On the other hand, if they are separated shortly after birth, the mother shows little reaction. Human beings show a parallel reaction, for a miscarriage or stillbirth is usually less traumatic than the death of a young child.

Nursing behavior. Among human beings as well as lower animals the sucking reflex is usually well developed at birth. This reflex stimulates the ejection of the milk from the mammary gland to the nipple region, a process that takes from several seconds to a minute or two.

The reason for the delay is that oxytocin, produced by the posterior pituitary, must travel through the blood stream and reach the mammary gland in sufficient quantity to be effective. The sucking activity also stimulates secretion of the pituitary hormone, prolactin, which controls milk production. This

is demonstrated by the fact that lactation usually continues as long as sucking is maintained. In some societies children are not weaned until they reach puberty, but in over 60 per cent of cultures studied by Whiting and Child (1953) weaning was found to begin between the ages of two and three.

Animals are often far less active than human beings in initiating nursing behavior. Rats and macaque monkeys simply remain quiet and allow their pups to find the nipple. A weak baby macaque will therefore starve to death in his mother's arms if he does not make contact (Lehrman, 1953; Tinklepaugh, 1942). The relief of pain or discomfort due to distention of the mammary glands is one of the most common motives for nursing among women. It is doubtful, however, whether the urge to nurse is an essential component of the maternal drive, since many women do not experience this impulse or have an active distaste for the process. Lehrman (1961) believes that the process is not initiated among animals by the need for relieving discomfort. The physical mechanism that does start the activity, however, is not fully understood.

Many psychoanalysts stress the importance of breast over bottle feeding because of the effect of early emotional as well as physical gratification on later adjustment. However, studies indicate that the method of feeding is probably less important than the attitude of the mother during the process. A mother who breast-feeds resentfully may do harm to her child, while one who is loving and happy in using the bottle will make the process highly pleasurable and successful. It is significant that no positive correlation has been found between the duration of breast feeding and general adjustment or emotional security in adolescence (Peterson and Spano, 1941). Studies have also shown that the way weaning is carried out is more important than the time at which it is done. *See* MOTHERING, MATERNAL

DEPRIVATION, FEEDING BEHAVIOR, NEW-
BORN INFANT.

The question as to whether the maternal drive is an instinct is seldom
discussed today. Wiesner and Sheard
(1933) have suggested that it is highly
artificial to apply the term to this drive,
since even in rats maternal behavior is
not a fixed, sterotyped pattern that automatically runs off independent of external stimulation. Rather, there are
large individual differences in every
component of maternal behavior, including nursing and nest-building. Moreover,
the same animal may react differently at
different times, depending on outward
stimulation and inner physiological condition. It has even been found that virgin female and male animals will perform maternal acts under certain conditions. The trend is therefore to avoid the
instinct label and to put the emphasis on
the specific conditions that underlie maternal behavior. In the animal these conditions are basically physiological, but
among human beings they tend to be
psychological and cultural as well. If we
describe human maternal behavior as instinctual, we are likely to overlook these
factors as well as the varied forms which
this drive is likely to take. *See* INSTINCT.

MAZE. A network of pathways and
blind alleys between a starting point
and a goal, used to study learning and
problem-solving in animals and human
beings.

There are many types of mazes, but
the process of solving them is similar in
all cases. The subject starts at a given
point, takes one path or another, arrives at "choice points" where he must
decide whether to go left or right, and
continues this procedure until he reaches
the end (PLATE 28). In most mazes the
subject reaches a dead end or blind
alley if he makes a wrong turn, and
has to retrace his steps; but in some
types, called open mazes, there are no
blind alleys and the problem is to see
whether the subject takes a longer or

shorter route, and whether he takes the
same route each time he tries. In any
case, mazes provide an opportunity to
study how human beings and animals
learn a series of interrelated acts that
lead to a goal. As an investigative tool
they have two distinct advantages: the
complexity of the problem can be altered at will, and the progress of the
learning can be readily measured in
terms of both the time required to
reach the goal and the number of
errors made on each trial.

The first experimental maze was built
by W. S. Small in 1900, and was a
miniature replica of the famous hedge
maze at the Hampton Court Palace in
England. Many of the early studies
were limited to this maze, but later investigators found it unnecessarily complex and irregular, and devised many
other types. The simplest patterns are
the T and Y mazes, which have only
one choice point, but a number of
these units are often linked together to
form more complicated sequences.
These mazes fall into two categories,
linear and circular. In the linear type
the goal is more or less directly ahead,
and the subject always moves in the
same general direction. In the circular
type, the goal is near the starting point
and can be reached only by frequent
changes of direction.

Mazes can also be classified into spatial and temporal. In the spatial type,
the choice points are located in different
parts of the maze, and the subject can
theoretically respond to a variety of
cues, such as the way the light falls or
the closeness of a certain turn to a wall
or other object outside the maze. There
are more of these extramaze cues in
the circular than the linear design, and
the circular is therefore easier to solve.

The temporal maze was designed to
eliminate these external cues completely,
and therefore limit the subject to the
use of memory and reasoning. Here a
simple T design is usually used, and the
subject is required to make a left or

right turn at a single choice point. The maze is so constructed that the subject is led back to this point after he makes each choice—like driving up a street, making a right or left turn, and coming around the block to reach the same corner again. A complex sequence, such as RRLL (right-right-left-left), can be required in this type of maze, and the subject must make the right choice even though the choice point looks the same every time. See ALTERNATION.

Mazes which are especially designed for human beings take several forms. "Body mazes" are too cumbersome to be widely used, since they have to be large enough for the subject to walk through. More common are the small mazes which the subject tries to solve while blindfolded. In the stylus type he moves a pencil or stylus through grooved paths, and in the finger relief type he moves his fingertips along elevated wire pathways. The paper and pencil type, similar to the mazes sometimes printed in newspapers, are also occasionally used. One of these, the Porteus Maze, was developed not only to test learning ability but also forethought, mental alertness, nervousness, and excitability. Today it is not considered a valid test for any of these characteristics except learning ability.

Experiments with finger and stylus mazes have led to a surprising discovery. Human beings do not perform any better than white rats when they are both tested on comparable maze patterns. There seem to be two major explanations for this finding. First, the human subjects were not able to avail themselves of their superior reasoning power because the mazes did not have any logical pattern; second, the rats were probably more highly motivated because physical need (hunger, thirst) drove them to work as hard as they could to reach the goal of food or water. (The human subjects were only working to do the experimenter a favor, and were therefore more easily distracted by noises and voices outside the laboratory.)

Throughout the years maze experiments have led to many other findings. These will be discussed in other articles, but can be summarized here: (1) learning does not take place unless the organism is motivated by hunger, ambition, or some other significant drive; (2) reaching a goal and receiving a reward reinforces the learning and makes it last; (3) both animals and human beings learn most quickly when different types of cues, such as visual, tactile, and auditory, are available simultaneously; (4) distributed practice, in which several practice sessions are spaced widely apart, is generally superior to massed practice, in which the trials come one after another; (5) most animals cannot solve temporal maze problems of any complexity, but human beings possess an almost unlimited ability because of their use of language. See LEARNING (GENERAL), REINFORCEMENT, LEARNING AIDS, LEARNING TECHNIQUES.

MCDOUGALL, WILLIAM (1871–1938). McDougall, the major exponent of the instinctivist approach to behavior was a native of Lancashire, England. After studying at Manchester and Cambridge, he received medical training at the University of London. His purpose, however, was not to practice medicine but to study the brain and nervous system as a means of understanding "human nature." While at Cambridge he participated in an anthropological expedition to the Torres Straits, and wrote The Pagan Tribes of Borneo with Dr. Charles Hose. Between 1900 and 1906 he engaged in experimental studies of vision, first at Göttingen and then at the University College, London. These investigations, as well as studies on attention, fatigue, and hypnotism, can be termed psychophysical, since the introspective observations he made were interpreted largely along physiological lines. His findings were incorporated in a book, *Physiological Psychology* (1905), which marked the end of his interest in neurological explanations of behavior. From there on, McDougall adopted a biological viewpoint, largely as a result of his admiration for William James.

Between 1904 and 1920 McDougall served as Wilde Reader on Mental Philosophy at Oxford, a position that permitted him to continue his research and to exert an influence on many students who later became prominent psychologists. His primary interest, as Murphy (1949) has put it, was in "making psychology really important by getting to the mainsprings of conduct which had so long been forgotten." In 1908 he published *Introduction to Social Psychology,* the first book on this subject except for a work by E. A. Ross published in the same year. In this volume, regarded as McDougall's most important contribution, the thesis is developed that all human action and interaction stem from instinctive forces which constitute our hereditary endowment, but which can be modified through experience. In his view, every primary instinct has an emotional counterpart—for example, the instinct of flight produces the emotion of fear, the instinct of repulsion is accompanied by the emotion of disgust. The book also traces the development of social life from its dynamic, irrational origins, and takes the position that broad classes of social responses—suggestion, sympathy, and imitation—have an instinctual foundation. He later termed this approach "hormic psychology," which holds that all activity not only has an instinctive basis, but is purposive and goal-directed.

The *Introduction to Social Psychology* marked the beginning of a new era, and "swept everything before it" (Murphy 1949). Psychologists began to view all behavior in dynamic, Darwinian terms, and vied with each other in "inventing" instincts to "explain" activities not covered by McDougall. Many

writers attributed World War I to a "clash of instincts," and social scientists in all fields, including Veblen, were influenced by the "instinct doctrine." The trend reached absurd proportions when one investigator listed over a hundred instincts, including the instinct to steal apples from a neighbor's orchard. But, starting with Knight Dunlap's critique in 1919, there was mounting dissatisfaction with the tendency to evoke this magic word to explain every type of behavior. The doctrine was assailed as loose, vague, unscientific, and soon began to fall into disrepute. After its decline, in the middle 20s, it left a theoretical vacuum which began to be filled when the experimental method of cultural anthropology came into vogue in social psychology.

Another of McDougall's earlier works also had a widespread influence—his *Body and Mind: A History and Defense of Animism* (1911). In this book he supported the interactionist approach to the mind-body problem, holding that "the mind itself must be regarded as a potent cause in development and evolution." This view, combined with his emphasis on purposive striving, alienated him from the dominant trends of the time, which conceived behavior entirely in terms of conditioning and stimulus-response mechanisms. Although McDougall entitled one of his works *Psychology, the Study of Behavior* (1914), he was anything but a behaviorist; and in spite of the fact that he regarded instincts as the wellsprings of action, he constantly insisted that the mind can influence the body, and that cognitive awareness is needed to guide behavior toward one's goals. "Present action depends on knowing whither it is directed." (Boring, 1950)

McDougall was a highly individual thinker who defended many unpopular causes. At a time when his colleagues were leaning toward determinism, he held that purposive behavior involves indeterminateness, and that the mind therefore has some degree of freedom. In the face of a staunch belief in the Mendelian law among his contemporaries, he embraced the Lamarckian theory and bred successive generations of white rats to prove that acquired characteristics can be inherited. (Others have concluded that his results did not support the theory.) While most scientists were emphasizing a completely environmentalist view, he supported eugenics as the road to human improvement. And while others were seeking to limit psychology to observable phenomena, he showed a continuing interest in psychical research—and when he took a position at Duke University in 1927 he sponsored the ESP investigations of J. B. Rhine.

McDougall was an active participant in many scientific societies and served as associate editor of the *British Journal of Psychology* from the year it was established. His twenty-four books dealt not only with psychology in a stricter sense, but with ethics and international problems. They include, in addition to those mentioned above, *Abnormal Psychology* (1926), *The Group Mind* (1920), *Outline of Psychology* (1923), *Character and Conduct of Life* (1927), *Modern Materialism and Emergent Evolution* (1929), *World Chaos* (1931), *Religion and Science of Life* (1924), *The Frontiers of Psychology* (1934), and *The Riddle of Life* (1938). His obituary, written by one of his students, J. C. Flugel (1939), contains these words: "For he was acutely conscious of the important role that psychology has to play in human affairs, and at the same time regretfully aware that it was at present unfit to play this role, partly because of its humble and backward position in the hierarchy of sciences and partly because of dissensions among psychologists themselves."

MECHANISM (Mental Mechanism). In psychiatry, mechanism is a general term for a large group of psychological processes through which we meet the demands of reality, protect our personality, satisfy our inner needs, and allay our conflicts and tensions.

The mental mechanisms are gradually acquired in the course of our growth, operate largely on an automatic level, and are responsible for our ability to adapt to the requirements of life. Among them are perception, fantasy, memory, thinking, language, and the entire array of defense mechanisms. All these processes, and more, have been developed over a long period of evolution in man's effort to cope with his environment and meet his inner needs.

Each of the mechanisms serves particular purposes in helping the individual develop a healthy personality and adjust to the physical and social world. Perception enables us to recognize and interpret experiences and events. Memory stores knowledge so that we can call upon it when needed. Fantasy makes it possible to imagine the past and future, and envisage new ideas. Language enables us to retain and express our thoughts, and to communicate them to others. All these mechanisms play an essential role in thinking, especially when we are concerned with the solution of problems. When they function effectively, they also help us maintain our mental health. If, however, we fail to adapt to reality and meet our emotional needs, we may develop the characteristic symptoms of personality disorder, which practically always involve disturbances in the mechanisms of language, perception, thought, memory, and fantasy.

In addition to the "adaptive processes" just mentioned, there is a group of mental mechanisms which are more directly and exclusively concerned with our conflicting impulses, our problems and tensions, and our efforts to defend the integrity of our personality —in a word, with our mental health and well-being. These are the defense mechanisms such as repression, identification, rationalization, compensation, and regression. We all make use of these devices in our attempts to alleviate anxiety, manage hostile and aggressive impulses, and maintain self-esteem. They frequently help to make life bearable and in themselves are not necessarily pathological. If, however, they are used to excess, they are bound to interfere with our relationship to ourselves and other people, and may therefore play a large part in mental and emotional disorder.

Two examples of these defense processes are the "compensatory mechanism" in which a basically shy or submissive person may become aggressive or overbearing; and the "scapegoat mechanism," in which resentful or frustrated individuals focus their anger on innocent people, blaming them for their own defects or difficulties. If the latter tendency is carried to the extreme, it may be indicative of a paranoid trend. See DEFENSE MECHANISM.

MEDICAL PSYCHOLOGY. An area of applied psychology devoted to collaboration with physicians on diagnosis, treatment, rehabilitation, and prevention, as well as research in such areas as psychopharmacology, psychosomatic medicine, and emotional reactions to illness. (The term medical psychology is used here as a parallel to educational, legal, and clinical psychology, and not as equivalent to psychiatry, as it is sometimes used in Europe.)

The period since World War II has brought medicine and psychology into closer contact. Not only have physicians recognized that psychology is involved in the doctor-patient relationship and in the patient's motivation to recover, but they have become increasingly aware of the emotional factors associated with illness itself. This trend has in turn prompted many pediatricians, internists, obstetricians, and others to consult with psychologists on problems of diagnosis. It has also led to collaboration in medical research and medical education. Some of the specific areas of collaboration will now be outlined.

Psychologists are contributing to medical diagnosis in three major ways. First, physicians frequently refer patients to them for assessment, and the results of their tests and examinations are integrated with medical data. Studies by Hinsie and others indicate that emotional factors are directly involved in at least 50 per cent of all cases seen by the physician. Second, psychological research on interviewing and communication is now being applied to the doctor-patient relationship. Research of this kind increases the physician's awareness of such aspects of the situation as the importance of using understandable language, ambivalent attitudes of patients toward treatment, their suggestibility, and their tendency to read unintended meanings into the doctor's comments, gestures, or tone of voice. Third, psychological studies of introspection have brought a new awareness of the difficulties of obtaining accurate reports on such questions as localization of pain, sensory reactions, and precisely what is perceived during an eye examination. See IATROGENIC ILLNESS.

Although psychologists do not themselves administer medical treatment, psychologically oriented physicians are now taking into account their patients' cultural background and personal history, as well as their attitude toward themselves. They realize that these factors can be important in determining their own approach and procedures. In a growing number of hospitals psychologists themselves are serving as consultants to ward physicians and nurses on problems of patient care, particularly in dealing with orthopedic disabilities, tuberculosis, and other chronic disorders. They also play an important role on rehabilitation teams, dealing with such problems as assessment of motor and intellectual skills in planning a remedial program, appraising the adjustment of the individual to his disability, and providing personal and vocational counseling.

The field of preventive medicine is now expanding, and techniques developed by psychologists are being applied on an increasing scale. Survey procedures are being used in many ways— for example, to discover why people oppose water fluoridation, or why they neglect to be vaccinated for polio. Interviews with patients who fail to report for treatment after a diagnosis of cancer have shown that one third attribute their hesitation to fear and unwillingness to recognize the existence of the disorder. Delay in seeking diagnosis and treatment was found to be most prevalent on the lower economic and educational levels. The public education programs on cancer and other diseases have not only made use of information gathered in surveys of this kind, but have also utilized many of the techniques of media and motivation research developed by consumer psychology. See PUBLIC OPINION SURVEYS.

One of the most significant changes that has taken place in the last twenty years is the increasing involvement of psychology in medical education. Practically every medical school employs psychologists. In some of these schools they give only a few lectures, but in others they present entire courses on such subjects as general psychology, psychodiagnostic techniques, abnormal psychology, psychology of personality, and in some instances developmental psychology, electroencephalography, psychotherapy, and research methods. A few medical schools have established departments of medical psychology or behavioral science. Psychologists also participate in the training of residents in pediatrics, neurology, and ophthalmol-

ogy, and may help to train nurses, occupational therapists, physical therapists, and social workers. In addition, they often spend a good deal of time in case conferences, collaborative diagnostic studies, joint research projects, and student counseling. Dental schools rarely offer courses in psychology, but about one half of them employ part-time psychologists for testing and counseling. Some psychologists also conduct workshops for practicing dentists on interpersonal relationships with patients.

Another rapidly growing area is that of psychological research on medical problems. The approach is usually an interdisciplinary one, involving collaboration with physiologists, pharmacologists, neurologists, biochemists, and other specialists. The range of projects is broad, including many subjects dealt with elsewhere in this book: motion sickness, electroencephalography, space travel, sensory deprivation, psychopharmacology, and the nature and relief of pain. In the testing of drugs, for example, psychologists have developed techniques for detecting side effects on psychological functioning ("behavioral toxicity"), and have designed and carried out basic experiments on both animal and human subjects. In the investigations of pain, they have engaged in collaborative studies of placebo effects and hypnotic analgesia, and have also tested the effectiveness of different drugs on different kinds of pain. A particularly interesting result of these studies is the discovery that some drugs eliminate the discomfort and anxiety associated with pain without raising the pain threshold—in other words, the patient can still identify the pain but no longer finds it distressing. Finally, psychologists have applied their research techniques to the development of tests of diagnostic skills for administration to medical students. See PLACEBO.

Two other spheres of medical activity come within the competence of psychologists. They have contributed heavily to the development of the psychosomatic approach, particularly through stress experiments with animals, case history studies of human beings, and personality testing of patients with ulcers, migraine, and other psychophysiologic disorders. And they have recently begun to turn their attention to the opposite side of the coin, the study of psychological reactions to physical illness or disability, a field known as somatopsychology. Since these two areas are covered by other articles, they will not be discussed at this point. *See* SOMATOPSYCHOLOGY, PSYCHOPHYSIOLOGIC DISORDERS, as well as individual disorders listed under that topic in the Category Index.

MEDULLA OBLONGATA (Myelencephalon). The "bulbar" area located at the lower part of the brain stem, which extends upward from the spinal cord. It is one of the three structures of the hindbrain, the most primitive part of the brain. The other structures are the pons and cerebellum.

At an earlier stage of evolution, the medulla was an important sensory and motor center. In fish, it was devoted largely to movement and contained special "vagal lobes" for the sense of taste. In man and other mammals it is partly a transmission center and partly a control center. Many tracts pass through this region conducting impulses upward and downward between the cord and the higher centers of the brain. It is also the site of entrance or exit for eight of the cranial nerves, V to XII, which are involved in facial movement, hearing, taste receptors in the tongue and pharynx, neck and tongue muscles, and control of the heart and blood vessels. In addition, it contains autonomic nuclei which control the fundamental processes of breathing, heartbeat, and blood pressure. For this reason the medulla is sometimes called the vital center of the brain.

MELANCHOLIA. A functional mental disorder, usually psychotic in nature, characterized by severe depression.

The melancholic patient is painfully dejected, inactive, withdrawn and may be afflicted with feelings of worthlessness as well as hopelessness. There appears to be no adequate reason for this state of mind, and it is believed to stem primarily from deep, unconscious sources. *See* AFFECTIVE PSYCHOSIS.

The term melancholia has a long history. Hippocrates, the "father of medicine" (c. 460 to 377), described the symptoms and course of melancholia in detail and distinguished it from mania, or extreme excitement. He recognized that both these states are mental illnesses, but attributed them to organic causes. In addition he described a "melancholic" temperament which he attributed to an excess of black bile.

The term is falling into disuse, and has been largely replaced by "depression" and the specific types of depression, such as acute, agitated, and retarded. Some psychiatrists use the term involutional melancholia to designate the depression that sometimes occurs in the involutional period, but the American Psychiatric Association favors the more general term involutional psychotic reaction. The reason is that while most psychotic reactions in the involutional period are depressive (i.e. melancholic) in character, some patients exhibit paranoid or other types of reaction. *See* DEPRESSION, MANIC-DEPRESSIVE REACTION (GENERAL), PSYCHOTIC DEPRESSIVE REACTION, INVOLUTIONAL PSYCHOTIC REACTION.

MELANCHOLIC PERSONALITY. A personality pattern disturbance characterized by a constant mild depression and an inability to enjoy life.

Melancholic individuals are subdued and morose, but generally kind, sympathetic, and helpful to the point of submissiveness. They tend to be over-conscientious, industrious, and perfectionistic in their activities, but usually deprecate their contributions and worry about minor mistakes. They are constantly fearful of disapproval, and if anyone criticizes them, they suffer in silence instead of defending themselves. When faced with new problems, they are usually indecisive, insecure, and easily discouraged.

This entire personality pattern is highly resistant to change, and there is a predisposition to affective disorder, including manic-depressive psychosis. *See* PERSONALITY PATTERN DISTURBANCE.

MEMORY IMPROVEMENT. It is an all-too-obvious fact that there are wide variations in memory ability. Some people complain that their memory is like a sieve; others have a phenomenal capacity to recall almost anything they have seen or heard. There is considerable agreement among psychologists that these wide variations are only in part due to natural endowment. The rest—and it is probably the major part—is due to techniques used in noting, learning, and recalling the material. In general, people with so-called good memories have been found to use efficient methods, while people with poor memories use inefficient methods. The question, then, is: What are the most effective ways to learn and memorize?

Before reviewing the principles which have been most fully verified, it might be well to consider some of the faulty suggestions and procedures that frequently parade under the name of memory improvement. First, it is often assumed that memory in general can be improved through practice in memorizing. This has been demonstrated to be false, since experiments have shown that the mere memorization of lists of names and numbers, or even poems, has no detectable effect. Memory is not a muscle that grows stronger simply through exercise. Second, mnemonic devices often appear to be helpful crutches, but they cannot be relied upon. Is "Thirty days hath September" followed by "April, June, and November" or "April, May, and December?" More important, a memory "system" that is based on such devices is bound to be highly artificial. Is it really sensible to attempt to memorize a list of objects by picturing them in the four corners of a room, or to memorize the French irregular verbs by making up a story which incorporates them? The trouble with these techniques is that they give us more to remember than we had in the first place; and often the mnemonic device is harder to recall than the facts themselves.

Third, commercial memory courses often operate on the principle that any association will be an aid to memory. The student therefore has to struggle to find associative links, and all too often ends up with a series of irrelevant and farfetched details. Every time he wants to remember a telephone number he has to rack his brain for a date or mathematical formula to associate with it, and every time he meets a new person he has to make a special effort to find some feature that will tie up with his name. Here, too, the procedure is artificial, circuitous, and burdensome.

This is not to say that such tricks are totally ineffective. They actually do help many people to remember the kind of things that memory courses stress—that is, statistics, names of clients, stock numbers, etc. The teacher dramatically demonstrates his own ability by rattling off the names of the entire class after the first session; and some of his students will be able to perform similar feats after the course is over. But the question is whether these achievements are worth all the time, effort, and money. Most of the data is rote material that can be more efficiently stored in a manual or notebook than in the mind. And as for material that is really useful and important, this can generally be remembered well enough by practicing simple, direct learning techniques.

Let us say we have trouble with names, as so many people do. First, it is important to narrow our sights and try to remember only the names of people who mean something to us. Second, the basic reason we do not remember the names of people we meet is that we do not attend to them fully, usually because there is some tension or distraction involved in a social introduction. Therefore, the important thing is to listen carefully to the name, say it aloud in firm tones, and then repeat it a few times during the conversation. Third, it is useful to look squarely at the individual to get a clear visual picture of his features, and then to refresh our memory with a few glances as we repeat his name during the conversation. Some people also find it helpful to imagine the name written on a blackboard, but this is usually unnecessary. The four cues Stop, Look, Listen, and Repeat should be sufficient. If they don't work, it is probably best to resign ourselves and join the host of people who "just can't remember names."

But recalling names and other factual details is usually not the core of the problem. The important question is how to improve our memory for the books we read, the courses we take, and the information we need in our work and social life. Here the key lies in applying sound learning principles to the kind of material we want to remember. Psychologists have developed and tested these principles over many years, and there is considerable agreement that the following are particularly effective:

Self-recitation. After reading a section or chapter, close the book and ask yourself questions. If you cannot give the answers, consult the book immediately. About 40 per cent of one's time should be spent in this type of active review. It is far more effective than merely rereading the material.

Overlearning—that is, studying material beyond the point where we can repeat it once or twice. Self-recitation and recitation to others are both methods of overlearning. It is best to concentrate on material which you tend to forget easily and not go over material you have no trouble learning. Overlearning is particularly useful with rote material such as telephone numbers; it can usually be carried out by repeating the material aloud or writing it down. Tests have shown, however, that the law of diminishing returns applies to this technique. In an experiment involving memorization of words, Group A learned the material just well enough to repeat it once, Group B repeated the list one and one-half times as much as Group A, and Group C twice as many times. On recall tests, Group B was almost 50 per cent better than Group A, but Group C was only 25 per cent better than Group B (Krueger, 1929).

Overlearning is also important in habit formation. This accounts for the fact that we often show unexpected proficiency in activities we have learned at an earlier period but have not practiced for years—for example, bicycle riding or typing. *See* HABIT.

Periodic review. Review should begin very soon after studying, since tests have shown that we tend to forget most rapidly just after we have been exposed to the material. Later review enables us to forestall the natural process of attrition that sets in as time goes on. Frequent regular reviews are generally economical because they take less time than infrequent reviews at longer intervals. This technique not only contributes to overlearning, but conforms to one of the cardinal principles of learning, that distributed (spaced) practice is usually superior to massed practice. *See* FORGETTING.

Principle learning. Memory can be

greatly improved by finding a logical pattern in the material we want to retain. Social security numbers and dog tags have to be learned by rote since they have no intrinsic meaning; but meaningful patterns of one kind or another can be found in most material that is worth remembering. The way to remember a play or a novel is to concentrate on the plot and fit the details into this framework. Even facts like the names of the twelve cranial nerves, which give anatomy students so much trouble, can be remembered if we find a principle around which to organize them—for example, if we study the etymology of the terms or the contribution of each nerve to actual human experience. It is almost always easier to remember a principle than to remember the details; and we can usually work out the details from the principle that brings them together. Similarly, it is much more efficient, as well as more interesting and useful, to learn the principles of geometry than to memorize the individual proofs. Principle learning is associative learning at its best. It facilitates memory by binding the material we study to a wider body of knowledge.

Finally, tests have shown that *mental set* is an important factor in memory. If we deliberately set ourselves to concentrate and remember, we will be sure to increase our power of retention. It also helps to remind ourselves, on occasion, that "This is important," or to underline essential points in a book or jot them down in a notebook. Many experiments have proved that anything which lends emphasis to the impressions we receive will heighten recall.

There is no royal road to memory improvement, but much can be accomplished if we put these five or six principles in practice—with determination. *See* LEARNING TECHNIQUES.

MEMORY STORAGE. The problem of where and how memories are stored in the nervous system has long been a subject of both conjecture and research. Earlier investigators suggested that experiences produce more or less lasting changes in the nerve fibers or in the synaptic junctures between fibers, and named these changes "memory traces" or "engrams." More recent research has sought to describe the memory process in specific terms, and has introduced a number of new possibilities.

Reverberating circuits. This theory holds that memory is due to the continuous operation, or "reverberation," of loops of neurons. It rests on the fact that electrical stimulation in isolated brain tissue continues for several seconds after stimulation (Burns, 1951), and also on the idea that some neurons appear to form closed pathways in which impulses might go round and round for longer periods of time (Hebb, 1955). If, for example, we are instructed to add a series of numbers, many neurons will be activated, but one circular pathway continues to excite and re-excite itself as a "holding mechanism"; and as a result the instruction to add the numbers continues to exert control over the thinking process (Hebb, 1958). The theory holds that the brain probably contains a huge number of storage systems in the form of reverberating circuits that keep going until new stimuli mesh with them and lead to recollection.

Electroencephalographic records support this theory, since they show that the brain is continuously active even in sleep. Moreover, the brain rhythms change when we work on problems, probably because new circuits are activated. Also, experiences have shown that animals will not remember how to run a maze if they are given a massive electric shock right after their trial runs—presumably because the shock disrupts the circuits (Gerard, 1959). The same experimenter has also introduced evidence against this theory.

He taught hamsters to run a maze, and then reduced their temperature by 40 per cent. This put them in a condition of hibernation, in which the brain waves disappeared almost completely. In spite of this fact memory was not obliterated. When the animals were warmed up, they could still remember how to run the maze (Gerard, 1953).

New nerve endings. Injured nerve cells do not regenerate, as other cells do, but they can grow new endings (axons and dendrites). This suggests that when neurons repeatedly fire together, they may sprout new connections that in some way store our memories. This is an older theory, but it has not been discarded since recent studies conducted with an electron microscope have revealed wide variations in the number and size of the synaptic "knobs" of nerve cells. There are the structures in which the nerve endings from various cells are grouped.

Recorded messages. Since all neurons fire as a whole and then go through a period of inactivity (the refractory phase), it has been suggested that neurons might be turned on and off in patterned groups. In this theory, the brain would resemble a digital computer which stores information for future use. It might also work like a television tape which stores patterns of magnetized charges in iron filings embedded on a plastic ribbon. The experiments of Penfield on electrical stimulation of certain areas of the cortex lend support to this theory. *See* HYPERMNESIA.

Chemical memory. This theory is based on the fact that electrical energy can be stored by chemical substances, the principle on which the storage battery is based. To account for specific memories, the energy must be put in coded form. The nearest analogy appears to be the genetic system, in which complex molecules of DNA (deoxyribonucleic acid) guide the development of the organism according to a fixed code. It may well be that proteins in the glia cells which support and nourish the neurons play an important role in this memory process, since there is evidence of chemical interchanges between the two types of cells, the glia cells and the nerve cells (Galambos, 1961). Also, direct stimulation of the glia cells has been found to produce electrical responses and mechanical contractions (Hild, Chang, and Tasaki, 1958).

Although the specific process is not fully known, there is a growing conviction that memory is chemically coded, and may be aroused when an appropriate enzyme is released by the activity of a particular set of neurons. Hydén (1959, 1963) has suggested that DNA is primarily responsible for "racial memory" in the sense that it is the source of genetic instructions which determine the basic characteristics of every human being, while various forms of its derivative, RNA (ribonucleic acid), act as its assistants in controlling specific cellular functions. He believes that one of these functions is the encoding of the organism's individual memories. A number of experimental investigations have lent at least tentative support to this theory. It has been found, for example, that the RNA in certain cells of the nervous system of animals is altered when they are given a particular kind of training. Moreover, when these animals are injected with chemicals that block the formation of RNA during the training period, they tend to learn very little if anything at all.

Experiments on flatworms (planaria) have provided even more direct evidence of the role of RNA in memory (McConnell, 1966; McConnell et al., 1963). The investigators knew that these worms respond with a strong muscular contraction when placed in water and subjected to a brief electrical current. With this response in mind, they developed a classical conditioning procedure in which the onset of the shock was repeatedly paired with the shining of a bright light until the contraction response was elicited by the light alone. Next, a substance containing RNA was extracted from the bodies of the conditioned planaria and injected directly into the body cavities of untrained flatworms. When these worms were subjected to the same Pavlovian training as the original worms, they learned the conditioned response more quickly than a group of control animals injected with RNA from untrained planaria. Other investigators have obtained similar results in rats (Babich et al., 1965; Fjerdingstad et al., 1965) and have also found that the RNA transfer effect applied only to the stimulus used in the learning task and was not the result of a generalized improvement in learning ability.

These experiments suggest that a specific learned ability, or memory, can be transmitted from one animal to another via RNA—and consequently there has been much speculation about the possibility of transmitting knowledge from individual to individual by injection. At the moment, however, the results obtained by the original investigators have not been successfully replicated in other laboratories. But if they are ultimately substantiated, it will mean that RNA is the chemical mediator for memory. This will still leave the problem of how the molecule encodes information and how the injections of RNA affect the organism that receives them.

MENARCHE. The first menstruation, marking the start of a new phase in the feminine life cycle.

The menarche usually occurs between the eleventh and seventeenth years, and was at one time taken as a sign of sexual maturity. Today, however, it is known that menstruation usually begins before the ovaries are capable of producing mature ova, and therefore

sexual maturity is not complete. Nevertheless, the menarche is the central event of the period of puberty, and a long step on the road to womanhood.

Most girls experience intense emotional reactions to the onset of menstruation. The majority welcome it as a sign of maturity and feel a sense of accomplishment. A minority, however, look upon this event with fear, anxiety, and resentment. These attitudes are due to a variety of influences, but the most important are the girl's general emotional security, the information she has acquired about the process, and the mother's feelings about sex and marriage.

In our society most girls study hygiene and personal development at school, and a fairly full and sympathetic account of the menstrual process is generally included in these courses. Ordinarily this helps to allay anxiety and prepare the way for the menarche. But the relationship of the girl to her mother, and the mother's attitude toward womanhood, marriage, and bearing children are usually more influential than the learning acquired at school. If the girl closely identifies with her mother, and the mother instills a sense of pride in playing the full feminine role in life, the girl will accept the beginning of menstruation as a sign of progress toward becoming a complete woman. She will then be able to override her normal feelings of apprehensiveness, and accept the physical distress as incidental to a larger goal. Even if this distress is greater than average because of some constitutional tendency or physical disorder, it will not be aggravated by emotional problems and the initial difficulties will usually subside in time.

Some girls, however, react in a completely different way. The onset of menstruation is marked by feelings of anxiety and protest. They rebel against this reminder of their future sexual role, either because their relationship with their mother has been filled with friction, or because the mother has impressed them with the trials and tribulations of pleasing a husband, bearing children, and carrying on the responsibilities of the home. These negative attitudes are often accentuated by further emotional factors, such as inferiority feelings, the idea that menstruation is "unclean," and an association between bleeding and injury, or between the pain of menstruation and the anticipated pain of the first sexual experience or the birth process itself.

Girls who experience emotional reactions of these kinds should be given an opportunity for counseling or psychotherapy, since their attitudes toward menstruation are so intimately related not only to their present well-being but their future role in life. See MENSTRUAL DISORDERS.

MENINGITIS. A bacterial inflammation of the meninges, the membranes covering the brain cortex. In some cases the infection spreads to underlying brain tissue and causes irreversible destruction.

Delirium occurs early in the course of the disease and takes the form of confusion, rambling speech, disorientation, and restlessness. In acute cases the patient becomes noisy and violent, and may have convulsions, after which he lapses into a coma. If he recovers, he may suffer aftereffects that include muscle weakness and blurred vision. The latter symptom is usually due to a choking of the optic nerve resulting from intracranial pressure—a condition known as papilledema ("choked disc"), which is also found in other disorders such as brain tumor, skull fracture, and encephalitis. Residual psychological symptoms rarely occur except in cases where the disease precipitates a neurosis or psychosis in a predisposed individual. Some patients, however, suffer brain damage resulting in perma-nent impairment of sensory processes, motor abilities, and mental capacity.

Since meningitis is relatively rare today as a result of widespread use of antibiotics, it accounts for somewhat less than 1 per cent of first admissions to mental hospitals and institutions for the mentally retarded. See MENTAL RETARDATION (CAUSES).

Illustrative Case: MENINGITIS

This forty-eight-year-old woman was admitted to the hospital with a history of a sore throat and increasingly severe headache developing over the previous three days. At the time of admission she was having difficulty swallowing anything other than liquids. She was rather lethargic but could be roused and at such times complained of severe headache.

Physical examination revealed an acutely ill woman, temperature 103.5°, rapid pulse and respirations. Her neck was stiff. Spinal fluid examination revealed an increased pressure, high cell count, predominately polys. Meningococci were demonstrated in the spinal fluid and a diagnosis of meningococcus meningitis was made. Antibiotic therapy was begun immediately. On the first evening of her admission to the hospital this patient became agitated. She complained of nausea. She attempted to get out of bed, claiming that she saw a woman walking toward her who was apparently going to hurt her. She was reassured by the nurses and quieted down. However, several hours later she became noisy, agitated, and quite anxious. She said she knew there was someone else in the room who would harm her. She mistook a small stand in the corner for a person crouching ready to spring at her. At this time she was disoriented, confused, and extremely fearful. Once again, however, she was reassured by the physician and nurse. She went back to sleep and by the next morning had shown considerable improvement in both her mental and physical state. She continued to improve and was subsequently diagnosed as cured. There was no recurrence of her acute mental syndrome. She remained lucid, co-operative, and in good contact.

A brief review of her history revealed some marital difficulties between her and her husband. She felt he was showing undue interest in another woman and she bitterly resented his attentions to this woman. The description she gave of the hallucinatory woman and her husband's friend were remarkably similar. There undoubtedly had been a good deal of resentment between the two women. In acute toxic situations the patient's delusions or hallucinations are influenced by his own personality and conflicts with which he is struggling. After the acute toxic condition subsides, the patient loses the psychotic evidences and returns to the premorbid personality adjustment. (English and Finch, 1964)

MENINGOVASCULAR SYPHILIS. A form of cerebral syphilis in which the blood vessels and brain coverings (meninges) are attacked by the spirochete germ. The damage is usually diffuse rather than localized, and the symptoms are quite different from those in meningo-encephalitic syphilis (general paresis), in which the neural tissue itself is destroyed. In many cases, however, there is a mixture of types.

Meningovascular syphilis is relatively rare and constitutes less than 1 per cent of first admissions to mental hospitals. It takes two major forms: syphilitic meningitis and vascular neurosyphilis.

Syphilitic meningitis may involve either impairment in absorption of the cerebrospinal fluid ("acute syphilitic hydrocephalus"), inflammation of the base of the brain ("basilar meningitis"), or inflammation of the meninges around the upper part of the brain ("vertical meningitis"). The hydrocephalic type, which is rare, is characterized by headache, nausea, vomiting, and stiff neck. In the basilar type the major symptoms are headache, dulled mentality, impairment of memory for recent events, sleepiness, and in some cases confusion, delirium, and stupor. The cranial nerves may be affected, resulting in such symptoms as double vision, facial anesthesia, and deafness. The vertical type involves more extensive areas of the brain and produces a wide range of symptoms.

These include severe headaches, dizziness, irritability, loss of concentration, retarded thought and speech functions, and sometimes confusion and delirium. In contrast to general paresis, syphilitic meningitis does not lead to serious impairment of the personality, delusions, or serious disturbance of behavior, judgment, and social reactions.

Vascular neurosyphilis usually accompanies the early stages of syphilitic meningitis. Early symptoms are intermittent headaches, often worse at night, dizziness, insomnia, irritability, emotional instability, increasing apathy, and impairment of memory. Vascular (circulatory) accidents frequently occur, causing temporary neurological disturbances, such as aphasia and hemiplegia (paralysis of one side of the body), and resulting in some loss of intellectual capacity.

The treatment of choice for all types of meningovascular syphilis is penicillin, and excellent results are achieved unless permanent damage to neural tissue has already taken place. For other details on diagnosis, treatment, and prevention, *see* SYPHILIS.

MENOPAUSE (Climacteric). The menopause, which marks the end of the reproductive cycle in women, generally starts between the early forties and the late fifties and ordinarily lasts between two and three years. During this period there is a gradual reduction in ovarian hormones and the menstrual flow decreases until it ceases altogether.

Today the menopause is approached from the psychophysiologic or psychosomatic point of view, since physical and emotional factors are so closely interwoven during the entire period. Both the physiological changes and the psychological reactions vary widely from woman to woman. In many women, perhaps the majority, the glandular changes are so gradual and the attitude so healthy that symptoms often expected during menopause occur only in the slightest degree. A few women may even be totally unaware of the transition. At the other end of the scale are those women who experience a variety of distressing symptoms such as hot flashes, chills, irritability, mood swings, dizziness, excessive perspiration, palpitation, depression, joint pains, fatigue, intolerance of emotional tension. Few women show all these symptoms, and in individual cases they may vary in intensity from mild to severe.

Many attempts have been made to explain this wide range of responses to the change of life. Physiological and constitutional factors may be partially responsible for the differences. These factors affect the timing of the menopause, the speed of the process, and the specific character of the hormonal imbalance that occurs. Undoubtedly physical changes are instrumental in producing severe symptoms in some cases and mild ones in others. It is known, too, that menopause usually sets in earlier and is accompanied by more intense reactions among women who have not borne children than among women who have. The differences here are believed to be due in part at least to differences in the physical condition of the ovaries.

These physical factors, however, do not operate by themselves. They are constantly under the influence of emotional changes associated directly with the secretions of hormones, as well as the individual woman's personality makeup and attitude toward the change of life. As Therese F. Benedek (1959) has put it, "When the gonadal stimulation (that is, sexual and reproductive life) subsides permanently the healthy woman is not severely threatened by this loss. The accomplishments of the reproductive period—not only the propagation function but also the total developmental achievement of the personality, its lasting sublimation, its capacity to love and to do for others— will sustain the personality when the

gonadal stimulation abates and the woman faces the change of life."

Personality and attitude affect the change of life in many ways. Although the acute reactions of the woman who has not had children are believed to be partially due to physical factors, they are probably even more the result of feelings of regret or frustration at not attaining complete fulfillment as a woman. The anticipation of the menopause is another significant factor both for those who have and for those who have not had children. For some women it signifies a loss of attractiveness and sexual ability—even though this is not usually the case—and therefore it is a severe blow to their ego. They take it as a sign that they are growing old, useless and unwanted. As a result, they become acutely aware of any sign of aging, and believe they have reached the final turning point in life and can look forward to nothing but mental, social, and physical deterioration.

These women usually experience the symptoms of menopause in their most intense form—but they invariably ascribe them solely to the physical changes and stresses of the period. Yet the fact is that most of the emotional symptoms have existed before and are now aggravated by tension and anxiety. Earlier personality weaknesses or faulty reaction patterns come to the fore in exaggerated form. The endocrine changes are merely the trigger that precipitates the emotional disturbances. In fact, personality studies have shown that many of these tendencies can be traced to the years before menstruation itself began, and it is significant that women who suffered from premenstrual depressions or dymenorrhea usually react with the greatest severity to cessation of menstruation.

The emotional symptoms that develop in these cases vary widely since they depend on the total personality of the individual woman. Often these reactions are most acute where there is no evidence of serious endocrine imbalance, an indication that they are psychological in origin. Some women lose their capacity to respond sexually, or to love others as before. They often grow selfish and self-centered. Some become highly irritable and impatient, others turn their hostility inward and become angry with themselves. Tendencies to depression and hypochondria manifest themselves in exaggerated degree. The meticulous housekeeper becomes perfectionistic to the extreme, as if she had to prove her worth and usefulness. The woman who has long been assailed with doubts about her adequacy or ability may now develop acute feelings of inferiority, or accuse herself of lost opportunities and a wasted life. The sensitive woman may become hypersensitive. The anxious woman may develop a phobia. The woman who has tended to blame others for her lot may begin to express paranoid ideas. In a few cases these processes develop into full-blown psychoses. *See* INVOLUTIONAL PSYCHOTIC REACTION.

Most women of today react to the change of life in a totally different way. They look upon the menopause, or climacteric, as a normal, natural event that merely signifies the end of their reproductive period. By the time it occurs they have usually fulfilled their maternal needs; if they have not, they have fully adjusted themselves to that fact of life. They realize that the menopause does not mean the end of their sexual life, but may even mean the beginning of a new phase in which sexual enjoyment and sexual drive actually increase because they are no longer hampered by anxiety over pregnancy. Moreover, now that they are relieved of the pressures and responsibilities of raising children, they find time for new outlets and absorb themselves in the hobbies and community activities they have long wished to pursue. At the same time they find new ways to enjoy family life—particularly

in relaxed devotion to home and husband, and in the many gratifications that arise from watching their children raise a family and from developing the role of cherished, helpful grandparents.

When the menopause is taken as a challenge to reorganize life and develop new satisfactions instead of being looked upon as a sign of failing resources, most women find that their energy level increases and their physical and emotional health actually improve. To them, the menopause is not the beginning of decline but a further stage in development.

The term climacteric, as opposed to menopause, may be applied to men as well as women. Among men it refers to a period of life, occurring about ten years later than in women, when psychological reactions to glandular changes—more than the changes themselves—produce symptoms in some individuals. This syndrome is less well defined and less frequent in males, and includes such symptoms as nocturnal frequency, fatigue, flushes, indecision, decreased sexual desire, and reduced potency. Anxiety over diminished potency, or simply the fear of becoming less potent, is believed to be the major factor, although it may be combined with concern over being "put on the shelf," feelings of inadequacy, or apprehension over possible illness in old age. Common reactions among the more neurotic are depression and a desperate attempt to prove their sexual vigor. In a few men the depression may rise to psychotic proportions, just as it does in some women during the involutional period.

Illustrative Case: MENOPAUSE

A forty-eight-year-old woman complained of anxiety, palpitations, depression, and apathy of about six months' duration. Her menopause had begun about a year before, and although she still suffered from mild vasomotor instability, most of her signs of autonomic imbalance had disappeared. Hormone treatment had been prescribed when she first became anxious and depressed, but she had not improved.

She was a shy, intelligent woman whose husband worked long hours and was preoccupied with his job. She had always found it difficult to make friends and had devoted herself to her two children. Recognizing that she was inclined to overprotect them, she had conscientiously tried to permit them their independence. The onset of her distress coincided with her daughter's engagement announcement and followed closely her son's departure for college.

The doctor knew that her husband was fairly set in his devotion to business and realized that since his patient had always been too shy to make social contacts before she became depressed, she could not be expected to do so now.

After making sure that she was not suffering from a psychotic or suicidal depression, he invited her to come in for a brief conference at a stated time each week and prescribed mild sedation as an adjunct to his psychologic support. At these conferences they discussed her marriage, her family, and her interests, and he encouraged her to express her loneliness for her children and her feeling of futility and uselessness. Although it was evident that she did not have enough to keep her busy, the doctor did not try to redirect her interests into channels of his choice but helped her to discuss possibilities of her own. Eventually, she brought out, rather self-consciously, that she had once been interested in painting. The doctor then gently and patiently encouraged her until she enrolled in a course at the art museum. There she gradually enlarged her circle of acquaintances, and as her interest developed, her symptoms subsided. (Aldrich, 1966)

MENSTRUAL DISORDERS. In psychiatry, psychophysiologic (psychosomatic) disorders associated with menstruation.

The relation between the menstrual cycle and emotions is a reciprocal one. The glandular changes that initiate the cycle produce emotional responses, and attitudes and feelings toward the process often affect both the regularity and amount of menstrual flow. This interaction can be demonstrated in the normal cycle as well as in various disturbances that may arise, such as premenstrual tension, dysmenorrhea, amenorrhea, menorrhagia, and menopausal reactions. The disorders can best be understood in the light of the normal cycle.

The normal cycle. Changes in the emotional state have been found to parallel the hormonal changes that occur in the normal cycle. At the beginning of the cycle, when the production of the female hormone, estrogen, gradually rises, women experience an increase in sex drive accompanied by sexual dreams and fantasies. This is ordinarily a period of emotional well-being that spreads to other activities as well. These responses reach their height when ovulation occurs and the organism is ready for conception. However, if the sex drive remains unsatisfied, the frustration may produce tension, irritability, and restlessness. Emotionally immature or inhibited women may unconsciously defend themselves against the increase in sex drive by becoming particularly hostile toward men during this period.

After ovulation, sexual tension diminishes, interest in heterosexual contact recedes, and the woman enters a relaxed, passive, receptive phase in preparation for motherhood—often accompanied by dreams and fantasies about having children. Conflicts and anxieties may, however, turn the wish for pregnancy into fear, and neurotic women transform the desire for children into the wish to be a child and into complaints about insufficient love and care from others.

As hormonal production declines, the premenstrual phase begins, and in varying degrees women are tense, irritable, anxious, and easily upset. When the menstrual flow occurs, these mood changes subside and most women experience a sense of relief. Some, however, go through a depressive phase during which they talk about sorrowful events, dwell on their physical complaints, depreciate themselves, or feel disgusted about the entire process. The depressive reaction is usually due to feelings of failure in achieving pregnancy, and the attitudes of depreciation and revulsion reflect the notion that women are inferior to men, and that menstruation is a curse that has befallen them. These reactions disappear when the new cycle starts.

Premenstrual tension is one of the most common of the menstrual disorders. One type occurs in women whose mothers have derogated the feminine role, characterized sexual activity as disgusting, and described the monthly period as an illness. From the very start of menstruation these women have looked upon the process as ugly and repugnant, and invariably complain about it as a sickness, demand unnecessary care and attention, and experience feelings of helpless anger and depression while it goes on. Another type of premenstrual tension occurs in young women who have accepted the menarche (onset of menstruation) with pride but who are afflicted with hidden conflicts and feelings of guilt due to sexual temptations or sexual behavior, or because of other personality disturbances. These weaknesses are brought to the surface by the glandular imbalance that takes place prior to menstruation. Some become depressed, withdrawn, or hypersensitive, while others complain of migraine headaches or eat and drink to excess. Since emotional control is reduced during this period, kleptomania or other psychopathic behavior has been found to occur more often in this phase than at other times. See KLEPTOMANIA.

Painful menstruation (dysmenorrhea) may take many forms, including pains resembling labor pangs, distention, abdominal distress, nausea, and migraine. These symptoms may be due to various organic conditions such as immature pelvic organs, faulty response to sex

hormones, or circulatory conditions— but in many cases they are found in women who are filled with anxieties and doubts about their role as wife, mother, and homemaker. Some of them have never had enough training for womanhood, while others are strongly identified with a mother who complains about her lot. Their negative attitudes toward sex and motherhood make them hypersensitive to pain, and their emotional tension undoubtedly aggravates any physical disorders to which they are predisposed during the menstrual period.

Profuse and persistent bleeding (menorrhagia), occasionally results from unusual emotional tension associated with anticipation of intercourse that is either greatly feared or greatly desired, or both. Young brides are sometimes afflicted during the honeymoon; and the condition also occurs when husband and wife come together after a long separation. Excessive bleeding may also be due to ovarian imbalance, and may therefore occur in young girls when the menstrual cycle is being established, and in older women at the onset of menopause. It is particularly upsetting to young girls since it not only interferes with their activities but causes self-consciousness and fear of embarrassment. It may also make them exaggerate the difficulties of being a woman. These anxieties and resentments may actually prolong the condition, and special efforts should be made to help these young women understand and accept the entire menstrual process as a sign of maturity rather than a source of distress.

Scanty menstruation (oligomenorrhea) and absence of menstruation (amenorrhea) may result from delayed sexual maturation due to insufficient gonad secretion (hypogonadism). More often these conditions are considered an unconscious defense against sexuality. Among adolescent girls scanty menstruation is often accompanied by overeating, which is itself a substitute for sexual expression. Almost invariably these girls do not want to have anything to do with menstruation because it is the "painful," "dangerous," "dirty" part of sex—yet they continue to have fantasies about a life rich in romance. The absence of menstruation, like impotence in men, is often associated with depression, and disappears when this mood changes.

In the rare condition known as *pseudocyesis,* certain women show all the usual signs of pregnancy, including absence of menstruation, distention of the abdomen, and breast changes, even though conception has not taken place. They are usually immature, hysterical personalities who have strong conflicts over childbearing. See FALSE PREGNANCY, MENARCHE, MENOPAUSE, INVOLUTIONAL PSYCHOTIC REACTION.

Illustrative Case: MENSTRUAL DISORDERS

Miss S.I., aged twenty-four years, complained of severe dysmenorrhea. Violent pains assailed her during the entire menstrual period; and for several days before and for several days after the period there was extreme lassitude and irritability. Physical examination revealed no pathology, and the use of ovarian extracts proved to no avail. Further examination revealed that the patient was "nervous," that she startled easily, that she had always been easily excitable, and irritable. The most important "cause" in this girl's case was the role of the dominant, irritable, demanding, and highly neurotic mother, who by her attempts to control the lives and actions of her children had rendered them unhappy and unstable. One of the important elements of therapy was to train this girl to change her attitude toward the mother, so that she would listen carefully to what the mother had to say, and then, in her own mind, decide what was the right thing to do. She was then to tell her mother, objectively, quietly, and unemotionally what her conclusions were and, where possible, to act on her own conclusions. Her entire attitude toward life was to be converted from the emotionally dependent, cringing, unself-reliant type of reaction to that of an independent, reliant person responsible for her own decisions and actions. When the patient learned this procedure, in addition to other changes, she lost her "nervousness," and her dysmenorrhea could be easily relieved by aspirin. (Kraines, 1948)

MENTAL AGE (MA). An individual's level of intellectual development, determined by comparing his performance on intelligence tests with the performance of average individuals of a given age— for example, a five-year-old who scores as well as the average seven-year-old would be assigned a mental age of seven.

The concept of mental age was originated by Alfred Binet, the French psychologist who developed the intelligence test. He believed that mental ability grows regularly from infancy on and can be scaled by creating test items appropriate to a wide range of ages and abilities. In constructing a test, these items are given to a large and representative group of children, and the age at which a majority master each of them is noted—for example, "Brother is a boy, sister is a _____" is placed at age seven. Binet's procedure was later refined at Stanford University to include six items for each year, with each correct item worth two months MA credit. A child's MA is calculated by first noting his basal MA, which is the level at which all tests are passed, and adding two months for each item passed above that level until all items are failed for a given year. See BINET, STANFORD-BINET TEST.

An example will clarify this procedure. If Bill, a six-year-old, passes all items through mental age six, two items at the seven-year level and one at the eight-year level, his over-all MA is six years six months. This means that the boy has the mental ability of a six-and-a-half-year-old child. The MA is considered a measure of absolute ability; if Bill had been five or eight, his MA would still be six and a half. To find a figure that would indicate his development relative to his age, we would divide his MA by his CA or chronological age, and multiply by 100 to eliminate the decimals. This figure is the IQ, which would be about 108 in Bill's case. *See* INTELLIGENCE TESTS.

Although the MA is less often used than the IQ, it has some independent value. We can say, for example, that an MA of about six years is required before a child can do well in first grade. Usually, however, the chronological age and not the mental age determines admission to school, and as a result children of widely different mental development tend to be lumped together. In a study conducted in a large midwestern school, the MA for first-graders ranged from four years seven months to eight years five months even though the CA's hovered around six years six months. This kind of situation can have detrimental effects, especially on children at both extremes of the MA scale. Those at the lower end benefit little from the teaching and become discouraged; those at the higher end learn so fast that they often become bored and restless.

Many schools attempt to overcome these problems by paying greater attention to the MA than to the CA. One solution is to advance the brighter children to the next grade; another is to keep them with their own mental age group but to offer them more individual instruction. A few schools are experimenting with the more unorthodox solution of ungraded classes during the first three years of elementary school.

MENTAL HEALTH. There is no single, accepted definition of mental health. Some psychiatrists and psychologists define it in negative terms as absence of symptoms—or, better, absence of symptoms that interfere substantially with the individual's sense of well-being and ability to meet the demands of life. Most specialists, however, prefer a positive formulation, in terms of establishing con-structive relationships with other people, releasing inner resources and potentialities, withstanding normal amounts of stress, and accepting one's self. On three points there appears to be practically complete agreement: that mental health is not synonymous with contentment or peace of mind, that it does not preclude emotional conflicts and upsets, and that it does not mean adaptation and adjustment in the sense of conformity and conventionality. The following is a representative sampling of definitions:

"Mental health is a state of well-being in which the individual has a satisfactory capacity for work, for relations with others, is able to love someone other than himself, is free of disabling symptoms such as severe tension, anxiety, depression and phobia, and is unhampered by serious mental conflicts." (Polatin, 1964)

Mental health is "that state in the interrelationship of the individual and his environment in which the personality is relatively stable, and the environmental stresses are within its absorptive capacity." (Marmor and Pumpian-Mindlin, 1950)

"Let us define mental health as the adjustment of human beings to the world and to each other with a maximum of effectiveness and happiness. Not just efficiency, or just contentment —or the grace of obeying the rules of the game cheerfully. It is all of these together. It is the ability to maintain an even temper, an alert intelligence, socially considerate behavior, and a happy disposition." (Karl Menninger, 1945)

"Mental health is the ability to handle everyday demands and situations, including our own emotional upsets, without excessive stress and strain. A mentally healthy person, therefore, has a sense of well-being and functions effectively in life. He can work regularly, think clearly, manage his emotions, enjoy life, and keep on reasonably good terms with most people, including himself." (Goldenson)

As these definitions indicate, mental health is a highly variable and relative quantity. There are different degrees of mental health as there are different degrees of physical health. If most of the ingredients exist in low degree, the individual is vulnerable to mental disorder of one kind or another, depending on his particular personality weaknesses, such as schizoid or paranoid tendencies. If the components exist in high degree, the individual is usually capable of enduring large amounts of stress without developing crippling symptoms. However, generalizations of this kind must be qualified in two ways: first, individuals who appear to be vulnerable may possess hidden strengths to offset their weaknesses; and second, those who appear sound and "well adjusted" may harbor weaknesses that can be exploited by certain types of situations. It seems to be a fact that no one is totally invulnerable—that "every man has his breaking point"—but this point varies widely and often unpredictably from person to person.

How can mental health be achieved and maintained? There are three general types of approach: primary prevention, consisting of attempts to lay a foundation of positive mental health during the development of the individual; secondary prevention, consisting of prompt care and treatment with the aim of arresting disorders in their earliest stages; and tertiary prevention, comprising rehabilitative measures designed to prevent relapse and forestall or reduce disabilities arising out of mental disorder. The latter two types of prevention are discussed in full under other topics and will only be mentioned in this article.

The activities involved in safeguarding mental health fall into three general categories: biological, psychological, and sociological. *Biological preventive measures* include: prenatal care for the mother to prevent mental defects arising from malnutrition, German measles, etc.; adequate obstetric services to prevent birth injury or anoxia; general health measures in childhood to reinforce resistance to both physical and psychological stress; thorough, periodic medical examinations throughout life to insure early detection of organic disorder; safety measures to prevent head injury and ingestion or inhalation of toxic substances in the home or at work; immunization and other medical measures to prevent infectious diseases that might lead to brain inflammations; adequate nutrition to prevent deficiency disorders that might develop into mental disturbance; and application of eugenic measures to prevent the birth of children to parents with known hereditary defects or diseases.

Psychological preventive measures include: adequate mothering in infancy and childhood; an atmosphere of love, approval, and encouragement; feeding schedules, toilet training, and social training adjusted to the child's needs and developmental pace; freedom to experiment and explore the surroundings; firm, consistent but kind discipline; extra emotional support and assistance during critical periods of stress, such as hospitalization or loss of a parent; cultivation of frustration tolerance through practice in facing difficulties independently, and through the development of mental, social, and physical competence; adequate opportunity to express feelings and emotions freely; encouragement of emotional control where the situation requires it; cultivation of positive emotions, such as love and humor, with help in handling negative emotions such as fear and anger; promotion of constructive interpersonal relationships through the encouragement of co-operative attitudes, sense of responsibility, and sensitivity to the needs of others; adequate preparation for crucial turning-points in life—especially going to school, adolescence, marriage, getting a job, having children, and retirement; and cultivation of a positive, constructive philosophy so that life itself will have value, meaning, and purpose.

The sociological preventive measures are far less under the control of the individual or his family than the biological and psychological measures, since they depend on the organization of society and its institutions. In general, these preventive measures include all efforts to reduce the social stresses that lead to personality distortion and breakdown, as well as all organized attempts to provide a positively healthful environment for every citizen. These comprise: housing projects to eliminate slums; adequate recreational facilities; programs to control drug traffic, alcoholism, and syphilitic infection; epidemiological studies to determine the incidence and distribution of mental disorders, and to identify general sociological conditions of stress such as social discrimination, as well as trouble spots where special action should be taken; and the building of community programs designed to make maximum use of institutions, agencies, and all types of leaders in maintaining the mental health of the population in a given area. *See* COMMUNITY PSYCHIATRY, MENTAL HYGIENE, REHABILITATION, COMMUNITY MENTAL HEALTH CENTERS.

Finally, what is the state of our nation's mental health? The answer can be given by quoting some recent statistics. Approximately nineteen million people in the United States, including four million children under fourteen, are in need of treatment for some form of mental or emotional disorder, mild or severe. This figure represents about 10 per cent of the population. An estimated one million are afflicted with psychotic disorders, ten million suffer from psychoneuroses, and the remainder need treatment for chronic alcoholism, personality disorders, acute or chronic brain syndromes, psychophysiologic disorders, drug addiction, or transient situational disturbances. In the course of a year about four million of these individuals receive help—over 1,600,000 in hospitals, one million in outpatient clinics, and 1,300,000 in private offices. Over half of the nation's hospital beds are occupied by mental patients, most of whom are classified as psychotics; and approximately half of all patients who go to physicians for medical or surgical treatment suffer from disorders with psychological complications. The over-all meaning of these statistics is that mental disorder is our country's greatest health problem. *See* NORMALITY, ECOLOGICAL STUDIES.

MENTAL HEALTH AND ECONOMIC LEVEL. A recent and promising development in the mental health field is the long-overdue recognition that patients on different socioeconomic levels require different therapeutic approaches. Most of the recognized techniques of psychotherapy have been devised by middle-class individuals for use with middle-class patients. Psychologists and psychiatrists at the National Institute of Labor Education, the William Alanson White Institute, and union health centers have shown that many of these methods cannot be effectively applied to low-income people. Recognition of this fact is of special importance today because of the trend toward community mental health centers, which will undoubtedly expand treatment opportunities for individuals at the lower end of the economic scale. Heretofore "blue collar" workers have for the most part been allowed to drift along until serious disorders or dire emergencies arise, and then they have been relegated to city and state institutions. Even when they were offered psychotherapy in community clinics, most of them found the approach uncongenial and dropped out.

The question, then, is what kind of therapy will be both acceptable and effective with low-income patients. The first step is to recognize that they do require their own therapeutic approach. Typically, middle-class therapy treats the patient's problem as internal, emotional, and originating in relationships that go back to childhood. The major techniques are discussion, free association, and other verbal methods; and the goal of the therapy is self-understanding and personality growth. The low-income client, on the other hand, believes that the causes of his problem are external and physical, and stem from present situations rather than the past. He expects treatment to eliminate his symptoms and produce specific changes in behavior and physical health. In his eyes the therapist is a physician who will give him concrete directions and practical solutions. He prefers home visits to the formality of the office, and is confused and repelled by too much talk and analysis. If given a choice, he prefers techniques that utilize physical activity and social intercourse.

In view of these differences, Riessman and others strongly recommend that therapists not only make a special study of treatment techniques which will be appropriate to low-income people, but also become familiar with their goals, hopes, traditions, and general style of life.

As a consequence of these findings, many changes in the therapeutic process are already being tried. The usual intake procedures have been foreshortened or postponed, and the patient is encouraged to air his problems and feelings as soon as he comes in. This helps to satisfy his need for a down-to-earth approach, and also gives the therapist valuable diagnostic material: "The first stage should be cathartic, supportive, informal, and should provide immediate service and appropriate advice." (Riessman, 1964)

A number of special techniques have been found to be particularly effective during the therapeutic process itself. One of them is role-playing centered around the patient's specific problems. This approach has long been popular in educational programs of labor unions, and is well suited to the low-income client's interest in group action and interaction. It also encourages the patient to express himself openly and creates an informal setting which brings the therapist into closer rapport with the patient's way of life. A second approach is to make full use of nonprofessional auxiliaries, or "indigenous nonprofessionals," drawn from the same background as the client himself. This "helper principle" is effective because it establishes a bridge between the therapist (who is usually a middle-class individual) and the client's life at home.

A third technique has been called "personality adjustment through social action" (Wittenberg, 1948). It has been found that low-income people greatly benefit from becoming involved with labor unions, block committees, hobby groups, or religious activities. Activity of this kind gives them the strength to handle their psychological difficulties, and reduces dependence on the therapist.

In addition to these techniques, these clients have been found to derive psychological benefit from auxiliary physical treatments, because of their general belief that their problems are physically caused. The therapist therefore includes tranquilizers, diets, and muscle relaxation in his treatment program.

During the past few years a number of large unions have begun to offer mental health service to their members on an organized basis. One promising example is a project carried out by the Hillman Health Center of the Amalgamated Clothing Workers of America, under grants from the National Institute of Mental Health and the Vocational Rehabilitation Administration (Wiener, 1966). The program is a venture in preventive medicine, since it is designed to enable disturbed workers to hold their jobs while undergoing treatment at co-operating hospitals and, where necessary, to provide for re-training or less taxing jobs. Among the early findings of this project are these: (1) the union health insurance depart-ment is an important case-finding source, since workers with emotional problems frequently stay away from their jobs and make insurance claims; (2) the business agent, who organizes and services union members, is not only a logical source for case referrals, but can often serve as a constructive member of the clinical team, since he is in direct touch with both the client and his job; (3) patients sent to clinics for treatment are more likely to "stick" if they are prepared for referral and if the referring agent (the project in this case) has a working relationship with the clinic; (4) the great majority of cases required less than three months of treatment and fewer than eight face-to-face interviews; (5) it is important to have the clinic see the patient im-mediately, even if the first meeting is brief. It must be recognized, of course, that the treatment goals in this type of program are largely limited to changes in attitude and behavior and do not in-volve the reconstruction of the person-ality.

A representative case is that of Mrs. R., who walked off the job for no apparent reason, but later returned and within a few hours threw a piece of metal at one of the workers who had "started making faces at me." The busi-ness agent urged her to go to the clinic and called to make an appointment with a psychiatrist. She broke the first appointment, explaining, "If I kept it you would think I was crazy." The business agent replied that he did not think she was crazy, but that she had an emotional problem and could be helped. When she again hesitated, he offered to accompany her, and the clinic rearranged its schedule in order to see her immediately. The psychiatrist found that Mrs. R. felt that other people were

making grimaces at her in social as well as work settings, and identified her per-sonal problem as one of guilt and anx-iety aroused by an extramarital situa-tion. He prescribed a tranquilizer (Stel-azine) and asked her to return to work immediately, making another appoint-ment.

Meanwhile, the business agent dis-cussed Mrs. R. with the clinic social worker, who was acting as case co-ordinator. He informed her that she had been employed for nine years as a ticket sewer, a critical and precise op-eration, and had been an excellent worker. However, during the preceding five months, shortly after her brother had been murdered, she had been mix-ing up the tickets and had begun to complain that her fellow workers were talking about her. To keep Mrs. R. at work, the business agent accompanied her to the job and enlisted the co-opera-tion of her boss and her fellow workers. The psychiatrist continued the medica-tion and interviewed Mrs. R. weekly, focusing attention on her personal and family problems as well as her feelings of guilt. She soon reported that the other workers were more friendly, and recognized that "All the things peo-ple were doing to me, I see now were in my imagination." After about six weeks of treatment, she appeared calm and relaxed, was working up to par, and treatment was terminated.

A second example is the Union Ther-apy Project organized in 1963 by the William Alanson White Institute in New York City. Recognizing that out-patient treatment is rarely provided for blue-collar workers, thirteen graduates of the Institute banded together and signed a contract with United Auto Workers Local 259 to render ten ther-apy hours and three hours of social work time in the evenings at a nominal fee to be paid by the union welfare fund. The first step was to educate the union members toward mental health and to correct the prevailing idea that treatment means that the patient is "psycho" or "nuts." To this end, discussions were held at union meetings and articles were placed in the local's newspaper. Treatment service was offered as part of the union's health and welfare plan, and patients were seen immediately instead of being put on a waiting list.

In this program, the therapists employ a short-term modified analytic approach geared to an understanding of blue-collar values and outlook on life. Flexibility is maintained, and the therapy is adapted to the patients rather than the patients to the therapy. There is little probing into the unconscious, and in many cases the therapist deals with the family as a group rather than with the patient alone. Regular seminars are held at the Institute to discuss cases and discover the most effective approach and the most helpful type of therapist. As in the Clothing Workers Project, shop stewards are the chief case-finders, since they are respected by the members and can spot trouble in its early stages.

MENTAL HEALTH CLINIC. "An outpatient psychiatric service unit having a psychiatrist in attendance at regularly scheduled hours who takes medical responsibility for all clinic patients" (National Institute of Mental Health, 1957). Such centers are located within the community, often in neighborhoods where the need is greatest so that patients may obtain help as close to home as possible. The typical clinic employs a team approach in which psychiatrists, psychologists, and psychiatric social workers offer a wide range of treatment services, including help with child behavior difficulties, excessive drinking, marital problems, depression, anxiety, psychiatric emergencies, and the diagnosis of psychotic disorders.

As the report of the Joint Commission on Mental Illness and Health (1962) points out, the mental health clinic occupies a "pivotal position" for early treatment on an outpatient basis and for aftercare of discharged patients; "it is also the fulcrum of efforts to remove the barriers isolating mental hospitals from the community." According to a statistical study for the year 1961 there were at the time about 1600 of these clinics serving an estimated 665,-000 (Bahn et al., 1963), but today the number is slightly over 2000 and the number of persons treated per year is approximately one million. About half of the clinics studied by Bahn were operated by state mental hospitals and other state agencies, 300 by voluntary agencies under state aid, 64 by the Veterans Administration, and 400 are under private auspices. Some clinics serve children or adults only, but most of them serve both.

There is a rapid annual turnover of patients who come to these clinics, with 60 per cent newly admitted, 10 per cent readmitted, and 30 per cent continued from the previous year. The most common diagnoses for children are transient situational personality disorders without underlying personality disturbance (36%), personality disorders or behavioral defects with little evidence of anxiety or stress (21%), and mental deficiency (17.6%). Patients below and above eighteen years of age are about equally represented. Boys outnumber girls by about two to one, but adult males are only slightly in excess of adult females. The most common diagnoses for adult patients are personality disorders (32%), psychoneurotic disorders (30.9%), psychotic disorders, especially schizophrenic reactions (19.5%). Bahn and her associates found, however, that out of every ten for whom service was terminated, eight received diagnostic evaluation with only three of them receiving treatment, while the other two were usually referred elsewhere. Of the patients treated, one-fifth had only one face-to-face interview and three-fifths fewer than five face-to-face interviews.

The psychoneurotic patients received the most attention and showed the greatest improvement: 70 to 80 per cent were improved.

As a result of its investigations, the Commission recommended that community mental health clinics should be regarded as a "main line of defense in reducing the need of many persons with major mental illness for prolonged or repeated hospitalization" and stated that the goal of the National Mental Health Program should be to establish one fully staffed, full-time clinic for each 50,000 of population. The Commission also felt that clinics providing intensive psychotherapy for children should be developed and expanded, and that a state aid program should provide training for child psychiatrists, who were "in short supply." As for adult patients, the Commission recommended that the principal function of such clinics should be (a) to provide treatment by a basic mental health team for persons with acute mental illness, (b) to care for incompletely recovered mental patients either short of admission to a hospital or after discharge, and (c) to provide a headquarters base for mental health consultants working with other treatment centers, schools, and social agencies. *See* COMMUNITY MENTAL HEALTH CENTERS.

MENTAL HOSPITAL. In 1965 there were 497 hospitals exclusively devoted to mental patients in this country. Of these, 332 were Government hospitals (244 state, 45 county, 41 Veterans Administration, and two other Federal hospitals), and 165 were private hospitals. In addition, approximately 495 community general hospitals (about one out of 11) had separate psychiatric units, about 500 other general hospitals admitted psychiatric patients to their regular medical facilities, and another 2000 admitted mental patients on an emergency basis. Many mental patients were also housed in old-age homes and in-

stitutions for the chronically diseased. In all, 51 per cent of the hospital beds in the country were occupied by psychiatric patients, with about 98 per cent in public hospitals and 2 per cent in private institutions. Taking turnover into consideration, approximately 1,500,000 mental patients receive hospital care and treatment in the course of a year.

The annual cost of hospital treatment for mental patients is about two billion dollars, but the cost per patient varies widely in different institutions. In 1965 state hospitals spent an average of $6.74 per day per resident patient, ranging from $3.18 in Mississippi to $23.02 in Alaska. Veterans Administration hospitals spent an average of $15.47; private mental hospitals, $21.99, and short-term general and special hospitals, $41.58. Veterans do not pay for hospital care, and patients in state institutions are charged only according to their ability to pay. The difference in rates is partially reflected in the personnel figures of the different institutions. Many private mental hospitals have a ratio of two full-time employees (attendants, maintenance workers, etc.) per patient, while the national average for public hospitals is only one employee for every three patients. The doctor-patient ratio is approximately one to 25 in private institutions and one to 100 in public hospitals.

In recent years practically every aspect of the mental hospital has undergone modification, including the physical plant, organizational structure, staff roles, treatment methods, and relationship to the community (PLATES 29, 30). Since these changes can best be understood when viewed against a historical background, we will briefly outline the development of the mental hospital from its beginnings in the early 1800s to the present time. Following Greenblatt and Levenson (1965), this review will be divided into three periods: the moral treatment era, the decline of moral treatment, and the "road back" during the past thirty to forty years.

The era of moral treatment dates from the founding of the first American mental institutions to the Civil War. The earliest private institutions were the New York Lunatic Asylum (1808), the Friends Asylum (Philadelphia, 1817), McLean Asylum (Waverly, Mass., 1818), Bloomingdale Asylum (White Plains, N.Y., 1821), and the Hartford Retreat (Hartford, Conn., 1824). The earliest public hospitals were Manhattan State (New York, 1825), Western State (Staunton, Va., 1828), and Worcester State (Worcester, Mass., 1833).

Under the leadership of Benjamin Rush, who brought to this country many of the reforms initiated by Philippe Pinel in France and William Tuke in England, these hospitals abandoned the harsh, punitive practices which prevailed in the eighteenth century. The patients were, for the most part, handled with compassion and understanding; and the superintendent sought to establish a personal relationship with each one in order to become aware of his thoughts, feelings, and behavior patterns. Charles Dickens' *American Notes for General Circulation* contains one of the clearest statements of the moral treatment approach, which, in his words, emphasized "trust of patient, interaction between patients and staff without paralyzing fear, little or no use of restraint, a diversity of occupations and recreations, and the expectation that behavior could become well modulated even in the severely deranged and that the future held out promise for these unfortunates if they were cared for properly."

There is evidence that this promise was realized in many cases—in fact, one hospital reported that 70 per cent of its patients were discharged as recovered or improved at the end of one year. Of these, 50 per cent returned to the hospital, but many were discharged or resettled later on. Though some of the publicized reports would fail to meet the rigid statistical requirements of today, they nevertheless suggest that a humane, optimistic approach can be effective, especially in hospitals organized along the general lines of a therapeutic community.

Moral treatment began to decline after the Civil War for a number of reasons. The influx of immigrants brought in patients who were considered morally and educationally degraded; the hospitals became so large that competent personnel could not be found; the idea of running the institutions for a profit took hold as a result of the industrial revolution, and low-grade attendants were hired; above all, the patients no longer came into direct contact with the superintendent or others who were responsible for their recovery. While these changes took place, moral treatment was further undermined on a theoretical level. One of the leading psychiatrists of the day, Pliny Earle, held that the form of mental illness itself was changing and becoming increasingly malignant. A well-known sociologist, W. G. Sumner, developed a Darwinian theory which viewed all illness as a form of unfitness determined by the laws of nature, and the best that could be done was to help the unfit to survive. But most important of all, the prevailing European doctrine that all mental illness was due to brain lesions invaded America; and since no way to remedy these lesions could be found, the mental hospitals gradually abandoned all semblance of treatment and became custodial institutions.

The third period began at the end of the nineteenth century after the great crusade of Dorothea Dix, and continued in the early twentieth century due largely to the work of Clifford Beers. The trend toward custodial care was gradually reversed, and the concept of moral treatment was revived. Progress, however, was slow because the hospitals were filled with chronic, deteriorated patients whose virtually hopeless condition was due more often to long institutionalization than to pathology. The "road back" was further handicapped by the fact that the hospitals were huge and impersonal, staffed by underpaid and incompetent employees, and situated far from medical schools and population centers. During the period from 1910 to 1920, however, two trends originating in Germany had considerable effect on hospital treatment of the mentally ill in America. The organic viewpoint advocated by Griesinger in the nineteenth century was further developed by Kraepelin and coupled with description and classification of mental disorders as separate and distinct illnesses which run a predictable course. Although this approach turned attention away from the psychological and social aspects of mental illness, it had the positive effect of focusing research efforts on disorders that involved brain pathology requiring hospital treatment, such as general paresis, cerebral arteriosclerosis, senile brain disease, and toxic psychoses. *See* GRIESINGER, KRAEPELIN, DESCRIPTIVE PSYCHIATRY, ORGANICISM, DIX, BEERS.

It took two world wars and a depression to demonstrate the need for a vigorous attack on mental disorders as a social as well as a personal problem. After the First World War, the public was startled to learn that there had been almost as many emotional casualties as physical casualties. The success of Franklin D. Roosevelt's social reforms following the depression of 1929–32 suggested that the Federal Government might play a part in maintaining and improving the mental health of its citizens. The need for large-scale help was again demonstrated in World War II when about 40 per cent of our young men were found to be emotionally unfit for military service, with another large percentage suffering breakdowns in the service itself. As a result of all these factors, a national mental health movement began to take shape.

This movement was accelerated by the development of intensive therapeutic techniques which went far beyond moral treatment. During the 1920s the organic approach was challenged by the psychodynamic doctrine of Freud, and a little later the holistic approach which integrated the physical, the psychological, and the sociological was developed under the leadership of Meyer, Southard, White, Sullivan, and Jelliffe. Between the 1930s and the 1950s all three components of this comprehensive approach were rapidly advanced. The introduction of electroshock therapy and insulin coma therapy in the 1930s brought new physical treatments into hospital psychiatry. Psychosurgery offered another promising procedure for last resort cases, though this drastic technique was overdone and is infrequently used today. In the 1950s tranquilizers and antidepressants were added to the hospital armamentarium; as a result, both excited and depressive patients became more manageable and more amenable to other therapeutic methods. On the psychological level all these new approaches opened the way to a wider use of group as well as individual psychotherapy, as well as to more highly developed forms of rehabilitative procedures such as industrial and recreational therapy. On the social level, it became possible to introduce the concept of an open hospital, to organize the environment as a therapeutic community in the fullest sense of the term, and to establish closer ties between the institution and the community outside.

These changes in the hospital picture were greatly advanced by the passage of the National Mental Health Act, which provided support for programs of basic research, training of professional workers, and improved rehabilitation services. At the same time, the citizens of the country were awakened to the mental health needs of the nation by the National Association for Mental Health and other organizations. By the 1960s a national movement against mental illness was in full swing.

Now let us look at some of the changes currently in progress. They are actually so numerous, and in some cases so radical, that they amount to a revolution in the entire mental hospital picture. Since most of these innovations are discussed under separate topics, we will confine ourselves to an over-all view at this point.

Physical structure. The massive, prisonlike buildings designed according to the "Kirkbride plan" are gradually being replaced by facilities with less than a thousand beds. Large wards are being broken up and an increasing number of patients are living in smaller units with a more intimate and homelike atmosphere. Greater attention is being given to décor, and hard hospital benches are being replaced by comfortable chairs. More rooms are being set aside for special activities such as music and dance sessions. *See* KIRKBRIDE.

General organization. Administration is less centralized, and the individual units are given semiautonomous status. Many staff roles have been redefined— for example, the attendant has been upgraded to "psychiatric aide," and the recreation specialists and rehabilitation counselors participate in staff conferences as members of the therapeutic team. The patients themselves are now conceived as participants in the therapeutic process. They advance their own recovery by engaging in group discussions and by serving on committees which make recommendations affecting their lives in the hospital. All these changes help to make the entire institution a therapeutic milieu.

Community links. The barriers between hospital and community are being broken down by wider use of volunteers, frequent visits of patients in the community, attendance by local citizens at hospital social events, and a trend toward having staff workers live in nearby communities rather than on the hospital grounds, in order to keep them in contact with the world at large.

The open hospital. Barred windows, locked wards, forceful methods of restraint are rapidly disappearing, along with the excessive use of such sedation techniques as tub baths, wet sheet packs, and heavy doses of hypnotic drugs. Seclusion is still occasionally required for violent cases, but on a short-term basis. "Maximum security units" have been largely eliminated, except for some hospitals for the criminally insane. Three factors are primarily responsible for these changes: tranquilizing drugs, the idea of the therapeutic community, and the concept of the patient as a sick person rather than a madman.

Admission, orientation, discharge. Admission procedures are now designed to allay the patient's anxiety and to assure that his rights and privileges will be respected. After admission, steps are taken to orient him to the hospital organization and help him adjust to ward life. Discharge procedures have been eased in many places, largely because many patients can be maintained on drugs, and readmission has also been simplified. As the concept of the hospital has changed from custodial institution to a center for intensive treatment, the number of voluntary commitments has increased.

Transitional arrangements. Opportunities for partial hospitalization and services that bridge the gap between hospital and community life have multiplied. The most important new facilities are the day hospital, in which the patient is treated at the hospital during the day but lives with his family at night; the night hospital, which offers overnight treatment for patients who work during the day; the halfway house, a residential center for patients who have no home or no suitable place to live; the sheltered workshop, which provides supervised working conditions outside the hospital for patients who have not fully recovered; the therapeutic farm, for patients who need long-term, inexpensive care and rehabilitation; the five-day hospital, which enables the patient to return to his family on weekends; and the foster-family, to promote convalescence and readjustment to family life before returning to the community.

Outpatient and emergency services. Many state and general hospitals have established outpatient departments designed to reduce the need for full hospitalization. An increasing number of hospitals and community centers are also offering special emergency care—for example, the Home Treatment Service of the Boston State Hospital and the Community Extension Service of the Massachusetts Mental Health Center. One study has shown that 40 to 50 per cent of patients who receive emergency treatment are able to stay out of the hospital.

Finally, modern treatments and the use of community facilities have had a significant effect on the mental hospital picture in America. In 1966 only 20 per cent of all psychiatric patients were treated in state institutions, as contrasted with 75 per cent two decades before. This change was due primarily to an increase in the use of general hospitals, outpatient clinics, and private office care. The number of resident patients has been dropping every year since the introduction of psychotropic drugs. Between 1955 and 1967 there was an over-all reduction of 133,000 patients in public mental hospitals, and in 1967 alone there was a drop of 26,000—from 452,000 to 426,000. Yet, in spite of this 24 per cent decrease since 1955, the actual number of patients treated each year has risen 15 per cent, since the average length of stay for new patients has been materially shortened. This is particularly true of the more advanced hospitals where intensive techniques are employed. In these institutions 80 per cent of newly admitted patients are discharged within six months to a year. In some states, notably Iowa, California, Connecticut, and Kansas, the average hospital stay of all first admissions is now about two months. For schizophrenic patients, who occupy half the beds in mental hospitals, the chances for release within a year have risen from 20 per cent to 80 per cent. Moreover, readmission rates are now as low as 10 per cent for patients receiving continuing aftercare and rehabilitation. *See* DAY HOSPITAL, NIGHT HOSPITAL, FAMILY CARE, SHELTERED WORKSHOP, HALFWAY HOUSE, MILIEU THERAPY, SOCIAL BREAKDOWN SYNDROME.

MENTAL HYGIENE. Systematic efforts directed to promoting mental health and preventing mental illness. The term is falling into disuse and is being replaced by the term mental health, as in such phrases as "Department of Mental Health" and "mental health measures."

The term was first applied in the nineteenth century to a regimen of prudent living designed to preserve the health of the mind, just as various sanitary and prophylactic measures were recommended to maintain the health of the body. In America it was used by Clifford Beers, at the suggestion of Adolf Meyer, to designate his movement for public education on the understanding of mental illness and the plight of the mental patient. The organization he founded for this purpose, the National Committee for Mental Hygiene, is now known as the National Association for Mental Health. The current program of that organization is a good indication of the broadening of the concept of mental hygiene in recent years, for it offers, in addition to his original goals, a comprehensive program involving research, voluntary services, rehabilitation, community psychiatric services, and counseling. A similar widening has taken place in mental hygiene clinics, which are now being enlarged into or replaced by community mental health centers offering a wide variety of services, including diagnosis and treatment of disorders not requiring hospitalization, and mental health education for all segments of the population. *See* NATIONAL ASSO-CIATION FOR MENTAL HEALTH, COMMU-NITY MENTAL HEALTH CENTERS, MENTAL HEALTH CLINIC, BEERS

An authoritative account of the broadened field of mental hygiene is presented by Lemkau in his article, "Mental Hygiene," in the *American Handbook of Psychiatry* (1959). He finds four major emphases in this field: (1) the prevention of mental diseases, (2) the interpretation of psychiatric problems and opportunities to the general public, (3) the promotion of mental health in the general population, and (4) application of the philosophy of public health to psychiatry. Some examples of each of these will be given.

1. Preventive efforts have been most successful in acute mental disorders in which one causal factor predominates, as in (a) the control of delirium due to infectious diseases through administration of sulfa drugs; (b) the use of enriched food, vitamins, etc., in preventing psychoses associated with nutritional and metabolic disorders, such as pellagra and pernicious anemia; (c) prevention of general paresis through early treatment of syphilitic infection; (d) compensation for nutritional deficiences in certain conditions causing mental retardation, especially phenylketonuria; (e) prevention of cerebral arteriosclerosis by treatment of diabetes mellitus; (f) prevention of certain types of mental deficiency and brain damage by avoiding obstetrical complications; (g) the use of public health and industrial measures to prevent lead poisoning and other toxic conditions which produce psychoses; (h) prevention of head injury disorders through improved safety measures.

Prevention is less successful where motivational and social factors are involved, as in alcoholism, syphilis, and such behavior disorders as juvenile delinquency, prostitution, and drug addiction. These conditions require an individual approach, including promotion of healthy family life, as well as a social approach aimed at the pathological components of the subculture (such as antisocial gangs) which influence the attitudes and behavior of young people. Primary prevention of complex disorders such as schizophrenia is virtually impossible at this time, since the causal factors are still largely unknown. However, secondary prevention—arrest of the disorder by early treatment—is frequently feasible.

2. The second approach is the promotion of mental health in the population as a whole. This is done largely through educational and counseling programs designed to develop attitudes and provide information that will have a preventive effect. One example is the "anticipatory guidance" given to parents in well-baby clinics and through government pamphlets on such subjects as feeding problems, sleep difficulties, and temper tantrums "not only to avoid pathological reactions in the child but to promote intrafamilial relationships of understanding" (Lemkau). A second example is the guidance program offered to specific groups at periods of peak concern, illustrated by family life and premarital courses given in schools or community centers, classes for mothers and fathers to be, and monthly leaflets mailed to new parents.

There is also a growing trend to include mental health information in the training of teachers, nurses, clergymen, and physicians, since they are frequently in a position to provide basic guidance and deal with unhealthy patterns of behavior before they become fixed. Educational programs are also directed at such problems as increasing the capacity to function in spite of symptoms (instead of demanding "perfect" mental health), and showing how damaged individuals, such as retarded children, can be protected from unnecessary stresses and given opportunities for satisfying activity suited to their resources.

3. The third type of mental health activity consists of calling the public's attention to services for prevention, treatment, and rehabilitation. This is one of the functions of the National Association of Mental Health and its affiliates, which conduct information programs via the public media as well as through schools, churches, and industry. The community mental health centers now in the making will also conduct their own information programs to make their services known to the public. Programs of both types will attempt to erase the stigma attached to mental illness and to motivate individuals to seek the help they need. The social worker is one of the key figures in this process, but much can also be accomplished by well-informed ministers, school guidance counselors, family physicians, and counseling departments in industrial firms.

4. Finally, during the past twenty years the development of a public health philosophy has added a new dimension to mental hygiene. This approach is based on a redefinition of health as "complete physical, mental, and social well-being," and recognition that every available instrumentality must be utilized if we are to promote total health in the total population. This comprehensive approach is, at the present, "an aim enunciated far ahead of the possibility of its accomplishment in any field of health, by no means excluding the field of mental hygiene" (Lemkau). The reason for this deficiency is that organized health efforts are now scattered among a wide variety of agencies, and co-ordination of all efforts is therefore a massive problem.

The envisagement of the "total mental health functioning of the community as an integrated whole" is an essential part of that problem. As the Group for the Advancement of Psychiatry has shown, it will involve making a survey and evaluation of a huge number and variety of services—including, at the local level, prenatal clinics, day-care centers, schools, recreational programs, industrial health, welfare agencies, courts, outpatient and inpatient services, and activities of lay and professional groups concerned with mental health; and at the state level, agencies paralleling the local services, as well as commitment procedures, organization of the state mental health office, and specific services such as state mental hospitals, institutions for the mentally retarded and epileptic, penal institutions, reformatories, and training schools. Also included would be rehabilitation services, psychiatric departments of general hospitals, foster home and adoption services, marriage counseling, and services to the aged.

Consolidation of all these services and facilities is a mammoth task, but progress has been made in some states through three general approaches: centralization of planning services in the state department of mental hygiene; establishment of independent local mental health authorities, or boards, for planning and administering programs with state aid and supervision; and consolidation of planning and services under state and local departments of health. These three efforts exist in a variety of combinations, but "the essential point is that all are pointing to a vision of a system of integrated functions from prevention applied to the total population, case finding early in the course of illness, early and effective treatment either in a hospital or in the local community, and, finally, rehabilitation to ensure sustained health and social productivity. This is the challenge faced by the mental hygienist." (Lemkau, 1959)

MENTAL IMPAIRMENT TESTS.
Tests for diagnosing intellectual impair-

ment or deterioration resulting from brain damage, psychotic disorders, or other pathological conditions.

With the exception of the Wechsler Scales, the tests described below have been developed primarily for clinical purposes. They are based on two major principles—first, that certain mental activities (especially memory, spatial perception, and abstraction or concept formation) are particularly sensitive to pathological processes; and second, old, well-established functions such as vocabulary are likely to be less affected by brain damage and mental disturbance than newly acquired learning. In order to assess these abilities in relation to each other, most of the tests are designed to measure the performance of the subject on different types of items.

As Freeman (1962) has pointed out, these tests, as a group, have not been adequately standardized or validated and "do not, as yet, provide a self-sufficient method for measuring mental deterioration, except in the more marked cases. However, clinicians who have used them are in substantial agreement that they are valuable in providing opportunities for observation of mental operations under controlled conditions in which prescribed materials are used. In such situations, an experienced psychologist is able to make important qualitative observations (of levels of abstraction or concreteness, rigidity or flexibility, bizarre responses, etc.) in addition to deriving, at times, quantitative values for the subject's performance." Because of their limitations, the tests that follow are generally used in conjunction with other techniques, such as projective methods, interviews, and direct observations of behavior.

Babcock-Levy Test. Scores made on a vocabulary test are compared with scores on other measures of mental "efficiency," on the principle stated above that vocabulary withstands the effects of age or mental illness better

than other functions. The subject's "vocabulary age" is determined by scores obtained on the vocabulary test of the Stanford-Binet. The tests which yield an "efficiency score" consist of items that emphasize information, recall of meaningful and meaningless material, motor speed (in writing, tracing etc.), and simple learning (immediate reproduction of a paragraph, or drawing designs from memory).

From these results an over-all efficiency index is computed, and compared with norms for different disorders such as paresis and schizophrenia as set up by the authors of the test. Since there is considerable overlapping between scores for different groups, these indices have to be supplemented by other information. Some investigators have gone beyond the use of the efficiency index by itself to the analysis of the *patterns* of performance in different patients—for example, schizophrenics have been found to perform poorly on recall of meaningful material, since they tend to omit many details, distort others, and introduce bizarre ideas. On rote repetition of digits, however, they do much better.

The tests are considered useful, though some psychologists believe they measure other functions than those named by the authors, such as, attention, concentration, coherence of thought, and visual imagery.

Hunt-Minnesota Test for Brain Damage. Here, too, the Stanford-Binet Vocabulary Test is employed as a point of reference for evaluating the subject's performance on other memory tests. These tests, six in number, involve exposure of series of paired designs and paired words. The subject is asked to reproduce one of the designs or recall one of the words in each pair when the other is presented. This is done either immediately or after a short lapse of time. Nine interpolated tests are also included as "validity indicators." These consist of information items, counting forwards and backwards, etc., and are given to determine whether the subject is too unco-operative, disturbed, or deteriorated to be tested.

The test has been standardized by comparing the performance of a relatively small number of patients with organic cerebral damage with a control group of other patients without brain damage. Although additional validation is needed, extreme scores are considered indicative. However, they should be carefully analyzed both qualitatively and quantitatively, and should be checked against other evidence.

The Benton Visual Retention Test is designed to detect disturbances in both memory and spatial perception. Ten designs of increasing complexity are individually presented on cards, and the subject is required to reproduce each of them as soon as it has been removed. Other items present drawings for copying or for reproduction after a short exposure or a fifteen-second delay. Scores are calculated in terms of number of correct reproductions and number of errors, and are interpreted in relation to the subject's I.Q. as obtained on any standardized verbal intelligence test, or in comparison with educational and vocational data if the I.Q. is not available.

The Bender Visual Motor Gestalt Test involves the perception of spatial relations. The subject is required to copy simple designs, a technique that was originally used for the diagnosis of aphasia. Details of this test are given under a separate heading. *See* BENDER GESTALT TEST.

The Grassi Block Substitution Test is an adaptation and extension of the Kohs Block Design which requires the subject to copy given designs with one-inch cubes of different colors. This instrument is still in the experimental stage, but appears to be promising, especially for detection of brain damage.

The *Goldstein-Scheerer Tests of Abstract and Concrete Thinking* are based on the principle that emotional disturbances interfere with thinking processes, and particularly with the ability to form abstract concepts that involve such operations as analysis, synthesis, shifting from one aspect to another, and keeping several aspects in mind at once. The examiner notes the way the subject attacks the problems and not merely the results achieved—in other words, interpretation depends on qualitative observations rather than on objective scoring techniques. Undoubtedly the tests would be more useful if scaled ratings and norms could be applied.

The series comprises five tests. The Cube Test consists of copying colored designs with cubes, all but one of which come from the Kohs series. The examiner notes whether the subject uses analytical reasoning in perceiving relationships or merely makes a direct, concrete approach. A graduated series of designs of decreasing difficulty is presented if the subject fails on the first attempt. On these new trials the design is enlarged to actual block size, or block models are presented. Abnormal subjects fail to benefit from these additional cues.

The Color-Sorting Test includes (a) presentation of woolen skeins of different hue and tint—the subject selects one and is then asked to pick others that go with it, and (b) presentation of three skeins differing in hue, brightness, and saturation from which the subject makes a selection according to hue or brightness. The investigators report that pathological patients cannot shift from the concrete task of matching on the first test to the abstract task of selecting and classifying on the second.

The Object-Sorting Test presents groups of about thirty objects (some for males, some for females) which the subjects are instructed to sort and classify on the basis of use, form, material, pairings, and groupings (such as dinner table settings). In the Color-Form Sorting Test, the subject sorts geometric figures according to their color or form, and is asked to describe what he is doing in order to discover whether he is using concepts. There are a number of signs of concrete as opposed to abstract thinking: a subject cannot grasp the principle or account for his grouping, or he may depend on sensory impression alone, or be unable to shift from one impression to another or to generalize from one performance to another.

Finally, in the Stick Test, the subject is shown geometric figures of increasing complexity and uses a set of sticks to copy them directly or reproduce them from memory. The tendency to associate the figures with concrete objects is interpreted as a concrete response.

The Goldstein-Scheerer series as a whole is of considerable value in diagnosing cases of marked mental defect or deterioration, but is less suited to detection of slight deficits.

The Kasanin-Hanfmann Test (PLATE 28) is a modification of the Vigotsky Test. The subject is presented with twenty-two blocks varying in color and shape, each with a nonsense name printed on the bottom, corresponding to one of four categories: tall-wide, flat-wide, tall-narrow, flat-narrow. The examiner selects a sample and asks the subject to pick out all others of the same kind. If he makes a mistake, the examiner turns the wrong block over to show that it carries a different nonsense name from the others. The subject continues working, with the aid of clues given by the examiner, until he arrives at the correct solution or fails altogether. He is then asked to state the principle of classification and to re-sort the blocks. *See* VIGOTSKY TEST.

Like the Goldstein-Scheerer series, this test is based on concept formation. However, the problems are considerably more difficult and are therefore not suitable for persons of lower intellectual levels or for patients who do not show deterioration in dealing with more familiar material. Scoring is based on both objective and qualitative judgment, including the subject's ability to interpret the task, to utilize concepts in attacking it, to verbalize the principles involved, and to arrive at a correct solution. A scoring plan is offered, but the values assigned have not been experimentally determined. The authors of the test were primarily concerned with the diagnosis of schizophrenia, but Rapaport (1945) has used it in constructing clinical descriptions of various types of cases, since it shows, among other things, the amount of rigidity, persistence, and flexibility which different subjects exhibit in tackling difficult and frustrating problems.

Other sorting tests are the Kahn Test of Symbol Arrangement and the Wisconsin Card-Sorting Test. So far, the research data on these tests appear promising.

Wechsler Scales. Wechsler, Rapaport and others have developed techniques for using the Wechsler Adult Intelligence Scale in the diagnosis of mental impairment. These procedures are all based on a "profile analysis" which shows the individual's relative performance on the eleven subtests. Three methods are used: first, the measurement of pattern, or variation, among the scores, as indicated by the average deviation (AD). Wechsler found that larger AD's are indicative of pathology, especially in schizophrenia. Second, characteristic score patterns have been constructed for organic brain disorders, schizophrenia, juvenile delinquency, anxiety states, and mental deficiency. For example, schizophrenic patients tend to score much lower on Object Assembly than Block Design, and have low Similarities scores but high Vocabulary and Information scores. The third procedure is based on the finding that tests requiring past learning show less decline than those involving speed, new learning, and perception of new relationships. The "hold" tests (those that do not show decline) include Vocabulary, Information, Object Assembly, and Picture Arrangement, while the "don't hold" tests comprise Digit Span, Similarities, Digit Symbol, and Block Design. The relation between the two types is computed to find the "deterioration index," which is then compared with the norm for the subject's age level.

The use of the profiles for diagnostic purposes has been criticized on a number of counts. The reliability of the subtests is not high enough to indicate any but large differences. Differences which Wechsler regarded as diagnostic have been found to occur frequently in the normal population. Also, large amounts of scatter may be due to conditions other than pathology, such as educational, occupational, and cultural factors. (Wechsler was aware of this and suggested that it be taken into consideration.)

The deterioration index may be thrown askew by the fact that many older people in the standardization sample had received less education than the younger subjects. Moreover, most of the studies of diagnostic interpretations based on the profiles have yielded negative or inconclusive results. In some studies the deterioration index has not successfully differentiated between mental defect and psychosis, between schizophrenia and neurosis, or between patients with brain damage and those with functional disorders. Most compelling, no significant relationship has been found between deterioration scores and actual decline in test scores on follow-up studies. On the other hand, the deterioration index has received some support from recent factorial analysis, and there seems to be a relation between scores on certain of the subtests and data derived from EEG studies. Also, low Digit Spans have been

found to occur more often among the brain-damaged than among normal subjects. These results indicate that at least some of the score patterns may be valuable in diagnosis.

In spite of their limitations, the Wechsler Scales are not only useful measures of intellectual level, but also give the clinician an opportunity to observe responses that may be indicative of personality disorder—for example, bizarre associations, excessive self-reference, or evidences of confusion. These cannot be accepted as conclusive signs by themselves, but must be regarded as leads or hypotheses requiring further verification.

The *Kahn Test of Symbol Arrangement* consists of sixteen plastic objects (heart, anchor, etc.) varying in size, color, and thickness. The subject arranges and sorts these objects in various ways, and tells what they mean to him. The object of the test is to identify the subject's cultural-symbolic thinking and to construct a psychograph based on his individual symbol pattern. By comparing this pattern with typical patterns of normal and clinical groups obtained through standardization on over 2000 adults and 200 children, the examiner can identify normals, neurotics, schizophrenics, and patients with organic brain pathology. The test is used primarily in clinics, hospitals, and correctional institutions, and can be employed with verbally blocked or unresponsive patients because of its manipulative aspects. Reliability and validity studies have yielded impressive results.

Tests for Aphasia. A number of tests and examinations have been developed specifically for evaluating linguistic impairment due to brain damage. The recently created Minnesota Test for Differential Diagnosis of Aphasia, developed by H. Schuell, assesses the type and extent of the disorder, as well as the prognosis for recovery, in each of five language areas. The stimulus material consists of two sets of cards and common objects supplied by the examiner. A monograph explains how to interpret the five parts of the test. "Examining for Aphasia," Second Edition (J. Eisenson), consists of a standardized procedure for systematically exploring the language functions of aphasics. A manual provides detailed instructions, explanatory matter, and fourteen plates of stimulus material in black and white and color. The Orzeck Aphasia Evaluation is designed for thorough assessment of apraxia, agnosia, and sensory suppression. The new Sklar Aphasia Scale, based on information theory and factor analysis, consists of four subtests for objective evaluation of speech loss and potential for recovery through exploration of the effectiveness of basic communication channels.

Other impairment tests. Another useful indicator of brain damage is the Memory-for-Designs Test (F. K. Graham, B. S. Kendall), which measures perceptual-motor performance of subjects from 8.5 to 60 years of age through immediate reproduction of printed designs from memory. It has proved effective for rapid screening purposes, since it takes only ten minutes to administer. Among the many other tests in use today are: the Hooper Visual Organization Test, which uses pictorial material for the differentiation of functional and motivational disorders due to brain pathology; the Grayson Perceptualization Test, involving reading at elementary levels; the widely used Shipley-Institute for Living Scale; the ten-minute Sherman Mental Impairment Test for young adults; and a new test battery constructed by A. J. Ayres, consisting of the Southern California Kinesthesia and Tactile Perception Tests, the Southern California Figure-Ground Visual Perception Tests, the Southern California Motor Accuracy Test, and the Ayres Space Test. *See* APHASIA, MINIMAL BRAIN DYSFUNCTION.

MENTAL PATIENT ORGANIZATIONS. Social clubs or other organizations formed to help former mental patients readjust to community life.

These organizations are based on the fact that it often takes a discharged mental patient several months before he can feel at ease in social relationships. Membership in a club in which others are facing similar problems usually helps to prevent him from withdrawing, and lends him the group support he needs to get through this trying period.

The Joint Commission on Mental Illness and Health (1962) has reported the existence of about 70 of these organizations in 26 states. The largest was Recovery, Inc., which claimed 250 groups in 20 states, with a total membership of over 4000. In most instances groups meet in donated or rented quarters on regular evenings, and are primarily concerned with social life and the maintenance of morale. Many of these clubs have been short-lived. However, they tend to be more stable if they have professional consultants or leaders and are affiliated with professional organizations such as clinics, community agencies, hospitals, and mental health associations.

Mental patient organizations are of three types. First, the largest number of the independent groups are *social clubs,* whose purpose is primarily recreational. Some of these clubs are limited to ex-mental patients, but others include friends and relatives of the patients as well. Second, there are a small number of *mental patient aid societies,* consisting of ex-patients, their relatives, and other members of the community. These societies conduct projects such as Christmas parties and clothing collections for patients as well as ex-patients, and are often concerned with bringing the mental hospital patient to the attention of the community. The third type is the small *therapy group* which is devoted to discussing problems of personal and community life, and the establishment of constructive relationships among the members. An excellent example is Recovery, Inc. In some cases the therapy groups are led by professionals affiliated with hospitals or clinics; in others, there is no professional affiliation or leader, and the purpose is largely to maintain morale. Frequently both types of therapy groups also engage in social-recreational activities. See GROUP PSYCHOTHERAPY.

Closely related to these organizations are the *social rehabilitation centers* for ex-mental patients. The best known is Fountain House, in New York City. It is an outgrowth of an ex-patient club, but has been reorganized to include a staff of consultants, a professional advisory board, and a large number of volunteers. The center provides space for a lounge, dining room, offices, classes, and various activities. There is an evening program for ex-patients who work full time, and a pre-vocational program during the day for those who are not yet able to work. In addition to social activities, Fountain House offers opportunities for actual work experiences, such as typing, that contribute to the organization. It also operates a number of neighborhood clubs for ex-patients. See REHABILITATION.

MENTAL RETARDATION AND MENTAL DISORDER. There have been surprisingly few thoroughgoing studies of the relationship between mental retardation and mental disorder. The scattered investigations made so far point toward a few general conclusions, but are somewhat lacking in supporting data. First, there is no necessary connection between mental retardation and mental disorder. The two are quite different conditions, since mental retardation is primarily an intellectual deficiency and mental disorder an emotional or organic illness. Second, the incidence of mental disorder is, nevertheless, somewhat higher among the re-

tarded than among the normal. Third, on the whole we can say that mentally retarded individuals are susceptible to the same general types of mental disorder as are people of normal intelligence.

The second and third points need more elaboration than the first. The higher incidence of mental disorder among the retarded is not due to any intrinsic relationship between these two conditions, but to the life situation of the retarded in our culture. The strains of life are simply too much for many of these individuals. By far the largest number of retardates are in the mild category, and therefore have sufficient intelligence to be aware not only of their defect but of the frustrations it produces. Too often they find themselves in educational, vocational, or social situations that are beyond their capabilities. In many cases, too, their sense of inadequacy and insecurity is aggravated by ridicule and rejection. Often, too, the mother develops a sense of shame or failure because her child is subnormal, and becomes so depressed and tearful that the child wonders what is the matter. As a result he may become confused or feel vaguely guilty.

Moreover, the retarded child is denied many of the ordinary satisfactions of life, such as new and exciting experiences or approval and recognition from other people—yet he has the same types of emotional needs as the normal child. It is an accepted fact that retarded individuals are often more incapacitated by their emotional difficulties than by their intellectual defect.

Although retarded individuals are prone to the same general types of mental disorders as are intellectually normal people, the incidence and often the manifestation of the disorders are quite different in the two groups. In view of the retardate's situation in life, it is not surprising that in contrast to the intellectually normal, the great majority of the mental disorders are of the reactive type—that is, they are responses to external frustration and stresses rather than to internal conflict. Some of them react by becoming depressed or agitated, while a few become excited and emotionally volatile.

Children who suffer from severe brain damage rather than developmental defect sometimes exhibit symptoms that may be mistaken for childhood schizophrenia: distorted perception, stereotyped behavior, bizarre movements, and outbursts of temper. Others may show reactions that resemble the behavior of a postencephalitic child—that is, they are highly irritable, destructive, and antisocial. See EPIDEMIC ENCEPHALITIS.

A small minority of retarded individuals develop psychotic reactions. In most cases the symptoms are fewer in number and simpler in nature than with people of normal intelligence—for example, paranoid delusions are less systematized, and hallucinations are less clear and definite. Moreover, these reactions are generally more transitory, and there are both more spontaneous recoveries and more relapses than among normal individuals. The transient character of these disorders is a further indication that they tend to be situational and reactive in origin. See "mild" illustrative case, under MENTAL RETARDATION (TYPES).

Retarded individuals do not as a rule present behavior problems, since they are usually gentle and mild-mannered. As just indicated, a few of them have periods of hostility and aggressiveness, but this is generally a reaction to ill treatment, excessive burdens, or frustrations resulting from brain damage.

Contrary to popular opinion in the past and even the present, the mentally subnormal are not as a group predisposed to criminal behavior. True, there is a somewhat higher-than-average proportion of juvenile delinquency among borderline individuals (children with IQ's in the 70 to 90 range), and children in the mild category (50 to 70 IQ) occasionally commit offenses. In these cases, however, the delinquency is not caused by mental defect alone, but by a combination of factors such as parental neglect or ill treatment, school failure or dropout, difficulty in finding and holding a job, and lack of opportunity for wholesome recreation. As a result, some of these children drift into relationships with undesirable individuals or gangs. And since they are unable to foresee the full consequences of their actions, and have a desire for approval and acceptance, they may be led into delinquent behavior without fully realizing what they are doing.

Among retarded boys delinquent behavior usually takes the form of truancy or petty stealing, and among retarded girls it most frequently takes the form of sex offenses. But few if any of these children can be classed as confirmed, "hard-core" delinquents, and as a rule they respond well to a program of guidance, training, and opportunity for constructive living within their intellectual limitations.

Illustrative Case: MENTAL RETARDATION AND SCHIZOPHRENIA

The patient was born after prolonged labor that terminated in a difficult instrumental delivery under deep anesthesia. It is probable that during this period the blood supply to her brain contained too little oxygen. At the time of birth her face was badly marked by the instruments, unlike her two younger siblings, and some degree of mild facial deformity remained. Her parents did not notice any retardation in her early development. She was a little slower than the younger siblings in starting to talk and walk, and her speech was more difficult to understand, but there was no evidence of obvious damage to her nervous system. She entered school at the age of six, and, although she had some difficulties, particularly in arithmetic, was advanced from grade to grade each year until she reached seventh grade. She repeated the grade but made little progress beyond that of the preceding year. As no special instruction was available for retarded children, her parents were advised to keep her at home. Her brother and sister went on to complete high school as the parents had.

The patient remained at home and never went out to work. She helped her mother very little and complained of nervousness and inability to concentrate. Her parents did not consider her behavior abnormal until one day, when she was nineteen, she went out and failed to return home. She was found standing in a lane and did not seem to know why she was there. During the next three years she became increasingly seclusive, stopped going to church, and remained in the house most of the time.

When she was twenty-one her parents thought there was an improvement in her condition because she started to become more talkative, but her conversation soon became quite disconnected and unintelligible. In addition, she started to destroy her clothing, throw dishes and furniture about the house, scream and shout without apparent reason, and move about constantly. Suddenly her condition changed to one of stupor and withdrawal and she remained in bed for several weeks. When she again became acutely excited and disturbed she was admitted to the state hospital for the first time. She was twenty-two.

When asked how old she was, she replied, "Must be ninety-nine. It's my great-grandmother. I knew one in the first battalion." When asked her age again, she replied, "Somewhere in the millions. At the barracks. That's all I know since I died on the first of May." When asked the year, she said, "Leap year, I don't know. Over ninety-nine millions. It's the boy and girl question. I think my sister is doing this. They went all through the barracks. I went to Europe."

She was given convulsive therapy (induced by injections of Metrazol) which controlled her episode of catatonic excitement. Because of additional episodes of both stupor and excitement, she remained in the hospital for over two years before she stabilized and was able to return home to live with her parents. During the next thirteen years she was at home without any recurrence of acute symptomatology. She had no outside interests or friends. Then, again, she became uncommunicative, inactive, spent all her time in bed, stopped eating and lost weight; she was readmitted to the hospital at the age of thirty-nine.

ECT had become available, in the meantime, and she was given a short course of treatment to which she responded promptly. When she was rational and had been off treatment for several weeks, a full-scale IQ of 55 was obtained and it was estimated that her intellectual function had never been higher than a moron level. She subsequently went home with her parents but promptly had another attack of acute excitement which was readily controlled by chloropromazine. Long-term medication, however, did not control her tendency to recurrent catatonic episodes, particularly the states of stupor. After repeated visits at home she was readmitted to the hospital for long-term custodial care with periodic symptomatic treatment for her acute episodes. (Rosen and Gregory, 1965)

Illustrative Case: MENTAL RETARDATION AND INFECTIOUS DISEASE

Flora M. is a slightly obese eleven-year-old girl who was admitted to the psychiatric hospital with a history of mental retardation and emotional disturbance. In school, the girl had been placed in a slow learners' class, but was too hyperactive to be continued in that setting. The child talked constantly, and her attention span was very limited.

In terms of the early developmental history, the child had two convulsions when she was ten months old. These convulsions were associated with a high fever accompanying an infectious disease. When three years old, the child vomited a number of times and had another convulsion. Following the convulsion, she regressed from singing songs and making complete sentences to phrases and scattered words. At four years of age, her overactivity became pronounced. From age four to seven, she attended nursery school where she was easily distracted and did not take part in group activities. She was then placed in a special class for slow learners, but her behavior problems became so serious that it was necessary to discontinue the training. Also she presented increasingly difficult problems in management in the home. The parent, who found it easier to accept their daughter as emotionally disturbed than as retarded, agreed to have her hospitalized. The psychological examination showed her to have an IQ of 45. (Kisker, 1964)

MENTAL RETARDATION (CAUSES).
Mental retardation is not a single disorder, syndrome, or clinical entity. Rather, it is a symptom associated with a large number of conditions that affect the development and functioning of the organism. Older etiological (causal) classifications have proved to be too crude for present-day use. One of these is the division into *primary* or *endogenous* cases, which are presumably due to heredity; and *secondary,* or *exogenous,* resulting from known brain disease or injury. Another is the division into causes acting *before birth* (infections such as German measles, endocrine or nutritional disorder, injury, radiation, oxygen deficiency, toxic conditions, or faulty heredity); causes acting *at birth* (birth injury, asphyxiation, prematurity); and causes acting *after birth* (encephalitis, meningitis, head injury, toxic conditions, vitamin deficiency). These divisions are now being superseded by the recent American Association on Mental Deficiency classification, which divides the one hundred or more specific causal factors into eight descriptive categories.

(1) *Sociocultural* factors. Deprived families living in city tenements and rural slums contribute disproportionately to the number of mentally retarded. The President's Panel on Mental Retardation (1962) has indicated that in some slum areas 10 to 30 per cent of school-age children are retarded, in contrast to 1 to 2 per cent in more privileged neighborhoods. This is only partly due to the fact that parents of low intelligence (and sometimes poor heredity) tend to live in deprived areas. The full explanation lies in the over-all lack of stimulation, opportunity, and motivation inextricably linked with poverty and neglect. Studies have shown that under such conditions many potentially normal children can become retarded in intellectual development. *See* PSEUDORETARDATION.

(2) *Genetic chromosomal factors.* Mild retardation is sometimes due to poor heredity. It is hard to pinpoint the genetic factor since many genes are probably involved, and in some cases the retardation is due to the collaboration of meager endowment with cultural deprivation. Moderate or severe deficiency may sometimes be due to single mutant genes or chromosomal abnormalities. These include many metabolic conditions, such as those mentioned in the next category, as well as mongolism (Down's syndrome), Klinefelter's syndrome, and Turner's syndrome. *See* these topics.

(3) *Biochemical or metabolic disorders.* These include about twenty-five rare metabolic diseases involving lipid (fat), carbohydrate, and protein abnormalities, most of which result from inherited defects. The most frequent and best understood is phenylketonuria (PKU). Others are congenital galactosemia, maple sugar urine disease, congenital porphyria, familial goiterous cretinism, gargoylism, Hurler's syndrome, Tay-Sachs disease, Niemann-Pick disease, Fröhlich's syndrome. *See* these topics.

(4) *Infections.* A number of viral infections transmitted from mother to fetus may result in congenital brain damage and mental retardation. The most important are German measles (congenital rubella) occurring during the first eight weeks of pregnancy, congenital syphilis, cytomegalic inclusion body disease, and toxoplasmosis. Other infectious diseases may occur either before or shortly after birth, particularly meningitis and epidemic encephalitis. *See* these topics.

(5) *Toxic agents.* These include carbon monoxide and lead poisoning of the mother while carrying the child, or of the child directly during the early years; encephalitis (brain inflam-

mation) due to antitetanus serum, typhoid vaccine or other immunological agents given the child early in life; drugs taken by the mother during pregnancy, or administered to the infant directly. Bilirubin encephalopathy (kernicterus), due to Rh or other blood incompatibilities, occasionally causes mental retardation, although it may be prevented by blood transfusions. Kernicterus may also be associated with prematurity or neonatal sepsis (infection in the newborn). See BILIRUBIN ENCEPHALOPATHY, CARBON MONOXIDE POISONING, LEAD POISONING.

(6) *Trauma or physical agents.* Although modern obstetrical methods have materially reduced birth injuries, some cases of mental retardation are still due to brain damage resulting from malposition of the fetus, forceps delivery, a combination of large head and small pelvis, or anoxia (lack of oxygen) due to delayed breathing or overdosage of drugs which depress respiration. Anoxia may also occur as a result of surgery, heart attacks, or near drowning in the child's early years. Accidental head injuries sometimes result in permanent brain damage, but not so frequently as many people assume. See HEAD INJURY (CHRONIC)

(7) *Ionizing radiation.* X-ray treatments administered to the pregnant mother in the region of the uterus may lead to birth defects in the child. The explosion of atomic bombs over Hiroshima and Nagasaki resulted in many defective children. Excessive radioactivity in the atmosphere is believed to act on the fertilized ovum directly, and may also produce gene mutations in the germ cells of adults, leading to the birth of children with gross mental and physical defects. Some authorities believe the testing of nuclear weapons has already polluted the atmosphere sufficiently to endanger future generations.

(8) *Other causes.* The incidence of mental retardation in very small premature babies (under three pounds at birth) is about ten times as great as in normal births. Children afflicted with brain tumors or other neoplasms may develop severe brain damage and consequent mental defect. Unknown factors operating prenatally may cause gross malformations of brain and skull structure. Among these defects are anencephaly (complete absence of cerebrum, cerebellum, and flat bones of the skull), macrogyria (only a few, broad convolutions, with wide sulci or fissures), microgyria (small brain with close-set convolutions and shallow fissures), porencephaly (large funnel-shaped cavities in the brain connecting with the ventricles), hydrocephaly (enlargement of cranium due to pressure of spinal fluid), hypertelorism or Grieg's disease (broad skull, widely separated eyes), macrocephaly (large head due to proliferation of supportive tissue in the brain), microcephaly (small, pointed head), and craniostenosis (premature closing of the cranial bones producing such skull distortions as acrocephaly or oxycephaly, a steeple-shaped or tower skull, and scaphocephaly, a long, narrow, boat-shaped skull. Congenital hydrocephaly produces mild to severe deficiency, while cases of microcephaly usually fall into the severe or profound category. Serious or prolonged emotional disturbances may also result in mental retardation in a limited number of cases. See BRAIN TUMOR DISORDERS, NEUROFIBROMATOSIS, TRIGEMINAL ANGIOMATOSIS, TUBEROUS SCLEROSIS, PREMATURITY, HYDROCEPHALY, ACROCEPHALY, MACROCEPHALY, MICROCEPHALY, BIRTH ADJUSTMENTS.

As the above classification indicates, many causes of mental retardation have been found. An estimated 50 to 60 per cent operate before birth, 8 per cent during birth and 25 to 30 per cent after birth. Those operating before birth are, on the whole, the least understood.

The fact that so many causes have

been isolated should not be interpreted as implying that the problem of etiology is near a solution. Actually, the specialist is able to identify the exact causal pattern in only about 25 per cent of cases. A great deal of research remains to be carried out in this vital area. *See* MINIMAL BRAIN DYSFUNCTION.

MENTAL RETARDATION (PREVENTION, CARE, AND TREATMENT). Considerable progress has been made in the care and treatment of the mentally retarded in recent years. In the past the major emphasis was on custodial care in large institutions; today it is on a comprehensive approach that includes medical treatment, parent education, special classes in schools, vocational training, sheltered workshops, and, where institutionalization is necessary, small residential centers within the community. The combined effect of these approaches has been to demonstrate that far more retarded people can be helped to lead happy, productive lives than was thought possible a generation ago.

Many of the most promising developments have been in the medical field. In all cases early diagnosis and prompt treatment are essential to prevent brain damage where this is possible, since it is irreversible once it has occurred. Regular administration of thyroxin is remarkably effective with hypothyroidism (cretinism), and as a result very few of these cases are confined to hospitals today. Recently developed surgical techniques have arrested many cases of hydrocephaly. Surgery has also proved helpful in many cases of retardation associated with brain tumors and craniostenosis. Special diets are frequently successful with phenylketonuria (PKU) and galactosemia, and seem to be promising in treating maple sugar urine disease. Bilirubin encephalopathy (kernicterus) can sometimes be forestalled by blood transfusions. Congenital syphilis usually responds to penicillin, and epi-

demic meningitis to the sulfa drugs. *See* these topics.

Medical treatment in the form of tranquilizing drugs can also be applied to the minority of mentally retarded children who develop hyperactive, destructive, or withdrawn behavior. Chloropromazine has been found effective in controlling disturbed behavior in about two-thirds of cases, although individual reactions vary widely. Drugs do not improve the basic intelligence of these children, but in some cases help them to develop their potential more fully and to function more effectively.

The use of psychotherapy with retarded persons dates from the middle 1950s, since before that time it was assumed that average or above average mental ability was essential to this form of treatment. In support of this view a number of studies appeared to indicate that the higher the intelligence, the better the chances for successful psychological treatment. However, in recent years a number of psychologists and psychiatrists have made systematic attempts to utilize psychotherapy with the retarded, particularly on a group basis, and this form of treatment has proved effective in many instances. As a result, group psychotherapy is now a widely accepted treatment technique for selected cases of mental retardation. Again, it does not increase intellectual ability, but it may help the individual accept his limitations and achieve a better social, emotional, and vocational adjustment. *See* ART THERAPY.

The problem of education and training for the mentally retarded begins with the task of identification and diagnosis. Only children with fairly gross defects are likely to be diagnosed in infancy; others are not identified until the pre-school years when a developmental mental lag begins to be apparent; still others are not discovered until they have had several years of schooling. Adequate diagnosis requires not only an intelligence test but an over-all medical, educational, and social evaluation. Great care must be exercised to distinguish mental retardation from other conditions such as simple schizophrenia, cerebral palsy, and perceptual disorders. Today a number of institutions operate pre-admission or outpatient clinics for diagnosis, and in addition there are traveling clinical teams as well as approximately 100 full-time clinics, usually associated with hospitals, health departments, medical schools, and community centers.

One of the major objects of diagnosis is to determine the degree to which the retarded child is academically *educable*, or, if not educable, *trainable*. The child is usually considered educable if his rate of intellectual development is from one half to three quarters of what is expected of a normal child of the same age, and if he can be expected to reach fourth- or fifth-grade achievement in academic subjects (with or without special education), even though he is incapable of mastering formal reading until he has reached nine to twelve years of age. He must also be able to communicate adequately in normal situations, handle the usual demands of social and personal give and take, and in most cases develop occupational skills that will lead to economic independence later in life. *See* MENTAL RETARDATION (TYPES).

Although facilities for education and training are far from adequate today, many promising types of schools have been developed. On the pre-school level, there are special day-care centers which offer stimulating activities and special training. These centers not only enhance the children's development, but also relieve the parents of the burden of caring for them, so that the mother may spend more time with her other children, and take a job if necessary. On the elementary level, children may be transported to special schools for the retarded or, more often, attend special classes in regular schools. In larger

school systems these classes may be homogeneous—that is, made up of children close in chronological and mental age; in smaller systems they are usually heterogeneous, covering a wide chronological and intellectual range. *See* NURSERY SCHOOL EXPERIENCE.

On the secondary level the young person may in some cases spend part of each day in a special class with an adjusted program and part in regular classes devoted to physical education, arts and crafts, industrial arts, home economics, music, and other activity subjects. In other cases, the retarded are placed in a slow section of regular classes where they are given individual attention.

A few large cities have special occupational high schools for apprenticeship training and preparation for relatively unskilled jobs. About forty states have instituted special classes for training the mentally retarded, but at present there is a shortage of teachers and facilities. The fact that training can be highly effective has been strikingly demonstrated in a New York City study cited by Kisker (1964), in which children with IQs between 40 and 50 attended classes. The results show that only 26 per cent were subsequently institutionalized, 27 per cent of those residing in the community were working for pay at the time of the study, and another 9 per cent had worked for pay at one time or another. (Saenger, 1957)

Another important approach, the sheltered workshop, has proved highly successful for both the educable and the trainable. The work is performed for actual companies, under subcontract, and usually consists of repetitive hand or machine operations such as packaging, stapling, and punching carried out in a controlled environment under the supervision of specially trained individuals. The educable retarded usually travel to and from work on their own at times that avoid the rush hours. Many of them develop their work skills to a point where they can take regular jobs in the outside world. The trainable group, on the other hand, continue to work under supervision and are rarely capable of outside employment.

The Federal Office of Vocational Rehabilitation makes grants to states for work projects, vocational training centers, and counseling for the mentally retarded who are capable of following a vocation. In addition, home training and counseling are now offered to their parents by many public and private agencies. They receive instruction and guidance on meeting the physical, emotional, and social needs of these children, and on the special problems that are bound to arise as they grow older. Through counseling, they are given an understanding of the child's present status and future possibilities, the nature of the diagnosis, and the need for long-range planning for education and training, or for institutionalization where necessary. One of the most important aspects of the counseling process is emotional support for the parents, to help them accept the retarded child and themselves as well.

Today it is widely recognized that significant progress in the field of mental retardation can be made only through organized research and the application of new knowledge on a broad social basis. The White House Conference of 1960 advocated a broad approach to the problem, aimed at (1) stimulating basic research in the field of genetics and genetics counseling as a means of preventing the hereditary forms of mental retardation; (2) initiating programs for the early diagnosis and treatment of such conditions as phenylketonuria, hypothyroidism, and blood-factor incompatibilities through public health services and hospitals; and (3) focusing special attention on the care and treatment of mentally retarded children in deprived groups, including the prevention of mental retardation caused by impoverished environments, and improvement in economic, social, educational, and nutritional conditions.

The White House Conference advocated research not only on the medical aspects of mental retardation, but on the social, behavioral, and educational aspects as well, including the nature of the intellectual skills required for independent functioning in different sectors of society, individual differences in ability among the mentally retarded beyond the unitary IQ index, development of guidelines for grouping children educationally according to their learning characteristics, assessment of the cumulative effects of continuous programs aimed at mental, social, intellectual, and vocational development of the mentally retarded, and ways of modifying the unfavorable stereotype of the mentally retarded prevalent among public and professional groups.

The greatest stimulus to research has been the availability of Federal funds through the National Institute of Mental Health, the National Institute of Neurological Diseases and Blindness, and other governmental agencies. Substantial grants are being made to hospitals, medical schools, universities, and private laboratories throughout the country as part of a total Health, Education, and Welfare expenditure for the mentally retarded, which rose from 1.7 million dollars in 1950 to 26 million in 1961, about 11 million of which was devoted to research. There has been a corresponding increase in the research projects supported by private agencies such as the Ford Foundation and the Joseph Kennedy, Jr., Foundation. But in spite of these promising developments, it is recognized that the problem of retardation will require a substantially increased outlay of funds and effort in the years ahead.

MENTAL RETARDATION (TYPES). Mental retardation is a deficiency in intellectual capacity which renders the individual to some degree ineffective in meeting the ordinary demands of life.

The formal definition adopted by the American Association of Mental Deficiency characterizes mental retardation as "subaverage general intellectual functioning which originates during the developmental period and is associated with impairment of adaptive behavior." The deficiency reveals itself in three primary ways: delayed physical and mental maturation during the early years; a defective capacity for thinking, learning, and solving problems during the school years and later; and inability to make adequate social and occupational adjustments.

At present there are an estimated 5,600,000 mentally retarded individuals in the United States—that is, about 3 per cent of the population, with males slightly outnumbering females. The incidence is highest in rural areas and on the lower socioeconomic levels. About 4 per cent of the total, or 215,000 persons, are now living in a total of 336 institutions (154 public, 182 private) specifically provided for the retarded.

Classification of the mentally retarded is based on the two factors emphasized in the definition, intellectual capacity and adjustive resources. Although some states use the IQ alone to determine mental deficiency, with 70 as the borderline, this should not be considered sufficient by itself. Many intelligence tests are overweighted for verbal ability or reflect a particular cultural environment. The standard tests are also inadequate in assessing the general intellectual level of children who are emotionally disturbed or who have special defects such as blindness, deafness, spasticity, or reading disability due to brain damage or perceptual disorder. Moreover, the ability to meet everyday problems and the ability to get along with other people—both of which are good measures of "adjustive resources" —are not accurately reflected in the

general IQ. Some people with IQ's in the 50 to 60 range can get along better than others with IQ's in the 60 to 70 range due to the fact that they have more adequate personalities, emotional capacities, and habit patterns.

The two factors, measured intelligence and adaptive behavior, were both taken into account by the recent President's Panel on Mental Retardation (1962) when it adopted a fourfold classification into mild, moderate, severe, and profound. These categories are in close agreement with an earlier grouping by the American Association on Mental Deficiency into four "levels," and completely supersede older classifications such as moron, imbecile, and idiot.

Mild (IQ of approximately 50 to 70, Level IV). This is by far the largest group, comprising about five million persons. Although slow in mental development, they cannot usually be distinguished from other children until they are well into school. Their intellectual level as adults compares to that of an eight- to eleven-year-old child, and their social adjustment compares to that of the average adolescent, except that they are likely to show less imagination, flexibility, and judgment. There is usually no brain pathology or other physical defect, and they are therefore close to normal in sensori-motor performance.

Mild retardates are "educable" in regular academic subjects through the sixth grade, which they do not usually reach until the late teens. After that they require special training. They usually need supervision and guidance because of lack of judgment and foresight, but most of them can learn simple occupational skills and become self-supporting.

Moderate (IQ 35 to 50, Level III), comprising about 350,000 persons who reach the intellectual level of an average four- to seven-year-old child in adult life. Moderate retardates, and those on lower levels, can usually be identified in infancy. They develop fair communication skills and some are sufficiently educable to learn to read and write if special classes are available. The more alert individuals may reach a fourth-grade level by the late teens, but they can never deal with complex concepts. The moderately retarded lack "personality," and have little social awareness, but are generally affable and likable. Occasional individuals show aggressive tendencies. They are usually afflicted with physical abnormalities or deformities, and are clumsy and awkward due to poor co-ordination. Yet the majority can learn to take care of themselves, behave acceptably, and do some simple productive work within the family or in a sheltered workshop. They all, however, require considerable supervision, and many have to be institutionalized.

Severe (IQ 20 to 35, Level II), comprising about 200,000 persons who reach the intellectual level of an average two- to three-year-old child. Though capable of learning to speak on a simple level, they cannot acquire academic skills of any kind. However, they are sufficiently "trainable" to dress and feed themselves, and can generally master elementary health and safety behavior. A few can be taught to do simple manual work. They usually suffer from sensory and motor defects as well as physical anomalies, and are highly susceptible to disease. Constant supervision, preferably in an institution, is required.

Profound (IQ below 20, Level I), a group of about 85,000 persons who show such severe sensori-motor defects, physical anomalies, and general mental deficiency that they cannot profit from training even in self-maintenance. Although some of these retardates are capable of rudimentary speech and motor functions, they remain completely dependent on the care and supervision of other people. Because of their physical abnormalities and susceptibility to disease, they usually do not live longer than a few years.

For case illustrations, *see* MICROCEPHALY, MONGOLISM, MENTAL RETARDATION AND MENTAL DISORDER, and the following examples.

Illustrative Case: MENTAL RETARDATION (MILD)

An attractive young woman of twenty-four was brought to a state psychiatric hospital by members of a social agency who considered her seriously disturbed. The eldest of an impoverished rural family of six children, the patient had early showed indication of consistent developmental retardation. She had completed the eighth grade in her country school at the age of eighteen; standardized tests located her in the lower moron group. When her mother died, the patient was left without supervision. She was, accordingly, placed in a state training school, but at the end of two years her father insisted upon her release. The girl tried to get and hold jobs which would enable her to contribute to the meager family income. Her vocational history, however, was characterized by frequent changes in job, irritability toward her employers, and increasing anxiety over her inability to help out at home. The housework and maid service which she performed at tourist homes throughout the state brought her into contact with male guests, and their behavior toward her ranged from casual flirtation to open sexual advances. During this period the patient suffered from repeated gastrointestinal distress which her physicians were inclined to relate to the circumstances of her mother's death.

In a desperate attempt to achieve the vocational independence and security upon which her family's economic welfare largely depended, the patient went to a city, where she obtained a job as night waitress in a short-order restaurant, and took a room at a girls' boardinghouse. Here she found the pace of city life increasingly difficult. There were the responsibilities of saving her earnings to pay her rent, of providing herself with food and of contributing to her family's support, and the problems raised by the continued advances of some of her male customers at the restaurant.

She returned to her room alone early one morning and went to bed; but shortly afterward she became convinced that there was a man in her room. Her search failed to reveal anyone, but the conviction remained. Her loud complaints brought her neighbors, the proprietors of the boardinghouse, and finally the police, who could neither find the supposed intruder nor convince her that she was safe. She remained so excited and terrified that medical help was called for and she was hospitalized, still insisting that men were following her and that she could see them. In the hospital she became more calm; but it was agreed that she could not return to the complex urban setting. She was eventually returned to the simplified, protected environment of the training school, away from the demands of adult vocational independence, which had proved intolerable and damaging to her. (Cameron and Magaret, 1951)

Illustrative Case: MENTAL RETARDATION (MODERATE)

Male. Age nine. Never attended school.
Chief Complaint: Patient can say only a few words, and these are very indistinct. He acts in a strange way and does not seem to understand what is going on about him. Soils himself frequently.
Family History: Father forty, born in Wisconsin, works in oil field. Has had syphilis and was treated until two years ago. Mother twenty-four, born in Washington. Mother also had syphilis and was also treated until two years ago. Father alcoholic. No siblings.
Personal History: Premature birth. Patient did not walk until three and a half years. Did not talk until six years. Now says only a few indistinct words. Appetite very poor. Does not care to play with other children.
Physical Examination: Patient appears weak. Reaction of pupils to light very sluggish. Two upper incisors peg-shaped (Hutchinson's teeth). Scars at corner of mouth. Nose slightly saddle-shaped.
Mental Examination: Patient's expression dull, somewhat apathetic. Mental age four years by California Test of Mental Maturity, IQ 44.
Present Status: Patient has been placed in an institution for the mentally defective. (Thorpe, Katz, and Lewis, 1961)

MERCURY POISONING. A toxic disorder produced by inhalation of mercury; classified by the American Psychiatric Association under brain syndromes resulting from drug or poison intoxication.,

Workers in factories where scientific instruments or felt hats are manufactured, or in plants where gold is extracted from silver, sometimes inhale volatile mercury in sufficient quantities to develop chronic intoxication. The most prominent mental symptoms are irritability, fear, loss of confidence, and occasional outbursts of anger. Physical symptoms include generalized tremors and weakened arm muscles. There is no specific therapy except BAL (British Anti-Lewisite, or dimercaprol), but the symptoms usually subside of themselves in time and leave few if any after effects. *See* BRAIN DISORDERS.

MESMER, FRANZ ANTON (1784–1815). Mesmer, the controversial precursor of hypnotherapy, was born in Austria, studied philosophy at a Jesuit university in Bavaria, and medicine and theology at the University of Vienna. Early in his career he became interested in the teachings of the Renaissance physician Paracelsus (1493–1541), who had discarded the vague humoral theories of Hippocrates in favor of the view that mental illness was due to disturbing experiences and faulty personality development. While Mesmer was impressed by this theory, he was even more influenced by the treatment methods used by Paracelsus and the Flemish chemist Jan Baptista van Helmont (1577–1644). Paracelsus applied medications derived from minerals which were supposed to capture beneficial magnetic forces emanating from the heavenly bodies, and van Helmont added the further point that magnetic fluids radiated from the human body and could be focused on the minds and bodies of other people through an act of will. Both of these men assumed that the human body was inherently polarized into positive and negative, and if this polarity could be coupled with that of the Universal Spirit, the resulting power could be harnessed to cure illness.

Mesmer wrote his doctoral thesis on the magnetic effects of the planets on the human body. He became convinced, however, that the celestial forces could be attracted and applied through the use of metallic magnets rather than the mineral medications of Paracelsus. A number of influences contributed to this theory. He was living at a time when new scientific discoveries were being made in electricity, optics, and magnetism, and many people sought to apply this knowledge to medical problems. Many of them were charlatans whose only interest was to conceal their quackery beneath the veneer of science. In England a showman named James Graham witnessed Benjamin Franklin's experiments on lightning and then opened a Temple of Health in which his "patients" bathed in electrically magnetized water in a bizarre setting reminiscent of ancient religious rites. In the American colonies a physician, Elisha Perkins, patented a set of brass and copper tractors which were supposed to draw pain from the limbs, and even George Washington purchased a pair. But apparently Mesmer was more directly influenced by a demonstration in which Father Maximilian Hell claimed to cure an emotional illness by applying magnetized plates to the patient's body.

After witnessing Father Hell's demonstration, Mesmer decided to try his hand at the art. One of his first cases was a woman who had been suffering from periodic attacks of neuralgia, convulsions, and agitation; but when he placed magnets over her stomach and legs, she was free from complaints for six hours. He then continued his treatments with other patients, offering the theory that the magnets captured the magnetic fluids from the atmosphere and revitalized their nervous systems. It apparently did not occur to Mesmer or

his colleagues that his "cures" were actually effected through hypnosis, and that they were primarily due to the power of suggestion and the interpersonal relationship between doctor and patient.

In treating his patients Mesmer adopted the mannerisms of a showman, and arrogantly claimed that through his techniques "the art of healing reaches its final perfection." It is not surprising, therefore, that he was asked to appear before the Faculty of Medicine in Vienna to demonstrate and defend his techniques. After due deliberation, that body concluded that his cures were a product of imagination rather than magnetism, and he was expelled from the medical profession.

Mesmer soon left Vienna for Paris, in the hope that his ideas would be accepted in the more liberal atmosphere of the French capital. There he constructed a "baquet," a huge tub containing magnetized water, with metal rods protruding from all sides. His patients were required to sit in a closed circle around the baquet, hand in hand, and the rods were placed on the ailing parts of their bodies. To add to the effect, he dressed in a lilac robe and passed among his devotees, touching them with a magnetized wand. This procedure was designed to increase his rapport with the patients, thereby stimulating the flow of magnetic fluid, or "animal magnetism," to a point where the patients reached a "grand crisis," which apparently was a convulsive seizure. Mesmer maintained that the crisis was a major factor in achieving a cure.

Mesmerism became the talk of Parisian society, and many famous people including Thomas Carlyle and Philippe Pinel attended his séances. But again he became the target of criticism, and the French government itself offered him 20,000 francs to reveal his "secret." When he refused to tell what he actually did not know, he fell into further disrepute. In 1784 two committees, one appointed by the Académie des Sciences and the other by the Faculté de Médecine, undertook an official study of mesmerism. These committees included some of the most distinguished scientists of the time, among them Antoine Lavoisier and Benjamin Franklin. Mesmer himself refused to be investigated, but one of his followers, Charles D'Eslon, physician to Louis XVI's brother, volunteered to discuss and illustrate his work.

At the end of the investigation a public report was issued in which the commission unanimously agreed that the magnetic fluid was a hoax, and attributed Mesmer's apparent cures to the fact that one person has the direct power to influence another through the vehicle of the imagination. They also submitted a secret report to Louis XVI in which they gravely warned that the grand crisis might become habitual and hereditary, and eventually assume epidemic proportions. In addition, they pointed out that women were especially susceptible to the grand crisis and that there was a risk of seduction while they were in this helpless state. Mesmerism was therefore labeled morally dangerous as well as medically unsound.

After this report was issued, Mesmer entered upon a personal decline and soon went into retirement. A few reputable physicians, however, continued to experiment with mesmerism, but abandoned his astrological explanations and his extravagant claims of a "final cure." The Marquis de Puységur (1751–1825), for example, discovered that the technique could be used to bring about a somnambulistic state instead of a grand crisis, and that in this condition even dull people showed clarity of thought and appeared to be clairvoyant. As a consequence, many physicians of the time presented their patients to mesmerized individuals for diagnosis, and mediums allowed themselves to be put in a somnambulistic state in order to predict future events.

Along another line, a British physician, John Elliotson (1791–1868), suggested that mesmerism might be used as an anesthetic; and not long after, a surgeon named James Esdaile (1808–59) reported that he had applied this technique in performing over two hundred major operations on convicts in India. These reports were generally met with either disbelief or outrage, since mesmerism continued to be associated with the occult until late in the nineteenth century. See CHARCOT, HYPNOSIS, FREUD, HYPNOTHERAPY.

METABOLIC DISORDERS. Many psychiatric conditions result from disturbances in the chemical processes of the body—that is, disturbances of metabolism. Disorders of this kind frequently produce changes in brain function of either an acute or chronic character and may lead to a wide variety of personality disturbances. They are classified by the American Psychiatric Association (1952) under acute brain syndrome associated with metabolic disturbance or chronic brain syndrome associated with disturbance of metabolism, growth, or nutrition.

Psychiatric disorders resulting from metabolic disturbances fall into the following groups: (1) *endocrine disorders* involving the thyroid, pituitary, adrenal, or parathyroid glands (*see* THYROID GLAND, MYXEDEMA, VIRILISM, ACROMEGALY, FRÖHLICH'S SYNDROME, ADDISON'S DISEASE, HYPOCALCEMIA, CUSHING'S SYNDROME; (2) *nutritional deficiencies* (*see* STARVATION REACTIONS, PELLAGRINOUS PSYCHOSIS, DEHYDRATION REACTIONS, DIABETIC REACTIONS, BERI BERI, WERNICKE'S SYNDROME, KORSAKOFF'S SYNDROME, HYPOGLYCEMIA, HYPOGLYCEMIC STATES; and (3) *other metabolic disorders* (*see* PORPHYRIA, POSTPARTUM PSYCHOSIS, POSTOPERATIVE DISORDERS, EXHAUSTION DELIRIUM, HEPATOLENTICULAR DEGENERATION, ALZHEIMER'S DISEASE.

In general, metabolic disorders produce psychological symptoms that range from mild changes in feeling and attitude to serious mental illness. These changes are related not only to the physical disorder but to the basic personality of the patient. A well-integrated individual can usually withstand the stress of metabolic disturbance far better than a marginally adjusted person. A neurotic reaction or a frank psychosis may be precipitated in predisposed patients, and cannot be eliminated simply by correcting the physical disorder.

Many types of factors are involved in producing these psychiatric conditions. In endocrine disorders there is a constant interaction between physical and psychological factors, and it has been found that the same type of hormonal change will vitally affect the emotional life of one individual and have little influence upon another. If the glandular condition brings about gross changes in the "body image"—for example by producing masculine features in a young woman—the patient is almost bound to be emotionally disturbed. *See* BODY IMAGE.

Nutritional deficiencies and other metabolic disorders generally have a depressive effect on body functions, and this may lead to a wide variety of psychological symptoms. Among these are apathy, irritability, anxiety, and in extreme cases, confusion, delirium, and stupor. The nature and extent of postoperative disturbances depend not only on toxic and infectious complications, but on the attitudes of the patient toward the affected organ. Postpartum reactions have been found to depend as much upon the personality of the patient, her adjustment to married life, and her attitude toward having a child as upon the metabolic and other physical factors involved in childbirth. For mental deficiency associated with metabolic disorders, *see* MENTAL RETARDATION (CAUSES).

METACONTRAST. A perceptual phenomenon in which one stimulus interferes with another that has just preceded it.

Our perceptions seem so quick and immediate that it is hard to imagine that they take time to develop. Experiments employing an instrument that can flash figures at rapid rates (a tachistoscope) have demonstrated that when certain figures are presented in quick succession, the development of the contours of the second figure sometimes prevents the first figure from becoming visible. These figures must be in a certain relationship to each other. In one experiment, the first figure was a solid black circle and the second one a black ring. The centers of these figures coincided, and the outer border of the first figure just fitted within the inner border of the second. Further, the effect only occurs when the two figures are presented repeatedly in succession, and when the time interval between them is optimal. The figures just described were seen for 12 to 20 thousandth of a second and the interval period was between .120 and .240 seconds. (Werner, 1935)

When these conditions were met, the contours of the first figure seemed to be "absorbed" into those of the second one. Since the second figure had a white interior, the black interior of the first figure did not appear—apparently because it did not have enough time to develop a definite border. The same results were obtained when the first figure was presented to one eye and the second to the other eye. This indicates that metacontrast is at least in part due to a brain mechanism.

It was also found that any factor that sets the first figure off as a "strong figure"—for example, using a striped instead of a solid circle—will make it somewhat resistant to the effects of the second figure. On the other hand, metacontrast has also been obtained when the second stimulus was an intense one relative to the first, but did not have the contour relationship outlined above. This suggests that any strong stimulus following a weaker one at an optimal interval may produce metacontrast. This is illustrated by the fact that the same effect can be obtained in hearing, smell, and possibly other senses. A strong tone which quickly follows a weaker tone will mask the perception of the first tone. Likewise a strong, pleasantly scented odor can be used to mask an objectionable one. Masking and metacontrast are similar if not identical phenomena.

The significance of metacontrast is that it conclusively demonstrates that perceptions take a certain length of time to develop and can be influenced by other forms of stimulation during this period. See MASKING.

METAPSYCHOLOGY (literally "beyond psychology"). A psychological theory that cannot be proved or disproved by observation or reasoning.

The term is applied to psychological speculation, usually in the form of a systematic attempt to deal with philosophic problems that relate to human behavior. Among these problems are the relation between mind and body and the place of mind in the universe. Such issues tend to lie beyond the facts and principles of scientific psychology.

Sometimes a broad psychological theory, such as psychoanalysis or Jung's analytic psychology, is characterized as metapsychology by critics who believe it is founded primarily on speculation rather than scientific observation or experimentation.

Freud himself used the term in a different sense. He applied it to a comprehensive system, particularly his own, that approaches every mental process from three aspects: the dynamic (its cause and effect relationships in psychic life), the topographical (its position in the total structure of the mind, that is, whether it belongs to the id, ego, or superego), and the economic (its function in utilizing psychological energy—the libido—in the psychic economy). See PSYCHOANALYSIS (THEORY).

METRAZOL THERAPY. A form of shock therapy introduced by the Hungarian psychiatrist, Ladislaus von Meduna, in 1935. He had observed that in schizophrenic patients who were also afflicted with epilepsy the psychotic symptoms tended to disappear following seizures. This led to a search for a means of producing artificial epileptiform convulsions. He eventually tried intravenous injections of metrazol. With this drug he succeeded in producing predictable convulsions, and the effect upon schizophrenic patients appeared highly promising.

Metrazol was widely administered for a time as an alternative to insulin coma therapy, but it soon began to fall into disuse because of its unfortunate effects on a large number of patients. Fractures were frequent during the convulsions, intense feelings of dread were experienced just before losing consciousness, and the incidence of fatality was high. The technique, however, achieved one important result. It focused attention on the beneficial effect of convulsive treatment, and thereby helped to pave the way for electroconvulsive therapy. See ELECTROSHOCK THERAPY, INSULIN SHOCK THERAPY.

MEYER, ADOLF (1866–1950). Meyer, the founder of the holistic approach in psychiatry, was born in Switzerland and received his medical degree at the University of Zürich. While still a young man he came to America to serve as pathologist at the Illinois Eastern Hospital for the Insane, and later at the State Hospital in Worcester, Massachusetts. In these positions he attempted to discover the neurological and anatomical bases of psychiatric disorders by making post-mortem examinations of cases of general paresis, acute mania, senile dementia, and epilepsy. His investigations yielded such meager results that he concluded that studies of pathology can be made only while the patient is alive, and that they must ultimately be geared to prevention.

Meyer was given a full opportunity to study living patients when he was appointed director of the New York State Psychiatric Institute in 1902. There he began to develop an integrated, dynamic approach that included not only the physiological but the emotional and social aspects of behavior (Meyer, 1951). In 1910 he accepted the chair of psychiatry at Johns Hopkins Medical School, and soon afterwards established the school's Henry Phipps Psychiatric Clinic. He remained at Johns Hopkins until his retirement in 1941. From that center he exerted a profound and widespread influence on practically every aspect of the mental health field—therapy, prevention, professional education and hospital organization—an influence that earned him the title of Dean of American Psychiatry.

Meyer adopted the "common sense" view that mental illness is a function of maladaptive habit patterns, and that psychotherapy is essentially a process of re-education in which faulty patterns are replaced by more effective ones (Lief, 1948). This relatively simple approach did much to change the character of American mental hospitals. It helped to counteract the air of hopelessness that pervaded these institutions by showing the therapist that something concrete and effective could be done to help the patient. It stimulated an interest in the individual history of the patient and the environmental forces which acted upon him, since a full knowledge of his background and situation were considered a key to his inefficient functioning. He turned the attention of psychiatrists away from nosological categories, and encouraged them to come to grips with the patient himself. See ANAMNESIS, RE-EDUCATION.

Meyer took an equally affirmative stand on the subject of prevention, believing that an enlightened public could avoid many of the faulty habit patterns which constitute mental illness. He therefore devoted himself to mass education on mental health and became a dominant force in the mental hygiene movement. When Clifford Beers got in touch with him during his campaign for mental hospital reform, Meyer urged him to publish *The Mind That Found Itself* because he felt the book might help to stimulate the public to action. He was instrumental in establishing the Connecticut Society for Mental Hygiene and, shortly afterward, the National Committee for Mental Hygiene, an organization which devoted itself to improving conditions in mental institutions and to educating the public on the nature of mental illness and its prevention. See BEERS, NATIONAL ASSOCIATION FOR MENTAL HEALTH.

Finally, Meyer recognized that the patient's relationship with the "outside" world must be considered an integral aspect of the treatment program. First, if the patient is to live comfortably at home and in the community, the stigma of "insanity" must be removed so that he will be accepted simply as a person who has recovered from an illness. Meyer sought to get this idea across through the mental hygiene movement. And second, he realized the importance of finding out about the character of the patient's home, the milieu to which he was to return. He therefore took a simple but revolutionary step. He sent his wife to the homes of his patients to gather information about their life history, the course of their illness, and the family's attitudes toward them. This procedure provided valuable information in planning both the treatment process and the after-care program. It was also the origin of psychiatric social work. Most important, his visits with the family not only helped to create an atmosphere of understanding and acceptance toward the returning patient, but helped to relieve conflicts and tensions that were instrumental in bringing on his disorder. This new program was in a sense an epitome of Meyer's entire approach. It put the emphasis on practical adjustment to life, on re-education of both the patient and his family, and on prevention of future emotional difficulties. *See* PSYCHOBIOLOGY, PSYCHIATRIC SOCIAL WORK, PARERGASIA.

MICROCEPHALY (literally, "small-headedness"). An abnormally small head associated with impaired brain development and mental retardation.

The microcephalic has a miniature brain, an extremely small cranium, and an elongated, cone-shaped head with receding forehead and chin. Other physical characteristics vary considerably, but usually include small stature and relatively normal muscular development. There are also wide differences in disposition, although many microcephalics tend to be restless but good-natured. The degree of mental defect is generally profound or severe, with little use of language. Some cases fall in the moderate category.

Microcephaly seems to be caused by a variety of factors. Some cases are believed to be due to a single recessive gene; others result from environmental factors that interfere with brain development, particularly infectious disease or radiation treatment in the pelvic region during the mother's pregnancy. Significantly, a number of cases followed the explosion of the atomic bomb in Hiroshima. Moreover, it was found that pregnant women who were close to the center of the explosion gave birth to the most severe cases. *See* TOXOPLASMOSIS.

To prevent this defect, extra precautions against radiation treatment, German measles, and other diseases are recommended during pregnancy. But once the condition occurs, there is no

known treatment, and institutionalization is recommended for all microcephalics. Many of them can learn to dress and feed themselves, and some can perform simple physical work under supervision. Their span of life is somewhat shorter than average, and they constitute about 5 per cent of our mentally retarded population. *See* MENTAL RETARDATION (CAUSES).

Illustrative Case: MICROCEPHALY

Male. Age five. Never at school. Born in United States.

Chief Complaint: History given by mother, who stated that the child is unlike her other children because he does not speak a word and acts idiotically. The patient is said to run about the house, rushing here and there for no apparent reason, throws things away that are given to him, soils himself, and drools from the mouth. He does not show any affection whatsoever.

Family History: Father born in Italy, in United States 20 years, living and well. Mother born in Italy, in United States 10 years, living and well at 44. Children: 7 living, 3 stillbirths, no miscarriages . . .

Personal History: Normal birth, labor of very short duration. Breast-fed 14 months, dentition 9 months, walked 1.5 years, cannot talk as yet.

Physical Examination: Head very small, especially in bitemporal dimension, ears unusually large in proportion, forehead recedes markedly, chin very small.

During History-taking: Patient presented vacuous expression, stood with mouth open, apparently did not understand anything said to him, could not even be made to imitate gesture. He scrawled on the blackboard and even took up an eraser to erase something, but quickly dropped it and jumped away. Became very rebellious during examination . . .

Psychologist's Comments: Patient does not speak but will touch examiner's hand and try to draw her attention in this way. Makes inarticulate sounds. Seems to be in very good humor. Makes no intelligent response to Binet. Tries to chew testing material and grabs at everything in sight (Adapted from Bisch, 1925)

MIGRAINE. A severe recurrent headache, usually occurring on one side of the head, and frequently accompanied by nausea, vomiting, spots before the eyes, diarrhea or constipation. Because of these symptoms migraine is often called a "sick" or "bilious" headache.

Headache is one of the oldest disorders on record and probably the most widespread of all medical symptoms. According to Wolff, nine out of ten cases are psychologically determined. Of the many types of headache, migraine is believed to afflict about 7 to 8 per cent of the population at one time or another, and is especially prevalent among women and city-dwellers. It is classified as a psychophysiologic, or psychosomatic, disorder of the cardiovascular type. In establishing a diagnosis a number of tests are usually performed—skull X-ray, EEG, visual acuity, blood sugar—to rule out possible organic causes such as tumor, acute infection with fever, disease of the ear, nose, or sinuses, eye diseases (particularly glaucoma), increased intracranial pressure, head injury, or vascular disease.

Hereditary predisposition is believed to play a role in 50 to 80 per cent of cases, but the precipitating cause is usually psychological stress, although some attacks may be precipitated by fatigue, starvation, abnormal hormone levels, bright sunshine, or, according to recent reports, consumption of foods high in tyramine, such as aged cheese, chocolate, and citrus foods. The stress acts upon the autonomous nervous system, producing a dilation of the pain-sensitive arteries of the brain. Though the pain is one-sided in most cases, it sometimes occurs on both sides or shifts from one side of the head to the other. The condition rarely lasts more than a few hours, and the pain may take different forms: dull, hammering, throbbing, pressing, or vise-like.

The personality pattern of migraine victims is fairly well defined (Wolff, 1937, 1948). They are usually ambitious, perfectionistic, highly competitive individuals who tend to be overcritical of others but unable to accept criticism of themselves. Sexual disturbances are common, particularly frigidity and disgust. As housekeepers, they are likely to be fussy and meticulous; as workers, they feel compelled to keep everything in rigid order. When defeated, disappointed, or frustrated, they "hold everything in" and may nurse resentments for long periods of time. These repressed feelings create emotional tensions that activate the sympathetic nervous system and send blood throbbing through the arteries of the brain.

Temporary relief from migraine can often be achieved through the use of carefully prescribed sedatives, but lasting recovery usually requires intensive psychotherapy. During psychological treatment the therapist encourages the patient to give free expression to his feelings, find constructive outlets for anger and resentment, and develop new reaction patterns which will enable him to be less critical of others and less demanding of himself. If at the same time he can find ways of reducing external stress, the migraine will be almost certain to subside.

Prevention can take a short-term or a long-term form. A person who is subject to migraine may learn to head off the kinds of situation that precipitate an attack. He may also be taught to spot warning signals (such as visual disturbances) that precede attacks, and take prescribed medication. Long-range prevention is especially important where there is a history of migraine in the family. In such cases special efforts should be made to encourage a child who appears to be prone to headaches to talk out anger, cope constructively with his difficulties, and set flexible, realistic goals for himself.

Illustrative Case: MIGRAINE

A married woman aged thirty-three had migraine of six years' duration; it had been growing worse in the last six months, attacks occurring once or twice a week. The illness had its onset with growing domestic tension, culminating in her husband's sister coming to live in her home. The sister quarreled continuously with both the patient and the patient's husband. The latter had been unemployed for four years. The family was on relief; and the patient, besides keeping house and caring for two children, supplemented the family income by peddling stockings. She was a meticulous, "fussy" housekeeper. "When I am home I don't sit down for five minutes. I always find something to do. I've got a worrisome nature; and besides, having a man around the house seven days a week, you can't keep your house 'just so.'"

The patient was a tense, anxious, driving, and ambitious woman who was thoroughly dissatisfied with her lot and looked on her life as miserably lacking. Despite an unusually small income, she gave her children advantages that could come only from good management.

The patient had been the youngest of seven children and had been considered a timid, bashful, obedient child. "There was never a question of being forced or told to do things. I was always a funny person— wanted things done just right."

At the age of eleven many responsibilities were loaded on her, primarily the care of her sister's babies. This, and the oppressive influence of a dominating father, caused her to resent her home life bitterly. She ultimately succeeded in going to business school and also took piano lessons; she learned to play moderately well. "I am very ambitious. I wanted a career as a piano player. I used to give piano lessons, but I was no success at it. I was deathly tired of my home. I was tired of 'hand-me-downs' all the time. My whole trouble was I wanted more than I had in life. It made me resentful and nasty." Consequently she grasped the first opportunity for marriage, explaining, "I married my husband just to get away from home." Her sexual and married life were unsatisfactory. (Wolff, 1937)

MILIEU. Although the term milieu means environment in general, the emphasis in psychiatry and mental health is on the immediate social setting of the individual. This setting is considered primarily from the emotional and interpersonal point of view.

The milieu within the home is believed to be the most significant factor in both normal and abnormal development, but other environments also play a role in personality and adjustment. The most important of these are the school, recreation area, church, and neighborhood. The climate of the home and the character of the immediate neighborhood are believed to be crucial both in the maintenance of mental health and in the development of many psychological disorders. *See* MILIEU THERAPY, ETIOLOGY.

MILIEU THERAPY (Therapeutic Community). Psychological treatment through modification of the patient's life circumstances or immediate environment; also called environmental therapy and situational therapy.

Milieu therapy goes beyond the usual "environmental manipulations," such as changing a patient's housing conditions or removing a child to a foster home by court order. It is an attempt to organize the patient's environment in such a way that it will be most conducive to recovery. The emphasis is on both the social and the physical setting, though the social setting is considered the more essential. Family therapy is sometimes regarded as a form of milieu therapy since it is aimed at improving the patient's interpersonal environment and alleviating the stresses that tend to produce or aggravate his emotional difficulties. The most widely recognized example of milieu therapy, however, is found in the more advanced mental institutions of today.

The term therapeutic community, coined by the English psychiatrist Maxwell Jones (1953), is now applied to a mental hospital that utilizes milieu therapy. Its object is to organize the entire environment and every detail of institutional life into a continuous program of treatment. As Linn (1959) says, "In former days there was a tendency to regard treatment in the mental hospital as that which takes place during the fraction of a second when the current flows from an electroshock apparatus, or during the longer intervals involved in other therapies . . . In the therapeutic community the whole of the time which the patient spends in the hospital is thought of as treatment time, and everything that happens to the patient is part of the treatment program . . . Viewed in this way, the aesthetic qualities of the grounds and the inner appointments, the way the food is served, and the behavior of all personnel, without exception, are part of the program. All activities are organized with regard to maximal therapeutic effectiveness. The promotion of wholesome interaction between patients is part of the plan."

The therapeutic community of today had its roots in the "moral treatment" of a century ago, which in essence treated the patient as a sick human being rather than as a criminal or wild beast. This movement originated with Philippe Pinel and William Tuke in Europe, but spread to America where Benjamin Rush, Isaac Ray, and Thomas Kirkbride insisted upon the importance of a comfortable, healthy environment with a minimum of restraint and a kindly attitude on the part of attendants. Though little intensive treatment of any kind was given, the total milieu was viewed as a therapeutic instrument in itself. See PINEL, TUKE, RUSH, RAY, KIRKBRIDE.

In our time this concept has been expanded in many directions, with a double purpose in mind: first, to encourage the patients to modify their social attitudes and behavior through group activities; and second, to forestall the disabling effects of hospitalization itself—that is, to prevent the "social breakdown syndrome" from setting in. This syndrome is akin to what used to be called "asylum lunacy" or "institutional neurosis," and consists of such symptoms as withdrawal, loss of interest in the world, and preoccupation with fantasies, often accompanied by quarrelsomeness, resentfulness, and hostility. It is now recognized that "much of the disability seen in the mentally ill is neither inherent in the mental process nor an inevitable accompaniment of mental disorders" but is the result of a limited routine existence in an isolated institution (American Public Health Association, 1962). See SOCIAL BREAKDOWN SYNDROME.

The therapeutic community, then, is designed both to promote recovery and to prevent institutional disabilities. As Kraft (1966) points out, it is based on the view that some part of every patient is well, and that the entire milieu should be focused on that part. Though it does not replace other forms of treatment, such as electroshock therapy, group therapy, or individual psychotherapy, it attempts to make the total environment a "school for living" in which the patient can learn and test out new attitudes and behavior, develop constructive social relationships, and take greater responsibility for his own recovery and the recovery of other patients as well. It is not aimed primarily at alleviation of symptoms and emotional distress, but at drawing the patient into normal relationships and activities which will give him the confidence, self-esteem, and competence he will need in meeting the demands of the wider community beyond the hospital.

The organization of the therapeutic community varies widely from institution to institution, but there are a number of common elements. First, every type of "supportive" therapy—recreational, occupational, industrial, educational—is viewed as an opportunity for social interaction between patient and patient, and staff and patient. The discussions involved in planning projects and carrying them out are considered as important as the activities themselves, and are looked upon as an opportunity for therapeutic intervention. Second, patients are frequently enlisted as aides to the therapist in solving staff problems such as handling a suicidal patient or opening lines of communication to those who are withdrawn or inaccessible. This type of activity has a beneficial effect on the patient who is called upon as well as the patient who needs the help, since it increases his insight and gives him a sense of participation.

Third, while Maxwell Jones trained special "social therapists" for his therapeutic community, the trend in America is to make every member of the staff a social therapist by awakening them to the fact that every transaction with a patient can be used for therapeutic purposes. Fourth, patients are given opportunities to participate in decision-making activities as an aid to recovery. (Some resist this type of participation since they feel they are in the hospital only to "receive" treatment; exploration of this point of view often has a therapeutic effect.) Two of the major forms of participation are (a) *patient-government,* in which patients organize themselves for various purposes, such as discussing and making recommendations on rules and regulations, planning social events, improving the hospital décor, conducting tours for visitors, and orienting new patients to hospital life; and (b) daily *community meetings* attended by both staff and patients for the airing of problems as they arise. These meetings are usually followed by staff conferences called to examine their content as a cue to the therapeutic needs of the patients. They are also a valuable means of training staff members in the milieu therapy approach.

The therapeutic community concept has been adopted by a great majority of mental institutions, and is also applied in halfway houses, rehabilitation facilities, residential treatment centers for adolescents, and correctional institutions. At present no conclusions can be drawn as to the most ap-

propriate setting or population for this approach, and no definitive evaluations have been made. However, the effect of milieu therapy is generally considered beneficial both as a stimulus for recovery and as preparation for life in the community. *See* SOCIOTHERAPY, SOCIAL PSYCHIATRY, FAMILY THERAPY, MENTAL HOSPITAL.

MINIMAL BRAIN DYSFUNCTION. A relatively mild impairment of brain function that subtly affects perception, learning, and behavior, but without reducing over-all intellectual capacity to the subnormal range.

A task force of the United States Department of Health, Education, and Welfare has recently offered the following definition, applying the term to "children of near average, average, or above average general intelligence with certain learning or behavioral disabilities ranging from mild to severe, which are associated with deviations of function of the central nervous system. These deviations may manifest themselves by various combinations of impairment in perception, conceptualization, language, memory, and control of attention, impulse, or motor function" (Clements, 1966). The authors of this definition add, "During the school years, a variety of learning disabilities is the most prominent manifestation of the condition which can be designated by this term." In view of this emphasis on educational adjustment, the term learning disability, or subtle learning disorder, is often applied to this condition today.

The term minimal brain dysfunction is now preferred to older terms, such as minimal brain damage or injury, diffuse brain damage and organicity, which attribute the condition to physical causes. Such causes cannot always be found, and the symptoms may in some cases result from early sensory deprivation—that is, lack of stimulation needed to promote normal brain functioning. It must be recognized, however, that many of the symptoms of minimal brain dysfunction are also found in severe disorders in which brain injury or defect can be clearly established, as in cerebral palsy, organic mental deficiency, epilepsy, aphasia, blindness, and deafness. An estimated 1 per cent of the school population show serious impairments due to these disorders, while an estimated 5 to 10 per cent are believed to be affected with learning disorders due to minimal brain dysfunction.

Even though the causes of this condition are often unknown, and may in some cases be psychological, evidence of disease or injury that may affect the nervous system can sometimes be found in the child's background. Three types of factors may be involved: prenatal factors (genetic variations, infections such as German measles, Rh antibodies); paranatal factors, occurring during birth (anoxia, birth injury, prematurity), and postnatal factors (head injury, early infections such as meningitis, brain tumor, recurrent convulsions).

The existence of the minimal type of brain dysfunction, or learning disorder, has been recognized for only about twenty years. The original investigations arose out of a study of brain-damaged soldiers conducted by Alfred Strauss. Others who contributed to the concept are Bender, Goldstein and Scheerer, Horton, Gesell and Amatruda. The entire category is still regarded as a shady and difficult area in which diagnosis is frequently indefinite and examination techniques inexact. However, many studies of symptoms have been made, and a number of useful tests, such as those described in the illustrative case at the end of this article and the one shown in *Fig. 19,* p. 465, have been developed. *See* MENTAL IMPAIRMENT TESTS.

One of the major difficulties is that the manifestations of this disorder, or group of disorders, are extremely varied and may appear in many different combinations. The following list of symptoms, though incomplete, will give some indication of the wide range of disturbances in this general syndrome.

Perceptual disturbances: (a) the child cannot integrate what he sees and hears, perceives only parts rather than wholes, such as letters but not words, isolated sounds instead of sentences, one part of an act like lacing shoes instead of the entire act—therefore has trouble in drawing, reading, talking, singing, buttoning clothes; (b) cannot place his own body in space and therefore judges distance, size, and direction poorly; frequently trips and bumps into things, and is slow in mastering running, skipping, throwing, catching; (c) confuses background with foreground, and cannot see or draw things in perspective; (d) perseveration: writes one letter over and over, covers entire page with one crayon color, talks about one subject incessantly for days or weeks; (e) cannot "filter out" or "tune out" unimportant details such as trivial sights and sounds like the ticking of a clock or a view outside the window, and therefore has a short attention span and is constantly sidetracked and distracted; (f) has a faulty body image since he is not sure where the parts of his body are at a given time, and therefore has trouble imitating simple movements or postures, or in putting together a jigsaw of a human figure correctly; (g) has difficulty in spatial relationships: may be unable to find the corner or center of a square, or see the difference between a vertical and horizontal line, or between a straight and curved line; shows poor, crabbed, irregular handwriting and frequent reversals in reading, writing, putting on shoes and other clothing.

Conceptual disturbances: (a) has difficulty in forming associations, discriminating differences, summoning of images; (b) cannot adequately use words as symbols for meaning, and therefore shows impairment in thinking and communication; (c) has difficulty in thinking abstractly, due to inability to see similarities and to generalize from the specific instances, and therefore thinks concretely and literally and does poorly in most academic work; (d) some brain-injured children are extremely talkative but fail to communicate meaningfully—they engage in repetitious chatter echoed from TV or other people's conversation, often dominated by words and phrases chanted over and over.

Behavior disturbances: (a) general emotional immaturity: talks, acts, and reacts like a much younger child, and shows great emotional lability (laughs one moment, cries the next); (b) general lack of control (sometimes termed hyperkinetic impulse disorder); hyperactive, impulsive, irritable, and disinhibited, with a tendency to run, scream, cry without restraint, and be talkative, restless, and volatile; (c) destructive: generally untidy with books, papers, and clothing, breaks toys and other belongings; (d) aggressive: especially when he is shunned or ridiculed by others; may hurt himself as well as others, and is defensively hostile toward adults, including teachers; (e) animistic: often invests inanimate objects with life, such as making two pencils fight each other, or two books run a race; (f) often appears bewildered, anxious, frustrated due to awareness of his inadequacy and failure in coping with reality; (g) in general, behavior is disorganized, unpredictable, and bizarre, and the child often appears to be clowning, though this may merely be a cover for poor performance or poor understanding.

As the above description indicates, the range of impairments in minimal brain dysfunction is extremely wide. Each child must therefore be diagnosed and treated individually. Some authorities, however, have found it useful to divide the impairments into broad groupings for purposes of teaching and training. Epps et al. (1958) suggest the following classification based on the work of Lisa Gellner. First, the visual-somatic group, who are handicapped primarily in the kinesthetic area. These children have little or no "muscle intelligence" and cannot use their eyes in guiding their hands. They show poor eye-hand coordination in such activities as cutting, pasting, and writing, have difficulty copying the body movements of others, and frequently have poor form and depth perception which makes it hard for them to identify two- and three-dimensional objects. On the other hand, these children can usually learn to read and speak well, discriminate colors, enjoy music, and understand the language of others.

A second large group, termed visual-autonomic, suffer from visual handicaps alone. These children show a short visual attention span and memory, poor color discrimination, poor reading ability, and poor number concepts. Since they usually have an adequate kinesthetic sense, they generally have no speech handicap and can learn through action games, moving toys, and auditory cues. The third group, termed auditory-somatic, are mute and have severe speech defects. These children show no interest in spoken language and cannot repeat words they hear—however, since they have no visual handicaps, they can differentiate colors, forms, and pictured objects, and can learn to write and use their hands and bodies well. The fourth, or auditory-autonomic group, can repeat words they hear, but without understanding. Also, they cannot speak spontaneously, name objects, answer questions, or understand the stories they hear. These children tend to be detached and autistic due to frustration experienced in trying to communicate with others. In their educational program emphasis should be on gesture, mimicry, silent reading, and visual cues such as pictures and three-dimensional objects.

In attempting to overcome learning

disabilities, the teacher selects the most appropriate training techniques for the particular child, and in many cases devises his own methods as the need arises. We will only attempt to give a few examples of activities and materials to indicate the wide range of available approaches. Among them are: lifelike rubber animals for tactile-kinesthetic training, improvement of depth perception, and learning to associate names or sounds with objects; colored wooden beads for recognizing form, responding to color, developing hand coordination by stringing, sorting by color or size; an electric jigsaw for developing manual ability and awareness of form; nesting boxes for tactile experience, size concepts, and perception of relationships; formboard and jigsaw puzzles for developing perception of color and form; rattles, tops, wind-up toys, large bolts and nuts, scissors and pick-up sticks for improving motor coordination; circle marching, and singing games (London Bridge, Farmer in the Dell) for improving social behavior; common games such as spinners, ten pins, jacks, follow-the-leader, and pantomime play to overcome autism, withdrawal, aggressiveness, or other behavior disturbances; structured materials (Lincoln Logs, Tinker Toys, hammer and nail sets) as well as unstructured materials (modeling clay, building blocks) for eye-hand coordination, development of the senses of sight and touch, emotional and creative expression; varied musical activities (listening to dramatized stories, group singing, rhythm band, activity records) to develop auditory understanding, stimulate kinesthetic responses, promote group behavior; picture books and viewers to introduce the child to reading and to establish associations between words and pictures; finger plays (Ten Little Indians, Grandmother's Eyeglasses) to promote finger awareness and group activity; development of number concepts through grouping and counting activities ("Put two cars in the garage"), pick-up sticks, sandpaper numbers, dominoes, rubber stamps, number cards, Bingo; development of reading readiness through matching pictures with each other and matching pictures with words, word stamps, primer typewriter or printer, copying names of objects, phonic games, dramatizing stories; developing writing readiness through tracing letters and numbers with fingerpaint, crayons, and sandpaper numbers.

Another, and radically different, approach to learning disorders due to brain dysfunction has been developed by Robert J. Doman, Glenn Doman, and Carl H. Delacato at the Institutes for the Achievement of Human Potential in Philadelphia. Their procedures are based on the theory that the nervous system must go through a definite series of developmental stages before it can operate at its full potential—and that many children with perceptual, motor, and cognitive disorders have skipped or contracted one or more of these stages due to brain injury or lack of opportunity to perform basic functions that stimulate the neural organization of the brain. Each child is diagnosed against a profile of normal development, and special "patterning exercises" involving such activities as creeping, crawling, and walking in certain patterns (as well as visual exercises and sensory stimulation) are prescribed to enable the child to retrace the step-by-step organization of the central nervous system and develop the missing abilities. The technique is applied not only to severely brain-injured children but to children with subtle learning disorders, particularly in reading ability, where the emphasis is on the development of clear-cut laterality (sidedness) since many of these children show mixed dominance. The Institutes have treated hundreds of children and claim that about one third have been brought up to normal and another third improved. The procedures and the theory behind them, however, are regarded as insufficiently validated and have recently (1968), been severely criticized by a group of eight major organizations, including The American Association on Mental Deficiency, The American Congress of Rehabilitation Medicine, The Canadian Association for Children with Learning Disabilities, and The American Academy for Cerebral Palsy.

The following case illustrates some of the diagnostic procedures and remedial techniques in use at a leading school for children with brain dysfunction, The Marianne Frostig Center of Educational Therapy. In this school a symptom-diagnosis is made of each child, based on a careful assessment of strength and weaknesses in six developmental areas, through the use of tests and observations: sensori-motor development, perception, language, higher-thought processes, social adjustment, and emotional development. The school recognizes that the educational approach must often be supplemented by other approaches such as speech correction, medical therapy, and occupational therapy.

Illustrative Case: MINIMAL BRAIN DYSFUNCTION

Ricpa, a nine-and-a-half-year-old boy, had shown poor school adjustment since kindergarten and was now in the low third grade. Shy, withdrawn, completely unable to keep up with his classmates and in evident despair over his failure, he was referred to the Marianne Frostig School for Educational Therapy for full-time schooling. The boy had been adopted early in life and little was known about his natural parents, his prenatal history, or his delivery. However, he had been a healthy-looking baby except for a slight ptosis (drooping of one eyelid). His medical history showed only severe infantile colic, chicken pox, mumps, and one overnight hospitalization due to a cut chin at the age of two. He began self-feeding at nine months but was not completely weaned from the bottle until three years of age. He crawled very little, cut his first tooth at nine months, and walked at fifteen

months. Toilet training, described by his mother as "difficult," was completed at three years of age. The mother could not remember when he said his first words, but his first sentence was spoken between two and two-and-a-half.

From the age of two through five, Ricpa had frequent nightmares and was beset by a fear of animals "getting" him at night. Though he refused at times to go to nursery school, he had no difficulty with peer relationships. In kindergarten and first grade, however, he became somewhat hyperactive and showed a poor attention span. From the second grade on he complained about going to school and developed nervous mannerisms. A year or so later he began to have difficulties with his peers and felt that the other children were picking on him. The Wide Range Achievement Test, administered at age nine and a half showed grade 3.8 in reading (vocabulary), 2.5 in arithmetic fundamentals, and 2.3 in spelling. The physician reported that he was in good health, with no signs of visual, hearing, or neurological impairment, although the Center found a weakness in the trunk muscles, poor fine motor coordination, and a very slight ptosis of one eyelid.

Ricpa was placed in a group of forty youngsters who worked at grade levels ranging from second to fourth. An educational program was developed for him covering the following areas:

(a) *Sensori-motor development.* Testing showed that the boy was not only deficient in the areas just mentioned, but also that he was clumsy in all his movements and scored very low in directionality.

(b) *Visual and auditory perception.* Testing and qualitative analysis showed that "position in space" and "spatial relationships" were both difficult for him. He had no trouble with auditory perception of single sounds and words, but was found to be deficient in perceiving and remembering auditory sequences and in associating auditory with visual stimuli. Spelling and acquisition of number facts were therefore both very difficult for him.

(c) *Higher thought processes.* In the Wechsler Intelligence Scale for Children, Ricpa had a verbal IQ of 92; performance IQ of 90 and full-scale IQ of 91 (at the bottom of the normal range). His highest scores were made on the Picture Completion and Block Design, and his lowest on Coding, Information, Arithmetic, and Object Assembly, probably due to difficulty in keeping an idea in mind, visual imagery, auditory coding, visual-motor planning, and perception of position in space. His score on Picture Arrangement, though near-average, was probably lowered by his difficulty in sequential thinking and his score on Similarities by difficulty in forming concepts.

(d) *Language.* Performance on the Illinois Test for Psycholinguistic Abilities confirmed his deficiency in the areas of auditory decoding and motor encoding. Longer sentences and paragraphs were very poorly understood. He scored even lower in visual-motor association, as reflected in his inability to learn spelling, and in auditory vocal sequencing, a further sign of a general difficulty in learning sequences.

General observation of this boy also revealed a slow tempo of all movements and delayed reaction time. In class he was always the last one to react to the teacher's signal, and also the last to finish his work. This general slowness was considered the underlying and most basic difficulty which hindered his progress. He seemed to be slow in his thought processes and slow in his ability to grasp spoken sentences and to memorize sequences, and therefore lost track of them and became confused.

Remedial work included: (1) exercises in visualization, in which the boy was required to visualize carefully graduated tasks in reading, spelling, and arithmetic; (2) workbook exercises designed to develop perception of position in space and spatial relationships; (3) exercises in keeping an idea in mind while solving arithmetic problems; (4) practice in listening to, memorizing, and repeating sequences; (5) training in tasks requiring organization of information, including coding exercises, word problems requiring reasoning, verbal discussion and elaboration of information, and written expression of these discussions; (6) practice in writing, designed to train him in organizing his movements, improving his directionality, and increasing his ability to associate movements with visual input; (7) work in reading beginning at a low third-grade level; (8) practice in spelling words taken from the reading, and using color cues to help him visualize and remember the sequences of letters; (9) training in mathematics by having him look

at a number fact (4 plus 5 makes 9) in order to picture it in his head before writing it down from memory; (10) work in following oral directions, to overcome his difficulty in decoding auditory sequences; and (11) participation in the school's physical education program, with special exercises designed to increase speed of movement, visual-motor coordination, and directionality.

Finally, the emotional attitudes of this seriously handicapped child had to be taken into account. In order to ameliorate his poor self-image, it was necessary to insure that he was continually able to experience success. This was done by presenting his work in carefully graduated steps. As Ricpa experienced success and his self-image changed, he began to make friends with the other children. His social adjustment, as is so often the case, depended upon his ability to feel that he could be successful and worth something.

So far as Ricpa's growth is concerned, as reflected by test scores, a retest with the Wide Range Achievement Test (May 25, 1965) showed: reading vocabulary: grade 5.0 (December 1964: 3.8); arithmetic fundamentals: 4.5 (December 1964: 2.5); spelling: 3.4 (December 1964: 2.3). Intelligence, language, and perception were again tested in November 1966. Ricpa showed a gain of 8 points on his intelligence test (7 in the verbal; 9 in the performance part). (Frostig, 1965, condensed)

MINNESOTA MULTIPHASIC PERSONALITY INVENTORY (MMPI). A self-report test designed to measure all important phases of personality.

The MMPI was originally designed by Hathaway and McKinley (1942), to assess personality traits commonly found in "disabling psychological abnormality." Since then it has been broadened to include normal subjects, and is now given primarily to individuals over sixteen years of age who have the ability to read. It has become one of the most widely applied inventories, both clinically and experimentally, and has been a significant factor in the growth of clinical psychology during and after World War II.

The test consists of 550 statements,

each printed on a separate card—for example, "It takes a lot of argument to convince some people of the truth," "I wish I could be as happy as others seem to be," "I believe I am being plotted against." The subject sorts the cards into "True," "False," and "Cannot Say" categories in terms of their application to himself. The test is usually administered individually, but a group form in which the statements are printed in a test booklet is also available.

The statements cover twenty-six different subjects, including family and marital affairs, sexual attitudes, delusions, phobias, obsessive states, religious attitudes, psychosomatic conditions, and general health. They deal with observable behavior, feelings, general social attitudes, and pathological symptoms. Though the items are presented in mixed order, they can be grouped together to form a number of separate scales. The original test contained nine categories used in traditional psychiatric diagnoses, based on Kraepelin's classification: (1) hypochondria (concern with bodily functions and health); (2) depression (pessimism, low morale, feelings of uselessness); (3) hysteria (extreme psychological immaturity); (4) psychopathic deviate (indifferent to social mores and ethics, incapable of deep feelings); (5) masculine-feminine interest (to detect homosexuality); (6) paranoia (suspicious, with delusions of persecution); (7) psychasthenia (scores here correlated positively with schizophrenic scores); (8) schizophrenia; (9) hypomania (overactivity characteristic of mania, or extremely active person who gets into trouble through excessive or inappropriate activity). Each of the "clinical scales" consists of items that differentiated between a specific clinical group and a control group of approximately 700 persons.

Since its initial publication, the 550 statements have been used as an "item pool" for the development of about 200 new scales. One of these, a social introversion scale, is now regularly included with MMPI. It has been found to correlate fairly closely with the number of extracurricular activities of high school and college students. Several other scales assess traits of normal individuals—for instance, dependency, ego strength, prejudice, dominance, and social status.

The response profiles are used for differential diagnosis, since they indicate whether an individual falls within one or another diagnostic group. They are also used for personality description as contrasted with clinical purposes, and have been found valuable in screening and counseling. A special feature is the inclusion of four validity scales to check on carelessness, misunderstanding, malingering, and the effects of special attitudes toward taking the test. The first of these consists of a validity score (F) obtained from a set of items rarely answered by the standardization group in the way they are scored. These items represent undesirable behavior but do not fall into a pattern of abnormality; therefore a high F score might indicate a lack of comprehension, carelessness, malingering, or scoring errors. The second indicator is a Q score designated by (?): too many "Cannot Say" responses invalidate the other categories. The third is a lie score (L): items that would be falsely answered by a subject who wants to present himself in a favorable light—for example, "I never tell a lie." A high score here leaves other responses open to question. The fourth indicator is a correction score (K): a set of items that shows whether the person is excessively defensive and "fakes good," or excessively frank and self-critical and "fakes bad."

Investigators have recently sought to drop the traditional Kraepelinian classification, since it is now believed to be highly artificial. The emphasis today is on the score patterns or profiles, and a numerical system of coding is used. An "Atlas for the Clinical Use of the MMPI" provides coded profiles and short case histories of 968 patients arranged according to similarity of pattern. A similar codebook has been based on the responses of four thousand college students, and is used in counseling centers. The test is currently being validated by the accumulation of data on persons who represent each profile or code.

The MMPI is widely employed for a number of purposes. It is frequently included in test batteries for employee selection and student counseling, as a means of obtaining a picture of the individual's personality and revealing pathological tendencies. It is also used as a general screening device for students, servicemen, and others, to indicate whether they would benefit from therapy. Although the test manual cautions against literal interpretation of the clinical scales, the scores readily distinguish undifferentiated pathological individuals as a whole from normal individuals. If they are applied with clinical judgment, they are also helpful in identifying hypochondria, paranoia, schizophrenia, and especially depressive tendencies. In 1943 McKinley and Hathaway predicted the final diagnosis of new psychiatric admissions with better than 60 per cent accuracy. In 1953 Hathaway and Monachesi showed that the profiles of delinquent and nondelinquent girls differed significantly; and in 1963 they found that the instrument reveals emerging patterns of disorder, so that tendencies toward delinquency and school dropout could be predicted in the ninth grade.

The MMPI has been criticized on several counts. The old psychiatric categories are still retained even though the labels have been eliminated. The reliabilities of some of the scales are lower than desirable. As a whole, the test has not been adequately standardized, since it is based on a sample in one city (Minneapolis) rather than on a representative national population. It is particularly questionable when used in cultures other than our own. Nevertheless it has proved effective for many purposes and deserves continued use, as well as continued research in the direction of improved validation.

MITCHELL, SILAS WEIR (1829–1914). Mitchell, chief proponent of the "rest cure" approach, was a man of many talents, attaining distinction not only as a neurologist and practitioner, but as a poet and novelist. After graduating from the Jefferson Medical School he studied abroad with a noted physiologist, Claude Bernard, and returned to engage in research on blood chemistry. During the Civil War he served as a surgeon in the Union Army, and later published articles and books on gunshot wounds and nerve injuries. His volume *Injuries of the Nerves and Their Consequences* (1872) is considered an outstanding contribution to our knowledge of peripheral nerve functioning. Among his other neurological contributions were studies of cerebellum physiology, postparalytic chorea, and a detailed description of a rare but painful nerve disease, eurymelalgia, which involves the blood vessels of the feet and the hands—a disorder which became known as Weir Mitchell's disease. *See* CAUSALGIA, HALLUCINOGEN.

Mitchell's interest in neurology led him to concentrate on somatic aspects of mental and emotional disorders. He served for over forty years at the Philadelphia Hospital and Infirmary for Nervous Diseases, making that institution a pioneering center in the diagnosis and treatment of the "nervous" patient. His book *Wear and Tear*, published in 1871, initiated a campaign for a new type of regimen. In it he pointed out that many people were suffering from nervous disorders as a result of the hectic pace of life in the "Railroad Age," a life that did not provide an adequate amount of rest and recreation. He also maintained that many early breakdowns in women came about because these sensitive creatures were allowed to attend college. At any rate, his book struck a responsive chord and was widely read by doctor and layman alike.

Mitchell's first book on nervous disorders was followed by a number of articles advocating rest in the treatment of disease. In 1877 he brought his ideas together in an even more influential volume entitled *Fat and Blood.* In it he proposed a treatment plan which he had begun to formulate during the Civil War as a result of observation of states of exhaustion resulting from combat. He believed that the pressures of the business world produced a similar condition, neurasthenia, and recommended a treatment plan that included not only extended rest but physiotherapy, electrotherapy, massage, and adequate diet. He also recognized that subtle psychological factors may be involved in nervous disorders. He suggested, for example, that patients should be isolated from surroundings that have helped to bring about their illness; and he realized that they may sometimes use their ailment to dominate their families and demand extra care and attention. However, nutrition and rest—"Dr. Diet and Dr. Quiet," as he called them—were the basic elements in what became known as the "Weir Mitchell Rest Cure." *See* NEURASTHENIA, SECONDARY GAIN.

Mitchell's book was translated into French, German, Italian, and Russian, and his regimen was widely adopted throughout the entire Western world during the 1880s. It should not be confused with mere "bed rest," the simple solution of the layman, for it includes an active rebuilding of the patient's body in surroundings that relieved him as much as possible from the emotional burdens of life. This remained the dominant approach to nerv-ous disorders for over thirty years. But when psychoanalysis and other forms of psychotherapy came to the fore, its importance gradually diminished, and by 1920 rest cures had been relegated to a secondary role in the treatment of neurosis.

MONGOLISM (Down's Syndrome). A relatively common type of mental deficiency in which the facial features superficially resemble Mongolian characteristics.

The mongoloid child has almond-shaped, slanting eyes, with thick eyelids, a flat nose, and round skull. The hair is straight and sparse, the tongue is large and fissured, the hands and feet are stubby, and motor coordination is usually poor. The voice is generally deep, palm and fingerprints have unusual characteristics. Frequently the abdomen is large and the sex organs underdeveloped.

A majority of these children have docile, affectionate dispositions and an unexpected ability to imitate others. These characteristics may conceal the seriousness of the mental defect: approximately 75 per cent are moderately retarded, 5 per cent mildly retarded, and the rest severely retarded. ("Mongolian idiot" is usually a misnomer.) There seems to be little connection between the number of physical symptoms and the degree of mental retardation.

The causes of mongolism have not been definitely determined. Faulty heredity was at one time the major theory, but has been discarded because the condition rarely occurs more than once in the same family. It may be due to glandular imbalance (probably in the pituitary system) resulting from faulty metabolism in prenatal life. Recent studies, however, suggest that a congenital genetic defect is involved, since it has been found that the cells of practically all mongoloids have an extra chromosome (trisomy 21). It is suspected that this defect originated in the egg cell just after fertilization, a theory which gains some support from the fact that the disorder occurs most frequently when the mother is older than thirty-five. Preventive measures therefore include extra precautions against glandular and dietary deficiencies during pregnancy, as well as avoidance of unnecessary radiation treatments.

The life expectancy of mongoloids is far less than average, since they are especially susceptible to circulatory, gastro-intestinal, and respiratory disorders, and about 10 per cent have congenital heart defects. There is no effective treatment, but most mongoloid children can be taught acceptable social behavior, self-help skills, and routine manual work under supervision, particularly since they have such agreeable dispositions.

Illustrative Case: MONGOLISM

The patient was thirty-five years old when she was admitted to a state institution for the first time. Her lifelong mental deficiency and associated behavior pattern had not changed, but economic difficulties in the family had necessitated her institutionalization. Her elder sister cared for four children and an aged father, in addition to the patient, and had been forced to go to work to support the family after her husband became ill.

The patient was the third and youngest child in the family. Her father had been about forty-seven and her mother about forty years old when she was born. The birth apparently had been a normal full-term delivery. Her development, however, was retarded from birth; she began to walk when she was nearly five and talked at the age of nine or ten but had difficulties with articulation. At the age of ten she was enrolled in school, but, unable to make any progress, was sent home after a few weeks. She was never able to help with any work and was wholly dependent upon the family. Her mother died when she was twenty-seven and she and her father moved in with the sister. The patient was able to dress and

feed herself and her toilet habits were satisfactory.

She liked to play with a doll, guitar, and skipping rope, and to scribble on paper. She also watched television and listened to the radio. She was mongoloid in appearance, good-natured, cheerful, and cooperative. There was no history of antisocial behavior. On arrival in the hospital she talked little and frequently laughed for no apparent reason. She answered questions to the best of her ability, but many of her replies were unintelligible. She gave her name correctly but said she was three years old. She could not tell where she lived.

She said that she went to school and could read but was unable to name letters of the alphabet or numbers. Formal intelligence testing by means of the Stanford-Binet showed her to have an IQ of 26 and the mental development of an average three-and-one-half- to four-year-old child. She was in the lower part of the imbecile range. Her adjustment to institutional routine was uneventful. (Rosen and Gregory, 1965)

MONOIDEISM. Obsession with a single idea and inability to think of anything else; harping on one idea.

In its extreme form, monoideism is most frequently observed in senile disorders and schizophrenic reactions. Historically the term was used by Pierre Janet for "the theory according to which an idea detached from other ideas will exercise an unusually powerful force in the mind." The theory was applied particularly to hysteria, which he believed to be due to "idées fixes" split off from consciousness as a result of stress or trauma acting upon a constitutionally weak nervous system. He attributed the concept of monoideism to Descartes and Condillac, and applied it also to hypnosis. "The magnetizers (hypnotists) were well aware that suggestion was more powerful when the subjects were 'isolated,' that is to say when they were apparently unable to perceive any phenomena except the personality of the magnetizer and his utterances" (Janet, 1925). This theory remains one of the major explanations of hypnosis today, although the term monoideism has fallen into disuse. *See* JANET.

MONOMANIA. An obsolete term for "partial insanity"; a condition in which the patient is believed to be pathological on one subject alone, but sound and healthy in every other respect.

In the nineteenth century the term was applied most frequently to paranoid conditions. It is occasionally used today to indicate that in "true" paranoia the patient's major symptoms consist of a logical system of delusions based on a single false premise. This usage, however, does not imply that he is healthy in all other respects.

In the earlier period various types of monomania were cited by different authors, apparently to stress the fact that a single symptom was most prominent. Among these were affective monomania, corresponding to the manic phase of manic-depressive reaction (lypemania was suggested by Esquirol for the depressive phase); homicidal monomania; monomanie boulimique, or insatiable hunger; monomanie du vol or kleptomania; monomanie érotique, or erotomania; monomanie incendière or pyromania; instinctive monomania, corresponding to what is now called obsessive-compulsive reaction; and intellectual monomania, which appears to be equivalent to paranoia. Most of these are now viewed as symptoms rather than separate syndromes or clinical entities.

The concept of partial insanity has been discarded, since mental disorders (of the functional type, at least) have been found to stem from disturbances in the total personality. Nevertheless it has played an important part in the history of legal psychiatry, since the defendant in the historic M'Naghten case was acquitted on the basis of partial insanity when it was shown that he was suffering from a delusion of persecution. This led to the establish-ment of the "right-and-wrong rule," which in essence stated that if a defendant is to be considered innocent by virtue of insanity, or partial insanity, he must have had such a serious defect of reasoning power that he did not recognize the wrongness of his act. Isaac Ray, America's pioneer forensic psychiatrist, opposed this test, and in 1869 the Supreme Court of New Hampshire was the first to sweep it aside and recognize simply that a defendant is not criminally responsible if his unlawful act is the result of mental disease or defect. According to this momentous decision, the question of the defendant's mental condition was not a matter of law but rested on the testimony of psychiatric experts. The M'Naghten Rule, however, still remains the criterion for acquittal in most states. *See* LEGAL PSYCHIATRY.

MONOTONY. Most research on monotony has been concerned with industrial work, since monotonous tasks frequently lead to lowered output and greater energy expenditure than varied and interesting tasks. The reason appears to be that many workers resent these jobs because they find them boring; and the necessity of forcing themselves to keep at the work results in overfatigue. This relationship between boredom and fatigue is not, however, a universal one. Workers can become tired after a long spell of interesting work, and light but monotonous jobs can be highly boring without leading to fatigue. *See* FATIGUE.

Earlier studies by the Industrial Fatigue Research Board in England (1929) showed a tendency to large fluctuations in output as well as a sharp end spurt among workers who reported they were bored. Apparently the fluctuations were due primarily to lapses of attention, and the end spurt to the necessity of catching up when they realized that their output was below normal. More recent studies, however, have shown that the work curves of bored and interested workers do not differ materially, probably because all workers have to keep up with the pace that is set for them (Smith, 1953).

Monotony and boredom depend upon many factors: the nature of the task, the working environment, the incentives, the worker's intelligence level and personality. Some studies indicate that semiautomatic tasks are the most boring since they require constant attention without arousing much interest. A completely routine and repetitive job such as packing light bulbs is often less boring, since it requires so little concentration that the worker can let his thoughts wander or talk with his neighbors.

The surroundings and contact with fellow workers have much to do with monotony. On the whole, uniform, single-operation tasks performed in plants where the workers are far apart and are given no bonuses or other special incentives tend to be the most monotonous of all. In an interview study of assembly-line operators in an automobile factory, the percentage of men who judged their work boring was 67 per cent for single-operation jobs, 56 per cent for jobs involving two to four operations, and only 30 per cent where there were five or more operations (Walker and Guest, 1952).

On the whole, more intelligent persons tend to find repetitive tasks boring, but no appreciable differences in intelligence have been found between people who do and people who do not find a *particular* job boring. There is, however, a close association between personality and susceptibility to boredom. To take one example, a research study has shown that women sewing machine operators who found the work most boring tended to dislike the regularity of daily routine, to be dissatisfied with their personal and home life, to show a strong interest in leisure activities, and to be under twenty years of age. On the other hand, those who did not find the work dull were relatively placid, contented, and rigid.

These individual differences in susceptibility suggest that one way of combating monotony is to pay greater attention to personality characteristics in placing people on jobs. Other remedies are: carefully scheduling rest pauses, improving the working environment, placing machines in such a position that operators can converse, introducing music, arousing interest through films and plant tours, and carefully planning the work itself. Such planning might include job rotation and grouping the work itself into broader units or batches so that the worker performs varied operations and has a greater feeling of satisfaction as each unit is completed.

MORALE (Industrial). Morale is a complex psychological state that appears to be compounded of belief in the value of the activity, feelings of personal worth, enthusiasm, interest, and satisfaction. The worker with high morale likes his job, becomes personally involved in it, works close to his maximum, and often has a lower absentee, accident, spoilage, and turnover rate than the worker with low morale. He also tends to work well with others and show a high degree of "team spirit." In a word, a worker's attitudes affect not only his output but his total job adjustment.

The recognition of the importance of morale and motivation dates largely from the celebrated "Hawthorne Studies" conducted by the Western Electric Company between 1924 and 1939 and published by Mayo in 1933 and Roethlisberger and Dickson in 1939. These studies were originally designed to assess the effects of changes in ventilation, illumination, rest pauses, work schedules, pay rates, and other practical conditions on productivity. It was found that improvement in these conditions generally increased worker performance.

However, the experimenters found, to their surprise, that even when the poorer conditions were reinstated, productivity continued to improve. A detailed study revealed the reason: the experimenters had inadvertently introduced many *human* factors that apparently spurred productivity by increasing the morale of the workers chosen for the experiment. They had been given a comfortable room of their own; were not under the usual supervision; worked in a small group that developed camaraderie and group spirit; were allowed to converse freely; received special attention from the experimenter; were consulted about the changes to be introduced—and, in general, felt they were important and were making a special contribution. As a by-product of these findings, the term "Hawthorne effect" is frequently used to indicate that the mere fact of participating in an experiment may itself influence behavior.

This early study focused attention on the importance of employee attitudes. The results were later amplified and confirmed by intensive interviews with over 21,000 workers on what they liked and disliked about the job, the working conditions, and type of supervision. This turned up another unanticipated finding: the opportunity to air their views, especially in unstructured interviews, was welcomed by the workers and itself had a favorable effect on their attitudes. It also revealed that worker morale was greatly influenced by such considerations as job status symbols and the nature of the work group. These results led to experiments which showed that small informal groups of workers adopt leaders of their own and tend to set their own pace, exerting social pressure on those who are either above or below their arbitrary standards.

Studies of the individual attitudes and lives of the workers in these experimental groups led to still another series of experiments that demonstrated the value of employee counseling designed to help them with their personal and interpersonal problems both inside the plant and at home. The net effect of the entire series of investigations was to introduce the "human relations" movement in industry, and to stimulate numerous inquiries into employee attitudes, factors in job satisfaction, supervisory practices, communication techniques, employee participation, work groups, and job design. Some of the major results of these studies will now be summarized.

Attitude measurement. Surveys of employee attitudes are now an accepted practice and serve many purposes: to assess morale and motivation; suggest changes in policy, procedures, or working conditions; provide a basis for selection in training programs; and appraise the effect of different factors on job performance. They are carried out on an anonymous or confidential basis, and include: (a) interviews with a whole unit or with representatives, as well as exit interviews with employees leaving the company; (b) opinion questionnaires on such matters as the cafeteria, vacation policy, opportunity for advancement, pay, working conditions, supervisor-employee relations; (c) attitude scales on overall satisfaction or attitudes toward the company ("on the whole, the company treats us well," "you've got to know the right people to get ahead in this company"); (d) trained observers assigned to special departments to study attitudes, group structure, and relationships; (e) indirect techniques such as word association, picture interpretation, sentence completion, and writing a letter on "My Job"; (f) nominating technique for investigating group structure —naming the "best worker," "who would make the best supervisor"—with the nominees plotted on a sociogram. *See* SOCIOMETRY.

Job satisfaction. Several attitude surveys have indicated that when applicants are asked what they want from their jobs, the men tend to rank security, opportunity for advancement, and interesting work at the top of the list, in that order; pay, pride in the company, congenial co-workers, and a fair and considerate supervisor occupy a middle position; while hours, working conditions, and employee benefits are considered least important. Among women, type of work ranks highest and the differences between the values given to the other factors is smaller. Some studies indicate that pay should be nearer the top. Lower-level workers tend to emphasize security and agreeable relations with co-workers and supervisors; higher-level workers stress opportunities for self-expression, interesting work, and leadership opportunities. It should be noted that the lower-level jobs actually provide less opportunity for self-expression or leadership so that the worker *must* seek his satisfaction from other factors.

Many studies have shown that absentee, tardiness, accident, and turnover rates are consistently highest among workers with poor attitudes. However, there is no simple relation between job satisfaction and productivity, probably because worker performance is influenced by individual goals—for example, high productivity may be sacrificed by the worker who insists on perfect quality. A study of accountants and engineers conducted by Herzberg et al. (1959) showed that among these workers satisfaction depended upon the job itself—especially on opportunities for growth and self-realization spurred by recognition of achievement, the taking on of responsibilities, advancement, and the nature of the work; while dissatisfactions were primarily due to the context in which the job was performed, including such factors as objectionable company policies, incompetent supervisors, and unsatisfactory working conditions. Only the intrinsic job factors

(the satisfiers) affected job productivity; the context factors (dissatisfiers), on the other hand, had an effect on other aspects of the work such as absenteeism, emotional adjustment, and job turnover. This suggests that a program directed toward improved human relations and better working conditions would be valuable in reducing dissatisfaction but not in promoting better job performance—a hypothesis that needs to be tested with other types of workers.

Supervision. Many studies have shown that the supervisor has a significant effect on employee attitudes, absenteeism, accident rate, grievances, turnover, and productivity as well. An extensive comparison of supervisory practices in a variety of organizations and industries conducted by the Institute of Social Research of the University of Michigan (Likert, 1961) has indicated that supervisors in high-producing units are likely to be employee-centered, and those in low-producing units, job-centered. The employee-centered supervisors tend to be concerned about the problems of the workers, to be friendly and encouraging, and to apply only general supervision while allowing the worker much individual freedom. They also spend a good deal of time in planning the work, motivating the workers and keeping them informed about company policy. Job-centered supervisors are primarily concerned about production and exercise more rigid control over worker activities. When managers of the two types of units were exchanged in one company, production shifted accordingly—though, interestingly, the favorable change occurred more rapidly than the unfavorable.

The Ohio State Leadership Studies (Startle, 1956) have shown that the most effective leaders in many different situations tend to show "consideration" (friendliness), also that they tend to "initiate structure"—that is, actively plan and direct activities. In other words, effective leaders tend to be *both* employee-centered and job-oriented, though they are not authoritarian in their attempts to set goals and supervise the work.

Other studies have shed light on the relation of the supervisor and his own supervisors. Pelz (1952), for example, has shown that employees tend to be entirely satisfied if the supervisor not only sides with them but gets his recommendations on their behalf accepted by management.

None of these points, however, can be considered general rules since much depends on the personality pattern of the supervisor, the characteristics of the workers, and the managerial climate and organization in which the supervisor functions. Moreover, it must be recognized that "human relations" cannot take the place of skill in organizing and directing the work itself. *See* LEADERSHIP.

Communication. There is a growing amount of evidence that the communication process has an important bearing on employee attitudes and morale. One study has shown an inverse relation between absenteeism and freedom to discuss problems among both white- and blue-collar workers of the same company (Likert, 1961). Other investigations have explored the relative value of different types of communication—for example, Dahle (1954) found that oral communication was understood and retained better than written, but a combination of the two was still more effective. A written communication has the advantage of greater accuracy, authoritativeness, and permanence; oral communications are more personal and can be reinforced by gestures and tone of voice.

Much can be done, however, to improve communication in business and industry—for example, by adapting memos, union agreements, and other written matter to the level of the reader, and by offering reading, speech, and writing programs to executives. From the viewpoint of morale, it is particularly important to keep open the lines of communication to superiors, so that employees will feel free to present not only their grievances but their ideas for improving the operation. Another important requirement is to inform employees in advance about changes that will affect them and their work. Likert's investigations have shown that superiors frequently *believe* they have imparted this information, but in many cases this was actually not done or did not get across to the workers.

A highly useful approach to improved communication is to analyze its flow through an organization or part of an organization. One method is to record all communications that pass a given spot, such as an executive's desk throughout the day. Another is to follow a specific item of information by asking each individual whether he knows about it and, if so, from whom he received it and whether it differs from the information presented by the investigator. This method is particularly useful in tracing distortions and in assessing the value of different media of communications. It has been found that even the decisions of the chief executive may be distorted by "selective filtering" through an assistant.

Another technique is to make a laboratory study of different types of "communication nets" by having a small group of subjects sit at a table separated from each other by radial partitions (*Fig. 37*). The group is given a problem that can be solved only by a pooling of information, and notes are passed from person to person through slots in the partitions. Since these slots can be opened or closed by the experimenter, different types of arrangements can be set up. Studies have shown that a wheel pattern in which one individual acts as the central source of information yielded the best results in terms of speed, accuracy, and stability of organization; but a leaderless

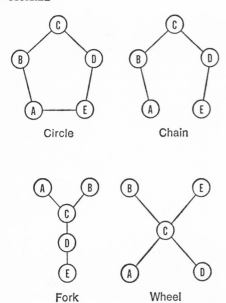

Circle   Chain

Fork   Wheel

Fig. 37. Four types of "communication nets" used in problem-solving experiments. Problems are solved more easily if subjects can communicate in the direction indicated by the circular pattern and the wheel.

circular pattern in which information could travel freely back and forth among the members yielded better morale and greater ability to adapt to sudden and confusing changes of task.

Organization. Psychologists concerned with industrial morale have made special contributions to three areas of organizational structure. The first is employee participation in decision-making. Likert advocates a thoroughgoing use of the group dynamic approach by proposing that every employee participate in decision-making work groups. The total organization would consist of overlapping groups, with each foreman engaging in conferences with his own work unit and participating in similar conferences with other foremen and their supervisor at the next higher level, and so on from echelon to echelon. He believes that this would improve performance since the employees would be more likely to accept higher goals when they had a voice in setting them up.

A study conducted by the Harwood Manufacturing Company (Coch and French, 1948) has demonstrated improvement in performance through participation of this kind. When a change in work assignment was contemplated, four groups were formed: two groups actively participated with management in making the decision; one group had a representative participate and discuss the new developments with the other members; and the fourth, serving as a control group, was merely informed of the change in the usual way. The full-participating groups showed far less drop in productivity after the change-over, as well as faster recovery, fewer grievances, and a higher ultimate level of output than the control group. The partially participating group yielded results between these two. At a later date the control group was given full participation before another change in production, and its record at that time equaled that of the experimental groups.

The second method is to assign employees to work groups according to sociometric principles—that is, to form teams according to the workers' own choices of mates. Studies both in industry and in the military service have shown that this procedure reduces production costs and turnover to some extent. It generates loyalty to the group, which has a positive effect on attitudes and absenteeism, but the effect on actual productivity may be either positive or negative, depending on the character of the group's relations with the organization and supervisors. Where motivation is high, productivity is increased; but where it is low, the group may agree to restrict its own output. Other studies have shown that the "geography of production" also affects turnover, grievances, and other indices of job satisfaction. An assembly line arrangement will usually reduce morale

since it does not permit enough contact between the employees.

Finally, a growing number of companies are attempting to increase motivation and work satisfaction through
"job design." Industrial engineers have
stressed the need for specialization on
one task as a means of reducing costs,
but psychologists have found that this
tends to make the job monotonous and
uninteresting. They have therefore introduced such procedures as job rotation, participation in planning the job,
and enlarging the job to include a longer
and more varied sequence of operations,
with greater responsibility for testing
the product and controlling the way
the job is done. Herz and his associates
have emphasized the importance of permitting the worker to structure his own
job, since this gives him a sense of
personal achievement. They also point
out that some workers function best as
individuals, while others operate most
effectively as members of a closely knit
team. This points to the need for fuller
respect for individual differences.

MOTHERING. In a psychological
sense, mothering refers primarily to
three aspects of the relationship between mother and child: emotional
warmth, personal care, and sensory
stimulation. All three are considered
essential to healthy personality development, and are particularly important in
infancy and the early years of childhood.

Emotional warmth comprises genuine
affection, coddling, and caressing, as
well as encouragement, admiration, and
reassurance. In a word, it includes
everything that makes a baby feel loved,
accepted, and wanted. It is the basic
ingredient, pervading all other aspects
of mothering. Personal care consists of
tending to the child when he is hungry,
wet, cold, or uncomfortable in any way
(but without making an unnecessary
"fuss"). It also includes soothing the
child when he is distressed or anxious,

helping him adapt to a comfortable
feeding schedule (comfortable for the
parents as well as the baby), finding a
formula and a bottle that are right for
him, encouraging him to accept new
foods at the proper time, and expending
the time, effort, and ingenuity necessary
for successful toilet training.

Sensory stimulation, the third ingredient, is less often associated with
mothering than warmth and tender care,
yet recent studies of sensory deprivation indicate that it should be an integral part of the mother's relationship
to her child. The stimulation should
awaken and develop all types of experience: touch, hearing, sight, taste,
smell, balance, and movement. Some of
the ways in which this can be done are:
talking, laughing, and humming to the
baby; providing him with play materials
of different shapes, colors, and textures;
showing him how to play by playing
with him; helping him become aware of
the different sounds of the world, including music as well as noise; giving
him foods of different taste, texture,
and smell as he grows; helping him
achieve co-ordination and balance
through free movement and the use of
play apparatus geared to his age and
ability; and helping him adapt to the
sight and sound of other people.

Mothering in its fullest sense gives the
child a solid start in life, since it fulfills
his basic needs and lays the foundation
for future development. It provides a
sense of security, makes him feel at
home in the world, helps him form a
positive self-image, and prepares him to
meet reality on his own.

The term mothering denotes a general relationship to the child rather than
specific behavior of a single person.
While it is true that the mother is herself the most important figure in a
child's life during the infancy period, it
is also true that a mother substitute (or
surrogate) can meet the child's psychological and physical needs if the actual
mother is not available. An aunt, foster

mother, nurse, or worker in an institution for children can serve as a mother figure, provided she is warm and accepting. Moreover, the child can and should be "mothered" by his father in all three senses described above. There is a great deal of evidence that young children feel happier and more secure when both parents take a full interest in them. The father's participation is particularly important when the mother is ill or absent from the home.

For the effects of insufficient mothering, *see* MATERNAL DEPRIVATION and MARASMUS.

MOTIVATION. The dynamics of behavior; the process of initiating, sustaining, and directing the activities of the organism.

Motivation is a broad area that deals with all types of internal forces—physical and psychological, conscious and unconscious—and all types of activities from our most commonplace needs to our loftiest aspirations. With this scope in mind it is not surprising that many terms are employed in this field and that the technical vocabulary is not fixed. The term motive appears to be the most neutral and inclusive word, applying to any internal force that activates and gives direction to behavior. Other terms, when strictly used, emphasize different aspects of motivation—for example, need stresses the element of lack or want; drive or urge, the impelling and energizing aspects; incentive, the goal aspect. Still other terms are used to designate complex determinants of behavior: interests, attitudes, and purposes.

This article will survey the field of motivation rather than discuss individual motives such as the hunger drive or the need for achievement. In general, motives are divided into two broad types. The ones in the first group, *physiological, primary, or organic motives,* are based on physical conditions that drive the organism to activity. They break down into two subtypes: basic motives which depend on physiological need (hunger, thirst, elimination, pain, and those based to a somewhat lesser extent on physiological need—sex and maternal drives); and basic motives which stem from unspecified physiological conditions (activity, manipulation, investigation, and stimulation).

The motives of the second general type, *personal and social, or secondary,* are acquired in the course of life as a result of individual and social experience, although they may in some cases be indirectly derived from physiological need. Some of these motives, such as gregariousness (or affiliation) and imitation, appear to be universal or almost universal tendencies, probably because they begin to appear in childhood and are deeply rooted in feelings of helplessness and dependence. (The term coenotrope, Greek for "common habit," is sometimes applied to these motives.) Others, such as the motives for achievement, competition, co-operation, and aggressiveness are more clearly conditioned by the particular society or cultural group, as anthropological studies have shown. A third group are far more personal and include our individual appetites, aversions, and interests, as well as goals, habits, and desires that stem from our general attitudes, interests, and level of aspiration. *See* the Category Index, under Motivation, for individual topics.

Many other classifications of human motives have been proposed. Thomas (1923) believed that the entire welter of needs, drives, and urges could be reduced to four "wishes": security, recognition, response from one's fellows, and new experience. Maslow (1954) has listed six types of needs ranging from stronger and lower to weaker and higher, contending that we cannot be free to satisfy our higher needs until our lower needs are met. His "hierarchy of needs" includes the following: (1) Physiological needs: hunger, thirst, air, etc.; (2) Safety needs: freedom from threat and danger, and the need to ally oneself with the familiar and secure; (3) Belongingness and love needs: affiliation and acceptance; (4) Esteem needs: achievement, strength, competition, reputation, status, prestige; (5) Need for self-actualization: self-fulfillment, realization of potentialities; (6) Cognitive needs: the need to understand, curiosity, tackling the unknown and mysterious.

Murray (1938) has offered a comprehensive inventory of motives that includes twelve viscerogenic or physiological needs, and twenty-eight psychogenic needs. Since many of his psychogenic needs are not listed by others, and have been given special names, we will enumerate them all with a word or two of explanation where needed: acquisition, conservation (collecting, repairing), orderliness, retention (hoarding, frugality), construction, superiority, achievement, recognition, exhibition (self-dramatization, exciting or amusing others), inviolacy (preserving one's self-respect and good name), avoidance of inferiority (avoiding shame, failure, and ridicule), defensiveness (self-justification), counteraction (overcoming defeat), dominance, deference, similance (imitating or agreeing with others), autonomy (independence), contrariness, aggression, abasement, avoidance of blame, affiliation, rejection (to be discriminating or exclude others), nurturance (to aid and protect others), succorance (to seek aid and be dependent on others), play, cognizance (to explore and satisfy curiosity), exposition (to explain and give information). The major value of such a list is to serve as a reminder of the kinds of behavior which a complete theory of motivation must encompass.

Any enumeration of the various forces that activate behavior, such as those given in the preceding paragraphs, is bound to be chaotic and confusing. When we look at human beings in general, we find not only many types of motives, but many degrees and levels of motivation—and when we abandon the over-all view and look at individuals, we face even more complex problems. It therefore seems easier to answer the general question, why men write novels or paint pictures, than to explain why this particular man writes this particular novel or paints this particular picture. As Hilgard and Atkinson (1967) point out, "Why men behave as they do has intrigued thinkers from early times; much of the thematic material in literature, art, and drama is concerned with goal-striving, ambition, jealousy, heroism, sacrifice, love, hostility—all intensely motivated behavior. Because of the variety and richness of these themes, it is no wonder that a psychology of motivation has difficulty achieving a simple and orderly theory of motivation that will be adequate to the subject matter."

These difficulties are compounded by such facts as the following: the same motive may be expressed in different ways (we may show antagonism by attacking or by ignoring our opponent); motives are not always expressed directly but often appear in disguised form (a girl may dream of being chased by a wolf instead of a man); and any single act may express several motives (an author may work for both fame and money, and the child may steal both to defy authority and as a "cry for help" for inner problems of which he is not fully aware). In view of these complexities it is not surprising that a number of different approaches to human motivation have been suggested in recent years. Three of the most influential will be briefly outlined: behavior theory, the theory of unconscious motivation, and cognitive theory. *See also* DRIVE REDUCTION THEORY.

Behavior theory is based on the idea that drives are generated by needs, or wants, and that we come to satisfy them in habitual ways through a learning process—that is, behavior that is rewarded (reinforced) by satisfying the need is usually repeated. In their account, Whiting and Child (1953) have proposed a scheme of "behavior systems" which consists of important motives leading to common satisfactions. They place particular emphasis on five of these systems, three of which have a physiological basis (oral: hunger; anal: elimination; and sexual) and two of which are acquired in early childhood as a result of helplessness and frustration (dependency and aggression). The wide differences in the expression of these motives in different cultures and within the same culture are due largely to child training and the methods of rewarding and punishing behavior. Much light can be thrown on adult behavior by discovering general themes within each behavior system, and by tracing them back to childhood experience and cultural conditioning.

Transformations of the hunger drive will illustrate this theory. This drive, which stems from the infant's helplessness and need for nutriments, becomes differentiated into an "oral drive" that generates ordinary food-related behavior (sucking, chewing, etc.) and a "dependency motive" as well, since the child is dependent on others for the food he receives. In the course of human development, each of these drives gives rise to its own social behavior, customs, and institutions. The oral drive and related behavior lead to food production and conservation (hunting, fishing, canning, refrigeration, etc.); food preparation and social eating (cooking, menus and recipes, table manners, preferences and aversions); food ceremonies (fasts, taboos, sacrifices, wakes); other mouth satisfactions (alcoholism, drug addiction, chewing gum, smoking, oral symptoms); resistance to eating or overeating (dieting, anorexia nervosa). The dependency motive, on the other hand, is reflected in our relations with other people (dependence on parents, teachers, friends, spouse, physician; homesickness); relations with groups (religious fellowships, social clubs, and other organizations that satisfy our dependency needs and need to belong); and resistance to overdependency (as expressed in such motives as autonomy and achievement). Each of these themes, however, has its variations from individual to individual. Some people, for instance, pay more attention to food than others; some become habitual joiners while others are relatively detached. The behavior systems approach appears to be most valuable when it focuses on these individual variations and not merely on the common sources of our motives. For other examples of this approach, *see* AFFILIATIVE DRIVE and AGGRESSION.

The second theory, that of unconscious motivation, focuses on impulses of which we are not aware rather than on the expression of drives in overt behavior. The fact that much of our behavior is influenced by unconscious factors has long been recognized by novelists and playwrights, but the first systematic study of these factors was undertaken by Freud. As a result of his work, we now have a theoretical framework which applies both to normal and neurotic reactions, and which provides a basis for psychoanalytic therapy. Since the analytic approach is described under a number of separate topics, we will confine ourselves here to an enumeration of examples of unconscious motivation and a brief review of experimental studies in support of this approach.

Unconscious motives are expressed in everyday life through slips of the tongue, memory, or hand. These "symptomatic acts," as they are sometimes called, frequently reveal feelings that are unknown to ourselves—for example, forgetting an appointment with an individual against whom we have an unconscious hostility, or with a person who merely resembles this individual. A second common example is the dream which expresses our fears or sexual desires in disguised form. A third is a tendency to acquire neurotic symptoms which save us from threatening situations or satisfy desires for dependence, sympathy, or domination over others. A fourth is the effect of unconscious conflicts upon our behavior—for example, a young girl experienced such a dread of running water that she was terrified by the sound of drinking fountains and the sight of rivers, and had to be forceably bathed by several members of the family. Her fear continued until the age of twenty, when an aunt whom she had not seen for thirteen years visited her. The aunt's first words were, "I have never told." This led to recall of an accident experienced by the girl at the age of seven while walking in the woods with her aunt. In spite of a promise of obedience made to her mother, the little girl had run off and was later found screaming in terror. She had become wedged between two rocks in a stream, and a small waterfall was pouring down on her head. The aunt rescued her, dried her clothes, and promised never to tell her mother. The girl had unconsciously repressed (forgotten) the harrowing experience (Bagby 1928). *See* DREAM INTERPRETATION (MODERN), PARAPRAXIS.

Unconscious motivation has been strikingly demonstrated through the use of hypnotic suggestion. Erickson (1939) hypnotized a student and told him he would later be visited in his room by a professor who would engage him in an endless, boring conversation. The next day the professor came in (by prearrangement) and as he talked on and on, the student showed increasing signs of restlessness. Finally the young man got up and walked toward the open door of the room. The professor asked him where he was going and his answer was, "Oh, I was just going to shut the bore —I mean door!" For an example of the experimental induction of unconscious

conflict, see the illustrative case at the end of this article.

Using another technique, Clark (1952) has demonstrated the Freudian principle that the sexual drive may be indirectly expressed, or "sublimated," in art and fantasy. He had two groups of male students view pictures of attractive nude females, then write stories while looking at another set of pictures of neutral subject-matter. One group, however, had viewed the nude pictures in the classroom and the other in the fraternity after a beer party. The results showed that sexual arousal in the classroom did not increase overt sexual imagery— probably because of suppression due to anxiety—but did increase the amount of symbolic or indirect expression of sex in the form of fantasy. Sexual arousal under the influence of beer, on the other hand, led to an increase in overt sexual imagery due to the fact that the alcohol reduced anxiety and suppression —and, correspondingly, there was no increase in indirect or symbolic expression.

The cognitive theory of motivation— the third approach—does not deny the influence of unconscious factors or early conditioning, but calls attention to the fact that we are also motivated by more or less clearly thought-out purposes, plans, and expectations. Choosing and preparing for an occupation, for example, requires a conscious assessment of interests and abilities, a weighing of alternatives, the setting up of both short-term and long-term goals, and the capacity to commit ourselves to them. We must also adopt "step-plans" that help us avoid activities and distractions that keep us from attaining our basic goal. *See* LEVEL OF ASPIRATION.

Many revealing experiments have been performed on goal-setting, particularly as related to level of aspiration and achievement motivation. First, it has been found that feelings of success and failure are not experienced when the task is either too difficult or too easy, but only in the middle range between the point where success is highly probable but failure possible, and the point where failure is highly probable but success possible. Second, we tend to adjust our goals and expectations to conform to groups to which we belong, and raise or lower them when we compare them with high- and low-prestige groups. Third, some individuals are more motivated by pleasure in success, and others by fear of failure—Sears (1940) found that children with a history of success set realistic goals, while those with a history of failure set goals very low in order to avoid defeat or very high to save them from feelings of failure. Along the same general lines, Atkinson (1964) has demonstrated that success-oriented individuals, who have high achievement motivation, work hardest at a task of intermediate difficulty when the outcome has a fifty-fifty chance of success or failure; while anxiety-ridden individuals, who have an intense fear of failure, are most anxious in the middle range of difficulty and prefer either extreme.

Each of the theories of motivation just outlined sheds light on important features of human behavior. At this point it is not a question of choosing between them, but of constructing a broader theory that will incorporate their major insights.

Illustrative Case: MOTIVATION, UNCONSCIOUS

During profound hypnosis the subject (a confirmed smoker) was instructed to feel that smoking was a bad habit, that he both loved and hated it, that he wanted to get over the habit but that he felt it was too strong a habit to break, that he would be very reluctant to smoke and would give anything not to smoke, but that he would find himself compelled to smoke; and that after he was awakened he would experience all of these feelings, though not remembering that he had been told to have them.

After he was awakened the subject was drawn into a casual conversation with the hypnotist, who, lighting one himself, offered him a cigarette. The subject waved it aside with the explanation that he had his own and that he preferred Camels, and promptly began to reach for his own pack. Instead of looking in his customary pocket, however, he seemed to forget where he carried his cigarettes and searched fruitlessly through all of his other pockets with a gradually increasing concern. Finally, after having sought them repeatedly in all his other pockets, he located his cigarettes in their usual place. He took them out, engaged in a brief conversation as he dallied with the pack, and then began a search for matches, which he failed to find. During his search for matches he replaced the cigarettes in his pocket and began using both hands, finally locating the matches too in their usual pocket. Having done this, he now began using both hands to search for his cigarettes. He finally located them but found that he had once more misplaced his matches. This time, however, he kept his cigarettes in hand while attempting to locate the matches. He then placed a cigarette in his mouth and struck a match. As he struck it, however, he began a conversation which so engrossed him that he forgot the match and allowed it to burn his finger tips, whereupon, with a grimace of pain, he tossed it in the ashtray. Immediately he took another match, but again introduced a diverting topic by asking the audience in a humorous fashion if they knew the "Scotch" way of lighting a cigarette. As interest was shown, he carefully split the match through the middle. One half of the match he replaced in his pocket in a time-consuming manner and tried to light his cigarette with the other half. When it gave too feeble a flame he discarded it and had to search for the second half. . . . A member of the audience stepped up and proffered him a light, but as the lighted match drew near to the top of his cigarette the subject sneezed and blew it out. . . . He took another, holding it in his mouth while he reached for his matches, started a conversation, and took the cigarette out so that he would talk more freely. It was observed that he took the cigarette out with his hand held in the reverse position to that which he usually used, and after completing his remarks he put the dry end of the cigarette in his mouth, exposing the wet end. He then tried to light this, held the match to the tip in the proper fashion, puffed vigorously, finally got a puff of smoke and then blew out the match. Naturally the wet end of the cigarette did not burn satisfactorily and quickly went out. (Erickson, 1939)

MOTIVATION RESEARCH. Although the term motivation research can be applied in a broad sense to any scientific attempts to find the motives behind human behavior, it is usually reserved for techniques designed to uncover the specific personal motives that underlie buying behavior. It is therefore an important approach in advertising and consumer psychology.

Motivation research contrasts sharply with the traditional methods used in advertising research. The usual emphasis is on collecting data about customers or potential customers, such as their income, age, sex, and education, as well as the amount they buy and the price they are willing to pay for specific articles. This approach provides valuable information but does not reveal all the reasons *why* people buy or refuse to buy products. Motivation research, on the other hand, delves as deeply as possible into the inner urges and personality needs of the consumer, since these are believed to be important determiners of buying behavior. Its approach is therefore clinical, intensive, and qualitative rather than statistical, extensive, and quantitative.

Many techniques are used in motivation research; the following are some of the most effective:

Depth interviewing, designed to tap the more deep-seated motives, is frequently employed today. The interviewer may use a fairly structured approach in which he starts with fixed questions but encourages his subject to express himself freely. This approach was employed, for example, in determining why and with whom people drink beer. It was found that the principal customers are the "middle majority group" who drink beer with friends as an "inexpensive, non-intoxicating drink

which oils the wheels of socializing." For this reason the ads of today avoid the "Man of Distinction" appeal but instead show hearty, active men and wholesome girls engaging in informal social life in modest surroundings. A study has also been conducted to determine why members drop out of book clubs. Intensive interviews revealed that one of the major reasons was a feeling of guilt for letting the books pile up unread, and it was therefore suggested that the clubs emphasize library building in their ads.

A few specialists, notably Ernest Dichter, advocate a frankly psychoanalytic, free-association technique designed to probe emotional reactions, symbolic meanings, and fantasies associated with the product, even tracing them to childhood experiences. According to Dichter, depth interviewing has revealed that the strong interest in convertibles among men represents a symbolic desire for a mistress, while the four-door sedan symbolizes the practical side of life and the plain girl they marry. He concluded that the hard-top combines the marital, family motives with the romance and adventure of a mistress. Whether due to these hidden reasons or not, this model has become an outstanding success.

Group interviews are conducted with either a specially assembled consumer panel or a group, such as a club, which is already in existence. A round-table technique is usually employed, since it is believed to elicit deeper reactions to the product or service under discussion. This approach enables the subjects to react to each other's opinions as well as to the questions of the interviewer.

Projective devices. Almost every kind of technique has been employed. One type is the word association test, in which key words are mixed with background words—for example, a test designed to uncover associations to "butter" contained the key words "buttery, snack, sizzling, bun, and aroma" as well as such neutral words as owl, friend, and cold. It was found that, among other things, people responded to butter with words like smeary, fatty, greasy, yellow, and heavy rather than words having to do with taste (Lucas and Britt, 1963). *See* WORD ASSOCIATION TEST.

A second type of projective technique is the sentence completion method. One test sounded out attitudes and feelings about automobiles by asking the subjects to complete forty statements, including "Driving very fast in a car is . . .", "The most enjoyable thing when you go to buy a car is . . .", and "The best kind of car is one that . . ." (MacLeod, 1958). Picture interpretation tests on the order of the Thematic Apperception Test, and cartoon tests similar to the Rosenzweig Picture Frustration Test, are also used. These are based on the theory that the subject's resistances may be overcome and his deeper feelings elicited if he tells a story suggested by an ambiguous picture, or fills in an empty balloon in a cartoon. In one study, subjects were presented with a picture in which a druggist is showing his customer two bottles, saying, "This widely known brand of aspirin gives you 100 tablets for 67 cents, and the other brand gives you 100 tablets for 27 cents. Which would you like?" The subject is then asked to fill in the response of the customer. *See* SENTENCE COMPLETION METHOD.

Role playing, or visualization. This technique uses fictitious situations into which the individual projects himself. An example is the "Shopping List Technique" used in a classic study of attitudes toward instant coffee. A conventional survey had revealed that most people who said they disliked instant coffee objected to its flavor, but the investigators suspected that this was merely an easy way to get rid of the interviewer. Two shopping lists were then printed, alike in every respect except that list A contained "Nestlé Instant Coffee" and list B included "Maxwell House Coffee, drip grind." Respondents were then asked to characterize the shoppers who had made up the lists. The technique revealed that women who were shown list A tended to characterize the shopper as lazy (48%), a poor planner (48%), a spendthrift (12%), and not a good wife (16%), while those who were shown list B seldom or never used such terms (Haire, 1950). Apparently the inclusion of a prepared food item made the difference.

Questionnaires. Motivation research sometimes uses indirect rather than direct questions. The general result obtained in the study just described was confirmed by an investigation that presented this question: "For which among these six listed reasons do you think a woman might use soup mixes?" Seventy-three per cent of regular users, 48 per cent of infrequent users, and 21 per cent of non-users checked "She thinks soup mixes are as good as home-made soups," while "She is lazy" was checked by 35 per cent of regular users, 47 per cent of infrequent users, and 60 per cent of non-users. In another study, people were asked how fast they would like to drive if they knew they would not be arrested. Owners of an expensive automobile of flashy design gave speeds that averaged 123 miles per hour, while owners of another expensive car of simple and conservative design gave answers averaging 73 miles per hour. These figures suggested that a drive for power may accompany an urge for flamboyant and conspicuous consumption. (Herzog, reported in Ruch, 1963)

Motivation research has both strengths and weaknesses. It frequently serves as a source of hypotheses to be tested by more objective methods, and is therefore particularly useful in the early, exploratory stages of consumer research. It can also be a fertile source of advertising appeals for the copywriter to use, since depth interviewing, projective methods, and other approaches frequently turn up ideas that would not otherwise be thought of. On the other hand, this type of research is an expensive procedure, requires highly trained investigators, and cannot be used on a wide scale. Moreover, since the samplings are small, too much weight might be given to individual responses which are often of a highly personal nature. There is little doubt that under intensive interviewing many respondents will fall back on stereotypes or say whatever comes to mind, whether or not these comments have anything to do with their actual buying behavior. The respondent may also answer as he thinks the interviewer wants him to answer; and the interviewer's own bias, conscious or unconscious, may have a significant effect on the stress he puts on certain answers. This seems to apply particularly to the so-called "psychoanalytic approach," which may over-emphasize such fanciful notions as the idea that people enjoy soup because it reminds them of the warmth, comfort, and security of the womb. *See* ADVERTISING RESEARCH.

MOTOR DEVELOPMENT. The development of muscular coordination and control required for physical activities and skills.

At birth the human infant is completely helpless. His first years are largely devoted to gaining control over his body. This increasing motor ability represents more than just a physical development, since it contributes to every phase of the child's personality and adjustment. It enables him to obtain the exercise he needs for physical health, and the release of tension and pent-up energy he needs for mental health. It brings him into satisfying social contact with other children, and enables him to keep occupied when he is alone. It helps him to achieve independence by doing more and more

things for himself, and it increases his self-confidence and security, especially when he develops skills which are approved by others. There is evidence for many of these findings in tests which show that children who develop high motor ability are in general better adjusted and more active, popular, cooperative, and resourceful than children with low motor ability (Rarick and McKee, 1949).

Motor development tends to follow predictable patterns and to proceed according to fairly well-defined principles. First, the process is primarily based on maturation, since the nerves, muscles, and skeleton must be developed before co-ordinated activity can occur. The cerebellum, which controls balance, grows most rapidly in the first year and a half. This enables the child to sit up, stand, and walk. The cerebrum and the muscles required for fine co-ordination develop more gradually. Second, learning can take place only when maturation has laid the foundation. If attempts are made to train the child before his body is "ready," as in toilet training, he will encounter many setbacks and will probably become high-strung, stubborn, and resentful. Moreover, as studies of twins have demonstrated, the later-trained child will, in most cases, quickly catch up with the earlier trained (Gesell and Thompson, 1929). Third, development follows three predictable patterns: (a) cephalocaudal (head to tail)—that is, the child raises his head before he raises his trunk; (b) proximo-distal (from the mid-line of the body outward)—that is, the shoulders are controlled before the hands and fingers; and (c) mass to specific: gross, random movements occur before refined movements. Fourth, the stages of development of basic activities such as walking follow a predictable sequence. Fifth, there are differences among children in the *rate* of development, owing to variations in constitution and in opportunity for practice.

For this reason the sequences which will now be given should not be regarded as a rigid timetable.

Eye control. Eye co-ordination is extremely poor at birth, but the average baby can pursue a moving light by the third or fourth week, focus on a stationary object at two months, follow a moving object in any direction at three months, and blink voluntarily at four months.

Smiling. A reflex or "gastric" smile may occur as early as the first week, but a genuine smile, perhaps the first sign of social behavior, does not usually occur until the third month.

Head control. Although the newborn may raise his head momentarily, it takes a month for him to hold it in a horizontal plane, and another three months before he can maintain it in an upright position.

Trunk control. The infant cannot turn his body at birth. By the second month he can turn from side to back, and by six months can turn completely around from stomach to stomach.

Sitting. He pulls himself to a sitting position at four months, sits with support at five months, and can usually sit alone for about ten minutes by the ninth or tenth month.

Elimination. On the average, bowel control begins at six months and bladder control between fifteen and sixteen months, but full bowel control (with occasional lapses) is not achieved until two years, and night bladder control is not attained until three or three and half years. *See* TOILET TRAINING.

Arm and hand movements. Poorly co-ordinated defensive movements may occur in the first few days of life, but reaching and grasping take about six months to develop since they require the co-ordinated movement of eyes and hands. In reaching for a cube, the infant makes backhand and circuitous sweeps at four months, and usually does not make a direct approach until the end of the year. The grasping reflex, in which the whole hand is used, appears almost at birth; but thumb opposition does not occur until the third or fourth month. It takes another month or so until the average baby accepts an object that is handed to him.

Leg and foot movements. Reflex stepping movements begin at birth or before, but the complex co-ordinations required for walking take nine to fifteen months to develop. The infant first has to strengthen his muscles by kicking, squirming, pushing, and rolling. By the sixth or seventh month he pushes himself along in a backward direction in a sitting position ("hitching"), and forward by crawling on his stomach. In the ninth month the average baby begins to develop cross-coordination by raising his trunk and propelling himself with one leg at a time—that is, by making creeping movements. A month later he begins to stand with support, and before his first birthday he is likely to be standing alone. From that time it is only a few days or weeks until he takes his first step with support. Less than a month later he will probably be able to walk independently, although a smooth and stable gait is not achieved until two to three years of age.

In contrast to the maturational activities just described, motor skills do not develop by themselves, but must be learned. Children can acquire the rudiments of the grosser skills, such as climbing and throwing, by imitation and experimentation; but even these skills require special training and practice if they are to be developed to a high degree. In general, studies indicate that speed and accuracy of movement show their most rapid increase during early childhood, but improvement continues until the teens. Steadiness and strength also improve with age, but the greatest increase in strength occurs after puberty when the muscles grow rapidly in size.

Needless to say, the finer skills, such as those required for carpentry or playing a musical instrument, require even more specialized practice, guidance, and motivation than the coarser skills. Patient, interested, experienced instructors who give generous encouragement and set reasonable levels of aspiration can make all the difference not only in developing these skills but in helping the child derive the maximum satisfaction from them. Here are some of the approximate norms for common skills—but again, the individual variations are great because of differences in hereditary endowment and learning opportunities:

Hand skills. The one-year-old can usually hold a pencil and remove a paper cap from his head; the two-year-old can scribble, string large beads, open a box, and build a four-block tower; the three-year-old can build a three-block bridge, crudely copy a circle, and dry dishes. By five the average child can copy a square, trace a diamond, draw a recognizable picture of a man, and tie a single knot.

A number of specific growth patterns have been exhaustively investigated. The six-year-old can make a crude table or boat out of wood, model clay, make cookies, sew, and help with most household tasks. The sequence for feeding is: the eight-month-old baby can hold his bottle in his mouth, and is able to remove it by himself a month later; by twelve months he can hold his cup momentarily and try to feed himself with a spoon; by his second birthday he can also use a fork; the following year he begins to spread jam with a knife, and by four he can cut with it. The sequence for dressing is: pulling off socks and shoes at one and a half years; rapid improvement during the next two years; complete ability to dress himself by five years, except for tying his shoelaces with a bowknot. Between four and five the child also learns to bathe himself and brush his hair and teeth.

The sequence for writing is: before three years the child does little more than scribble; by three and a half or four he prints a few large capitals; by five he prints his first name in large, irregular letters with many reversals; by six he can print the entire alphabet as well as the numbers from 1 to 20, and can copy words; by seven, most children can write but the letters are large and irregular, with printed capitals and many errors; between eight and nine printing is given up and the letters become smaller and neater (especially among girls), and there is the beginning of an individual style.

Sequences for many play activities have also been studied. The sequence for block-building is: between one and two the child simply handles, carries, and piles the blocks at random; between two and three he makes simple designs by placing them in a row and begins to experiment with structures such as towers, bridges, and walls; by four and five he uses block structures in his dramatic play; and between five and six he attempts to reproduce actual buildings and bridges (Johnson, 1933). The sequence for wagon play is: pushes the wagon but hesitates to climb in at 21 months; gets in with right knee but does not move at 24 months; gets in and propels it forward and backward at 30 months; coasts down an incline and hauls dirt at 36 months; and by the age of four, uses it for a make-believe game of moving van, and stands up in it while another child pushes: "Look, everybody, I'm standin' up riding!" (Jones, 1939).

Psychologists have also investigated the correlations among different motor abilities, such as throwing, climbing, and jumping. In general there are low correlations, since a child may show little skill in one performance but still do well in others. The reason is that these activities depend on different combinations of factors, including not only strength, speed, and size, but interest and self-confidence. The relationship between intelligence and motor ability has also been studied. It is fairly close during the first few years of life, but there is little or no correlation later on. Children who do not do well academically may therefore be able to succeed in athletics or arts and crafts, and this can be a major factor in the achievement of satisfaction and in the preservation of their self-esteem and mental health.

Finally, little or no correlation has been found between motor ability and socioeconomic level. As Jersild (1960) points out: "So here is an additional facet of the rule of motor abilities in the larger affairs of life: they provide, to a degree, a democratizing influence. The child who might be discriminated against when appraised in terms of his intelligence quotient or academic grades, may be able to make the grade in other important matters if he is given a chance to develop his motor potentialities." See SEX DIFFERENCES, HANDEDNESS.

MULTIPLE PERSONALITY (Dual Personality).

A rare dissociative reaction in which two or more relatively independent personality systems develop in the same individual.

Only about a hundred cases of this highly publicized disorder can be found in psychiatric records. Each of the personalities has characteristic and well-developed emotional reactions, thought processes, behavior patterns, and mannerisms. Secondary personalities often give themselves different names, wear different clothes, and have different handwriting from the primary personality. Usually the personalities are strikingly different and even opposite: one may be inhibited, the other uninhibited; one timid, the other aggressive; one thrifty, the other extravagant; one prudish, the other promiscuous.

The patient changes over from one personality to the other suddenly and without warning, for periods lasting from a few minutes to a few years.

Generally the two or more personalities are not aware of each other, but occasionally the second or "co-conscious" personality is aware of the thoughts and reactions of the primary, dominant personality: B knows A, but A does not know B. In some cases B indicates his awareness of A through automatic writing or by performing some mischievous action such as charging extravagant purchases to A at a department store. See AUTOMATIC WRITING AND DRAWING, PRINCE.

Multiple personality is a gross exaggeration of normal behavior. All but the dullest among us have conflicting tendencies and occasionally do things that are surprising to ourselves as well as to others. Such tendencies may be a dynamic source of creative ideas and flexible adjustment, and contribute substantially to the excitement and satisfaction of living. Practically all of us can harness our conflicting urges and direct them to positive purposes. A few individuals, however, have such acutely incompatible urges that they do not succeed in adjusting their different personality tendencies to each other, and when subjected to stress may unconsciously adopt another solution. They cut away the unacceptable side of their personality and mold it into a separate self which appears to act on its own. In this way they are able to put forbidden urges into practice without feeling the tension and guilt that would haunt them if they were carried out in normal life. In a word, multiple personality enables them to eat their cake and have it too.

Naturally this is no satisfactory solution to conflict. The personality is still at war with itself even if the armies are kept apart. The way to solve emotional problems is through integration not disintegration, through association not disassociation. The first step in integrating the personality is to bring the secondary personality fully to the awareness of the primary personality. This is usually accomplished by applying special techniques, such as hypnotic suggestion or sodium amytal interviews. The therapy is generally successful.

Multiple personality is not to be confused with schizophrenia, which literally means split personality. In schizophrenia the split is not between different total personalities, but between different processes of the same personality. The individual is so disorganized and fragmented that his thinking, motor activity, and emotions are at odds with each other. *See* SCHIZOPHRENIC REACTIONS (GENERAL).

Illustrative Case: MULTIPLE PERSONALITY (A DOUBLE LIFE)

". . . in general demeanor, Maud was quite different from Sara. She walked with a swinging, bouncing gait contrasted to Sara's sedate one. While Sara was depressed, Maud was ebullient and happy, even though suicidal. Suicide and death meant nothing to Maud, and she saw nothing wrong or depressing in them.

". . . in so far as she could Maud dressed differently from Sara. Sara had two pairs of slippers. One was a worn pair of plain grey mules; the other, gaudy, striped, high-heeled, open-toed sandals. Sara always wore the mules. Maud would throw them aside in disgust and don the sandals. Sara used no make-up. Maud used a lot of rouge and lipstick, painted her fingernails and toenails deep red, and put a red ribbon in her hair. She liked red and was quickly attracted by anything of that color. Sara's favorite color was blue.

"Sara was a mature, intelligent individual. Her mental age was 19.2 years I.Q. 128. A psychometric done on Maud showed a mental age of 6.6, I.Q. 43. Sara's vocabulary was larger than Maud's, and she took an intelligent interest in words new to her. When Maud heard a new word, she would laugh and mispronounce it, or say, 'That was a twenty-five-cent one.' In sharp contrast to Sara, Maud's grammar was atrocious. A typical statement was, 'I didn't do nuttin'.' Sara's handwriting was more mature than Maud's.

"Sara did not smoke and was very awkward when she attempted it. Maud had a compulsion to smoke. At times she insisted she 'had to' and would become agitated and even violent if cigarettes were denied her. She would smoke chain fashion as many cigarettes as were permitted but two would satisfy her for a while . . .

Maud had no conscience, no sense of right and wrong. She saw no reason for not always doing as she pleased. She felt no guilt over her incestuous and promiscuous sexual relationships. Sara on the other hand had marked guilt feelings over her previous immoral sexual behavior.

"It seemed that Sara changed to Maud at the point when Sara's feeling of guilt was greatest." (Lipton, 1943)

Illustrative Case: MULTIPLE PERSONALITY (THE THERAPIST WITHIN)

During a demonstration of hypnosis, Dr. Milton H. Erickson discovered that his best subject, a Miss Damon, experienced a strange fit of terror. To get at the reason for this reaction, he decided to try automatic writing. The girl, a college student, was given an advanced book on psychology to read, and a pencil was placed in her hand hidden from view behind a pile of books. Almost at once the hand began to write about "fears."

When the girl was questioned, she revealed that she had recently been troubled by an intense dread of cats and an uncontrollable impulse to close doors, even to the point of getting up in the middle of the night. At the same time, her hand continued writing, but the words were practically illegible. She was shown what her hand had written, but she was able to decipher only a few of the words, such as trance, my, and catalepsy. She then "asked laughingly, 'Did I really write that nonsense?' Both the investigator and his assistant replied affirmatively and in the same amused tone. At the moment the subject was leaning forward over the desk and her hand was out of her peripheral vision. As the verbal reply was given to her question, her hand was observed to write 'No,' of which Miss Damon remained unaware. Immediately the investigator asked, as if speaking directly to the subject, 'What do you mean?' And while Miss Damon puzzled over what she meant, her hand wrote 'Can't.' Again speaking as if to Miss Damon, the question was asked, 'Why?', to which her hand replied, 'Damon doesn't know these things.'"

When asked "Who does know?", the following exchange occurred: "A (answer): Me. Q (question): Me? A: Brown. Q: Who? A: Me—Brown—B. Q: Explain. A: D (Damon) is D, B is B. Q: B know D? A: Yes. Q: D know B? A: No. No. Q: B part of D? A: No. B is B; D is D. Q: Can I talk to B? A: Are . . . Q: What do you want? A: Help D. Q: Why? A: D afraid. Q: Do you know what D is afraid of? A: Yes; D, no. Q: Why? A: D afraid, forgot, don't want to know. . . .

The secretary then read the questions and her answers were shown to Miss Damon. She attended carefully with a look of increasing understanding, finally remarking, "Why, that must really mean I have a dual personality," and then was greatly startled that her hand emphatically wrote "Right." Recovering her poise, Miss Damon asked, "Can I talk to you?" "Sure." "Can you talk to me?" "Yes." "Is your name really Brown?"

"Yes." "What is your full name?" "Jane Brown."

The hand then wrote "D forgets something a long time ago" and directed the doctor to "Ask, ask, ask." An eerie interchange unfolded in the hours that followed. Brown, a physically non-existent personality, actually served as the psychiatrist in the case and prompted and prodded the professor to ask question after question. She reassured him when he was on the right track, called him "dumb" when he went off. By writing certain key words on the paper (as in a word association test), Brown gradually revived Miss Damon's memory of her childhood. But the further back she went, the more resistant the girl became.

After about two hours, as she was trying to recall events that occurred before she was four years of age, the hand wrote "niaise" on the pad. Miss Damon looked at this strange word, and experienced a fit of terror. At once Brown ordered the doctor to put Miss Damon into a trance and give her a mirror, which she was to hold in such a way that it reflected only the blank ceiling. Miss Damon took one look at the mirror and turned away in terror. Brown then wrote, "It's all right, E. D just scared. Got to be. Then feel better. Just comfort."

The doctor made a few soothing remarks, and Brown continued, "D no at 7:30."

As the fateful hour approached, Miss Damon gradually lost her fear, and at the appointed minute suddenly exclaimed in amazement that she saw her grandfather's face in the mirror. This immediately brought to her mind an experience that occurred at the age of three. In a word, the little girl had mischievously run out of the house leaving the door open, and could not find her way back. When she was finally located, her grandfather, a French Canadian, scolded her severely and called her "niaise"—simpleton. To impress her with the gravity of her offense, he told her how he, too, had once left a door open, and a muskrat had invaded the pantry, eating everything in sight. Between them, Brown and the doctor brought Miss Damon to the realization that, in her three-year-old mind, she had confused her own experience with her grandfather's, and had inwardly taken the blame for the catastrophe in *his* story. Now, years later, she was closing the door she had once left open, and dreaded cats, which she somehow associated with the intruding muskrat.

After the interview, which lasted almost three hours, Miss Damon's symptoms disappeared completely—and with them went her unsuspected alter ego, Brown, now that her psychiatric mission had been accomplished. (Erickson and Kubie, 1939)

MULTIPLE THERAPY. Any form of psychotherapy carried out simultaneously by two or more therapists.

The term multiple therapy was first used by Rudolf Dreikurs, a follower of Alfred Adler. The technique is occasionally used in family therapy and group therapy as well as individual therapy. In an article published in 1960, Mullan and Sangiuliano report that they initially utilized a second therapist only when an impasse occurred or a crisis situation, such as a suicide threat, presented itself. However, it became clear to them that the second therapist was permanently helpful with certain types of patients, such as men who had difficulty relating to the opposite sex. In these cases the second therapist was often introduced at the start of the process and not merely when it reached an impasse.

In most instances, however, the second therapist is brought into the picture in the midst of the therapeutic process, and his presence usually has a number of effects. Frequently the patient's dreams become Oedipal in nature as a result of the triangular situation, and this becomes an important source of information on the struggle within the original family. Moreover, the patient and the two therapists form a symbolic family in which the original relationships can be re-enacted. And as the patient learns to deal with the symbolic relationships of the therapeutic situation, he begins to alter his basic attitudes and deal more effectively with his real relationships.

Mullan and Sangiuliano summarize a number of advantages cited by various practitioners of multiple therapy. The following eight points appear to be particularly significant. First, introduction of a second therapist in the course of the treatment process has a stimulating effect, since the patient has been relating to only one symbolic parent (the first therapist), and is now forced to reconstruct his relationship to his other parent, represented by the second therapist. Second, the inclusion of another therapist adds a note of insecurity for the therapist himself. It confronts him with his own limitations and challenges him to re-examine his approach. (For this reason, some therapists resist the introduction of a colleague into the picture.) Third, the intensity of the therapeutic field is increased by the presence of two therapists and by their own interactions. Fourth, the more complex situation adds to the number of possible relationships which can be utilized in the therapeutic process. Fifth, interaction between the therapists helps them change and grow, and this can have a therapeutic effect on the patients they are treating. Sixth, each therapist may complement or supplement the other both in insight and approach. Seventh, therapeutic impasses can be more easily avoided or dissolved than they can with a single therapist; and then, if it becomes advisable, the patient can be readily transferred entirely to one of the therapists. Eighth, the presence of two therapists helps to reinforce interpretations and gives a more powerful and effective ending to the therapy.

MUNSELL SYSTEM. A systematic arrangement of colors in terms of hue, saturation, and brightness, used as a reference standard.

The system arose from the need for a single standard of comparison so that color specifications could be clearly stated and carried out in industry. Manufacturers had a great deal of trouble in the early part of this century because there were a number of different standards instead of a uniform means of defining any particular color. A. H. Munsell studied the problem and proposed a single system in 1915. He later refined and restated his standards in the *Munsell Book of Color,* published in 1929. In this system every color is classified and numbered according to the three dimensions of hue, saturation ("chroma"), and brightness ("value"). These dimensions are marked off on charts in equal-appearing gradations.

To find these equal-appearing gradations, Munsell prepared sets of cards which showed every color in different degrees of saturation (richness) and brightness. He then gave the cards for each color to a group of subjects, and asked them to divide them, first into equal steps of increasing brightness, and after that into steps of increasing saturation. The resulting gradations were then arranged in systematic order, and a number was assigned to each of them. The book reproduces these gradations in the form of rectangular slips of heavy paper painted with permanent water color. Any color that can be reproduced by mixing pigments can be found in it, and any manufacturer who needs to produce standard colors merely has to refer to a number in the Munsell System. *See* COLOR CIRCLE, COLOR SOLID.

MUNSTERBERG, HUGO (1863–1916). Münsterberg was a versatile student of the human sciences, noted equally for his contributions to philosophy and to applied psychology. Born in Germany, he was a pupil of Wilhelm Wundt in Leipzig and later taught in German universities. William James became interested in him after reading his criticisms of Wundt's structuralist psychology, and invited him to take over the psychological laboratory at Harvard University. He remained there from 1892 until his death. Among his works are: *Principles of Psychology* (1900), *The Eternal Life* (1905), *Science and Idealism* (1906), *Philosophy of Value* (1908), *Psychology of Industrial Efficiency* (1913), and *Psychology: General and Applied* (1915).

Münsterberg did not have as direct an influence on American psychology as some of his contemporaries, partly because of his great interest in philosophy, and partly because he was attracted to the undeveloped areas of of psychic research, legal and industrial psychology. He also alienated himself from many of his colleagues by publishing articles which were interpreted as pro-German at the outbreak of World War I. Nevertheless his work gave impetus to several important trends in the field. First, he proposed an "action theory" which helped to turn attention to psychological processes as contrasted to the analysis of states of consciousness. He attempted to discover the basic physiological correlates of mental acts, and concluded that they always involve a complete circuit from sensory receptor to motor response— in other words, consciousness tends toward action. This view has been in-

corporated in the modern organismic approach. *See* ACT PSYCHOLOGY.

Second, Münsterberg did pioneer work in the field of social psychology. He was one of the first to attempt an experimental study of group behavior. An example was his classroom experiment in which students were asked to estimate the number of dots appearing on a screen. The results showed that decisions made in the group setting differed materially from those made when alone, due to the influence of members of the group on each another. *See* SOCIAL NORM.

Third, and perhaps most important, he showed how psychology could be used in education, industry, criminology, and business. In education, he helped to further the mental testing movement as well as the study of individual differences, although he confined himself largely to tests of sensory ability similar to those devised by Cattell. In industrial psychology, he showed the importance of scientific studies of fatigue and its influence on output. In legal psychology, he not only served as expert witness in many court cases, but performed experiments and demonstrations on the reliability of testimony. His activities in these more practical fields have earned him the title of "Founder of Applied Psychology," according to Boring (1950).

MUSIC AND WORK. Work has been done to the accompaniment of music ever since the first work songs were created, but psychological research on industrial music dates back only thirty years. Some of the early studies reported significant effects not only on worker morale but on productivity as well. More recent and more refined investigations have questioned some of these claims. Nevertheless a survey made by Scott and others in 1961 indicated that about one third of all sizable manufacturing companies had introduced

848

MUSIC TESTS

music programs of one kind or another.

Before summarizing the present status of the subject, it might be useful to review two influential studies, one involving complex work and the other a simple, routine task. The subjects in the first experiment were 142 women working in a rug factory; their job required long training and a high degree of manipulative skill, visual memory, and color discrimination. Music was played for eighty minutes a day four days a week for five weeks, but the types of programs and the music-free day were varied from week to week. There were no significant changes in output on either the music or the music-free days—perhaps, as the investigators suggested, because the workers had established stable activity patterns that could not be easily influenced. However, when they were asked whether the music should be continued, 84.5 per cent said yes, 14.5 per cent said it made no difference, and only 1 per cent said no (McGehee and Gardner, 1949).

The subjects in the second study were forty-two women who performed highly repetitive production-line tasks in the manufacture of terminals for radios. Half of them were on the day shift, half on the night shift. Carefully scheduled music programs were played for twelve weeks, and productivity during music and non-music shifts was compared. The experimenter reported that "Production under varying conditions of music increased from 4 to 25%. The average increase on the day shift was 7%; on the night shift 17%." There was no decline in the effectiveness of the music over the entire period, and interviews at the end showed that there was also no decline in the enthusiasm of the workers (Smith, 1947).

A thorough review of all major investigations has been made by Uhrbrock (1961). His conclusions indicate that

companies would be well advised to investigate the work situation, the type of job, and the attitudes of the employees before deciding whether to adopt a music program—and if it is adopted, no one should expect miraculous results. Here are his major points:

First, many of the claims for increased production as a result of music have not been scientifically established. Second, at least three investigators have reported that "Young, inexperienced employees engaged in *simple,* repetitive, monotonous tasks increased their output when stimulated by music." Third, experienced factory workers whose work patterns were stabilized and who were performing complex tasks did not increase their production. Fourth, factory employees in general prefer working where music is played. Fifth, changes in blood pressure in some subjects indicate that feelings of euphoria during periods of musical stimulation have a physiological basis. Sixth, the majority prefer instrumental to vocal music at work. Seventh, not all workers like work music; from one to ten per cent are annoyed by it. Eighth, the quality of work can be adversely affected by music, and the output can be lowered even when the worker reports it was "quite pleasant." Ninth, the older the worker, the less he is likely to prefer working to music.

MUSIC TESTS. A number of standardized tests have been developed for measuring musical aptitude and for predicting success or failure in musical study. All five of the following tests are presented on phonograph records and in this way assure uniformity of presentation and allow for group administration. In general, music tests have been found most useful in detecting very good and very poor prospects for musical instruction, but are less effective in measuring the gradations between these extremes (Freeman, 1962).

Seashore Measures of Musical Talent (fourth grade to adult). This test, the first to be developed, presents pairs of tones or tonal sequences on records or tapes in six different groups, covering pitch, loudness, rhythm, time, timbre, and tonal memory. In the pitch test, for example, two tones, a and b, are sounded in sequence, and the subject indicates whether b is higher or lower than a. In the rhythm test, the subject compares two tonal patterns and states whether they are the same or different. Several items of increasing difficulty are included in each group. The individual scores on the six tests are not combined into a single total, but are presented in profile form.

The scores on the individual tests are given in percentiles, and can be compared with norms reported for grades 4–5, 6–8, and 9–16. The six items are based on Seashore's analysis of measurable sensory abilities required for both the appreciation and production of music, and can be used to identify people who are so deficient in these capacities that it would be fruitless to devote themselves to the study of music. They are also helpful in locating specific deficiencies of otherwise able students. Attempts to validate the tests by comparing scores with actual achievement and teacher ratings in music schools have been disappointing. This indicates that prediction of success in music studies requires much more than information on sensory capacities. Interestingly, the Seashore tests have proven quite valid in predicting performance on jobs that are essentially based on these capacities, such as radio telegrapher.

Kwalwasser-Dykema Music Tests (*elementary and high school*). This series consists of ten short tests measuring the six Seashore functions, as well as facility in reading musical notation and certain aspects of musical appreciation. The tests have been widely used in schools, probably because they take less

than an hour to administer and appear to provide a great deal of information. However, studies have shown that many of the subtests have low reliabilities, since they are too short and too lacking in discriminative items. Consequently the scores obtained from this test are of questionable value.

Wing Standardized Tests of Musical Intelligence. (eight years to adult). These tests are an answer to the frequent objection that the Seashore approach atomizes musical ability instead of viewing it as a unitary aptitude. They present meaningful piano music instead of individual tones or phrases, and the results are combined into a single score representing general musical ability or "musical intelligence."

Seven subtests are administered, each representing a musical dimension emphasized by music teachers and examiners: rhythmic accent, memory, pitch change, chord analysis, harmony, intensity, and phrasing. Studies indicate that the reliabilities of the total scores are very high, and correlations with teacher ratings are at least .60. The items are generally on a more complex level than in the Seashore test, and involve judgment of esthetic merit as well as sensory capacity. Not surprisingly, the Wing tests are especially useful in testing older children and adults, and in identifying talented individuals who would profit from further training.

Drake Musical Test (eight years to adult). This test effectively measures two basic functions. On one part, the subject listens to a two-part melody and then compares it from memory with other versions. If he decides that one of the versions is not the same, he must state whether it differs in key, time, or notes. The other part is a rhythm test designed to measure the subject's ability to keep time by maintaining a metronome beat silently. High reliabilities have been reported for both tests, and scores show substantial validity as predictors of future ratings on musical study and performance.

Aliferis Music Achievement Test. The major difference between this test and others is that it is designed for use with entering college freshmen who wish to enroll in music courses. The functions tested are much the same as on other recent tests: "auditory-visual discrimination of melodic, harmonic, and rhythmic elements and idioms." It fares reasonably well in studies of validity, with correlations of .50 to .60 between the total scores and grades in music courses.

MUSIC THERAPY. The application of the art of music in supportive treatment. This may be in the form of music appreciation sessions, concerts, group instruction, or individual practice. Music therapy is sometimes combined with a dance therapy program. *See* DANCE THERAPY.

Music therapy was originally developed for mental patients but has also been found effective with the mentally retarded and the physically handicapped, including the blind, the crippled, and the cerebral palsied. In their most advanced form, music therapy programs are planned not only for groups of patients, but also to meet the particular needs of individuals. As with other forms of therapy these programs are the final responsibility of the physician in charge, but in this case a music specialist collaborates with him in making out the treatment plans.

At the present time about four hundred hospitals and other institutions offer music therapy programs. Therapists should be specially trained and registered according to requirements set up by the National Association of Music Therapy. Eleven colleges and universities throughout the country have been accredited by the Association. They offer courses not only in all phases of music but in psychology, sociology, and other relevant subjects. The field is a growing one, and at present the demand for music therapists exceeds the supply.

Music therapy has a number of special values in the field of mental health. As pointed out by Marian Chace and others, most mental patients tend to be isolated, and music gives them an opportunity for nonverbal communication and shared experiences which create an "empathic bond" with other people. Listening or performing with others helps to break through the barriers of individual illness and reestablish social relationships. At the same time, it gives each patient a chance to release his own emotions and respond in his own personal way. These objectives can best be achieved if the leader does not impose his own taste but allows the group or the individual patient a wide range of choice. In group activities most therapists agree that the members should be selected on the basis of their interests in a particular form of music, and not on the basis of their type of disorder. In general, it has been found that the musical interests of mental patients are the same as they were before the onset of illness.

The chief function of the music therapist is to make an ample choice of music experience available, and to establish an emotional climate which will encourage relaxation, enjoyment, spontaneity, and self-confidence among the patients. Though specific musical forms —group singing, music appreciation, individual performance—have their own values, the general atmosphere is believed to be the key factor.

An example of well-planned music therapy is the program at the Veterans Administration Hospital in Topeka, Kansas. This institution offers individual and group instruction, music appreciation for larger groups, and environmental or background music for parties, dancing, sports, and meals. Facilities include an attractively furnished, noninstitutional music clinic for group instruction, as well as a record library, piano, tape recorder, and small sound-proofed studios for practice. Musical activities may be prescribed by physicians for therapeutic purposes, or may simply serve as leisure-time pursuits. The staff consists of two professional musicians assisted by several volunteers who occasionally take interested patients to music stores or broadcasting studios in the community.

MUTISM. This term has three basic meanings. First, inability to speak due to congenital or early deafness, as in deaf-mutism. Second, voluntary refusal to speak, as in certain religious orders or in children who use silence as a means of expressing anger. And third, involuntary inhibition of speech, a condition found in certain psychiatric disorders.

Among psychiatric patients mutism is a functional, or psychogenic, symptom which probably arises from underlying conflicts. It appears to symbolize either withdrawal from a threatening world, or hostility toward other people, or in some cases both of these reactions at once. Psychogenic mutism is most commonly observed in the catatonic form of schizophrenia, where it is usually interpreted as a manifestation of negativism. It is also found in profound depression and in hysterical stupor, a conversion reaction. See NEGATIVISM.

MYXEDEMA. A disorder brought about by a marked thyroid deficiency in adults. The hypothyroidism is frequently due to a diet lacking in iodine, but may also occur after thyroidectomy and in women undergoing menopause.

The symptoms of myxedema are both mental and physical. The patient becomes profoundly fatigued, listless, overweight, emotionally labile, and retarded in thought and action. His speech is slow, his comprehension and memory are poor, and he may become irritable and restless.

In severe cases previous personality defects may combine with the disturbed brain metabolism to produce psychotic reactions. Many of these patients develop a marked depression or a paranoid reaction with hallucinations and delusions of persecution.

The standard treatment for myxedema is administration of thyroid extract in the hospital. The symptoms are usually relieved in cases where the brain has not suffered permanent damage. The hormone treatment is also applied in the early stages of hypothyroidism, and for this reason severe myxedema is a rarity today. See CRETINISM, THYROID GLAND.

Illustrative Case: MYXEDEMA

A thirty-nine-year-old woman was hospitalized after five years of emotional instability and outbursts of temper. During the previous two years marked changes had occurred in her appearance: her weight had increased, her face had become puffy, skin and hair had turned very dry, and her voice had coarsened. She had become intolerant of cold, chronically fatigued, constipated, and short of breath. Her ankles had begun to swell and she complained of headaches, nausea, vomiting, and excessive menstruation. She slept twelve hours a day.

When hospitalized, the patient was disheveled and in an obvious state of anguish. Her speech was repetitive and stereotyped and she blocked frequently. Her attention span was short and she could not concentrate well; her abstract thinking was impaired and her memory for recent events poor. Her affective responses were very labile and fluctuated from a tearful, agitated depression to resentful hostility. Among the most striking of her symptoms, however, were the transient delusions of reference, influence, and persecution, along with varied hallucinations. The latter ran the gamut of hearing, vision, smell, and taste; relatives appeared to be talking to her and she told a nurse's aide, "I hear all these voices—all day I have—but you are the first voice I believe—yes, I do—I believe I can trust you. You are pure. I used to be like you—a nurse's aide helping people." She had had two illegitimate children before her current marriage to an alcoholic with whom she got along badly. The voices she heard talked about her, accused her of immorality, and threatened her. She felt that everyone was watching her. At one time she believed that all her relatives were dead.

Her MMPI was elevated on the paranoid and psychopathic deviate scales. An intelligence test yielded an IQ of 73 and a memory test yielded an even poorer score. On clinical examination it became obvious that she was suffering from a severe thyroid deficiency. Her basal metabolic rate was —32 per cent and other tests of thyroid functioning were consistent. Concomitantly, she suffered from anemia and impaired heart functioning, which are common in advanced hypothyroidism. Treatment by thyroid extract was begun, and after two weeks marked physical and behavioral improvement was noted.

Six weeks after admission, the patient's measured IQ was 93, although her memory was borderline and she still manifested a defect in foresight and planning. On an MMPI retest the paranoid psychopathic scales were normal. The delusions and hallucinations disappeared completely. Her anemia and cardiac functioning improved greatly and her weight went down. Soon afterward she was able to leave the hospital on a daily maintenance dose of thyroid extract. (Rosen and Gregory, (1965)

N

NAIL BITING. Nail biting is one of the most common habit disturbances among children, and is classified by The American Psychiatric Association as a "special symptom reaction" under Personality Disorders. It frequently starts at five or six years of age, but the incidence is greatest in adolescence, after which it usually declines rapidly. About one fifth of all children and adolescents bite their fingernails. Girls and boys seem to be equally prone to this habit during the early years, but males outnumber females at later ages, probably because older girls and women are more concerned about their appearance and more sensitive to social disapproval.

Several explanations for persistent nail biting have been advanced, but the most widely accepted is the theory of tension reduction. Apparently the habit provides a physical outlet that relieves anxiety, since it is most pronounced during periods of stress. This theory is supported by the fact that the incidence is particularly high among stutterers and among children raised in institutions, as well as during adolescence when emotional tension usually reaches a peak. Studies also indicate that nail biters as a group are more anxious than non-nail biters. Moreover, they frequently realize they are engaging in the habit to relieve tension as well as to use up extra energy and keep busy.

Three other explanations have been suggested. It has been considered (1) a substitute for masturbation, (2) a fixation at the oral stage of development, or (3) an outlet for hostile impulses. These explanations may apply in certain cases, especially when they are combined with the theory of tension reduction. Children who have been taught that masturbation is wrong may start to bite their nails because it is a somewhat pleasurable activity and directs their attention away from their sex organs. They may, however, *continue* the biting because they have found that it also relieves their inner tensions. Similarly, the child discovers early in life that the mouth and lips give him pleasure (oral gratification), and this pleasure is enhanced by nail biting. Children who are denied other pleasures—institutional children, for instance—may be arrested, or "fixated," at the oral stage where satisfaction is derived primarily from sucking and chewing. Others may regress to this early stage when they go through stressful situations such as moving to a new neighborhood or entering a new school. Finally, nail biting is sometimes interpreted as an aggressive act which can readily be used as an outlet for anger and resentment. In support of this theory, studies have shown that nail biters are usually "intropunitive"—that is, they tend to blame or punish themselves instead of directing their hostility against others. When they are angry with their parents or other people, they use nail biting as a safe way to discharge their tension.

Persistent nail biting may be treated by alleviating stressful situations and by helping the child to handle his problems more effectively. Children can also be taught to release tension and resentment in constructive ways, such as talking out their problems with a sympathetic person. Tranquilizing drugs may be a useful adjunct to these approaches during periods of special strain and tension. Appointments with a manicurist do not usually work unless efforts are also made to reduce tension. Symptomatic approaches, such as punishment, forcing the child to wear gloves, or applying a bitter substance to the nails, are rarely recommended. *See* PERSONALITY DISORDERS.

NARCISSISM. Self-love, usually to an excessive degree.

The term narcissism derives from a Greek legend. The youth Narcissus rejected the maiden Echo, who died of a broken heart. As punishment, Nemesis, the god of revenge, made him fall in love with his reflection in the water until he pined away of self-admiration. He was then transformed into a flower, the narcissus, an early spring plant that grows and nourishes itself in water.

In general, narcissism is regarded as an expression of emotional immaturity. The normal individual advances from childhood love of self to adult concern and love for others, from egoism to some degree of altruism. The immature or disturbed individual remains overconcerned with himself. He seeks to escape responsibility and the risk of failure by being totally self-involved. At the same time he compensates for feelings of inadequacy by exaggerating his own personal qualities.

Narcissism is an important concept in psychoanalysis. Freud distinguished two forms, primary and secondary. Primary narcissism occurs in the earliest stages of development in which the child's libido or pleasure drive is turned toward his own body and its satisfactions rather than toward the environment or "object relations." According to this theory, young children form a narcissistic "ego ideal" consisting of an image of their own perfection and omnipotence. This is partly because their slightest gesture leads to satisfaction of their nutritional needs, partly the result of their increasing abilities, and partly a reaction to feelings of anxiety and helplessness. If an individual's emotional development is fixated at this stage, his behavior will be dominated by self-love and self-interest.

Secondary narcissism develops out of the desire of the child to identify with the parents and partake of their omnipotence. This leads to overestimation both of the parents and of himself. In later life an immature, disturbed, or senile individual may cease to be interested in other people and regress to a stage where he is wholly concerned with himself. In so doing, he may return to the overidealized image of his ego which he built up in his childhood by identification with fond and admiring parents. This type of reaction also occurs in psychotic patients (especially schizophrenics) who lose contact with outer reality and unconsciously seek satisfaction in fantasies and delusions of grandeur. The patient's inner life is so central in schizophrenia that the psychosis is often described as a narcissistic disorder. See EGOMANIA, IDENTIFICATION, INCORPORATION, EGO IDEAL.

NARCOLEPSY. A rare disorder characterized by a sudden irresistible urge to sleep.

The narcoleptic patient may be overcome by the need to sleep at any time during the day, regardless of the situation or the activity in which he is engaged. He immediately collapses or lies down, falls into what appears to be a natural sleep for a few seconds to thirty minutes, and awakens refreshed. Nocturnal sleep is not affected even though the sleep attacks may occur several times a day.

Some cases of narcolepsy appear to be organic, others psychogenic. The condition was at one time thought to be a variant of epilepsy, but this theory has been discarded by most investigators since the electroencephalograph of patients subject to sleep attacks shows normal brain waves when they are awake and alert. However, many patients show electrical patterns of drowsiness, the first stage of sleep, during an examination following an attack, and for this reason a dysfunction of the reticular activating system is often suspected. This theory is supported by the fact that a history of epidemic encephalitis has been obtained in many cases. As Noyes and Kolb (1963) suggest, narcolepsy may be a sequel or continuing form of that disease, or it may be due to a "localized encephalitis, trauma, or neoplasm" (tumor) in the hypothalamus, which contains a center that controls sleep. The disorder is most frequently found in young males and is often associated with sexual impotence and obesity. Dextroamphetamine (Dexedrine) is usually administered to counteract the attacks. See RETICULAR FORMATION, EPIDEMIC ENCEPHALITIS, HYPOTHALAMUS, AMPHETAMINES.

Neurotic sleep attacks may last for a few minutes, a few hours or even many years. (The more extended attacks are sometimes termed psychogenic hypersomnia). The disorder is usually classified as a dissociative reaction since, like amnesia and fugue, it appears to be a means of cutting one's self off from a distressing situation. Kisker (1964) compares it to the "still reaction" of animals who protect themselves from danger by playing dead, and cites the fact that the common expression "He makes me tired" implies a desire to escape into sleep, and that many people find it hard to wake up in the morning when they have problems to face. Neurotic sleep attacks are exaggerations of these tendencies dictated by unconscious needs: "Cases have been reported in which soldiers have fallen asleep during a bombardment, preachers and professors have fallen asleep while lecturing or delivering sermons, a sign painter fell asleep while on the scaffold, and a man who was having a tooth pulled fell asleep in the dentist's chair."

Studies have shown that many individuals subject to sleep attacks harbor intense resentment against a rigid life pattern, usually laid down by the parents, plus an inability to change the pattern due to a passive personality and strong emotional dependence. In such cases the attack probably represents a desire to escape from domination, and is frequently precipitated by an emotional outburst that provokes intense anxiety. Sleep, then, is a means of avoiding the anxiety-producing situation. The reaction seems to be illustrated, in part at least, by the following extreme case cited by Kisker: "A young woman in South Africa was in love with a man who committed suicide after her parents opposed their marriage. The girl was so overcome with grief, and felt such strong hostility toward her parents, that she fell asleep and remained asleep for thirty-three years."

Amphetamines are less effective with psychogenic than with organic cases, but in some cases psychotherapy has proven useful. *See* CATAPLEXY.

Illustrative Case: NARCOLEPSY

Patient was a twenty-three-year-old colored college student, first seen in surgical dispensary for infected umbilicus. Referred to neurological dispensary because of complaint that he was unable to stay awake. Neurological examination revealed a tense, asthenic boy with overactive reflexes, excessive perspiration, and bilateral lid ptosis (drooping eyelids).

Patient had first become aware of urge to fall asleep, difficult to resist, six years before, at age of seventeen. During next four years desire for sleep grew more intense and it became increasingly difficult to remain awake. At one time drove truck off road because he had fallen asleep. Gave up driving because could not trust himself at wheel. He said, "I wasn't able to shake it off." During two years preceding visit to hospital, sleepiness at time became irresistible.

Personal Development: Had always, from childhood, felt physically small and incompetent. Had grown up in uneducated, low-standard Negro family. Had always done well in school and been favorite of teachers. Had finished high school at head of class at seventeen, having done four years' work in three by attending night school. Always timid, felt that security lay in "brains rather than brawn." Since five had been preoccupied about parentage, wondering whether he had been adopted or not. This issue became of absorbing interest to him, but he never made any direct attempt to clear up the matter.

In the dispensary he recalled that, at eleven, he had gone to court with his supposed parents, although he did not know why. Through the psychiatric social service it was possible to obtain the actual facts about this boy. His suspicion that he was adopted was found to be correct, and it was learned that he was the son of a white woman and a colored man. Had been legally adopted by family with whom he lived. Present whereabouts of own parents or any further information about them not ascertainable. Information was presented to patient, who seemed pleased by it. He became more comfortable and attacks of sleep diminished and completely disappeared. Gave up the Benzedrine tablets which he had taken previously, and for several months was free of symptoms and stopped return visits to psychiatrist of his own accord.

However, through a letter of inquiry, contact was re-established with him two years later. It was found that sleeping attacks had recurred and were still present, and that again he was caught up in tangle of attitudes about parentage. Thought "about nothing else." In last conference with him, he stated that he had, at present time, no close relationship with anyone. Admitted feelings of terrible resentment against foster parents, which he never showed. Seemed to blame them in some way for emotional dilemma in which he found himself, but attitude was one of self-pity, with no apparent impulse to attempt amelioration of his lot. (Langworthy and Betz, 1944)

NARCOSYNTHESIS. A treatment technique in which narcotic drugs are used to stimulate the recall of crucial repressed experiences, followed by a "synthesis" of these experiences with the patient's emotional life.

The technique was developed by R. R. Grinker and J. P. Spiegel during the war as a rapid treatment for combat fatigue cases involving severe battle trauma. Intravenous injections of sodium pentothal (or sodium amytal) were used to produce a drowsy, suggestible state in which the patient could be encouraged to bring damaging experiences to the surface—experiences which had been unconsciously repressed and "forgotten" because they were so threatening and disturbing to the ego. Under the influence of the drug, servicemen were able to relive these experiences with startling realism and emotional intensity: "The terror exhibited in the moments of supreme danger, such as the imminent explosion of shell, the death of a friend before the patient's eyes, the absence of cover under a heavy dive-bombing attack, is electrifying to watch" (Grinker and Spiegel, 1945).

"Abreactions" of this kind helped these patients discharge much of their emotional tension, relieve such symptoms as mutism and agitation, and reduce anxiety to a point where they could talk openly about the fears or guilt feelings which had caused them to repress the painful experience. With the psychiatrist's help, they were able to achieve a better understanding of their reactions, and accept and assimilate the disturbing events. As a result, most of them regained their full confidence and stability.

The majority of these combat cases were "reactive" conditions—that is, the patient was responding to battle experiences which were so overpowering that they caused a temporary breakdown in an otherwise normal individual. In these instances only one or two narcotic interviews were usually needed. But in cases where the traumatic experiences served to activate and bring to the surface already existing neurotic tendencies, more extended treatment was required.

Today narcosynthesis is one of the standard treatments for acute anxiety states, and for reactions to severe traumatic experiences. It is also used in cases of amnesia to facilitate the recovery of lost memories, and in conversion hysteria to remove such symptoms as paralysis or blindness. Many psychiatrists prefer narcosynthesis to hypnosis as a means of releasing the unconscious, since it requires less time, is more certain, and does not involve dependence on the therapist. The technique is also well accepted by patients, because it appears to be a physical procedure and does not appear to put them under the "spell" of another person. See ABREACTION, NARCOTHERAPY, HYPNOTHERAPY.

Illustrative Case: NARCOSYNTHESIS

In *Men Under Stress* (1945) Grinker and Spiegel cite the case of a bombardier who fainted during two missions just as his plane reached an altitude of ten thousand feet. A psychiatrist assigned to the case learned that just prior to these experiences the man had been confined to a base hospital for four weeks due to a chest injury. It had been incurred during an air raid when his plane had been struck by a shell and he had fallen heavily against the bombsight. He had recovered consciousness just in time to release his bombs successfully. Knowing this, the doctor suspected that the fainting spells were due to anxiety created by this harrowing experience.

The bombardier, however, scoffed at the idea of feeling anxious, and asked to be returned to combat flying with a unit that would not operate above nine thousand feet. The doctor felt that the man's insistence on this impractical assignment, plus his rather theatrical display of bravado, might be a reaction to buried fear. To test this hypothesis, he decided to use sodium pentothal as a means of getting him to relive his accident. Under the drug the bombardier quickly re-created the mission—but, surprisingly, went through it with little indication of fear.

Still unsatisfied, the doctor decided to accompany him on a practice flight and observe his reactions in the air. As they left the ground, the bombardier was in his usual jocular mood, but just as the plane reached ten thousand feet, he suddenly grew pale and began gasping for breath. The doctor prevented him from fainting by ordering him to breathe slowly and deeply. As they descended, the man regained his composure and insisted that his faintness was simply due to his old chest injury. He brushed aside the idea of psychological treatment.

Weeks later, after a trial return to duty which produced even more acute anxiety symptoms, the bombardier was returned home for rest. He soon became tense and depressed, and had frequent nightmares about falling in an airplane. He finally sought treatment, and the doctor who examined him turned out to be the same one he had seen overseas. The psychiatrist again tried sodium pentothal, and this time the account of the bombing mission had quite a different flavor:

"Going up to north Italy . . . have to take evasive action . . . flak and fighters around . . . plenty of evasive action . . . got to have it. Well, the plane suddenly shook, pulled up back of three other ships, rolled over on its back . . . falling down . . . down . . . down . . . down . . . down we fell, falling down . . . falling down, fast, faster . . . faster . . . faster. I didn't expect it. We came out of it but I was hurt . . . my chest hurt bad . . . my head was hurting . . . I was scared. Me scared! I didn't think I'd ever be scared . . . didn't think any man could scare me."

This intense abreaction broke through the bombardier's defenses, and he was at last able to give voice to his true feelings: "I know it now. But I didn't know it before. I know I'm scared of falling out of an airplane." This admission opened the way to a realization that he had never allowed himself to admit weakness of any kind. With the doctor's help, he gradually recognized that the fainting spells were protective devices adopted by his unconscious to get him out of flying without revealing his feelings of panic even to himself.

As the interviews continued, the bombardier's false self-image of fearlessness was gradually traced to sources in his childhood. From about ten years of age on, he had reacted against a weak alcoholic father, and identified closely with a grandfather who set rigid standards of responsible behavior. As the man gained insight into himself, his depression—which had been caused by feelings of failure—gradually dissolved and his confidence returned—but without the false bravado which had made him repress his experience. (Adapted from Grinker and Spiegel, 1945)

NARCOTHERAPY. Diagnosis and treatment of psychiatric disorders through the use of drugs that produce the sleeplike state known as narcosis. The two most widely used narcotics are sodium pentothal and sodium amytal. Sodium amytal is classified as a hypnotic; sodium pentothal as an anesthetic, and is frequently used for this purpose in surgery. Since the psychological effects and applications of these drugs overlap, they will be considered together.

Carefully controlled doses, given by injection, produce three major effects: they relax and soothe the patient, release pent-up emotion, and heighten suggestibility. These qualities make them particularly effective for the symptomatic relief of acute tension and anxiety attacks, states of acute panic, and agitated stupor following catastrophic experiences such as rape, fires, or earthquakes. They are equally helpful in breaking through hysterical amnesia, in relieving the agitation and self-reproach that accompany moderately severe depression, and in allaying apprehension prior to electroshock therapy.

Narcotic drugs are also utilized for various diagnostic and prognostic purposes, especially in establishing rapport and eliciting blocked material during a psychiatric examination, in testing for organic brain disease, and in predicting the response of schizophrenics to electroshock and insulin therapy. The use of these drugs as "truth serums" is usually prohibited by the courts, but in any event the technique is considered highly dubious from a psychological point of view, since there is no certainty that the suspect will confess or that the absence of confession means innocence rather than ability to resist effects of the drug. Moreover, individuals who are anxiety-ridden, ingratiating, depressed, or masochistic may be "confession-prone" even though they may be innocent of crime.

One of the major applications of narcotic drugs is in psychotherapy. In the *abreaction technique,* they are used to bring a repressed traumatic event to the surface. This enables the patient to relive the experience and discharge the emotion attached to it. There is usually no attempt at interpretation; nevertheless, symptomatic cures are sometimes achieved with a single injection. In *narcosynthesis,* which is described in full under a separate topic, intense emotions associated with traumatic events are also re-experienced, but the therapeutic effort is primarily devoted to helping the patient gain insight into his reactions and integrate them with the rest of his experience. The technique was developed primarily for use in severe anxiety and panic states resulting from battle experiences. In *narcosuggestion,* drug injections are used to increase the acceptance of suggestions made by the therapist. This is a strictly supportive approach, since no attempt is made to uncover the unconscious sources of the patient's difficulties. The drugs are also occasionally employed in the induction of hypnosis when that technique is used in psychotherapy. *See* HYPNOTHERAPY.

Far more common than any of these procedures is the technique of *narcoanalysis.* This is a form of relatively brief psychoanalysis first developed by Horsley (1936), in which narcosis is used to help the patient gain insight into the unconscious forces and events that underlie his symptoms. Repeated injections are given in order to establish quick rapport between doctor and patient, to facilitate the preliminary exploration of the patient's feelings, to help him "ventilate" pent-up emotions of anger, fear, etc.; to uncover significant childhood experiences and enable him to relive them where advisable. Suggestions given under narcosis may also be used to increase the patient's tolerance toward unconscious material that might be threatening, and to help him reorient his thinking and attitudes. In its fully developed form, narcoanalysis overlaps considerably with narcosynthesis in spite of the fact that the latter technique puts special emphasis on traumatic experiences. *See* NARCOSYNTHESIS, ABREACTION.

Illustrative Case: NARCOTHERAPY

A twenty-one-year-old unmarried Jewish girl was admitted to the hospital with a history, furnished by companions, that during the previous three weeks she became uncommunicative and resistant to care, and that she had occasionally begun to complain vaguely of being "followed" and "slowly poisoned." Since the patient had apparently developed her illness while en route from Lithuania to Chicago, where her distant relatives knew little about her, and since the patient refused to answer questions in English, French, German, and Russian as spoken by various members of the staff, sodium amytal was tried in an attempt to obtain a working history. The first few drops of the injection produced a remarkable effect: the patient, previously suspicious and resistive, seemed to drop her reserve and began to sigh and then to cry softly. Soon she became relatively alert and responsive, and thereafter, in a polite, ingratiating manner and with normal inflection and affectivity, answered in good English (which, she said, she had learned at school) any question put to her. This period of responsiveness on her part persisted for half an hour, after which, however, she would tire, withdraw her interest, and gradually resume her previous evasiveness and mute stolidity. The administration of additional sodium amytal at this point had little or no effect other than to induce drowsiness or sleep, but if the injection were deferred until the next day, another period of rapport and productivity would be induced.

In this way it was possible to obtain a detailed and highly significant subjective account of emotional conflicts that had led to and precipitated her present illness. These consisted of early familial separations, almost incredible hardships under the Communist oppression, the Nazi terror, then the Soviet reoccupation, the heartbreak of repeatedly unsuccessful attempts to escape, and, as a final blow, her seduction and desertion by a man to whom she had entrusted her fate. In view of the dramatic effects of amytal, various other drugs (hyoscine, histamine, atropine, Adrenalin, and ergotoxine) were tried to physiologic tolerance, but none produced effects similar to those of amytal. Tragically, complications related to her illegal entry forced the immigration authorities to return her to Lithuania before therapy could be completed. (Masserman, 1955)

NATIONAL ASSOCIATION FOR MENTAL HEALTH. The national voluntary citizens' organization working to combat mental illness and advance mental health.

The Association was formed in 1950 by a merger of three organizations. The oldest was the National Committee for Mental Hygiene, organized by Clifford Beers in 1909 as a citizens' movement to fight conditions of brutality and neglect in mental institutions and to advocate treatment as opposed to custodial care. Though it never comprised more than a small body of dedicated people, the Committee nevertheless initiated the mental health clinic movement in America, started a nationwide program of public education on mental illness, effectively crusaded for reforms in mental hospitals, and collaborated with the American Psychiatric Association and other organizations in bringing the federal government into the area of mental health through the enactment of the National Mental Health Act in 1946 and the creation of the National Institute of Mental Health. The second organization was the National Mental Health Foundation, which advocated higher standards of care and treatment, publicized the need for a comprehensive prevention program, provided educational materials to interested groups, and recruited college students for summer volunteer work in mental hospitals. The third, the Psychiatric Foundation, was set up by the American Psychiatric Association and the American Neurological Society to inspect mental hospitals and raise funds for the study, relief, and cure of mental illness. See BEERS.

Today the National Association for Mental Health includes more than eight hundred affiliates in forty-eight states, with an enrollment of over a million members and volunteers. Its programs are carried out by the affiliates with assistance, guidance, and materials from the national headquarters in New York.

These activities fall into the following nine categories. First, *research:* the Research Foundation carries on a co-ordinated program on basic functions of human behavior with the goal of improving treatment, prevention, and rehabilitation procedures; it has also sponsored a special program of research on schizophrenia for the past thirty years. Second, *mental hospitals:* the Association works toward improvement of care and treatment through consultation with hospital officials, more liberal financing, information programs designed to elicit public interest and support; recruits, trains, and places hospital volunteers; and works for admission and discharge procedures which assure the patient his rights as a sick person. Third, *rehabilitation:* the Association develops programs of social, vocational, and medical rehabilitation for returned patients, including ex-patient clubs, foster home and convalescent home placement, regular or sheltered workshop employment, and follow-up medical care in the community.

Fourth, *childhood mental illness:* the Association helps to set up day-care and residential treatment centers and to organize special educational programs for mentally disturbed children; works for separate and special treatment for children confined to state mental hospitals. Fifth, *community services:* helps to establish psychiatric services in general hospitals, and to set up mental health clinics for children and adults; establishes counseling, guidance, and consultation services for schools, businesses, and courts. Sixth, *assistance to families:* helps families of the mentally sick to find and use treatment services, to understand their illness, and to learn how they can speed their recovery and rehabilitation. Seventh, *information services:* sponsors services providing information on treatment, counseling, and guidance, for both individuals and referral agencies such as schools, courts, and business firms; conducts a joint information service with the American Psychiatric Association, providing scientific data on the entire mental health field.

Eighth, *education:* the Association carries on a widespread program to help the public achieve sound mental health, and to recognize and understand mental illness if it occurs; publishes books and pamphlets, and distributes films on mental health and emotional problems; conducts workshops, conferences, and seminars for doctors, nurses, social workers, clergymen, and the police, as well as for business and labor groups and various categories of the public such as families of the mentally ill, teen-agers, parents, and the aged; publishes a professional quarterly, *Mental Hygiene.* Ninth, *public interest and action:* carries on intensive campaigns of public education through the mass media in collaboration with the Advertising Council, and organizes the annual Mental Health Week in collaboration with the National Institute of Mental Health.

The entire program of the National Association for Mental Health, including its eight hundred affiliates, is supported by voluntary contributions from individuals, business firms, and foundations.

NATIONAL INSTITUTE OF MENTAL HEALTH (NIMH). In response to increased public awareness of the need for more research, training, and services in the mental health field, Congress passed the epoch-making National Mental Health Act in 1946. This act authorized the Public Health Service to establish the National Institute of Mental Health in Bethesda, Maryland. In 1949 the Institute opened its doors and became the headquarters for the federal government's comprehensive program designed to (a) assist in the development of state and community mental health services; (b) support research into the causes, prevention, and treat-

ment of mental illness; and (c) support the training of psychiatrists, psychologists, psychiatric social workers, psychiatric nurses, and other mental health workers. These functions are carried out by grants made to states and institutions and agencies within the states. Applications and grants are reviewed by the National Advisory Mental Health Council, consisting of twelve members from outside the federal government, all of whom are distinguished in medicine, science, education, or public affairs.

The development of community services was greatly advanced by the Community Mental Health Centers Construction Act of 1963, whose objective was to provide comprehensive, co-ordinated mental health services within the communities themselves, and thus avoid removal of patients to isolated state institutions. Each state must submit a State Plan to the NIMH for review and approval before construction grants are approved. In addition, three other types of grants-in-aid are made to the states. First, *formula grants,* based on a formula determined by the state's population, the extent of the problem, and the financial need. These grants are matched dollar for dollar by the state and allocated for distribution to local agencies which provide public mental health education, consultation services, rehabilitation services for former mental patients, and local clinics for prevention and treatment of alcoholism, drug addiction, and other problems. Second, *project grants* made to state and local agencies, hospitals, research facilities, educational institutions, and individuals to support the development of improved methods of diagnosis, care, treatment, and rehabilitation of the mentally ill, including such special areas as public education in mental health, aging, drug addiction, mental retardation, juvenile delinquency, and alcoholism—all with the ultimate aim of translating research findings into actual practice in community programs, as well as to stimulate governments, foundations, and research agencies to provide additional funds for similar activities. Third, *professional and technical assistance* to the states for the development of programs applying new research findings to everyday operations, primarily through demonstration projects, conferences, surveys, and consultation through the regional offices of the Department of Health, Education, and Welfare. In addition, the Institute has established the Hospital Improvement Project Grant Program to aid state mental hospitals and institutions for the retarded to update their standards and procedures, and to establish new services, such as special facilities for children and the aged.

The NIMH is now an independent bureau in the Department of Health, Education, and Welfare. It is primarily a research facility, conducting research not only in its own laboratories but supporting research in medical schools, hospitals, clinics, universities, and other institutions. These projects cut across many fields of specialization and include, among many others, studies on biochemical factors in schizophrenia, the epidemiology of mental illness, the use of psychoactive drugs, the influence of parental attitudes on psychological development, the impact of community structure on individual behavior, and the psychological processes of learning, memory, and perception. The Institute also supports studies in social problem areas, such as aging, juvenile delinquency, and mental retardation.

The training program of the NIMH awards funds to universities, hospitals, clinics, and schools of medicine, nursing, social work, and public health, to support training at the graduate level. Practically every medical school department of psychiatry in the country, and almost all the major graduate departments of psychology, social work, and nursing receive such grants, both

to support teaching personnel and to provide traineeships. In addition, special grants have recently been made to support psychiatric training of general practitioners, graduate mental health research in the biological and social sciences, and for teaching undergraduate medical students in the field of human behavior. A variety of research fellowships are also available for the training of promising graduate students and for additional training of experienced scientists to help relieve the present manpower shortage in the mental health field. The NIMH also helps mental health agencies and institutions develop their own in-service programs designed to increase the effectiveness of members of the staff in hospitals, clinics, and training schools.

NECROMANIA (literally, mania for the dead). Pathological preoccupation with dead bodies.

The interest in corpses is usually of a sexual character and may in some cases take the form of necrophilia, an erotic attraction to the dead. Necromaniacs frequently dream about dead bodies and show a morbid interest in funerals, cemeteries ("taphophilia"), morgues, and autopsies. Some of them take jobs, such as embalmer, in which they constantly work with the dead. Hinsie and Campbell (1960) cite a case in which the patient could achieve satisfactory intercourse only when his partner repeatedly asserted that she was dead. *See* NECROPHILIA.

NECROPHILIA (literally, love of corpses). A sexual deviation consisting of a morbid sexual interest in dead bodies.

This perversion seems to be confined to men. The necrophile achieves sexual arousal and gratification by viewing or having intercourse with a female corpse, followed in some instances by mutilation of the body. He may kill the victim himself, but more frequently removes bodies from graves. Kisker (1964) cites the case of a man in England who murdered a young woman and slept beside her body for the next eighteen nights. There is usually no interest in normal sexual relations.

Necrophiliac fantasies are more frequent than necrophiliac acts. Also, as Thorpe, Katz and Lewis (1961) point out, "Some necrophiliacs gain satisfaction from contact with simulated corpses. In the larger cities they sometimes visit prostitutes who permit themselves to be put in a hypnotic or sleep-like state. They are sometimes waxed to give a lifeless appearance. Under these conditions the necrophiliac gains sexual gratification."

Necrophilia has been recognized since antiquity but is quite rare. It is the result of a deep-seated emotional disturbance which Krafft-Ebing and others attribute to fear of failure or rejection in sexual relations. The individual avoids the risk of humiliation by choosing a sexual object that can offer no resistance of any kind. This explanation may be partially correct, but it does not account for mutilation of the corpse or the fact that necrophiles often show no interest in intercourse with living women. Fear of rejection may be a sufficient explanation for milder sexual disorders, such as voyeurism and exhibitionism, but the necrophile is afflicted by a far more severe disturbance. He is usually psychotic, but the exact nature of his disorder has yet to be determined. See NECROMANIA.

NEGATIVISM. The persistent tendency to resist the suggestions of others. The reaction may be either a normal form of behavior at an early stage in the child's development, or a symptom of psychiatric disorder later in life.

In its earlier form, which usually occurs between the ages of eighteen months and four years, negativism is a healthy expression of the child's growing need to assert himself and attain in-

dependence. During this period his world is expanding and his skills and confidence are developing; but at the same time heavy demands are placed on him to form civilized habits and learn the rules and regulations of life. Negativism therefore serves two purposes: by refusing to conform, the child tests his ability and right to assert himself, and at the same time resists the burdens put upon him. He answers the "noes" he hears from others with his own "I won'ts," which take the form of "holding back" in the bathroom, turning a deaf ear to requests, dawdling, arguing, persistent questioning—and in more extreme cases, of refusing to eat or swallow, or even holding his breath till he turns blue. See BREATH HOLDING.

Parents can help their children (and themselves) through this difficult phase by recognizing that it is necessary and useful; by refraining from treating the child merely as perverse, willful, or headstrong; and by limiting their own noes and don'ts to the most necessary. They should realize, too, that children become more resistive if they are needlessly interfered with, given abrupt or contradictory commands, allowed to become overfatigued, or so neglected that they use negativism as a bid for attention. Overt negativism usually subsides after the third year, when the child discovers more constructive ways of asserting himself. It often crops up again in the teen-age period when the adolescent is struggling for independence and rights of his own. In immature individuals, however, it may become a permanent character trait. See PSYCHOSEXUAL DEVELOPMENT, ANAL CHARACTER.

Among adults, and some children, negativism may be interpreted as a psychological defense reaction which can be carried to great extremes. It takes the form not only of noncompliance and resistance to the suggestions of others, but of doing the exact opposite of what is requested. In mental patients it may also be expressed in mutism and refusal of food or care. Negativism of this kind is considered an aggressive act through which the patient gratifies his need for acting out resentments and hostilities. It may also be motivated by an unconscious desire to attract the interest and concern of others. The symptom is especially common in catatonic schizophrenic patients, where it is interpreted as an expression of the need to withdraw from a threatening world; and in senile patients, where it is usually a regression to childish techniques of expressing anger or gaining attention.

NEOLOGISM. A new word coined for a particular purpose, such as "astronaut" or "serendipity." Among psychiatric patients, neologisms are generally "contaminations" (Freud's word) and condensations of two or more words, and are embedded in a more or less incoherent stream of thought. An example cited by Bleuler is "gruesor," derived from gruesome and sorrowful.

The meaning of these invented words is often highly obscure, particularly since symbolism is frequently employed. Where they can be explained, they are usually found to refer to people, experiences, and inner conflicts closely related to the patient's disturbance. In some cases the patient himself will indicate what the new words mean, or will provide clues that help the psychiatrist decipher the hidden meaning. *See* SCHIZOPHRENIC REACTIONS (GENERAL), WORD SALAD.

The persistent use of neologisms is usually indicative of a schizophrenic psychosis, as in the following psychiatric interview. (The psychiatrist's questions are placed in parentheses.)

Illustrative Case: NEOLOGISM

I'm a cut donator, donated by double sacrifice. I get two days for every one. That's known as double sacrifice; in other words, standard cut donator. You know, we considered it. He couldn't have anything for the cut, or for these patients. All of them are double sacrifice because it's unlawful for it to be donated any more. (Well, what do you do here?) I do what is known as the double criminal treatment. Something that he badly wanted, he gets that, and seven days' criminal protection. That's all he gets, and the rest I do for my friend. (Who is the other person that gets all this?) That's the way the asylum cut is donated. (But who is the other person?) He's a criminal. He gets so much. He gets twenty years' criminal treatment, would make forty years; and he gets seven days' criminal protection and that makes fourteen days. That's all he gets. (And what are you?) What is known as cut donator Christ. None of them couldn't be able to have anything; so it was to be true works or prove true to have anything, too. He gets two days, and that twenty years makes forty years. He loses by causing. He's what is known as a murder. He causes that. He's a murder by cause because he causes that. He can't get anything else. A double sacrifice is what is known as where murder turns, turns the friend into a cut donator and that's what makes a daughter-son. (A daughter-son?) Effeminate. A turned Christ. The criminal is a birth murder because he makes him a double. He gets two days' work for every day's work. . . . (What is a "birth murder?" A birth murder is a murder that turns a cut donator Christ into a double daughter-son. He's turned effeminate and weak. He makes him a double by making him weak. He gets two days' work for every one day's work because after he's made a double, he gets twice as much as it is. He's considered worth twice that much more. He has to be sacrificed to be a double. (Cameron, 1947)

NERVE CONDUCTION. The process by which impulses are carried by nerve cells.

Our knowledge of nerve conduction has gone through a number of stages. Early thinkers, such as Descartes, believed that impulses in the form of "animal spirits" were carried through the body in hollow tubes. In 1791 Galvani used the newly developed Leyden jar to make a frog leg twitch, but he mistakenly concluded that the animal tissue itself generated electricity. In 1800 Volta showed that electricity of this type could be obtained without placing animal tissue in the circuit, and therefore concluded that it was the property of inorganic substances. Nevertheless the association of nerve impulse with electricity continued, and in 1834 Johannes Müller asserted that it was clearly electrical in nature, although he felt that its speed could not be measured because it was close to the speed of light. A few years later his student, DuBois-Reymond, adumbrated the present theory of nerve conduction by suggesting the concept of polarization and by insisting that the impulse was not instantaneous but actually finite and measurable. As Boring (1950) points out, "It was these experiments of DuBois that brought the nervous impulse out of the mystic realm of animal spirits and the pneumatics of the soul into the realm of materialistic science."

DuBois' work prompted his friend Helmholtz to measure the speed of nerve conduction in 1850. Shortly after, in 1866, Bernstein discovered that the outside of the membrane of the fiber is positively charged during its resting state, while the inside is negatively charged. He described the impulse itself as a "wave of negativity" generated by changes occurring along the cell membrane. When the nerve fiber is stimulated, the negative charge spreads to the outside, sweeping along the fiber as a wave of depolarization. The speed of this impulse, or "spike potential" as it is now called, has been found to vary with the thickness of the fiber. Most fibers are between .001 and .02 mm. in diameter. Recent measurements have shown that the rate of conduction, expressed in meters per second, is six times the diameter in thousandths of a millimeter. Thus, a fiber with a diameter of .010 mm. will conduct at the rate of sixty meters per second.

In 1899 F. Gotch and G. J. Burch showed that for a brief period after a nerve fires it cannot be fired again. This period, during which it is recovering its excitability, is called the refractory phase. In 1912 E. D. Adrian and K. Lucas plotted the curve of recovery and found an absolute refractory period during which no stimulation no matter how intense will fire the fiber, and a relative refractory period occurring directly afterward, during which an intense stimulus will set it off. These two investigators also discovered the all-or-none principle, which states that a stimulus which is above the threshold of a given fiber will excite the entire fiber, and if it is below the threshold strength it will not excite it at all. See NEURON, SYNAPSE, ALL-OR-NONE LAW.

NERVOUS BREAKDOWN. A vague, popular, "polite" term for mental illness, most frequently applied to acute conditions that require immediate treatment.

Nervous breakdown is a scrap-basket expression that does not refer to any particular disorder or clinical entity. Rather, it is a euphemism frequently used to conceal the real nature of the condition. It seems to imply that the individual has simply been under a strain and his nerves have given way, a theory of neurosis that held sway around the turn of the century. In other words, it suggests that the disorder is largely or wholly physical, and deliberately obscures the idea that it might have something to do with his personality or emotions. The reason is that mental disorder is still regarded by many people as a social disgrace, and purely physical causes are not considered to be as much of a stigma as personality problems. Because of this fact, the term is sometimes used with a knowing look. See NEURASTHENIA, MITCHELL, JANET.

NERVOUS SYSTEM. The human nervous system consists of the brain, spinal cord, and nerves. It serves to co-ordinate the various sense organs, glands, and muscles of the body, and no physi-

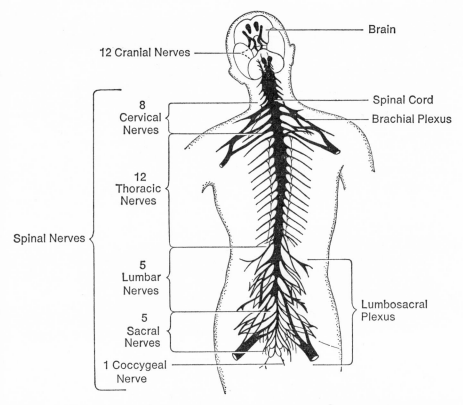

Brain

12 Cranial Nerves

Spinal Cord

Brachial Plexus

8
Cervical
Nerves

12
Thoracic
Nerves

Spinal Nerves

5
Lumbar
Nerves

Lumbosacral
Plexus

5
Sacral
Nerves

1 Coccygeal
Nerve

Fig. 38. The nervous system, comprising the central nervous system (nerve fibers in the brain and spinal cord, integrating all messages), and the peripheral nervous system (nerve fibers outside the brain and spinal cord, connecting with sense organs, muscles, and glands).

cal or mental activity can take place without its intervention.

There are two ways of describing the nervous system, one of which is primarily structural and the other primarily functional. Structurally, the system is divided into two parts (*Fig. 38*): (a) the central nervous system, which consists of the nerve cells and supporting tissue within the bony case formed by the skull and spine, and which serves to co-ordinate, connect, and integrate incoming and outgoing messages; and (b) the peripheral nervous system, made up of fibers and cell bodies outside the brain and spinal cord, serving the dual purpose of bringing the messages from the receptors (sense organs) to the cen-

tral system and transmitting messages from the central system to the effectors (muscles and glands). The two functional divisions are (a) the somatic nervous system, which serves the sense organs and skeletal muscles; and (b) the autonomic nervous system (*Fig. 39*), which regulates the internal activities of the organism and prepares it to meet situations of stress.

The second method of dividing the nervous system cuts across the first, since the autonomic ·and somatic divisions both have cerebral and peripheral components. The best way of presenting a bird's-eye view of the entire system is to describe the various components which are peripherally oriented,

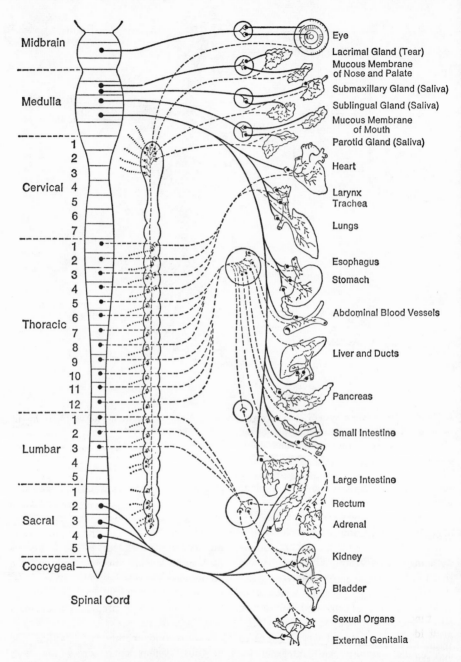

Fig. 39. The autonomic division of the nervous system. Note that sympathetic fibers (broken lines) and parasympathetic fibers (solid lines) usually go to the same organs—one advancing, the other retarding their activity.

followed by the components which are centrally oriented.

The peripheral somatic system includes the twelve cranial nerves, which have their central terminations inside the skull; and the thirty-one spinal nerves, which connect with different segments of the spinal cord. Each set of tracts contains both sensory and motor fibers. The cranial nerves serve functions primarily located in the head. They receive sensations from receptors for smell, vision, hearing, and taste; and activate effectors involved in speech, mastication, and facial movement. The only one of the twelve that extends beyond the cranium is the vagus nerve, which serves the heart, blood vessels, and viscera. The sensory branches of the spinal nerves carry messages from receptors in the skin, blood vessels, muscles, tendons, joints, and visceral organs; the motor branches innervate the striated muscles of the arms, legs, and body. The clusters, or ganglia, of sensory cells and synapses for the sensory spinal nerves lie outside the spinal cord and are therefore classed as peripheral; the cell bodies of the spinal motor nerves lie within the cord and are therefore classed as central. All in all, the somatic system is primarily concerned with adjustments between the organism and the external world.

The peripheral autonomic system, on the other hand, is principally concerned with the internal adjustments of the organism. It differs from the somatic system in functioning more or less as a whole, and in serving the glands and smooth muscles of the internal organs and blood vessels, as opposed to the striated muscles of the skeleton. Its two general parts, however, function in opposition to each other and work toward adjustment in different ways. The parasympathetic system maintains the routine activities of the organism by regulating heart rate, salivation, gastric secretions, and other functions under normal conditions. Its ganglia lie outside the spinal cord and work somewhat independently of each other. The sympathetic system mobilizes the organism for heavy work or emergency situations by constricting the blood vessels, accelerating the heart rate, dilating the lungs, releasing sugar stored in the liver, and inhibiting the digestive processes. These ganglia form a chain outside the spinal cord and work closely together to produce patterns of response. The two systems function in an interlocking manner to promote survival under all conditions.

The central nervous system comprises the spinal cord and the five distinct divisions of the brain: the myelencephalon, metencephalon, mesencephalon, diencephalon, and telencephalon. The primary function of the spinal cord is transmission. It handles all messages traveling from the receptors up to the brain, and from the brain down to the effectors, except those carried by the cranial nerves. Its secondary function is simple integration, since it serves as a connecting center for many reflex activities such as heartbeat and respiration.

The brain structures are best described in the order of evolutionary development. The oldest is the myelencephalon, or medulla, which connects the spinal cord to the brain. Many nerve tracts pass through it on the way to the higher areas, but it also contains vital centers of its own for breathing, heartbeat, and blood pressure. Next, the metencephalon consists primarily of the cerebellum, which receives and relays messages having to do with balance and motor co-ordination; and the pons, which transmits messages upward and also acts as a sensory and motor center for the mouth and face. The myelencephalon and metencephalon together make up the hindbrain.

The mesencephalon, or midbrain, is a small bridge between the hindbrain and the higher brain centers. Its tectum, or roof, is involved in vision and hearing. The next two divisions, the diencephalon and telencephalon, constitute the forebrain. The diencephalon contains a number of complex structures: the thalamus, which is the main relay station between the spinal cord and lower brain centers and the various parts of the telencephalon; the pituitary gland, important in growth, sex activity, and stimulation of other glands; the mammillary bodies, which appear to be involved in emotion; the optic tracts; and the hypothalamus, which connects with the higher centers, the pituitary gland and medulla, and serves as a central control center for autonomic functions, including hormonal secretions, metabolism, emotional reactions, and physiological activities associated with hunger, thirst, sleep, temperature, and sex.

Finally, the telencephalon, the highest, farthest advanced, and most complex part of the brain, consists primarily of the two cerebral hemispheres, connected by the corpus callosum, and the two olfactory bulbs which lie just above the smell receptors in the nasal passages. These hemispheres and their outer layer, the cerebral cortex, are largely responsible for the psychological functions of perception, memory, thinking, reasoning, and planning. Other structures of the telencephalon, buried beneath the cortex, have recently been found to be deeply involved in the control of emotion and motivation. The most important are the septal area and the amygdala, which work hand in hand with the hypothalamus. Another recent discovery is the reticular activating system, a network of ascending and descending fibers which are not actually a part of the telencephalon, but extend from higher to lower centers, and serve to regulate the activity level of the cortex. *See* topics on the Physical Basis of Behavior in the Category Index.

NEURASTHENIA (literally, nerve weakness). An obsolescent term for a neurotic condition marked by severe fatigue, bodily weakness, poor concentration, feelings of inadequacy, and mental and physical listlessness. Other complaints include headaches, insomnia, muscular pains, and poor appetite.

The term originated with the American psychiatrist George Miller Beard (1839–83) in 1869. He believed the symptoms were due to weakness or exhaustion of the nervous system produced primarily by overwork, while others thought they were caused by excessive masturbation. Today the condition is attributed to psychological factors such as emotional conflicts, prolonged anxiety or tension, sexual dissatisfactions, frustration, and boredom. The adjective neurasthenic is still used occasionally to characterize a general neurotic fatigability, but the American Psychiatric Association does not include neurasthenia in its latest classification of disorders (1952). The tendency is to drop the term and assign some of the symptoms to anxiety reactions, others to conversion reaction, and the greater part to psychophysiologic disorders. Some authors, supported by factor-analytic studies (Guilford, 1959), believe the symptoms constitute a separate neurotic pattern which they term asthenic reaction. *See* ASTHENIC REACTION, HYPOCHONDRIASIS, MITCHELL, JANET.

NEUROFIBROMATOSIS (Von Recklinghausen's Disease). A disorder transmitted by a dominant gene, causing mild or moderate mental defect in about one third of the cases. The clinical symptoms are skin lesions (neurofibromata), areas of skin pigmentation (café au lait), and small tumors in the retina and other tissues. The mental defect is due to diffuse damage to brain cells. Treatment is primarily palliative; painful tumors may be surgically excised or subjected to X-ray. *See* MENTAL RETARDATION (CAUSES).

NEURON (Nerve Cell). The basic structural unit of the nervous system, which transmits impulses from one part of the body to another.

The nervous system is a vast communication network which receives energy from the environment and transforms it into signals that produce appropriate responses in different parts of the organism. The neuron is a specialized cell which has the capacity to conduct these signals in the form of nerve impulses. The brain alone contains an estimated 9.3 billion of these cells.

Neurons differ greatly in shape and size but have certain common features (*Fig. 40*). They all have a relatively large cell body, or soma, and two types of elongated fibers extending from it. One set of fibers, known as dendrites, are always the receiving end of the cell; the other, called the axon, the transmitting end. The size of these struc-

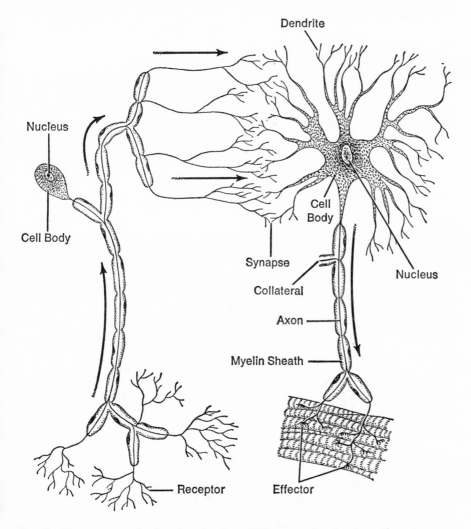

Fig. 40. Two neurons showing the direction of the nerve impulse from the sensory, or afferent, neuron at the left, across the synapse to the motor, or efferent, neuron at the right.

tures depends on their function. The closely packed neurons in the brain have very short fibers; neurons that serve the skin of the toes have very long dendrites and shorter axons, while those serving the muscles of the big toe have very long axons and short dendrites. Neurons also vary in diameter, and as a rule the larger the cell, the faster it conducts the nerve impulse. *See* NERVE CONDUCTION.

There are three general types of neurons. The sensory or afferent neurons carry messages from the sense organs to the spinal cord; the motor or efferent neurons conduct impulses from the spinal cord to the glands and muscles; and the connecting or correlation neurons are found within the brain and spinal cord. The correlation neurons often have elaborately ramified sets of dendrites that make connections with hundreds of other cells. It is an interesting fact that each of these neurons is a separate, anatomically independent unit, with a gap between them across which the nerve impulse must pass. *See* SYNAPSE.

Nerve cells differ in one other important respect. Some have axons which are covered with a fatty insulation material called a myelin sheath. The axons outside the brain and spinal cord also have a thin membrane, called neurilemma, outside this sheath, which is important in the regeneration of fibers that have been severed or injured. The neurilemma is not found inside the brain or spinal cord. This means that a nerve fiber in the arm or leg can sometimes mend itself, but most of the fibers in the brain and spinal cord cannot. For this reason nerve destruction caused by a stroke or head injury usually leads to irreparable damage. *See* DEMYELINATING DISORDERS.

Although the central nervous system does not contain neurilemma, it does house a related type of structure called a glia cell. For a long time it was thought that these cells merely supply mechanical support for the neurons, but recent research indicates that they may play a vital part in the conduction and excitation of nerve impulses, particularly in learning and memory processes. *See* MEMORY STORAGE.

NEUROTIC DEPRESSIVE REACTION (Reactive Depression). An acute depression precipitated by an intensely distressing situation such as loss of a job, death of a loved person, or financial setback. The condition may last for weeks or months, but usually clears up in time with proper treatment. Neurotic depressive reactions of one degree or another account for an estimated 20 to 30 per cent of all psychoneurotic disorders.

The appearance of the depressed individual is one of deep dejection and discouragement; his facial expression is dull and masklike. He complains that he feels apprehensive, cannot sleep well, and is unable to concentrate. These symptoms are usually accompanied by a reduced level of activity and initiative, decreased self-confidence, feelings of loneliness and helplessness, restricted interests, tenseness, vague hostility, loss of appetite, and various bodily complaints. Everyday tasks are performed with difficulty, and in extreme cases the patient may sit by himself, cease talking, and threaten suicide. Sometimes the suicidal threat is made to extract sympathy and attention from others, but it should always be taken seriously. Neurotic depressives, however, do not make actual suicidal attempts as often as psychotic depressives, and they do not manifest the retardation, agitation, and delusions which are usually found in psychotic depressives. A neurotic depression may in some cases progress to a psychotic depression.

Neurotic depressives are predisposed to overreact to situations from which most individuals "bounce back." Characteristically, they have low ego strength, little ability to tolerate stress, a rigid conscience, sensitivity to guilt feelings, and introversive tendencies. They are usually overdependent individuals who bottle up their anger or feelings of rebellion and blame themselves for failures and losses. Many of them, however, have hostile fantasies against people they love and depend upon, and feel so guilty about these feelings that if one of these people is hurt or killed, they feel inwardly responsible even when it is no fault of their own. In these cases the depression may be viewed as an "intropunitive reaction"—that is, a turning of hostility or anger against the self rather than outward. Psychoanalytic theory attributes the feelings of helpless dependency and loss of appetite (or in some cases excessive appetite) found in many depressive patients to fixation at the oral level of psychosexual development.

Antidepressant drugs and supportive therapy are usually effective in relieving neurotic reactive depressions, although electroshock is sometimes applied as an emergency measure. Hospitalization may be necessary, particularly when there is an active danger of suicide. When the symptoms have been reduced to a manageable level, psychotherapy is introduced to help the patient change his neurotic patterns of adjustment. This treatment is usually successful, since the patient can clearly recognize the situations that produced the depression, although he needs help in understanding why he overreacted. *See* PSYCHOTIC DEPRESSIVE REACTION.

Illustrative Case: NEUROTIC DEPRESSIVE REACTION

Hannah M., a fifty-year-old mother of two children, consulted a psychiatrist in private practice, seeking help for feelings of depression which she could not overcome. A divorcée, she was living with her son and his wife in their comfortable home in the suburbs of a large eastern city.

In discussing her background, Hannah tended to emphasize her general unhappiness, rather than to focus on relations with specific individuals. She was the youngest of seven children born to parents advanced in years, and was six years younger than the sibling closest to her in age. She always felt keenly that she was not wanted either by her parents or her siblings—especially her three sisters, who were expected to play a major role in caring for her as when she was a young child. Instead of being given a bedroom with the others in the family, Hannah was relegated to a cot in her father's small study in the rear of the house. Eventually she was given the room abandoned by a brother who married, but when an older sister decided that she preferred Hannah's new room to her own, Hannah was forced to trade, thus giving up what had been a symbol of her acceptance by the family. This incident seemed to Hannah to typify the lightness with which her feelings were regarded by her parents and siblings. She recalled also that her clothes were always the castoffs of her older sisters and that she was frequently told that she was ugly and stupid by members of the family.

Hannah completed high school and just a few years later, after a year in secretarial school and two years in office work, married a man she didn't know very well in an effort to establish a home of her own. Her husband proved to be an improvident person who couldn't hold a job for any length of time, and who soon began to be unfaithful. Hannah had two sons in rapid succession, and the combination of the responsibility of caring for them, the austere life she had to lead, and her husband's infidelity caused her to become very anxious and angry and to withdraw from interaction with friends and family. When this condition failed to clear up in a short time, her family doctor insisted that she take a vacation away from her family. She therefore went on a three-month visit to her favorite aunt who lived in a distant city. While away, Hannah's children were left in the care of a sister, and, during this time, her youngest, a two-year-old boy, sustained a head injury when struck by an automobile—an accident which Hannah felt resulted in his later severe mental retardation. When she returned home, Hannah's husband left her and filed for a divorce, which she did not contest. She then went to work as a secretary to support her family and managed to provide enough to permit her oldest son to have a good education. Eventually her son became successful in the insurance business and, after he married, he insisted that his mother and younger brother, who needed much care, come and live with him and his wife.

Hannah's current complaint had its onset about a year after her retarded child died. He suffered a lingering illness and was cared for devotedly by Hannah to the last. She was overcome by fear and depression when he died and felt guilty for having to leave him years before when she was away for a rest. Hannah also began worrying that she was too much of a burden on others and went out of her way to avoid being an imposition or an expense to her older son. Her obsessive fear that she might harm someone made it impossible for Hannah to work and she slept poorly. Just before coming to the psychiatrist she began to think about committing suicide.

In an interview Hannah appeared to be in acute distress. She cried and wrung her hands. A constant theme she expressed involved her not wanting to cause concern or to be a burden on her children. She was accepted for treatment and was seen in a series of sixteen supportive interviews. During this time she developed some insight into her problems and her depression subsided. Hannah was then able to plan more realistically and shortly after was able to return to work. (Zax and Stricker, 1963)

NEUROTIC PERSONALITY. A pattern of personality traits which renders the individual susceptible to an actual or "symptom" neurosis.

The neurotic personality does not exhibit a specific pattern of symptoms, but shows tendencies which may (or may not) develop into one or another neurotic reaction type. The persistently tense, apprehensive, insecure person is prone to anxiety neurosis; the overly cautious, meticulous, orderly individual is more likely to develop an obsessive-compulsive reaction. Other individuals may have a tendency toward the fixed, irrational fears of the phobic patient, the chronic fatigue of an asthenic, or

the bodily complaints that characterize conversion reaction.

In addition to these special tendencies, neurotic personalities have a number of fairly common traits. Many of them are morally rigid and unable to recognize or give full expression to their sexual or hostile impulses. Their attitudes toward other people are usually ambivalent; they hold them at arm's length even though they may crave closeness, or veer from co-operative to nonco-operative attitudes. They have an unstable concept of themselves and are therefore unsure of their goals, sometimes expecting too much, sometimes too little of themselves. They usually lead unsatisfactory or distorted sex lives. They are constantly at the mercy of feelings of insecurity, self-doubt, guilt, or anxiety, and make excessive use of defensive reactions, such as rationalizing away their shortcomings, displacing their anger or disappointment to others, or denying the reality of their problems.

Some neurotic personalities remain fairly well stabilized; others develop outright neuroses with clearly defined symptom patterns. Still others can be characterized as borderline cases, since their neurotic traits and symptoms are not sufficiently disabling or clear-cut to constitute a full-blown neurosis.

The transition from neurotic personality to neurosis cannot always be satisfactorily explained, but three types of precipitating factors often appear to be responsible. First, a sudden change in the individual's life situation, such as a new job, a promotion, or parenthood, especially when the new situation exposes long-standing weaknesses, revives latent fears and conflicts, or puts too heavy a burden on faulty behavior patterns and defenses. Second, a single traumatic experience, or a prolonged series of stresses, that weakens his psychological defenses and brings his anxieties to the surface—for example, business failure, social ostracism, debilitating illness, or death of a loved one. Third, the slow corrosion that occurs when an individual gradually uses up his resources in overcoming feelings of inadequacy, insecurity, or rejection. In such a case he may break down under the weight of the ordinary responsibilities and difficulties of life. Any one of these three factors may exploit the neurotic personality tendencies and lead to one or another type of symptom neurosis. See PSYCHONEUROTIC DISORDERS (TYPES AND CAUSES), PERSONALITY PATTERN DISTURBANCE, PERSONALITY TRAIT DISTURBANCE.

NEWBORN INFANT (Neonate). Anyone who looks through the window of a hospital nursery is bound to be impressed by the fact that individuality begins at birth, or before. Practically any group of newborn infants show startling variations in both physical and psychological characteristics—in size, shape, general appearance, physical maturity, as well as activity level, feeding behavior, and emotional adjustment. There are, however, certain normal limits to these variations, and it is important to know these in order to establish a base line for assessing future development, and to predict whether a specific child will be faced with difficulties. This article will therefore outline the physical characteristics, behavior, and beginnings of personality which are generally found in newborn infants.

Newborn infants average 7.5 lbs. in weight and 19.5 inches in length, with a range of 3 to 16 lbs. and 17 to 21 inches. Girls are slightly larger than boys, but the differences are wide within both sex groups. These variations depend on many factors, such as family tendencies, maternal diet, economic status (infants in poorer districts are smaller than in better districts due to maternal nutrition), ordinal position (the firstborn usually weighs less than later-born infants), and fetal activity (excessive activity leads to underweight).

At birth the typical infant has bluish-gray eyes which roll about in an un-co-ordinated manner. His neck is short and creased, his tear glands do not secrete, his skin is deep pink but likely to be blotchy, his muscles are small and poorly controlled, and his bones are soft and flexible. Compared to an adult, his proportions seem almost grotesque, since his head seems too large for his body, his cranium too high, his face too broad and flat, his arms and legs too short, his shoulders too narrow, and his abdomen too large. In a word, he is hardly the cherub his parents are likely to expect—and this is even more the case when the infant is bruised or misshapen due to a difficult birth, or red and wizened because he arrived ahead of schedule. Even though his appearance usually improves greatly within two or three weeks, the shock of the first impression may have a disturbing effect on parents who are not prepared for it.

When he first enters the world, the human infant is more immature and therefore more helpless than any newborn animal. His autonomic nervous system is so undeveloped that it cannot adequately regulate the basic homeostatic processes, and consequently pulse rate, respiration, blood pressure, body temperature, sleep, and elimination are all highly unstable. He is totally incapable of voluntary activity and therefore behaves in a random, purposeless fashion. Even though he can move and has a considerable repertoire of reflexes, he constantly makes diffuse and unco-ordinated responses.

The senses of smell, taste, pain, and temperature are ready to function at birth or shortly after, but the two distance senses of hearing and vision are poorly developed. The infant therefore can respond to light merely by turning his head or closing his eyelids, but he cannot focus his eyes or follow a quickly moving object. In most cases he is totally deaf at birth since the middle ear is filled with amniotic fluid, but even when it drains out, hearing usually remains poor for a time because the inner ear is not completely formed.

The cerebral cortex is also undeveloped at birth, and the neonate is incapable of learning, with the possible exception of the formation of unstable conditioned responses in feeding. The combination of poor muscular co-ordination and undeveloped mentality makes it impossible for him to communicate his needs in any specific way. All he can do is squirm or kick or cry when he is hungry or uncomfortable, and others have to guess what he wants.

The human infant, then, is so immature at birth that he would be unable to survive without constant care. If his parents give him an adequate amount of attention, he will be relaxed and happy, and his development will proceed normally. On the other hand, if he gets either too much or too little care, he may be seriously and lastingly damaged. Anxious mothers keep their children in a helpless condition after the infant stage has passed by fussing over them and waiting on them night and day. This makes them dependent and deprives them of opportunities to learn skills needed for growing up at a normal rate. On the other hand, some infants are raised in homes or institutions where they receive too little warmth and attention during infancy. This often has drastic effects on all phases of development, physical, emotional, social, and intellectual. See MATERNAL DEPRIVATION, MOTHERING.

Finally, it is important to re-emphasize the wide variations among normal newborn infants, due largely to hereditary factors but also to prenatal environment and the birth experience itself. Some neonates look like the typical advertisement of a chubby baby, while others look like wrinkled old men. One child will quickly fall into regular patterns of feeding and sleeping, another will have trouble taking his food and falling asleep. There is a high degree of individuality too in the nature and amount of crying, and in activity patterns, for some infants are almost constantly fretful and restless while others appear relaxed and tranquil.

In view of these variations, it is highly unwise for parents to establish rigid expectations or measure their own infants against others. Such expectations pave the way for disappointment, anxiety, and tenseness—reactions which are bound to be upsetting not only to the parents but to the baby as well. False expectations also make the parents turn a deaf ear to reassurance from the doctor. A far wiser approach would be to recognize that every child has a "right" to an individual personality and an individual rate of development from the moment of birth onward. See BIRTH ADJUSTMENTS.

NIEMANN-PICK DISEASE. A rare congenital disorder of lipid (fat) metabolism affecting the brain, liver, and spleen, and causing severe mental retardation.

The condition is believed to be due to a single recessive gene, and usually sets in during infancy. The neurological features are almost identical with those in Tay-Sachs disease, but there are large deposits of fat in the liver, spleen, and other tissues in addition to the brain. There is also a resemblance to Gaucher's disease except that the lipid involved in Gaucher's is kerasin, while a phosphatide is involved in Niemann-Pick. Victims of the disease become dehydrated, lose weight, and suffer from progressive paralysis. They usually do not survive more than a few years. See TAY-SACHS DISEASE, MENTAL RETARDATION (CAUSES).

NIGHT HOSPITAL (Night Care Program). A psychiatric unit offering treatment and residential care to patients after working hours. In most cases the patients reside at the hospital, but they may also live in the community and come to the hospital in the evenings for psychotherapy and supportive activities such as recreational or occupational therapy.

The night care program offers a number of advantages. Basically its function is to provide help without interrupting employment or other daytime responsibilities. It is particularly well suited to patients who are in the process of recovery and who would benefit from a gradual transition from hospital life to community life. Many of these patients can be released sooner than usual from full hospitalization since they will still receive therapeutic support even after they have begun to work. In addition, the opportunity to receive night care often encourages disturbed individuals to apply for the help they need, since they do not have to reveal to their employers that they are receiving treatment. Finally, the night operation makes fuller and more economic use of hospital facilities, and also provides an overnight service for psychiatric emergencies. *See* MENTAL HOSPITAL.

NIGHTMARE. An intense, acutely disturbing anxiety dream which is ordinarily remembered upon waking. Nightmares are sometimes distinguished from pavor nocturnus ("night terror") in which the individual, usually a child, awakens screaming and disoriented, may hallucinate people or animals in the room, then usually drops off to sleep without remembering the episode.

The prime motif in nightmares is helpless terror. Typically, the dreamer is plunged into an extremely threatening situation, feels overwhelmed by agonizing dread, makes futile attempts to escape, finds every avenue closed, becomes helplessly paralyzed, develops a mounting sense of oppression, and awakens in a cold sweat. Anyone who has experienced a nightmare will agree that it is one of the most upsetting and painful experiences he has ever undergone. The question is why we have them and what they represent.

The most common explanation is that nightmares are simply due to the emotional residue left by harrowing experiences. Such experiences generate more emotion than we can handle at the time they occur, and the terror dream is an unconscious attempt to express that emotion and get it out of our system. This theory is applied particularly to nightmares that re-enact accidents, illnesses, or life-and-death struggles such as war experiences. The battle dreams of soldiers sometimes persist for months or even years, presumably because there is such an enormous load of emotion due to repeated situations in which life and limb are threatened.

The fact is that nightmares are a singularly unsuccessful means of ridding ourselves of anxiety and tension. Not only are they usually a poor outlet for emotion, but in many instances they even seem to reawaken and prolong our terror instead of alleviating it. The reason for this failure is probably that a mere revival of an experience does not necessarily give us a new understanding of it or a new ability to grapple with it and master it. As R. W. White (1964) has pointed out, "These nightmares . . . again display the failure to rationalize the original danger. Occurring as they do in sleep, when defenses are relaxed, and throwing the patient into renewed anxiety, they accomplish nothing in the way of new learning." This is the difference between a nightmare and a re-enactment of traumatic experiences under hypnosis or narcosis. Through the latter techniques, the therapist helps the patient gain conscious insight into his experience and acquire new methods of dealing with it. This type of treatment loosens the hold of the trauma, and the anxiety reaction usually subsides. *See* HYPNOTHERAPY, NARCOTHERAPY.

Some psychoanalysts offer a different explanation of nightmares. They base their theory on the idea that human beings have an unconscious masochistic drive, an impulse to experience pain and suffering. The nightmare is then interpreted as a form of self-punishment. Even though there may be little evidence for a universal drive of this kind, the explanation may apply in individual cases where the traumatic experience is associated, consciously or unconsciously, with guilt feelings. In fact, the experience may have been traumatic largely *because* of such feelings. This explanation is consistent with Freud's original interpretation of nightmares. He viewed them as volcanic eruptions of repressed impulses accompanied by intense, paralyzing anxiety. He held that ordinarily the events and images which constitute our dreams effectively disguise and conceal our dangerous impulses. Occasionally, however, this "dream work" fails, and our guilty wishes and threatening fears burst their bounds and overwhelm us with terrifying fantasies.

Freud also believed that the repressed impulses which motivate nightmares are either sexual or aggressive in nature, or both. Typically, they are not expressed in direct form but are represented by symbolic figures or events, such as beating a fierce animal to death, falling from a great height, being chased by a monster, or being trapped in a deep cavern with no way out and no air to breathe. *See* DREAM INTERPRETATION (MODERN).

NIHILISM (Nihilistic Delusion). In psychiatry, the delusion of nonexistence. The patient believes he no longer exists, that his mind or a part of his body is missing, or that the world itself has ceased to be.

This delusion takes a variety of forms: "My brain has rotted away," "I died twenty-five years ago, and now only my spirit remains," "I lost my left eye in a car accident," "My whole family is dead and gone and I haven't a friend left alive," "This is a dream world, all shadow and no substance," "I am only an empty shell. I have no stomach, no liver, no genital organs."

Nihilistic delusions occur primarily in schizophrenic reactions and depressive states, particularly in acute depression. They are also observed in occasional cases of general paresis, psychosis with cerebral arteriosclerosis, and the depressed and agitated type of senile dementia. There are several interpretations of these delusions, none of them final. In schizophrenia they appear to be due to the autistic feelings and fantasies that develop as the patient divorces himself from the world. He may feel that reality no longer exists because he is not in contact with it. It seems quite understandable, too, that a person who dwells in fantasy will begin to feel that all things, including himself, are shadowy and tenuous. And if he feels that he is a changed personality, as many schizophrenics do, it is not a long step to believing that he no linger exists.

Another theory holds that nihilism arises out of fear and anxiety. The patient is so afraid that others will run off and abandon him, or die and leave him alone, that he comes to believe that this has already happened. It is possible that the patient rejects reality because he feels, or fears, that it has rejected him. He may also develop such a fear of disease (hypochondriacal delusion) that he becomes convinced that his body has actually rotted away. This particular type of delusion is more common in depressed states than in schizophrenia. It is frequently tied up with delusions of sin, since the patient thinks of his fancied disease as punishment for some horrible misdeed he has committed. *See* DELUSION, DENIAL OF REALITY, COTARD'S SYNDROME, DEPERSONALIZATION.

Illustrative Case: NIHILISM (in involutional patient)

"The beauty of the earth and the glory of the sky do not now exist; the seasons are not the seasons of yesteryear; the flowers, the trees and the birds are not raised in the glory of old time; people display only repulsiveness, deceit and all forms of wickedness. All, all is gone; those days are bygone splendor, and things can never be changed; body, soul and spirit have been altered until I have become a weariness to myself. . . . The beautiful furniture; the beautiful needlework—clean and beautiful people—think of them all, all buried: these things are literally under the earth. That is all over; all is gone, absolutely, and here am I. I wish I had never seen the world, and now I have ruined it." (Henderson and Gillespie, 1940)

NOISE CONDITIONS. Noise is defined as aperiodic sound—that is, sound produced by irregular vibrations. Although noises may be high or low, they have no clear-cut pitch—in contrast to tones, which are based on regular vibrations and have a definite pitch. Some common examples are the hiss of escaping steam, the rustle of leaves, and the clatter of a typewriter. Most of the sounds we hear are actually mixtures of tone and noise; conversation occurs on a background of noise, and even a violin emits a certain amount of noise, especially when played by a beginner.

The standard unit for measuring noise is the decibel. Zero on a decibel meter represents the threshold for audition, the lowest sound pressure that can be heard. A whisper registers 20 decibels, a quiet office 40, normal conversation 60, a bus 80, a subway train 100, a jet plane and a punch press 110, loud thunder 120. Noises above 145 decibels are distinctly painful. Below 90, they do not do any physical harm; above 110 prolonged exposure, especially to high-pitched sounds, produces temporary or permanent deafness as well as nervous symptoms. The greater the length of exposure, the greater the degree of hearing loss, particularly in the 4000 to 8000 cycle (waves per second) range (Glorig and Wheeler, 1955). *See* DEAFNESS, HEARING.

The psychological effects of noise are not easy to assess. Some studies show an impairment of factory operations requiring speed under conditions of 90 decibel noise (Broussard et al., 1953). Another study, by Broadbent and Little (1960), revealed a significant drop in the number of errors made in film processing when the sound level was reduced from 99 to 89 decibels by soundproofing the room. Other investigations indicate that complex mental tasks and monitoring tasks are more seriously affected than simple pen and paper and sensori-motor tasks.

We generally go through several stages in our response to noise. At first it has a distracting effect and we slow down; after that we may work and concentrate harder in order to overcome its effects; and finally we adapt ourselves fairly well, although our performance level will usually be lower on the whole than under less noisy conditions. It is now an accepted fact that noise is a source of both psychological and physical stress, and in the long run we become more fatigued, produce less, and make more errors under noisy than under quiet conditions. (Jerison, 1959)

There appear to be large individual differences in the effects of particular types of noise, but it may be said that intense, continuous noise not only interferes with production to some extent, but leads to worker discomfort and dissatisfaction. Fortunately the sound level can be substantially reduced in almost any plant through acoustical ceilings, sound-absorbent mountings, machine enclosures, baffles, careful maintenance of equipment, and substitution of quieter for noisy operations, such as welding or riveting. Where the noise cannot be reduced to a reasonable level by such measures, the use of earplugs ("ear wardens") may be required.

NONSENSE FIGURE. A figure composed of lines, contours, or marks that are intended to be meaningless; used for experimental purposes.

Nonsense figures, like nonsense syllables, are used by psychologists primarily in exploring memory and learning behavior. One object is to uncover the bare essentials of these processes by presenting material that does not closely resemble anything the subject has ever experienced before. Another is to enable all subjects to face exactly the same problem, since each of them presumably sees the stimulus for the first time. This provides a base line for the experiment. In a typical procedure the subject is presented the figure for a short period of time, and is then required to reproduce it from memory. *See* NONSENSE SYLLABLE.

Experiments on nonsense figures have produced some interesting results. First, they are found to vary greatly in difficulty; some are hard, others easy to reproduce. A moderately hard figure, shown to the subject on a memory drum (PLATE 18), takes almost as long to memorize as a twenty-digit list of numbers. Second, nonsense figures, like their verbal counterparts, are not entirely nonsensical. Even when they seem to be totally meaningless and unrecognizable when viewed as a whole, they can usually be broken down into component patterns, and each element can then be associated with a meaningful figure it seems to resemble. Third, this fact explains the ease or difficulty of memorizing the total figure; the more meaningful patterns we see, the easier it is to memorize the figure.

Fourth, human beings seem to have such a strong need to perceive patterns instead of fragments that practically any nonsense figure *as a whole* will eventually be fitted into a category. Fifth, when subjects reproduce nonsense figures from memory, they tend to emphasize these patterns and make the figure as a whole resemble a real object. Many of these tendencies argue strongly in favor of the Gestalt theory of perception. *See* GESTALT PSYCHOLOGY.

NONSENSE SYLLABLE. A syllable expressly constructed to convey as little meaning as possible; used for research purposes.

The nonsense syllable was invented by the German psychologist Hermann Ebbinghaus in 1885 during his pioneer studies of memory and learning. He found that he could not accurately measure the learning process when he had his subjects memorize ordinary words, since some of them were more familiar than others, and they also tended to evoke special associations. In an effort to set up a wide range of unfamiliar and equally difficult items, he created lists of meaningless syllables such as TAF, CIZ, ZOV, and used them in his experiments.

Recent research on nonsense syllables has led to new and revealing findings. Most important is the fact that they are not equally nonsensical. In a typical experiment, a series of syllables is briefly shown to a large number of subjects, and their associations are recorded. (*See* PLATE 32) Almost all subjects were found to have associations for REV, PIL, and COL, but there were practically none for XZF, QJH, and LAJ. It has also found that the associations are often influenced by abbreviations currently in use: LAJ is apt to suggest LBJ today. Tables of low, medium, and high associative value have been constructed for experimental use.

The classic nonsense syllable consists of two consonants separated by a vowel. A first cousin of these syllables is a unit called a trigraph, which consists of three consonants. Trigraphs have also been calibrated for meaningfulness. DPT, PMK and FNK, for example, are high, while XZF, QJH, and ZGT are low in the associative scale.

The fact that most nonsense syllables and trigraphs actually arouse some associations and make some sense is compelling evidence that we either find or create meaning in most of our experiences. Many psychologists believe this is a basic human tendency. *See* EBBINGHAUS, REMEMBERING, FORGETTING.

NOREPINEPHRINE (Noradrenalin). A substance secreted by the medulla of the adrenal gland.

Since it has important effects on the activity of the sympathetic nervous system, noradrenalin is known as a "neurohormone." These effects are of two general types. The secretion helps to mobilize energy in meeting emergencies and stress situations; and it is instrumental in producing intense emotional activity, particularly the expression of anger and hostility. The adrenal gland does not act alone, however, but collaborates with other organs, especially the hypothalamus, the pituitary gland, and the cerebral cortex. The exact relationships among these components are a subject of continuing research. It is hoped that these investigations will not only clarify the physical changes that occur in emotion but also the personality changes that take place in neurosis and psychosis. *See* ADRENAL GLAND.

NORMALITY. The problem of defining psychological normality runs into many difficulties. First, there is no sharp dividing line between normal and abnormal behavior, but rather a continuous and imperceptible gradation from good to poor adjustment and from apparent absence of symptoms to extreme pathology. Second, the same individual may shift from time to time to different positions along this continuum, since his adjustment will be better at one point than at another. Third, human nature is so varied that it is not possible to set up a fixed standard or ideal model which will satisfy either the scientist or the layman. Fourth, a definition of normality in terms of a statistical norm would overemphasize the average individual and tend to exclude deviations from the majority, such as geniuses, nonconformists, and even

people who are completely free from conflicts. Fifth, a definition in terms of adaptation is bound to stress adjustment to a particular society at a particular time, and overlook the fact that what is considered normal in one society or one segment of a society may be considered abnormal in another, and what is normal for one period may be abnormal for another.

Even though there are no rigid standards of normality, certain flexible yardsticks are frequently applied. The most important are: a "reasonable degree" of internal harmony or personality integration—ability to think, feel, and act in a co-ordinated way, or, negatively speaking, freedom from disruptive conflicts; ability to meet the demands of an average "socially acceptable" (noncriminal, nondeviant) environment in a relatively mature, realistic, and nondefensive manner; freedom from extreme emotional distress (unhappiness, upset, apprehensiveness, etc.) without going to the opposite extremes of apathy or unwarranted euphoria; and absence of clear-cut symptoms of mental disorder, or "psychopathology," such as phobias, obsessions, compulsions, sexual deviations, excessive anxiety, confusion, disorientation, or mental incompetence. (For an enumeration of the various types of symptoms, *see* SYMPTOM, PSYCHOPATHOLOGY; and for a further discussion of normality, *see* MENTAL HEALTH, a term which is usually used interchangeably with normality in psychiatry and psychology.)

NOSOLOGY (literally, "study of disease"). The classification of diseases, or the branch of medicine that deals with naming and classifying diseases.

Nosology has an extremely important place in psychiatry, as it does in general medicine. It is not merely a matter of labeling or pigeonholing disorders, but of discovering their most indicative symptoms and the grouping of symptoms into syndromes. Any psychiatric condition must be recognized and correctly diagnosed before appropriate therapy can be applied and a secure prognosis made. It is not always easy, however, to make a diagnosis in psychiatry since the same symptoms are frequently found in different disorders. Moreover, many disorders cannot be confined to one or another category, and a "mixed" diagnosis must often be made.

In addition to its important role in diagnosis and treatment, classification plays a major role in developing prevention programs and research projects. It must be recognized, however, that a nosological approach can be carried to the extreme, as it was during the "descriptive era" in the nineteenth century, when the various disorders were considered separate and distinct. At that time greater emphasis was placed on naming diseases and describing symptoms than on searching for all possible causal factors and attempting to interpret the inner meaning of symptoms for the particular patient. In the dynamic psychiatry of today these aspects are fully recognized.

Emil Kraepelin (1856–1926) is considered the greatest nosologist in the history of psychiatry. He accumulated a vast mass of clinical observations, and defined and classified practically all the severe disorders now known to exist. The study of psychiatric nosology, however, is a continuing process and is responsible for the nomenclature and classification published by the American Psychiatric Association in 1952 and used in this encyclopedia. Among the newer categories are the various personality pattern and trait disturbances, and the transient situational personality disorders that occur in both childhood and adulthood. *See* KRAEPELIN, DESCRIPTIVE PSYCHIATRY, DIFFERENTIAL DIAGNOSIS.

NURSERY SCHOOL EXPERIENCE. Many studies have been made of the effect of nursery school on the intel-

lectual, social, and emotional development of the child. The experience appears to have a somewhat positive effect on IQ scores for most children, although this may be largely due to greater familiarity with materials and tasks that are typical of intelligence tests, and partly to increased rapport with adults. The effect appears to be most pronounced in deprived children, as indicated by recent studies as well as an earlier experiment performed by Skeels, Updegraff et al. (1938). The latter investigators compared a group of orphanage children who attended nursery school with a group that did not have this experience. They found that after twenty months the experimental group showed an average gain of 4.6 IQ points, while the control group showed an average loss of 4.6 points.

Nursery school children make their greatest gains in the area of social adjustment. When compared with children who have not had this experience, they usually show considerably more independence, spontaneity, self-reliance, curiosity, and ability to react constructively to failure (Van Alstyne and Hattwick, 1939; Walsh, 1931). They also show increased sociability and participation in group activities, as well as improvement in self-help, skill, and resourcefulness in using play materials and equipment. On the whole these positive effects have been found to persist into elementary school.

These trends, however, are not universal, since children respond in their own way, and the experience is better suited to some than to others. It would therefore be a mistake to assume that a few months in nursery school will automatically change a child's behavior patterns or remedy his shortcomings. Changes can certainly take place, but they depend largely upon the atmosphere of the school and the sensitivity of the teacher. Thompson (1944) has shown that in a school where the teachers were warm, helpful, and perceptive, the children rated far higher in constructive activity, social participation, and leadership than children who attended a school in which the teacher gave little guidance and rarely participated in their activities. It seems to be true that a great many teachers spend far more time on such externals as arranging materials and helping the children with their clothing than they do on their emotional needs. But when they do pay attention to the individual child and his problems, and set the stage for growth experiences, remarkable progress frequently takes place, as the illustrative case at the end of this article indicates.

The value of nursery school for the handicapped and retarded is being increasingly recognized, although few clinics and communities offer adequate facilities. Under the guidance of specially trained teachers, blind children profit greatly from the opportunity for social play and development of compensatory skills. The earlier they start, the better, since they will more readily learn to respond to touch, taste and smell stimuli, and to orient themselves by other means than sight. Moreover, school activities prevent them from withdrawing into isolation, and also compensate for parental overprotection and oversolicitude. The benefits are equally great for the mildly and moderately retarded. These children usually respond best to the stimulation provided by group games, musical and rhythmic activities, and the chance to play with brightly colored materials of different shapes and sizes. Just as important is practice in tending to their own needs, as in toileting, changing their clothes, and keeping their "cubby" orderly.

A nursery school recently organized by the New York University Institute of Rehabilitation Medicine has demonstrated that children with severe disabilities resulting from congenital defects as well as brain and spinal diseases profit immensely from opportunities for varied sensory experience and activity as well as for emotional release. The school's gaily colored room has been especially designed for these children, with cut-out tables for patients in wheel chairs, easels slanted to permit the armless child to paint with his feet, toys and puzzles fitted with knob-like handles for those who cannot grasp well, and easily opened shelves and cabinets to encourage independence. Finally, special nursery schools have been organized for children suffering from emotional disturbances, such as those conducted by the Child Development Center and the Riverside Church in New York City.

The following case illustrates the use of one nursery school activity, dramatic play, as an instrument for growth and self-realization. Four-year-old Donnie, living in a fatherless home, was described by his teachers as "a quiet and scared kid" who could not participate in the usual group activities for fear that "I will get my clothes dirty." The brief excerpts from the observer's protocols show how he was gradually able to free himself from timidity and feminine tendencies and adopt a more masculine role.

Illustrative Case: NURSERY SCHOOL EXPERIENCE.

First Record. "Donnie and Alice are pushing doll carriages round and round the room. Donnie seems to be very happy this morning. As he pushes his carriage into an enclosure, he turns to Alice, saying, 'Bring yours in this way—this way,' indicating the opening. She continues on, however, and he follows her to the enclosure on the other side of the room. . . . Donnie lies down on the play bed for a moment, than gets up and they walk back to the house holding hands. They sit down there for a moment and, holding hands, walk back to the enclosure. They sit on the bed and whisper.

Second Record, five months later. Donnie now shows an interest in more exciting play with boys, but cannot participate fully. "He goes over to join his friend Rex who, with Eddie, is building blocks. Donnie kneels and watches them, saying nothing. The two other boys make a ramp for a car to glide down and Donnie makes a humming sound and then, 'Be-eep, beep,' as the car slides down. . . . The three children pile blocks on top of the car and Donnie says, 'Put 'em all in the garbage can. Hee.' Next they pretend they are burning the car up. Rex is the leader in this play. He announces, 'I'm goin' in the fire,' and lies down over the blocks. Jackie [who has joined the group] follows suit. Donnie is somewhat hesitant about getting in and draws back. Jackie: 'C'mon, Donnie, let's burn him [Rex] up.' Donnie starts to whine about the car which is under the pile of blocks and tries to get it out: 'I want it *now*.' The other children excitedly drop bricks on Rex, and Donnie halfheartedly does the same."

Third Record. Donnie attempts to change his conception of himself—a car is a symbol of power and driving it is a mark of mastery. 'Ivan, Rex and Donnie have made a large block structure in a sort of square. The observer asks what this is and Donnie replies, 'A jeep car.' He is standing looking at the car when Buddy comes along and tries to knock it down. A few of the blocks tumble and Ivan yells; Donnie and Rex build the car up again. During all this Donnie has said nothing. Suddenly, as if he had been thinking it over all this while, he says in a plaintive way, 'I have to drive, let me in, let me in.' Despite having said this he does nothing about it, probably because he is afraid of being pushed away."

Fourth Record. Building a car gives him the courage to boss others and defy an old enemy, though he uses the car as a place for sleep and refuge. "Again Donnie says, 'I wanta play with the car.' It seems as if he is the 'boss' as he says to Rex, 'Get me two blocks to put here.' Rex complies and Donnie says, 'Get in the car.' They both climb in. The two boys continue building their car and proudly display it to the teacher. Donnie: 'We could sleep in the car, couldn't we?' He seems very satisfied. . . . Buddy, who is in a very aggressive mood, comes along to disturb the peace. As Donnie watches him come over, his whole face puckers in fear. Bud pushes him; Donnie gets quite red and tries to push him

off. He whines and sticks out his tongue (which is the first sign this observer had seen of an attempt at aggressive defense)."

Fifth Record. Donnie assumes masculine roles and carries out his power fantasies. "The children are having their free play in the big gym hall. Donnie sees a small ladder and props it up against the radiator. Oblivious of the others, he climbs it and says to the observer, 'Who wants their windows cleaned?' He makes a few cleaning gestures, comes down, holds out his hand and says, 'Here, thirty cents.' . . . Donnie is now playing another game of his own making. He puts the ladder against the water fountains, above which is a ledge piled with big square blocks. He climbs the ladder, lifts the blocks off one by one and moves them to another place. He tells the observer they are ice. Since they are big and bulky and Donnie is rather small, he strains as he carries them but seems rather proud of his success, looking at the observer as if to say, 'Look what I'm doing!' Bud and Donnie have a tussle over one of the blocks. To the observer's surprise, Donnie clings to it with all his strength and manages to keep it (without calling for the teacher). The other children want to join in this game and Donnie readily lets them." (Hartley, Frank, and Goldenson, 1952)

NYMPHOMANIA (Andromania). A sexual deviation in females consisting of an excessive or insatiable desire for gratification.

In nymphomaniacs, the desire for sexual stimulation and gratification is so intense and insistent that it tends to overshadow all other activities. Many of these women not only engage in promiscuous intercourse but also masturbate several times a day. The sources of the drive are closely parallel to those for satyriasis, excessive desire for sexual activity in the male. Many nymphomaniacs are basically frigid women who are unconsciously attempting to prove their sexual normality and adequacy. In some cases constant intercourse is an unconscious attempt to deny or disguise latent, unrecognized homosexual tendencies. Psychoanalysts usually trace this compulsive need to early childhood. Redlich and Freedman (1966) state, "Both the 'Don Juan' with a need for sexual intercourse with countless women and an inability to enter into a deeper relationship, and his counterpart, the nymphomanic woman, have profound character neuroses. Usually, seduction in childhood and pathological attachments to frustrating or permissive parental figures are found in the life histories of such patients; paradoxically, the promiscuous 'save themselves' for an unobtainable 'true love' "—that is, they make a sharp distinction between sex as a physical need (or way of making a living) and an expression of love and devotion. This enables them to obtain immediate gratification while at the same time preserving a romantic, idealistic hope.

Other causal factors may apply in certain cases. In some women excessive sexual activity may be a response to emotional tension, though this is more likely to be the case with males than with females, since tension usually diminishes sexual desire in women. Today very few investigators attribute the drive to excessive hormone secretions, but there is a possibility that a small number of cases are due to lesions in the amygdala, a structure located at the base of the brain. *See* PROMISCUITY, PROSTITUTION, EROTOMANIA, SATYRIASIS, AMYGDALA.

Illustrative Case: NYMPHOMANIA

Margaret W., age thirty-eight, married, requested psychological help for her excessive desire for sexual gratification. She had consulted her physician for some type of medication that would reduce her sexual drive. Her physician, after evaluating the situation, referred her for psychotherapy.

Ever since she was in grammar school Margaret had evidenced a strong sexual drive. She was a chronic masturbator at the age of ten. Her parents at that time took her to the family doctor, who reassured them she would grow out of it. She had her first sexual intercourse at thirteen and had

numerous affairs by the time she was eighteen. At that time she became pregnant and married the man who was the father. After two years of marriage she was deserted. She has had three marriages since and they all have ended in divorce. While married she would carry on several affairs with a variety of men—her neighbor, the insurance agent, a grocery clerk, and often a man whom she had simply picked up.

Margaret's parents were divorced when she was three. She never knew her real father. Mother went to work after the divorce and placed Margaret in a boarding home during the day. Her mother was always tired, irritable, and temperamental. She resented having to go to work and take care of the baby without any support from the father. At night Margaret was put to bed early so that mother could relax. Margaret can recall that she engaged in some masturbation at the age of about five (when she started school).

When Margaret was seven her mother remarried. The stepfather was a severe and strict person. He rarely gave Margaret any affection although he brought her home toys from time to time. When Margaret misbehaved he would strap her with his belt, sometimes with the buckle end. She recalls resenting her mother for marrying him, and resenting her stepfather for being so strict and harsh with her.

As a child Margaret was always tense and high-strung. She would cry easily and sometimes would cry herself to sleep. She had frequent nightmares and on several occasions walked in her sleep. She was quiet and shy and had difficulty in making friends. At school she did poorly in her academic subjects but got along well with the students and teachers.

Throughout the years the masturbation continued and increased as she got older. In high school she recalls masturbating several times a day. Then she heard that it was wrong, and that it would cause her to become insane. She tried hard to stop the habit but was never able to be successful. While in high school she started to run around with a number of "fast" boys and had sexual relations with several of them. It was while she was in her senior year that she became pregnant and got married. She never went back to school to get her diploma.

Margaret was aware of her sexual problem. She stated that at about twenty-five she consulted a doctor for her condition and was given some type of medication. It did not give her any relief. She decided she would try to change herself by getting her mind on other things. Her strong desires continued to be present and she continued to engage in sexual relations. A few months ago she again decided to try and do something about her strong sexual desires. She consulted her physician, who referred her for psychotherapy. (Thorpe, Katz and Lewis, 1961)

O

OBESITY. In psychiatry, a psychophysiologic disorder of the gastrointestinal system characterized by an excessive drive to eat (bulimia) and overweight.

In medical examinations an individual is generally described às obese if his weight is at least 20 per cent over the standard for his age and sex. However, a growing number of authorities advocate using the "preferred weight" for the *individual* as the norm, in view of the large constitutional differences in body build. In any case, a person becomes obese for one basic reason: he has an excessive drive to eat and takes in more calories than his body can consume. The calories are then stored in the form of fat. The critical amount varies from individual to individual because of basic differences in metabolism and activity level. But, generally speaking, any person will tend to gain weight if his caloric intake exceeds his energy expenditure—and if this continues for a substantial period of time, he is bound to become obese.

Today the great majority of cases of obesity are considered psychophysiologic, or psychosomatic, in origin—that is, the excessive drive to eat is due to psychological factors. This is not to deny that *some* cases are basically glandular, for it is a well-known fact that an underactive thyroid keeps metabolism at a low level and leads to overweight. In addition, two centers in the hypothalamus are now known to be involved in the eating process—one controlling the act of feeding, and the other the level of satiation—and damage to either of them can produce excessive appetite, or "hyperphagia." However, glandular deficiency and brain injury are believed to account for fewer than 5 per cent of obesity cases. The other 95 per cent are due primarily to behavior patterns stemming from parental influences and emotional difficulties, but often abetted by a constitutional tendency toward overweight.

The tendency to obesity usually begins in childhood. In many cases the parents set a pattern of overeating due to such causes as cultural influences and their own upbringing. Often overweight themselves, they may unconsciously want their children to identify with them and become as heavy as they are. In some cases, they may force food upon their children because they were half-starved in their own childhood due to war or poverty, and sometimes because of the mistaken impression that "a fat child is a healthy child" and that "a double chin is like a spare tire." In any event, the child soon realizes that he can win the approval of his parents by the simple and usually pleasant process of eating "well," a pattern that is often reinforced by the offer of extra desserts as rewards for good behavior. The net effect is to establish a high level of consumption that will produce "developmental obesity" and remain as a fixed pattern all the rest of his life.

Overemphasis on food not only creates faulty eating patterns, but faulty emotional patterns as well. When the child is made to feel that eating a great deal will gain him the love and attention of his parents, food will tend to take on the unconscious symbolic meaning of approval and acceptance. As a consequence, the young person may develop a drive to "raid the icebox" when he feels disappointed, lonely, or rejected. At these times, he craves food not because his body requires it, but because his emotions demand it. Moreover, if his frustrations continue, and food becomes a *habitual* refuge, he may begin to develop a full-blown case of psychosomatic obesity.

The major characteristics of such cases are these: first, they show a truly *compulsive,* uncontrollable drive to overeat; their motto, paraphrasing that of the alcoholic, would be "One bite is too many, a thousand are not enough." Second, this drive stems from deep-seated personality needs. Many psychoanalysts believe it originated in frustrations experienced during the oral phase of psychosexual development, the stage at which the child is preoccupied with the mouth and eating. If the child is neglected or deprived during this period, the oral needs of infancy may be carried over to adult life. Studies by Bruch (1958) have shown that many obese individuals felt unwanted, inadequate, and insecure as children, and began to overeat not only to attract approving attention from their parents, but to become big, important, and conspicuous in their own eyes. This compensatory drive to be important is frequently expressed in grandiose daydreams. However, as overweight develops, they find that their huge size and ungainliness interfere with participation in sports and social activities—and they also find that it attracts ridicule instead of admiration. They then begin to "retreat behind a wall of fat," using their obesity as a rationalization for

their failures ("Nobody loves a fat girl"), and as a means of escaping the risks and anxieties that so often accompany social relationships. In some cases these include marriage itself, for the fat girl may have a fear of sex and childbearing. The entire situation then creates a vicious circle, for the obese person experiences so many dissatisfactions that he cannot endure the extra discomfort—and the symbolic loss of love—that would be involved in dieting. Instead, he usually eats more than ever as a substitute for the life satisfactions he is missing due to his obesity.

To be effective, treatment of cases of psychosomatic obesity is not confined to the usual medical therapy, but is directed at the total personality of the patient. Psychotherapy is needed in order to make these people aware of the unconscious purposes served by their excessive drive to eat. With children it is usually advisable to interview or actually treat the parents whose attitudes have encouraged them to establish faulty eating patterns, to seek refuge in food, or to overeat as a means of eliciting affection and approval. The attempt to increase the patient's insight is accompanied by emotional re-education to help him become more self-reliant, sociable, and self-confident. A diet is not usually prescribed until the patient, child or adult, has arrived at some self-understanding and is capable of some degree of self-regulation. When a regimen is proposed, it usually includes exercise as well as a weight reduction diet. Efforts are also made to help the patient find new interests and satisfactions in life so that eating will not remain his major gratification. With adults, group therapy has been found particularly effective, since the members of the group help each other attain the necessary insight and also provide group support, encouragement, and a measure of competition, which reinforce their attempts to keep to the regimen. Hypnotic suggestion may also be employed to help obese patients maintain their diet. *See* BU-LIMIA.

Illustrative Case: OBESITY

Let us take, as an illustration, the behavior of a young unmarried woman who came to a psychiatric clinic complaining of fatigue, inefficiency, excessive daydreaming, and a voracious appetite. She said she had been growing increasingly tired and lethargic since her graduation from college two years before. Although she had accepted several temporary jobs teaching dramatics in small schools, she neglected her work more and more, spent long periods lying on her bed, and memorized and recited lengthy excerpts from religious tracts. Finally she gave up working altogether and remained at home alone in her room.

Six months before she came to the clinic, our patient began to eat voraciously. She took three or four generous helpings at each meal, and between meals ate large quantities of food from the refrigerator. Although the pantry was always open to her, on several occasions her parents found her in the barn, eating grain and garbage which had been put there for the farm animals. She excused this behavior merely by saying that she was hungry. During this six-month period she gained forty pounds. Examinations in the clinic excluded the possibility of endocrine or general metabolic disturbance; but there was considerable evidence to indicate that the uncontrollable eating had become a substitute satisfaction which reduced the tension of her unappeased affectional needs.

The patient was the oldest of seven children. For the first five years of her life she had been the only child, indulged and overprotected by her mother. Then came the second child, a girl, and the patient was abruptly cut off from the fondling, petting, praise, and attention which had formerly been hers. Later in childhood, the younger sister consistently excelled her in school and made friends more easily than she. In adolescence the sister enjoyed pretty clothes, dancing, and the company of boys, which the patient herself characterized as "having a good time in a wicked way." Throughout her life, the patient compared herself unfavorably with her sister, calling herself "dumb," shy and "old-maidish." She had

few boy friends, went to college dances alone, and was always critical of any young man who came to call on her. Her fantasies and dreams, however, centered around love affairs, marriage, and childbearing. Her younger sister became engaged and then married six months before the patient came to the clinic—the time at which, it will be recalled, the patient began her voracious eating.

In the hospital, the patient appeared apathetic, preoccupied, and somewhat disorganized in her behavior. Asked about her overeating, she said, "I guess it's my sex. . . . I'm a little eager for marriage, I ought to be taken care of. . . . My hands are weak." Her spontaneous comments were usually confined to complaints of hunger. On an obesity diet she achieved only a negligible loss of weight; she continually attempted to take food surreptitiously from the other patients. Prolonged therapy directed, not toward her overeating, but toward the needs for affection and acceptance which food had come to satisfy indirectly, brought some improvement. (Cameron and Magaret, 1951)

OBJECT RELATIONSHIP. A psychoanalytic term for emotional attachment to another person, as opposed to concern and love for one's self.

According to this theory the human being starts life as a complete narcissist, with his libido centered on himself alone. As he grows, he gradually directs this psychosexual energy outward, toward other things and people. Some individuals, however, develop a greater capacity than others for object relationships. These are the warm, responsive people who readily form bonds of love and devotion. Others fail to develop this capacity for several reasons. They may be neurotically fixated, or arrested, at an earlier narcissistic stage. They may have experienced rejection and frustration in early childhood, and become incapable of attachment to others because their parents were not attached to them. Or they may have lost their capacity later in life because of disappointed expectations or unrequited affection.

It is significant that one of the major

symptoms in the most severe of all mental illnesses, schizophrenia, is the inability to respond or feel close to other people. *See* LIBIDO, NARCISSISM, FIXATION.

OBJECTIVE PSYCHOTHERAPY. A treatment procedure carried out in writing in order to reduce the subjectivity involved in a personal relationship between patient and therapist. The technique was developed by Benjamin Karpman primarily for use with institutionalized patients and patients with mild to moderate emotional disturbances.

The first step in the procedure is a series of face-to-face interviews in which the therapist explains the importance of emotions in life, discusses neurosis as an emotional illness which can be cured only by understanding and not by will power. He also assures the patient that everything possible will be done for him and that he will benefit from the treatment. After this initial orientation, the therapist meets with the patient for brief periods several times a week, not for therapeutic interviews, but only to explain instructions and give and receive written material. During the first of these contacts, he gives the patient a set of about twenty questions designed to elicit general autobiographical material, including his relationships with his mother, father, siblings, friends; his early sexual interests; and his social environment. The patient is instructed to give explicit answers, but with emphasis on the emotional aspects of his experiences. At the next meeting the therapist hands the patient a memorandum which notes the highlights and explains the significance of his answers in common-sense terms. Karpman finds that this memorandum not only holds the patient's interest but often gives him a first glimpse of insight into himself.

In the next phase of the treatment the patient is asked to submit written accounts of his dreams. When he receives this material, the therapist briefly explains the processes involved in dreams, such as symbolism, and then makes interpretations. These are again on a common-sense level, but based on the autobiographical material already supplied. The interpretations are given to the patient in writing, and he is then asked to elaborate on his dream and make his own comments in written form. Karpman finds this technique particularly useful not only in providing insight but in showing the patient that many of his thoughts are under conscious control. During this phase of the treatment the patient is also assigned readings on psychopathology and psychotherapy from such authors as Freud, Menninger, Janet, McDougall, Prince, and Stekel. The books are chosen with the patient's level of intelligence and emotional needs in mind. The object is twofold: to educate without indoctrination, and to stimulate the recall of forgotten experiences. *See* BIBLIOTHERAPY.

Next, the therapist prepares a second set of written questions based on the patient's comments on his dreams, his reactions to the reading material, and his type of disorder. These questions are designed to reach deeper into his personality and "are likely to bring forth rather definitely some of the underlying psychogenetic mechanisms" (Karpman, 1949). They are handled in the same way as the first set, that is, the patient submits his answers in writing. A third and usually final set of questions is then given the patient, using the same ground rules as the other two. When the entire question and answer interchange has been completed, the therapist presents a "memorandum as a whole" to the patient, summarizing all the insights obtained in the process.

Karpman maintains that each neurosis is unique and that the therapeutic tools must be adjusted to the individual needs of the patient as well as the personality of the therapist. He therefore does not present objective psychotherapy as the only valid approach, although he believes it has proven effective in many cases of moderate disorder, including institutionalized criminals. If he finds that his initial questionnaire does not yield enough information, he switches to a more traditional psychoanalytic approach, but he also suggests that the therapist may in some cases switch from the traditional procedure to the shorter method of objective psychotherapy, using the material gathered in free association as a basis for written questions. The therapist must therefore remain flexible and alert to the situation that will be most effective with a particular patient.

OBSESSION. A persistent, intrusive idea or impulse which the individual does not want but cannot eliminate from consciousness.

Obsessions may be experienced by both normal and disturbed persons. They are considered normal when they do not arise from deep anxieties or conflicts or markedly interfere with mental processes or emotional adjustment. Such obsessions do not completely dominate our mind and behavior, and usually disappear when we develop new interests or solve our immediate problems. Examples of normal obsessions are a musical theme running constantly through our head, a nagging worry or premonition of disaster, and the repetition, or "perseveration," of a more or less meaningless phrase or quotation. Obsessional thoughts of this kind frequently arise when we are overfatigued, tense, or anxious.

In contrast, morbid obsessions appear more irrational and completely dominate consciousness and behavior. They are often more complex than the normal variety—for example, an individual may feel compelled to ruminate about an insoluble metaphysical problem such as why the world exists and what will ultimately happen to it. An obsession of this kind can occupy an individual's whole attention for days or weeks on end, sometimes to such an extent that he gives up his job and social life. These ruminations are frequently called intellectual obsessions. Obsessive fears are another type, and include phobias such as a dread of contamination or fear of thinking bad thoughts. A third type consists of obsessive impulses—for example, one patient may keep thinking about stabbing his wife and another may be haunted by the urge to shout some obscene word. A fourth type is obsessive fantasy. A common example is the mother's recurrent mental picture of her son lying dead on the battlefield. *See* OBSESSIVE-COMPULSIVE REACTION, OBSESSIVE PERSONALITY.

OBSESSIVE-COMPULSIVE REACTION. A psychoneurotic reaction characterized by a persistent impulse to think certain thoughts (obsessions) or carry out certain actions (compulsions). Obsessions and compulsions are usually found in the same patient, but one type of reaction may be more prominent than the other. The individual usually realizes that his behavior is unreasonable but is powerless to control it.

Obsessive-compulsive reactions are gross exaggerations of the common tendency to dwell on the same idea, such as a haunting melody, a single phrase or sentence, or to perform the same act, such as scratching one's head or touching every picket in a fence. In the neurotic form, however, these ideas or actions obtrude themselves with overpowering insistence, monopolize the mind, restrict the personality and interfere with everyday activities. Moreover, they are frequently more pointless, absurd, or repugnant than the usual preoccupations. Some individuals ruminate for days on end about infinity or creation or why a chair has four legs. Others have recurrent fantasies about killing a beloved member of the family or shouting blasphemous words in church, and no matter how hard they try, they cannot get rid of these ideas. Fortunately they rarely carry out unethical or violent acts, although they may become extremely apprehensive about doing so.

Obsessive-compulsive reactions of one kind or another are among the most common psychoneurotic disorders, constituting an estimated 20 to 30 per cent of the total number of cases.

Obsessions vie with phobias in number and variety. Some obsessive thoughts are disturbing only because they waste so much time—for example, counting to seven seventy-seven times, or occupying one's self with an insoluble scientific problem such as perpetual motion. Other obsessions may be a source of torment to the individual—for instance, preoccupation with thoughts about death and disease, or the feeling that one is going insane. One particularly distressing variety of obsession is "folie du doute" (madness of doubt), a persistent vacillation and indecision even about the simplest matters such as whether to make a telephone call or cross a street. Feelings of doubt are often accompanied by compulsive acts, such as checking the front door lock a dozen times, even to the point of getting up in the middle of the night.

Compulsions are usually stereotyped, repetitive acts ranging from simple behavior, such as crossing one's t's in a certain way or snapping one's fingers a certain number of times, to complex rituals such as placing one's clothes in a certain order and saying a nonsensical rhyme every night before going to bed. The performance of these actions brings a feeling of relief and satisfaction; if they are neglected or resisted, the individual is filled with uneasiness and tension. During periods of stress, compulsions become particularly irresistible and multiply to a point where they dominate the entire waking life. These activities may be annoying but they are rarely harmful to others. Compul-

sive stealing (kleptomania) and fire-setting (pyromania) are the most important exceptions. *See* these topics.

Cameron (1947) classifies compulsive behavior into six major but not mutually exclusive categories: *compulsive repetition* of acts, as in checking again and again to see whether the door has been locked; *serial compulsions:* carrying out sequences of acts or adhering rigidly to a certain order of behavior, as in dressing; *compulsive restraint* or *coercion:* the irresistible need to hold one's self or others in check by demanding devotion to routine or detail; *compulsive orderliness:* overconcern with simple everyday arrangements, with unbearable anxiety if there is any variation; *compulsive magic:* putting faith in signs, rituals, incantations and stereotyped actions, such as touching every third picket in a fence; and *antisocial compulsions:* the irresistible need to perform criminal acts, such as setting fires, stealing, committing murder or suicide.

The same underlying factors apply to both obsessions and compulsions, since they are aspects of a single type of neurotic reaction. In general they are both defenses against anxiety, but any one of several different mechanisms may be employed. First, *substitution.* Some individuals screen out disturbing ideas or threatening impulses by substituting meaningless thoughts and activities. The man who is failing in business may become preoccupied with trivial problems in accounting; the woman who feels guilty about her sexual impulses may endlessly arrange and rearrange the furniture in her home. In a case cited by Freud a patient blocked off a fear of insanity by continually brooding over the question "Why must I breathe?" In rare instances the individual may apply himself compulsively to social issues or scientific questions and thus may solve other problems even if he cannot solve his own.

A second pattern is the *isolation* of impulses from their emotional origins ("isolation of affect"). An individual with obsessive fantasies of aggression may feel they are forced upon him against his will and therefore are no fault of his own. In this way he denies that he actually harbors dangerous impulses. In one case, a man was obsessed with "horrible thoughts" of hitting his son over the head with a hammer. He could not explain his obsession, but analysis revealed that his wife had suffered so much pain during the birth of the child that she refused him sexual relations from then on. In addition she lavished most of her attention on the boy. In this case the man's obsession was the combined result of repressed hostility toward the son and an unconscious desire to get him out of the way in order to regain his former marital happiness. Both motives had been successfully cut off from recognition, and in this way the man was freed from responsibility for his violent thoughts.

A guilty reaction resulting from forbidden impulses or acts frequently gives rise to obsessions and compulsions. The man who hates and wants to harm his wife may feel compelled to pray for her a hundred times a day. The boy who has engaged in sexual play may wash his hands a hundred times a day or daub himself with mercurochrome until he looks like an Indian war dancer —yet if he is asked why he does these things, he will maintain that he simply has a special sensitivity to germs. An obsessive fear of contaminating others may also arise from feelings of guilt, and the individual may feel compelled to wear gloves constantly or refrain from bodily contact of any kind. These are all methods of counteracting, expiating, or atoning for dangerous impulses. The technical term for this reaction is *undoing. See* this topic.

Two other patterns are particularly noteworthy. Some people deny their underlying wishes by going to the opposite extreme—the mechanism of *reaction formation.* An individual with strong unconscious homosexual desires may devote himself completely to organizations dealing with the problem of homosexuality. Similarly, Masserman (1961) relates the case of the successful executive who hated the responsibility of marriage and being a father. This man was in the habit of calling his children's school three times a day to see if they were safe and sound, and he never came home without bringing presents to his entire family. Through these compulsive activities he was hiding his true feelings from himself as well as from others.

Finally, many individuals defend themselves against anxiety by organizing every aspect of their lives in a meticulous and rigid manner. They usually have an obsession for schedules, budgets, and invariable routines. These preoccupations give them a sense of security, but they also serve to screen out dangerous impulses since there just isn't time or place for them. The price they pay, however, is a high one, for they inevitably lead narrow, predictable, unimaginative lives. *See* COMPULSIVE PERSONALITY, OBSESSIVE PERSONALITY.

Although obsessive-compulsives do not all fall into a single personality pattern, they do tend to be restricted, methodical, obstinate, and overcontrolled individuals. They lack spontaneity and verve, and live by rules and regulations. Many of them are overconscientious, submissive, and conventional, and have unhealthy attitudes toward sex. Frequently their parents have had the same perfectionistic drives and the same intolerance of disorder, and have tried to push their children ahead too fast.

Like other neurotics, obsessive-compulsives have strong feelings of inadequacy and are excessively susceptible to guilt feelings. To them the world as a whole is a dangerous place, and they are caught between threatening impulses from within themselves and threatening situations from outside. Their obsessive thoughts and rigid routines may be interpreted as attempts to appease fate and block off anxiety. Their rituals have a semimagic quality that recalls the rites and incantations of primitive tribes.

The whole psychic economy of these individuals is precarious, and to maintain peace of mind they must constantly readjust its shaky balance by thinking of things they do not want to think about or performing actions they do not want to carry out. It is not surprising, then, that the acutely obsessive individual finds it difficult to live with himself, and others find it next to impossible to live with him.

Obsessive-compulsive reactions frequently present difficult problems of diagnosis. Normal defensive traits shade so gradually into neurotic behavior that it is necessary to ask how seriously the life of the individual is disturbed and whether his obsessive behavior is gathering force. Obsessive thinking and compulsive rituals may be confused with the ruminations and mannerisms of the early schizophrenic. A schizophrenic, however, shows less tension and fails to see how absurd his compulsions are. He is also likely to believe that external influences are forcing him to think and act as he does. As Bleuler has put it, the neurotic struggles *against* his obsession, and the delusional patient struggles *with* it. Manic-depressive patients are frequently afflicted with obsessional ideas in the depressive phase, but investigation will disclose that the depression preceded the obsessive ideas. The depression is therefore the basic reaction.

Obsessive-compulsive patients are frequently more resistant to treatment than other psychoneurotics because of the rigidity of their personalities. Most cases require long-term psychotherapy with the double aim of revealing the sources of the compulsive character traits and the unconscious meaning and purpose of the rituals and obsessive thoughts. Feelings of guilt and tendencies to over-conscientiousness and perfectionism can sometimes be explored in short-term therapy, and re-educational techniques may also be effective in helping the patient modify his extreme reactions. During this process the therapist usually encourages him to discover and cultivate latent interests in order to reduce preoccupation with meaningless and repetitious activities, and to promote the kind of personality growth he most needs.

Illustrative Case: OBSESSIVE-COMPULSIVE REACTION

". . . This boy's excessive cleanliness first showed itself at the age of thirteen, when it was noticed that he washed his hands many times during the day. Later he began to bathe frequently. Frequently he stayed two or three hours in the bathtub. On a number of occasions he daubed iodine on his hands and face. He told his parents that he had scratched himself and wanted to prevent infection. In addition to iodine, he had bought mercurochrome and other antiseptics for use in 'emergencies.' He also used a boric acid solution to wash his eyes every evening. The parents stated that he refused to play ordinary games with other children because he did not want to soil his hands. When asked to explain his concern regarding cleanliness, he stated that he realized that he washed more than other boys, but that in his case there were real reasons. He believed that his skin was of such a texture that it retained dirt and germs, and he therefore was forced to wash and scrub himself.

"No amount of persuasion was successful in deterring the boy from this until his original conflicts began to be solved. He stated that he had been greatly worried about his guilt regarding his previous activities with other boys. His parents discovered that he took part in sex play and punished him. They had frequently lectured him on the evils of 'immoral' behavior and on one occasion, when he was nine, made him sign a pledge never to smoke or drink even beer. They also told him how some terrible diseases result from masturbation. . . . He stated that he had 'sworn off' masturbating on many occasions, and after each time he masturbated he felt thoroughly ashamed of himself. He also believed that he was deficient in character and will power because he could not stop. He stated, 'I know it's a dirty habit and if anyone finds me out they will think terrible things about me.' After many interviews and much discussion, he began to change his attitude regarding the immorality of his past behavior and the possible consequences of his supposed moral transgressions. His excessive cleanliness gradually decreased and he was able to take part in the activities of other boys without feelings of unpleasantness from soiling his hands and clothes." (Sherman, 1938)

OBSESSIVE PERSONALITY. A personality trait disturbance characterized by perfectionism, excessive orderliness, indecisiveness, and constant worry over trifles. Obsessive individuals must have their desk arranged in a certain order, must eat at certain times, and usually pay a great deal of attention to cleanliness. They are often overconcerned about making a good impression, and try to consider every alternative in making the slightest decision. As a result, they tend to be irritating to other people, especially when they try to impose their rigid standards on them, or keep them waiting while they make up their minds.

The obsessive tendencies just mentioned are classified as character traits rather than neurotic symptoms. Although they frequently stem from feelings of guilt or anxiety, these feelings tend to be less acute and compelling than in cases of obsessional neurosis. Nor do the obsessional thoughts intrude so persistently or take as irrational a form as they do in neurotic patients. However, if individuals with obsessive tendencies are subjected to great stress, they may develop a full-blown neurosis. *See* NEUROTIC PERSONALITY, OBSESSIVE-COMPULSIVE REACTION, PERSONALITY TRAIT DISTURBANCE.

OCCUPATIONAL NEUROSIS. A neurotic reaction to one's occupation.

The individual with an occupational neurosis becomes so tense and anxious, or develops such incapacitating physical symptoms, that he finds it difficult or impossible to continue work. An author may become afflicted with writer's cramp and be unable to write or type; a violinist may find it impossible to raise his arm (musician's cramp); a taxi driver may become powerless to turn the steering wheel; a seamstress may find she cannot cut the cloth or thread the needle (seamstress' cramp). No organic cause can be found in such cases —not even in the case of the telephone operator who develops a chronic ringing in the ears.

Reactions of this kind are sometimes described as traumatic, but newer studies have shown that they are rarely precipitated by a single traumatic event. It seems more reasonable to classify occupational neurosis as a conversion or hysterical reaction, since the symptoms are usually physical in nature but produced by emotional conflicts. These conflicts may be due to situations or unconscious factors that are not basically work-connected, although the condition often appears to be precipitated by anxieties about failure on the job, resentment against superiors, distaste for working conditions, near-accidents, or occupational hazards. In many cases fatigue and tension lower the emotional threshold to a point where the workers' desire to escape from his distressing situation produces overt symptoms. In this respect the reaction bears a resemblance to combat neurosis. *See* COMBAT REACTION, CONVERSION REACTION, COMPENSATION NEUROSIS.

Illustrative Case: OCCUPATIONAL NEUROSIS

A nineteen-year-old unmarried woman was brought for consultation because of an intention tremor [a tremor occurring only when performing a deliberate action] in her left hand which had compelled her to give up her job. A year earlier she had obtained employment as an elevator operator in a department store for the purpose of saving money toward her marriage. Her fiancé, who at that time had moved to a better job in another city, had begun by writing her twice weekly and visiting her once a month. After a few months, however, his letters grew cooler and less frequent; he kept putting off visiting her on various plausible pretexts, and when he finally did come he behaved in a strained and preoccupied manner. In response to her worried promptings, her fiancé agreed that his changed behavior was the result of business cares, but a few days after he had left, he sent the patient a letter which stated bluntly that he had decided to marry someone else.

The patient was very much shaken by this sudden collapse of her life plans. She felt deeply humiliated at being rejected after she had so confidently told everyone whom she could, almost daily, of her marital plans. Back at work she found that she could no longer reach for and hold the elevator clutch because of a coarse intention tremor which appeared each time she tried. The symptom received strong reinforcement from the reactions of her fellow workers to it. With their genuine sympathy they mingled the inevitable frightening anecdotes which people in all walks of life seem to save for such occasions.

The patient responded well to brief therapy, which, in addition to personal reorientation, included an immediate change in vocation, and a move to another neighborhood where her adversity would not be known. Her initial resistance to any interpretation of the tremor other than that of a "palsy" gave way as treatment progressed. She succeeded in recalling that the trembling in her left hand was originally not an isolated phenomenon, as it later became, but had been part of a generalized trembling which immediately followed her receipt of the bad news. She remembered that, after reading the letter, she had found considerable difficulty with the manipulations involved in eating and in putting on her things before going to work. "I was shaky all over," she said. However, the other tremors diminished, while the one in the hand upon whose steadiness her job depended grew worse. In the course of therapy, the patient gradually lost her symptom as she worked out the factors precipitating and perpetuating it,

and as she recognized its significance as a public statement of her inability to go on any longer with her plans. (Cameron, 1947)

OCCUPATIONAL PSYCHIATRY (Industrial Psychiatry). The practice of psychiatry in a work setting, on either a full-time or consultative basis.

This growing field represents "a promising meeting-ground between preventive psychiatry and occupational medicine" (Powles and Ross, 1966). It offers the psychiatrist a unique opportunity to provide a variety of mental health services, since practically all men and a large percentage of women spend half their waking hours in an office or plant. Some of these services are "patient-centered," others "environment-centered." The patient-centered services take the form of emergency psychiatric treatment, diagnosis, case-finding, and referral to clinics or social agencies. The psychiatrist also acts as a consultant to the plant physician, and may advise or serve as referee in disability and compensation cases.

Environment-centered services are of two general types. First, the psychiatrist will be concerned with reducing the physical and psychological risks in the plant by drawing on his knowledge of the effects of noise, ionizing radiation, toxic substances, air pollution, etc. Second, he will be concerned with the "psychosocial matrix" of the plant, and will seek to establish constructive relationships on all levels—between executives and supervisors, between foremen and workers, and between the workers themselves. In so doing, he will call upon his knowledge of such matters as group dynamics, morale factors, the importance of "ventilating" grievances, and the nature and effects of defense mechanisms. He will be particularly aware that the attitudes of the supervisor, such as coldness and irritability, may foster unhealthy reactions not only in an individual but in a whole group of workers. He will also be concerned with out-of-plant situations, since marital and other home problems may seriously affect productivity and relationships on the job. His objective will be to handle, or see that others handle, all types of mental health hazards, so that both the neurotic and the average worker will function as well as possible in the work environment. In carrying out these functions, he must be able to "communicate with non-psychiatrists" and with individuals and groups on management, supervisor, and worker levels.

Powles and Ross offer a "suggestive list of syndromes" to indicate more specifically the range of problems on which the occupational psychiatrist may apply his professional knowledge. They include: absenteeism, accident syndrome, back disabilities, cardiac difficulty, compensation neurosis, executive neurosis, grievance proneness, group phobias, intoxications, moonlighting (compulsive working after hours), pulmonary disorders, prejudice, retirement concerns, supervisor neurosis, "traumatic" neurosis, wildcat strikes, and problems of women and younger employees. See ACCIDENT PRONENESS, SAFETY PSYCHOLOGY, COMPENSATION NEUROSIS, VENTILATION CONDITIONS, NOISE CONDITIONS, CARBON MONOXIDE POISONING, LEAD POISONING, MORALE (INDUSTRIAL), PREJUDICE, AGING, OCCUPATIONAL NEUROSIS, GROUP DYNAMICS.

OCCUPATIONAL THERAPY. A form of supportive therapy consisting of activities involving skill, such as weaving or typing (see PLATE 34).

The primary purpose of occupational therapy is to further the recovery of mental patients through activities that keep them interested and alert, increase their self-confidence, promote their social relationships, and give them a sense of accomplishment. Its importance lies in the fact that most institutional patients tend to feel lonely, rejected, isolated, inadequate, and deeply self-con-

cerned. Working with their hands keeps them from lapsing into inertia, focuses their attention outside themselves, brings them into contact with others, and gives them an opportunity to re-establish their self-esteem by producing something of worth.

Since mental patients are extremely varied in background and interests, the occupational therapist must be prepared to offer a wide range of activities. Among them are sketching, weaving, clay modeling, woodworking, painting, needlework, ceramics, leatherwork, indoor or outdoor gardening, and sculpting. In a modern therapeutic center these activities are not approached from the "busywork" viewpoint; the emphasis is rather on self-expression, the development of skill, and the achievement of personal satisfaction. In many cases volunteers are called in to teach their own specialties, and at the same time to bring patients into closer contact with the community beyond the hospital. Some of the activities, such as typing, stenography, or the operation of power tools and business machines are directly oriented toward a vocation, and therefore have the added value of preparing the patient for the future. This is sometimes termed industrial therapy.

Effective occupational therapy is not a haphazard affair. It involves careful planning for each *individual patient. The psychiatrist usually makes recommendations concerning the patient's needs. The occupational therapist then explores his interests and skills, and together they plan activities which will be congenial and at the same time fulfill the therapeutic objectives set by the physician. If these activities are used as preparation for an actual vocation, the occupational therapist usually works closely with the vocational counselor in planning the program.

An occupational therapist must possess a variety of manual skills and the ability to impart them to others.

Just as important is an active imagination, an outgoing attitude, and a genuine desire to help mentally disturbed people regain their health and independence. The educational requirements, as established by the American Medical Association and the American Occupational Therapy Association, include four years at a college or university offering a curriculum in occupational therapy, leading to the degree of B.S. or B.A. in occupational therapy, followed by nine months of clinical experience. College graduates who have received their undergraduate degree in another field may take an eighteen-month advanced course on both academic and clinical aspects of the subject. The American Occupational Therapy Association conducts a national registration examination, and successful candidates are entitled to use the initials O.T.R. (Occupational Therapy, Registered) after their name. In the past most of the therapists were women, but in recent years there has been a steady increase in the number of men in the field.

ODDITY METHOD. A procedure for testing the ability to use concepts. A subject is presented with three or more items to see if he can pick out the odd one, the one that does not belong with the rest.

The oddity method can be applied with or without the use of language. In a typical verbal test, the subject is asked, Which of the following does not belong with the other: skyscraper, temple, cathedral, prayer? In a performance test, the subject looks at a group of actual items or pictures and picks out the odd one. This form of the test can be applied to young children and even certain animals. In one setup three hollow geometrical forms are presented, with a reward such as candy or fruit placed under the odd-shaped one. After the subject solves this problem,

he is presented with other sets of three to see if he continues to choose the odd shape. This would indicate whether he could detect a relationship, and, presumably, form a concept.

The oddity method is used in experimental work (Cofer, 1951) as well as intelligence tests. It offers an alternative to the usual ways of determining whether a subject can understand concepts—that is, by defining terms, giving illustrations, or picking out examples from a group of items (for instance, pointing to vegetables in a group of foods). The verbal oddity test shows whether the subject can understand several concepts at once. It also indicates whether he can form his own concept, or hypothesis, and use it in finding the odd item. Experiments indicate that people can often solve oddity problems even when they cannot give adequate definitions. They have learned their concepts through experience, and they have a practical rather than theoretical understanding of them.

Interestingly, it has been found that the order of presentation often determines the basic concept that is used in searching for the odd item. In the example given above, the word "prayer" is usually selected as the one that does not belong. But if prayer is given first, the subject thinks in terms of religious rather than architectural concepts, and usually selects "skyscraper" as the odd item. This ties up with other observations which show the importance of "primacy"—that is, the beginning of a speech or article generally has the greatest effect.

Experiments with performance items indicate that chimpanzees as well as children are capable of solving some of the oddity problems (PLATES 36 AND 37). In other words, concept formation is possible even without the use of language. *See* CONCEPT FORMATION.

OEDIPUS COMPLEX (Oedipus Situation). In psychoanalytic theory, the erotic attachment of the son for the mother, accompanied by attitudes of rivalry and hostility toward the father. The corresponding relationship between daughter and father is sometimes referred to as the Electra complex, but the term Oedipus complex is frequently applied to both situations.

The name Oedipus complex derives from a Greek myth in which Laius, king of Thebes, was told by an oracle that he would be killed by his son. Accordingly, when the boy, Oedipus, was born he gave him to a shepherd to leave on a mountain to die—but instead, the compassionate shepherd gave him to the king of Corinth to raise. At puberty, the young man journeyed to Thebes and on the way killed Laius in a quarrel, not realizing that he was his true father. On arrival, he solved a riddle presented by the Sphinx and as a reward was given Jocasta, the queen, as a wife. When the relationship to Jocasta finally came to light, she hanged herself. Oedipus then put out his eyes and wandered about with his daughter, Antigone, until he was destroyed by avenging deities.

According to Freud, every boy symbolically relives this drama by experiencing incestuous desires for his mother and regarding his father as a hated rival.

The psychoanalytic theory holds that the Oedipus situation, or "family romance," arises in the phallic period of psychosexual development, gathering force between the ages of three and seven. Freud believed it to be a universal phenomenon, holding that it is the source of the powerful taboos against incest found in practically every culture. Most anthropologists, however, deny its universality since there are many cultures in which it does not appear.

Freud's position is also rejected by many psychiatric theorists. Horney (1939) denied that the Oedipus complex is either normal or universal, and

viewed it as a neurotic relationship fostered by parents who caress their children erotically, allow them to witness sex scenes, or adopt provocative and seductive attitudes toward their children of the opposite sex. Kanner (1948) claimed that the relationship was "imposed" by Freud and his followers and that the theory was not based on observation of children. Adler interpreted the boy's conflict with his father and his desire to possess the mother in terms of a striving for superiority—that is, the boy wants to prove he is stronger and more attractive than his father. He also held that boys who are pampered by the mothers are likely to overindulge in sexual fantasies about her; and suggested that the girl's attachment to the father and hostility toward the mother stem from a desire to reject feminine inferiority and identify with the superior status of the male. See MASCULINE PROTEST.

Many types of evidence have been offered to show that the Oedipus situation is common, if not universal, in our culture. Young boys frequently ask the mother which one she loves most, their father or themselves. They may also have dreams or fantasies in which the father goes away, dies, or meets with an accident. The popular song containing the line "I want a girl just like the girl who married dear old dad" is a perennial favorite with male quartets. On the other side of the coin, many mothers "court" their sons, and are overcritical of their daughters or try to marry them off as soon as possible. Similarly, many fathers constantly criticize and deprecate their sons, and at the same time make "dates" with their daughters and show little enthusiasm for their boy friends. Whether these attitudes are an *expression* of a basic Oedipal situation, or *originate* this situation, it is an undeniable fact that they do occur.

According to the Freudian theory, the Oedipus situation is relinquished in favor of external interests during the latency period (ages six to eleven). It is then revived briefly in puberty, and is normally resolved during adolescence. Two major factors are responsible for this resolution. First, as he develops, the boy identifies increasingly with the male role in life and incorporates his father's goals and standards into his own patterns of behavior. Likewise the maturing girl gradually finds gratification and fulfillment in the feminine role, as a result both of the mother's encouragement and the father's admiration.

The second agent for resolution of the Oedipus situation is the castration complex. This complex stems from the boy's unconscious concern about retaliation by the father for his attentions to the mother, and takes the form of fear of injury to his sexual organs. This forces the son to repress his incestuous feelings for his mother, and when he reaches puberty he begins to direct his libido toward girls of his own age. Freud held that the daughter also experiences castration fantasies, though they are viewed as one of the sources rather than the outcome of the Oedipal attachment—that is, when girls discover that they lack a penis, they blame this difference on the mother, and the effect is to reinforce their hostility toward mother and their attachment to the father. In their case, the Oedipal relationship is gradually given up because of feelings of shame and guilt, as well as the threat of losing their mother's love, and not because of castration fear. According to the theory, the female Oedipus complex is never resolved as completely as the male complex, and for this reason women remain psychologically closer to their fathers than to their mothers.

Freud (1930) stated: "One says rightly that the Oedipus complex is the nuclear concept of the neuroses, that it represents the essential part of the content of neuroses. It is the culminating point of infantile sexuality, which through its after-effects decisively influences the sexuality of the adult." He held that many cases of neurotic, psychotic, and character disorder stem from an inadequate resolution of this situation. It is believed to be a major source for phobias (fear of pointed objects, a phallic symbol), compulsions ("undoing" or atoning behavior due to guilt feelings), and conversion reactions (hysterical paralysis of the hand that wants to caress the mother). A schizophrenic patient may reflect the Oedipus situation by believing that he is not the child of his parents, that his mother is his wife, that his father does not exist, or that he has been deprived of his sexual organs.

Kisker (1964) cites the play *Black Chiffon,* in which a mother is so attached to her son that when she discovers that his fiancée wears a black nightgown, she is driven to steal a similar nightgown from a shop: "This theft was motivated by her deep-seated desire to compete with the girl for her son's affections and at the same time to be punished for her forbidden unconscious wishes." He also cites the case of a father who shot his daughter and himself on her wedding day because "the load is more than I can bear."

Far more common are the men who remain bachelors and the women who become spinsters as a result of strong attachment to the parent of the opposite sex, the daughter who postpones marriage for years because of a father fixation; the adult son who lives with his widowed mother, spends his life fruitlessly looking for a mother substitute, or marries a woman much older than himself; and the many men and women who adopt ("introject") characteristics of the parent of the opposite sex and become either latent or overt homosexuals. *See* PSYCHOSEXUAL DEVELOPMENT, INCEST, SEX ROLE, CASTRATION COMPLEX, IDENTIFICATION.

OLIGOPHRENIA (literally, "small mentality"). A term for mental retardation or mental deficiency, more commonly used in Europe than the United States. Until recently the term appeared in the title of one congenital form of retardation, phenylpyruvic oligophrenia, but that defect is now called phenylketonuria (PKU). *See* this topic.

ONANISM. Sexual intercourse with withdrawal just before ejaculation; coitus interruptus.

The term derives from the Bible (Genesis 38:9): "And Onan knew that the seed should not be his; and it came to pass, when he went in unto his brother's wife, that he spilled it on the ground, lest that he should give seed to his brother." Due to a misinterpretation of this passage, onanism is often incorrectly used as a synonym for masturbation.

Coitus interruptus is sometimes used for purposes of contraception, though it may fail because the preorgastic secretion contains spermatozoa in 25 per cent of males. As to the psychological effects, there is considerable disagreement. Lowen (1961) states: "Any attempt to control or restrain the mounting genital excitation at this time is unpleasant and may be painful. Such a procedure frequently results in a shock to the body." Lehfeldt (1961) believes it may have other effects: ". . . it is certain that the method often produces psychological disturbances such as lack of female orgasm or male impotence, which may lead to marital maladjustment. Switching to a different contraceptive technique usually cures these ills." As to lasting psychological harm, Gutheil (1959) has this to say: "Early psychiatrists (including Freud) believed that coitus interruptus—like masturbation—was harmful, and that it led to a so-called 'actual neurosis.' Today, this concept is no longer considered valid."

ONLY CHILDREN (Onliness). Attitudes toward the only child are still influenced by the opinions of an earlier day. Among the most frequently quoted statements is one by G. Stanley Hall, who said in 1907, "Being an only child is a disease in itself," and another by the Blantons in 1927, "The only child is greatly handicapped. He cannot be expected to go through life with the same capacity for adjustment that the child reared in a family with other children has." Others have insisted that, due to his unique position in the family, the only child is bound to be spoiled, egotistical, domineering, and therefore unpopular with his peers. In any case, he would seem to be doomed to be, in psychological terms, "maladjusted," and in lay terms, a "brat."

Recent research has given us quite a different picture of the only child. In the first place the attitude of the parents and the climate of the home determine whether or not onliness is a disadvantage; the presence or absence of siblings does not by itself have a drastic effect on personality development (Shaffer and Shoben, 1956). In the second place, there is no "typical" only child just as there is no typical child with brothers and sisters. It is true that the child, and his parents as well, are in a special situation by virtue of the fact that he is an "only"—but this situation can be an advantage as well as a disadvantage. As Johnson and Medinnus pointed out in a recent book (1965), "Several studies have compared only with *non*-only college students on standard behavior and adjustment tests as well as on achievement (Fenton, 1928; Campbell, 1933; Dyer, 1945), whereas other studies have employed teacher ratings of elementary school children (Fenton, 1928; Gilford and Worcester, 1930). In general, the findings have indicated no essential differences between only and other children."

The reason there are no essential personality differences is probably twofold: first, there are plus factors in the situation that compensate for the difficulties of being an only child; and second, parents are usually aware of these difficulties and find ways of offsetting them. The only child as a rule spends more time with adults and identifies more completely with them; he therefore tends to be more mature than other children, and maturity has been found to contribute to social adjustment. He also advances more rapidly in language development (Davis, 1931), and there is some evidence that he is superior in intellectual achievement (Faris, 1940; McCurdy, 1957; West, 1960). The latter finding is probably due not only to stimulation from adults, but to the richer imaginative life of children who are not constantly involved in social relationships.

These plus factors help to counterbalance the disadvantages of being an only child. Parents have also learned that all children must learn to adjust to their peers as early as possible in life. They therefore make special efforts to give the only child nursery school experience and to involve him in after-school activities at later ages. This is easier, of course, in urban than in rural areas, but even the country child has more opportunities for social contact than ever before due to increased transportation and communication facilities. Sometimes these relationships are more satisfying and less disruptive than the jealousies and rivalries that take place between siblings. Moreover, an ample program of social and extracurricular activities for the only child will make him more independent and keep his mother from showering too much attention on him. See BIRTH ORDER.

ORAL CHARACTER. In psychoanalytic theory, a pattern of personal traits determined by drives originating in the oral stage of psychosexual development.

The oral character stems from the earliest phase of development, when the child's life centers around the mouth and its functions. Since this stage is divided into two periods, the oral sucking period and the oral biting period, there are different types of oral character. In the oral sucking period, extending from birth to about eight months, the child is strongly attached to the mother and derives his basic pleasure from feeding. If this process is emotionally and physically satisfying, he goes on to the next, or anal stage without difficulty. He does, however, retain his capacity for oral satisfaction, as manifested in normal pleasure derived from thumbsucking, eating, sucking on a pen or pencil, smoking, and kissing. See THUMBSUCKING.

If, on the other hand, the child experiences frustrations and conflicts during the oral sucking stage—for example, if his mother's attitude is cold and mechanical during the feeding process, or if he is under tension during the weaning period—he may become fixated (arrested) at this stage and develop lasting oral habits and character traits. According to the Freudian theory, these residual expressions of oral sexuality may take the form of persistent thumbsucking, stuttering, chain smoking, extreme talkativeness, tics involving the mouth, or a compulsion for oral sexual contact. Severely regressed schizophrenic patients may also exhibit symptoms of an oral nature, such as verbigeration and voracious eating. See VERBIGERATION, BULIMIA.

Psychoanalytic theory also traces many character traits to an oral origin. If the individual has experienced full satisfaction at the nursing stage, he may identify with the "giving" mother and become generous and altruistic. Early oral satisfaction is also believed to lead to optimism, self-assurance, and a normal degree of narcissism. However, if the individual has been deprived during the oral period, he may develop neurotic character traits such as pessimism and dependence on others for satisfaction of immediate needs. These individuals constantly demand that others look after them and are usually unwilling to give anything in return. See INCORPORATION.

The oral biting period yields a different set of behavior patterns and character traits, on both a normal and neurotic level. During this second stage of oral sexuality, which lasts from the eighth to the eighteenth month, the child ceases to identify with his mother and comes to feel that he is an independent person. He also begins to feel both love and hate for his mother— love when she satisfies him, hate when she refuses or neglects to satisfy him. During this period, cruelty and aggression make their first appearance, and the child shows his hostility by biting the mother's breast or the nipple of his bottle during the nursing period. This is most likely to occur as a response to feelings of anger and insecurity experienced during the weaning period.

Expressions of oral biting carry over to later life in the form of nail biting; spitting; sticking out the tongue; chewing a pencil, pipe, or gum. When any of these activities take extreme form, they are viewed as expressions of delayed or fixated oral aggressive drives. Various forms of oral sadism are also regarded as expressions of the biting stage. A common example is the habit of making caustic, "biting" remarks; another is the tendency of lovers to nibble at various parts of each other's bodies. The most extreme forms are found in the cannibalistic rites of primitive tribes, in the biting manias of the Middle Ages, and in rare cases of mental disease that involve a compulsion to devour human flesh. See EXOTIC PSYCHOSES, SADISM.

ORGANIC DISORDER. An impairment of function due to a demonstrable abnormality in the structure or biochemistry of bodily tissues or organs.

The term "organic disorder" is used in contradistinction to "functional disorder," which is applied to conditions that are due to psychological rather than physical factors. In psychiatry, the term organic disorder covers a broad spectrum that includes both acute and chronic disturbances of psychological functions that are due to infectious disease, toxic conditions, circulatory dysfunction (as in cerebral arteriosclerosis and brain hemorrhage), head injury, congenital or inherited brain defect, brain tumor, menopause, encephalitis, cerebral dysrhythmia, metabolic disturbance, irradiation, and brain atrophy.

Organic psychiatric disorders have been classified by the American Psychiatric Association under the headings Acute Brain Disorders, Chronic Brain Disorders, and Mental Retardation. See BRAIN DISORDERS, MENTAL RETARDATION (TYPES).

ORGANIC SENSES. Sensitivity to changes occurring inside the body through receptors located in the internal organs.

A great deal of activity is constantly taking place in the interior of our bodies, but relatively little of it comes to our attention. We occasionally notice the beating of our hearts or the churning of our intestines, but few people become aware of the movements that occur in their liver and spleen. It usually takes an illness or upset to make us realize that we have these organs at all, and even then we may not be able to localize the sensations accurately.

Relatively little is known about the organic senses, since the receptors are virtually inaccessible to experimentation. Anatomical studies indicate that the number of sensory fibers embedded in some of our visceral organs is only about one tenth the number of motor fibers leading to them. There are some pressure and pain endings in the internal organs, but they are unevenly distributed. The liver, spleen, kidneys, and intestines can be squeezed, cut, or cauterized under local anesthetic. Yet these organs can at times give rise to the most intense pain. Intestinal colic is extremely distressing to babies, and there are few pains more excruciating than those caused by gallstones and kidney stones. See PAIN SENSE.

The most extensively studied organ is the stomach. It is sensitive to warm and cold substances, alcohol and other chemicals, and spices such as mustard and peppermint. When it is empty, its walls rub together and we experience the pangs associated with hunger. After a particularly heavy meal we may experience a feeling of pressure due to distention. But we are hardly ever aware of this organ in its ordinary state. See HUNGER.

Many specialists believe the sensations we receive from our visceral organs are almost always a combination of pain, pressure, and other senses, such as hot and cold. The reason is that these sensations usually involve gross areas of the body containing many kinds of receptors. A typical example is nausea, a complex reaction made up of general discomfort in the stomach region, muscular weakness, and various circulatory disturbances including sweating, paling, "goose flesh," and chills.

Organic sensitivity has been found to decrease with age. This accounts for the fact that coronary thrombosis, appendicitis, and other painful disorders of the internal organs may be experienced by older people without acute discomfort.

ORGANICISM (Organic Viewpoint). The theory that all disorders, both physical and mental, have an organic basis.

Those who adhere to this point of view in psychiatry hold that all psychotic disorders, and possibly the more severe neurotic disorders as well, are due to structural brain changes or biochemical disturbances of the nervous or glandular systems. The disorders include not only brain syndromes caused by infectious diseases, nutritional disorders, toxic substances, head injury, and other physical conditions, but also disorders usually classified as functional, such as schizophrenic and manic-depressive reactions.

The organic viewpoint got its start in early Greek and Roman times when Hippocrates, Galen, and others ascribed mental disorders to disturbances in the brain, liver, heart, or other organs. This was a distinct advance over the prevailing view that mental illness was due to possession by demons or spirits. Little was done, however, to build on the theories of these early physicians, and demonology remained the dominant theme throughout the Middle Ages and early modern era. In 1757 Albrecht von Haller advocated the post-mortem study of brains of the insane, but the organic viewpoint was not systematically developed until Wilhelm Griesinger and Emil Kraepelin became convinced that all mental illness could be explained in terms of brain pathology. This was the prime approach in the first general period of modern psychiatry, beginning in the latter part of the nineteenth century, and it resulted in such great advances as the discovery of the effects of brain tumor, toxic conditions, syphilitic infection, arteriosclerosis, and brain injury on mental functions. It also led to the first thoroughgoing description and classification of mental illnesses and the first clear-cut triumph over a mental disorder by medical science—the successful treatment of general paresis, first by malaria therapy and later by penicillin.

As a result of these discoveries, the great majority of medical men in the early part of the twentieth century accepted the organic viewpoint, and strong impetus was given to research in the fields of physiology, anatomy, neurology, and biochemistry to discover the underlying causes of all types of mental disorder. These investigations were continued throughout the period when the psychological and holistic points of view were being developed, and have contributed heavily to three types of advance. First, the discovery and delineation of many organic psychoses and conditions causing mental retardation—among them, psychoses associated with nutritional disorders, glandular disorders, and infectious diseases; and mental deficiency due to encephalitis, German measles and other infections, brain injury and anoxia at birth, chromosomal anomalies, and metabolic disorders such as phenylketonuria and galactosemia.

Second, physical treatments, including insulin shock, electroconvulsive therapy, psychosurgery, tranquilizers, and energizers—all of which are applied to conditions usually believed to be functional, such as schizophrenic and depressive reactions—as well as vitamins and special diets for nutritional disorders (pellagra, phenylketonuria), replacement therapy for endocrine disorders (hypothyroidism, for example), and sedatives for convulsive disorders. Third, the fuller recognition of the collaboration between physical and psychological factors in reactions to stress and in such psychophysiologic (psychosomatic) reactions as asthma and migraine; and the possibility that organic conditions and hereditary tendencies may be involved in the etiology of schizophrenia and manic-depressive reactions. See ETIOLOGY, GRIESINGER, KRAEPELIN, HIPPOCRATES, GALEN.

ORGANISMIC THEORY. A holistic theory of personality developed primarily by Kurt Goldstein (1879–1965).

Organismic theory views the individual as a totality and emphasizes the integration of personality. Although its roots go back to Aristotle, the modern formulation stems largely from two sources: the Gestalt approach in general and, more specifically, a study of brain-injured soldiers during World War I. Gestalt psychology holds that the mind has a basic tendency to organize experience into patterns and configurations, and Goldstein applied this principle to the study of personality when he found that the symptoms of brain-damaged individuals could be under-

stood only when they were viewed as a manifestation of the organism as a whole, and not as products of a particular lesion or illness. This observation led to the more general theory that any event whatever, either psychological or physiological, occurs within the context of the total organism and must be viewed in a holistic light.

Goldstein was basically opposed to the atomization of experience into reflexes, stimulus-response bonds, or any other isolated components. He believed that the key to the normal personality lies in its unity, consistency, and organization; in contrast, the pathological personality is fragmented and disorganized. The unity that resides in any particular individual can only be appreciated and understood by seeing every aspect of his functioning together: his performances (conscious, voluntary activities); his attitudes, feelings, and inner experiences; and the way his body functions. According to Goldstein, more is to be gained from an intensive, holistic study of a single individual than from any statistical study of groups, a point of view that has made his approach more popular among clinicians than among experimental psychologists.

Organismic theory explains personality largely in terms of one basic principle: human beings are guided by a sovereign drive for self-actualization or self-realization. Goldstein maintained that each individual tries to fulfill his inherent potentialities in the most complete way open to him. Like Rousseau, he believed that natural man is good, but his environment can be a detriment since it often prevents him from acting according to his inherent nature. Yet in spite of obstacles, the human being has an urge for self-realization which gives unity and direction to his life, motivating him to select activities and experiences which contribute to his growth.

The master motive, self-actualization, underlies all other drives. According to the organismic theory it is the only motive we have, but it is expressed in many ways because different people have different innate potentialities and develop within different cultures and environments. Thus any drive that fulfills and replenishes the individual is a form of self-actualization, whether it be sex, hunger, power, or achievement, but each person develops his own pattern of drives to call upon as he needs them. According to Goldstein, this process is largely a conscious one. He views the unconscious as primarily an area to which these drives recede until they again become useful for self-realization (Goldstein, 1939).

Although self-actualization is primary in the organismic theory, a second concept also plays an important part. To explain the coherence, consistency, and orderliness he found in the human personality, Goldstein invoked the principle of equalization. He believed the organism has a basic tendency to maintain an average, balanced state—for example, if we hear a noise to the right of us, we turn in that direction in order to equalize the distribution of energy which was upset by the noise. Similarly, we bring ourselves back to a normal temperature by turning on an electric fan when it is hot; and in the emotional sphere, we let off steam by talking a blue streak when we are tense. In each of these instances disturbing influences throw us out of gear and we do what we can to regain our equilibrium.

Both of these concepts, self-actualization and equalization, recognize the importance of the environment. It is the medium which provides both the obstacles and the opportunities affecting growth. We must "come to terms" with our particular environment—on our own terms or on its terms. The more effective individuals are able to master their environment and utilize it for growth and self-realization; the less ef-fective merely accept it and adjust to it. The process of growing and mastering the environment is not a static affair, however, for in the course of our development we go through different stages, face different tasks, and have to reorganize our attitudes and behavior according to new requirements. This calls for a flexible but integrated approach to life if we are to remain normal. The pathological individual isolates one process from the total pattern of life and develops a fixed habit, for instance, of aggression or submission, which he employs in all circumstances, whether it is appropriate or not.

Many criticisms have been leveled at the organismic theory. The concept of self-actualization is too general and cannot be put to experimental test. The inner growth and maturation of the individual are stressed so much that the effects of learning are minimized. The emphasis on uniqueness of personality and on qualitative evaluation precludes the use of standardized objective tests. Nevertheless, the general approach of holism is widely employed today, and Goldstein has undoubtedly contributed greatly to its acceptance. It is largely due to his work that clinicians recognize the value of an intensive study of the individual patient in his natural setting instead of limiting themselves to the usual diagnostic tests. *See* MENTAL IMPAIRMENT TESTS.

ORGAN NEUROSIS. The psychoanalytic term for a neurosis in which bodily disturbances are prominent symptoms.

The term recognizes the fact that unconscious mental processes can produce such physical conditions as stomach upsets, paralysis, blindness, and headaches. The concept is a broad one that usually includes both psychophysiologic (psychosomatic) and conversion (hysterical) reactions. *See* PSYCHOPHYSIOLOGIC DISORDERS (GENERAL), CONVERSION REACTION.

ORGONE THERAPY (Vegetotherapy). The therapeutic approach of Wilhelm Reich (1897–1957), based on the dissipation of sexual tensions through the attainment of full orgasm.

Reich was originally a member of the psychoanalytic movement, but between 1924 and 1934 developed an approach of his own which he termed character analysis. In essence, he held that many patients protect themselves with a "character armor," a set of resistances which stand in the way of the analyst's attempts to penetrate to unconscious levels of the personality. These resistances consist of such attitudes as overaggressiveness, cynicism, passivity, and ingratiating tendencies. As a preliminary step, they must be cleared away by making the patient aware of them and by tracing them to their sources. In this process Reich used every clue available, including the patient's gestures, expressions, and posture as well as his actual utterances.

Reich regarded the character armor as a defense erected by the patient against revealing his unconscious libidinal (sexual) tendencies. When he felt that the patient's "education for analysis" had been completed, and his resistances removed, he adopted the orthodox analytic approaches such as free association and dream analysis in order to help the patient work through the depressed infantile sexual material which he believed to be at the root of neurosis. It was at this point that Reich began to part company with the classical analytic theory. Though he ostensibly broke with Freud in 1932 over the concept of the death instinct, the basic reason was probably that he believed Freud did not go far enough in his emphasis on the libido. Freud had pointed out the importance of eliminating infantile sexual tendencies of an oral, anal, autoerotic nature, and of achieving mature, "genital" expression of sexuality as *one* indication of improved functioning. With Reich, however, the achievement of "full orgastic potency" became the *only* measure of psychological well-being.

Reich based this theory on the idea that the orgasm is the emotional-energy regulator of the body, whose purpose is to dissipate sexual tensions. If it is not experienced, or if it is not equal in strength to the individual's sexual tensions, his emotional energy will be expressed through nonsexual, neurotic channels. A neurotic may therefore experience orgasm, but it will not be strong enough to release his particular sexual tensions—that is, he does not achieve *"full* orgastic potency."

Reich held that the anti-sexual, puritanical mores of Western society have so inhibited man's orgastic ability that only a few people are capable of full potency. It is therefore the task of psychoanalysis to revive the orgastic ability of mankind. In seeking to disseminate this doctrine, he formed "sexpolitical" units in the Socialist Party of Austria, and later in the German Communist Party. However, he was considered a corrupting influence and was expelled not only from these parties, but from Denmark, Sweden, and Norway, as well as from the International Psychoanalytic Association. He then came to the United States and taught for a time at the New School for Social Research.

Reich came to believe that the orgasm derives its power from a cosmic force which he termed orgone energy (1942). He advanced the theory that this energy emanates ultimately from the sun, and held that it not only pervades the atmosphere, giving the sky its bluish color, but can be found in all plants and animals. He even claimed to have found microscopic energy vesicles or "bions," charged with this energy, on the skin surfaces during sexual excitement. And he maintained that this vital force had the power not only of producing orgasm but of killing rot germs and bringing about a cure for diseases ranging from the common cold to cancer.

According to this theory, the primary function of orgone energy in psychiatric therapy is to restore the individual to full orgastic potency. For this purpose Reich designed an "orgone box," or "orgone accumulator," which, he believed, could capture the energy from the surrounding atmosphere and concentrate it on the sexual organs. The box resembles a telephone booth, but to attract the orgone energy it must be made of metal and lined with an organic material such as wood or fiber. The patient sits in the box for fifteen to forty-five minutes at a time and, according to Reich, frequently reports that he experiences hot, prickling sensations during the recharging process. The treatment can be speeded up by massaging the entire body, since this releases the orgone energy which has accumulated in the tissues and at the same time reduces muscular and emotional rigidities that prevent the orgasm reflex from functioning.

The major objective of orgone therapy, or "character analytic vegetotherapy," as he also called it, is to destroy the character armor with which the individual has surrounded himself as a result of his anxieties. If this is accomplished, he will be able to return to his proper biological functioning—that is, the achievement of full potency, which discharges present tensions and keeps others from developing. Needless to say, this theory finds little if any acceptance today, not only because of Reich's fanciful concept of cosmic energy, but because it is a well-known fact that many highly disturbed individuals are capable of full orgastic potency.

ORIENTATION. Awareness of one's self in relation to time, place, and person.

An individual who can identify and locate himself in his environment as to place, time, circumstances, and other people is said to be oriented. He knows who he is, what date it is, where he is, why he is there, and whom he is talking to. If he is confused about these facts, he is said to be disoriented. In a psychiatric examination, especially in a mental hospital, orientation is determined largely by answers to such questions as What is your name? What do you do for a living? Where are you now? Why are you here? Who do you think I am? What is today's date? *See* DISORIENTATION, PSYCHIATRIC EXAMINATION.

ORTHOPSYCHIATRY. An approach to mental health, or, as the name implies, "straight-mindedness," "through interdisciplinary treatment before a troubled person's problem becomes severe" (American Orthopsychiatric Association). This collaborative approach is reflected in the membership of the Association, which consists of psychiatrists, psychologists, social workers, sociologists, nurses, educators, and members of related professions.

The American Orthopsychiatric Association was founded in 1923 "to unite and provide a common meeting ground for those engaged in the study and treatment of problems of human behavior," and "to foster research and spread information concerning scientific work in the field of human behavior, including all forms of abnormal behavior." The current membership numbers about 2800, including about 12 fellows. The principal forum of the Association is its annual meeting which revolves around a single major theme, such as orthopsychiatry and the law, mental health programs in underdeveloped countries, and social change in its relation to the underprivileged. In addition, the meeting includes panels and workshops devoted to various clinical areas, such as group therapy, residential treatment, childhood schizophrenia, delinquency, aging, and community psychiatry.

The Association's work is uniquely problem-centered, and its professional committees are therefore grouped around such issues as alternatives to war, minority group problems, psychosocial diagnosis and classification, psychotherapy, and research education. Its official journal, the *American Journal of Orthopsychiatry,* reports current findings in research and therapy, and contains articles on a broad range of mental health topics, but with a heavy emphasis on the child. A representative recent issue, for example, included articles on the training of volunteers to work with the mentally retarded, mental illness among children of blue-collar workers, marriage roles and family treatment, an interview method for assessing alcoholism, and social group work in child guidance.

OSS ASSESSMENT TESTS. A series of personality tests, primarily of the situational type, devised for the selection of candidates for strategic missions during World War II.

When the Office of Strategic Services, the forerunner of today's Central Intelligence Agency, was organized, one of the major problems was that of selecting men to carry on special operations aimed at destroying the morale of enemy troops, organizing and training resistance groups, and gathering information behind enemy lines. The psychologist Henry A. Murray, who had developed the Thematic Apperception Test at Harvard University, was assigned the difficult task of finding a method of choosing the type of person best suited for this kind of assignment. The assessment program which Murray and his staff devised was considered an important contribution not only to the war effort but to personality testing in general.

The investigators adopted the over-all viewpoint of German military psychologists, who believed that observation of behavior on complex tasks involving intellect, emotion, and physical behavior would be more indicative than a study of the candidate's education, employment record, or performance on standard personality or intelligence tests. They therefore constructed a series of situational or "work sample" tests that required the candidates to face stresses, conflicts, and problems of the same general nature as in the situations they would later confront. The program took three days to administer, and during this period a concerted effort was made not only to determine the candidate's performance on the tests, but to evaluate his personality as a whole. This over-all, or "holistic" approach was one of the most unique and successful features of the program.

The first step was to give each candidate a fictitious name to prevent his test mates from identifying his service status or civilian origin. From then on almost everything he did was recorded —the way he greeted the staff, whether he followed or led in informal activities, his actual conversations about subjects that revealed his attitudes, purposes, prejudices, and religious faith. During the three-day period he took many written tests, including aptitude and projective tests, and answered questionnaires designed to elicit information about his life and personality. This material was later analyzed and used to guide the line of questioning which an examiner took in a clinical interview. This part of the process turned out to be one of the most revealing of all the procedures.

The candidate was then given a series of "stress interviews" to discover how well he could withstand extreme intellectual and emotional strain. He was asked, for example, to concoct a story and then defend it against merciless cross-examination while sitting in a ramrod position with a bright light shining in his eyes. To build up further tension, the examiners fired questions and accusations with increasing rapidity, till the candidate was faced with continual harassment from all sides. While he was being questioned, an observer rated his emotional control in terms of flushing, swearing, swallowing, stuttering, and other signs of tension. As soon as the stress interview was over, he was questioned under relaxed conditions in an attempt to lower his guard and break down his story.

The interview tests enabled the examiners to gauge the intellectual resourcefulness, emotional stability, and security consciousness of the subjects. These characteristics were further explored in situational stress tests. One task, labeled the Wall Test, required several candidates to move a heavy eight-foot log, and themselves, over two ten-foot walls separated by a deep imaginary canyon eight feet wide. No leader was assigned to the group, but the staff noted which men took over as leaders and whether leadership shifted from one to another. These observations not only helped them locate "natural" leaders, but gave them insight into the way the men interacted with each other. To obtain an even fuller picture of each individual, the observers also noted their energy level, initiative, and ideas, as well as their reactions when their suggestions were rejected by others.

The candidates were subjected to a number of other situational stress tests. Perhaps the most frustrating was a construction task which required a man to build a five-foot cube with a set of large Tinker Toys within a given period of time. The parts were so big that he was given two assistants, who were actually psychologists secretly trained to needle him and interfere with his completion of the task. The psychologists later made an extensive report on the way the candidate handled the situation.

After the three-day ordeal was over, the examiners pooled their observations, interviews, and test results to produce a final assessment of the candidate. This intensive, holistic approach yielded a massive amount of information and greatly increased the chances of choosing able men. Unfortunately their assignments were so unique and widely separated that no systematic study was made of the validity of the program, but the staff members believed it was basically successful. Moreover, they felt they had developed an approach to personality assessment which could be used in three positive ways: to select personnel for unique or important jobs, to gain further insight into personality dynamics, and to train clinical psychologists and psychiatrists (OSS Assessment Staff, 1948).

Today intensive interviewing for high level positions sometimes takes on characteristics of a stress test, but the more complex situational tests used by the OSS are not administered because of the time, equipment and trained personnel they require. However, a variant of the leaderless group technique known as Leaderless Group Discussion (LGD) is widely applied in the selection of industrial executives, management trainees, military officers, teachers, and social workers. In this procedure a group is assigned a topic for discussion during a specified period, and examiners observe and rate each person's performance. The technique has proved highly effective, since the examiners' ratings have been found to correlate significantly with performance in actual job situations. *See* PERSONNEL SELECTION.

OVERACHIEVER. A student whose academic performance exceeds his ability as measured by intelligence tests.

There are undoubtedly more underachievers than overachievers at every educational level, but the number of overachievers is probably larger than usual today due to parental anxiety about college and the increased competition for college entrance. In general, academic pressure is greatest in middle-income homes, and these families are responsible for the largest number of overachievers. Most of these children are girls, since they are more likely than boys to conform to parental standards. Moreover, academic achievement tends to win more "peer acceptance" among girls than among boys.

Overachievement is sometimes due to special situations, such as the threat of failure or a desire to please a particular teacher. In these cases it is likely to be temporary and limited to a certain subject. Long-term overachievement, on the other hand, generally stems from the home, not the school, and from the inner emotional needs of the child rather than from an incidental external circumstance. These children respond to their parents' prodding (or bribing) by doing their utmost, often because they feel this is the best way of winning approval and love. They may also have underlying fears and insecurities —fear that they may not be able to measure up, or anxiety over losing their parents' affection. Some parents intensify these feelings by making comparisons with other children, including the child's brothers and sisters, or by repeated references to members of the family who failed because they were lazy or unambitious.

It is an interesting and understandable fact that a great many overachievers have been found to be inwardly hostile not only toward their parents but toward the school as well. The reason these children overwork is not that they are basically interested in their studies or even because they have a strong desire to achieve—rather, they work because they fear failure or want to prove their adequacy (which they frequently doubt). The typical overachiever feels guilty if he takes time away from his studies to enjoy himself, and he often antagonizes his classmates because he is so tense, competitive, and eager for success and teacher approval. Like the underachiever, he rarely has a completely satisfying and happy experience in school. See UNDERACHIEVER.

OVERDETERMINATION. The theory that several factors play a role in determining a single reaction; or, more specifically, that a single symptom may serve more than one unconscious need.

The Freudian theory holds that most dreams and neurotic reactions are overdetermined, and for this reason the analyst must probe beyond the first unconscious factors that present themselves. The images that occur in a dream frequently represent two or more impulses—for example, dreaming of the death of a parent may stem from both a latent wish that he might come to harm and a latent fear that this might occur. Similarly, a conversion symptom may serve two or more purposes at once—for example, a violinist who feels unprepared for a concert may suddenly develop a stiff arm. This relieves him of the anxiety involved in making an appearance, excuses him from personal responsibility, and may at the same time help him satisfy an unconscious desire for sympathy and attention. See PRIMARY GAIN, SECONDARY GAIN.

OVERPROTECTION ("Momism"). Every young child needs a great deal of care, attention, and "mothering," and every older child needs help and guidance in meeting the situations of life. The overprotective parent, however, goes too far and turns care into coddling and guidance into domination. She (it is usually but not always the mother) hovers over the child, tries to anticipate his every need, and guards him against every risk. She constantly worries about his health, showers him with excessive physical affection, and becomes oversolicitous at his slightest injury or discomfort. No other interest is allowed to compete with her concern for the child.

The effects of overprotectiveness are clear. The child fails to develop independence because he can never venture out on his own. He becomes timid because he is constantly warned against danger and is permitted to associate only with the quietest and gentlest children. He becomes uncertain and apprehensive because he has not learned to cope with the most ordinary obstacles. And all these characteristics together make it difficult for him to adjust to everyday situations and be accepted by his peers.

Overprotection and overindulgence frequently go together. The parents not only shower the child with care, but with gifts and privileges as well. This combination is particularly devastating, since it not only prevents him from learning to think and act for himself, but encourages him to believe that everything will come his way as a matter of course. Such children are likely to lack emotional control, to be oversensitive to criticism, and to have a low frustration tolerance. They are also afraid of growing up and making their own way in life. In school they usually make extra bids for attention, show little sense of responsibility, and tend to be selfish, spoiled, and socially immature.

Overprotective attitudes arise from many causes. Mothers shower their children with excessive care and attention because they are uncertain and inexperienced, overanxious due to the miscarriage or death of another infant, or unhappy and sexually dissatisfied in their marriages. They may also become overprotective because their child has had a severe illness or suffers from a handicap, because they themselves were emotionally impoverished early in life, or simply because they have a domineering personality. There is also considerable evidence that many parents become overprotective and overindulgent in order to conceal or compensate for feelings of rejection and hostility toward the child. These parents give their children physical care and material advantages in place of genuine affection. *See* MOTHERING.

Illustrative Case: OVERPROTECTION

(Male, 8 years). Excessive Contact: When he was an infant, mother could never leave him for an instant. When he was two years old, she had moods of despondency because she could not get away from him. She feels worried and unhappy when patient is out of her sight. Has been sleeping with him the past six months because he has called her. Lies down with him at night. Extra nursing care has been required because of his frequent colds. Mother says they are attached like Siamese twins.

Prolongation of Infantile Care: Mother dresses him every day (age 8), takes him to school every morning and calls for him every afternoon. When at school in the morning she pays the waiter for his lunch and tells waiter what to give him. Breast-fed 13 months. Mother fed him the first five years. Mother still goes to the bathroom with him and waits for him. Mother insists on holding his hand when they walk together. Resents his walking alone. . . .

Prevention of Independent Character: The mother changed the patient to another school because the walk there was a little shorter. She never allowed him to play with other children because they were rough, until age 8. He is now allowed to play with boys in front of the father's store. Mother hired an older boy to accompany him to school because he complained that the boys molested him.

Maternal Control: Anxious, obedient child. Accepts mother's domination. Accepts mother's infantile methods of discipline without protest. Mother's "slightest disapproval" is very effective in making him mind. He wants to do exactly what the mother does, helps her with the housework, and is overresponsive to her approval or disapproval. (Levy, 1938)

P

PAIN DRIVE (Pain Avoidance). A drive directed to the removal of noxious stimulation.

This basic drive is activated by special sense organs in the form of free nerve endings embedded in the skin, internal organs, and blood vessels. Stimulation of these nerve endings produces sensations of pain via the hypothalamus and reticular formation. The sensations serve as warning signals of possible tissue damage, and whenever possible we react, usually reflexly, by moving away from the source of stimulation. This type of response works reasonably well for external stimuli such as sharp objects, but avoidance of pain is much more difficult when the source is internal. In such cases we may become dependent, and sometimes overdependent, on the use of various drugs, including the usual analgesics for physical distress and the tranquilizers for "psychic pain."

Preoccupation with pain and discomfort is immense, to judge not only by the enormous sale of pain-killing drugs, but by our endlessly repeated expressions "How are you?" "How is your health?" and "Take it easy." Although many of us have been taught in childhood to override minor distress, others have been encouraged by oversolicitous parents to react with anxiety to the slightest discomfort. But in spite of these variations in response, it is an undeniable fact that a continual toothache or headache can make all other activities difficult if not impossible. It also seems true that extreme or annoying pain can generate more compelling motivation than any other drive.

Some psychologists contend that pain motivation is basically different from that of other primary drives such as hunger, thirst, and sex, since it is directed toward the elimination of a source of stimulation rather than toward positive satisfaction. Others, however, point out that elimination of pain or discomfort—a dry throat, for example —is involved in all these drives, and that they are all directed toward survival of the individual or the species. The issue is still under debate. *See* DRIVE REDUCTION THEORY.

Research on the psychology of pain has not advanced as far as research on the physiological mechanisms involved, nor as far as the use of drugs or surgery for relief. The subject is highly complex, and attempts have been made to attack it from a number of angles. First, studies show that pain ordinarily functions well as a warning system, since we can usually report the sensation before we are forced to wince or withdraw. However, large variations in pain sensitivity exist among individuals, and even within the same individual at different times. Organic and social factors may both be involved: a person with a hangover may be driven close to "madness" by sounds he would ordinarily not notice, and a player in a team game or a soldier in combat may be completely unaware of an injury that would ordinarily be excruciating. This point has been put to experimental test: Seidman et al. (1957) found that subjects will tolerate a stronger shock when the experience is presumably shared by a partner than when they are alone. It has also been found that a few people are born with a total inability to feel pain. This is more of an affliction than a blessing since it prevents them from using pain as a warning signal.

Second, there is evidence that the reaction to pain is largely a question of learning and training. Most children do not cry when they first fall, even if they injure themselves; but when their mothers have picked them up and anxiously asked, "Are you hurt?" a few times, they usually learn to wail as if they had been damaged for life. These reactions on the part of the mother, plus constant warnings about getting hurt, encourage the child to feel helpless and to exaggerate his slightest feeling of discomfort. Other parents, however, take the much more sensible course of encouraging a more stoical attitude. This difference in upbringing is one of the major factors that account for the variations in pain response in later life. Interestingly, similar variations can be produced experimentally in animals. Melzack and Scott (1957) have shown that dogs reared in isolation and with a minimum of stimulation did not show the usual emotional response to electric shocks, pin pricks, and even a flame held close to the nose. Pavlov (1927) and Masserman (1943) have also shown that even the physiological responses to painful stimuli such as pulse and respiratory changes can be extinguished by repeatedly pairing an electric shock with a food reward. This indicates that pain responses can be unlearned as well as learned.

Third, psychologists have studied a number of special methods for relieving pain. They have shown experimentally that hypnosis can attenuate the reaction, and have helped to develop its use in childbirth, dentistry, and surgery. They have examined patients who have been subjected to prefrontal lobotomies for the alleviation of continual pain and have found that the sensation is still present, although it does not bring discomfort until attention is directed to it. In other words, the signal is still there but the patient is no longer able to interpret its symbolic meaning as a warning—a form of aphasia known as asymbolia. See APHASIA.

The "placebo effect" has also been the subject of many experiments. Reactions to placebos are an impressive illustration of the power of suggestion, for it has been found that totally inert substances will frequently alleviate pain, provided the subject believes they are drugs that will actually do the job. Suggestion can, of course, produce the opposite effect as well: expectation can double our pain in the dentist's chair. And speaking of dentists, the use of nitrous oxide (laughing gas) lends support to Pavlov's experiment which showed that positive rewards can reduce the sensation of pain, for the gas puts the patient in a pleasant state of mind in which he feels some pain but is not bothered by it. See PLACEBO.

The psychoanalytic theory has added still another dimension to the study of pain. More than any other investigator, Freud made therapists aware of the overwhelming power of "psychic pain." This pain, which he termed anxiety, is a pervasive feeling of uneasiness and impending doom which he believed to stem from early traumatic experiences or unconscious conflicts. To rid himself of this distressing feeling, the individual unconsciously resorts to a wide variety of defensive reactions, the most important of which is repression. Excessive use of these reactions underlies the various forms of neurosis. Since anxiety is basically a feeling of imminent danger, Freud's account of psychological pain conforms closely to the accepted interpretation of physical pain as a warning signal. See DEFENSE MECHANISM, SADISM, MASOCHISM, REPRESSION, ANXIETY.

PAIN SENSE. The sensory mechanism for pain consists of free nerve endings, and the sensation is felt only when a stimulus is strong enough to bring about actual tissue damage. Pain is therefore an indispensable signal that our organism is being injured, though it does not always work perfectly. A severe case of sunburn is one example of the failure of this signaling system.

Pain spots are more numerous than any other sensitivity spots, probably because they are more necessary for survival. They are not evenly distributed, however; the eyelids and neck contain many spots, but the sole of the foot and the ball of the thumb are relatively insensitive because they contain so few pain nerve endings. These facts explain why doctors often draw samples of blood from the thumb, and also why we use the expression "He's a pain in the neck." Pain receptors are poorly developed in our internal organs as compared with the outer surface of the body. The liver, spleen, and kidneys can be cut or burned without causing pain, and certain types of brain operations can be performed without anesthesia. The intense pain we feel when we have a stomach ache probably comes from a pulling or stretching of the tissues.

Pain can be caused by excessive stimulation of many kinds, including intense lights, loud sounds, and extremes of heat or cold, as well as the more obvious sources such as cuts and bruises. There is considerable variation in pain sensitivity from person to person, probably due to constitutional differences, early training, and emotional makeup. There are also rare individuals who are born with no pain sensitivity whatever. These people often suffer severe mishaps, such as seriously burning themselves, because their brain receives no information that the situation has become dangerous. Normal individuals become less sensitive to persistent pain through the process of adaptation. See SENSORY ADAPTATION, CAUSALGIA.

Pain may be felt in other areas than at the point where it originates. Heart disease may be felt as pain in the left arm, kidney trouble in the back and groin, and stomach distress in the abdominal wall. These "referred" pains are caused by the transmission of impulses through groups of nerve fibers that lie close together in the spinal cord. Pain can also be falsely referred to a limb or other body part that has been amputated. See PHANTOM REACTION.

Psychological factors are extremely important in the origin and perception of pain. Anxious, timid, or neurotic people tend to react strongly to a minimum amount of pain. Chronic nervous tension, which these people often experience, causes muscles to contract continually, and these spasms may produce enough pain to bring them to a doctor's office. Physicians often prescribe placebos for conditions of this type. These dummy pills, which the patient believes are drugs, have a purely psychological effect on anxiety and pain, but can often bring as much relief as medications. Unfortunately they are not effective with all patients. See PLACEBO.

Distraction can also be helpful. When we attend to something besides the painful stimulus, pain is diminished or may even disappear. This is why dentists use distraction, often in the form of bad jokes. We are also likely to feel less pain in the dentist's chair if we spend less time anticipating the ordeal. Anxiety over medical tests can make an otherwise neutral situation extremely painful. This is similar to anxiety over illness. We feel acute pain when the nature of the illness is still a mystery, but once a diagnosis is made and we have professional assurance of recovery, our pain reaction is likely to subside.

Most people report that they experience a minimum of pain when they feel they have control over the pain-producing stimulus. For this reason children will often tolerate medication if they are allowed to take it themselves; and most people prefer to extract splinters by themselves rather than have others do it. The same applies to the discomfort of tickling.

The close relationship between fear and pain has been demonstrated by cross-cultural comparisons of reactions to childbirth. In some cultures the woman works in the fields until the hour the child is born, and resumes her work almost immediately afterward (see *The Good Earth,* by Pearl Buck). In our society a woman is taught from childhood on that giving birth is both extremely painful and potentially dangerous. The expression "labor pains" reinforces her fears. The suffering that many women report during delivery may in large part reflect these expectations. The same principle can be applied to common mishaps such as falling and cutting ourselves. These experiences may not be really painful the first time they occur to us as children but, as pointed out in the article "Pain Drive," we may *report* that they were painful merely because an adult expects us to do so and anxiously inquires if we are hurt. In other words, they become painful largely because they are *supposed* to be painful. Pain may "adapt out" slowly for the same reason: we all know that a toothache is supposed to last for a long time, and this may be one reason it does.

These illustrations strongly indicate that suggestion plays an important part in the psychology of pain. This is supported by the fact that we tend to be more anxious when we get a pain in the head or genitals or heart region than in other parts of our body. Our fears, as well as our pain, are undoubtedly heightened by the widely publicized idea that disturbances in these areas may be a serious threat to both mental and physical well-being.

PAIRED ASSOCIATES LEARNING.
A technique for studying learning. Words, syllables, digits, or other items are learned in pairs, and the subject is later tested on his ability to give the second member of the pair when the first is presented. In a typical paired associates experiment, the names of states are paired with colors: Ohio-Red, Delaware-Blue, etc. After they are presented together a number of times, the names of the states are given, and the subject tries to respond with the correct colors. Any two items may be paired in this fashion. To control the exposure time, they are usually presented on a memory drum (PLATE 32).

This type of procedure has two major advantages. First, it is closely related to actual experience, since much of our thinking is a chain of associations, acquired by "serial learning," in which one response becomes a stimulus for the next, as in counting to one hundred, playing a piece of music, or reciting a poem. It is also relevant to more specific tasks, such as learning a foreign language vocabulary, since we pair the new words with their English equivalents. Second, the procedure lends itself to experimental investigation of many aspects of the learning process, particularly proactive inhibition, retroactive inhibition, and transfer of training.

In testing for proactive inhibition, or forward-acting interference, the experimenter attempts to find out whether learning one set of pairs will interfere with the learning of subsequent pairs. Here the subject learns to associate the states with one set of colors, and later with a second set of colors. If the second learning takes longer, as it usually does, it is evidence for proactive inhibition. The subject may then be asked to relearn the first set of associations, and if he takes significantly longer than he did the first time he learned it, this is taken as evidence of retroactive or backward-acting inhibition. *See* FORGETTING, MEMORY IMPROVEMENT.

The object of the transfer of learning tests is to discover whether previous learning can have a positive effect on subsequent learning—for example, whether studying one language helps us with another. A typical experiment consists of learning paired nonsense syllables such as MIR-PED, TEC-ZOX, REQ-KIV, and then learning another list in which the first syllables are changed. Does it help or hinder us if we already know the second syllables? The answer is that it usually helps. However, it has been found that the *amount* of transfer varies with different syllables. If the new syllables are similar to the old ones, the effect is considerably stronger than if they are not similar. This means that an American will probably learn Spanish more easily than Chinese. *See* TRANSFER OF TRAINING.

PANIC. An acute reaction of confusion and terror arising out of a situation of overwhelming danger and threat; complete demoralization characterized by irrational, nonadaptive behavior.

The study of panic presents special problems. Experimentation is virtually impossible since the situations would be dangerous to the participants. Observation is hard to carry out during an actual panic because people involved in the situation are usually too disturbed or distraught to give a completely accurate account of what goes on. Nevertheless, a few objective observations have been made, and there is considerable agreement among psychologists on at least the general features of panic behavior.

A. L. Strauss (1944) has examined the literature on the subject and finds that most authors describe panic in terms of "collective surprise and shock, suggestion, mass imitation, mental contagion, shattering of group bonds, wild flight." He also finds that the following additional features are frequently associated with panic reactions: "hallucinations, heightened imagination, tension, insecurity, uncertainty, confusion,

anxiety, loss of faith in leaders." P. B. Foreman (1953) emphasizes the factor of extremely impulsive action, and the individual's attempt to keep alive regardless of the rules and customs that ordinarily govern behavior. He points out that panic involves a "milling of people which merges into flight when avenues of escape are blocked." He also notes that not all people react with the same type of panic response, since they differ in abilities, prior experiences, and the way they perceive the crisis.

Brown (1965) reports that panic is usually described as an emotional, irrational, and disorderly form of escape or avoidance behavior in which the responses of the individual take "ruthless precedence" over the safety of others. At the same time he finds that "most writers invoke at least one aspect of contagion, such as mimicry, suggestion, and imitative activity." Brown himself gives several examples of the "mental homogeneity" that occurs in the escape group, notably (a) the tendency to stampede for exit, which may result in "collective suicide," as in the disastrous Cocoanut Grove fire in Boston (Veltford and Lee, 1943); (b) the collective self-sacrifice that occurs in marine disasters, when the men herd women and children into lifeboats with no one strong enough to row, while they go down with the ship; (c) the tendency to give aid to others while disregarding one's own wounds, as occurred during the atomic bombings of Hiroshima and Nagasaki (Janis, 1951); and (d) the wave of suicide that occurs when people jump off a sinking ship to certain death.

A variety of conditions can lay the groundwork for panic. In his summary, Strauss points out that exhaustion, previous shock, intoxication, bad health, and poor nourishment frequently set the stage for the heightened emotional tension and tendency to fantasy which most writers believe to be central factors in the etiology of panic. These conditions also lead to physical weakness, which reduces the individual's ability to think and act rationally. Moreover, when people become tense and exhausted, they tend to be highly suggestible, and this stage of mind leads to exaggeration of the threat to life, as well as indiscriminate imitation and mass contagion. This is especially likely to occur when the group lacks a leader or loses faith in its leadership.

As Strauss points out, the above factors fall into three general categories: physiological (fatigue, etc.), psychological (anxiety, etc.), and sociological (lack of group solidarity). He makes the interesting comment that the conditions which produce panic may also give rise to other mass phenomena such as collective fanaticism, collective exaltation, collective heroism, and collective hysteria. He suggests that all these forms of irrational behavior are closely related to each other, since in some situations, such as a battle, there may be a rapid shift from one form to another—for example, from fanaticism to exaltation to panic. It is quite possible that the same causal factors, and the same remedies, apply to all these kinds of collective behavior.

In his review of over fifty incidents of panic, Foreman distinguishes prior and predisposing conditions from immediate causes. Among the former he mentions acute fatigue, worry induced by lack of information, and chronic social unrest due, for example, to wartime rumors of new lethal weapons possessed by the enemy. The precipitating cause of panic, on the other hand, is a shock stimulus linked to the following factors: a sudden interruption of action, a startling perception of crisis, confusion brought about by inability to interpret events reasonably or in terms of prior situations. Situations of this kind are followed by acute feelings of terror, and often by screams, shouts, and excited physical movement that oc-

cur when all attempts to understand and master the situation are blocked. According to Foreman's account, the full state of panic is the product of this entire chain of reactions, and reaches its climax when a group of people are precipitated into flight by the devastating, incomprehensible situation—or in some cases by the rumor that an event which has previously produced panic, such as poison gas, is going to recur.

Brown points out that most writers have not distinguished between panic in unorganized collectivities, as in a theater, and in organized groups such as an army. He quotes La Piere's statement that panic occurs when a group encounters an unexpected danger for which there are no "regimental" responses (1938), and then points out that an army frequently faces such situations without panicking and that preparation for regimental behavior does not always prevent panic from occurring. Brown suggests that the prime factor in the army and other organized groups may be leadership. Many writers, including Freud, have stressed loss of confidence in leaders as a cause of panic. Freud viewed the members of an army as children of the commanding officer, and compared the panic that breaks out when a general deserts or loses his head to the panic experienced by a neurotic when affectional ties are broken. In World War II the Germans emphasized the importance of leadership in preventing panic, since a strong leader gives the group solidarity and a sense of invincible power. This theory was actually based on experiments in which panic was induced in soldiers, civilians, and children to discover how to render storm troopers "panic-proof."

As to unorganized groups Brown cites the conclusion of Mintz (1951), who opposes the idea that panic is caused by intense emotional excitement spreading by contagion and interfering with adaptive behavior. Mintz claims, on the basis of experiments, that it is due to a breakdown of co-operation because of a change in the "reward structure" of the situation. This he explains by pointing out that certain individuals in the group act for their own advantage and interfere with the activities of others, and soon everyone is milling about in terror: "If everyone cooperates in a theater fire and leaves in orderly fashion, a person waiting in line will not be in a position which appears to be sacrificing his interests. But if a minority of people stop cooperating and push and jam the exit, the person waiting in line is put into conflict and would be mistaken to now wait in line."

Brown, however, suggests that the essential problem is that of identifying the minority who *incite* others to panic. He believes that these individuals are probably not antisocial or deficient in co-operative impulses, but tend to be excitable and "panicky." But again, he asks, what makes them more panic-prone than others? He insists that a study of the personality of these individuals is as necessary as the study of the situation itself, but so far no such study has been undertaken.

Many suggestions have been made for the prevention and control of panic. Most investigators put the major emphasis on intelligent leadership. Effective leaders must be capable of inspiring confidence, maintaining discipline, and eliciting co-operation. It has even been suggested that one or more individuals in every establishment such as a theater or restaurant be selected on the basis of personality tests, and then be given special training in techniques for handling emergencies. Some writers also stress the need for training the group itself to respond automatically in critical situations. One simple method is to train children to march to a one-two-three-four command, or to martial music.

Other writers stress the importance of intelligent action, maintaining that people can keep themselves under control if they know what is going on and are informed about their duties in critical situations. This, of course, requires training and preparation for possible disaster, as in fire, lifeboat, and air raid drills. Still others emphasize the desirability of distracting the attention of the group during a threatening situation by such devices as singing, telling jokes, or assigning activities to keep them busy. It is also important to attempt to forestall physical debility —for example, by supplying hot coffee, food, and blankets, by providing conditions for rest and relaxation, and by discouraging the excessive use of alcohol. *See* CIVILIAN CATASTROPHE REACTION, EMERGENCY PSYCHOTHERAPY, MASS BEHAVIOR, MASS HYSTERIA.

PARALOGICAL THINKING (Paralogia). False, illogical thinking found particularly in schizophrenic reactions.

Paralogical thinking may take many forms. A patient who is preoccupied with his own subjective thoughts and fantasies may give answers to questions that are either wrong or beside the point. His interests and attention are narrowed to a point where his thinking becomes restricted and unrealistic. Here is an example: "Is something weighing heavily on your mind?" "Yes, iron is heavy" (Bleuler, 1911). Some patients draw false inferences to protect themselves from the truth. In one case a schizophrenic patient learned that his girl friend, with whom he had never had intercourse, had become pregnant. He immediately concluded that the conception was immaculate, that the girl was the Virgin Mary, and that he himself was God.

Paralogia may also take the form of distorting reality to conform to personal desires or delusional ideas. If a nurse smiles at a schizophrenic patient it may be enough to convince him that she is his mistress. If a paranoid patient sees two people looking his way while conversing, he is apt to conclude that they are talking about him; if he hears a bell ringing he may believe it is summoning him to Judgment.

A special kind of paralogical thinking is sometimes found among prisoners awaiting trial. When they are asked questions of any kind, some of them give false or illogical answers even though they seem to know better. This tendency may stem from an unconscious desire to prove that they are too stupid to be held responsible for their criminal behavior. *See* GANSER SYNDROME.

Paralogical thinking is sometimes described as prelogical or paleological thinking, since the thought processes are similar to those found in children and primitive man. On this theory it represents a regression to the stage in human development when the mind was dominated by feeling and perception rather than by logic and reasoning. One of the major characteristics of such primitive thinking is concreteness. Like a small child, the schizophrenic has difficulty with abstract concepts—for example, if he is asked to give the meaning of the proverb "A new broom sweeps clean," he will say something like "No, it doesn't because the bristles are stiff." A second characteristic is its fallacious, dreamlike logic. In his study of schizophrenic thinking, Bleuler (1911) cited a patient who was convinced that he was Switzerland. Such a thought could not even be entertained by the normal mind—but this patient's thinking followed the line, "Switzerland loves freedom. I love freedom. I am Switzerland."

PARAMNESIA. A falsification or distortion of memory; a confusion of fact with fantasy in recalling events.

We have all experienced some of the "tricks" that memory can play on us. Sometimes we feel we have witnessed an event when we actually read about it in a newspaper or saw it in a newsreel or on television. Many of our so-called memories of early childhood arise in this fashion. Our elders tell us about our behavior at two or three years of age, and we come to believe that we recall this behavior directly. Experiences of this kind are termed simple paramnesia.

Simple paramnesia comes about through a faulty linkage of events. We fuse two or more contents that originally arose at different times or in different contexts. The reasons cannot always be found, but they can sometimes be traced to our emotional reactions. We may feel we have actually witnessed an accident because the newspaper account had a dramatic impact on us or aroused latent fears. Stories of our childhood are usually so pleasant, amusing, or flattering that we adopt them as our own. This is particularly likely to happen if we reinforce them by repeating them to others. In the course of such repetition another form of memory distortion is likely to occur: we unconsciously alter the stories to make them even more entertaining or flattering.

The déjà vu ("already seen") experience is another common form of paramnesia. This is an illusion of recognition or identification in which a new event is experienced with a strong feeling of familiarity. In visiting a small town for the first time we may suddenly have an odd, mystifying feeling that we have been there before. Here, too, there is a convergence or fusion of experiences, but there are several possible explanations of the way it occurs. First, years before, we may have passed through a town with striking features or general characteristics which the present scene resembles. We might also have seen a photograph or motion picture of a similar town. Second, it is possible that just as we entered the town we quickly glanced down the street, but only closely inspected the scene sometime later. The sense of familiarity might therefore be due to that momentary glance. Third, Freud has suggested that the déjà vu experience sometimes comes about through the actualization of a daydream. Before our arrival we may have attempted to picture how the town would look—and this daydream, or a fragment of it, might have been accurate enough to give us the feeling that we have actually been in the town before.

Fourth, the present scene might remind us of a night dream in which we happened to picture a similar town. This might explain the air of mystery that often surrounds these experiences, for they would then be the echo of a dream instead of an actual experience. This explanation is reinforced by the fact that we sometimes wonder whether we dreamed about certain events, or whether they actually happened. Finally, not merely vision but other senses might help to produce the déjà vu reaction. In some cases similar sounds, smells, or even tastes might originate or bolster the feeling that we have gone through the experience before.

Déjà vu experiences have been reported since antiquity. They play an important role in the ancient doctrine of reincarnation, or rebirth after death ("déjà vécu," already lived). The Hindus believed that when we have feelings of familiarity in novel situations, we are actually conjuring up experiences from another life. Plato offered a somewhat similar theory. He believed that our souls have had an opportunity to view basic ideas in a heavenly realm between incarnations, and all knowledge is therefore a "reminiscence" or recollection of these ideas already imprinted on our minds. See PLATO.

A related phenomenon is déjà raconté, the illusion of "already told." When we start to tell a story or describe an incident to a friend, we sometimes have the distinct feeling that we have told him the same thing before.

This form of paramnesia is considered especially significant in psychotherapy. When a patient has such a feeling, it probably means that the material was actually close to being verbalized for some time, but was repressed. The therapist pays special attention to such disclosures, since they may provide a clue to the patient's difficulties.

Paramnesia may also come about through the influence of suggestion. If someone insists that we have made a certain statement or performed a certain action, we may begin to doubt our own minds and perhaps end up with a false memory. This problem frequently arises in legal testimony. It is one reason for ruling out leading questions such as "Wasn't Mr. Smith walking with you at the time?" Any evidence gained from such questions is legally inadmissible. The proper question would be, "Where was Mr. Smith walking at the time?"

Many forms of paramnesia occur in psychiatric disorders. The déjà vu experience is found in schizophrenia, extreme fatigue and intoxication, and in the dreamlike "twilight state" that sometimes occurs in psychomotor epilepsy. In addition, epileptic patients as well as drowning persons may experience the phenomenon of "panoramic memory" in which they feel they are suddenly remembering forgotten stretches of their lives. These patients, as well as schizophrenics, sometimes experience the opposite of déjà vu—that is, jamais vu, a false feeling of unfamiliarity in situations which they have actually gone through. Other forms of paramnesia are discussed elsewhere in this volume, particularly confabulation, in which a senile or Korsakoff's patient fabricates events to fill in memory gaps; and retrospective falsification, in which memories are embroidered with imaginary details to meet unconscious needs. The latter type of falsification occurs in most extreme form among paranoid patients, though, like other kinds of paramnesia, it is frequently found in normal people as well. *See* KORSAKOFF'S SYNDROME, CONFABULATION, FORGETTING, ILLUSION, HYPERMNESIA, TWILIGHT STATE.

PARANOIA. A psychotic disorder marked by slowly developing, systematized delusions of persecution and/or grandeur.

Paranoia is a gross exaggeration of tendencies often found among normal individuals. Many people tend to be slightly suspicious and blame others for their failures, or feel that they have not been given a "fair shake." They cannot accept their lot in life and instead of making constructive attempts to change it, they become envious, bitter, and nurse grievances for fancied injustices. If these tendencies become the dominant pattern of adjustment, the individual may develop a "paranoid personality." This kind of person is hypersensitive, irascible, and feels slighted and resentful at the slightest provocation. In his dealings with other people he is overaggressive, intolerant, and hypercritical, and he usually subscribes to the philosophy of "getting the other fellow before he gets you." Such a person surrounds himself with an armor of arrogance and superiority, and is totally incapable of admitting any defects or weaknesses in himself. Yet the faults he finds in others are usually his own, and his picture of other people is a mirror of himself.

Many paranoid personalities become stabilized and simply remain hostile, mistrustful, self-assertive people who overuse the mechanism of projection. In others, however, these characteristics are gradually and insidiously intensified until they reach a psychotic level characterized by rigid delusions of grandeur or persecution. The question is how and why this happens in some individuals and not in others.

No definite evidence of hereditary or constitutional factors has been found in this disorder. One recent study re-vealed an abnormal amount of psychosis among the relatives of older paranoiacs, but these reactions did not include paranoia. No body type seems to be predominant, nor is there consistent evidence of endocrine disorder, head injury, focal infection, or other conditions causing brain pathology.

Psychological factors of several kinds appear to be responsible for paranoid conditions. Future paranoid patients generally grow up in families where the parents are overbearing, critical, and ambitious. As children they are made to feel that they will not be accepted or loved unless they measure up and prove themselves superior. Under the impact of these excessive pressures, usually reinforced with punishment, they soon become sullen, resentful, and stubborn, and fail to develop warm relationships or normal patterns of play with other children. Attitudes of superiority and arrogance, taken over from their parents, further interfere with their social relationships. As a result, they are not accepted by their peers, and, instead of becoming more friendly and congenial, they become aloof and isolated. Instead of realizing that they are being rejected because of their own attitudes, they become increasingly hostile, suspicious, and sensitive to unintentional slights. As they grow older, they become even more aggressive, humorless, and domineering, constantly finding fault with others and demanding recognition for themselves.

The paranoiac's outward air of superiority is actually a cover for inward feelings of inadequacy. He betrays his inner doubt through his oversensitivity to criticism, craving for praise, and overzealous performance in most activities. The origin of the inadequacy feelings usually becomes apparent when the full case history is known. The paranoid individual has so frequently failed to live up to expectations, has been so severely criticized in his early life, has antagonized so many people, and has experienced so many rebuffs that he is haunted by a sense of failure. Nevertheless he is totally unaware that he is reacting to feelings of inadequacy and disappointment in himself.

Instead of looking inward to find the source of his difficulty, he protects himself from intolerable feelings of failure, and at the same time expresses his intense feelings of hostility, by falling back on his usual pattern of blaming others for everything that happens. The more he does so, the more problems he generates. His aggressive attitudes arouse the anger and resentment of other people, and this in turn feeds the fires of his own hostility. This "self-perpetuating cycle" continues until he loses friend after friend and job after job.

As his problems multiply, so do his defensive reactions. He becomes increasingly sensitive to any hint of criticism, begins to feel that others are talking about him behind his back, and searches for hidden meanings in glances and gestures. Next, he gets the idea that others are actively working against him, and out of this feeling he gradually builds a rigid and elaborate delusional system. This system is usually limited to one area of his life—job, marriage, etc.—but within that area it increasingly dominates his mind. He comes to see himself surrounded by a "pseudo-community" of real or imaginary persons who are organized for the sole purpose of conspiring against him. He then uses his intellectual ability —which is usually above average—to "prove" that its spies are everywhere, and ingeniously finds "evidence" that they are tampering with his mail, spreading lies about him, thwarting his plans, and stealing his ideas. Anyone who points out evidence to the contrary is immediately under suspicion himself.

The delusional system, then, usually takes a persecutory form; but it is frequently accompanied by grandiose ideas. The delusions of grandeur originate not only from the paranoid individual's long-ingrained attitudes of superiority, but from the feeling that he must be an extremely important person if so many enemies spend their time conspiring against him. The content of these delusions varies, but he always sees himself as the champion of good and his enemies as the incarnation of evil. *See* DELUSION, GRANDIOSE DELUSIONS.

The delusions of a paranoiac may center around many different areas of life, and at one time a great deal of attention was paid to classifying the various types. The "litigious type," for example, is constantly in court defending his rights or seeking redress for exaggerated or fancied wrongs. The "erotic type" is certain that a woman of great wealth and position is in love with him, and inevitably finds disguised evidence of requited affection in newspaper photographs or even the flight of birds. The "exalted type" may claim to have invented a device that will halt all wars, or may form a new religious sect and parade in flowing garments and equally flowing hair. Attempts to categorize all types of delusions have been found fruitless, however, since they take almost any form. More important is the fact that each delusion has a central theme, and the individual appears fairly normal and well adjusted in other respects.

Still more important are the dynamics behind the development of the delusion. Research has provided some confirmation for a theory suggested by Freud, that faulty sexual attitudes or homosexual tendencies contribute to the development of paranoia (Rosen and Kiene, 1946). Many paranoiacs have been subjected to rigid, prudish ideas about sex during childhood, and show evidence of severe sexual maladjustment in adult life. Because of their distorted sexuality as well as their difficult personalities, few of them get married, and those who do marry usually become unsatisfactory mates. One of their most disturbing patterns is extreme jealousy, and many specialists believe that this feeling may originate in homosexual tendencies and is a reflection of their own desires toward the fancied rival or toward other members of their own sex. Similarly, the delusion of being persecuted by others is sometimes interpreted as a projection of their own defensive hatred aroused by guilty homosexual feelings: "I love him" becomes "I do not love him" or "I hate him," and this unacceptable feeling is transformed into "He hates me" and then "I am persecuted by him." Erotic delusions are also interpreted as denials of homosexual impulses: "I do not love him—I love her" becomes, by projection, "She loves me." Grandiose delusions are still another way of denying these impulses: "I do not love him—in fact, I do not love anyone but myself." These mechanisms are attributed to female as well as male paranoiacs.

The sexual interpretations, however, probably apply to only a limited number of cases. Most authorities today believe that the fundamental source of paranoia lies, as suggested above, in unconscious and unbearable feelings of dissatisfaction and inferiority growing out of failure to meet the goals set by the parents, as well as out of an inability to gain acceptance from peers. The paranoid individual, in a word, cannot accept disappointment in himself, and reacts by developing fictions of superiority and by blaming his shortcomings on the machinations of others.

In contrast to paranoid states, "true" paranoia does not clear up by itself, and no adequate treatment has been found. Some psychiatrists advocate keeping patients in the community unless their behavior is disturbing or dangerous, since confinement in a hospital may arouse further resentment and extend their delusional system. Tranquil-izers are sometimes helpful in relieving tension and anxiety, and in some cases they may open the way to psychotherapy. Electroshock therapy may also be tried in an attempt to break up the delusional system and render the patient accessible to a psychological approach. In psychotherapy, however, great care must be taken to steer a midline between directly challenging the patient's delusions and reinforcing them by implying agreement. Some patients become fairly co-operative in exploring their difficulties and considering alternative explanations for their delusional ideas. This approach occasionally leads to recovery, but more often merely reduces the hold which the delusions have on the patient, or makes him more reserved in expressing them. Some of these patients can be released from the hospital. In many cases, however, facilities for psychotherapy are lacking, or the treatment is ineffective, and they must remain in the hospital. They are frequently the most difficult of all patients because of their attitudes of superiority toward others, and their belief that treatment is simply another form of persecution by their enemies. *See* PARANOID STATES, SCHIZOPHRENIA (PARANOID TYPE).

Illustrative Case: PARANOIA

A typical case is that of a forty-one-year-old white male, who came to the hospital because he annoyed the officers of a trust company. He was a quiet, serious, intent person. He had always been a brilliant student, had started to work early, and had worked himself up in the banking business. He was married but did not get along well with his wife. He stated that she resented his interest in his mother. He was divorced in 1925, and soon after resigned from the bank in which he worked. He was a person of good habits and had not been in any previous difficulty. The patient developed the idea after resignation from the bank that a wealthy businessman who had obtained him his job in the bank had established a large trust fund with the company for which he worked, and that this trust fund was for his benefit. He believed that the trust company had worked various swindles against him in order to deprive him of his rights. He met objections to the validity of his contentions rather cleverly and pointed out that the daily newspapers contained items that should make us realize that financiers are not always men of integrity, and that in these times a bank is not at all anxious to lose control of a large sum of money. If pressed further, he would smile and say with dignity that there was no reason for him to discuss his private affairs. When asked about hallucinations or other false beliefs, the patient would become indignant and say that these would be signs of a mental illness. The patient refused treatment and was not again seen. In this case his whole line of reasoning was entirely logical, except for the fact that there was no fund in the trust company for him, and the fact that he justified his suspicion of the head of this particular bank by reading accounts of embezzlements by clerks, cashiers, etc., of other banks in various parts of the country. This was coupled with a rigid, meticulous, rather dignified mien and a history of marital difficulties. (Ewalt, Strecker, and Ebaugh, 1957)

PARANOID REACTION (GENERAL).

A psychotic reaction marked by more or less systematized delusions without personality disorganization or deterioration. The term was first applied to persecutory and grandoise states by Karl Ludwig Kahlbaum in 1863, and became a separate clinical entity through the work of Emil Kraepelin. It derives from the Greek words "para" (beside, in the sense of change) and "nous" (intellect, reason), and was originally used to designate mental disorder in general.

Two types of paranoid reactions are currently distinguished. In *paranoia* ("true paranoia"), the delusions develop insidiously and gradually crystallize into an intricate, rigid, and logical system. Hallucinations are usually absent, and delusions of persecution and/or grandeur dominate a relatively intact personality that appears normal in other respects. In *paranoid states* the delu-

sions are transient, less systematic and logical, and are sometimes accompanied by hallucinations.

Paranoid reactions comprise less than 1 per cent of all first admissions, but hospital statistics do not reflect their actual incidence, since many paranoiacs can exercise enough self-control to avoid commitment. They probably constitute a large proportion of the cranks, bigots, self-appointed saviors, fanatical reformers, and chronic litigants in our population. At present the male-female ratio is about equal, though these disorders were at one time more common among men. The average age at first admission is fifty, with most cases ranging from twenty-five to sixty-five. Their intellectual and educational level is usually above average. *See* PARANOIA, PARANOID STATES, SCHIZOPHRENIA (PARANOID TYPE), FOLIE À DEUX.

PARANOID STATES.

A psychotic disorder characterized by transient, poorly systematized delusions.

Paranoid states appear to be intermediate between "true" paranoia and paranoid schizophrenia. The delusions are usually persecutory in nature, but are less systematized, clear-cut, and elaborate than those in paranoia. At times they may be accompanied by hallucinations. Other thought processes may also be disturbed, and the patient may be less coherent and logical than the paranoiac. On the other hand, his thinking is not bizarre, fragmentary, or disorganized, and he is not thoroughly out of touch with reality, as are patients afflicted with paranoid schizophrenia. Kraepelin used the term "paraphrenia" to designate this type of reaction, but this term is not in use today.

The background and dynamics of paranoid states are similar to those in paranoia, but instead of a gradual and insidious development of symptoms, there is usually a fairly sudden onset following a traumatic experience or a period of overwhelming emotional stress. Though occasionally chronic, most of these cases are transient and clear up spontaneously after a few days or weeks. Psychotropic drugs are now used to reduce the severity of the symptoms and hasten recovery. The patient may also receive brief psychotherapy to prevent a recurrence.

PARAPHASIA. A speech disturbance in which incorrect, distorted, or inappropriate words are used.

Paraphasia may be one of the many forms of aphasia, in which language defects occur as a result of brain defect or injury. It is sometimes observed in Pick's disease and Alzheimer's disease, and is occasionally associated with epilepsy. It may also be a stress reaction and therefore psychological in origin. One of the more common forms occurs in hospital patients who have difficulty adapting themselves to the fact of illness. Weinstein and Kahn (1959) point out that some patients habitually misname objects related to their hospitalization: a hypodermic needle becomes a "tie pin," a head bandage is a "turban," a wheelchair is a "spinning wheel." Sometimes the name expresses their feelings about themselves —for example, an electronics engineer called an electric light bulb a "used-up radio tube."

The use of incorrect but related words is not uncommon in schizophrenia, and is usually termed metonymy rather than paraphasia. One patient, for example, referred to losing the "piece of string" instead of the "thread" of his conversation. Such expressions are not mere figures of speech or attempts at humor, since these patients are usually completely unaware of any error and continue to use them even after they have been corrected. *See* PARALOGICAL THINKING.

PARAPRAXIS (literally, "misaction"). A behavioral error or lapse due to unconscious motivation, such as a revealing slip of the tongue, pen, or memory, mislaying of an object, an unintentional pun, or a "purposive" accident.

Freud was the first to make any extensive study of parapraxes, and published his findings in a popular book, *The Psychopathology of Everyday Life* (1904). He interpreted these common occurrences along psychoanalytic lines and offered them as evidence of the influence of unconscious wishes, feelings, and drives on ordinary behavior. According to his theory, the psyche automatically erects defenses against unacceptable or threatening impulses, but occasionally these impulses break through and express themselves in the form of "symptomatic acts." He therefore suggested that one way of discovering the unconscious factors that motivate an individual would be to study the errors he makes in his actions or conversation. In keeping with his general technique, he sought to interpret them through free association. However, the analysis of parapraxes did not become a major feature of psychoanalysis, for he felt that dreams and fantasies provided a more fruitful and dependable avenue to the unconscious. He simply made use of them if they happened to turn up.

Practically all of us commit unconscious errors at one time or another. We distort or forget the names of people we dislike. We make faux pas at parties, lose articles that have unpleasant associations, trip as we enter an office where we expect to be "put on the carpet." We reveal ourselves by misspelling words (erotic for erratic), by failing to recognize people we ought to remember, or by making "Freudian slips" in our conversation. A classic example is the remark made by an admirer of Theodore Roosevelt, whose campaign motto was "A square deal." At a supper party where no one got enough to eat, the guests were discussing Roosevelt's policies, when this man injected the comment, "You can say what you please about Teddy, but there is one thing he can always be relied upon to do. He'll always give you a square meal." *See* PSYCHOANALYSIS (THERAPY), MOTIVATION (GENERAL).

PARATAXIC DISTORTION (literally, parataxis means abnormal arrangement or response). A term applied by H. S. Sullivan to the tendency to distort perception and judgment, particularly in interpersonal relationships, as a result of a pattern set by earlier experiences.

The pattern in question arises primarily out of the young child's relationships with his parents. If, for example, he has been rejected, treated coldly, or criticized too much, he develops an exaggerated sense of unworthiness, a large "bad-me" and a small "good-me," to use Sullivan's terms. As this child matures, he interprets other people's remarks and attitudes in the light of these earlier conceptions of himself. These misinterpretations, or "parataxic distortions of experience," prevent him from developing patterns of response that will eliminate his feelings of anxiety. They also lead him to overuse protective measures, or dynamisms, such as ignoring or separating himself from sources of disturbance. As a consequence he may develop neurotic or even psychotic reactions, such as withdrawal from all interpersonal relationships into an autistic world of his own making.

In Sullivan's view the early patterns are not completely rigid, for they may be consciously or unconsciously modified by later experiences. If this does not occur, and they continue to dominate the personality, psychotherapy may be required. In this process, the therapist helps the patient recognize his distorted thoughts and feelings by comparing them with the evaluations of others, a process Sullivan termed "consensual validation." The major force that encourages the patient to modify his irrational tendencies is the interpersonal relationship he establishes with the therapist. *See* SULLIVAN.

PARATHYROID GLANDS. Two pairs of small endocrine glands adjacent to the thyroid gland in the neck, which regulate calcium metabolism and maintain the normal excitability of the nervous system.

The parathyroid glands secrete parathormone, which controls the body's calcium-phosphorus balance. If the parathormone level is high, the calcium level is high and the phosphorus level low, and vice versa. This mechanism indirectly controls the amount of calcium deposited in bone as well as the functioning of the nervous system, since a low blood calcium level increases the irritability of nervous tissue. This means that if the gland does not produce enough hormone, the muscles begin to twitch and the reflexes are hypersensitive—and if the deficiency is severe the patient becomes afflicted with general tetany, muscle cramps, convulsions and emotional lability. *See* HYPOCALCEMIA.

PARERGASIA. This term, which literally means "perverted functioning," was employed by both Emil Kraepelin and Adolf Meyer. In his *Textbook of Psychiatry* (1927), Kraepelin applied it to a form of parabulia (disturbance of volition or will) in which a patient's impulse to perform an act is interrupted by what he called cross impulses. For example, if he starts to reach for a cup he may abruptly brush his hand through his hair instead; and if he then grasps the cup, he may fling it away instead of putting it to his mouth. Another term for this type of response is derailment of volition. *See* ABULIA.

Adolf Meyer used the term in a broader sense, as a replacement for dementia praecox. He believed this disorder could be best understood in terms of disorganization of behavior resulting from progressive maladjustment—that is, "a substitution of inefficient and faulty attempts to avoid difficulties rather than to meet them by decisive action." He applied the term parergasia to these disorganized reactions to emphasize their distorted character.

Meyer (1951) described parergasic reactions as "twists and fundamental or fancy-born incongruities more or less foreign to average, mature waking life . . . Disturbances developing in particular constitutional types and expressed in vague autistic fancy, projections, passivity, paranoid systematization, formal disorders of language and behavior, incongruity of affect and motivity disturbances." The term was never generally adopted, and the term dementia praecox was replaced by schizophrenia instead. Nevertheless Meyer's emphasis on personality disorganization is considered a major contribution to the understanding of this disorder.

PARKINSON'S DISEASE. A chronic degenerative disease of the central nervous system, usually occurring between the ages of fifty and seventy. Atrophy takes place primarily in the thalamus, basal ganglia, and reticulating activating system, all of which are concerned with motor control.

Initial symptoms are usually rigidity and tremor in the muscles of one arm, gradually spreading to the leg on the same side of the body, then to the neck and face, and finally to the limbs on the other side. In time the face becomes masklike, speech grows halting and indistinct, and there is usually a tendency to lean stiffly forward and walk at a half run. This is called a "festinating gait," a term derived from an archaic word for "hurry." There is little or no effect on intelligence, but the patient may develop psychological symptoms which result from his reaction to the disease. These usually include apathy and inactivity, social withdrawal, and inability to concentrate and maintain intellectual interest.

There are an estimated half million cases of Parkinson's in this country. The cause of the disease is unknown, although one type is associated with arteriosclerosis. Spellman (1962) has found indications of inherited metabolic defects in a small percentage of cases, but most studies of the disease point toward an acquired deficiency in brain metabolism, possibly caused by a virus that attacks nerve cells leading to the motor cortex. Parkinsonian symptoms may also result from epidemic encephalitis, carbon monoxide poisoning, and brain tumors.

No treatment yet devised is completely effective. Early detection, however, is essential, since antispasmodic and muscle relaxant drugs can be used to relieve rigidity and tremors, and psychotherapy is often effective in controlling the psychological reactions. Recently surgical methods have been developed which have been successful in arresting the progress of the disorder in about 90 per cent of the cases. In one technique, defective cells in the thalamus (which switches impulses to the brain's motor centers) are destroyed by carefully dripping a freezing solution into the affected area (cryosurgery). *See* BRAIN DISORDERS.

PASSIVE-AGGRESSIVE PERSONALITY. A personality trait disturbance characterized by immaturity and failure to develop an adequate balance between dependence and independence, and between aggressiveness and submissiveness.

This failure may be exhibited in three ways. In the *passive-dependent reaction type,* the individual is timid, helpless, and totally lacking in self-confidence. He is "afraid of his own shadow," constantly requires reassurance, and depends on others to make his decisions. These individuals were generally raised by dominant parents, and reacted by repressing their resentment and becoming oversubmissive. In adulthood they still avoid all open expression of anger or aggression, but gain an unconscious outlet for their hostile impulses by making excessive demands and forcing others to take responsibility for them.

In the *passive-aggressive reaction type,* hostile urges are closer to the surface and are expressed in a sullen, disgruntled attitude and actions that obstruct the wishes of others. These are the people who frustrate their associates by postponing decisions, constantly raising objections, or taking ineffective action. In some cases their hostility is more open and they become chronic complainers. These behavior patterns can sometimes be traced to childhood—in particular, to suppressed anger against an overdemanding and overcritical father.

In the *actively aggressive type,* resentment is directly on the surface, and the individual has a constant chip on his shoulder. In response to frustration of any kind he becomes irritated, openly hostile, and sometimes violent. Even without provocation, these individuals may express their aggressiveness in caustic remarks, lengthy arguments, or cutthroat competition. They rebel against the authority of others, yet often try to assume unwarranted authority themselves. If they succeed in attaining a position of even slight power, they are likely to overreach themselves and in some cases develop grandiose fantasies. Most of them show an early history of open hostility toward the father, with strong dependence underneath. Their aggressiveness in adulthood is usually interpreted as an extreme reaction to unconscious feelings of dependency. *See* PERSONALITY TRAIT DISTURBANCE.

Illustrative Case: PASSIVE-AGGRESSIVE PERSONALITY

The parents of this ten-year-old boy requested their pediatrician to refer them to a psychiatrist. They felt that their home life had become chronically unhappy and frequently disrupted by the obstinate characteristics of their son. On initial interview they reported that he was a marked underachiever in school in spite of a superior intelligence. He seemed to avoid every task that was given him both in school and at home. There were short periods where he seemed happy and contented, but most of the time he obviously was not. While he was not considered to be an aggressive behavior problem either by his parents or by his teacher, as his mother put it, "He drives us all to distraction." One of the biggest difficulties in family life occurred with the parents' attempts to help the boy do his homework. These evening sessions stretched to as long as two hours, during which the parents became increasingly exasperated while the boy produced little in the way of accomplishment.

The parents were highly intellectual, well-educated people who had devoted a great deal of energy to their child's rapid progression through new accomplishments. They were rather worrisome people who placed excessive demands upon both themselves and their child. During his preschool years they were unaware that he was developing a passive-rebellious syndrome, but after he entered school, the first structured situation in his life, it became increasingly evident that he was unable to accept any authority.

This child's treatment entailed work with both parents and the boy. The parents were encouraged to remove themselves from the homework situation and other similar situations which could be either ignored or delegated to some other authority. They were helped to relax their own goals for him and to be accepting of more ordinary childish behavior from their son. At the same time the boy was helped to understand some of his own needs to resist authority in all forms. He had grown sufficiently unhappy with his over-all adjustment that he was a reasonably willing candidate for assistance. Within a period of about six months, during which he was seen weekly, he began to make academic gains with the help of an outside tutor, and his parents began to relax their demands upon him. The number of conflicts within the household diminished, and family life in general was much happier. The child still presented many passive-aggressive features, but these were rapidly diminishing. (English and Finch, 1964)

PASTORAL COUNSELING. Counseling offered by a pastor, chaplain, or other religious worker, and designed to integrate spiritual values with a psychological approach.

Pastoral counseling can be traced back to the prophets, priests, and medicine men in man's early cultures. Like them, the modern counselor serves as a guide and advisor on the problems of life. But unlike them, he bases his practice not only on religious beliefs, but on information and skills derived from psychology, psychiatry, social work, and other "helping professions." The first person to recognize the need for special preparation for this work was Anton Boisen, who became the first clinically trained chaplain at a mental hospital (Worcester State), and inaugurated the first program of supervised clinical training for pastors at a mental hospital in 1925. A decade later a physician, R. Cabot and a pastor, R. Dicks introduced seminars on pastoral care of the physically ill in Massachusetts General Hospital. These first steps, taken by Protestants, were followed by the development of training programs by Jews and Roman Catholics. Today the major seminaries of all faiths offer courses in pastoral counseling, usually supplemented by workshops, institutes, and clinical experience in mental hospitals, clinics, prisons, or residential treatment centers for children and adolescents.

The trained pastoral counselor carries on his work in conjunction with his duties as clergyman in a religious institution; as chaplain in a hospital, correctional institution, or the armed services; or as a member of the staff of an independent counseling center organized by representatives of a religious faith. In general, he deals with personal problems of a social, emotional, or religious nature which tend to be of a less deviant character than those handled by psychiatrists. The bulk of these problems have to do with marriage, child-rearing, grief, physical illness and suffering, guilt over moral transgressions, and questions of religious belief. In addition, each denomination has its own special problems—for example, a Roman Catholic may become deeply concerned if he does not gain relief from feelings of guilt through confession and absolution; a Jew may be troubled by questions concerning his identity, intermarriage, or changing religious practices; a Protestant may be assailed with guilt because he leads too worldly a life or is unable to fulfill the Scriptural command to forgive and love all men.

In his approach to these problems, the pastoral counselor calls upon the psychological insight and interviewing skills he has acquired during his training, but combines them with a religiously inspired approach. He does not attempt to delve into the unconscious or uncover repressed experiences, but focuses on the individual's present need for emotional relief, personal guidance, and spiritual sustenance. These needs may take a different form in different settings: the convict may seek strength to resist temptation when he is freed; the delinquent adolescent may need sexual guidance or help in finding an occupational interest; the institutionalized patient may feel isolated from humanity, or may be obsessed with religious thoughts which he does not understand. And an ever-increasing number of average, normal people not only need help in solving personal difficulties but in finding a meaning for their lives. *See* EXISTENTIALISM.

Though the approaches of pastoral counselors differ widely, they tend to have a number of general characteristics in common. As Loomis (1963) points out, all pastoral counselors (1) accept the person as he is no matter how deeply disturbed or degraded he may be; (2) serve as representatives of God and of their denomination, and expect the client to accept their religious role; (3) allay feelings of guilt not only through emotional catharsis but through the channels of forgiveness provided by their faith; (4) attempt to restore the individual to sounder relationships with others through a sense of spiritual fellowship; and (5) help him achieve a new integration of values—social, emotional, and spiritual—through the medium of his faith.

Pastoral counseling is a developing field. Some of the major current trends are the following: (a) closer co-operation between clergymen and other professions dealing with human problems, especially through the inclusion of clergymen on the staff of mental health centers, clinics, and community councils; (b) increased recognition by psychiatry of the value of pastoral counseling as an approach to problems, as a form of supportive therapy, and as a source of valuable psychological data; (c) establishment of pastoral counseling centers or clinics in which troubled persons receive counseling and candidates receive training; (d) development of group pastoral counseling dealing with teen-age problems, preparation for marriage, parent guidance, and difficulties faced by the aging members of the congregation; (e) certification of pastoral counselors by such bodies as the Council for Clinical Training and the Institute of Pastoral Care; (f) greater exchange of ideas among pastoral counselors through such publications as *Pastoral Psychology* and *Pastoral Counseling;* and (g) increased awareness of the role of the religious institution itself in maintaining mental health by providing its members with emotional security, a sense of personal identity, continuity with a heritage, a feeling of belonging, and a wider perspective on human existence.

PATHOGNOMONIC. This term, meaning "indicative of a disease," is used in both physical medicine and psychiatry. It is usually applied to a symptom or group of symptoms that is considered characteristic or diagnostic of a specific disorder. The group or "constellation" of symptoms is called a syndrome. The term "pathognomonic signs" is frequently used, particularly in Rorschach testing, where it is applied to responses which seem to be indicative of a certain disorder.

PATHOLOGICAL   INTOXICATION. An acute psychotic episode occurring in (1) individuals whose tolerance for alcohol is low due to an unstable personality or epileptic tendencies, and (2) relatively normal individuals who drink after being subjected to prolonged stress, debilitating illness, or an exhausting experience. The disorder is also known as mania a potu, "madness from drink."

The onset of the disturbance is sudden and may even follow moderate drinking. The patient becomes confused and disoriented, and experiences hallucinations which lead to impulsive acts or outright violence. Some cases of this kind are probably instances of epileptic furor: "There is an increasing tendency to consider that such episodes with their disturbances of consciousness and perhaps crimes of violence are really instances of psychomotor epilepsy released by alcohol in persons predisposed to such seizures" (Noyes and Kolb, 1963). In one study (Binswanger, 1935), 26 out of 174 patients had been charged with such crimes as manslaughter, arson, and sexual assault. The disturbance lasts for a few minutes to a day or more, followed by prolonged sleep. There is a complete amnesia for the episode. *See* FUROR.

Treatment is essentially the same as for other cases of acute alcoholism: a restful environment, enriched diet, sweetened fruit juice, and the tranquilizer, chlorpromazine.

Illustrative Case: PATHOLOGICAL INTOX-
ICATION

N.W., aged twenty-eight, was seen in jail while awaiting trial on a charge of drunkenness and disorderly conduct. The patient's father had committed suicide as he was about to be sent to a hospital for mental diseases. The patient himself was described as being a friendly but quick-tempered and restless individual whose marriage had terminated in early divorce. He was said never to have been particularly alcoholic, but on one July 4 he celebrated the holiday by drinking two bottles of beer and a glass of wine. Soon afterward he attempted to fling himself down an eighty-foot embankment and was so greatly excited that he was taken to the police station for the night. The next morning he had no recollection of the affair.

Ten months later the patient called late one afternoon to see friends, who invited him to sample what they considered choice varieties of whiskey and gin. He accepted their invitation and drank somewhat more heavily than usual. Soon after leaving the home of his friends he was observed by a police officer to be acting strangely. As the officer spoke to him he attacked him. While the officer was calling for help, the patient disappeared. About fifteen minutes later two women were startled to see a strange man thrust his head through a closed window of their living room and shout, "Help! Murder!" It was the patient, who then ran on to another house, where he rang the doorbell insistently. As the occupant answered the summons he again screamed, "Murder!" and ran to the street once more, where he broke the windshields and headlights of several parked automobiles and tore out the seats and pulled parts from other cars. At this point he was seized and taken to the police station where, on awakening the following morning, he had no recollection of his experiences of the previous night. (Noyes and Kolb, 1963)

PAVLOV, IVAN PETROVICH (1849–1936).

Pavlov, the discoverer of the conditioned reflex, was the son of a priest attached to a church in Ryazan, Russia. He started to follow in his father's footsteps by attending a theological seminary (1866–70), but became interested in science after reading J. M. Secherov's *Reflexes of the Brain,* and decided to attend St. Petersburg University. While there he studied under a number of famous men, including the physicist D. I. Mendeleyev, the chemist Alexander Butlerov, and the physiologist I. F. Tyson, who aroused his interest in the study of the central nervous system. After receiving his medical degree in 1883, he traveled and studied in Europe, and in 1890 was appointed to the chair of pharmacology at the Military Medical Academy.

Pavlov's first major interest was in the physiology of digestion. His work on this problem began in Europe when he and Heidenhain discovered the nerves governing pancreatic secretion. He continued his investigation in the physiology department at the Institute of Experimental Medicine in Leningrad, which he organized in 1890 and directed for the rest of his life. In this work he introduced what has been called the "chronic method," a procedure in which dogs were trained to lie quietly on the operating table without anesthesia while experiments were being performed. In this "natural" setting he found that the nervous system co-ordinates digestive activities through reflex regulation of the organs involved. His findings were published in his only book, *Work of the Digestive Glands* (1897).

Pavlov is most widely known for his studies of conditioning, which were an outgrowth of his work on digestion. He noticed that gastric and salivary secretions occurred in his dogs when they heard the rattling of dishes or the footsteps of his assistant as he prepared food to be used in an experiment. For a long time he ignored these reactions, which he called "psychic stimulations," since his sole interest was in physiology. But when they began to interfere with his investigations of the digestive system, he finally decided to study them systematically. This work

930

was initiated in 1901, and he thought it would take him only a year or two, but shortly before his death thirty-five years later he remarked that his investigations of what he called the "science of higher nervous activity" had just begun.

Pavlov's lectures and papers on the subject of conditioning were published in English translation in three volumes, *Conditioned Reflexes* (1927), *Lectures on Conditioned Reflexes* (1928), and *Conditioned Reflexes in Psychiatry* (1941). His theories, however, came to the attention of American scientists long before these volumes appeared, through an article by Yerkes and Margulis in the *Psychological Bulletin* in 1909. Since his discoveries are described in the present volume under other headings, especially under CONDITIONING, only his general approach will be outlined here.

Pavlov's orientation was strictly physiological. He used the secretion of the salivary gland in his experiments because this was the easiest way to measure the effects of psychic, or sensory, stimulation that occurred at a distance. He found that if a tuning fork was sounded simultaneously with the presentation of meat powder, and if this was repeated a number of times, the unlearned or "unconditioned" response of salivation could be produced by the tuning fork alone. He called this newly established response a "conditioned reflex," since it was conditional upon the fact that the new stimulus was presented along with a stimulus that had originally been effective in producing it. His early work focused on such questions as the number of repetitions and the optimal time intervals needed to bring about conditioning, as well as the inhibition and extinction of the response. He also discovered that the method could be used to test an animal's ability to discriminate between different stimuli, such as tones of 508 versus 512 cycles.

The experiments on discrimination led Pavlov to an investigation of the production and elimination of "experimental neuroses" in animals. The first step was to condition an animal to respond to a circle of light and not to respond to an ellipse. After this he systematically varied the shape of the ellipse to make it more and more circular. This procedure, according to Pavlov, overtaxes the discriminatory powers of the animal and it becomes confused, negativistic, anxious—in other words, neurotic. Further experiments showed that rest, retraining, and drugs could be used effectively in clearing up the condition. *See* EXPERIMENTAL NEUROSIS.

This discovery convinced Pavlov that functional illness could be remedied through therapy, and in time his approach was applied to human beings. The basis of this treatment, which is now widely used in Communist countries, is Pavlov's theory that neurosis is due to an imbalance in the excitatory and inhibitory functions of the cerebral cortex, an imbalance that is produced by overburdening the nervous system. The major techniques are prolonged sleep treatment to allow the nerve cells to recover from fatigue, the use of sedative and tranquilizing drugs, verbal psychotherapy, as well as educational and environmental reorientation. *See* SLEEP TREATMENT.

These studies of the functioning of the human nervous system introduced a new element which his original studies of animals had not uncovered. He had found that there are only two sources of higher nervous activity in animals: the unconditioned reflex system, which governs inborn reaction patterns to certain stimuli—for example, salivation at the sight of food; and the sensory conditioning system, or "first signaling system," which enables the organism to adapt to changes in its environment—for example, a deer learns through conditioning to react by fleeing when he merely sees the track or receives the scent of a predatory animal. The latter process "ties" the original unconditioned reflex to particular environmental signals that are important for survival. Man, according to Pavlov, possesses both of these systems, but has a "second signaling system" in addition. The core of this system is language, which makes possible such processes as thought before action and generalization from experience. However, if this system loses control over the other two systems, for whatever reason (and Pavlov was relatively uninterested in the reasons), a dissociation of systems occurs and efforts must be made to restore the balance through therapy.

Pavlov became a celebrated figure in his own time, and his influence on psychology has been extremely widespread. His work on the digestive system won him the Nobel Prize in 1904, the first received by a Russian. He was elected to the Russian Academy of Sciences in 1907, and to the Royal Society in London the same year. When the Communists took over, Lenin gave him funds and a free hand to carry on his research. Through Pavlov's efforts and those of his colleague V. M. Bekhterev and the American behaviorist John B. Watson, conditioning became established as a basic concept in the explanation of animal and human learning.

PEAK-CLIPPING.

Increasing the intelligibility of transmitted speech by "clipping," or eliminating, high intensity sounds and amplifying the low intensities.

Peak-clipping is accomplished by special circuits in radio transmitters, walkie-talkies, public address systems, and hearing aids. It is based on experiments of physiological psychologists and acoustical specialists who have shown that the high intensity (loud) components of speech contribute little to intelligibility. The reason is that these components are usually (in English, at least) the low frequency (low-pitched)

sounds, mainly vowels, and these are not so essential to understanding as the high frequency sounds, which are primarily consonants. The technique therefore cuts out the lower tones and amplifies the higher tones of speech. This enables the hearing aid or other system to utilize its power to the best advantage. It also helps to eliminate noise in the system since noise is primarily high intensity, low frequency sound.

Peak-clipped speech sounds rough and distorted, but its comprehensibility is increased. If the reverse is done, by a process called center-clipping, in which the low intensity, high frequency tones are eliminated, speech becomes totally incomprehensible. Both processes are known as "amplitude distortions," and are important for both their practical applications and their theoretical implications in the study of speech perception.

PEDOPHILIA (literally "Love of Children").

A sexual deviation involving sexual activity of any type with a child who has not reached puberty.

Pedophiles are usually men who fondle a child of either sex, exhibit themselves, or attempt intercourse. They may occasionally induce the child to manipulate their own sex organs, and sometimes engage in anal or oral homosexual contact with young boys. Deviates of this type vary in educational background and fall into two major age groups, one around thirty years and the other from fifty years up. A few are adolescents who are retarded in social and psychosexual development. The older group have usually been married and tend to seek out younger children; the younger group more often become involved with adolescent girls. Pedophiles are more likely to use force than any other sex offenders except rapists.

Thorpe, Katz, and Lewis (1961) describe the dynamics of pedophilia in the following terms: "Pedophiliacs are particularly afflicted with anxiety regarding their sexual potency. Like the rapist, the pedophiliac is not a hypersexed individual, but one whose sexual impulses are distorted by crippling anxiety. A large number give histories of impotence or partial impotence. It is evident that the pedophiliac's inferiority feelings lead him to search for younger and less formidable love objects whose ignorance would prevent his deficiency from becoming obvious. The child sexual object saves the offender's ego from blows which might prove destructive to his mental equilibrium."

The psychological pattern is somewhat different for the two age groups. Younger male offenders generally feel inadequate and are afraid of rejection when they approach women. They seek contact with children in order to meet sexual needs without the risk of failure and humiliation. These men are usually unable to establish normal sexual relationships with women of their own age and do not play an adequate role in the community. Many of them are ambulatory schizophrenics or schizoid personalities who do not realize how eccentric their behavior is. They usually rationalize their actions by blaming them on alcohol or claiming that they were seduced by the boy or girl—a claim that has been substantiated in a few cases. In this connection it is interesting that most of the offenders and their victims knew each other before the incident.

Middle-aged offenders are frequently borderline psychotics, or in some cases overt psychotics who are conflicted over homosexual tendencies. Instead of becoming full homosexuals, they occasionally molest or seduce underage boys. The oldest group of offenders is composed largely of senile psychotics who have lost the ability to inhibit their impulses as a result of chronic alcoholism, paresis, or brain disease of the senile or arteriosclerotic type. Some are actually impotent, others are fearful of

losing their potency and are seeking to reassure themselves. In some cases these men are lonely individuals who simply want to show affection to a small girl, but the child has been warned so frequently about strange men that she becomes hysterical, and as a result the man is imprisoned for attempted rape.

Pedophilia is treated as a serious offense since the offender subjects children to traumatic experiences and sometimes physical injury. Legal prosecution is usually a further ordeal for the child, and for this reason many cases go unreported. Most states have laws confining pedophiles to prison or mental hospitals for sexual offenders. Today, however, an increasing number are serving indeterminate sentences in hospitals and are receiving treatment and rehabilitation. The results so far are highly promising.

Illustrative Case: PEDOPHILIA

W.L., fifty-seven, man slightly below average height and weight, acknowledged to have pedophiliac tendencies. Resides with younger sister, aged forty-five, who keeps him under strict surveillance. W.L. admits he has had desire for sexual contact with children for many years, but has only within recent years made any overt advances.

Parents died when he was of preschool age. Reared by relatives until fifteen, when he ran away from aunt with whom he was living. Met girl who attracted him when twenty-four and married her after a three-week courtship. Most unhappily married, separated after living with wife for six weeks.

Always felt inferior and insecure. States he is still afraid to face adults. Has never been successful in his work (cabinetmaker).

Acknowledges that only young girls are sexually attractive to him. Has tried sexual intercourse with a number of women, mostly prostitutes, and has never felt sexually satisfied. Attains sexual satisfaction only when manipulating the genitalia of a young girl.

Tendencies brought to attention of sister, who now lives with him and supervises him. Has been cautioned not to permit himself to get too close to children. Has never presented himself for medical or psychological treatment. (Thorpe, Katz, and Lewis, 1961)

PELLAGRINOUS PSYCHOSIS (Psychosis with Pellagra).

A metabolic disorder produced by a severe deficiency of vitamin B (niacin, nicotinic acid). Deficiencies of thiamine, riboflavin, and ascorbic acid may also be involved.

The incidence of pellagrinous psychosis in this country has sharply declined in recent years due to the availability of enriched bread and emphasis on a balanced diet. Nevertheless it is still a problem in deprived or backward communities as well as among alcoholics, drug addicts, and aged, destitute individuals who live alone. The vitamin deficiency produces changes in the nerve and blood systems of the brain, resulting in a variety of psychological symptoms as well as gastrointestinal disturbances and skin lesions. (The word pellagra comes from pelle agra, meaning "rough skin" in Italian.) Early symptoms of pellagra include irritability, forgetfulness, restlessness, vague headaches, and general sluggishness. From 5 to 10 per cent of victims develop more severe symptoms, including confusion, delirium, Korsakoff's syndrome, and hallucinations. Some patients become overexcited, while others become depressed and anxious, depending on their previous personality pattern.

If the disease is not arrested, it may lead to extensive brain damage, producing stupor, convulsions, paralysis, and permanent mental deterioration. But if large doses of niacin and other dietary components are administered before brain damage occurs, the prognosis is positive. See BRAIN DISORDERS, BERI BERI.

Illustrative Case: PELLAGRINOUS PSYCHOSIS

M.G., female, white. In this patient pellagra had existed three years. From informant it was learned that patient had complained of pains, generally distributed about body, vertigo, stiffness of muscles, and general weakness.

Upon admission to hospital, had typical pellagrous rash and loose bowels. Mentally confused, could give no account of trip to hospital or happenings of previous two weeks; frequently paid no heed to questions asked, but said over and over again, "I'm scared, I'm scared. What are you going to do to me? Am I going to be killed? I don't like to be left by myself." Knew in vague way that she was in hospital, but did not know its location, nor did she know the day or the month, and made no effort to fix hour of the day. Retention very defective. Counted from one to twenty in ten seconds with difficulty, and made no effort to reverse, nor would she perform simple mental calculations. Frequently remarked, "I have pellagra; I have been in bed two weeks. Oh, I don't remember; I don't remember." Although patient denied hallucinations, from her behavior at times it was thought that they probably existed. At times patient appeared more clear than at others; she would show certain degree of insight into her condition, at one time stating that she knew there was something wrong with her mind, that everything seemed "strange" and unfamiliar.

Patient ultimately recovered and showed well-marked amnesia for previous confused state. Certain happenings were more readily recalled; these coincided with periods of relative clearness. (Rosanoff, 1938)

PENIS ENVY.

The desire of the female for male sex organs.

According to psychoanalytic theory, when the young girl discovers that the boy has a conspicuous genital organ which she does not have, she inevitably develops the belief that she lacks or has lost a crucial part of the body, and desires to possess it. She feels "handicapped and ill-treated" (Freud's words) and blames her mother for the loss. At the same time she becomes jealous of her mother for being able to possess her father, whom she both loves and envies. This composite feeling marks the beginning of the Oedipus (or Electra) complex, at around three years of age.

Penis envy arouses feelings of anxiety which parallel the castration anxiety experienced by boys. To allay this anxiety, the child unconsciously represses the envy and therefore is not aware that it exists. She also renounces her special attraction to her father since it cannot be gratified. Nevertheless she continues to love, admire, and identify with him, and as a consequence adopts many of his basic standards and values.

Psychoanalysts also use the term in a broader sense to denote the envy of the female for male characteristics, status and advantages in society. In any event, they believe that penis envy has a significant effect on character development in the female. The way she "works through" this feeling determines largely whether she fully accepts herself as a woman, or takes the opposite course of denying the loss by feeling "compelled to behave as though she were a man" (Freud). *See* OEDIPUS COMPLEX, CASTRATION COMPLEX.

Illustrative Case: PENIS ENVY

A young lady of five had just finished having a bath with her younger brother. As she was rubbing herself down with a towel, she said to her father, "Daddy, I wish I had a bottom like Charlie's." Her father, half-amused, replied, "Why is that? You have a nice bottom yourself." To which she answered, "Because I like those kind of bottoms better." Here, direct and without adornment, is the little girl's envy of the male genital and her wish to have the same for herself. Not long after, the same little girl recounted at breakfast a dream of the night before: "Mummy," she said, "I dreamed last night that some men were trying to hurt me with pistols and you chased them away with your sword." Here again is the theme of attacking men which loomed so large in Sarah J.'s fears. In this instance it was not a waking fantasy, but a dream—the product of the sleeping youngster's inner life of imagination and fancy.

. . . If one investigates children systematically, it becomes apparent that fantasies of this nature are characteristic of

the period of from three to six, with a peak of intensity in the fifth year of life. A two-year-old does not have such preoccupations and concerns. They appear as a part of the process of the growth and development of the maturing child, and characterize that phase of the child's known as the Oedipal period.

This is a time of life for the little girl when she dwells on the basic facts of human life and relationships. She is curious about the relationship between her mother and father; she experiences strong desires to possess her father and to eliminate her mother ("Wouldn't it be nice, Daddy," said a young lady cheerfully, "if Mummy died, and you and I were married?"); she is fascinated by babies and the idea of pregnancy; she notes the difference between the sexes and is concerned because, unlike the boy, she has no visible genital; she resents the difference and is envious of the boy for what she considers his superior equipment. As she tries to explain these mysteries to herself, the answers come in the form of the common fantasies of childhood— that, for example, a man's attack has injured her genitals, or that she has harmed herself by masturbation. (Nemiah, 1961)

PEPTIC ULCER. A craterlike wound in the inner wall of the stomach or duodenum resulting from the corrosive effects of acid-containing digestive juices. Although certain types of food and drink stimulate the secretion of these juices, it is an established fact that emotional stress and strain are a major causal factor in many cases. For this reason peptic ulcer is classified in psychiatry as a psychophysiologic (psychosomatic) disorder of the gastrointestinal system.

Family quarrels, business reversals, and other problems produce temporary stomach upsets in most people, and if these stresses are sufficiently severe and persistent, they may result in actual lesions. Brady (1958) has shown that stress situations can have the same effect on monkeys (PLATE 17). Many authorities, however, believe that this reaction occurs only in individuals who have a predisposition to oversecretion. They are sometimes referred to as "high pepsinogen secreters."

Modern society with its pressures and uncertainties is particularly conducive to the formation of ulcers, and it has been estimated that one out of ten people are afflicted at some time in life. The disorder is especially prevalent in large urban centers where the strain and tempo are greatest. (One indicative study showed that the incidence was fairly low among Negroes living in the South, but the rate among Negroes who had lived in Chicago for more than five years was the same as for whites. Steigmann, 1936.) Three times as many males as females suffer from ulcers, but the incidence among females is increasing. Recent studies have shown that ulcers are more prevalent in children than had previously been recognized.

Although social and cultural factors help to account for the over-all prevalence of ulcers, specific types of situations and behavior patterns are believed to be responsible in many individual patients. A few cases seem to fall into the category of acute stress reactions—for example, the combat soldier who is subjected to situations of extreme tension, frustration, and threat to life may develop gastrointestional upsets that lead to ulcers. But most of the psychosomatic cases seem to be associated with a particular personality pattern. Alexander (1952) and others have found that these patients tend to be tense, hard-driving, and aggressive on the surface, but this façade hides an underlying wish to be passive, dependent, and cared for by others. As children they learned to associate food with affection, and as adults they continue to express their desire for loving care by overactivity of the digestive system when they find themselves in competitive or threatening situations. Evidence for this theory was found in the fact that when these individuals were under stress, their craving to be loved and "babied" was expressed in fantasies and dreams. Moreover, when they were confined to bed and cared for by a nurse, their ulcers frequently cleared up without medication.

Other investigators (Mittelmann and Wolff, 1942) maintain that ulcer patients are not always hard-driving, but agree that they tend to demand the care and attention of others. When these demands are denied or frustrated, they become angry and their digestion becomes upset.

Although psychoanalysis has been successful in treating ulcer patients, this long-term procedure is seldom undertaken. Bland diets, frequent feeding, drugs, and rest have proven effective in most cases, particularly when medical measures are coupled with direct counseling in which the patient is encouraged to lead a more relaxed way of life. If the ulcer condition is persistent and recurrent, and there is evidence that it is a response to emotional conflicts, short-term psychotherapy is usually indicated. A major aim of this approach is to help the patient accept his "dependency longings," that is, his need for regular opportunities to let down and be cared for by others.

Illustrative Case: PEPTIC ULCER

The patient was the fourth of five boys. His father was an unsuccessful farmer whom the patient had disliked from an early age on and never respected. His mother, to whom he felt much closer, was nervous, frail, and had numerous bodily complaints which the family physician regarded as 90 per cent emotional. Nevertheless, she criticized and dominated her husband and nagged her sons into striving for the success that their father had never achieved.

Poverty and a small physical stature contributed to making the patient feel inferior to other children, but he compensated by striving for academic achievement. He was very intelligent and although he worked in a store during noon hours, after school, and on Saturdays he was at the top of his classes.

He completed college and two years of law school in evening classes. In World War II he rose from private to captain. At the age of twenty-four he married and subsequently became the father of three children.

He was as ambitious and hard-driving in his career as he had been in school and in the Army. He began to work for a large company at the age of twenty-one and over the ensuing twenty-five years rose to a senior executive position. He felt personally responsible for much of the company's growth and expansion. He was away from home traveling on company business a great deal, worked evenings and weekends, ate irregularly, and for fifteen years never took a vacation with his family. But after reaching a high position he began to feel that his talents—which were considerable but which he undoubtedly overvalued—and his dedication were neither appreciated nor adequately rewarded. His future seemed bleak, with little opportunity for future advancement financially or in prestige. Every morning he felt sick over the prospect of another day's exhausting demands and inadequate rewards. However, he did not express his feelings of frustration and resentment while at work but became increasingly irritable at home. He also began to drink and smoke very heavily. At this point he developed stomach ulcers. Sedative medication reduced his pain but he continued to drink and became increasingly depressed. An added blow occurred when his eldest daughter married after graduation from high school instead of going on to college; his heart had been set on seeing all his children obtain college degrees. He became extremely unreliable on the job, often failing to keep business appointments, and finally was dropped by the company for alcoholism and unreliability.

Shortly thereafter he was referred for psychiatric treatment. He was angry, tense, tremulous, and depressed. As a consequence of losing his position, he was confronted with the necessity of re-evaluating his goals and patterns of behavior. He was treated in psychotherapy and by minor tranquilizers and his tension and depression diminished. Being an intelligent man, he was able to acquire insight rapidly; his compulsive ambition decreased, he cut down on smoking and drinking, and his ulcer symptoms receded. He took a less demanding position with another company and during a two-year follow-up period there was no recurrence of the ulcers and alcoholism. (Rosen and Gregory, 1965)

PERCEPTION. The process of becoming aware of objects, qualities, or relations via the sense organs; includes such activities as observing, recognizing, discriminating, and grasping meaning.

The specific character of perception can probably best be described by differentiating it from two other processes, sensation and attention. The various sensations provide a basis for perception, since they give us the data from which we construct our knowledge of the world. Sight and hearing provide sensory data for most of our perceptual experiences, but other senses may also be involved. Perception is not mere awareness of these data, but the process of organizing and interpreting them. It is perception, therefore, that gives them their meaning as objects, events, signs, experiences, and sources of understanding. It enables us to look beyond mere spots of color or bits of sound to observe a painting, recognize a friend, hear a piece of music, read a book.

Perception must also be distinguished from attention. Although it is true that we must attend in order to perceive, attention is simply the process of *focusing* on a limited range of stimuli and becoming especially aware of them, while perception is the process of *interpreting* these stimuli.

This article will be limited to an enumeration of the various aspects of perception which have been subjected to psychological investigation. Its object is to provide an over-all view of the subject, and to direct the reader to the topics in which the details are presented. A problem of first importance is our ability to perceive enduring, stable, identifiable objects and events as opposed to a constantly shifting series of sense qualities. This problem has led to a study of the various "constancies" on which the stability of objects depends: color and brightness constancy, shape constancy, size constancy, and location constancy—that is, we tend to see an object as having a standard size, shape, color, etc., even though it may be viewed in different lights or from an angle or a distance. Perceptual constancy—a term that includes all these types of stability—introduces a second major problem, that of discovering principles that explain the organization of perception. One basic type of organization, found in both visual and auditory perception, is the tendency of a figure (a wallpaper design, a voice) to stand out from its background. Other organizational principles are the tendency to group dots or lines or sounds together according to factors such as position, "closure," or similarity, as well as the tendency to perceive objects and events according to past experiences, expectation, emotion, or suggestion. A study of perceptual illusions, including illusions of shape, size, and movement, has refined our knowledge of the principles of perception, and has helped to explain many inaccuracies in our judgments.

Still another problem is that of depth perception, our ability to construct a three-dimensional world out of two-dimensional cues, in both vision and audition. This phenomenon, as well as the phenomena of perceptual constancy and perceptual organization, raises the basic question of whether our structuring of the world is due primarily to innate tendencies or to the learning process. Some light has been thrown on this problem by studies of animals raised in the dark, individuals whose vision has been restored, and the ability of small children to perceive depth in visual cliff experiments. Finally, the controversial problem of extrasensory perception—perception in the absence of sense organ stimulation—has also been a subject of continuing experimental research. *See* ATTENTION, PERCEPTUAL

CONSTANCY, ILLUSION, PERCEPTUAL DISTORTION, GESTALT PSYCHOLOGY, DEPTH PERCEPTION, VISUAL CLIFF, VISION, EXTRASENSORY PERCEPTION, SUBITIZING.

PERCEPTUAL CONSTANCY (Object Constancy). The tendency for objects to appear the same despite wide variations in the standpoint from which they are viewed.

In spite of the fact that the stimuli that impinge on our sense organs continually change, our perceptual world remains relatively constant. A man does not look like a midget when seen at a distance, nor does he grow into a giant as we approach him. Our environment would be too chaotic for survival if every change in physical stimulation brought with it an expansion or shrinkage in the actual color, shape, brightness, or size of an object. Perceptual constancy therefore permits us to deal more effectively with the world because it remains more or less the same under varying conditions.

This striking mechanism is so automatic that we rarely think about it, but a simple experiment will show how remarkable it is. Look at a person fifty feet away. The size of the image that falls on the retina of the eye—the "proximal stimulus"—can be estimated by holding up a pencil at arm's length and comparing its size with the apparent size of the person in the distance—the "distal stimulus." Next, do the same thing with a person ten feet from you. In the first case the pencil will appear much larger than the person; in the second, much smaller—yet both of these widely different images lead to correct estimates of his actual size. This is termed *size constancy.*

Our perception of the size of objects is greatly influenced by cues to distance and depth such as differences in brightness and perspective. If these cues are present we do not see distant objects as smaller than similar ones close at hand, but we perceive them as farther

away (PLATE 28). *See* DEPTH PERCEP-
TION.

Object constancy appears to be partly
due to learning. A very young child
will draw a man of the same size regardless of his position in the picture;
later he will reduce his size if he is
in the distance. Japanese and other Oriental art, as well as the primitive school
of painting, ignore object constancy.
Some authorities believe these are deliberate attempts to recapture our earlier, more "natural" view of the world.

Size constancy tends to break down
at large distances. From the top of a
very tall building the people in the
street look like ants, not human beings
of normal size. This fact points to the
survival value of perceptual constancy.
At great distances there is no need for
constancy because faraway objects pose
little threat or are of little interest to
us. But when they move closer, we
often have to deal directly with them,
and perceptual constancy helps us do
so since it enables us to judge their
actual size.

We also experience *brightness and
color constancy*. Coal looks black even
in very bright light, and snow continues to look white even at night.
Colored objects retain their natural
color even when the color of the illumination is altered. An important factor in color constancy is the remembered color of familiar objects. In one
study the same piece of orange paper
was used to cut out figures identified
as a banana, lemon, tangerine, carrot,
cooked lobster, and tomato. When subjects were asked to match colored
pieces of paper to these orange cutouts,
there was a marked tendency to distort the matched color in the direction
of the natural color of these foods.
This occurred even when the subjects
knew that all cutouts came from the
same orange paper. (Bruner, Postman,
and Rodrigues, 1951)

Brightness constancy results from our
tendency to respond to the amount of
light reflected from an object's surface
rather than the way it looks under
different illumination. Another way of
stating this is that we respond to the
object's "albedo," which is the percentage of the light falling on it that it
reflects. A white object, for example,
will reflect about 80 per cent of the
sunlight that falls on it. It will also
appear white in a poorly lighted room
because it reflects the same percentage
of light—that is, its albedo is 80 per
cent. Coal is seen as black whether
in sunlight or shadow because in either
case it reflects the same small amount
of the incidental light.

We also experience *shape constancy*.
A door is seen as a rectangle even
if it is partly open. A plate looks
round and not elliptical even if we view
it from an angle. Shape constancy,
like the other types of object constancy,
makes objects appear stable despite the
fact that the stimulation arriving from
them is constantly changing.

Object constancy does not do a perfect job. Our perceptions are usually
a compromise between what we know
an object to be and the way it appears at the moment to our senses
(that is, its "retinal size"). Things at
a distance actually appear slightly
smaller to us; white objects are not
quite so white in relative darkness as
under good illumination. But this compromise corresponds much more closely
to the usual way we interact with the
object than to the way it strikes us
at the moment. Much of the stability
of our world derives from such constancy.

PERCEPTUAL DISTORTION. An inaccurate interpretation of perceptual experience; a distorted impression of
things or people.

Perceptual distortions may be due to
(a) the effect of drugs such as mescaline or lysergic acid (LSD), (b) severe
mental disease, particularly schizophrenia, (c) sensory deprivation, or (d) the

influence of an individual's needs, values, and attitudes. Since the first three of these are dealt with under separate topics, this article will be devoted to the fourth. *See* HALLUCINOGEN, LYSERGIC ACID, SCHIZOPHRENIC REACTIONS (GENERAL), SENSORY DEPRIVATION.

Most people perceive concrete, clear-cut objects such as chairs and tables in much the same way. This can be proved by asking them to match photographs with objects they are looking at. But when the perceptual field is complex and ambiguous, there is much less agreement. In this case different individuals tend to interpret the situation in different ways, and one of the principal reasons is that they focus on aspects that are in accord with their needs and interests.

We have all had experiences in which our wishes influence our perceptions. If we walk down a street hoping to meet someone we have often seen in that section of town, we may readily convince ourselves that a person we see in the distance is actually our friend. If it turns out that we are mistaken, it is because we saw a resemblance where none really existed. Under the influence of anticipation, we paid attention only to those cues that supported our hope, and overlooked obvious details that would have disappointed our desire. In a word, we were victims of perceptual distortion.

Advertisers make extensive use of the fact that we tend to perceive what we want to perceive. They try to build up an expectation of desirable qualities in their products so that we will have a positive reaction to them. Cigarette advertisements seem to be especially effective in this respect. As a result, habitual smokers claim to have a strong preference for one particular brand because it alone delivers the satisfaction they seek. This is usually an example of perceptual distortion, since blindfold tests have demonstrated that relatively few smokers can distinguish their own brand from others. The same has been shown to apply to various cola drinks.

There are any number of examples of the effect of suggestion and "wishful thinking" on perception. People who are very hungry tend to see ambiguous objects as food: the circular ashtray on the dinner table may, at a quick glance, appear to be a hamburger. The expression "Love is blind" suggests that under the influence of emotion we are aware only of the good qualities of the loved one, and probably exaggerate even those. The saying "the honeymoon is over" indicates that perception has returned to normal and we recognize that our mate has the usual quota of faults. *See* SUGGESTION.

Selective perception is especially evident in judgments based on prejudice. A prejudiced person will comment that a Negro in soiled work clothes "looks filthy" or "shiftless," but will see a white person wearing the same clothing as a good man coming back from a hard day's work. Since most social situations are ambiguous it is relatively easy to perpetuate such interpretations. Moreover, attitudes of this type persist because people either avoid or reinterpret information that would correct them. Experiments have also demonstrated that material which is congenial to an emotionally toned attitude is learned much more easily than material which is opposed to it. *See* COGNITIVE DISSONANCE, PREJUDICE, STEREOTYPE.

The value we attribute to an object may influence our perception of it. In an oft-quoted experiment, Bruner and Goodman (1947) found that poor children tend to overestimate the size of coins to a greater extent than rich children. The coins loomed larger in their minds because they had a greater need for them. Their distorted perception may also be due to the fact that in our culture there is often a connection between size and value. The bigger the object the more valuable it may seem to be—for instance, we usually assume that a big car is more expensive and roadworthy than a smaller one.

Most situations are perceived against an established frame of reference, a system that helps to organize and interpret complex events. One safe way of bringing order into our confusing experiences is to see what everybody else sees, a kind of strength in numbers approach. This is one reason for the continuation of prejudice, especially in the South, where many white people are brought up to view Negroes as inferior. It also accounts for the prevalence of fads, and the fact that a new clothing style appears less strange and more "normal" as we see many people wearing it—until a new fashion comes along and displaces it. In a word, we automatically mold our perceptions to conform to the prevailing trend. See SOCIAL NORM, RUMOR, MASS BEHAVIOR.

PERPLEXITY STATES. A form of mental confusion in which the patient is assailed with doubt and uncertainty about his own thoughts.

Perplexity is one of the more transient disorders of thinking found primarily in schizophrenia. The patient "is at a loss when trying to understand why and how his thought processes are operating" (Landis and Mettler, 1964). These authors cite, as one example, the shifting explanations given by a paranoid patient to account for her ideas of persecution: "As far as I know they used an oscillograph on me, but I might be mistaken . . . Whether a dictaphone was actually in the apartment upstairs or not I don't know, I wasn't there . . . I did feel the effects of something. I couldn't say what it was, gas or not. I really heard the gas stove move but I could be mistaken . . . People across the street appeared to be signaling. It is possible I was wrong . . . There might not have been a scandal in the papers about me. The psychiatrists told me there was, but I didn't read the news . . . I was taking the psychiatrist's word for granted that he was a criminologist. That is, so far as I know. I couldn't swear he was." (Milici, 1937)

Another form of perplexity is observed in patients suffering from a diffuse impairment of brain functions, as in toxic, infectious, or head injury disorders. Since these cases involve a disturbance of consciousness rather than disordered thinking, the patients are not perplexed by the thoughts and ideas that pass through their minds, as in schizophrenia, but are bewildered by their inability to concentrate, understand questions, or grasp the situation. They therefore wear a puzzled, distressed, and at times surprised expression on their faces.

PERSEVERATION. A persistent repetition of the same thought or activity.

Normal individuals are occasionally "haunted" by the same idea, mental image, phrase, or melody for hours or even days: "I can't get it out of my mind." This reaction sometimes occurs after an emotional experience that touches us deeply. In some cases, too, we may harp on one idea in order to screen out another. This is particularly likely to occur when we are disturbed, tense, or overfatigued.

Perseveration may also be a pathological symptom. In certain clinical cases the patient clings to the same idea involuntarily even though it may be totally inappropriate and irrelevant. Rigidity of this kind may serve an unconscious purpose since the patient probably derives some security from expressing a familiar idea or continuing to offer a solution that worked in the past.

This reaction frequently occurs among catatonic patients, who have withdrawn into themselves and have lost contact with the outside world. It is also observed in some cases of aphasia. The most persistent form, however, occurs in organic brain disease and senile dementia. In the latter cases perseveration is associated with intellectual impoverishment resulting from cerebral damage or atrophy. *See* VERBIGERATION, STEREOTYPY, SCHIZOPHRENIA (CATATONIC TYPE), SENILE PSYCHOSIS (GENERAL).

PERSONA (literally, "mask," as worn by actors in ancient Greece). A term applied by Carl Jung to the personality or façade we show to the world. He distinguishes the persona from our inner being, or anima (soul), since the persona is adopted and put on like a mask to meet the requirements of social life. It consists largely in the roles we play in society, roles that are based primarily on the customs and conventions of the culture and our need to conform to the expectations of others.

An individual may identify so strongly with his persona that he is influenced more by the role he is playing than by his inner self. Some people behave outwardly like a teacher or lawyer but have no feeling for these roles; others devote themselves so completely to their jobs that they forget how to be a human being. Jung calls the man who identifies himself with his persona a "personal man," and uses the term "individual man" for the one who identifies with the deeper components of his personality. *See* JUNG.

PERSONALITY DISORDERS (Character Disorders). These terms are currently used interchangeably for various types of pathological character structure that stem primarily from defective personality development rather than from unconscious conflicts or transient stresses.

Personality or character disorders are a relatively new addition to the classification of mental illness. They include a group of conditions characterized by faulty attitudes and personality trends which tend to manifest themselves in deviant or maladjusted behavior rather than in disturbances of emotional, perceptual, or intellectual functions. In most cases the individuals are unaware they have a personality disturbance, and do not seek psychological help. If they come to the attention of a psychiatrist or clinical psychologist at all, it is usually as a result of family pressure or behavior that brings them into court.

The Diagnostic Manual of the American Psychiatric Association (1952) describes personality disorders as "developmental defects or pathological trends in the personality structure, with minimal subjective anxiety, and little or no sense of distress. In most instances, the disorder is manifested by a lifelong pattern of action or behavior, rather than by mental or emotional symptoms." The category includes a wide range of disorders, from relatively mild conditions to some of the most serious forms of behavior disturbance. The current Manual divides them into four groups. The first is *personality pattern disturbances*, comprising personality types that are deeply entrenched and resistant to treatment: inadequate personality, schizoid personality, cyclothymic personality, paranoid personality, hypomanic personality, melancholic personality. The second includes *personality trait disturbances*, characterized by a dominant feature which is considered relatively superficial and amenable to change: immature personality, emotionally unstable personality, hysterical personality, passive-aggressive personality, compulsive personality, obsessive personality. Many specialists feel that the distinction between these two groups is too subtle for practical diagnostic purposes, and it is interesting that the latest classification of the American Medical Association (1961) groups them together under the general heading of personality disorder.

The third category is *sociopathic personality disturbances*, which include antisocial and dyssocial reactions (psychopathic and criminal behavior), sexual deviations, and addiction to alcohol or drugs. The fourth category is termed *special symptoms reactions,* and comprises such disorders as stuttering, nail biting, enuresis, tics, and compulsive gambling.

Even though relatively few individuals with personality disorders are treated in hospitals, the total percentage of first admissions to United States public mental hospitals falling into this general category was 16.6 per cent in 1963, according to the National Institute of Mental Health. This compares with 6.9 per cent for psychoneurotic disorders, 31.6 per cent for psychotic disorders, and 33.8 per cent for brain syndromes. *See* PERSONALITY PATTERN DISTURBANCE, PERSONALITY TRAIT DISTURBANCE, TRANSIENT SITUATIONAL PERSONALITY DISORDERS, and the appropriate topic on each individual disorder.

PERSONALITY INVENTORY (Self-Report Inventory). A personality test consisting of questions and statements about personal characteristics and behavior which the individual judges to apply or not to apply to himself. These tests measure either individual traits, such as introversion-extraversion, or over-all adjustment, and yield either a single score or a profile of scores representing several aspects of the personality at once.

In general, personality inventories compare the individual's self-report with a norm, or criterion, based on responses made by a large, representative group of people. An example is the early Thurstone Neurotic Inventory, which requires the individual to check "yes," "no," or "?" on such questions as: Are your feelings easily hurt? Do you like to be with other people a great deal? Do your interests change quickly? Scores on this test are based on a comparison with responses of groups of well-adjusted and groups of poorly adjusted people to the same questions.

Five major procedures have been employed in selecting and formulating

questions for personality inventories; each of them will be illustrated by a brief description of representative tests. The first technique used was *content validation,* based on a systematic study of behavior representing the personality characteristics to be measured. The questions on Woodworth's Personal Data Sheet, for example, stem from an investigation of representative neurotic and pre-neurotic symptoms, such as phobias and compulsions. The Mooney Problem Check List, now in wide use in high schools, contains student problems in such areas as health, sex, and social relations, gathered from surveys, interviews, and case records of four thousand young people. This inventory is used primarily in identifying problems for discussion and counseling. Other instruments which employ the content validation technique are the STS Youth Inventory, the Bell Adjustment Inventory (student and adult form), and the California Test of Personality, available in five forms from kindergarten to adult, and yielding a total adjustment score as well as separate scores for personal and social adjustment, social skills, school relations, and withdrawing tendencies.

In the second technique, *empirical criterion keying,* the items are selected and weighted according to an external criterion such as responses of mental patients or ratings made by a representative group of individuals. The criterion used in the early but durable Allport A-S Reaction Study, designed to measure ascendance-submission, is based on the responses of a large "standardization sample" to descriptions of typical situations encountered in school, on the job, etc. The subjects indicate what they would do in these situations, and are rated on a scale from ascendance (dominance, assertiveness) to submission (dependence, docility) both by themselves and by four associates. The individuals who take the test are scored according to norms derived from the standardization group. Another test constructed on the same principle is the Bernreuter Personality Inventory, which presents 125 yes-no questions on personality adjustment, with each response weighted for neuroticism, self-sufficiency, introversion, and dominance. (The questions are on the order of the examples from the Thurstone test cited above.) The most important and widely used test based on criterion keying is the Minnesota Multiphasic Personality Inventory, consisting of 550 items ("I am worried about sex matters," "I believe I am being plotted against," etc.), which have been found to differentiate between groups of patients in clinics or mental hospitals and groups of normal individuals on such characteristics as depression, hysteria, and paranoia. Since a separate article is devoted to the MMPI, it will not be discussed further at this point.

The third procedure, *factor analysis,* is based on intercorrelations among different items from many personality inventories. One of the tests resulting from this approach is the Ten-Factor Inventory known as the Guilford-Zimmerman Temperament Survey, which yields scores for the following traits, each based on thirty different items: general activity (liking for speed, vitality, efficiency), restraint, ascendance, sociability, emotional stability, objectivity, friendliness, thoughtfulness, personal relations, masculinity. Sample items, each to be answered with "yes," "?," or "no," are: You are often in low spirits; Most people use politeness to cover up what is really "cutthroat" competition. Norms for this test are derived primarily from college samples. By re-analyzing Guilford's data and by eliminating items reflecting abnormalities and maladjustments, Thurstone constructed the Thurstone Temperament Schedule for Normal Behavior, consisting of twenty items for each of the following traits: active, vigorous, impulsive, dominant, stable, social, reflective. Cattell has also employed factorial techniques in constructing a number of inventories, including the Sixteen Personality Factor Questionnaire, as well as separate inventories on anxiety, neuroticism, and introversion-extraversion. *See* FACTOR THEORY OF PERSONALITY (CATTELL).

The fourth method, *forced choice,* is also described under a separate topic. Briefly, inventories using this technique present paired statements or terms, and the subject is required to choose the alternative which appears to be most applicable or least applicable to himself. The alternatives in each item are carefully chosen to be equally desirable (or equally undesirable), and for this reason the subject's choices are believed to reflect his general view of himself rather than what he thinks the examiner "wants." In scoring this test, the choices are rated according to specific criteria which the inventory is designed to predict, such as academic achievement or success on a particular job. An example of the industrial application of the technique is the Jurgensen Classification Inventory, which includes such items as: Decide which reputation you would *most* prefer to have, and which you would *least* prefer to have: calm, alert, friendly; and, Mark the item you prefer with XX if your preference is strong and X if it is weak: Have interesting work with moderate pay, Have uninteresting work with high pay. Another test using the forced choice technique is the Personnel Inventory developed by Shipley and his associates as a psychiatric screening device. The items on this test are equated for social acceptability but differ sharply in frequency of choice by normal and maladjusted subjects. Two others are the Gordon Personal Profile, which yields an over-all adjustment score as well as individual scores on ascendance, responsibility, emotional stability, and sociability; and the Gordon Personal

Inventory, which measure cautiousness, original thinking, personal relations, and vigor.

Finally, a few self-report inventories are based on *personality theories*. The most notable and comprehensive of these is the Edwards Personal Preference Schedule (EPPS), designed to assess the strength of fifteen of the needs listed by H. A. Murray and his associates at the Harvard Psychological Clinic: achievement, deference, order, exhibition, autonomy, affiliation, intraception (to analyze one's motives and feelings and to observe and understand the feelings of others), succorance (to receive help, affection, sympathy, and understanding), dominance, abasement, nurturance (to help others and be generous), change (to do new and different things), endurance, heterosexuality, and aggression. A forced choice format was adopted for this inventory, with the items tested on college students and judged to be equal in social desirability—for example, (a) I like to be successful in things undertaken, and (b) I like to form new friendships. Norms were established on the basis of responses in twenty-nine colleges as well as eight thousand adult men and women. The test has been found highly reliable, and has been validated experimentally by putting subjects into situations that require different kinds of behavior. *See* PERSONOLOGY.

Other noteworthy self-report tests are: the Eysenck Personality Inventory, Cattell's IPAT Children's Personality Questionnaire and Junior-Senior High School Personality Questionnaire, the Personal Orientation Inventory, the Minnesota Counseling Inventory, and the Myers-Briggs Type Indicator based on Jung's theory of personality types (Extraversion or Introversion, Sensing or Intuition, Thinking or Feeling, Judgment or Perception).

In general, personality inventories are beset by many problems, most of which are shared by other types of personality tests: the difficulty of establishing adequate criteria for determining validity; the possibility of faking and malingering; and the almost exclusive emphasis on general traits, which tends to ignore the fact that the same individual may behave differently in different situations. In view of these limitations, many psychologists do not score the tests, but use them only to identify the problems to be discussed in interviews, or to throw light on various types of behavior. They also tend to pay more attention to poor scores than good scores, since the good scores are more ambiguous and might reflect a desire to create a favorable impression. Attempts to overcome the difficulties include: keying of individual items against highly specific criteria (for example, requirements for a particular job), the use of the forced choice technique, and the inclusion of more subtle items whose significance is unlikely to be recognized by the subject.

PERSONALITY PATTERN DISTURBANCE. A group of personality disorders comprising personality types that are deeply ingrained, resistant to change, and predisposed to develop into psychosis under stress.

In contrast to personality trait disturbances, which center around specific characteristics such as emotional instability and aggressiveness, these are pervasive disorders in which the organization of the entire personality appears to be involved. The afflicted individuals have many features which are lesser in degree but similar in kind to one or another psychotic reaction. Although they are peculiar, difficult, or even warped, they can usually function fairly well and remain in contact with reality so long as they are not exposed to overwhelming pressure or prolonged frustration. In some cases their functioning may be improved by long-term therapy, but basic change can seldom be achieved since their personality structure can rarely be altered.

The following are the major types of personality pattern disturbance. Each is described elsewhere as a separate topic.

(1) *Inadequate personality:* characterized by ineffectuality, poor judgment, lack of physical and psychological stamina, and general inability to meet intellectual, social, emotional, and physical demands. Tends to develop schizophrenia under stress.

(2) *Schizoid personality:* cold, aloof, unable to feel close to other people; fearful and cannot express hostility or endure competition; an introversive, eccentric daydreamer. Tends to develop schizophrenia under stress.

(3) *Cyclothymic personality:* an extravert who alternates between elation and dejection without adequate external cause. Tends to develop manic-depressive reaction under stress.

(4) *Paranoid personality:* hostile, mistrustful, self-assertive; intolerant, arrogant, hypercritical toward others but hypersensitive to criticism of himself. Tends to develop paranoia, paranoid states, or paranoid schizophrenia under stress. *See* PARANOIA.

(5) *Hypomanic personality:* lively, gregarious, uninhibited; easily swayed and carried away by enthusiasm; finds it hard to tolerate frustration or criticism. Tends to develop manic-depressive reaction under stress.

(6) *Melancholic personality:* morose and subdued, with a persistent mild depression and inability to enjoy life; kind, sympathetic, and overconscientious; insecure and fearful of disapproval. Tends to develop manic-depressive or involutional reaction under stress. *See* PERSONALITY DISORDERS.

PERSONALITY THEORIES. Personality may be defined as the pattern of characteristics and ways of behavior which accounts for an individual's unique adjustments to his total environment, it includes major traits, interests, values, attitudes, self-image, abilities, behavior patterns, and emotional patterns.

As this definition indicates, the human personality is a highly complex, multifaceted entity. Innumerable attempts have been made to find a single key to its nature, or at least to encompass its entire structure within a single theory. Before reviewing these attempts, it might be well to mention two general points on which there is considerable agreement. The first is that the individual does not arrive on the scene of life with a ready-made personality. Individuality is not part of our original equipment; it is gradually shaped through the operation of many forces —hereditary and constitutional tendencies, physical maturation, early training, identification with significant individuals, culturally conditioned values and roles, unique experiences and fortuitous events. The relative impact of these forces varies widely from individual to individual, and one theory will stress one type of influence more than another —but it would be hard to deny that all of them play some part in the formation of our personality.

The second point of agreement is that as the personality develops, it achieves some degree of integration, or "identity," to use Erikson's term (1959). The very concept of personality seems to imply a measure of unity, at least enough to account for the fact that a person can be recognized from day to day by something more than his appearance alone. But here again there is room for a variety of interpretations. Some writers insist that there is a central core from which all bahavior flows, others look for unity in a single dominant characteristic or hierarchy of characteristics, still others try to define the set of roles or values or motives which an individual calls his own. But whatever interpretation is preferred, it seems to be an accepted fact that there is some measure of internal structure in each personality.

Theories of personality can all be viewed as attempts to explain personal identity. As Hilgard and Atkinson (1967) point out, "A successful theory must weave together the various strands descriptive of individuality into a fabric that has enduring, identifiable features, unique for each individual yet permitting individuals to be compared to each other. There are many theories—partly because personality is so loosely defined that all theories do not deal with the same subject matter, partly because the facts upon which a finished theory must rest are not yet well enough known." The following summary will group the most influential theories under four headings: type theories, trait theories, developmental theories, and dynamic theories. Since these theories are described in detail under separate topics, we will indicate only their general character here for purposes of comparison.

Type theories classify people into categories, much as we classify plants, animals, and rocks. The typological approach is based on the common observation that the personalities of some people, at least, seem to revolve around a dominant characteristic or central theme. The theories represent three different bases of classification: (a) *physiology or body chemistry,* as in the ancient Greek classification into sanguine, phlegmatic, choleric, and melancholic temperaments according to one or another dominant humor or "body fluid"; and recent attempts to find a constitutional basis for personality in endocrine balance and autonomic patterns; (b) *physique or body type,* including the age-old tendency to associate personality traits with facial features (physiognomy), and the modern theories of Kretschmer, who divided people into three distinct physical types with corresponding personalities, and of Sheldon, who classifies individuals according to a balance between three major physical components and cor-

responding temperamental tendencies; and (c) *behavior, or psychological types,* especially Jung's division into extraverts and introverts, which has been challenged by tests showing that most people are ambiverts, and by factor analysis, which identifies various components of personality as opposed to personality types. *See* PHYSIOGNOMY, HUMORAL THEORY, CONSTITUTIONAL TYPES, JUNG, FACTOR THEORY OF PERSONALITY, EXTRAVERT, INTROVERT.

Trait theories attempt to do justice to the variations in human personality by describing individuals in terms of their position on a number of scales, each scale representing a different trait. The two major trait theories are: (a) *Allport's theory,* which rates individuals according to common traits or values (theoretical, economic, etc.) and unique personal dispositions (a single cardinal trait, a few central traits, and many secondary dispositions, interests, and attitudes); and (b) *Cattell's theory,* based on the discovery of a set of surface traits through cluster or correlational analysis, and a set of source traits through factor analysis, and tests designed to yield a trait profile, or psychograph, for each individual studied (*Fig. 41,* p. 957). *See* PERSONALITY TRAIT THEORY (ALLPORT), PERSONALITY TRAIT THEORY (CATTELL).

Developmental theories stress the continuity of human development, and hold that the way to understand an individual is to identify past experiences and situations which have shaped his personality. These theories fall into three general types: (a) *psychoanalytic theories,* including the Freudian approach which views character and personality as the product of experiences and fixations stemming from earlier stages of psychosexual development; and Erikson's approach, in which personal identity is achieved through a long process of resolving critical problems encountered at different stages of psychosocial development; (b) *learning theories,* such as that of Dollard and Miller (1950), which also recognize the importance of early experiences and their residues, but put special stress on the effects of training, reward and punishment, and cultural conditioning on the formation of basic habits, attitudes, and emotional responses; and (c) *role theories,* closely related to learning theories, which describe personality development in terms of the gradual acquisition of roles (such as boy, girl, student, worker), the role behavior prescribed by the particular culture, and the individual's ability to select his own roles and develop them in his own way. *See* PSYCHOSEXUAL DEVELOPMENT, ADOLESCENCE (THEORIES), SOCIAL ROLE, SEX ROLE, STIMULUS-RESPONSE ASSOCIATION.

Dynamic theories hold that the personality can be most fully understood by describing the interplay between various conscious and unconscious forces in the personality. As a theory of personality dynamics, psychoanalysis examines the individual's present conflicts between his id (instinctual sexual and aggressive drives), his superego (conscience and ideal self), and his ego (attempts to control behavior rationally and mediate between the id and the superego). Learning theory and role theory also have their dynamic aspects, since conflict and tension are bound to arise between our various habits and drives, and between the demands imposed by our different roles in society. Both learning and role theory attempt to define an individual's personality in terms of the way these conflicts are handled. Murray, on the other hand, explains the uniqueness of personality in terms of the individual expression of fundamental needs, such as sex, achievement, aggression, and affiliation. *See* PSYCHOANALYSIS (THEORY), EGO, ID, SUPEREGO, PERSONOLOGY.

PERSONALITY TRAIT DISTURBANCE.

A group of personality disorders centering around specific traits rather than total personality patterns, but with a common denominator of immaturity, inability to maintain emotional equilibrium, and failure to withstand even minor stress. Individuals with trait disturbances are not predisposed to psychotic breakdown, but revert to ineffectual childish behavior of one or another kind when they are subjected to heavy pressure or emotional conflict.

The following is an outline of the major trait disorders. Each is more fully described under a separate topic:

(1) *Emotionally unstable personality:* characterized by general excitability and inability to control emotional reactions; low stress tolerance; ineffective behavior and lack of judgment when under pressure; poorly controlled temper.

(2) *Passive-aggressive personality:* various forms of emotional dependence accompanied by open or hidden resentment: (a) passive dependence (helplessness, indecisiveness, leaning on others), (b) passive aggressiveness (obstinacy, procrastination, obstructionism), (c) active aggressiveness (irritability, temper outbursts, destructiveness).

(3) *Compulsive personality:* rigid, overconscientious, inhibited; perfectionistic, unimaginative, unable to relax.

(4) *Hysterical personality:* self-centered and wilful; prone to emotional outbursts and theatrical behavior to attract attention and dominate others.

(5) *Immature personality:* unable to tolerate frustration or stress; little control over emotions; reverts to infantile tactics and behavior when opposed.

(6) *Obsessive personality:* excessively orderly and cautious; worries over trifles; imposes severe standards on self and others. *See* PERSONALITY DISORDERS.

PERSONALITY TRAIT THEORY (Allport).

The theory that an individual's personality traits are the key to the uniqueness and consistency of his behavior.

The chief exponent of this theory was Gordon W. Allport (1897–1967) of Harvard University. In his view traits are motivational in nature, since they are determining tendencies or predispositions to behave in a certain way. No two persons are alike because each personality is made up of an individual set of traits. Moreover, the traits themselves differ from individual to individual and are never truly identical. There are, however, a few modes of adjustment which can be termed common traits merely for purposes of comparing one individual with another. But these comparisons are bound to be rough since different individuals express the same trait in different ways.

This emphasis on individual difference is reflected in Allport's definition of personality as "the dynamic organization within the individual of those psychophysical systems that define his unique adjustment to his environment" (1937). The dynamic character of the personality organization is manifested in two ways. First, the individual's traits are not separate and static, but interact with each other in determining characteristic actions and reactions. And second, they not only guide behavior but even initiate it—for instance, a person with a marked degree of sociability will actually create situations in which he comes in contact with people instead of merely waiting for a suitable occasion to express this tendency. Some traits have a greater influence on behavior than others, and in order to clarify the differences Allport set up the following classification: (a) *cardinal traits,* or master qualities which dominate the individual to such an extent that they affect the whole range of his behavior—for example, miserliness or overweening political ambition; (b) *central traits,* which usually form a cluster that describes the ordinary individual's personality fairly completely; and (c) *secondary traits,* which are of a more limited nature and not essential to personality description.

Traits are not merely dynamic, they are also *organized*—that is, they work together to form a unique, unified personality. To explain (or at least describe) this fact, Allport continually stressed the concept of the self or "proprium," the essence of the individual. The proprium is made up of our unique body sense, self-estimate, self-identity, and self-extensions (the ideas, organizations, objects, etc., in which we invest our ego). It is not an innate component of our lives, but is gradually developed as our attitudes, intentions, and values take shape. In line with modern ego theory, Allport believes the self is the root of the consistency which can be found in the personality.

How, then, does the personality develop? In spite of his emphasis on consistency, Allport offers a discontinuity theory of development. He holds that the infant differs radically from the adult, since the newborn is governed almost entirely by reflexes, primitive drives, and heredity. These are not enough to give him a personality, since the distinctive attitudes of the individual come from experience and interaction with the environment and not from biological urges. In the first few years of life the child is concerned largely with satisfying his physical needs and reducing his physical tensions; but in time a transformation takes place under the combined impact of maturation, imitation, learning, self-extension, and "functional autonomy," the tendency to develop new, independent drives. As a result, the purely biological organism gradually acquires a unique trait structure, a growing self-awareness and an individual set of goals, values, and aspirations. These free the growing child from bondage to his biological needs and enable him to develop a personality of his own. *See* FUNCTIONAL AUTONOMY.

Allport does not trace this process in detail, nor show exactly how the individual's traits develop. He believes, however, that the transformation takes place largely on a conscious, rational level, and claims that we can discover more about a *normal* person by asking him directly about his goals and intentions than by attempting to elicit his unconscious dynamics through projective tests. (The unconscious, however, may be helpful in explaining the grossly disturbed individual.)

Allport's characteristic emphasis on the future rather than the past is closely related to his theory of functional autonomy. He maintains that one of the major keys to personality development lies in the transformation of biological needs into independent, autonomous motives. The more the individual divorces himself from such drives as hunger, thirst, or shelter, the more mature he becomes. A highly developed person, for example, will eat not merely to satisfy his physical needs but will enjoy fine food or drink because they have an esthetic value—in fact, he will sip wine or taste a delectable dish even when he is not hungry or thirsty. Likewise, the mother whose children are grown and married and who has no financial needs may devote herself wholeheartedly to community service. Her motives may be far removed from her original maternal drive, for she may be responding to a need for achievement, a desire for recognition or status, or the moral urge to help the needy; and it may be that all these drives are operative at once.

The fact that different autonomous motives activate different personalities is an illustration of the infinite variety of personality which Allport constantly stresses. And the fact that each person develops his own expressions of individuality as he matures is evidence for his contention that present motivation is more closely allied to future goals than to drives which were dominant in the past.

Allport's theory contrasts sharply with the Freudian approach on a number of points. He bases his views on a study of normal individuals and contends that psychoanalysis arose from a clinical approach to neurosis which does not automatically lead to an understanding of normal people. This emphasis on the normal motivated him to carry on investigations of expressive movements, rumor and prejudice in "action settings" rather than in a laboratory, clinic, or therapist's chamber. He stresses the discontinuity between child and adult as well as between normal and abnormal, while Freud stresses the continuities. He believes that normal individuals are generally aware of their goals and intentions and are not merely driven by unconscious forces. And he emphasizes the rational and moral aspects of adjustment as opposed to the irrational and biological. It is interesting that polls conducted among clinicians have revealed that Allport's theory of personality is considered nearly as influential as Freud's (Schafer, Berg, and McCandless, 1951). *See* RUMOR, EXPRESSIVE BEHAVIOR, PREJUDICE.

Trait psychology has been criticized on a number of grounds: (1) it is loosely formulated and cannot readily be subjected to empirical test; (2) it does not offer a set of dimensions or general traits for studying different individuals, since it puts so much emphasis on uniqueness; (3) the process by which motives become autonomous is not spelled out; (4) Allport does not give sufficient weight to sociocultural and other environmental factors in the development of traits; and especially (5) he does not do justice to the continuity between infant and adult experience or between normal and abnormal. Allport has stated, however, that he does not deny the importance of the irrational, the biological, or the unconscious aspects of experience, but he deliberately presented the other side of the coin in order to counterbalance the current emphasis on these factors.

Allport's approach has been a strong stimulus to personality research. His emphasis on individual (idiographic) traits as opposed to universal (nomothetic) aspects of experience has directed attention to the uniqueness of behavior, and is regarded by many as a healthy corrective for the current stress on group averages and statistical norms. *See* ORGANISMIC THEORY, PERSONALITY THEORIES.

PERSONALITY TRAIT THEORY (Cattell). An approach to personality description originated by Raymond B. Cattell, based on an analysis of characteristics into surface traits and source traits.

A trait is a reasonably consistent personality characteristic which may be used to distinguish an individual from others. Trait names are actually a form of shorthand, each implying a certain pattern of behavior—for instance, if we say a girl is shy, we can predict that she will not show a normal interest in the opposite sex for someone of her age, will be reluctant to speak out in a group or talk about her personal life, etc. Trait names are therefore comprehensive ways of characterizing people. An unabridged dictionary contains about four thousand trait names (forthrightness, humility, boisterousness, etc.), as well as about eighteen thousand adjectives used to describe how people think, perceive, and act (Allport and Odbert, 1936).

Investigators concerned with describing personality in terms of traits devise tests, or scales, to determine the degree to which any individual possesses a particular trait or set of traits. Their major problem is to decide which of the huge number of traits to select. In 1946 Cattell attempted to solve this problem by first eliminating synonymous or nearly synonymous items, and bringing together those which appeared to be closely related. This procedure reduced the list to 171 traits, which he called "the personality sphere" since he believed they were all we need to make a complete description of personality. Next, he brought together in a single cluster traits which were highly correlated in the same individual. This reduced the number to thirty-five clusters—for example, warmth versus aloofness includes responsiveness versus unresponsiveness, affectionate versus cold, and even-tempered versus sensitive.

Cattell called these thirty-five traits "surface traits," since they were found by correlational analysis, and this process merely shows that they were discovered together, somewhat as a group of symptoms forms a syndrome in medical diagnosis. To cut the number down still further, he had judges rate groups of subjects on each of the traits, and then made a factor analysis of the results. In this way he uncovered twelve basic factors, or "source traits," from which it was possible to predict a person's score on each of the thirty-five surface traits. Each of them is a summary label for a group of traits—for instance, a person who has the source trait "cyclothymia" will be emotionally expressive and changeable, while "schizothymia" implies that an individual is anxious, close-mouthed, and reserved, and "bohemian unconcernedness" means that the person is eccentric, unconventional, and subject to hysterical upsets.

The source traits are conceived as underlying features which combine in various ways to determine the many surface traits. Cattell believed they stem from basic, unitary influences which he described as "physiological factors, temperament factors, degrees of dynamic integration, and exposure to social institutions." These influences, however, were never spelled out. Furthermore, although the traits were obtained in a variety of ways—by objective tests, self-ratings, life record scores—they were bound to be somewhat subjective. For this reason some of the trait descriptions appear forced, and the list as a whole can only be considered tentative (Anastasi, 1961).

Cattell and his associates developed a number of personality inventories based on these investigations. The most comprehensive, the Sixteen Personality Factor Questionnaire, for Ages 16 and Over, yields sixteen scores on such traits as aloof versus warm, submissive versus dominant, glum versus enthusiastic, emotional versus calm. This instrument has not proved reliable because of the shortness of the subtests. Similar inventories have been constructed for ages eight to twelve and twelve to eighteen, as well as separate instruments for such personality characteristics as anxiety, introversion-extraversion, and neuroticism. The latter are the IPAT Anxiety Scale, the Contact Personality Factor Test, and the IPAT Neurotic Personality Factor Test. They are all considered experimental since they have not been sufficiently standardized and validated. See PERSONALITY INVENTORIES.

Trait analysis has been criticized on a number of scores. It is essentially an atomistic approach to personality. It yields specific ratings on the traits that are emphasized, but these ratings tend to be confined to specific persons in specific circumstances, and cannot be generalized to other persons. Finally, the method can be used to summarize specific responses, but it cannot give a picture of the personality as a whole, or uncover basic principles of personality. See PERSONALITY THEORIES.

PERSONNEL SELECTION. The major object of personnel selection programs in business and industry is to choose the applicant who is best suited for a particular job. In constructing an effective program, the first step must be to study the job itself in order to determine the precise operations performed, the equipment to be used, the work conditions, the necessary training and experience, the rate of pay and other characteristics. This information is compiled into a "job description," which in turn determines the "worker requirements" that are necessary for effective performance. On the basis of these requirements, the selection procedures are developed.

These selection procedures include two general types of "predictors," as they are called: evaluations of the applicant based on (1) application forms, references, and interviews designed to obtain relevant biographical and interpersonal data on the applicant; and (2) tests of intelligence, special aptitudes, achievement, and personality, selected to measure the specific abilities and characteristics needed for the job. This article will review the current use of the first group of procedures; personnel tests will be considered under a separate topic.

Application forms. The *letter of application* is of little value for several reasons: the applicant does not know what information is most relevant for the job; he may omit negative factors or falsify his qualifications; and the characteristics of the letter itself (neatness, spelling, etc.) may have a disproportionate influence on the reader. *Application forms* are more effective than letters since the employer can specify the items which are most relevant to the job, and he will be better able to make comparisons because all applicants answer the same questions. In addition to the usual queries about age, dependents, job history, and education, special data may be sought—for example, information on scholastic achievement has been found to correlate well with success on higher level jobs, and data on extracurricular activities in school or college often provide a clue to leadership qualities. The selection of the items should be made on the basis of a job analysis and on actual research on job success wherever possible.

This more scientific approach has led to the *weighted application blank*, a refined technique in which positive or negative weights are assigned to each item, based upon criteria established for the specific job. The weights are determined by studies of employees over a period of years, to determine what factors correlate most highly with criteria—for example, if the job is for women and the criterion is job stability, the blank might show a weight of minus three for "having preschool children" and plus three for "having high school or older children." Weighted blanks have been developed for many jobs including life insurance salesmen, sales clerk, sales manager, secretarial workers, service station dealers, and high-level executives.

References. The object of references is to obtain information about the applicant from people who are acquainted with him. They are of particular value in verifying the applicant's job experience, but have limited use in predicting his performance, since the old and new jobs may be quite different. *Letters of recommendation* of the "To Whom It May Concern" variety are likely to contain only favorable statements and are too general to be of much value. Letters addressed directly to the employer are more helpful, especially when they are written in response to an inquiry which specifies the nature of the job and the information desired. A third type of letter, the *employment recommendation questionnaire* (ERQ), is still more satisfactory, since it contains specific questions selected in much the same way as the items on a weighted application blank. It may also include rating procedures such as a graphic rating scale or a forced-choice technique, designed to elicit information on the applicant's job performance, abilities, or personal characteristics.

Two other methods of investigating references are the *telephone checkup* and the *field investigation.* Telephoning yields a much higher proportion of completed inquiries than mailed questionnaires, and the respondents are likely to be more frank over the phone than in writing. Moreover, a trained telephone interviewer can pick up clues from the respondent's comments or tone of voice, and can then ask follow-up questions that elicit additional information about the applicant. Field investigations are expensive and time-consuming, but face-to-face interviews with persons who know the applicant can probably provide the most comprehensive and accurate information not only about job performance but about such characteristics as specific abilities, character, personality, and life style. In a study of applicants for civil service positions, material obtained by field investigations and by the ERQ technique correlated fairly well; but the field investigations revealed disqualifying features that escaped the questionnaire method, probably because many people would rather not respond to a written inquiry than give adverse information.

Interviews. All interviewing techniques have two unique advantages. First, they provide a "behavior sample" which permits the interviewer to note such traits as voice, use of language, nervous mannerisms, appearance, poise, and emotional control. And second, they provide a "reactional biography"—that is, they evoke not only the usual factual material but show how the applicant reacts to the events of his life. Through selective probing, a sensitive and skillful interviewer can gain insight into the applicant which no other technique can supply.

There are wide differences, however, among the interviewing procedures in use today. At one extreme is the traditional unorganized, impressionistic approach which varies from applicant to applicant and often fails to focus on relevant information. At the other extreme is the standardized approach which confines itself to a set list of questions without taking advantage of the opportunity for probing, following up cues, and personal interaction. Between the two extremes is the patterned (guided, systematic, semistructured) interview, which covers certain specified areas (work history, education, home situation, etc.) in a uniform sequence, but gives the interviewer a chance to guide the conversation into side channels and ask questions on points that need to be clarified.

Psychological research has thrown considerable light on several aspects of interviewing. First, the interview is subject to many sources of error, such as the halo effect, social stereotypes, indiscriminate use of hunches, incorrect recording, as well as the tendency of the interviewer to inject his own bias by suggesting ideas which the subject then follows, an effect which has been termed "contagious bias." Second, recordings of interviews have shown great variations in susceptibility to these errors, as well as in interviewing skill, and it is now widely recognized that interviewers should be selected with the same care as other technical personnel. Too often they are chosen because they do not fit other jobs or simply because they have "a way with people." A growing number of companies are also introducing intensive training programs, usually conducted by a consulting psychologist, in which basic principles of interviewing are explained and various techniques such as tape recordings, role playing, and supervised practice are utilized. See HALO EFFECT, STEREOTYPE.

Third, tests have been conducted in which a number of untrained but "experienced" interviewers have rated the same group of applicants, using the traditional unplanned type of interview. Their ratings were found to vary so widely that one interviewer might rank a given applicant first and another last. Recent studies of patterned interviews conducted by trained personnel have shown considerably more agreement between interviewers, and substantial correlations have been found between patterned interview ratings of predicted success and actual effectiveness on the job (McMurry, 1947).

PERSONNEL TESTS. The use of personnel tests is constantly increasing. At the present time over one half of all large companies and about 15 per cent of smaller companies include tests in their selection programs. The general practice is to administer a combination of tests, since job requirements are usually complex; and to integrate the results with data from interviews and other techniques. Since the major categories of tests are all described under separate headings, we will limit our comments here to an enumeration of the instruments in widest use today, and some comments on their application to personnel selection as distinguished from their use in educational and vocational counseling. See PERSONNEL SELECTION.

Intelligence Tests. Most intelligence tests are constructed with academic achievement rather than job performance in mind, and are generally more accurate in predicting success in school or college than in business and industry. However, since many jobs require different degrees of general mental ability as well as specific aptitudes, these tests have been found useful for preliminary screening of applicants. Standard intelligence tests used in schools are usually too long for this purpose, and therefore a number of short, easily administered and objectively scored instruments have been developed.

The most widely used industrial test is the Otis Self-Administering Test of Mental Ability, which has been found to correlate fairly well with success in clerical, assembly line, bank teller, and foreman jobs. An adaptation of this test, the Otis Employment Tests, is now under revision. An abridgement of the Otis, the Wonderlic Personnel Test, which takes only twelve minutes to administer, is especially useful in selecting clerical workers. The Adaptability Test, which yields a single score for verbal, numerical, and spatial items, has shown fair evidence of validity for salaried office jobs, clerical work, and for selection of teletype trainees, as well as particularly high validity for supervisory personnel (Tiffin and McCormick, 1965). The Wesman Personnel Classification Test, which yields separate verbal and numerical scores as well as a total score, includes more advanced items than other industrial tests, and is therefore better suited to higher-level personnel. The Oral Directions Test, presented on records, on the other hand, stresses perceptual and spatial items, and appears to be most useful in screening applicants for lower level jobs such as laborer, messenger, maintenance and service workers. It is part of a brief battery, the Personnel Tests for Industry, which also includes a five-minute Verbal Test and a twenty-minute Numerical Test. Several non-language tests, including the Purdue Non-Language Personnel Test and the Progressive Matrices, have been designed for illiterate or foreign-speaking applicants.

Intelligence tests have a number of industrial uses in addition to predicting job performance. Because of their academic character they are particularly helpful in selecting candidates for training programs; their correlations with success in these programs is often higher than with success on the job itself. They are valuable in reducing job turnover, since they help to prevent employment of workers who would be inefficient because they are underqualified, or who would become bored or restless because they are overqualified. They have proved helpful in determining promotion potential, especially when employees are hired in the expectation of being upgraded. On another level, industrial intelligence tests are particularly useful in determining the ability of mental defectives for purposes of job placement and vocational rehabilitation both in institutions and in industry. At the other end of the scale, special tests have been developed by Guilford and others for identifying individuals with creative talent and originality. *See* CREATIVITY TESTS, INTELLIGENCE TESTS.

Special Aptitude Tests. These tests are often tailor-made for particular requirements, but since some aptitudes are common to many jobs, a wide range of standardized tests is also available. Research has shown that it is important to set minimum standards for *vision* and *hearing* for many jobs both in industry and military installations, since sensory capacities have a significant effect on quality and quantity of output, spoilage and waste, accidents, and job turnover. A widely used device is the Ortho-Rater (PLATE 17), an apparatus which tests many visual characteristics at once: near acuity, far acuity, depth perception, muscular balance (phoria), and color discrimination. Individual and group audiometers are available for measuring auditory acuity, the most important single characteristic of hearing; sensitivity to other components such as pitch and loudness may also be measured as needed. *See* VISUAL ACUITY.

The standard *motor skills tests* usually involve simple functions such as inserting pins in holes, or assembling small parts. It is generally best to administer a number of different tests in determining capacity for packing, assembly, and machine operations. For more complex activities, such as piloting a plane, special tests are usually administered. Motor tests often have good predictive value, but their validity has to be checked for each specific job. Some of the *mechanical aptitude tests* also require motor skills, but the major emphasis is on perceptual speed and accuracy, spatial visualization, and mechanical comprehension. The tests involve such operations as determining how geometric forms fit together, assembling different objects like bicycle bells or mousetraps, and interpreting pictures which illustrate mechanical principles, or inserting pins in holes with tweezers or fingers (PLATE 3). The Minnesota Paper

Form Board has proved highly accurate in predicting performance in shop courses, grades in engineering, and job performance. It has also shown some validity in predicting achievement of dentistry and art students. Scores on the Bennett Test of Mechanical Comprehension correlate quite well with performance on many kinds of mechanical jobs, and proved to be one of the best predictors of pilot performance in World War II. *Clerical aptitude tests* yield fairly high correlations with job performance and ratings by office supervisors. However, intelligence tests or composite tests involving verbal and numerical items are usually more effective in selecting higher-level clerical workers such as bank tellers. *See* APTITUDE TESTS (SPECIAL).

Multiple Aptitude Batteries. These batteries are designed to measure different abilities and to provide a profile of scores rather than a single measurement. Among the traits tested by such batteries as the Differential Aptitude Tests (DAT), Flanagan Aptitude Classification Test (FACT), and the General Aptitude Test Battery (GATB) are mechanical reasoning, verbal reasoning, planning, space relations, clerical perception, and motor co-ordination (*Figs. 3, 4, 5, 6*). Up to the present these tests have been most widely used in vocational counseling, but they will probably be increasingly applied to personnel selection and placement.

When applicants are selected for a particular job, most personnel psychologists rely on a general intelligence test plus a group of special aptitude tests. But in dealing with a large manpower pool, it is often advantageous to administer a multiple battery in order to classify the applicants into a few broad categories that cut across many different jobs. Aptitude profiles for different occupations are now being determined, and validation studies are in progress. More of these studies have been made for the DAT than for the FACT and

GATB, but findings on all three batteries are promising. *See* APTITUDE TESTS (MULTIPLE).

Achievement Tests. In industry these tests are called trade tests, since they are designed to assess proficiency on the job rather than in school. Although they measure what the individual can do at the moment, they are useful in predicting future performance, and therefore play the same role as aptitude tests in selection of personnel. In addition, they are frequently employed in measuring the effectiveness of a training program, in determining when trainees have reached the desired level of proficiency, and in identifying employees who need special training or should be transferred or promoted.

Two general types of trade tests are in use today. One type deals with the *information* required for jobs like electrician or carpenter, and is administered in either oral or written form. The questions are based on specific details of the job, and have been carefully pretested for their ability to differentiate between experts, beginners, and workers in related occupations. Among the most widely used written tests are the Purdue Vocational Tests, and among the oral tests are those developed by the United States Employment Service for well over a hundred jobs.

Since it is not enough to test the applicant's information, *job skill tests* are also administered. These are usually of the "work sample" variety, since they are based upon actual operations performed on the job. Common examples are the driver's and pilot's license tests, and clerical tests that involve typing, taking shorthand notes, or solving bookkeeping problems. Industrial tests may involve the use of actual equipment in a plant or specially designed equipment, as in the Miniature Punch Press Test. Experimental tests for certain executive functions have also been tried—for instance, the "In-Basket Tests" which present the subject with a prepared set of incoming letters, memos, reports, and other items which he must process for a hypothetical job.

Personality Tests. The current emphasis on human relations in industry has brought with it a recognition of the importance of personality characteristics for both success and failure. Although workers interact on almost any type of job, personality is a particularly crucial consideration in operations that involve supervision or selling. So far, however, attempts to construct specific objective tests for these areas have not met with much success, probably because they involve intangible traits like social sensitivity and empathy, as well as personal values such as an interest in other people. However, promising studies have been made of the actions and interactions of salesmen in the course of a day's work, and other research has been done on the activities and the responsibilities of executives. Research of this kind may ultimately lead to new personnel selection instruments. *See* SALESMANSHIP.

Meanwhile, business and industry are making increasing use of four types of personality tests of a more general nature. First, even though *interest tests* are more widely used in vocational counseling than in personnel selection, they are sometimes used to see whether an applicant has the type of interests, values, and attitudes that make for success in the area under consideration (*Fig. 41*). The Kuder Preference Record is geared to broad areas (mechanical, scientific, persuasive, etc.), the Strong Vocational Interest Blank is based on patterns of interest associated with specific occupations, the Allport-Vernon-Lindzey Study of Values assesses the strength of the individual's basic approaches to life (theoretical, economic, social, etc.). The more recent Survey of Interpersonal Values shows the relative importance of different relationships to other people, such as sup-

port, conformity, recognition, independence, benevolence, and leadership.

Second, the *personality inventories* used in industry are usually designed to yield a profile of normal traits such as sociability, emotional stability, or achievement drive (*Fig. 41*). Many of them provide verification keys or use a forced-choice technique because of the tendency to give acceptable responses on self-report tests. Three widely used inventory tests are the Guilford-Zimmerman Temperament Survey, the Edwards Personal Preference Schedule (EPPS), and the Jurgensen Classification Inventory. *See* PERSONALITY INVENTORY.

Third, *projective techniques* are occasionally used for intensive individual evaluation of executives and for assessment of managerial potential. The Thematic Apperception Test (TAT), or adaptations of it, is probably most often chosen for this purpose. Another test, the Tomkins-Horn Picture Arrangement Test (PAT), has been especially designed for group administration to industrial personnel (*Fig. 41*). Material obtained through these or other projective techniques must be interpreted by a clinical psychologist. Although they may throw considerable light on the applicant, they cannot be regarded as tests in the usual sense of the term. *See* PROJECTIVE TESTS, THEMATIC APPERCEPTION TEST, TOMKINS-HORN PICTURE ARRANGEMENT TEST.

Fourth, another method of personnel evaluation which has been adapted to industrial use is the *situational test*. In this type of test the applicant is required to face a situation that calls for the type of attitudes or personality traits needed on the job itself. In this sense the test is actually a variation on the work sample technique described above. The most celebrated example is the OSS series of stress tests used during World War II. One type of industrial test involves typical face-to-face situations encountered by an administrator—for example, he may be required to carry

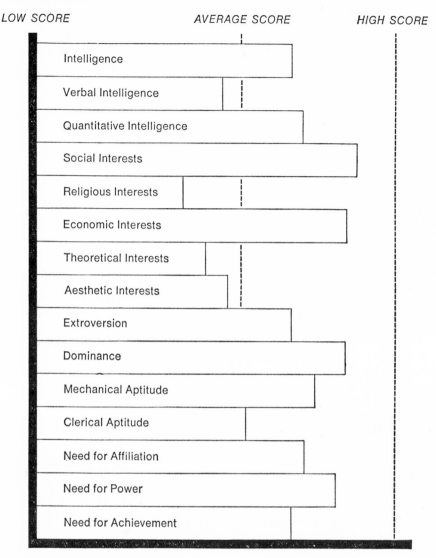

LOW SCORE   AVERAGE SCORE   HIGH SCORE

Intelligence

Verbal Intelligence

Quantitative Intelligence

Social Interests

Religious Interests

Economic Interests

Theoretical Interests

Aesthetic Interests

Extroversion

Dominance

Mechanical Aptitude

Clerical Aptitude

Need for Affiliation

Need for Power

Need for Achievement

Fig. 41. A psychograph, or trait profile, characterizing a single individual on a number of dimensions of personality and ability.

out an interview with a man playing the role of a qualified worker who has been falling down on the job (American Institute for Research, 1957). Another effective technique is the Leaderless Group Discussion in which a group of applicants, such as supervisors, sales trainees, or social workers, is assigned a topic for discussion. Observers rate each person's performance, but do not participate in the discussion. A number of studies have shown significant correlations between these ratings and future performance in jobs requiring interpersonal relations, oral communication, verbal problem-solving, and social acceptance. Here again the test is best interpreted as a work sample rather than a general test of personality traits. *See* OSS ASSESSMENT TESTS.

Psychologists recognize that personality tests are particularly subject to abuses on the part of both the applicant and the employer. It must be remembered that the employer can set up his own criteria in interpreting many of these tests, and he may also have tests constructed to suit his particular purposes. For his part, the sophisticated applicant can in some cases falsify his answers to fit the values which he believes are stressed by the company. These practices do not in themselves vitiate the tests. They do, however, serve as reminders of the necessity of (1) utilizing the services of highly professional psychologists, (2) selecting instruments that cannot be easily faked, and (3) integrating the results of personality tests with information on the applicant obtained from interviews and other sources.

PERSONNEL TRAINING. Training procedures designed to increase the efficiency of existing personnel in business and industry.

An ever-increasing number of companies are introducing planned, systematic training programs. Their major objectives are to help employees adjust to changes in industrial operations, to give them an opportunity for promotion, and to meet the growing need for higher-level personnel. This article will deal with training procedures instituted below the supervisory level. For training at the managerial level, *see* MANAGEMENT DEVELOPMENT.

Before World War II, personnel training was usually carried out without benefit of professional assistance, but since that time industrial psychologists have come to play a large part in well-organized programs geared to the special needs of the plant. They have also been instrumental in broadening the concept of personnel training so that it now includes not only the traditional goals of developing job knowledge and job skills, but the added goals of trans-

mitting information about company products and policies, and of improving the morale and interpersonal relations of the employees.

A wide variety of training programs are in use today, covering both new employees and experienced workers who are promising prospects for advancement or who would profit from refresher courses. In general, they fall into these three types: (a) *orientation training,* designed to acquaint new employees with the company and to develop favorable attitudes and motivations; (b) *on-the-job training,* given either informally, and often casually, by a supervisor, or, more formally and systematically by a special instructor; (c) *off-the-job training,* often given in a "vestibule" training school in which simulated equipment is used, and sometimes combined with on-the-job training to facilitate transfer to the actual work situation. In addition, some companies have special training programs for college graduates, who shift from department to department in order to prepare themselves for future management positions; a few offer courses of a cultural or recreational nature, and still fewer send selected employees to colleges or universities for additional education.

Four major steps are required in developing a training program: (1) determination of training needs, (2) task analysis, (3) selection of training procedures, media, aids, and devices, and (4) periodic evaluation, especially during a trial period. Each of these will be briefly described.

Training Needs. In planning a program, the specific training needs should first be systematically established through surveys of production, accidents, turnover and other records, as well as through interviews and conferences with foremen and other supervisors, and questionnaires to be answered by the employees themselves. Checklists are frequently employed in identifying entire departments or areas in which training may be desirable. Merit ratings are consulted when it is a question of locating individual employees who need training. A study by Mahler and Monroe (1952) has shown that training directors prefer five methods of determining training needs: informal observation, requests from management, talks with supervisors, group discussions, and analysis of reports.

Task Analysis. This is a detailed study of the job itself to identify the skills, information and attitudes required for successful performance. Task analysis closely resembles job analysis, but the worker's operation is usually broken down into finer units, since the purpose is to discover which activities require the most and which require the least training, as well as the most effective sequence in which training should be given. The procedures followed in making a task analysis are primarily: observation of workers, consultation with workers and supervisors, examination of operating manuals, and a study of records and reports that might help to locate areas of difficulty and causes of poor performance. *See* JOB ANALYSIS.

Training Procedures, Media, and Aids. Due largely to the influence of industrial and educational psychologists, industry is becoming increasingly aware that basic learning principles must be applied if training programs are to be effective. For this reason recent books such as Tiffin and McCormick (1965) include a review of learning principles, with comments on their application to training programs. Here are some of the major concepts with a few relevant questions: (1) *Motivation:* how much should the program stress material incentives like promotion and higher pay, as well as non-material incentives such as praise, encouragement, and realistic goals? (2) *Participation:* What is the best way for the worker to get a maximum of practice under guidance? (3) *Knowledge of Results, or "Feedback":* What can be done to let the learner know how well he is doing, so that correct behavior will be reinforced and errors eliminated? (4) *Distribution of Practice:* What is the optimal practice session, and how should the sessions be spaced? (5) *Whole versus part learning:* Is it best to learn this particular operation piecemeal, as a whole, or through a combination of the two? (6) *Freedom from Stress:* What is the best way to avoid anxiety, embarrassment, distraction, and other stress factors that interfere with learning? (7) *Transfer of Learning:* What is the best way to facilitate the application of the learning experience to the actual job?

In developing a program, the specialist must not only find answers for these questions, but select the training media and devices which are most appropriate for the specific job and the type of trainee. The methods in most common use below the supervisory level are:

Lectures: Usually given in person, but sometimes on film, television, or recordings, with the aid of charts, models, etc.; often used for orientation on plant organization or safety rules, but sometimes for preliminary explanations of job procedures.

Demonstrations: Especially useful in showing operations and use of equipment; should be followed by active participation and practice.

Training Manuals and other printed materials: especially suitable for orientation purposes or for learning long operational sequences, since the material can be read and consulted repeatedly.

Films and TV: A good substitute or supplement for lectures, since the best instructors can be used, and demonstrations can be viewed in closeup or slow motion; especially useful in discrimination training (for example, reading a radarscope), dramatic safety education, modification of attitudes, or viewing operations from the "subjective" standpoint of the worker himself.

Training Devices and Simulators:

Typical devices are flight trainers for student pilots, gunnery trainers for practice in visual tracking, apparatus for training technicians in trouble-shooting electronic equipment, and flight simulators which reproduce complete instrument panels, controls, engine sounds, and motions of the cockpit. Such devices have a number of advantages: active participation, repeated practice, emphasis on critical activities, and immediate feedback. The flight simulator, for example, requires the trainee to respond to situations presented on a motion picture screen as if he were actually operating the plane.

Programmed Instruction: This technique has the advantage of presenting material in small, easily mastered steps, and permits the subject to pace his own learning and test himself as he proceeds. Programs used in industrial training are usually presented on teaching machines, and sometimes on film, rather than in textbook form. In contrast to the automated training devices described above, they are confined to verbal material. Typical programs deal with retail selling, principles of life insurance, billing procedures, data-processing, and "verbal pretraining" of electronic maintenance technicians. *See* PROGRAMMED LEARNING.

Job Performance: That is, actually working under the guidance of an experienced employee, supervisor, or instructor. The traditional on-the-job training was a casual and unplanned affair, based on the faulty assumption that good performers make good teachers. Today this procedure has been vastly improved through systematic training of supervisors or selected employees, as well as the use of special instructors. Its effectiveness can also be increased through vestibule schools, which provide training in a separate room, and through apprenticeship programs which combine classroom instruction with guided practice on the job.

Finally, training programs can reach their maximum level of effectiveness only if they are periodically evaluated. This requires, first, setting up the criteria to be used, such as hourly output, time required, breakage, accidents, absenteeism, labor turnover; and second, making comparisons in job performance of the same group before and after training, or of a trained group with a control group, or between two or more groups trained by different methods. A number of studies have shown that training brings substantial results. In World War II, when a "whole learning" method was introduced in teaching Morse code to radio operators, the normal training time decreased from about thirty-seven to twenty-seven hours, and the number of failures fell from 15 to 3.4 per cent (Keller, 1943). Another study involved the use of a special practice and recording device in training employees to cut small tungsten discs. After only eleven weeks of training, these men reached a production level that ordinarily took five months to achieve, and at the same time the labor turnover and absentee rates were cut about 50 per cent, and the accident rate about 19 per cent (Lindahl, 1945). In still another study a systematic training program was conducted for shoe machinists, involving films, filmstrips, and training devices, with independent learning of different units followed by combining them in practice. As a result of this program, the normal training period was reduced from one year to about seven weeks. Moreover, during their first month of employment, the trainees made more money on piece rate than experienced workers who had received the usual unplanned on-the-job training. (Singleton, 1959)

PERSONOLOGY. A holistic theory of personality developed by Henry A. Murray, based on the concept of need.

Murray has offered a formal—and formidable—definition of personality in these terms: "Personality is the continuity of functional forms and forces manifested through sequences of organized regnant processes and overt behaviors from birth to death" (Kluckhohn et al., 1953). This definition means that personality is a set of enduring tendencies organized by the brain as a means of adapting to life. Still more simply, it is the mediator between the individual's needs and the demands of the environment.

The key to this approach lies in the concept of need, which is viewed as a force that organizes all mental processes—perception, apperception, action, intellect—in order to change an existing situation and reach a desired result. Needs can be aroused by either internal or external stimulation, and are instrumental in setting up and maintaining action until they are met. Murray and his colleagues at the Harvard Psychological Clinic attempted to identify the most fundamental human needs by conducting intensive studies of a limited number of subjects. In carrying out their investigations, they employed no less than twenty-five different procedures for assessing personality, and created a new technique, the Thematic Apperception Test (TAT), which was especially designed to elicit fantasy responses. This technique later became a widely accepted projective method. *See* this topic.

Over a score of fundamental needs were identified and divided into two types. The *primary* or *viscerogenic* needs arise from organic processes and lead to physical satisfaction: air, food, sex, urination, defecation, water, etc. *Secondary* or *psychogenic* needs are ultimately derived from primary needs, but are not associated with specific organic processes or physical satisfactions. Among them are achievement, dominance, recognition, aggression, exhibition, nurturance, construction, play, and affiliation. Each of these needs can be manifested in a number of ways—

for example, aggression is expressed in forcefully overcoming opposition, fighting, punishing others, etc.; play takes the form of laughing and making jokes, relaxation, dancing, games, social drinking; and the need for achievement is shown in accomplishing difficult tasks, mastering skills, developing ideas, or organizing human beings. Frequently several needs may be satisfied by a single activity. Competition in business can be a form of aggression, a game, and an expression of the need for achievement all at once.

In his conception of needs, Murray was greatly influenced by the psychoanalytic theory. Like Freud, he derived many of them from examining motivating forces and developmental patterns during childhood. He also recognized that some needs are overt and recognizable, while others are latent and repressed. Although he did not give as much prominence to sex and hostility as Freud, he nevertheless held that these drives as well as others, such as achievement, are "determinant needs," since they regulate large segments of behavior and enlist other, so-called "subsidiary needs" in their service. On the other hand, Murray did not follow Freud in relegating the primary impulses (the id) to a lower, more primitive order, since he viewed physical needs from the standpoint of survival. He also stressed the ego ideal more than did Freud—that is, the individual's concept of himself in fully realized form, which serves as a guiding image for his life. *See* ID, EGO IDEAL.

Two additional concepts are essential in Murray's basic formulation: perceptual press and thema. A press is a stimulus or situation which is capable of arousing a need. It is effective only when a need is present—for example, an apple appears desirable only when we are hungry and not when we are satiated. A given press may therefore be strong at one time and weak or nonexistent at another. Some of the more important presses in childhood are: birth of a sibling; feelings of physical, intellectual, or social inferiority; and family conditions such as an unsettled home, parental discord, or the absence of a parent. Presses of this kind act as instigating forces affecting both the arousal and expression of the child's fundamental needs. In other words, Murray's concept of press is a recognition of the influence of the social situation and other environmental factors upon the individual. This, too, is a departure from Freudian theory, which places far more emphasis on internal, unconscious factors than on the external situation.

According to Murray, needs and presses affect each other and produce the individual's characteristic reactions with his environment. These patterns of behavior are termed "themas." To give one example, a harshly treated child might develop rancorous resentments against all authority; these resentments may be expressed in present hostility toward his parents, or repressed and stored up for future expression. The TAT was originated as a means of discovering such themas and the situations or "presses" that gave rise to them. In this technique, the subject examines ambiguous pictures and makes up stories based on them. By using this instrument as well as other tests and observations, Murray believed it would be possible to construct a rounded, holistic conception of an individual's personality on both the conscious and unconscious levels.

Murray has offered a detailed, complex theory of personality based upon the expression of fundamental needs. It stresses the uniqueness of the individual, since each person manifests his needs and develops his themas in his own way. This emphasis has focused attention on the study of single individuals in depth as opposed to statistical investigation of large numbers of people. Murray felt that an intensive investigation of these single individuals would require many techniques, many approaches, and many observers. He therefore proposed a "diagnostic council" which would synthesize physical, social, and psychoanalytic findings, and arrive at a unified, holistic portrait of the personality. This comprehensive approach has been adopted by many specialists in the clinical field. See MOTIVATION (GENERAL), PERSONALITY INVENTORY, SOCIOMETRY, HOLISM.

PERSUASION THERAPY. The use of persuasion as an instrument in psychotherapy.

Today few if any students of psychology and psychiatry believe a patient can be literally talked out of an emotional disturbance. Nevertheless many therapists find a place for persuasion in dealing with at least the milder disorders. Instead of searching out the underlying causes or "psychodynamics" behind the problem, they may at times focus directly on faulty attitudes and patterns of behavior, and attempt to induce the patient to change them by appealing to his powers of reasoning, will, and self-criticism.

The persuasion technique is not so crude as a simple "snap out of it" approach. The therapist acts the part of a teacher rather than merely a morale builder. He usually begins by sympathetically exploring the patient's problem with him, and then goes on to point out that he is employing the wrong approach in dealing with it. He may explain, for example, that his patient's tendency to forget important appointments is an attempt to escape from the truth, or that he is using a demand for perfection as a means of dominating other people. In some cases the therapist may also relate drives of this sort to earlier experiences, such as constant criticism received by the patient when he was a child. He also encourages his patient to try to change his faulty patterns of adjustment, and expresses confidence that he can do so.

Persuasion has been proposed by some therapists—notably P. C. Dubois, Joseph Déjerine, and Alfred Adler—as an alternative to extended psychoanalytic therapy. Dubois viewed the process as an attempt to convince the patient by argument that his neurotic reactions were irrational; Déjérine and Adler believed an emotional change must take place and emphasized the value of warmth, interest, and encouragement on the part of the therapist. All three, however, believed it is not necessary or even desirable to attempt a thoroughgoing reconstruction of the personality when simpler and quicker methods of behavior change are possible. Critics of the technique maintain that such changes are likely to be superficial and temporary. *See* ADLER, RE-EDUCATION.

PHANTOM REACTION. A psychological disturbance occurring in individuals who have lost a limb or other body part. The reaction consists of various annoying or painful sensations and a feeling, for a time at least, that the missing member is still there.

Phantom phenomena are explained by the fact that every individual forms an image of his own body as a whole, and this image persists when he is deprived of part of his anatomy. Significantly, people who are born with a limb missing, or who undergo amputation very early in life, do not experience phantom reactions. On the other hand, studies of amputees have revealed that 98 per cent experienced a persistent feeling that the limb was still there after the operation (Noyes and Kolb, 1963).

Definite feelings are localized in the phantom limb. Most common is a mild tingling; but a pins-and-needles sensation may also be aroused by touching the stump. If disease occurs in other organs, such as the stomach, pain is sometimes felt in the phantom limb.

As time goes on an emotionally healthy amputee will automatically revise his body concept. The phantom appendage gradually appears to shrink and finally disappears, although manipulation of the stump may produce a sensation of movement in the missing extremity long afterward.

In some cases intensely annoying or painful sensations may be localized in the nonexistent limb, especially sensations of twisting, pulling, burning, or itching. If these sensations continue, it usually indicates that the patient is having difficulty in accepting his defect and adjusting to a prosthetic limb—or that he is experiencing acute family and occupational problems as a result of his loss. Occasionally the painful sensations are associated with fantasies concerning the disposal of the amputated limb.

These patients usually benefit from psychological treatment. The particular form of therapy is determined by the extent and nature of the disturbance. The techniques most commonly used are narcotherapy, hypnosis, electroshock, or suggestion accompanied by tranquilizing drugs.

Illustrative Case: PHANTOM REACTION

A fourteen-year-old boy was brought to the hospital to have his right leg amputated because of a malignant tumor. Shortly after the operation, he complained of intense pain and burning sensations in the phantom limb, and by the ninth day he was thrashing about the bed and threatening to jump out of the window. A psychiatrist was called in, and in time the boy revealed that his teacher had once told a story about an amputee who had developed a severe stinging sensation in his phantom limb. The leg had been disinterred and ants were found burrowing into it. The psychiatrist then asked the boy what he thought had been done to his own limb, and he answered that he thought it had been burned. He was assured that this was not so, and as a result his pain and overactivity subsided considerably.

The case, however, proved to be considerably more complicated. During four additional hours of psychotherapy, the psychiatrist learned that the boy's mother had developed a cancer of the breast, and although the breast was removed, she had died five years before his operation. The boy had developed a repressed hostility against his mother, and had never spoken of her since that time. When his leg was amputated, he unconsciously identified with his mother as an amputee, and his buried hostility was instrumental in bringing about his emotional disturbance.

In the course of psychotherapy the phantom pain disappeared and the boy became eager to have a prosthesis fitted. A year later his stepmother wrote that he had returned to his studies and was doing well in all respects. (Adapted from Noyes and Kolb, 1963)

PHENOMENOLOGY. The view that psychology, and all other science, should be ultimately based on a description of immediate experience—that is, on the process of attending to and grasping phenomena as they are directly presented. The initiator of the phenomenology movement was the German philosopher, Edmund Husserl (1859–1938).

Phenomenologists hold that science must take immediate experience—the "given"—as its starting point. Observation must come before explanation, otherwise we will miss the essential nature of the events we are trying to explain. This can be illustrated by the familiar Müller-Lyer illusion, which presents two equal lines side by side, one of which ends with arrows pointing inward and the other with arrows pointing outward (*Fig. 29a*). If a scientist were to rely on the usual empirical approach, he would simply measure the lines and find that they are equal, and that would be that. However, in doing so he would completely overlook the existence of the illusion itself, for to the observer the lines actually appear unequal. Only a phenomenological approach would take this fact into account.

This initial phase of phenomenological observation is essential to later phases of theorizing, for we must experience the phenomenon before we can go on to discover its causes. The phenomenologist, therefore, deliberately adopts an attitude of neutrality toward experience. He first accepts it as it is presented to consciousness without introducing analysis and speculation. This suggests what causal relationships are to be sought. In other words, we must see the colors, smell the odors, experience the illusions that are *there* before we can begin to explain them. The phenomenological approach, then, plays an important role as an introductory stage in psychological investigations. It is also important in psychiatry —for example, in attempting to get "inside the mind" of a schizophrenic patient or a person under the influence of a hallucinogenic drug.

Many of the early discoveries in the field of sensation stem from the phenomenological viewpoint. Among them were Goethe's acute observations of color phenomena, Purkinje's discovery of the effect that is now named after him (the shift of colors which occurs as darkness comes on), and Fechner's studies of size constancy, in which he showed that receding objects, such as a man walking away from us, appear to shrink very slowly in size even though the actual image on the retina of our eye grows rapidly smaller. The smell prism and color solid are also based on immediately observed data. In more recent psychology, the clearest example is the Gestalt approach to perception. This approach is basically phenomenological, since the Gestaltists hold that patterns and configurations are directly and immediately given, and not the result of later analysis or interpretation. *See* PERCEPTUAL CONSTANCY, COLOR SOLID, CONTRAST EFFECT, SMELL PRISM, DARK ADAPTATION, GESTALT PSYCHOLOGY.

Phenomenology is not a comprehensive theory of behavior. Rather, it is a point of departure for investigating the human being. Its main function is probably to serve as a reminder when the human sciences become involved in complex theories that get further and further away from actual experience. If we listen to the phenomenologist, we will go back to the foundations on which all science must be built—the sensations, feelings and fantasies which make up the raw data of the world as we see it. *See* EXISTENTIALISM.

PHENYLKETONURIA (PKU) (Phenylpyruvic Oligophrenia). A congenital metabolic disorder that may result in mental retardation. The newborn infant appears normal, but lacks an enzyme needed in the metabolism of phenylalanine, an amino acid found in protein foods.

Accumulation of phenylalanine in the blood can damage the brain during the first year of life, and produces such symptoms as vomiting, eczema, seizures, and a peculiar musty odor. If the condition is not arrested, it will lead to moderate or severe mental deficiency generally accompanied by defects in coordination and posture (bent head and body). Some victims suffer from persistent dermatitis and convulsions, and untreated patients may never learn to speak. Frequently the disorder is first detected through signs of mental defect, but the medical diagnosis is primarily based on the presence of phenylpyruvic acid in the urine.

About one per cent of all institutionalized mental defectives are PKU cases. The disorder is believed to be transmitted by a recessive gene, and occurs about once in ten thousand births. Authorities recommend that the urine of all infants be tested between the third and ninth weeks and frequently thereafter if there is evidence of this disorder in the family. A special diet low in phenylalanine will pre-vent or greatly limit brain damage in most cases. The child is usually fed a preparation such as Lofenalac, containing an acid hydrolyzate of casein, very low in phenylalanine, supplemented with additional amino acids, vitamins, and minerals.

In 1962 the National Institutes of Health and the Children's Bureau sponsored a PKU prevention program in which blood specimens of all newborn infants were tested as part of the hospital routine. Twenty-five PKU cases were located during the year and placed on preventive diets. If these children had not been treated, and had lived in institutions for the retarded until thirty-five to forty years of age, the cost to the state would have been over two million dollars more than the cost of the testing program—not to mention the value of potential earnings or the cost in terms of human suffering. About forty states now have laws requiring all newborn babies to be screened for the defect. *See* MENTAL RETARDATION (CAUSES).

PHOBIA. An intense obsessive fear which the individual cannot control even though he usually realizes that it is unreasonable.

Phobias may be focused on objects such as cats or knives, acts such as building a fire or sexual intercourse; or situations such as finding one's self alone on a street or being caught in a crowd. In any case the feelings of dread are out of all proportion to the apparent stimuli because they actually stem from sources deep within the personality.

In general, they arise in three ways: (a) from a single traumatic experience or a series of such experiences (being bitten by a large dog); (b) from unconscious anxieties which the feared objects or situations represent or symbolize; and (c) from a combination of these two sources—that is, the individual has had a disturbing experience in the past but revives it as a result of underlying conflicts and anxieties.

Almost anything can become an object of morbid dread, and it is therefore not possible to make a full inventory of phobias. At one time investigators vied with each other in devising Greek names for these fears. A dread of bees was termed melissophobia; dread of sermons, homilophobia; dread of virgins, parthenophobia; dread of crossing water, gephyrophobia; and fear of blushing in public, erthyrophobia. A few others are entomophobia (insects), eosophobia (dawn), gymnophobia (naked bodies), haptephobia (being touched), heliophobia (sunlight), gamophobia (marriage), emetophobia (vomiting), and enosiophobia (committing an unpardonable sin). Such terms display a greater knowledge of Greek and Latin than of psychology.

Today investigators concentrate on the *dynamics* of all phobias, and apply special names only to the most common varieties, such as acrophobia (high places); agoraphobia (open spaces), ailurophobia or galeophobia (cats), algophobia (pain), astraphobia (storms), claustrophobia (closed places), hematophobia (blood), mysophobia (contamination, germs), monophobia or eremophobia (being alone), nyctophobia (darkness), ocholophobia (crowds), pathophobia (disease), pyrophobia (fire), syphilophobia (syphilis), xenophobia (strangers), zoophobia (animals, or a particular animal). Some authorities include an all-embracing fear—panphobia, a dread of anything and everything—but others claim this is a form of diffuse anxiety rather than a true phobic reaction. *See* ANXIETY, PHOBIC REACTION.

Illustrative Case: PHOBIA, AGORAPHOBIA

Ellen R., a thirty-two-year-old woman, developed a severe case of agoraphobia in which she became terrified each time she attempted to leave her house. The phobia became so serious that she gave up her job, and remained home at all times. When she sought psychological help, it was found that when she was in her early teens she had been sexually promiscuous with several boys in the neighborhood. The patient changed her behavior when the family moved to another neighborhood, and she entered a new school. She experienced intense guilt feelings about her behavior, and she repressed all memories of it. The phobia which developed later in her life was based on the fear that she might lose control of herself, and be led into a life of prostitution. Without realizing what had happened, the patient had reactivated the entire episode some weeks earlier when she was going through some old papers and found a group photograph of herself at the time she had been promiscuous. The chain of unconscious associations triggered by the picture was responsible for the appearance of the agoraphobia at that particular time. (Kisker, 1964)

PHOBIC REACTION. A psychoneurosis characterized by persistent unrealistic fears, or phobias, of such an intense and dominating character that they interfere with everyday activities.

The individual who is afraid to enter an elevator or walk across an open field usually realizes that he has nothing to fear, yet he is powerless to help himself. If he persists in facing the dreaded situations, he is beset with feelings of uneasiness or suffers an anxiety attack that may reach panic proportions. In addition to his specific fears, he is usually afflicted with physiological signs of anxiety such as headaches, stomach upsets, dizzy spells and backaches. These symptoms usually arouse the further fear that he has a serious organic disease or is about to "crack up."

Phobic reactions are most frequently found among young adults and are far more common among women than men, possibly because intense fears are more socially acceptable in the female sex. Many phobias are rooted in the common experience of mankind—for example, fears of fire, disease, or darkness. Others are related to unique experiences or the individual workings of the unconscious. Recent investigations have shown that they may also be associated with the culture of the times. This is well illustrated by a study of four patients who developed a phobia for outer space. All four were worried that the earth would deviate from its course and be destroyed by a collision in outer space. They felt that artificial satellites increased this danger. Here is a portion of the record of one of these patients, a robust thirty-year-old schoolteacher:

"He felt unsafe 'because the earth is a ball spinning around and I am on it.' Occasionally the horizon seemed to tilt and if he looked at a picture he felt it was about to turn over. He became completely incapacitated and had to be admitted to a hospital with a fear 'of going to disappear into outer space.' . . . He had to keep reminding himself that the force of gravity was keeping him down—'otherwise I would float into space.' At this time he blamed his illness on his resentment of changes at work. Phrases which commonly occurred included: 'It's outer space that's getting me—the curvature of the globe makes everything insecure'; 'We are surrounded by a hostile envelopment—if I think about it I want to run for cover . . .' If he went outside and saw other people he would say, 'Do these other people realize what danger they are in on this spinning ball we call a globe?' His fear was summed up by himself as follows: 'Primitive man had a fear of the sun and the moon and the stars, and I am the same.'" (Kerry, 1960)

Phobic reactions must not be taken at face value. To understand them it is necessary to consider whether they are the result of early experiences and conditioning, or reflect unconscious conflicts and personality weaknesses. Conditioned fears can usually be explained by the standard concepts of learning theory. After a painful session at the dentist, a child might tense up every time the doctor's name is mentioned.

He might also come to fear anything associated with the experience, such as drills of any kind. In addition he might, through the process of "generalization," develop a fear of any man in a white coat, including researchers and street cleaners. Similarly, a single traumatic experience, such as a near-drowning, may lead to a lasting fear of water.

Fears can also be contracted from others. A phobic mother who cowers in the corner every time a thunderstorm approaches will probably communicate her fear to her children—and the more frequently this occurs, the more firmly will the conditioned response be established.

These conditioned fears are usually isolated responses that should not be put in the same category as deeply neurotic phobic reactions. True, they may be extremely upsetting. Also they probably persist longest in people who feel insecure, and may be revived during periods of personality stress. Nevertheless, they do not originate from internal conflicts, immaturities, inadequacies, or other typical neurotic sources.

In contrast, psychoneurotic phobic reactions are unconscious personality defenses. The individual who is in the grip of internal conflicts, or who is faced with a threatening situation, feels extremely anxious. He then displaces, or transfers, this anxiety to specific objects or situations that would not otherwise be feared. Usually the object or situation is related to the basic anxiety in a symbolic way—for example, a woman's phobia for pointed objects may represent a fear of men, or a phobia for black may symbolize a fear of death. Phobias of this kind are actually protective devices, since if the individual stays away from the feared object or situation, he succeeds to some extent in controlling his basic anxiety. In a word, by avoiding the symbol, he avoids some of the anxiety it represents.

Classical analysts believe that the anxiety leading to phobic defenses arises from sexual and especially Oedipal sources. This view is based largely on Freud's famous case of the boy Hans who had a morbid dread of horses. Freud believed that this was a displaced dread of his father, and the fear that he might castrate him for desiring to possess his mother. *See* CASTRATION COMPLEX.

More recent investigators trace phobic reactions to many other types of stress situations. For example, a young storekeeper whose business was in danger of failing found his small shop so stuffy and confining that he had to close it, thus saving himself the ignominy of failure. He was, of course, completely unaware of the source of his anxiety. Similarly, Arieti (1961) points out that many phobias represent fears, doubts, and uncertainties that have nothing to do with sex. A phobia for speaking in public may stem from a fear of revealing one's inadequacies, and a phobia for traveling may conceal the larger fear of making excursions into life.

These examples bring up another point about phobias. Like dream symbols, they must be interpreted in the light of the individual's own experience. The same feared object or situation may have totally different meanings for different people. A phobia for closed spaces (claustrophobia) may in one case represent a fear of becoming too intimate with other people; in another, it may symbolize fear of the sexual embrace; in a third, a fear of suffocation arising from some earlier experience—and in the storekeeper just mentioned, it was a face-saving device.

Neurotic fears, then, serve to protect the individual from conflicts, weaknesses, and anxieties. They may also protect him against his own dangerous impulses, usually of a sexual or aggressive nature. A child who harbors a strong and guilty wish to harm his parents may develop a fear of guns or sharp instruments of any kind. His fear helps him resist the temptation of using them against his parents. The man who develops a phobic avoidance of all bodies of water—lakes, rivers, swimming pools—may be unconsciously resisting an overwhelming impulse to drown his wife. In more than one case a phobia for syphilis has been traced to the fear of engaging in homosexual relations: by preventing all sexual relations, this phobia defends the individual against his guilty tendencies. On the other hand, an exaggerated fear of syphilis may represent an unconscious fear of punishment for engaging in any sexual relations at all—a fear that is sometimes instilled by parents as a means of keeping their children on the straight and narrow path.

Although these phobias protect the individual from the anxiety caused by unacceptable impulses, they hinder him in two ways. First, they conceal the true source of his difficulties, since he believes he is merely afflicted by a slightly odd but relatively unimportant fear. Second, they tend to restrict his life by preventing him from traveling or swimming or engaging in normal relationships. This is the price he pays for his neurosis.

There does not seem to be a specific phobic personality pattern. Some studies do indicate that phobic individuals tend to be somewhat immature, passive personalities who attempt to flee from their difficulties instead of facing them. They may also be dependent, helpless people who look to others for support —as illustrated by the fact that a person with acrophobia (fear of heights), will probably be able to climb a hill if he is accompanied by someone he trusts. Many phobic people come from families in which one or both parents are phobic. The parents may not only transmit specific fears, but set the stage for the expression of unconscious conflicts through phobias later on in life.

Treatment of phobic reactions may take several forms. A phobia which has resulted from a severe traumatic experience may be eliminated or at least mitigated by a program of reassurance and desensitization. This should be done as soon after the experience as is possible. A person who has almost drowned, for example, might be encouraged to go wading with a trusted friend, and after that he might swim with other people in shallow water, and in this way gradually extinguish his phobia.

Another deconditioning procedure consists in gradually associating the dreaded object or situation with a pleasant experience. This was successfully carried out in a recent case (Lazarus, 1960) in which an eight-year-old boy had developed an intense fear of moving vehicles as a result of a motor accident. The subject of transportation was introduced during an interview, and the boy was rewarded with chocolate each time he made a positive comment concerning any vehicle. He could soon talk freely about all types of moving vehicles. Next, the interviewer dramatized a series of accidents with toy cars, and gave the boy a piece of chocolate after each incident. Following this, the lad was seated in a non-moving vehicle and then in a slowly moving vehicle, with the same reinforcement applied each time. He was finally able to enjoy motoring without anxiety.

Where phobic reactions result from personality maladjustments rather than traumatic experiences, reconditioning techniques may also be used in alleviating the most disturbing symptoms, but extensive psychotherapy is often required to alter the basic behavior patterns that gave rise to them. *See* BEHAVIOR THERAPY, SCHOOL PHOBIA, PANIC.

Illustrative Case: PHOBIC REACTION

Anne A., an eighteen-year-old girl, was brought to the psychiatric outpatient clinic by her family, who stated that they were greatly concerned over the patient's irrational fear of small pets: dogs, cats, and even canaries. So marked was the patient's apprehensiveness in this regard that, to guard against the possibility that such an animal might somehow enter the house at night, she insisted on locking all the doors and windows of her house and those of her own and her parents' bedrooms, while leaving an intercommunicating door between the two rooms open. Psychiatric examination revealed many other obsessions, compulsions, and neurotic symptoms, but the apparent origin of the animal phobia was of particular interest. The circumstances may be outlined briefly as follows:

The patient had been a particularly indulged child until the age of four, but had then been almost completely displaced in her parents' affections when her mother gave birth to a long-anticipated son. The patient at first showed frank jealousy of her infant brother, but when this merely increased what she sensed to be her parents' rejection of her, she became an apparently devoted sister except for one significant displacement: she was persistently destructive to her brother's clothes and other belongings, and particularly so to such of his toys as were mechanically animated. The parents, distressed by the patient's aggressions but blind to their motivations, sought to cure her by giving her a kitten in order, as they remember it, "to show Anne how cute and lovable any little pet could be." Anne professed delight and seemed to cherish the kitten; once, however, in her parents' absence, she so mistreated it that they later found it dead. Her punishment, now prompted by an intuitive recognition by the parents of the unconscious intent of the patient's act, was made unusually severe. The patient's overt hostilities and destructiveness diminished, but unfortunately she developed various other neurotic patterns, prominent among which were a recurrent anxiety syndrome and a persistent fear of being alone with small animals of any description. Now thoroughly alarmed, the parents again began to shower attentions on the patient but, regrettably, mainly on the rationalized basis that she was a "sick, nervous child" who needed frequent medical and pediatric consultations. As may have been expected, this merely fixated the patient's phobias and other neurotic reactions until, after many years of well-meaning parental and medical mismanagement, she entered the Clinics for psychiatric therapy.

Comment. In this case then, it may be seen that the patient's persistent phobia of animals had little relation to fear of physical injury by them, but served quite other and deeply unconscious functions. On the one hand it protected her from temptations to express aggressions originally directed against her brother, and on the other it signified a reunion with her parents, as unconsciously symbolized by the open door between their bedrooms, and by the precautions against outside intruders. The secondary gain of her phobic state was also symbolic: i.e., it secured renewed attention and protective indulgence from her parents or from various surrogates such as nurses and doctors.

Thus, many phobias are defensive mechanisms that protect the neurotic patient from situations in which his own repressed aggressive or erotic impulses might become dangerous; and at the same time the behavior patterns induced by his phobias may bring him substitutive and regressive satisfactions. (Masserman, 1961)

PHRENOLOGY. The belief that different psychological faculties are located in specific areas of the brain, and that personality traits can be judged by the size and location of protrusions or "bumps" on the skull.

This theory of personality was proposed by Franz Josef Gall (1758–1828) in Germany in the early eighteen hundreds. It was later taken over by Johann Kaspar Spurzheim (1776–1832), who coined the term phrenology, meaning "science of the mind." In their hands the theory was more than a method of reading character, since it was based on the belief that anatomical and physical factors have a direct influence on mental behavior. The latter point of view played an important role in introducing the scientific study of the mind: "It is almost correct to say that scientific psychology was born of phrenology, out of wedlock with science." (Boring, 1950)

The phrenologists held that the mind is not unitary but consists of as many as thirty-seven independent faculties, such as benevolence, language, veneration, calculation, cautiousness, and amativeness, each localized in a specific region or "organ" of the brain. (*Fig. 42*). They also postulated three psychological types based on general body build, a foreshadowing of W. H. Sheldon's somatotypes: the mental, motive, and vital types. The thirty-seven faculties were all believed to be inherited propensities which affected the size and shape of the cranium in their particular part of the brain. Maps were constructed to indicate the location of each faculty, and character analysis was carried out by studying the prominent areas, or "bumps," which were supposed to show a high development of particular characteristics. The seat of "amativeness," for example, was supposed to be at the base of the skull, and people who had a large bump in this area were described as "alive to the charms of the other sex, polite, affable, and free in the company of others, successful in gaining their confidence and courageous in their defense." (Olin, 1910)

Phrenology was extremely popular in the first half of the nineteenth century, and was accepted by many eminent doctors, scientists, and educators. A number of societies were formed in the United States during the 1930s and 40s, and attempts were made to apply its principles in various fields. For example, some educators believed that child prodigies should have short school days because constant mental activity would permanently weaken the brain, and the bumps of defective children were studied to determine areas of educability. Many laymen attempted to practice phrenology, and charlatans offered secret lotions and special hats which were supposed to develop different organs of the brain.

The theories of phrenology had a considerable effect on the psychiatry of

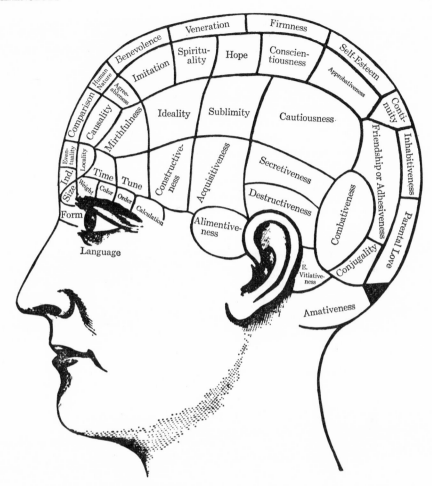

Fig. 42. Phrenology, an early attempt to "map" the brain.

the time. The emphasis on physical characteristics led many physicians to view mental illness as a brain disease, in opposition to the prevailing opinion that it was due to possession by the devil. They tried to find which brain organs were responsibile, and treated these areas by such methods as applying leeches to cut off their blood supply, trepanning, drugs, laxatives, and mustard plasters. Some conditions were also treated by simple rest, good food, and physical exercise. These techniques had a profound effect on diagnosis and treatment in the "lunatic asylums" in America. Many of their superintendents

abandoned attempts to defeat and exorcise the devil by beating, starvation, and solitary confinement and adopted more humane methods of treatment.

Modern research has indicated that there is no correspondence whatever between the phrenologists' map of the brain and the actual localization of functions. In fact, to take one example, when electrical stimulation is applied to the area which phrenologists attribute to "religiousness," the subject twitches his leg! Nevertheless the theory of phrenology helped to free psychology from metaphysics and encouraged the idea that mental phenomena can be studied objectively according to natural law. Its decline after the 1830s was largely due to the fact that it helped stimulate the kind of scientific experimentation that proved it incorrect. *See* CEREBRAL CORTEX, LASHLEY, FRANZ.

PHYSIOGNOMIC PERCEPTION. A term applied by Heinz Werner to the tendency to view the world in the light of emotional and motor qualities—that is, to endow things and people with expressive characteristics.

Werner believes the child's experience of the world is more physiognomic than the adult's. A child may, for example, perceive a lifeless object such as a stick as if it were an animate being, or he may say the number three looks "cross," or that a diamond-shaped figure looks "cruel." According to Werner this type of perception is more elementary than make-believe, and antedates the anthropomorphic tendency to project human characteristics into things. The child therefore does not actually project a cross face into the number three or a cruel person into the diamond-shaped figure. Rather, he invests them directly with these expressive characteristics.

Werner holds that many artists retain this "gift" of physiognomic perception. Abstractionists like Kandinsky, for example, perceive certain emotions in the lines they draw; and apparently those who appreciate their paintings must also find them emotionally expressive. The tendency may apply to figure-drawing as a projective technique. The use of smooth, curved lines is believed to imply less tension than sharp, jagged lines, and blurred or shaded lines are believed to be indicative of anxiety. Similarly, if an individual is given paper and pencil and instructed to let the pencil "move by itself" as he listens to music, the lines he draws will probably express the mood and feelings of the composition as he experiences it. *See* ESTHETICS, FIGURE DRAWING TEST.

Werner holds that many mentally ill individuals, particularly those affected with schizophrenic reactions, revert to a primitive, physiognomic perception of the world. Everything they see is construed in terms of their affective needs and reactions. A paranoid schizophrenic may therefore say, "The door is devouring me," or insist that people are scowling at him when they are actually smiling. Such changes in perception are likely to occur at the onset of the illness; it is not unusual for patients to complain that the world suddenly appears strange to them.

Similar changes in the appearance, or "physiognomy," of things have been observed in cases of brain lesion as well as mescaline and marijuana intoxication. There is little doubt that LSD produces similar reactions. The following statement of Werner's (1932) might apply to the experience of individuals under any of these influences: "In a very real sense it appears that the optical field submits to a process of dynamization, and things continually change in form, size, and position. The whole world becomes physiognomically alive." *See* HALLUCINOGEN, LYSERGIC ACID, SCHIZOPHRENIC REACTIONS (GENERAL), MARIJUANA.

PHYSIOGNOMY. The attempt to "read" personality from outward appearance, especially from the facial features.

Physiognomy is at least as old as Aristotle, who is believed to be the author of *Physiognomica,* a work which suggested that people who resemble certain types of animals also possess their temperamental characteristics—for instance, a bulldog indicates tenacity. He also held that races or nationalities can be typed according to appearance, suggesting that excessively dark people, such as Ethiopians, tend to be cowardly. Notions of this kind have been extremely persistent, and many systems of physiognomy have been constructed. In the eighteenth century Johann Lavater developed such a system, based on ancient lore and carefully selected examples of famous men. Toward the end of the nineteenth century Cesare Lombroso proposed that criminals could be identified by certain "stigmata of degeneracy" such as small, pointed ears, low foreheads, and close-set eyes. This theory was later revived by the anthropologist Ernest Hooton, who attributed such supposed characteristics to organic inferiority and primitivism. In the first quarter of the present century systems devised by Katherine Blackford and others were widely used in personnel selection.

Physiognomy has been a fertile field for quacks and charlatans, and a number of English monarchs actually outlawed the "profession." Yet even today there is a widespread belief that people with high brows are likely to be intellectual, blondes to be fickle, redheads temperamental, and the like. Psychologists and other scientists have therefore conducted a number of careful investigations to see if there is any possible evidence for this theory. The results can be summarily stated since they are practically 100 per cent negative. Lombroso's theory was proved false by actual measurements made by Goring, and Hooton's contentions were attacked by a fellow anthropologist, Alex Hrdlicka, who carefully examined one thousand juvenile delinquents and found no significant physical differences between these offenders and groups of noncriminals. In studies made by Hollingworth (1922), Hull (1928), and Paterson (1930), attempts were made to correlate such features as height of forehead, blondness, and convexity of profile with aptitudes and personality characteristics as determined by tests or ratings made by associates. No significant correlations were found in any of these investigations.

Psychologists class these physiognomic concepts as "social stereotypes" and contend that they are perpetuated not because they have a foundation in fact but because they are kept alive by literature, hearsay, and the desire to find some simple way of categorizing human beings. In many cases an individual may exploit a stereotype, just as Mussolini thrust forward his already prominent chin to give the impression that he was a man of power and determination. Moreover, the belief itself may have an effect on the behavior of suggestible people, especially when it is bolstered by the expectations of others. Anastasi's comments are much to the point: "If there is a widespread belief that a person with a receding chin is weak-willed, then such a person will tend to be judged as weak-willed by his associates. Actions that might be overlooked in another will be noticed and accepted as indices of weakness in this individual . . . The influence of social stereotypes may go even farther and modify the individual's own self-percept and his subsequent behavior development. What people expect of someone may be an important factor in determining his behavior" (1958). In other words, it is not the features themselves but the attitudes toward them that affect the personality. *See* EXPRESSIVE BEHAVIOR, STEREOTYPE, PREJUDICE.

PHYSIOLOGICAL PSYCHOLOGY. The scientific study of the physiological basis of human and animal behavior. Psychologists who work in this field are generally members of the divisions of physiological, comparative, or experimental psychology of the American Psychological Association. Although these three divisions include about 10 per cent of the members, the number who devote themselves primarily to physiological psychology is relatively small.

Historically, physiological psychology has been a meeting-ground for many lines of inquiry. As Morgan (1965) remarks, "Perhaps no subject draws upon so many different sciences and their methods as physiological psychology.

Every sort of pure and applied scientist —mathematician, physicist, chemist, physiologist, pharmacologist, anatomist, neurologist, psychiatrist, electrical engineer, as well as psychologist—has been taking part in our subject in one way or another. None can claim sole or even major rights to the subject, for each has contributed a share." In view of this fact, it would be impossible even to attempt a history of the subject at this point. However, many of the highlights are mentioned in other parts of this volume—among them, Descartes' mechanical conception of the body, Fechner's psychophysics, Helmholtz's theories of vision and hearing, Lashley's experiments on mass action, Cannon's hypothalamic theory of emotion, Berger's EEG studies, Papez's discovery of the limbic system, Penfield's work on electrical stimulation, and, most recently, the direct implantation of electrodes in the brain. See DESCARTES, PSYCHOPHYSICS, HELMHOLTZ, LASHLEY, CANNON, EMOTION (THEORIES), ELECTROENCEPHALOGRAPH, LIMBIC SYSTEM, HYPERMNESIA.

The central problem of physiological psychology is the relationship between psychological processes and the physiological events which underlie them—in other words, the age-old mind-body problem. However, this problem is not approached from the philosophical point of view but from the viewpoint of experimental research, and to a lesser extent, clinical study as well. The clinical approach is involved in psychosomatic studies which have thrown light on such subjects as the relation between emotional tension and peptic ulcers, as well as the effect of brain injuries, glandular disorders, and psychoactive drugs on psychological functions. As Morgan points out, this approach has so far yielded little of a concrete and fundamental nature because one cannot be sure exactly what is physiologically wrong with the patient; and it is usually not possible to find adequate controls for the sake of comparison, or to find

the kind of illnesses that will answer specific scientific questions.

Most of our knowledge about the physiological basis of behavior must come, therefore, from experiments, although it is acknowledged, as Morgan remarks, that "experiments in this field are not nearly so neat and often not so clear-cut as they are in the natural sciences." Moreover, most of them must be carried out on animals rather than on people since we would not run the risk of using many kinds of drugs and hormones on human subjects, nor destroy parts of their nervous or glandular systems at will. Nevertheless, our knowledge of evolution and the similarities in structure and physiology between man and animal has made it possible to transfer many of the findings to human beings.

The major divisions of the subject are the following. First, the peripheral nervous system, including the sense organs, muscles, and glands, cranial and spinal nerves, and autonomic nervous system. Second, the central nervous system, which includes the spinal cord, brain stem (hindbrain, midbrain, reticular formation), and forebrain (thalamus, hypothalamus, basal ganglia, limbic system, and the cerebral hemispheres). Third, the physiology of the neuron (potentials, excitation, conduction, synaptic transmission). Fourth, the internal chemical environment (metabolism, hormonal secretions, homeostasis). Fifth, the sensory functions (the chemical senses of taste and smell, the visual system and visual perception, the auditory system and auditory perception, and the somatic senses of temperature, pressure, pain, and kinesthesis). Sixth, the motor functions (the motor system, spinal reflexes, co-ordination, balance, posture). Seventh, emotion and motivation (mechanisms and theories of emotion, sleep and arousal, activity level, hunger and thirst, sexual behavior, instinctive behavior). Eighth, the physical bases of learning and memory (classical conditioning, avoidance conditioning, maze learning, discriminative learning, complex problem-solving). Ninth, brain disorders (aphasia, localization of function, recovery of function, psychological deficit). And tenth, psychochemistry (the biochemistry of memory traces, inborn errors such as mongolism, nutritional deficits, genetic predisposition, and the psychotropic drugs). These ten topics, based largely on Morgan's latest book (1965), represent the major subject matter of physiological psychology today. For individual articles, *see* the Category Index, under PHYSICAL BASIS OF BEHAVIOR, SENSATION AND PERCEPTION, MOTIVATION, LEARNING; also MEMORY STORAGE, CHEMOTHERAPY, APHASIA, BRAIN DISORDERS.

PICA (Cittosis). A craving for unnatural foods such as clay, plaster, ashes, hair, starch, and dirt. The term derives from the word for magpie, a bird which is said to eat anything.

Pica is a surprisingly prevalent tendency. It has been observed in retarded children, neurotic children, deprived groups, and pregnant women, as well as in chronic schizophrenic and senile patients who have apparently regressed to the stage where the child will put anything into its mouth, whether or not it is fit for consumption. Some normal children eat hair, mud, or the fluff from blankets for a short period.

Pica is also a cultural practice found among peoples throughout the world. The most common form is geophagy, the eating of clay and dirt. In some localities these substances are consumed as part of the normal diet, but more often they are eaten for special purposes or only when food is scarce. In China the practice dates back to the fifth century. In Africa, warriors have long taken bags of dirt with them when they had to fight at distant points, in the belief that they would gain strength from consuming the earth of their homeland. In Malay and Polynesia, clay is eaten today to reduce weight, maintain a slender figure, and as a standard food during pregnancy. In Siberia and Tibet it is used as a remedy for vomiting and diarrhea, as well as to "fortify the heart." In some areas "fossil meal," a diatomaceous earth, is used as a relish or a delicacy in its own right. Clay-eating is also practiced as a primitive religious rite.

In some cases pica is probably the result of a "specific hunger"—that is, an urge to eat substances which are needed but lacking in the body. This theory accounts for the fact that calcium-deficient children will sometimes eat chalk, plaster, or starch. The same type of explanation may also apply to some of the women who eat dirt during pregnancy, since the growing fetus requires extra minerals. However, according to Marcia Cooper (1957), who has made an extensive investigation of pica, this theory cannot account for the universality of the practice. She points out that the nutritive value of clay and dirt is almost nil, since these substances are inorganic and cannot be digested. Her own theory is that they were originally eaten during times of famine to fill the stomach and allay the pangs of hunger, and that later on some groups of people developed a taste for them, or a belief that they were effective for various disorders.

Pica practices can be extremely injurious. Children who eat painted plaster or chew painted toys sometimes develop brain syndromes due to lead poisoning. Slaves brought to America from West Africa often continued to eat earth, primarily to kill hunger pangs. Each had his own "clay hole" in a secret location. As a result of the clay-eating many of them became lethargic, debilitated, and anemic, and some even died. The practice of earth-eating persists among some American Negroes; in fact, a study by Dunston (1961) showed an incidence of 42.9 per cent among the Negro population in one area. This form of pica is particularly prevalent among pregnant women in the rural South, who believe the earth will strengthen the child. It actually does the reverse, and is responsible for many infant deaths, since it leads not only to serious iron-deficiency anemia but to a lower hemoglobin rate. In New York City, where clay or earth is not available, women have been known to eat starch instead. A hospital recently reported that a woman patient under treatment for anemia had been consuming three full boxes of starch (about three pounds) every day. *See* LEAD POISONING, HUNGER.

PICK'S DISEASE. A rare degenerative disease of the brain, first described in 1892 by the Czech psychiatrist Arnold Pick (1867–1926).

The disease occurs between the ages of forty-five and fifty and affects more women than men. For reasons unknown, the higher associative areas of the cortex, starting in the frontal and temporal lobes, begin to atrophy, as if in premature senility, and the mechanisms of speech and thinking are increasingly affected.

The onset of the disorder is gradual, and the earliest symptoms are usually difficulty in thinking and concentrating, memory defect, indifference, and inability to deal with new situations. One of the outstanding symptoms is inability to generalize and deal with abstractions. As the atrophy spreads to different brain areas, the patient becomes increasingly bewildered, either refuses to talk or talks in a rambling manner, and gradually loses the ability to read, write, and name objects (alexia, agraphia, nominal aphasia). Finally, extreme mental and physical deterioration sets in: Speech practically disappears, paralyses and contractures of the arms and legs occur, incontinence develops, and the patient becomes so debilitated that he has to be confined to bed. He does not usually survive more than four to six years after the onset of the disease.

It is sometimes difficult to distinguish Pick's disease from Alzheimer's disease, since the age of the patient and many of the symptoms are similar. In Pick's disease, however, there is more apathy and indifference and less agitation, anxiety and activity than in Alzheimer's. Memory defect occurs later in Pick's, and delusions, hallucinations, and confabulation rarely occur. Some investigations indicate that Pick's disease tends to run in families and is based on defective genes. There are no preventive measures, and treatment is limited to routine medical and custodial care. *See* ALZHEIMER'S DISEASE.

Illustrative Case: PICK'S DISEASE

Margaret J. a 60-year-old widow and mother of three children, was a completely normal and well-balanced person during her early life and adult years. She graduated from a large state university, was happily married, and engaged in an active social life. Among her three children, one became a professor. The family enjoyed a relatively high socioeconomic status, and the patient and her husband had many friends.

The first symptoms were noticed following the husband's death, when the patient was fifty-one. At that time, the patient became forgetful, irritable, and confused. There was also occasional difficulty in speaking. These symptoms gradually became severe, and an X-ray of the skull was made when the patient was fifty-four. The skull film showed atrophy of the prefrontal lobes. As a result of progressive deterioration, it became necessary to hospitalize the patient at age sixty. She was sometimes incontinent and careless about her toilet habits, at times she exhibited herself, and occasionally she attacked other patients.

At the time of the examination, the patient was pleasant and friendly, but she could not be examined because of difficulty in communication due to impairment of the speech centers in the brain. The patient made sounds with the rhythm and intonation of normal speech, yet the material was largely unintelligible on first hearing it. However, when recorded on tape, and played back several times, the thought content became increasingly clear. Following the death of the patient four months after her admission to the hospital, an autopsy revealed changes characteristic of Pick's disease. (Kisker, 1964)

PINEAL GLAND (Pineal Body). A small white structure, about one quarter of an inch long, deep in the center of the brain of all mammals (PLATE 1).

The existence of this body has been known for over two thousand years. In about A.D. 200 Galen noted that it was a single structure without the distinguishable right and left halves characteristic of other parts of the brain. He concluded from this fact, and from its strategic location, that it must be a valve which regulates the flow of thought from the higher centers of the brain. Descartes, writing in the seventeenth century, elaborated this idea and suggested that the organ was the place where the mind and body interacted. He therefore concluded that it was the "seat of the rational soul." According to his theory, the events of the world, perceived through the eyes, are transmitted to the pineal body by way of "strings" in the brain, and this organ then secretes "humors" which travel to the muscles through hollow tubes, causing them to make appropriate responses. *See* DESCARTES.

Recent research indicates that Descartes was probably right in one respect. The pineal body is actually a gland that regulates certain types of behavior through its secretions. This has been discovered by bringing together observations that at first seemed unrelated. First, for some time scientists have known that children with pineal tumors, which increase the activity of the pineal gland, show delayed sexual development. It was further observed that the structure could act as a "third eye" in cold-blooded animals such as frogs, converting light impulses of certain wavelengths into nerve impulses. Then, in 1958, A. B. Lerner isolated a compound in the pineal gland of cattle and called it melatonin. When this sub-

stance was injected in rats, he found it had an inhibitory effect on the estrous (sexual) cycle, while removal of the entire gland led to acceleration of this cycle. This left the question, What is the relation between the influence of the gland on the sexual cycle and its effect on light energy?

This question has been tentatively answered by further investigations. The pineal body apparently ceased to function as a third eye in mammals, since it lost its connection with the brain during the evolutionary process. Electron microscope studies have shown that many sympathetic nerve cells terminate directly in the pineal cells, and further experimentation has indicated that this system probably releases "neurohumors" which inhibit the synthesis of melatonin when certain amounts of light fall on the retina. In other words, the pineal gland does respond to the external world, as Descartes suggested. It seems to operate as a "biological clock" which reacts to changes in illumination. (Wurtman and Axelrod, 1965; Lerner, 1961)

There is some direct evidence for this idea: melatonin production in rats has been found to increase two- or threefold in the five hours following darkness. However, we do not yet know exactly how the pineal "clock" regulates the timing of the estrous cycle, or whether it is the primary center for controlling this function. Nor do we know whether it is involved only in sexual activity or regulates other rhythmic activities that are dependent on the passage of time.

PINEL, PHILIPPE (1745–1826). Pinel, the most revolutionary figure in French psychiatry during the eighteenth century, received his medical degree at the University of Toulouse, and moved to Paris in 1778. His interest in psychiatry and mental hospitals was awakened when he translated English works such as Cullen's *Institutions of Medicine,* and was intensified when a close friend became insane, ran into the woods, and was devoured by wolves. Shortly after this event, Pinel began to publish articles on mental diseases, and by 1793 had achieved sufficient recognition to be appointed head physician at the Bicêtre Hospital.

At the time the prevailing attitude toward the mentally ill was one of fear, suspicion, and disgust. The public believed they were possessed by the devil himself, and in the hospital they were caged in unheated cells, chained to walls, and fed inedible scraps. Nevertheless when Pinel assumed his new position, one of his first acts was to remove the chains and fetters from about a dozen of the inmates, some of whom had been kept in dungeons for over thirty years. Instead of regarding them as criminals or wild beasts, he declared that "the mentally deranged, far from being guilty people deserving of punishment are sick people whose miserable state deserves all the consideration that is due to suffering humanity. One should try with the most simple methods to restore their reason." (Zilboorg and Henry, 1941)

Pinel had to contend not only with the prejudices of the public but the opposition of the government. His act of humanity was performed at a time when France was torn by the distrust and strife that followed the Revolution of 1789, and he was soon suspected of hiding emigrés and priests who had secretly returned to the country. At one point he was even seized by an angry crowd who threatened to hang him—but his life was saved by one of the inmates he had freed from chains, and who had volunteered to serve as his bodyguard. Undaunted, he proposed to free all the inmates of Bicêtre from their chains—but to accomplish this, he had to present his case to the Bureau Central and the Commune. His proposal was met by these comments from Couthon, president of the Commune; "Why not proceed to the zoo and liberate the lions and tigers?" and

"Woe, to you, if you deceive me and if you hide enemies of the people among your insane!"

In spite of these warnings, Pinel convinced Couthon of the merit of his plan and invited him to Bicêtre to see it carried out. As he watched the 300 inmates screaming and clanking their chains, he asked Pinel, "Well, citizen, are you mad yourself that you want to unchain these animals?" Pinel's simple but classic reply was, "Citizen, it is my conviction that these mentally ill are intractable only because they are deprived of fresh air and of their liberty." (Zilboorg, and Henry, 1941)

The chains were removed, and the effects proved practical and beneficial. Building on this victory, Pinel went on to introduce a number of other sweeping reforms. He kept full records and compiled case histories on his patients, practices which have become a cornerstone of psychiatric research. He discontinued the accepted methods of bloodletting, ducking, and purging, and took the first steps toward psychotherapy by talking with his patients frequently, taking down anything of significance they uttered. He forbade the attendants to apply violence of any kind, and permitted the use of the strait jacket only when every humane approach had failed. He believed in the importance of the relationship between physician and patient, stressing kindness, humanity, and the ability to empathize. He also recognized the necessity of commanding respect through the physician's voice, manner, and glance, and insisted that it was better to stare a violent patient down than to use physical force. He was the first to pay full attention to efficient hospital management and to the arrangement of rooms and facilities in the institution.

In 1795 Pinel was appointed head of the Salpêtrière Hospital, where he continued his revolutionary policies by removing the chains of the inmates and reorganizing the institution as a hospital for the care and treatment of patients. During the years that followed, he served on the faculty of the University of Paris and wrote a number of influential books based on his observations and case studies. His three-volume *Nosographie Philosophique* (1798) classified mental illnesses into mania, melancholia, dementia, and idiocy. His *Traité Metaphilosophique sur la Manie* (1801) emphasized the need for studying individual cases, compiling detailed descriptions of the behavior of patients, and keeping accurate records of their responses to different treatments. He also recognized both hereditary and environmental factors in the etiology of mental illness. But the most important contribution of this volume was a full description of the "moral treatment" which he advocated in place of the strictly physical methods which were in vogue during his period. This form of treatment included talks with patients, encouragement and reassurance, occupational therapy, as well as improved diet and a humane approach in place of restraint. These views—reinforced by the efforts of Pinel's students and his successor Esquirol—established a new trend in French psychiatry for much of the 19th century. *See* ESQUIROL, TUKE, RUSH, RAY, KIRKBRIDE, MENTAL HOSPITAL.

PITUITARY GLAND (Hypophysis). An endocrine gland, located at the base of the brain (PLATE 1); it secretes hormones that regulate growth processes and activities of other endocrine glands. Because of its effect on other glands, the pituitary is sometimes called the body's "master gland."

The pituitary is part of the diencephalon, the lower and older region of the forebrain. It is connected to the hypothalamus by a stalk known as the infundibulum, and consists of two principal portions: the anterior part, or adenohypophysis, which appears to be primarily under blood control because it is not directly connected to the brain;

and the posterior part, or neurophysis, which is served by a pathway from the hypothalamus.

The anterior pituitary produces six hormones which are termed "trophic" (nourishing), since they stimulate other endocrine glands. Three of these, the gonadotrophic hormones, promote the activity of the gonads and control the female ovarian cycle: (1) the follicle-stimulating hormone (FSH) which brings the ovary to maturity; (2) the luteinizing hormone (LH) which causes the ovary to release its ovum (egg cell), also stimulating it to produce estrogens and to form the corpus luteum; and (3) the lactogenic hormone, prolactin (LTH), which stimulates the development of the mammary glands and the production of milk. The other three hormones are: (4) the thyrotrophic hormone, thyrotrophin, which regulates the activity of the thyroid gland; (5) the adrenotrophic or adrenocorticotrophic hormone (ACTH), which stimulates the adrenal cortex; and (6) somatotrophin, which promotes general body growth.

The posterior pituitary produces pituitrin, which has three effects: (1) it raises blood pressure by constricting blood vessels leading from the arteries; (2) it stimulates the smooth muscles, particularly in the uterus during childbirth; (3) it inhibits the excretion of urine through the kidneys ("antidiuretic effect"). In recent years these functions have been found to be largely under the control of two separate hormones: vasopressin, which raises blood pressure and controls thirst by retarding the flow of urine; and oxytocin, which stimulates the smooth muscles involved in nursing.

In more descriptive and general terms, the major functions of the pituitary are the regulation of metabolism, growth and sexual maturation. If the secretions are within normal limits, development proceeds on schedule; but if the gland is not functioning properly, gross abnormalities may appear. A deficiency of growth hormone in childhood may result in midgetism or dwarfism, and an excess may lead to giantism (gigantism). If persistent oversecretion occurs during adolescence or later, it may lead to acromegaly, a condition in which the hands, feet and jaw are abnormally enlarged. Giantism is usually accompanied by weakened muscles and sexual inadequacy, while acromegaly may give rise to personality disorder due to bodily deformity and hormone imbalance.

The gonadotrophic, or "middleman" hormones do not come into play until the child is eleven or twelve years of age. They then stimulate the gonads to secrete actively and promote the development of the entire reproductive system and secondary sexual characteristics.

Pituitary dysfunction can lead to abnormalities in function as well as structure. Among them are pubertas praecox, in which sexual maturity is reached as early as eight or nine years of age; delayed sexual maturation; sexual impotence and infertility; and adiposogenital dystrophy (Fröhlich's syndrome), characterized by obesity, low metabolism, underdeveloped genitals, and lack of drive. These conditions can sometimes be modified either by surgical removal of part of the gland when it is excessively large, or by hormone injections where there is a deficiency of secretion. Since psychological reactions are usually involved, psychotherapy is frequently recommended. *See* ACROMEGALY, DWARFISM, IMPOTENCE, INFERTILITY, MENSTRUAL DISORDERS, FRÖHLICH'S SYNDROME.

PLACEBO (literally "I shall please"). An inert substance administered in place of an active drug.

Originally the term placebo was applied to a relatively inactive substance, such as a bread pill or sugar pill, given to "placate" a patient who demanded medication. In present usage, it is a "dummy" pill or injection administered for therapeutic or experimental reasons.

Placebos may be used, for example, in place of sedatives to induce sleep or to alleviate pain. The doctor usually applies suggestion in giving the pill: "This will put you to sleep." Sometimes an actual sedative or painkiller would be harmful, but the placebo may have the same effect without risk of injury.

The placebo effect helps to explain the early success of medications that later prove worthless. During the period when many different treatments were tried for tuberculosis, practically any new drug was found to bring remarkable results on the first trials. When word got around that scientists questioned these treatments, or when less suggestible patients were given these drugs, the results invariably proved disappointing.

In general, placebos have their greatest effect in conditions that have a large emotional or psychosomatic component, and tuberculosis is one of these conditions. Asthma, headache, hay fever, tension, and postoperative pain are others. In a study of over 1000 patients afflicted with a variety of disorders, Beecher (1955) found that one in three reported relief from placebos. He also reported about 35 different toxic effects experienced by patients receiving dummy drugs.

Suggestible patients are particularly amenable to placebo effects, and are sometimes called "placebo reactors." Little investigation has been made of the personality of these reactors, but there are some indications that they tend to be more anxious than average individuals. The study conducted by Beecher points up the fact that reactions to placebos may be either positive or negative. If the patient has faith in drugs or in the doctor, the effects are likely to be highly positive, but where he is fearful, hostile or antagonistic to all pill-taking, the effects may be negative or even noxious.

Placebos are often used to good effect in conversion (hysterical) reactions, since these consist of bodily symptoms produced by emotional problems rather than organic disease. In fact, dummy pills can sometimes be of help in diagnosing these reactions. A patient who cannot speak above a whisper (aphonia) may suddenly get his voice back if his throat is sprayed with a new "wonder drug," even though that drug may be nothing but colored water. Although this technique may successfully relieve the patient's present complaint, it does not in itself cure the neurosis, and the alleviated symptom will probably be replaced by another within a short time.

Placebos are also used in experimental medicine. When a new drug is under test it is given to an experimental group, and their reactions are compared with those of a control group who receive a drug that looks and tastes the same but is actually an inert substance. The object is to determine whether any changes that take place are due to the drug itself and not to psychological factors such as suggestibility and expectation. To rule out these psychological factors even further the doctor himself usually does not know whether a particular patient is receiving the placebo or the medication (the "double-blind" technique). He may also try to eliminate known placebo reactors from the experiment. In spite of these precautions, the placebo is sometimes found to be as effective as the drug under test, at least for a short time, simply because a pill has been taken by a patient who needs help. For an example of this technique applied to drug-testing, see CLINICAL PSYCHOLOGY.

PLATO (428–347 B.C.). Born of aristocratic parents in Athens, Plato spent a number of years in the coterie surrounding Socrates. During this period he developed an interest in practical politics, but abandoned this career after the sentencing of his mentor in 399. The death of Socrates helped to convince him that the existing parties in Athens had no clear-cut philosophy to guide their efforts, and he is believed to have made a trip to Italy and Sicily to become acquainted with the teachings of the Pythagoreans. He returned with the conviction that the thoughts of Socrates, which he had recorded, could be taught to others. He therefore founded his Academy in about 387, and remained its guiding force for forty years. It became the first permanent organization for the study of both the exact and the human sciences, and in this sense was a forerunner of the modern university.

Plato's approach to the human being was in many ways the antithesis of scientific psychology. His distinction between the world of appearance and the world of reality separated sense perception from thought processes. His search for eternal forms and universal ideas through the dialectical method ruled out the observational, empirical approach. His extreme emphasis on mathematics as the foundation of all learning led to the doctrine of formal discipline, which has been disproved by experiments on the transfer of training. His view that knowledge is "reminiscence," a déjà vu experience which resurrected ideas already imprinted on the mind, focused on the static and unchanging as contrasted with the modern notion of a developing world and an evolving personality. His conception of the soul as an immaterial entity transcending and surviving the body is in direct opposition to modern psychology and psychiatry, which integrate body and mind. His division of the soul into three parts arranged in a hierarchical order—reason, spirit, and appetite—was a precursor of faculty psychology, which has been replaced by the holistic approach of today. His conviction that mankind can be divided into three types of people—three species—each representing one of the three categories of reason, spirit, and appetite conflicts with the modern view that human capacities do not differ in kind but only in degree. And his theory that the state must be organized according to these inborn differences represents the type of racial and class myth which the human sciences of our day have discredited.

And yet, in spite of the fact that many of Plato's ideas cannot be accepted today, he made many positive contributions to the study of the mind. Even though his dialectical method was directed to the discovery of unchangeable ideas, it nevertheless recognized the value of systematic thinking, and prepared the way for at least the more formal aspects of scientific method by showing how theories are constructed and inferences drawn. While our main emphasis today is on the changing world of sensation, or what Plato called "appearance," we still deal with abstract, general concepts, and search for the laws that govern nature.

There is evidence, too, that Plato anticipated the general notion of motivation in one of his works, the *Symposium,* where he suggested that an "irrational element" or emotional force termed Eros can lift the mind into the realm of the true and the beautiful. He also recognized that all men, with the possible exception of the philosopher-kings, tend to be dominated by will, emotion, and desire—a view that is not far from the modern concept of drives. His emphasis on symmetry, order, and balance influenced Fechner and others in their search for the laws governing esthetic perception. His ideal of intrapsychic harmony under the direction of reason finds an echo in the views of modern psychologists who stress rational control over primitive impulses. His educational program, with its graded series of tests and its broad curriculum that included the arts as well as the sciences, greatly influenced the development of educational psychology. Finally, his view that the social order must be based on the inner nature of man is reflected in the modern doctrine that the goal of society is to enable all individuals to fulfill their needs and realize themselves.

PLAY. Any activity which is freely sought and pursued for the sake of enjoyment.

The meaning of play can be clarified by contrasting it with work. Although work may be undertaken voluntarily, and may also give pleasure, it differs from play in one essential respect: it is basically directed toward some other end than enjoyment. The objective is usually economic gain, but sometimes it is achievement, prestige, or benefit to others. The amateur basketball player plays primarily for fun (although he may also be motivated by school spirit or a desire for recognition). The professional plays primarily for the income he receives, although he may have chosen this particular way of earning a living because it gives him pleasure.

It is an interesting fact that few if any activities can be classed exclusively as either work or play, since the determining factor is the attitude and not the activity. Moreover, an activity may shift from one to the other. A person may start to raise roses purely as a hobby, and later make his living out of selling them; or an individual who has made more money than he can use may continue to pursue his occupation simply because it gives him enjoyment. The child who said, "Play is what you want to do, work is what you have to do" put his finger on the basic distinction between the two.

Systematic studies of play have largely been devoted to the recreational activities of children rather than adults. It is now generally recognized that the urge to play is as natural as the urge to eat and sleep. Moreover, play is far more than a means of killing time or keeping the youngster out of mischief. Rather, it is a prime and indispensable instrument for growth, which—in one form or another—can contribute to every major phase of the child's life. It can benefit the child physically by exercising his muscles, releasing surplus energy and giving him practice in co-ordination, dexterity, and balance. It can cultivate his mental abilities by stimulating imagination, by challenging him to use skill and ingenuity in solving problems, and by bringing him into closer touch with his environment. It can develop his social capacities through give and take, co-operation and respect for rules. It can advance his moral development by making him aware of the standards of the group and the need for fairness, truthfulness, self-control, and sportsmanship. It can help him maintain his psychological equilibrium by providing an outlet for tensions and frustrations, and a chance to "play out" fears, anxieties and resentments in action. And finally, it gives the child who engages in different activities a chance to discover and test his interests, needs, and abilities, and therefore to learn more about himself. *See* PLAY THERAPY.

The child's earliest play experiences are solitary and exploratory. After the first few weeks of life, he begins to touch, suck, bite, and bang everything within reach. He seems to derive special delight from stimulating his senses, and it is important to let him play with blocks, pans, and other simple articles that make him aware of a wide variety of shapes, textures, and sounds. These experiences help to awaken his mind, sharpen his senses, and arouse his interest in the surroundings.

By the end of the second year the child begins to turn his attention to toys and activities of many kinds, and from there on the world of play expands in all directions, as the following summary, based on Hartley and Goldenson (1963), will show.

Dramatic Play. Taking different roles is one of the child's chief ways of testing himself, rehearsing for life, and preparing for real events such as visiting a dentist or going to school. It also enables him to transcend his limitations, identify with important figures, realize his wishes in imagination, and play out feelings of anger, jealousy, and fear within the safe realm of "let's pretend" and make-believe.

The sequence of make-believe play is somewhat as follows. *2 to 3:* imitates the sounds and movements of animals, trains, planes; later pretends to be a grownup keeping house, tending the baby, telephoning, driving a car. The years from three to six are the peak period for make-believe. *3 to 4:* imaginary companions are common for both sexes; girls play mother, nurse, cook; boys play pirate, space pilot, zoo keeper, postman. *5 to 6:* group activities and "realistic" situations become important, including playing family, running a store, staging an Indian attack, giving a tea party. *6 to 9:* acting out stories (Cinderella, George Washington), "dressing up," puppet plays; girls still play house but include more advanced activities such as entertaining guests; boys play hunt and chase games, act as spacemen and commandos. *9 to 12:* the focus is increasingly on the real world, and the child who visits a factory, fashion show, or newspaper office imagines himself in new roles; dramatic play now takes the form of charades, pantomimes, acting in school plays.

Indoor Games. Games do many things for the child. They develop visual acuity, co-ordination, logical thinking, vocabulary, and observation. They can also be used to detect and meet special needs, such as anagrams for the poor speller or numbers games for those who are weak in arithmetic. *1 to 3:* all babies enjoy finger play, pat-a-cake, peek-a-boo, hide-and-seek; one-year-olds need things to squeeze, pound, and knead; and two-year-olds like pegs to hammer, bean bags to throw, wooden puzzles to solve. *3 to 6:* three is the age for sorting, buttoning, stringing large beads, as well as for group games like Farmer in the Dell; the four-year-old enjoys picture lotto; and the five-year-old is ready for simple board games and alphabet blocks. *6 to 9:* the favorites are darts, jigsaw and wire puzzles, card games, number and letter games; later on, dominoes and checkers. *9 to 12:* the peak period for games requiring mental and manual skill: marbles, card tricks, vocabulary and number games, memory and observation tests, quizzes, table tennis, more advanced board games.

Outdoor Play and Sports. The major values of outdoor play are somewhat different from those of indoor play: exploring nature, experiencing risk and competition, developing team work and obedience to rules, playing the role of follower or leader, winning acceptance through skill and ability. *1 to 3:* the one-year-old enjoys push-and-pull toys, rocking horses, and low vehicles to ride on; soon he is picking up and examining pebbles, twigs, and shells, and a little later he is ready for a slide, a swing, a packing-case "house." *3 to 6:* the three-year-old runabout needs steps to climb, a wagon to haul things, a tricycle to ride; as he grows, he graduates to a jungle-gym, a scooter, a large beach ball, and then on to a skipping rope, roller skates, a sled—all to gratify his urge to develop strength, agility and nerve. *6 to 9:* six is the year for group games with much action and talk, few rules, and little teamwork: tag, London Bridge, cops and robbers; then come ball games, marbles, rope-jumping, hopscotch, bike riding, skating, water sports, treasure hunts, and baseball. *9 to 12:* the period for developing the more demanding skills of standard sports—not only physical skills, but team work, fair play, knowledge of the finer points of the game; but to get the most out of these sports, good instruction and regular practice are needed. Children also derive benefit and enjoyment from less organized activities such as hiking, bike trips, sailing, camping, skiing.

Constructive Activities. Practically all children have at least a potential interest in making useful articles and creating drawings, sculptures or paintings. These activities contribute to personality growth by providing opportunities to develop manual skills, solve "technical" problems, explore the properties of different materials, originate their own designs, express their feelings in matter and form, and experience the thrill of achievement. *1 to 3:* before he can construct and create, the young child must first have plenty of things to squeeze, pound, smear, and manipulate; between two and three, he builds nameless block structures, copies simple towers, makes mud pies and sand tunnels, and covers yards of paper with crayon scribbles, water paint and finger paint. *3 to 6:* gradually builds more complex structures and uses them in dramatic play; begins to use large wooden tools, puts plastic bricks and interlocking logs together, crudely draws people; and at five begins to mold play animals and paint "pictures" that he wants to keep and display. *6 to 9:* this is the age for steel, plastic, and wood construction sets and simple model-building; painting, drawing and clay work become more realistic and detailed; useful or decorative objects are made out of pipe cleaners, spools, cartons and clay, and collages out of practically anything. *9 to 12:* the peak of the childhood construction period: girls and boys alike make shelves, bookends, boxes, and treehouses, and experiment with various arts and crafts, using papier-mâché, metal, cardboard, leather, cloth, raffia, and other materials in making a wide variety of articles such as trays, bracelets, doll houses, mats, baskets, aprons, and greeting cards.

Musical Activities. A clacking rattle, a banging pan, a sparrow's chirp, a lullaby—all these help to develop the child's ear. But the first response to music is made with the entire body, not just the ears, and much of his enjoyment consists of clapping, swaying, and hopping about. *1 to 3*: all youngsters like bold, rhythmic melodies for energetic response, and soft, soothing tunes when they are tired; the toddler wants to hear his favorite records over and over, frequently chanting and "dancing" along with them. *3 to 6*: can remember simple melodies of nursery songs, folk songs, lullabies, and likes to sing but is rarely in tune; reacts to music by pretending he is a high-stepping horse, a marching soldier, a tugboat; five-year-olds can pick out simple tunes on the piano and may form a rhythm band. *6 to 9*: the age for experimentation with different instruments, group singing and musical games; by eight they are usually ready to start lessons on the piano, recorder or flute. *9 to 12*: most boys and girls enjoy mixed choruses and folk dancing, which help to overcome self-consciousness and bridge the gap between the sexes; strumming a guitar or ukelele can also be a social asset; and at eleven or twelve young people of both sexes are usually ready for band concerts, folk music performances and informal recitals.

Hobbies. A pastime becomes a hobby when it is pursued intensively and systematically. Hobbies are often the most beneficial and satisfying form of play since they develop habits of perseverance and thoroughness, give children the thrill of becoming an "authority," and express their individual personalities more fully than transient interests. No classification of hobbies can be exhaustive since the most rewarding and creative pursuits frequently arise out of one small facet of a subject. The following are a few examples, common and uncommon. *Collecting:* starts with trivial items at three and rises to a peak at ten for boys and eleven for girls, when the articles are usually carefully sorted, stored and sometimes displayed. The variety of collections is immense: not only stamps and coins,

but dried leaves and flowers, rocks, insects, shells, dolls, toy soldiers, postcards, recipes, posters, bottles, puppets. *Animal Hobbies:* raising hamsters, mice, guinea pigs, rabbits, fish, birds; grooming and showing a cat or dog; bee keeping; bird watching. *Arts and Crafts Hobbies:* weaving, engraving, sculpture, photography, woodworking, ceramics, jewelry making, dressmaking, bookbinding, printing. *Gardening Hobbies:* rock gardens, window gardens, greenhouse, plant breeding, hydroponics, special varieties. *Science Hobbies:* through the many kinds of scientific play, the child explores the natural world, satisfies his curiosity, learns some of the laws of nature, becomes acquainted with apparatus and instruments. In the early years children like to observe natural processes such as the movements of insects or the way water turns to steam or ice; they also like to use a magnifying glass, a compass, a magnet, and enjoy maintaining an aquarium or terrarium. During middle childhood they ask how-and-why questions, but enjoy learning for themselves by using instruments such as a prism, microscope or telescope, and by performing experiments with a chemistry set, electricity kit, or a seed and germination set. In later childhood they may develop a particular interest by visiting specialists, laboratories or museums; and they are also ready to use more advanced materials (if the family can afford them), such as a star-spotter, a photoelectric kit, a radio kit, an intercom system, a geology set, or even a computer kit.

PLAY THERAPY. The use of play activities in child psychotherapy.

Today play is probably the most widely used device among child therapists. The major reasons are: (1) play is a mirror of the child's emotional life; (2) it serves a cathartic function, helping the child give vent to his feelings and impulses; and (3) it enables him to test new approaches and new relationships. Moreover, it serves these functions on an activity rather than a verbal level, thereby making it possible to treat young children who cannot express themselves adequately in words.

In her basic book on play therapy, Virginia Axline (1947) distinguishes between two general types, directive and nondirective. In the directive approach, the therapist assumes responsibility for guidance and interpretation, and in the nondirective he allows the child to lead the way. Axline herself advocates a nondirective approach, maintaining that "play therapy is based upon the fact that play is the child's natural medium of self-expression. It is an opportunity which is given to the child to 'play out' his feelings and problems, just as in certain types of adult therapy an individual 'talks out' his difficulties." Her contention is that when the therapist allows the child to play freely in an accepting atmosphere, he will give expression to the accumulated feelings of tension, frustration, aggression and fear that stand in the way of healthy behavior and satisfying relationships. The play therapy room then becomes a place where the child can grow emotionally since it enables him to express whatever he wants to express, be whatever he desires to be, and do whatever he wishes to do with a minimum of adult interference.

Nondirective play therapy is based on Carl Rogers' view that a person, even a child, has the capacity to revise his own behavior. In Axline's approach, the therapist therefore plays a friendly, interested role but gives no direct suggestion. F. H. Allen (1942) also uses a nondirective approach, but believes the therapist should be somewhat more active. The major difference is that he engages the child in conversation, always focusing on present feelings, reactions and situations rather than on past experiences. The accepting attitude of the therapist encourages the child

to try new and more appropriate ways of dealing with his problems. Allen and Newell (1941) feel that excessively timid, overly meticulous, inhibited, repressed, and extremely hostile children benefit most from the spontaneous play technique. See RELATIONSHIP THERAPY.

The directive approach to play therapy actually originated before the nondirective. Though historically the first author to attempt to understand the psychology of the child through observations of his play was Rousseau (the *Emile*), the Austrian psychiatrist Hertha von Hug-Hellmuth was the first to report the use of this medium in analysis and therapy. Her account, published in 1921, aroused the interest of Melanie Klein and Anna Freud. While both utilized the play technique as a partial substitute for the more verbal methods of psychoanalysis, Klein (1932) attempted a strict interpretation of the child's activities according to such analytic concepts as Oedipal strivings, castration anxiety, and oral deprivation. Anna Freud (1928), on the other hand, put less emphasis on these concepts, and used play to elicit dreams, daydreams, free associations, and discussions of current difficulties. The psychoanalytic approach has also given rise to more controlled techniques in which the therapist structures the situation by offering materials, such as dolls, through which the child can depict his relationships with his parents or siblings (PLATE 39). The session begins with figures chosen by the therapist, but the child is encouraged to add whatever other scenes or actors he wants to use. The chief exponent of this approach in America is D. M. Levy (1939). See RELEASE THERAPY.

Another controlled approach was developed by J. C. Solomon in 1948. In his "active play therapy," the therapist gives the child a set of dolls and arouses his interest through such suggestions as "Let's pretend." He also asks questions based on the feelings and attitudes expressed by the child as he handles the dolls—for example, if the boy doll is described as sad, the therapist asks, "What made him sad?" or "How does it feel to be sad?" Such questions are designed to help the child achieve greater understanding of himself. In addition, Solomon encourages the child to express feelings of guilt or hostility, on the theory that he will become less afraid of these emotions and will no longer repress them. He also offers direct guidance in solving his problems by using such suggestions as "You needn't feel badly about that."

The use of play therapy in a group setting has recently been developed by Haim Ginott (1961). Experience has shown that the groups must be carefully selected, and that the technique is most effective with children who are withdrawn, immature or phobic. It is also useful for children who suffer from conduct and habit disorders, provided they feel a need for social acceptance and a desire to be like others. Ginott finds that this form of group therapy cannot be used with children who are extremely aggressive and sociopathic, or with children who show intense stress reactions or accelerated sexual drives. With those limitations, the groups are made up of children with different syndromes in order to allow them to identify and associate with personalities different from their own.

Ginott has also found that play sessions are helpful in making differential diagnoses. Brain-damaged children tend to show poor motor control, social ineptness, perseveration, various speech difficulties and overreaction to minutiae; the neurotic are usually excessively inhibited or excessively aggressive; the mentally retarded show little awareness of the functions of playthings, and no inventiveness in using them; the psychotic tend to exhibit language disturbances, extreme self-insulation, bizarre behavior, pathological

reaction to pain, and relentless insistence on the same activity. Normal children, on the other hand, avoid emotional extremes, form personal relationships with ease, take delight in the use of play materials, and use substitute outlets for primitive drives.

Specialists recommend that play therapy take place in a large soundproofed room equipped with a wide assortment of materials. For the age range between three and nine, where the technique is most effective, it should contain a blackboard, tables, climbing equipment, doll house, toy animals, a sink for water play, easel and water colors, fingerpaints, clay, blocks, puppets, housekeeping materials and more aggressive toys such as guns. For children of nine to thirteen there should be material for woodworking, leatherwork and similar crafts as well as material for sewing, knitting, weaving, and perhaps penny arcade machines such as a rifle gallery.

In a study of play and emotional growth on the preschool level, Hartley, Frank, and Goldenson (1952) have described and illustrated the special values of different materials and activities for different kinds of children. Building blocks provide the small child with an opportunity to experience pride in achievement, and to gain emotional release by tearing down his structures at will. If foot-square cardboard blocks are available, the timid child may build a rampart and retreat behind it until he gains the courage to play with other children. Water is an ideal medium for relaxing tensions and returning temporarily to the joys of infancy. Moreover, it is so undemanding that it can lure the unskilled child into activity; it can also afford welcome relief to the child who comes from a rigid home where he must always keep dry and clean. Clay provides the angry child with an opportunity to pound away strong feelings, and gives the passive child a chance to become active with things even if he cannot be active with people. Soft clay and fingerpaint enable small children to give vent to their basic urge to smear and mess, which Freudians associate with elimination drives. Through easel painting as well as fingerpainting, the inhibited child may drop his restraint for the first time and experiment with broad strokes and bright colors.

Any of these activities can open the way to spontaneous changes in personality as the child discovers that his new ways of behaving are satisfying to himself and approved by others. Play therapy of this kind is a form of emotional correction and self-education that even a small child can perform. See PLAY, NURSERY SCHOOL EXPERIENCE, EARLY INFANTILE AUTISM, SYMBIOTIC PSYCHOSIS.

PLEASURE. The feeling which accompanies the satisfaction of a drive or the achievement of a goal.

There are wide variations in the experience of pleasure. It ranges from a warm, glowing sensation to an acute, intense reaction that borders on pain. Some forms of pleasure appear to suffuse the entire body, while others are focused on specific regions, such as the stomach or sex organs. Moreover, pleasurable responses are associated with an extremely broad spectrum of behavior. We derive pleasure from the satisfaction of both our primary and secondary drives—that is, from the relief of physiological needs such as hunger, thirst, sex and relief from excessive heat or cold, as well as from psychological needs for social approval, affection, status, and the attainment of personal aspirations.

In view of this emphasis on satisfaction of need, some psychologists have proposed the general theory that all these drives set up tensions in the organism, and pleasure is experienced whenever we succeed in reducing these tensions (Hull, 1943). The theory has considerable merit, but there seem to be exceptions. First, we experience

many pleasures that are not associated with tension or specific needs—for example, many tastes, smells, and sounds seem to be inherently pleasant. Second, we frequently derive pleasure from tension itself and not just from the relief or relaxation of tension. Working *on* a problem gives us pleasure, not simply working it *out*. The exhilaration of a fast game of tennis gives us pleasure whether we win or lose. And even the tensions involved in emotions which are generally classified as unpleasant may give us some satisfaction. It seems true that some people enjoy the intense fear they experience on a roller-coaster ride as much as the relief they experience when it ends. It may be, however, that the tennis game and the roller-coaster ride help us to reduce other tensions or satisfy other needs which are not apparent on the surface. See DRIVE REDUCTION THEORY.

The difficulties of describing and explaining pleasure psychologically are matched by the difficulty of discovering its physiological basis. The autonomic nervous system appears to be closely involved, yet it has not been possible to find specific patterns of response, as has been done with fear and anger. Some investigators have suggested that pleasantness arises primarily from parasympathetic activity, since pleasurable sensations are associated with eating, warmth, and sex, which are governed by that system. Among these activities are dilation of blood vessels, secretion of saliva and gastric juices, vasodilation, and certain muscular responses leading up to orgasm (Allport, 1924; Arnold, 1960). On the other hand, many other parasympathetic activities are distinctly unpleasant: crying, salivary response to bad odors, gastric contractions causing vomiting, and the activity of the bladder and rectum during fear.

A great deal of additional research will be required before any conclusions are reached. Meanwhile another physiological approach appears to be promising. Animal experiments on direct brain stimulation, initiated by Olds in 1954, indicate that there are pleasure centers in the brain itself situated predominantly in the limbic system beneath the cerebral cortex. The specific mechanisms of arousal, however, are still unknown. *See* LIMBIC SYSTEM.

Still another approach to pleasure is that of tracing its development from childhood onward. The infant's first pleasure is derived from gratification of his physical needs for food, warmth, elimination and close physical contact; and he signifies his satisfaction by cooing, gurgling and relaxation. Soon he adds another important component to this pleasure repertoire: free and unimpeded activity. He loves to exercise his lungs, kick his legs, and use his mouth and hands to explore everything within reach. By two months of age he begins to express delight by smiling, and a little later by something resembling laughter. One of the best ways to elicit these responses is to play simple, energetic games like peek-a-boo with the child. As time goes on, his range of spontaneous activity increases, and within a few months he is shouting with joy as he frisks about like a puppy, testing his developing strength and skill by climbing over the furniture and up the steps. At this point the pleasure of sheer activity is supplemented by the thrill of adventure and conquest of both the outer world of things and the inner world of fear and hesitation.

The child's personality expands as his opportunities for joyful activity increase. Pleasure may not be the end and purpose of life, but it is one of the major reinforcements in the process of growth and learning. A broad variety of attractive play materials, contact with different kinds of children, a full opportunity to satisfy curiosity and develop skills— all these will help the child discover himself and widen his sources of satisfaction. And if he develops under the guidance of thoughtful and perceptive adults, he will learn to derive pleasure not only from satisfying his own needs, but from participating with others and helping to meet their needs as well.

A study conducted by Jersild and Tasch (1949) has thrown considerable light on these developing patterns. A large number of children ranging in age from six to eighteen were asked to describe "one of the happiest days of my life." The younger children mentioned birthdays, holidays, and other festive occasions far more frequently than any other events, but this category declined sharply after the twelfth year. Gifts were consistently cited at all ages, though less often in the oldest age group (15–18) than in the younger and middle groups. Sports, games, and outdoor activities were mentioned twice as often by boys as girls, but on the whole girls enjoyed traveling, camping and visiting various places of recreation just about as much as boys (except that older boys preferred these activities far more than older girls). Girls found their greatest happiness in relationships with people (friendship, companionship, return of relatives) about twice as frequently as boys in all age groups. Satisfactions connected with school were cited at all ages, but reached their peak in the 12–15 (grades seven to nine) group. Finally, two types of satisfactions were mentioned far more often by the oldest group (15–18) than any other group: self-improvement, including job competence; and benefits befalling others or mankind in general, including an end to war.

Interpreting these results, Jersild (1960) points out evidence that many of these experiences were gratifying because of their underlying significance for the child. A gift, for example, may be a token of good will, a symbol of acceptance, or an expression of confidence and not merely a material gain. The study as a whole indicates that even if children begin life as physical, egocentric creatures, they soon develop the capacity of enjoying richer, more varied, and more meaningful satisfactions. If properly nourished, the spectrum of pleasure can continue to widen and deepen throughout life.

PLEASURE PRINCIPLE. In psychoanalytic theory, the regulatory mechanism that motivates us to gratify our basic instincts or drives and thus reduce the unpleasant tension we experience when they press for satisfaction.

The pleasure principle acts in the service of the libido, the instinctual energy of the organism, which is directed to the immediate gratification of internal needs such as sex, hunger, thirst, and elimination. In the Freudian theory, the individual's mental life and personality development are basically influenced by the pleasurable satisfaction of these needs. As Hendrick (1963) points out, "The most fundamental of Freud's laws of instinctual activity is that the psychological (and social) activities are determined by a constant need to reduce emotional tension to a minimal level. These tensions are the propulsive factor in human life, and the production of the tensions is the function of the instincts. They are consciously perceived as painful or disagreeable feelings; activity is initiated by the need to perform some specific function which will reduce this instinctually produced tension; and the fulfillment of this tension-reducing function thereby evokes the mental experience of pleasure." See DRIVE REDUCTION THEORY.

The pleasure principle—the tendency to seek immediate gratification regardless of consequences—characterizes the early life of the child. Before long, however, another force, the reality principle, comes into operation, compelling the child to recognize the demands of the external world. He must therefore begin to deny or postpone his gratification, and through this process he gradually attains emotional maturity. The reality principle, however, does not set aside the pleasure principle, but simply modifies it, since the individual continues to be motivated by a desire to obtain maximum pleasure and maximum avoidance of pain. As Freud's disciple, Ferenczi, has put it: "The controller-in-chief of all reactions and thoughts is the 'pleasure principle,' the endeavour to escape if possible from unpleasant situations, and the desire to obtain the greatest possible gratification with the smallest possible effort" (1926). See PSYCHOANALYSIS (THEORY).

PONS. A protruding part of the brain stem just above the medulla (PLATE 1).

The pons is part of the hindbrain, the oldest portion of the brain, and contains several components: (1) transverse fibers that run to and from the cerebellum, (2) the "pontine nuclei" within this band of fibers, (3) ascending and descending tracts connecting to various levels of the nervous system, and (4) the nuclei of the trigeminal nerve (the fifth cranial nerve) which receives sensations from the face and tongue and helps to control the movements of the mouth. As the name implies, the pons, or "bridge" is primarily a transmission center between different areas of the nervous system. It also works with the cerebellum in controlling equilibrium, and assists the cerebral cortex in making our voluntary movements smooth and co-ordinated.

PORPHYRIA. An uncommon metabolic disorder resulting in excessive or abnormal porphyrins in the urine, usually giving it a reddish color. Porphyrins are breakdown products of hemoglobin; the term derives from the Greek word for purple. The disease occurs most frequently in women and produces both physical and psychological symptoms.

There are three major types of porphyria: congenital, which is probably due to a recessive gene and may lead to mental retardation; acute intermittent, thought to be a dominant trait that runs in families; and the mixed type, in which the patient suffers from such symptoms as colic, skin eruptions, photosensitivity, and extreme susceptibility to sunburn. Psychiatric symptoms are most often found in the acute type, together with abdominal pain and weakness or paralysis in the extremities. Convulsions and both sensory and motor aphasia are occasionally reported. In the earlier stages patients are anxious, irritable, and argumentative. If the disease progresses, they become agitated, depressed, and suffer from memory disturbance and delirium with hallucinations and delusions. A recent study (Macalpine and Hunter, 1969) indicates that many descendants of Mary Queen of Scots were afflicted with porphyria, including James I and George III of England and Frederick the Great of Prussia.

Early diagnosis is essential, and the tranquilizer, chlorpromazine, has been found to be the most helpful remedy. In some cases electroshock therapy is applied for the psychiatric symptoms. The outlook for life is generally good in the congenital and mixed types, but mortality is relatively high in the acute intermittent type. See MENTAL RETARDATION (CAUSES).

POSTOPERATIVE DISORDERS. Emotional disturbances of a neurotic or psychotic character following surgery.

Many factors contribute to these disorders. Metabolic changes resulting from such temporary conditions as acidosis and hypoglycemia (reduced blood sugar) are frequently responsible in part, but other physical factors, such as sedatives, the anesthetic, infections, and toxic or nutritional disturbances may also be involved. Psychological factors are of equal or greater importance. The patient may be assailed by general feelings of apprehension preceding the operation, specific fears of mutilation or death, uneasiness due to preoperative procedures or the sights and sounds of the operating room, and fear of losing consciousness under the anesthetic. All these influences may be aggravated by tensions which the patient brings to the hospital as a result of financial, occupational, or family problems.

These factors combine to produce anxiety or panic reactions in some postoperative patients. Hysterical symptoms may also occur, but less frequently. In occasional cases the reaction may reach psychotic proportions. Here the most common symptom is a transient delirium, with confusion, disorientation, hallucinations, and restlessness. Severe reactions of this type are most frequently observed after major amputations and operations on the brain, heart, eyes, or genitals. Reactions to loss of a leg or arm may also be complicated by the "phantom phenomenon." The removal of a cataract is sometimes followed by confusion, suspiciousness, fear, and paniclike excitement, particularly during the night. One of the major causes of this reaction is believed to be the sensory deprivation experienced by the patient when his eyes are covered during the postoperative period. See PHANTOM REACTION, SENSORY DEPRIVATION.

In occasional cases other reactions, such as manic states and depressive or schizophrenic symptoms may follow an operation. These sequelae are believed to occur only in previously disposed individuals. Like all the other postoperative disorders, they are precipitated by the combination of psychological and physical stress incident to surgery.

The question of postoperative disorders among children deserves special consideration. D. M. Levy (1945) was the first to make a systematic study of "psychic trauma" following tonsillectomies and other operations in young children. An analysis of the records of 124 children referred for behavior problems following operative procedures revealed clear-cut emotional effects in twenty-five, including prolonged night terrors, fears (of the dark, strangers, white-coated men, new experiences), dependency reactions (clinging to the mother, refusing to be out of earshot of her, demanding help in dressing), negativistic reactions (disobedience, temper tantrums, destructiveness). The largest percentage of sequelae occurred in children below three years (50 per cent): "The increased emotional hazard of the operation for the one and two year old child was related to their keener response to pain, poorer comprehension of the experience, greater dependence on the mother, less experience in social contacts outside the home and less facility in handling anxiety."

On the basis of these findings, Levy made the following recommendations: postponement of the operation until at least three years of age, especially if there is evidence of anxiety or undue dependency; an explanation to the child of what is to take place, to overcome reactions to the strange or surprising event; contact with the mother before and after the operation; and preparatory sedative and anesthetic in the bedroom to spare the child the experiences of riding through the corridors and of seeing instruments and the operating room.

Lester L. Coleman (1952), a surgeon who has performed hundreds of tonsillectomies, has confirmed Levy's findings, and offers the following suggestions on prevention of postoperative emotional disturbances. The physician should establish a friendly, trusting relationship with the child and give a straightforward explanation of the need for the operation in terms of fewer colds and more time for activities. The operation should not be discussed with the parents in front of the child, and he should not be told about it until a day or two before it occurs. He should be given a simple description of the hospital, operating room and nurses, and the need for the anesthetic should be explained. The fact that pain and discomfort will be experienced after the operation should not be concealed. The presence of one or both parents immediately before and after the operation is essential, and with four- or five-year-olds, one parent should, if possible, be present throughout the hospital stay. The physician himself should escort the child to the operating room. During the postoperative period the child should be permitted to express his anger, for "from a child's point of view an injustice has been done him," and "better this hostility than submerged emotional conflict." To prepare the child more fully for this experience, an illustrated children's book, *A Visit to the Hospital*, has been written under Dr. Coleman's direction. In his experience, "the thoroughly prepared child goes through the entire experience with little if any emotional trauma."

Illustrative Case: POSTOPERATIVE DISORDERS

The most frightening experience I had occurred just after my last operation. My first recollection was one of great difficulty in breathing and very confused, opaque surroundings. Finally, things came into focus and I found myself completely under water in a steel chamber with a dozen or so other people. All were holding on to handles fastened securely to the wall and were flutter-kicking their feet slowly as one would do in a swimming pool holding on to the edge . . . I complained bitterly that I could not hold my breath any longer and while I realized that it was probably necessary for me to remain under water, stated in no uncertain terms that I would like to come up for a breath of air and then promised that I would come right down again. They smiled and laughed and said no, that I must stay where I was. While academically I realized that I was probably in no danger, I became terrified of drowning, feeling that probably because of my condition I was not able to stay under water as long as they, so started to fight my way to the surface. As they both continued to hold me down, I suddenly got the thought that they were trying to drown me. . . .

In a very tiny room just off my room . . . there lived a person whom I never saw. This room must have been very thin because it was concealed in the wall between my room and the adjoining room which, I believe, was the nurses' sitting room. At night this person would open up an almost invisible slot in the wall between his room and mine from which tiny tentacles of wire would begin to appear.

Usually he would start out with just one seeking tentacle, which would work its way very, very slowly out of the slot and down one of the nearby walls, generally near the intersection with the ceiling. The manner in which these wires were moved was very ingenious. It was something like snaking a rope to make it go from one place to another while lying flat on the floor. This manipulator, by the faintest motion, could move a wire at a snail's pace. After the wire had reached possibly three or four feet, a second wire would follow along next to it holding, at its end, a very tiny device which he would use to support the first wire at the point where possibly gravity might have pulled it down off its precarious position on the wall. (Nemiah, 1961)

POSTPARTUM PSYCHOSIS. A psychotic episode following childbirth, usually schizophrenic but sometimes depressive in nature. At one time toxic-exhaustive psychoses, with confusion and delirium, were common following childbirth, but today these disorders are relatively rare due to improved obstetrical procedures and the use of antibiotics.

Postpartum psychosis is not considered a specific syndrome, but is classified as "reactive"—that is, a transitory reaction to both physiological and psychological factors involved in giving birth to a child. It has been found that already existing personality defects (the "premorbid personality") determine whether the patient will become more schizophrenic or more depressive. In either case there is a prior susceptibility

which is brought to the surface by the physical and emotional strains of childbirth and the need for accepting and caring for the baby.

Postpartum disorders differ little from other psychoses except for preoccupation with hostility or harm toward the newborn infant or toward the husband. In patients with schizophrenic tendencies, long-standing aloofness may turn into indifference or open antagonism toward the child and husband, followed by an acute breakdown in which the new mother becomes mentally confused and apprehensive and may develop hallucinations, delusions, and dreams in which the child is lost, kidnaped, or killed. In patients with depressive tendencies, ordinary "maternity blues" do not subside but progress to deep dejection, lethargy, self-accusations of sin or unworthiness, and a sense of futility. Here, too, there may be indifference toward the child or fears that it might be harmed; and in rare instances suicide or infanticide may follow.

Case studies have revealed that postpartum psychosis is frequently associated with such factors as immaturity, a history of maladjustment, an unstable marriage and unfavorable home conditions, physical illness and excessive fatigue, heavy financial burdens, added responsibilities due to the birth of the baby, and lack of desire for the baby on the part of the wife or husband. The attitude of the father toward his wife's pregnancy and toward his own fatherhood may add materially to the stress which the new mother experiences. All these conditions may be taken as warning signals which can lead to early detection or prevention.

Preventive measures include competent and understanding obstetrical care, alleviation of stresses in the family situation, and psychological preparation of both the wife and husband through individual discussions with the physician or classes for expectant mothers and fathers.

Psychotherapy and electroshock therapy are commonly used treatments in postpartum psychosis. The condition generally clears up within a short time and rarely recurs after later pregnancies.

PRECONSCIOUS (Foreconscious). A psychoanalytic term for thoughts which are not presently in awareness, but which can be recalled more or less readily.

The preconscious includes images, ideas or verbal expressions that can be called up with conscious effort. Examples of preconscious thoughts are the memory of what happened yesterday, early but accessible experiences, the face of a friend, or a verbal cliché. Sometimes the term "the preconscious" (or "the foreconscious") is used as if it were a special repository for these thoughts, as contrasted with "the unconscious," which consists of thought contents that can be brought to awareness only by special techniques or under special conditions, as in free association, hypnosis, or automatic writing. This is no simple process, however, since unconscious contents are at least temporarily barred from consciousness by internal forces such as repression—and before it is given external expression, all unconscious material must be critically examined by an agent, termed the censor, that resides in the preconscious and acts as a watchdog.

The preconscious, together with the conscious and the unconscious, make up Freud's early "topographical" theory proposed in 1913, which conceived the mind in terms of three regions or mental systems. In 1923, however, he propounded a "structural hypothesis" which described mental functioning in terms of the id, which represents instinctual drives, the ego as the mediator between the id and external reality, and the superego which comprises moral precepts and ideals. At that time the concept of the censor as a single agent was replaced by the process of censorship exercised by a "chain" of agencies, the superego, the ego, and the ego-ideal. *See* METAPSYCHOLOGY, FREUD, PSYCHOANALYSIS (THEORY), CENSOR, EGO, SUPEREGO, EGO IDEAL.

PREGENITAL. A psychoanalytic term for the stage of psychosexual development preceding "genital primacy," when the sex organs begin to exert a predominant influence on the organization of sexual behavior. The pregenital period comprises the oral and anal stages of early childhood, during which the libido, or pleasure drive, is concentrated on the mouth or the anus rather than the genital organs. This period covers approximately the first three years of life, and precedes the phallic stage, or stage of "phallic primacy" beginning in the third year, when the penis in the boy and the clitoris in the girl gradually become the central erotogenic zones. Complete genital primacy is not attained until puberty. *See* PSYCHOSEXUAL DEVELOPMENT.

PREJUDICE. Literally, prejudice means any kind of prejudgment, favorable or unfavorable; but in social psychology it is generally used in a negative sense. It may therefore be defined as "an unfavorable attitude toward an object which tends to be highly stereotyped, emotionally charged and not easily changed by contrary information" (Krech et al., 1962).

Today it is generally agreed that prejudices are never "instinctive." There is no inborn "dislike of the unlike" or innate distaste for people of certain races or nationalities. Observations made the world over have shown that children play indiscriminately with members of other ethnic groups, and are either unaware of obvious physical differences or accept them as a matter of course. Prejudices are therefore wholly due to *learning,* and are acquired primarily through interaction with other people who teach, directly or indirectly, that certain groups or certain individuals are to be scorned or disliked. This type of learning can occur so early in life that it antedates any genuine capacity for judgment, and is therefore accepted without question. Moreover, prejudicial attitudes are strongly reinforced by the fact that they are usually acquired from people who are admired and accepted as authorities, especially parents and other close relatives.

The fact that prejudices are often acquired in the first few years of life, and even before the child goes to school, has been amply proved by a number of investigations. One of the most notable is the study of Radke et al. (1949), in which children from a lower middle-class area of Philadelphia were asked to tell stories about pictures of simple social situations, such as a Negro boy watching white children playing ball, or a boy watching people emerge from a synagogue. The stories indicated that a high percentage of these children expressed definite racial or religious prejudices by the time they were five to eight years of age. In another study, evidence of active prejudice was found as early as four years (Ammons, 1950). In general, these early prejudices are no more than echoes of the attitudes of others, often with little or no understanding of their meaning. Allport (1954) cites the example of the little girl who ran home to ask, "Mother, what is the name of the children I am supposed to hate?", and Munn (1966) tells of a small boy who remarked, "I don't like colored people. I just like people who are black or white." His mother had repeatedly warned him against "colored people."

In spite of its early beginnings, prejudice is not inevitable. It depends upon two general factors which may or may not encourage this form of learning: the individual's group affiliations, and his own particular personality structure.

The factor of affiliation is a most important consideration because prejudice is "typically learned through the process of interacting with members of one's own group" (Newcomb, Turner, Converse, 1965), and not—as some people believe—from personal contact or disagreeable experiences with members of the target group. Such experiences, however, may be used to reinforce prejudices that already exist, and are often exaggerated or distorted in so doing. Many studies have shown that prejudices vary with the degree of contact with one's own group rather than with the "outgroup." Each culture develops its own specific prejudices. Generation after generation of white people in South Africa, for example, have expressed strong prejudice against Negroes, while the French, Russians, and Scandinavians exhibit little prejudice toward any people with colored skins. *See* SOCIAL DISTANCE.

There is also evidence that a fairly systematic teaching process is at work in many groups where prejudice is common. Horowitz and Horowitz (1938) investigated the attitudes and behavior of white children toward Negroes in a southern community, and found that both subtle and explicit teaching takes place. Some of the children mentioned specific instances of being punished for not maintaining the proper distance from Negro children, but many of them were scarcely aware of the more subtle means employed, such as the use of derogatory gestures or condescending tones of voice. This study and others also showed that a common and effective means of teaching ethnic distinctions is through the application of the double standard. The child learns that it is not proper to cheat, lie, or be rude to members of his own group, but these forms of behavior are quite acceptable in dealing with certain other groups.

Even where groups teach prejudice directly or indirectly, one person may more readily adopt the negative attitudes than another. According to Adorno et al. (1950), "Individuals are most receptive to ideologies that are most compatible with their over-all personality structures." In their analysis much emphasis is placed on the predisposition to prejudice among authoritarian personalities. Such individuals are overly obedient to strong authority and release their pent-up hostilities against members of minority groups whom they can attack with impunity. The specific targets are singled out by the dominant group as a whole, and the authoritarian person adopts the prejudices which are most widespread in his culture, but expresses his unfavorable attitudes with greater rigidity and intensity than his less authoritarian compatriots. In a word, the group provides the targets but the authoritarian personality determines the dynamics. *See* AUTHORITARIAN PERSONALITY.

It is an interesting fact that when these two factors are operative they sometimes affect the behavior of members of minority as well as majority groups—that is, the member of the minority group who has an authoritarian personality shares some of the prejudice of the majority toward his own group. An example is anti-Semitism among Jews. This type of prejudice may result from an unconscious desire to identify with the majority group, but it may also be due in part to two other factors. First, members of a target group become hypersensitive to the criticisms which the majority utilize to bolster their prejudices; they may therefore try to dissociate themselves from members of their own group who display objectionable characteristics. And second, people who are discriminated against develop resentments, which must have an outlet, and they frequently give vent to these feelings by turning against members of their own group whom they blame for their plight.

Another personality trend frequently associated with prejudice is the feeling of inadequacy. Ineffectual people often experience a sense of power in lording it over others, joining exclusive organizations, or using minority groups as scapegoats. Moreover, they derive strength, security, and group support from identifying with the majority against those who are "different."

A number of investigations have shown that prejudices are often brought to the surface and augmented by the frustrations and deprivations of adult life, especially when the individual already believes that some groups are basically more acceptable than others. Bettelheim and Janowitz (1950), for example, conducted a study of three groups of veterans of World War II. The first had found better jobs than before entering the service, the second held similar jobs before and after the war, and the third could not find as good a job after the war as before. Attitude tests indicated that the veterans who were descending the vocational ladder were far more anti-Semitic and anti-Negro than those who were rising.

A major characteristic of prejudice is the fact that it is not readily accessible to change. Any effective program must be directed both at its roots, not only in the individual social group and the personalities of susceptible individuals, but also in the wider culture. The study just cited indicates one approach: people will often be less prone to prejudice if changes in their economic status are in a favorable direction. This suggests, for example, that if the level of prosperity of both white and Negroes in the South were considerably increased, acts of hostility on both sides would decrease in the long run. A second step is to alter the *practices* which maintain prejudicial attitudes. One way is through legislation. Though this approach does not attack prejudice directly, it is effective in eliminating some of the overt and clearly observable forms of discrimination, such as segregation, which is both an effect and a source of prejudice. As New-comb points out, "The modification of behavior through legislation can serve to reduce the likelihood that succeeding generations of children will acquire attitudes of prejudice, and may even affect the attitudes of adults over fairly brief periods of time." A striking example of these effects is found in the unforeseen consequences of laws against discrimination in employment. Three years after passage of the New York State law (1952), the Commission Against Discrimination reported that only 5 per cent of the businessmen polled expressed disapproval of the law, even though a large number had expressed fears at the time of its inception. See COGNITIVE DISSONANCE.

But in spite of this example, it must be recognized that legislation and other forceful measures "are by no means always necessary, desirable or effective. Under most conditions legislation cannot be enforced unless there already exists considerable popular support for it in the larger community or society" (Newcomb, Turner, Converse). For this reason it is advisable to conduct an intensive educational program before legislative changes are introduced.

A third effective technique is to set up situations in which those who hold prejudices participate in joint endeavors with target groups. Association and communication enable individuals to know and appreciate each other, and frequently change their attitudes toward one another. During World War II this occurred in many of the mixed platoons, as well as in war factories where people of different races worked side by side. In many cases, however, there was a return to prejudiced attitudes when peacetime brought back the tensions associated with economic competition—yet these attitudes were frequently less intense than they had been before the experience of working together. In an indicative experiment performed at a summer camp, Sherif et al. (1961) forced a group of boys to co-operate with another group toward whom they had been extremely hostile. This led to favorable changes in attitude toward members of the disliked group.

There is considerable agreement among psychologists that a program designed to reduce prejudice must be far-reaching and many-sided. It must attempt to reduce personal susceptibility to prejudice, change practices which reinforce hostile attitudes, and provide opportunities for participation in joint enterprises by members of opposing groups. These three attacks must be backed by attempts to inculcate positive attitudes of fairness, justice, understanding, and sensitivity toward the feelings of others. If this process begins early in life, it will add the moral ingredient that can contribute so much to improved human relations. See PROPAGANDA, HOSTILITY.

PREMATURITY. An infant is considered premature if the gestation period has been less than thirty-nine weeks and, more commonly, if his birth weight is five pounds, eight ounces (2800 grams) or less, and his crown-rump length less than thirty-two centimeters.

About seven out of 100 births in the United States are premature, with the highest rates occurring among first-borns, multiple births, and at lower socioeconomic levels. In spite of medical advances the mortality rate is still high, accounting for one third of all deaths in the first year of life. Survival is rare if the birth weight is less than 1000 grams (two pounds, three ounces); an infant weighing over 1500 grams (three pounds, five ounces) has four times as great a chance for survival as one below that weight. Twice as many premature females survive as premature males. Congenital malformation and birth injury are considerably more prevalent among premature than among full-term babies, and the chances of respiratory difficulty, anemia, feeding problems, infection, and brain damage are especially great.

Little is known about the causes of prematurity. Besides uterine crowding in multiple births, various maternal conditions such as malnutrition, prolonged emotional stress, illness during pregnancy, and excessive smoking or drinking are frequently cited as possibilities. Strenuous physical activity is now mentioned less often than it was at one time. Some investigators have suggested that many cases could be prevented through injections of hormones which control uterine contractions.

Many studies have been made of the effects of prematurity on the personality and development of the child. It is rather generally agreed that when lasting ill effects of a psychological nature are found, they are likely to be due more to parental attitudes than to the condition itself. Physical development is clearly retarded during the first few months of life, and prematures (especially the small ones) sit, stand, and walk considerably later than full-term babies—however, by the time they are two years of age there are usually no detectable differences in motor ability. On the whole, premature children score the same as others on intelligence tests, but there are more cases of serious mental defect due to brain hemorrhage at birth. Speech development is apt to be delayed, baby talk persists longer, and stuttering is more frequent than among full-term children. As a group they also have more than their share of nervous traits and behavior disorders such as nail biting, prolonged thumbsucking, excessive masturbation, extreme shyness, and temper tantrums. Many of these reactions persist through adolescence. Their social adjustment appears to be better during the early years, when they are closely associated with their mothers, than in later childhood when many premature children continue to be dependent and passive, while others turn in the opposite direction and become assertive and aggressive.

The social and emotional difficulties associated with prematurity are believed to be due largely to the mother's overconcerned and overprotective attitude. Her extreme solicitude may arise from a number of sources: concern that the baby may not live or may be abnormal; separation from the baby when he is put into an incubator; his small size and unusual color; feelings of guilt and anxiety stemming from the traditional belief that she is somehow to blame for the early birth; the doctor's careful precautions in the hospital and the feeling that she will not be able to care for the delicate baby; and the extra financial burdens which prematurity imposes. A few parents overstimulate their children to make them catch up with others, but more often they treat them with such caution and solicitude that they become nervous and anxious about themselves. Many of these children become timid and are inclined to be "fringers" throughout childhood and even later. This is far less likely to occur if parents take only the necessary precautions until the baby catches up with himself, and resolve to give him normal amounts of independence instead of treating him as different or handicapped.

PRENATAL DEVELOPMENT. In recent years there has been a growing realization that the period between conception and birth is a crucial one for the development of the individual. If prenatal conditions are favorable, the child will grow normally and get a good start in life. If the conditions are unfavorable, he may be seriously and lastingly handicapped from the moment he enters the world. Moreover, it is impossible to attain a full understanding of human development without knowing what goes on during this essential period of life.

Information about prenatal development has been gathered from many sources: examination of embryos and fetuses removed from the mother's body, studies of animals, the use of instruments to detect movements and responses to stimuli during the gestation period, mothers' reports of fetal movements, and photographs taken at various stages of prenatal life. The developmental process starts with the fertilization of the ovum by the sperm, and proceeds with such remarkable rapidity that within the short space of 280 days, a single microscopic cell develops into an indescribably complex organism composed of 200 billion cells. What is more, this growth process proceeds according to a timetable that is orderly and predictable to the minutest detail. It even has a built-in safety factor which enables the organism to survive if birth occurs as much as one hundred days before the normal term. *See* PREMATURITY.

The prenatal period is divided into three stages. During the *period of the ovum,* an interval of two weeks, the fertilized egg lives off its own yolk, dividing many times until it forms a cluster of cells about the size of a pinhead. This cluster descends through the Fallopian tube and implants itself in the wall of the uterus on about the tenth day, deriving its nourishment from the mother's body from then on. During the *period of the embryo,* extending to the end of the second lunar month, growth and development are extremely rapid. By the end of the third week the heart starts to beat even though the organism is only a quarter of an inch long. The liver secretes during the seventh week, and by the end of two months the facial features, fingers and toes are well formed. At the same time the "accessory apparatus" develops, consisting of the placenta, the umbilical cord, and the amniotic sac. These structures provide the embryo with nourishment and protection. From a psychological point of view it is important to recognize that there are no nerves in the umbilical cord, and therefore no transfer of thoughts from the mother to the embryo is possible.

The third prenatal period, the *period of the fetus* extends from the end of the second lunar month to birth. No new features appear during this period, but growth and development are steady and sequential, following two principal directions: the cephalocaudal or headtail direction and the proximodistal direction, from the center of the body outward. In other words, the head develops more rapidly than the legs, and the internal organs reach full functioning before the hands and fingers. In fact, the heart, stomach, and other internal organs are well developed by the fifth month, and by the sixth or seventh month the fetus has reached the *age of viability,* which means that it has a chance of survival if birth occurs at that time.

There is a fairly definite timetable for activity as well as for physical development during the fetal period. The umbilical cord often becomes twisted in the second or third month, indicating that the unborn child turns around at that time. Peristaltic movements also start very early, probably by the seventh week. Most of the basic reflexes—swallowing, palmar, plantar, flexion, and Babinski—are established in the fourth and fifth months, and by birth all the others are present. Another type of reaction, known as mass activity or generalized movements, starts in the head region as early as the third month under appropriate stimulation. These movements become spontaneous a little later, and by the fourth and fifth month the head, arms and legs are capable of moving independently. In some fetuses these movements occur as much as 75 per cent of the time, but in others as little as 5 per cent; and some fetuses squirm while others kick or have hiccups.

The various movements increase in

strength and number up to the ninth month, and are most violent when the mother is fatigued. There is also evidence of fetal movements if the mother is frightened or suddenly becomes angry. Overactive fetuses tend to become underweight, since they use up their energy instead of storing it in the form of fat. Infants who have been active as fetuses tend to develop motor co-ordination earlier than average, but those who have been less active usually have less difficulty adjusting to the postnatal environment directly after birth. See PRENATAL INFLUENCES.

PRENATAL INFLUENCES. Influences on the developing organism between conception and birth, ordinarily a period of about forty weeks.

At one time there was a widespread belief that the unborn child can be affected by the mother's thoughts and experiences—for example, that watching a fire may produce strawberry-colored birthmarks, or that listening to music will make him musical. There is no evidence for these "old wives' tales," yet they still persist in some quarters. On the other hand, there is substantial evidence for a newer concept of prenatal influence: the child's health and development can be profoundly affected by the conditions in the womb and the health of the mother.

Although there is no direct connection between either the blood stream or the nervous system of the mother and the unborn child, many abnormal conditions can be transmitted through the placenta, the organ which carries nutrition to the fetus. If the mother does not take in enough oxygen because of acute respiratory infection or chronic anemia during the first three months of pregnancy, the child may be born with a cleft palate or hare lip. If she contracts German measles (rubella) during the first fourteen weeks of pregnancy, the chances are ten to one that her child will develop one or more types of

impairment, such as eye defects, mental retardation, cerebral palsy, dental deformity, and especially deafness (Wesselhoeft, 1947). Syphilis in the mother frequently causes not only miscarriages and stillbirths, but mental deficiency, blindness, and deafness. Gonorrhea used to be the major cause of congenital blindness, but the incidence has been greatly reduced through the use of a silver nitrate eyewash administered shortly after birth. A pronounced thyroid deficiency in the mother can produce cretinism in the offspring; lead poisoning can cause deaf-mutism and deformities; heavy doses of quinine taken by the mother during the malaria season has caused many cases of congenital deafness.

Other special conditions have also been found to produce serious effects: diabetes, large doses of barbiturates, and thalidomide. In addition, heavy smoking appears to be a factor in prematurity. In one study, women who smoked an average of thirty-one or more cigarettes a day had more than five times as many premature deliveries as nonsmokers. The early births, however, may have been caused by the tension, anxiety, or physical distress that led to the excessive smoking rather than by the smoking itself (Lowe, 1959).

Radiation is another hazard to the unborn. In Hiroshima and Nagasaki the number of deformed and defective babies was found to be directly proportionate to the distance of the mother from the blast (Wilson, 1954). The Federal Radiation Council has estimated that 110 children born to people now alive in the United States will show the effects of nuclear fall-out resulting from explosions in the atmosphere through 1961. X-ray treatment in the pelvic region is also a factor. In one investigation, fourteen microcephalic children were born to fifty-three mothers who had been overexposed during pregnancy (D. P. Murphy, 1928). Even natural radiation can have harmful effects. In an area of New York State that contains igneous rock, the rate of cleft palate and other congenital malformations is significantly higher than the incidence in the state as a whole (Gentry, Parkhurst, and Bulin, 1959).

Serious malnutrition resulting from poverty, disease, or war almost inevitably affects the growth and health of the fetus. Vitamin deficiency in the diet of expectant mothers leads not only to rickets and general physical weakness, but may also produce nervous instability and mental deficiency of greater or lesser degree (Sontag, 1941). During the siege of Leningrad and the occupation of Holland in World War II, the stillborn rate doubled, the prematurity rate was abnormally high, and the weight and length of the newborn children were considerably lower than usual. The incidence of these conditions returned to normal when the food supply was improved.

Does the emotional life of the mother affect the fetus? The answer here is conjectural, but some investigators believe that while there is no guarantee that a happy mother will have a happy and healthy child, it is quite possible that emotional disturbance can have a negative effect. Sontag (1946) suggests that tensions and anxieties cause glandular changes in the mother which affect the fetus and carry over into the period after birth. Wallin and Riley (1950) have found that women who are unhappy during pregnancy experience more nausea and vomiting than those who are happy. It is quite possible that their digestive difficulties might interfere with the child's nutrition and affect his development. There are also signs of a more direct effect, since Sontag and others have observed that fetuses show an increase in activity when their mothers are undergoing severe emotional stress. The idea that tension and anxiety during pregnancy can affect the growing organism and influence its adjustment after birth is supported by a

number of recent experiments on rats (Ader and Belfer, 1962), but so far there is no conclusive evidence for human beings.

PRIMAL SCENE. A psychoanalytic term for the individual's recollection or fancied recollection of his first observation of the sex act. The primal scene usually stems from infancy or early childhood, and ordinarily involves intercourse between his parents. It may also arise from a seduction scene or other heterosexual relationship.

When the primal scene is based on actual observation, the child usually misinterprets what he sees. If it is constructed by his imagination, it is generally suggested by fragmentary impressions such as sounds behind closed doors, the talk of other children, or the sexual behavior of animals. Whatever its source, Freud believed it has a potent effect on the formation of personality and may be a source of pathological reactions. If, for example, the child believes that one parent is hurting the other during the primal scene, his own attitude toward sexual relations may be seriously distorted. It is also possible that this idea may be a source of anxiety that affects his whole development.

The primal scene may produce clearcut neurotic symptoms in some cases. An extreme example is the young boy whose entire visual field was inverted— that is, he saw the whole world upside down. The reaction was traced under hypnosis to secret observation of his parents while they were having intercourse in the "woman above" position. This position was a shock to him since he had been led to expect the reverse.

Illustrative Case: PRIMAL SCENE

A sixteen-year-old boy was brought to the clinics with the complaint (among many others here irrelevant) that he was frightened of the dark and of being left alone in constricted quarters. Specific investigation of this particular symptom in his past history revealed that, as a child, the patient had been alternately pampered and neglected by his parents, and had become highly dependent, yet jealous and insecure in his relationships with them. When he was five, they took him on an automobile trip and one night all three were forced to share a single hotel bed. That night, for the first time, the child witnessed intercourse between his parents. He was greatly excited and frightened by this "primal scene," in which he fancied that his parents, oblivious to his needs, were engaged in some sort of horrifying struggle that he was helpless to control. He cried, was punished and then banished to a cot where he lay in silent terror for the rest of the night. The next day his contrite parents calmed his fears and within a week all parties concerned had apparently forgotten the whole incident completely. However, a significant displacement remained: the child began to suffer severe anxiety when left alone, or when taken into closets, darkened theaters, or other places symbolic of his traumatic experience. Nevertheless, it was only with great difficulty that either the parents or the patient could recollect the incident described or recognize its symptomatic residue. (Masserman, 1961)

PRIMARY GAIN. The basic psychological benefit derived from neurotic symptoms.

According to many theorists, and particularly Freud, neurotic symptoms serve the primary purpose of relieving or controlling anxiety generated by conflicting impulses. At the same time they may bring secondary advantages, or gains, in the form of escape from a distressing or threatening situation, or sympathy, service, and attention from others. As an example, a pianist who is preparing to face a particularly critical audience may suddenly find her finger joints so stiff that she cannot appear. The symptom enables her to resolve her conflict about keeping the engagement, since she is able to satisfy her desire to escape from it (a secondary gain) without feeling anxious or guilty (the primary gain), for she feels she cannot be blamed for her "physical"

ailment. Similarly, a man who has acquired an unconscious fear of death may feel compelled to say a certain prayer every hour on the hour. His compulsion also brings neurotic gains, since the praying allays his inward fear and at the same time assures him that he is behaving like a very religious man. *See* SECONDARY GAIN.

PRIMARY PROCESS. A psychoanalytic term for mental activity dominated by the instinctual demands of the id.

The primary process is viewed as an immediate expression of wishes and impulses which stem from the unconscious. It is a free and uninhibited discharge of psychic energy without regard to reality or logic. This unorganized mental activity is believed to occur in its clearest form in the thoughts and dreams of infants. It is characterized by illogical ideas, fantasies, and magical thinking.

The young child's fantastic notions about the things and events around him provide many examples of primary thought processes. He may talk with an imaginary companion or play with an inanimate object as if it were alive. He may feel that he is the center of the world and develop ideas of his own omnipotence. In his dream life he makes no distinction between image and reality, and sees things happen (or makes them happen) without regard to the laws of nature. His dreams, however, are not simply a hodgepodge of fantasy, but obey the same laws that govern adult dreams. These laws bring the primary thought processes of both children and adults within the province of science.

Primary thought processes are manifested in psychotic disorders of a regressive type, most notably in schizophrenia. The distorted logic, fragmentation, concreteness, and overinclusiveness found in schizophrenic thinking are believed to be indicative of the immediate discharge of impulses without regard to the demands of the environment. The patient lives as if he were in a dream world, making up his own words, confusing his wishes with reality, condensing many thoughts into a single phrase or gesture, drawing odd analogies, and using mysterious signs and symbols. Schizophrenics have therefore been said to "wear their unconscious on their sleeve."

Even more indicative of primary-process thinking is the conviction that other people can read their mind, and the assumption that their thoughts are omnipotent. It is not uncommon for a schizophrenic patient to sit motionless, holding his forefinger in a peculiar position because he is sure that the world will come to an end if he moves an inch. *See* SECONDARY PROCESS, MAGICAL THINKING, IMAGINARY COMPANION, SCHIZOPHRENIC REACTIONS (GENERAL), DREAM INTERPRETATION (MODERN), DAY-DREAMING, AUTISM, PARALOGICAL THINKING.

PRINCE, MORTON (1854–1929). Prince, an important contributor to the dynamic approach in psychiatry, was born in Massachusetts and received his medical degree at Harvard Medical School in 1879. He then continued his studies abroad, primarily in Paris, where he came into close contact with the work of Janet, Liébault, Bernheim, and Charcot. After his return to the United States, he served as physician for disorders of the nervous system at several Boston hospitals, and taught neurology first at the Harvard, then at the Tufts, Medical School. In 1906 he founded the *Journal of Abnormal Psychology,* which he edited for the rest of his life. Among his professional posts were terms as president of both the American Neurological Association and the American Psychopathological Association. Between 1926 and 1928 he taught dynamic and abnormal psychology at Harvard, and established its Psychological Clinic as a means of integrating clinical with academic psychology. Through all these activities he became one of the great pioneers in psychopathology and abnormal psychology.

Prince was the author of over a hundred scientific papers and a number of books, not only on psychological and neurological subjects, but on political issues as well. His technical works include *The Nature of the Mind and Human Automatism* (1885), *The Dissociation of a Personality* (1906), *The Unconscious* (1913), and *Clinical and Experimental Studies in Personality* (1929). During the war he wrote *The Psychology of the Kaiser* (1915) and *The Creed of Deutschtum* (1918). The former book was used as a guide by the British in organizing their propaganda campaign against Germany. Prince's war services earned him decorations from a number of Allied governments.

As a result of his studies with Janet in Paris, Prince acquired a lasting interest in the subject of dissociation. He developed his own interpretation of this process, putting the emphasis on unconscious conflicts which split one thought or one aspect of the personality from another—a view that was actually closer to the dynamic theories of Freud than to the more static approach of Janet. His interpretation was even more sharply opposed to the doctrines of the leading psychologists of the time, Wundt and Titchener, who limited psychology to the analysis of mental processes of which we are directly aware. He also insisted that psychiatry should develop treatment methods directly geared to the inner dynamics of emotional disturbance, an approach that offered a promising alternative to the Weir Mitchell "rest cure" technique which was in vogue during the first part of the twentieth century. *See* MITCHELL.

Prince's approach to abnormality was thoroughly eclectic. He viewed mental illness as the result of inappropriate habit patterns, conflicting tendencies in the personality, and in some cases as a consequence of dissociated systems. He held that two sets of opposing forces are active in any situation: constructive factors that lead to appropriate associative and integrative reactions, and destructive factors that tend toward dissociation and conflict. In his view, therapy is primarily a re-educational process in which the conflict which has fragmented the personality is dissolved and a new, dynamic integration is achieved. He used analysis, interpretation, and hypnosis as his major therapeutic tools, and described the change brought about in the patient as a kind of "repersonalization." He also suggested that both the conflicting trends in the personality and the process of integration could be most vividly observed in the treatment of cases of multiple personality. For this reason he devoted an entire work, *The Dissociation of a Personality* (1906), to the study of a single patient, Christine Beauchamp, who developed a total of five personalities, three major and two minor. Here is a brief account of this celebrated case:

As a child Christine was lonely, dreamy, and subject to mystical experiences in which she felt "saintly." She cultivated an attitude of meekness and humility, fasted frequently, and sought to put aside all "wicked thoughts." Terrified of her father, she adored her mother, whom she identified with the Madonna—but felt that her love was not returned. When the mother fell ill and died, Christine, now thirteen, took the blame upon herself. After living unhappily with her father for a few years, she ran away to become a nurse. At eighteen she fell in love with an older man whom she regarded as a "messenger from heaven"—but suffered a second major trauma when he kissed her at the entrance to the hospital. "Horrified" by his expression, and apparently consumed by guilt over her own sexual response, she returned to the solitary, brooding existence she had led as a child.

At this point dissociation set in, and a quiet, reserved, sickly personality whom Prince called "the Saint" took over and remained dominant until she was twenty-four. During that year she received a letter that revived the memory of the hospital scene, and as a result became highly agitated and hallucinated the entire episode. Immediately afterward she suddenly manifested a second personality, "the Realist," a sociable, self-assertive, impulsive individual who disliked whatever the Saint liked, such as older people and church.

At the end of this period a third personality, "Sally," began to make her appearance when the Saint's eyes were closed. Sally was "coconscious" with the Saint—that is, she knew everything the Saint thought and did, but the Saint was totally unaware of her. This personality was a mischievous imp who forced the Saint to think of other things while reading anything that bored her, embarrassed her by making her lie, destroyed her knitting, charged extravagant purchases to her at stores, hiked far into the woods and deliberately changed over to the Saint personality, forcing her to walk back because she knew the Saint disliked exercise and outdoor life. She also tried to trick the Realist, but this personality knew of her existence and managed to resist.

Utilizing hypnosis as his major technique, Prince sought to banish the mischievous Sally and merge the Saint and the Realist. The treatment was successful and Sally finally disappeared and could not be recalled. Miss Beauchamp later married and remained emotionally healthy. *See* MULTIPLE PERSONALITY.

PRISON PSYCHOSIS. A severe emotional disturbance precipitated by actual or anticipated imprisonment.

There are several types of prison disorders, all of which are believed to represent unconscious attempts to escape from an uncompromising and unbearable reality. They are therefore classified as "situational" psychoses. The patients are usually antisocial (psychopathic) personalities who have a strong antipathy to authority and are accustomed to do exactly what they want at any time. Such individuals find it extremely difficult to adjust to confinement or the thought of confinement, and if poorly integrated may develop psychotic reactions.

Situational prison psychoses are special types of reactions that must be distinguished from other psychotic disorders that develop among prisoners. The most common psychoses in prison are of the usual clinical types, especially schizophrenia and paranoid states. These disorders are due to long-standing tendencies that are merely released by the stress of imprisonment. In contrast, the "true" prison psychoses are limited and often brief reactions to the specific situation of confinement. They are most likely to occur among long-term prisoners relatively soon after they begin serving their sentences.

These prison psychoses tend to take one of two forms. Some prisoners develop delusions of ill treatment and become extremely irritable and querulous. They complain constantly and insist that everything possible is being done to make life miserable for them. Others develop delusions of innocence or pardon. They may hear voices that announce that they have been exonerated and are about to be freed, or they may convince themselves that they are completely innocent and become increasingly resentful against those who keep them in confinement.

Occasionally two other reactions are observed. A new prisoner may suddenly become highly excited and enraged, cursing and destroying anything he can lay his hands on. These attacks are usually brief, and represent a protest against confinement. Other prisoners may develop delusions of persecution, ideas of influence (that is, someone is controlling or putting ideas in their minds), hallucinations of poison gas, or severe attacks of anxiety and uneasiness.

Prisoners who become acutely psychotic are usually transferred to mental hospitals for treatment. Most of them recover fairly quickly, although life prisoners who cannot look forward to freedom may gradually deteriorate. They are generally given standard treatments for psychosis, and special efforts are made to keep the atmosphere as friendly and nonirritating as possible. They are also given an opportunity to occupy themselves with nondemanding recreational and occupational activities. For discussion of a special form of mental disorder that develops among prisoners under detention and awaiting trial, see GANSER SYNDROME.

Illustrative Case: PRISON PSYCHOSIS

Two brothers, one twenty and the other twenty-two years old, held up a messenger who was carrying money in an elevator. They both were armed with five revolvers. They were pursued by a policeman, who shot one of them, whom we shall call John, in the knee. He fell to the ground. As the policeman leaned over him, he shot and killed the policeman. He was taken to a hospital for treatment of his wound, and, when he recovered from that, he was taken for psychiatric observation because of his behavior. The other brother, George, was captured without being wounded but was severely beaten over the head. After a period of imprisonment he too was sent for observation to the psychiatric hospital. Both of them were repeatedly examined very carefully, and the conclusion arrived at by several psychiatrists with considerable experience in the field was that they were malingering. Another psychiatrist, who examined them in the prison several weeks later, was of the opinion that John was suffering at the time from a Ganser syndrome with reactive depression. He looked sad and gave few answers, and those he gave were approximate answers of the type described. When asked to put a key into a lock, he put his finger into a hole. When asked what happened to him, he began to weep, and said, "They took my sword away." At this point George presented the picture of schizophrenia of the catatonic type. He gave no replies, did not look at the examiner, and, when his extremities were moved, either resisted or retained them in the position in which they were placed. During the trial this brother, while sitting in the courtroom, would defecate in his trousers and try to eat his feces. Both of the brothers were sentenced to death. In prison, awaiting execution, both of them presented the picture of a catatonic stupor. They were mute, lay on the cot without moving, did not attend to their bodily needs, and had to be fed artificially. A committee of three psychiatrists appointed by the governor examined them and came to the conclusion that they were psychotic.

The life history of the two brothers was very instructive. From early childhood on, the history was full of incidents of the following kind. Having been abandoned by one of the parents, they lived with relatives who were alcoholics or petty criminals. They committed minor offenses in childhood and preadolescence and had been sent to reform schools. They continued with worse offenses and ended up with the final venture. These two cases illustrate the fusion of interpersonal problems and traumas continuously from early childhood, including identification with older people having delinquent and criminal orientations, and exposure to gang practices. They illustrate the problem of diagnosis of psychiatric states following capture, fear of imprisonment, fear of punishment, and the collapse of the magic omnipotent reliance on the self and on the group, when they felt that they would be crushed by retribution. (Maslow and Mittelmann, 1951)

PRISONER OF WAR REACTIONS. Personality disturbances occurring in individuals who have been subjected to the psychological and physical strains of the prisoner of war experience. Disturbances of this kind are described by the American Psychiatric Association as "gross stress reactions," and are classified as "transient situational personality disorders." They are termed "situational" because they are responses to severe, disrupting conditions of life as opposed to unconscious conflict or other sources of maladjustment; and they are described as "transient" because they generally subside by themselves or as a result of limited psychotherapy.

The psychological reactions of captured Americans following the fall of Bataan and Corregidor during World War II have been vividly described by a psychologically trained participant, Commander A. E. Nardini. Here are some of the highlights of his report:

First, the experience of being suddenly deprived of name, rank, identity, justice and all rights as a human being, coupled with physical misery and disease, frequently produced emotional shock and depression. These reactions contributed greatly to the massive death rate during the first months of imprisonment. (For a similar reaction, see ANACLITIC DEPRESSION.)

Second, there was a fairly widespread deterioration in attitude and behavior due to prolonged subjection to squalid living conditions, insufficient and inedible food, physical abuse, inadequate clothing, and extremes of temperature. "Hungry men were constantly reminded of their own nearness to death by observing the steady, relentless march to death of their comrades." They quibbled over food, took advantage of less clever fellow prisoners, bartered unethically, stole, and even curried favor with their captors. They found it hard to think or feel beyond the next bowl of rice. See STARVATION REACTIONS.

Third, distinct personality changes were observed—most often extreme irritability, unfriendliness, suspiciousness, and sullen withdrawal. The hostility generated by the extreme frustrations of the situation, coupled with constant subjection to shouting, slapping, and baiting by the Japanese was often turned toward other men, especially in mixed groups. Sometimes, however, it was turned inward and produced serious waves of depression.

Fourth, as they became debilitated from dysentery, fever, chills, pain, and apparently hopeless conditions, the men reacted with increasing apathy and despondency. The "apathy syndrome," utilizing the mechanism of emotional insulation, usually helped the prisoners maintain their stability in the face of stress. The feelings of hopelessness, however, had a much more destructive effect. Some men lost interest in living and gave up completely: "An ever-present sign of fatal withdrawal occurred three or four days before death when the man pulled his covers up over his head and lay passive, quiet and refusing food."

The conditions in the POW camps improved to some extent with the Chinese Communists, but the men were soon faced with the problem of brainwashing. The first step was to isolate them completely from the companionship and support of others; after that they were threatened with torture and death if they did not "confess" and collaborate. Most men found they could withstand their captors by "playing it cool"; they were, noncommittal, relatively uncommunicative, and would not allow themselves to become emotionally involved. Others, however, were softened up by the strain of isolation, the wretched living conditions and the constant bombardment with propaganda. They lost their power to discriminate, became increasingly suggestible, and developed a desperate need for someone to talk to. Their captors then "befriended" them, offered them extra food and other favors, and succeeded in getting a few men to "co-operate." See BRAINWASHING.

About one half of the prisoners taken by the Japanese, North Koreans, and Chinese Communists died in the POW camps. Those who survived tended to suffer from persistent aftereffects of a physical and psychological nature. Their symptoms usually fell into a pattern marked by fatigability, inability to withstand frustration, frequent resort to alcohol and sedatives, lowered resistance to illness, neurotic pains in hands and feet, irritability, and other symptoms of emotional instability, including the indiscriminate release of pent-up hostility. After a varying period of adjustment the majority of former POWs succeeded in adapting themselves to the requirements of civilian life.

What personal qualities are most conducive to survival in a POW camp? Although this question has not been thoroughly investigated, the following

have been suggested: a stoical but non-defeatist attitude, absorption in present activity, ability to control hostility and depression, maturity and ego strength, a strong sense of identity and self-respect, ability to keep on hoping, and an intense will to live (Nardini, 1962). See TRANSIENT SITUATIONAL PERSONALITY DISORDERS.

PROBLEM SOLVING. There is no need to justify the study of problem solving, since life is a continual series of obstacles, difficulties, and frustrations from beginning to end. In fact, this type of behavior is probably the most characteristic activity of the human being, especially at a time when every phase of our existence is rapidly changing and ideas which worked in the past can rarely be used in unchanged form today.

The method of attacking problems has changed far less than the problems themselves. About fifty years ago John Dewey and others outlined a typical sequence of events that applies to practically every type of reasoning, creative thinking, and problem solving—and more recent psychologists have done little more than refine and elaborate his four-step pattern:

1. *Motivation.* As Dewey pointed out, in his book *How We Think* (1910), all thinking arises from a desire to get out of some trouble. Before we use our minds, we must be faced with a difficulty, a challenge, an unsatisfied need. The motives may be extremely diverse: curiosity, greed, ambition, love—but there must be a motive. This simply starts us off, but the recognition that there *is* a problem is essential. Many situations are not problematic because we do not recognize them as problems. The arrogant person sees no need to change because he does not realize that his arrogance is creating a problem for himself as well as others; the dominating husband accepts his wife's inferior role, and his wife may herself accept it;

poverty, hunger and discrimination were taken for granted for centuries and only recently became genuine problems for society to face. The first problem, then, is to *see* the problem.

2. *Delimitation*. Before we can make any adequate attack, we must define and delimit the problem at hand. This is often the critical point of the process, the place where we either start off in a promising direction or bark up the wrong tree. Pinpointing the difficulty also helps us plan our efforts, look for information in the right places, and make observations or experiments that have some possibility of success. The poorly organized person plunges into the work without knowing what he is really looking for or what specific questions he is trying to answer. The well-organized person knows that the time he spends in defining the problem will be saved many times over in the long run. Science began to make strides against communicable diseases when Pasteur defined the problem in terms of the transmission of micro-organisms from one individual to another. In psychological counseling the client starts out with a vague feeling that "something is wrong," but this uneasiness usually begins to dissipate as soon as his problem is defined and spelled out.

3. *Hypothesis*. The next step is to develop a number of tentative solutions. This stage grows out of stage 2, since hypotheses must be based on essential aspects of the problem and not some incidental features or irrelevant details. They sometimes arise from the discovery of new information, but are more frequently suggested by prior knowledge. A person who has had considerable experience with similar problems can usually develop more plausible hypotheses than the novice in the field. He will also be less likely to stamp over old ground. The chief danger is that he may cling to old ideas and resist the new.

The negative effect of clinging to old ideas has been clearly illustrated in experiments on habitual set and "functional fixedness." As an example of the effects of set, Luchins (1942) devised seven problems in which the object was to show how a certain amount of water might be obtained by using containers as measures—for example, "If I have a twenty-nine-quart jar and a three-quart jar, how can I obtain twenty quarts?" The solution to each of the first five problems involved several steps; the sixth and seventh problems, however, could be solved either by a roundabout method which involved pouring the water from one jar to another several times, or by a simple and direct method. The experimenter found that 75 per cent of the subjects used the roundabout method, due to the set established in the first five trials. However, he was able to break this habit in another group of subjects by the simple expedient of warning them, "Don't be blind. Look sharp now," or by separating the practice and critical trials by a period of several days. Both of these measures encouraged the subjects to try a fresh approach.

A second experiment illustrates the fact that we are often blind to new uses of objects we are accustomed to employing in a certain way—that is, they become "functionally fixed." As one example, Adamson (1952) provided two groups of subjects with three candles, three cardboard boxes, five thumbtacks, and five matches, then asked them to find a way of mounting the candles on a vertical screen. In one case the objects were simply placed on a table in front of the subjects; in the other, the tacks, candles, and matches were placed in the boxes before giving them to the subjects. The problem was solved within twenty minutes by 86 per cent of the first group and only 41 per cent of the second. The solution consisted of melting the ends of the candle with match flames, sticking them onto the boxes, and then attaching the boxes to the screen with the thumb-tacks. The reason the second group had trouble finding the solution was that they were "fixated" on the use of boxes as *containers*. Since they had received the various materials in the boxes, they could not easily imagine using the boxes as *shelves* for the candles. The first group, on the other hand, were not hampered by this set and could more readily take a fresh approach to the problem. *See* SET, HABIT, CREATIVE THINKING.

A good hypothesis must be clearly defined and lead to a course of action through which it can be either verified or disproved. This does not close the door completely on hunches, since occasionally they turn out to be correct. It is important to recognize, however, that a hunch that remains vague and poorly formed is of no use in meeting a problem. It may even stand in the way of a genuine solution. Many people, scientists included, cling to pet hunches and some even unwittingly distort the facts to fit their theories. Such hunches can sometimes be traced to unconscious wishes.

4. *Testing*. The only way to tell whether any hypothesis is valid is to try it out. This process, however, is not always an external affair; we can often discard a hypothesis—and occasionally accept one—by visualizing the outcome and checking it against known facts. Einstein's theory of relativity is one of the few major instances where an idea was widely accepted before any definitive observations were made. Our space program combines the two approaches. Astrophysicists and other scientists deal with many aspects of space flight without leaving the blackboard; the astronauts test some of their hypotheses in the laboratory under simulated space conditions, and others in actual flight.

The testing of hypotheses is frequently a long and laborious process. Edison's problem was to find a substance that would glow without being consumed when electricity was passed through it.

He tried dozens of hypotheses in the form of such substances as carbon, platinum, straw, paper, tar, cellulose, and cork until he found that bamboo best fitted his requirements. Then he tested 6000 different bamboo specimens before choosing three that worked moderately well. The search did not end there, for these early filaments were later replaced by tungsten. *See* DEWEY.

PRODIGY. An individual who shows phenomenal ability in one or more activities, usually at an early age.

The precocious ability of the prodigy generally appears spontaneously, but contrary to common opinion, it does not arrive full-blown. It takes time to grow, but its development proceeds more rapidly and achieves a higher degree of perfection than the abilities of ordinary individuals. Much of this growth seems to be a process of inner maturation; but training, encouragement, and stimulation are usually necessary to bring it to full flower.

Genuine prodigies must be distinguished from (1) pseudo-prodigies, who may develop a high degree of skill, but only as a result of overtraining by overzealous parents or teachers, and not because they possess a remarkable potential; and from (2) idiot savants, who show remarkable skill in a limited area but fail to achieve complete understanding of what they are doing due to subnormal intelligence. *See* IDIOT SAVANT.

Although prodigies appear to possess uncanny powers, their abilities rarely differ in kind from those of ordinary individuals but generally only in degree. Most investigators today believe these abilities are based on superior basic endowment. There is no clear evidence, however, that prodigious talent is inherited according to Mendelian ratios, with the possible exception of musical ability.

There have been very few systematic, scientific studies of prodigies. We do, however, have a large body of biographical and anecdotal material on arithmetical, chess, memory, and musical prodigies; and some of these accounts throw considerable light on the nature of these abilities. The following is a representative sampling of cases illustrating each of these categories.

Arithmetical Prodigies. Carl Friedrich Gauss showed astonishing ability in performing mental calculations before the age of three, and repeatedly corrected his father's mistakes. He would often pursue the same problem for days or even weeks, and came to know "by heart" the square roots, squares, logs, and other properties of the first two thousand numbers. G. P. Bidder, known as the "calculating boy," mastered the numerator table up to ten million, and at thirteen years of age was able to give the answer almost instantly to problems of this kind: "Find the number whose cube, less 19, multiplied by its cube shall be equal to the cube of 6." Tom Fuller could correctly multiply two nine-digit numbers, and reduce a year and a half to seconds within two minutes. Oscar Verhaeghe could perform feats like raising 9,999,999 to the fifth power in one minute. T. H. Safford published four different almanac calendars at age ten, and also discovered new mathematical rules for calculating eclipses, and for the rising and setting of the moon. In addition, he successfully multiplied 365,365,365,-365,365,365 by itself within one minute.

A number of tentative conclusions can be drawn from these and other cases. First, the ability to perform these feats is not confined to individuals of high intelligence; in the above examples, Gauss became a renowned mathematician, Bidder a successful engineer, Safford a noted astronomer; but Tom Fuller and Oscar Verhaeghe were illiterate idiot savants. Second, lightning calculators develop an all-consuming interest in numbers and devote endless amounts of time to practicing and perfecting their skills. This constant preoccupation makes them so familiar with the properties of numbers (square roots, etc.) that they can call upon memory to give them the answer to a complex operation at a glance, in the same way that other people immediately know that 8 times 8 is 64. Third, they tend to specialize in certain areas, such as multiplication, squares, or the calendar, and often show less than average proficiency with other problems. Fourth, many if not all prodigies use systems or short cuts in solving problems, but only a few are willing or able to explain their methods. The idiot savant usually claims the answer just "pops into my head," but this may simply be an admission that he cannot put his system into words. Fifth, there is evidence that the huge amounts of practice make the process largely automatic and semiconscious—which may also explain why the answers seem to come to mind spontaneously. One famous calculator, Maurice Dagbert, played the violin from music he read for the first time while extracting the cube root of four different numbers, each in the hundred millions. On the other hand, many calculators go through various physical gyrations while calculating—Safford, for example, used to spin around the room like a top, biting his hands and rolling his eyes in their sockets as if in agony until he came up with the answer. Sixth, some calculators are aided by vivid visual imagery, or even eidetic imagery, which enables them to hold many numbers before their minds at once (Bousfield and Barry, 1933). A few, like Inaudi, who was studied by Binet, possess highly developed auditory imagery. *See* EIDETIC IMAGERY.

These observations do not fully explain arithmetical prodigies. They do, however, indicate that their ability is not a miracle but rather a higher development of known capacities through the influence of such factors as interest, practice, memory, special techniques, automatic activity, and specialization.

Chess Prodigies. There are so many similarities between "lightning calculators" and phenomenal chess players that the two abilities may have a common basis. Many of the great chess players manifested their ability at an early age: Capablanca, Reshevsky, Evans, Fischer, to name only a few. Some have developed a high degree of skill in other areas, but most of them show no particular distinction outside their field. Scheinfeld (1965) has suggested that "Apart from the fact that chess virtuosity requires specialization and constant application, it appears to develop capacities unrelated to other forms of achievement. Thus, Edward Lasker, himself a chess virtuoso, reported that studies of a dozen leading chess masters revealed unusual memory only for chess positions and no ability to think faster than average persons in other respects. The only distinctive capacities identified were those for objective and abstract thinking, highly disciplined wills and powers of concentration, good nerves, self-control, and confidence." Contrary to Scheinfeld's interpretation, these capacities can hardly be termed unrelated to other forms of achievement. We would rather say that partly by virtue of his natural endowment and partly by virtue of assiduous practice, the chess player has developed essentially basic abilities to a remarkably high degree. Moreover, other special capacities seem to be essential, especially visualization and foresight, which combine with abstract ability to enable the player to analyze possible consequences several moves in advance.

These intellectual powers suggest that chess is actually a form of mental calculation in which the player must continually recalculate his most advantageous moves on the basis of his opponent's plays and the total constellation or "Gestalt" of the board at any given time. Like the rapid calculator, the chess player develops an ability to see these patterns "in his mind's eye," so that they fall into place almost automatically. (This ability to visualize reached a peak in the blindfold play of George Koltanowsky, who has taken on as many as fifty-six players at once.) And, like the calculator, the chess player appears to draw heavily upon memory, for anyone who plays thousands of games is bound to find that similar combinations reappear, or that similar principles can be applied time and again. It is certainly indicative that Paul Morphy claimed to be able to recall the many thousands of games he engaged in after his chess ability matured, and that he once demonstrated his memory ability by correctly reproducing the entire sequence of moves he made while engaged in simultaneous games against eight players on the preceding night. While these facts about practice, memory, visualization, and systematization do not fully explain the remarkable ability of the chess prodigy, they at least help to bring it within the sphere of scientific investigation.

Memory prodigies. The feats of memory prodigies are so often cited that only a few examples need be given. Macaulay was apparently able to recall whole passages of volumes he read only once, and Daniel Webster is credited with knowing by heart not only the entire Bible, but *Paradise Lost* and all of Shakespeare's plays. General Smuts, who did not learn to read until twelve years of age, is said to have memorized the contents of the five thousand books in his library. Ben Jonson, Pascal, Grotius, and Leibnitz had similar reputations. In addition, every generation has its memory experts who make a living by performing before incredulous audiences. Among the most celebrated were James Crichton, who, while still a boy, could respond to questions in any of twelve languages; and W. J. M. Bottle, who used the stage name Datas because he specialized in such weighty facts as "When was a duty put on soap?" and "When were top hats invented?"

The explanation of memory ability, so far as it can be given, is based on the same types of factors found among the prodigies already discussed: exceptional inborn capacity combined with interest, practice, and in some cases special techniques such as mnemonic devices, or unique abilities such as eidetic imagery. Since no psychological investigations were made of men like Macaulay and Webster, we can only offer conjectures based on cases which have actually been studied. Doubtless a considerable portion of their ability was due to high basic intelligence in combination with, for want of a better term, a particularly plastic nervous system. Since this plasticity cannot as yet be explained in physiological terms, we can only surmise that connections can be established in some nervous systems more readily than in others. We cannot overlook the possibility that individuals such as Macaulay and Webster came from an environment which offered a wealth of cultural experiences and put a premium on intellectual accomplishment. Other so-called prodigies, such as Datas, probably possessed an unusually plastic nervous system, but were highly motivated to make the most of their ability by commercial considerations rather than cultural interests. There is a distinct possibility that Macaulay and Webster were gifted with either an especially vivid visual imagery or with eidetic imagery, a hypothesis suggested by a number of psychological investigations, such as the one by Bousfield and Barry cited above. This explanation may also apply to Datas, since early in his career he memorized dates by visualizing the events associated with them—for example, he would remember the date 1666 by picturing the great fire which occurred in London that year. He claimed that these impressions returned to him whenever he was questioned by

his audiences. He also established associations between the different facts he sought to memorize, so that one item would call up another in a chain reaction. This technique is still recommended in some memory-improvement courses which focus on memory for details like names and dates. *See* MEMORY IMPROVEMENT.

Musical prodigies. Exceptional musical talent usually manifests itself at an early age. The list of great musicians (including composers as well as performers) who have earned the title "child prodigy" is a long one. In an earlier day Mendelssohn, Mozart, Franck, Berlioz, Brahms, Chopin, Debussy, Liszt, Schumann, Dvorak, Haydn, and Handel all showed precocious musical ability. The same is true of many recent virtuosos, including Heifetz, Menuhin, Rubinstein, Ricci, Schnabel, Oistrakh, Richter, Stern, and Arrau. A study of thirty-five outstanding pianists, violinists, and conductors comprising the great majority of living virtuosos, as well as fifty students of the Juilliard Graduate School of Music, has shown that musical talent expressed itself at an average age of four and three quarters years in the virtuoso group and at five and a half in the Juilliard group (Scheinfeld, 1965). In many cases this talent appeared spontaneously, and often in unusual ways—for example, at the age of one and a half, Rubinstein used to sing little songs of his own making to express what he wanted and to identify various members of his family—yet his parents were too poor to own a single musical instrument.

Many great musicians and composers stemmed from highly musical backgrounds—among them, Bach, Purcell, and Mendelssohn. Evidence compiled by Scheinfeld from various sources argues in favor of a hereditary basis for outstanding musical ability, at least in the form of a predisposition that is most likely to express itself in virtuoso form when the environmental conditions are favorable to its development. Scheinfeld has suggested that the hereditary mechanism is "polygenic"—that is, involving a cluster of genes rather than a single gene. The following data would seem to favor this general interpretation.

First, in Scheinfeld's study, 70 per cent of the brothers and sisters of gifted individuals showed a talent when both parents had musical talent; 60 per cent when only one parent was talented; and only 15 per cent when neither parent was talented. Although these findings are compatible with an environmental interpretation, they strongly suggest a hereditary basis. The fact that musical talent sometimes appears where *no* member of the family has shown talent (as in the case of Toscanini), suggests that all the components of the musical cluster had not come together before.

Second, environment cannot by itself create musical talent, as is shown by the fact that one in four of the children of the virtuosos studied did not show any musical talent. Moreover, many parents give their children endless musical training to no avail, apparently because they do not possess the required genetic capacity. On the other hand, the basic ability can be so strong that it will develop even in an adverse environment, or, as in the case of Leonard Bernstein, where it is not recognized or cultivated at an early age.

Third, the argument that musical talent consists of a cluster of genetic traits is supported by the idea that it is probably not a single ability but a set of related aptitudes, including pitch, rhythm, tonal memory, etc., and it is therefore unlikely that a single gene could determine all of these abilities. Fourth, some of these abilities, such as excellent pitch, may be present in persons who have little or no general musical ability. Only the rare individual who, presumably, has all the required genes in high degree—and usually a stimulating environment as well—could become a prodigy. There have even been cases of idiot savants who showed unusual, though limited, musical aptitude —for example, a thirty-eight-year-old man with the mental age of ten (IQ 67), who had absolute pitch and a remarkable musical memory (Anastasi and Levee, 1960).

Scheinfeld concludes from all these indications that "What is inherited is a single 'talent susceptibility,' dependent for its expression on the interoperation of many factors—some from within the individual (sensory, mental, emotional, physical) and some from without (home, social and cultural environments, opportunities for training and recognition). In some individuals, the susceptibility to musical achievement is so strong (talent plus *drive*) that even in a minimal or adverse environment it will assert itself. And also, just as there are some few individuals with inherited musical capacities which can be developed to an astounding degree, there are others so limited or imperfect in genetic capacities that no amount of training can make them musical."

PRODROME (literally, "running before," "precursor"). An early or warning symptom of a disorder, either mental or physical.

In any illness there is likely to be a "prodromal phase" in which a number of premonitory symptoms appear. For example, some of the early signs of cerebral arteriosclerosis are fatigue, headaches, dizziness, drowsiness in the afternoon, and insidious impairment of physical and mental abilities. The first signs of schizophrenia are frequently isolation from other people, sensitivity to the remarks of others, and loss of interest in work or social life. Epileptic attacks are often preceded by premonitory sensory, motor, or visceral symptoms. The prodromal phase in alcoholic addiction is marked by amnesic episodes (blackouts), surreptitious drinking, preoccupation with drinking, gulping drinks, and avoidance of reference to drinking. *See* ALCOHOLIC ADDICTION, AURA.

Prodromal symptoms make it possible to detect many psychiatric disorders in their beginning stages, when treatment is most effective. It is therefore important for all practitioners, social workers, and others who deal with human problems to become acquainted with these symptoms—not necessarily to make specific diagnoses, but to recognize that the individual might be in need of special help.

A word should also be said about so-called prodromic dreams. The idea that dreams may contain warnings of impending disorders has a long history. In the fourth century B.C. Hippocrates suggested that symptoms of an illness may appear in dream symbolism long before it is evident in consciousness. Galen, writing in the second century A.D., was more equivocal. At times he attacked the idea of diagnosis through dreams, but he also mentioned cases in which dreams guided him to cures, holding that dreams of fire were caused by yellow bile and dreams of darkness by black bile. In the present century Carl Jung cited a number of dreams which he believed to be prodromic.

PROGRAMMED LEARNING (Automated Teaching, Programmed Instruction).

Self-instruction through a step-by-step presentation of information, with each step immediately followed by a test question. The object is to motivate and enhance the learning process through activity and immediate reinforcement.

A learning program is divided into a large number of "frames," each of which contains an item of information, plus a question that tests the student's understanding and the answer to the question in the preceding frame. The answers give an immediate "knowledge of results"—that is, the student discovers without delay whether or not he understands the material. If he finds he

has answered correctly, this knowledge reinforces his learning by rewarding him with the satisfaction of giving the right response. If he is wrong, he is prodded to review the preceding frame or frames until he understands them. Some programs are so arranged that the student can skip certain frames if he answers correctly, or study additional, more detailed frames if he gives the wrong answer.

Here are four frames from a typical program; the words to the left are covered (Galanter, 1963):

air 1. The stimulus for hearing a sound is an acoustic wave that travels through the _____ around us.

ear
ear 2. These acoustic waves enter the _____ where they cause the _____ drums to vibrate.

vibrate 3. Connected to the eardrum are three small bones called the *ossicles*. When the eardrum vibrates, the ossicles also _____.

ossicles 4. The third of these small bones, or _____, is connected to the *cochlea*, which is a coiled double tube.

Programmed learning arose largely out of experiments conducted by the psychologist B. F. Skinner on instrumental conditioning, a form of learning in which correct behavior is immediately rewarded. He found that a rat would learn to press a certain lever and a pigeon would learn to peck at a certain button if each correct response was "reinforced" by food. He later designed a piece of apparatus, now called a teaching machine, that would do essentially the same thing with human beings (1954). This device was a further development of a piece of apparatus originated by S. L. Pressey in 1926 for the self-scoring of examinations, but later used for self-instruction.

This approach to learning was gradually developed as an answer to the limitations of textbooks and other teaching techniques. The ordinary text presents material clearly enough but does not engage the active participation of the learner. Other approaches, such as lectures, films, and demonstrations stimulate interest as they provide information, but neither texts nor learning aids provide "knowledge of results" during the learning process. Quizzes and examinations are usually given too late to be used effectively as learning instruments. Class discussions are all to the good, but there is a limited amount of time for them, and today's classes are often too large to make them effective with every individual student. All these facts seemed to point toward one major need: a method that would enable the student to learn as much as possible by himself.

Programmed learning seemed to meet this need, whether it was printed in textbook form, or presented on a roll or sheets of paper or film for use in a teaching machine. The textbook and the teaching machine are based on the same essential characteristics: (1) they permit the programmer to divide his subject into easily comprehended steps; (2) they provide questions that have a small error rate—that is, the student can usually answer them correctly so that he learns by success rather than failure; (3) they present material in graduated form with easier material at the beginning and more difficult material later on when the student can absorb it best; (4) the division into frames with specific questions permits the program to be readily tested on large groups of students before it is offered to the schools; (5) the technique gives the learner an opportunity for repeated practice in order to master each stage before he goes on to the next; (6) it requires the student to involve himself fully and actively in the learning process through self-testing in every frame; (7) it clearly informs the learner of his strengths and weaknesses as he goes along; and, most important, (8) it gives

him a chance to proceed under his own steam and at his own pace.

During the development of programming, two types of presentation emerged. In the *linear design,* the student fills in an answer to a question, then uncovers the answer to find out whether he is right or wrong. (The answers are always covered in one way or another.) He progresses along a single track from one frame to the next, independently of whether or not his response is correct. In the *branching design,* he chooses from several alternative answers to questions, and the alternative he chooses determines what frame he sees next. A wrong choice may lead to an explanation of his error, additional instructional frames or even a retracing of steps or an alternative route. If he has done well for a number of frames, however, he may skip certain frames. This multiple-choice technique, however, has the educational disadvantage of testing recognition rather than recall—that is, the correct answer is always given and this serves as a reminder or hint to the student. This drawback is partially offset by the advantages gained by "branching" frames that rephrase the question, explain a mistake, or provide additional instruction.

Programs have been created for a wide variety of subjects, including mathematics, English grammar, spelling, natural science, electricity, astronomy, logic, and psychology, as well as bridge, chess, and even football. As yet there have not been a sufficient number of definitive tests of this technique, but the indications are that (1) the most successful and most easily constructed programs present material which has a clear-cut, logical, highly factual structure (biology would be a better candidate than philosophy); (2) the effectiveness of a program depends greatly on the programmer's ability to create frames in an orderly, graded progression without forcing the material into an artificial mold; (3) material that is broken up into short steps is most readily learned by average students but has a tendency to bore bright students; (4) the best results are achieved when the material is reviewed and related to other subject-matter; (5) the student retains at least as much material as he does with traditional instruction, but the learning process takes about one half the time (Galanter, 1963); (6) programmed texts and teaching machines are equally effective; (7) teachers can improve their teaching techniques by constructing programs; (8) programming effectively motivates children to study material which they can learn by themselves with little supervision, and this allows the teacher to devote class time to difficult concepts, discussions, and individual student questions. See LEARNING AIDS.

PROJECTION. The unconscious defense mechanism of shifting the blame or imputing one's faults to others.

Both of these behavior patterns are expressed in countless ways. The young child transfers blame to another person when he insists that "He hit me first," and the young man who gets into trouble with a girl is almost sure to say, "She led me on." Similarly, the cheater tries to justify himself by saying, "Everybody cheats once in a while," and the prejudiced person denies his bias by insisting, "I don't hate them, they hate me." Projection, then, is an all-too-common device for exonerating ourselves from responsibility and justifying faulty behavior. It may help to make us feel more comfortable for a time, but always at the expense of distorting the facts and deceiving ourselves. See DEFENSE MECHANISM.

A certain amount of projection can be expected as a natural human failing, but a constant pattern of blaming other people and ascribing our own faults to them is bound to interfere with good relationships. It not only prevents us from seeing ourselves as we really are, but generates attitudes of antagonism, intolerance, and suspicion. Some individuals facing problems they cannot handle may begin to feel they are living in a hostile, threatening world. They cannot bear the idea that they may be responsible in some degree for their own predicament, and therefore project the blame outward and suspect that others are causing them harm or plotting their downfall. If such an individual harbors hostile attitudes toward other people, he may turn the feeling around and begin to believe that they are out to get *him*. If he is deeply troubled by guilty sexual impulses, he may begin to accuse others of "pouring filth into his mind." Delusions of this kind are characteristic of the paranoid form of schizophrenia. See SCHIZOPHRENIA (PARANOID TYPE), PARANOIA.

PROJECTIVE PSYCHOTHERAPY. A procedure in which responses on various projective tests are used as raw material for therapy. The approach was developed by Molly Harrower primarily for use by clinical psychologists with analytic experience.

Practically any projective method may be used: Rorschach, Thematic Apperception, Sentence Completion, Figure Drawing, Szondi Test. The therapist gives the patient several different tests, then carefully selects the responses which he deems most provocative. These responses are read to the patient, who is encouraged to associate to them in much the same way that analytic patients make free associations to dream fragments. See PROJECTIVE TESTS.

In one of Harrower's cases (1956), for example, the Rorschach response "long-nosed wolf" was utilized. After several attempts at evasion, the patient, a young girl, revealed that the phrase referred to her father's nose, his self-consciousness about being a Jew, and his "animal, wolf-like expression." This led to the revelation that his "angry eyes" inspired her with terror. Other projective responses revealed that she hated, feared, and yet was fascinated by her father. However, she had repressed the intense feelings of aggression which she felt toward him. This in turn brought the realization that she had become romantically attached to a near-blind musician because of her fear of becoming involved with anyone who could see—a fear that was linked to the angry eyes of her father.

The responses of this patient to other projective tests exposed still another facet of her problem. On the "Most Unpleasant Concept" test, she drew a "spider," and on her Sentence Completion test she also showed fear of spiders. When asked to associate to this response, she related the spider to her father and revealed that as a child she used to keep spiders and burn them in effigy, thinking that she would thereby burn him. When this game began to frighten her, she attempted to keep a spider in view outside her window as reassurance. Recognition of the meaning of these responses led to distinct improvement, as indicated by her responses on still other projective tests.

There are a number of essential aspects of this technique. First, the therapist studies the patient's responses on several projective tests in order to discover which associations should be "fed back" to him. Second, one test is usually given before the sessions, and responses on this test are used as a baseline for measuring changes that take place during the therapeutic process. Third, the method is highly flexible; Harrower does not prescribe a single way of using the tests, a single sequence, nor the selection of the tests themselves. Fourth, the therapist must be deeply immersed in the patient's productions in order to "play them back" at the appropriate time. Fifth, the technique is not applicable to extremely disturbed patients and is most effective with patients who have a high IQ and who make productive and original Rorschach

responses. It is not effective with patients who show poor ego strength or who make bizarre responses. Sixth, the method cannot be used before the patient shows trust in the therapist and the therapy. And seventh, it is not offered as an exclusive procedure, but is most effective when used in conjunction with other approaches.

PROJECTIVE TESTS (Projective Methods or Techniques). Personality tests in which the subject reveals his characteristic traits, feelings, attitudes, and behavior patterns through his responses to relatively unstructured material such as ambiguous pictures or ink blots.

The term "projective technique" was first applied to this type of test by L. K. Frank in 1939, but the method had actually been in use for a number of years. Hermann Rorschach had begun to experiment with ink blots as a means of differentiating personality as early as 1911, and prior to that Alfred Binet had used them in studying imagination and invention. The method as a whole is based upon the unconscious process of projection in which the individual tends to attribute his own thoughts and reactions to other people and to impose his own interpretation on what he sees or hears. The test materials provide a stimulus situation designed to elicit these reactions. As Freeman (1962) points out, "He is said to project the inner aspects of his personality through his interpretations and creations, thereby involuntarily revealing traits that are below the surface and incapable of exposure by means of the questionnaire type of personality test."

The major feature of projective techniques consists of the presentation of a relatively unstructured task which lends itself to an almost unlimited variety of possible responses. To stimulate the subject to perceive and "structure" the situation in his own way, the material presented to him is usually vague, ambiguous or incomplete. The instructions are brief and general in order to allow free play to the imagination and free expression of feelings. In addition, the procedure may be disguised by presenting the task as a test of imagination or storytelling ability, or it may be introduced without any explanation of its purpose. One of the major advantages of the method is that the subject is not likely to fake his responses, since they do not involve factual information or answers to specific questions, and he has no way of knowing how they will be interpreted by the psychologist. The materials also have high interest value and are an effective means of establishing rapport between therapist and client.

Most of the projective instruments have been developed in clinical settings and are regarded as clinical tools. Some have evolved from tests of originality and imagination; others from art therapy or play therapy. In general, the technique is deeply influenced not only by psychoanalytic theory, with its emphasis on unconscious forces, but by Gestalt psychology which advocates a global, holistic approach to personality. As a result of both these influences, the examiner attempts to obtain a picture of the total structure and dynamics of the subject's personality, including emotional reactions, social relationships, evidences of maladjustment, motives, interests, attitudes, and intellectual level.

A wide variety of projective tests are presently available, though many of them have not as yet been fully evaluated. They can be classified in several ways—for example, type of stimulus presented, method of administration, or manner of interpretation—but probably the most useful is Lindzey's grouping into five types on the basis of type of response (1959): (1) *associative techniques:* the subject responds to a stimulus by giving the first word, image, or idea that occurs to him (examples are Word Association tests, Rorschach Inkblot Test); (2) *construction procedures:* the subject creates or constructs a story

or other production (Thematic Apperception Test, Make a Picture Story); (3) *completion tasks,* such as completing sentences or stories (Sentence Completion, Rosenzweig Picture Frustration Study, as well as story and argument completion tasks); (4) *choice or ordering devices,* requiring rearrangement of pictures, recording of preferences and the like (Szondi Test, Tomkins-Horn Picture Arrangement Test); (5) *expressive methods,* in which style or approach as well as finished production are evaluated in personality terms (Figure Drawing Test, House-Tree-Person Projective Technique, Play, Psychodrama).

Each of the above tests and techniques is described under a separate topic. Additional representative tests are also included in these topics. Other noteworthy projective techniques are: the Toy World Test, the Four Picture Test, the IES (Impulse, Ego, Superego) Test, the Group Personality Projective Test (using ambiguous "stick" drawings), and the Lowenfeld Mosaic Test.

PROMISCUITY. Transient unselective sexual relations with a variety of partners.

Promiscuity is considered a form of sexual delinquency, particularly in the case of girls who become temporarily involved with young men, or with men two or three times their age. Although they may receive gifts and even money, the relationship is not basically a commercial one, as it is in prostitution. Promiscuity may, however, lead to prostitution, and it is also one of the major factors in the spread of venereal disease, which has been increasing during the past few years.

Although psychologists and psychiatrists have not given promiscuity as much attention as it deserves, they have isolated several important causal factors. Faulty family life is a major contributor in many cases. A high percentage of these girls come from homes where the children are neglected and the parents lead disorganized lives. If the father is living at home, he is frequently shiftless or alcoholic; if he is not, the mother may herself set a pattern of promiscuous behavior. Girls who come from such homes generally feel lonely and rejected, and long to feel wanted and loved. They are vulnerable to practically any man who shows them attention and offers a change from their drab existence. Frequently they deceive themselves that the overnight affair will lead to a more lasting relationship—but when it does not, they always hope it will happen "next time."

In some cases the girls are not reaching for romance or acceptance, but are expressing defiance against an overstrict family. There may also be an element of revenge in their behavior, especially when their fathers have "run out" on them. Sexual promiscuity in young men may be due to a similar desire to feel wanted, to protest against rigid morality, or to get back at parents who have disappointed them. In addition, they are often motivated by a need to prove that they are sexually and socially adequate.

A second major factor is the impact of a "delinquent subculture"—a gang or other neighborhood group that sets a standard of loose sexual behavior. Promiscuity is often expected or even required if a girl is to be accepted as a member of the group. Like the boy who must prove his sexual prowess, she must demonstrate that she is attractive, desirable, and a "good sport." These appear to be far more powerful motives than the desire for sexual gratification, for studies indicate that while some promiscuous girls are sexually responsive, the majority are wholly or partially frigid. In many cases they are also uninformed or misinformed about the basic "facts of life." Too often their sex education is left entirely to their peers.

Finally, various kinds of defects and disorders may be important factors. Promiscuity is the most common form of delinquency among mentally retarded girls; they tend to be suggestible and easily influenced, and frequently enter into sexual relationships to gain acceptance and approval. Some sexual delinquents are affected with character disorders, particularly of the sociopathic type that is characterized by impulsive, amoral, and irresponsible behavior. In a few cases promiscuity is the result of loss of inner control due to borderline psychosis, manic reactions, or ambulatory schizophrenia. See ANTISOCIAL REACTION, PROSTITUTION, JUVENILE DELINQUENCY, NYMPHOMANIA.

Illustrative Case: PROMISCUITY

A fourteen-year-old girl was brought to a physician because of bilateral inflammation of the Fallopian tubes due to gonorrhea. She contracted this through having intercourse with an eighteen-year-old boy, following which she infected a boy of fifteen. She was fully developed sexually by this time, having reached her full height and having fully developed secondary sex characteristics (breasts, pubic, and axillary hair). She had been rather promiscuous for the last year, following her mother's second marriage. Her parents had been divorced when she was one year old, and she lived with her mother, with whom she was engaged in increasing rivalry and of whom she was very critical. A year before, she visited her father with the plan of staying for the summer, but they got into a violent quarrel, and the father asked her to leave. The mother was a superiorly gifted person, who, however, because of her occupation, was frequently away from home. The girl resented this as well as her mother's continued anxiety about her and the continuous pressure on her for superior performance. She frequently stayed with relatives. This was the case at the time the promiscuity started. The girl had enough trust in her mother to turn to her in the current and future difficulties and was brought by her to the physician for treatment.

After the girl was cured of the infection, she continued her promiscuity and became pregnant a year later. The pregnancy was interrupted on medical grounds. A year after that, she married, without her mother's consent, an irresponsible young man who deserted her after one month. The mother, with the girl's consent, had the marriage annulled. Her sexual problems and her other difficulties (strong feelings of inadequacy and guilt, considering herself unattractive, anxiety states, superficial relationships with people, erratic performance in her studies) were not straightened out until she underwent psychoanalytic treatment at the age of twenty. The behavior of this girl was determined by a feeling of abandonment (not having a home), rivalry with the mother, sexual preoccupation (the mother's marriage), thwarted positive Oedipal strivings (disappointment in the father's affection), feelings of inadequacy, anxiety, and guilt because of hostility to both parents, and constitutional elements (rapid maturing). The promiscuity was an attempt to solve the interpersonal and sexual problems and problems of self-evaluation, through genital activity and acceptance, although obviously in a defiant, self-debasing, and self-injurious manner. (Maslow and Mittelmann, 1951)

PROPAGANDA. A deliberate attempt to influence attitudes, beliefs, and behavior through the use of persuasion techniques.

One of the best ways to define propaganda is to compare it with education, since both processes have a significant effect on attitudes and behavior. The basic purpose of propaganda is to persuade; the object of education is to enlighten. The propagandist seeks to bring other people's ideas in line with his own; the educator seeks to bring their ideas in line with the facts. The appeal of propaganda is primarily to emotion; the appeal of education is primarily to reason. These distinctions are oversimplified and are given only to highlight the differences. They do not imply that propagandists as a whole have no regard for the facts or that educators never appeal to emotions. It must be recognized that the propagandist serves as an educator when he presents enlightening information in his own way and also that the educator sometimes borrows the techniques of the propagandist to make ideas more exciting and relevant to life.

Propaganda arises out of two basic needs. First, there are many situations in which individuals or groups find it important to persuade others to adopt their beliefs or to behave as they want them to behave. This is particularly the case in election campaigns, fund-raising activities, advertising and discussions of social issues such as birth control, Medicare, and race relations. Second, most people cling stubbornly to their ideas and avoid information that conflicts with their beliefs, and it therefore takes special efforts at persuasion to make them listen to the other side. These efforts are also needed when they are on the fence and pulled in different directions. To answer these needs, propagandists have created a whole armory of persuasion techniques, and a number of them have been experimentally tested by psychologists. In the summary that follows, the first six were isolated and given rather propagandistic names by the Institute of Propaganda Analysis during World War II (Miller, 1946). The others have been emphasized in more recent studies.

Name-calling, or more generally, the "loaded word" technique: The device of using emotionally toned words to create favorable or unfavorable attitudes. In the 1950s, many people who were branded with labels like Commie or pink found it next to impossible to obtain work in motion pictures or other professions. The following word pairs indicate that we can often choose a positive or a negative word in characterizing the same thing: slender–skinny, inexpensive–cheap, scent–stink, thrifty–stingy, earthy–dirty. The use of such "polite" or "impolite" words probably does less real harm than loaded words used to slant the news or reinforce prejudicial attitudes. The following terms were taken from reports of the same story. The first term in each pair was used by the Chicago *Tribune* and the second by the New York *Times:* government witch hunting–Senate investigation; Communist CIO leader–maritime leader; labor agitator–labor organizer; radical–progressive (Sargent, 1939). Studies have shown that loaded words such as labor agitator exert their greatest effect on people who do not have strong attitudes or beliefs on the subject under discussion. People who agree with the point of view expressed do not usually recognize that the words are loaded, since the report seems factually accurate to them. Those who are strongly opposed to it are often the only ones who recognize the propaganda as propaganda.

Transfer: Inducing acceptance through associating an idea or cause with an admired public figure or an accepted point of view. The propagandist tells his audience that his views are in keeping with Jeffersonian principles or the laws of nature. Father Coughlin identified his program with the Christian religion. Similarly, an advertiser may assure us that athletes, debutantes, or movie stars use the product he is publicizing.

Testimonial: Quoting actual endorsements by well-known individuals or unnamed "experts." This technique is similar to transfer except that the association is more explicit. Both devices are examples of "prestige suggestion"—and they are both based on the fact that people often want to identify with important individuals or ideas, and depend on "authority figures" to tell them what to do. And in both cases the "authority" may be highly questionable or totally irrelevant.

Prestige suggestion can be so powerful that it actually alters our perception of a person or situation. This has been proved by an experiment in which two groups of students were asked to rank various professions according to intellectual level and social usefulness. One group rated them without suggestion; the other was told that certain professions, such as politics, were ranked highest or lowest by a previous group.

These suggestions had a significant effect. When students were later asked to give specific examples, those who ranked politicians high named such figures as Roosevelt, Lehman, and La Guardia; those who ranked politicians low, cited Tammany Hall politicians and "the usual neighborhood politicians." *See* SUGGESTION.

Bandwagon effect: A form of "social suggestion" in which we are urged to follow a course of action because "Everybody's doing it, why not you?" Bandwagon appeals are based on people's lack of confidence and the tendency to conform. In a culture like our own, where so many situations are complex and ambiguous, a great many people simply follow the crowd. Moreover, there is a widespread tendency to apply a derogatory label such as immature or peculiar to the person who dares to be different.

The bandwagon effect was clearly demonstrated on a test in which three hundred high school seniors, three hundred college seniors and three hundred adults were asked to indicate their attitudes on controversial issues such as the effect of installment buying. The three groups were retested about a month later. One hundred from each group were given the questionnaires unchanged, since they were to be used as a control. The second hundred received the questionnaires with the majority opinion for each statement circled, and the third hundred received them with the expert opinion circled (the experts were individuals from public life and university faculties). Many people changed their attitudes on the retest, with more changes occurring in the "majority opinion" group than in the "expert opinion" group, and the least number of changes in the control group. The influence of the majority opinion was especially great among the high school students, who reversed themselves four times as often as the control group (Marple, 1933).

There is some evidence that the band-wagon effect is less pronounced in elections than in other issues. Roosevelt overwhelmed Landon in 1936, and Truman defeated Dewey by a large majority in 1952 in spite of the fact that highly publicized polls predicted a severe defeat in both instances. *See* PUBLIC OPINION SURVEYS.

Card-stacking: Attempting to influence opinion through deliberate distortions. Among the common devices are suppression of facts, overemphasis on selected facts, and manipulation of statistics. Another method is to quote the results of a rigged piece of "research." Theoretically a company could send expensive monogrammed fountain pens to superior court judges, and then send interviewers to ask them what pens they were using. They might later advertise, quite truthfully, that "the majority of superior court judges use our pens."

Glittering generalities: The use of vague but catchy phrases, slogans and "virtue words" to elicit favorable reactions. There are any number of examples: "our noble heritage," "our glorious future," "good clean government," and references to motherhood, patriotism, and civilization. Frequently these terms are used for their "halo effect" when a candidate wants to avoid taking a stand on specific issues. They are high in emotional tone but low in factual content. *See* STEREOTYPE, HALO EFFECT.

Plain folks appeal: The use of various techniques, such as photographs of a candidate pitching hay or pinching babies, which make the propagandist appear like a common man, a regular fellow. These activities have little if any relevance to the issue but are designed to make the audience identify with the speaker and to assure them that he knows their problems and will reflect their will.

Flogging the dead horse: Starting a propaganda communication with statements that elicit enthusiastic agreement.

The object is to create an atmosphere of acceptance which will carry over to the propaganda message itself. A pamphlet or speech that is basically anti-labor may begin with a discussion of other issues from a point of view that is favorable to labor. Experiments have shown that this technique influences attitudes more effectively than starting with statements that arouse disagreement, and that the effect carries over to communications on related topics (Weiss, 1957).

Appeal to prejudice: This is a particularly potent technique because propagandists play on emotion, and prejudices are basically emotional. The influence of prejudice on judgment was strikingly demonstrated by a study made during the Eisenhower-Stevenson campaign. Seventy per cent of Eisenhower supporters thought his health was good enough to carry him through a full term of office, but only 23 per cent of Stevenson supporters thought Eisenhower's health was adequate. An earlier poll, conducted in 1944, had resulted in similar findings: 84 per cent of Roosevelt supporters but only 47 per cent of Dewey supporters thought Roosevelt's health was adequate. In both cases the voters had an equal opportunity to read papers, listen to speeches, and draw their own conclusions (Gallup, 1956). Other studies have shown that prejudiced individuals are susceptible to propaganda that fits in with their beliefs, but are practically impervious to propaganda that opposes their prejudices. The negative ideas often fail to "register" at all—and in some cases the message is actually misinterpreted or reinterpreted to conform to their beliefs. *See* PREJUDICE.

Need arousal: To be effective, propaganda and other forms of suggestion must appeal to actual needs. The propagandist tries to "sell" the idea that the individual's own goals will be attained by believing or acting as he suggests. Advertisers engage in extensive "motivation research" to determine the needs and drives that move the public to action. Investigations have shown that the closer the relation to actual needs, the more effective the appeal. In one study, a group of students, all of whom had a high need for achievement, were given talks on "Teaching as a Career." All the talks presented teaching in a favorable light, but the one that made a direct connection between teaching and the satisfaction of achievement needs proved most effective (Di Vesta and Merwin, 1960). *See* MOTIVATION RESEARCH.

Another experiment (Weiss and Fine, 1958) showed that the same principle applies to negative as well as positive motivation and, incidentally, throws light on the effectiveness of hate propaganda. In the first stage of the experiment, one group of subjects was humiliated and insulted, and another was given a highly satisfying experience. One half of each group was later asked to read a message urging harsh, punitive treatment of juvenile delinquents; the other half heard a statement urging that America be very lenient in dealing with her allies. Later on an attitude test showed that the angered subjects advocated harsh treatment of delinquents and resisted the idea of leniency toward our allies considerably more often than the non-angered group. Hitler used a similar technique in arousing so-called Aryan Germans to such a pitch of anger that many of them were ready to accept a "final solution" to the "Jewish question."

Fear appeal: The arousal of fear is widely used for purposes of propaganda and attitude change, but experimental findings on this technique are largely negative. In one study, three groups of high school students were given lectures on dental hygiene—one under strong, the second under moderate, and the third under minimal conditions of fear arousal. Results showed that the higher the level of fear arousal, the less

they accepted the lecturer's point of view. Apparently intensive fear appeals provoke a "defensive avoidance" reaction in which the subjects tune out the message or assume that "it can't happen to me" (Janis and Feshbach, 1953). The important question seems to be how closely the situation touches the individual. If he is face to face with danger, he will be influenced by the appeal, but if he actually knows few people who are affected (as in smoking and lung cancer), he is likely to dismiss the message as "only statistics."

The effect of fear appeals and other types of propaganda also depends on the personality structure of the recipients. In another study dealing with dental hygiene practices, Goldstein (1959) showed that individuals who have a tendency to attack problems energetically ("copers") tend to respond positively to strong fear appeals, but hardly react at all to mild appeals; those who avoid unpleasantness as much as possible ("avoiders") are more influenced by the minimal fear appeal than by the strong fear appeal. A further study on the same subject showed that people who feel assured about their social desirability are more influenced by strong fear appeals, while minimal fear appeals are more effective with those who are less secure. Apparently the more secure individuals are able to "take" the stronger appeal, and the less secure tend to ward it off by ignoring it, turning a deaf ear, or refusing to believe it. The less secure people, however, are susceptible to the milder forms of propaganda. (Goldstein, 1960)

Other investigations of the effectiveness of propaganda have suggested five more fairly well-established principles. First, arguments that *appear* to state both sides of an argument are often more persuasive than arguments that are obviously one-sided, particularly with people who are initially opposed to the propagandist's viewpoint (Hovland, Lumsdaine and Sheffield, 1949).

Second, propaganda that advocates extreme changes seems to be more effective than pleas for small or moderate changes (Hovland and Pritzker, 1957). (This seems to support the "big lie" technique.) Third, propaganda aimed at bringing about opinion change in one area tends to spread to related issues (McGuire, 1960). Fourth, the order as well as the strength of arguments have an influential effect: more recent arguments tend to carry the most weight (Anderson, 1959). Fifth, the effects of propaganda often increase with time. If we know that certain statements are being made by a propagandist, we may discount them at first; later on we tend to remember the ideas but forget their source. This so-called "sleeper effect" occurs in gossip, rumor, and courtroom testimony. Lawyers sometimes bring up points they know will be "stricken from the record" since they realize that this does not erase their effect upon the minds of the jury. *See* BRAINWASHING and SENSORY DEPRIVATION for other propaganda effects.

PROSTITUTION. A form of sexual delinquency in which intercourse is performed indiscriminately for financial gain.

The actual number of prostitutes is hard to estimate since the practice is generally outlawed and carried on in secrecy. The *Kinsey Report* (1948) estimated that 69 per cent of the white male population in this country had had some contact with prostitutes—but many of these were single experiences, and prostitutes account for less than 5 per cent of the total sexual activity of the male population.

Many prostitutes would quarrel with the term "indiscriminate," since they claim to accommodate only a "select clientele." Such women make strict social distinctions between the lowly streetwalker, who accepts practically any assignment (and brothels themselves vary widely in social atmosphere); call girls who accept appointments only on recommendation; and women who maintain elegant apartments of their own and function as mistresses for limited groups of men. These distinctions probably arise from a mixture of motives. While all these women are basically indiscriminate, since they offer themselves to men who may not know or care about them, a semblance of selectivity assures them of their attractiveness and desirability and helps them to maintain a measure of self-respect: "After all, I don't take just anybody." Their attempts at selectivity also help them avoid the police and increase their financial return.

A social hierarchy also exists in male homosexual prostitution. "Street hustlers" have the lowest status. They are usually teen-age boys who may in some cases be homosexuals themselves, but in other cases engage in homosexuality simply as a way of making money—a practice that is usually learned from other members of a gang. Next is the "bar hustler" who finds his clients in bars frequented by homosexuals. Highest in prestige is the "call boy," who does not solicit in public. In some instances the major motive of these young men is robbery—a "shakedown" that sometimes leads to extreme violence.

Some recent investigators, notably Hollender (1961), question the idea that money is the sole motive in all cases of female prostitution. The common notion is that the prostitute or call girl regards her "profession" as simply a business venture. Intensive treatment of a number of these women, however, has indicated that in some cases they had been unable to form warm and satisfying personal relationships, and were actually seeking "human relatedness in a physical and non-personalized form." Their basically unselective choice of partners therefore represents both a need for human contact and a defense against intimacy. Many of these women, unlike most prostitutes, became emotionally aroused and experienced orgasm during their professional contacts.

Some psychoanalytic theorists explain prostitution in terms of penis envy and the Oedipus complex. They suggest that, in certain cases at least, the tendency toward promiscuous relations may stem from an unresolved urge to possess a penis and to overcome the feeling of deprivation which is believed to arise when the young girl discovers that she does not have this organ. The envious desire for a penis gathers force during the Oedipal stage (from three to five years of age) when she forms a strong sexual attachment to her father. On this theory, prostitution is a displacement of the desire for the father as well as an indirect means of obtaining a male organ and allaying the anxiety associated with penis envy. *See* PENIS ENVY, CASTRATION COMPLEX, OEDIPUS COMPLEX.

The factors that produce prostitution are, in most cases, similar to those that produce promiscuity: disorganized home life, rejection and neglect, resentment against parents, association with delinquent individuals or groups. Many of these women shy away from regular employment because they consider it dull or "square"; others are acutely aware of their lack of education and marketable skills and accept prostitution as an easy and undemanding way of making a living. They may also cherish the hope of meeting a "rich guy" and even of getting married. A few are married already, and preserve a semblance of morality by either reserving some type of sexual activity for their husbands, or by refraining from certain activities, such as oral-genital contact, with their husbands and reserving these for their business practice alone. Some prostitutes become increasingly aware of the empty nature of their existence and eventually seek a more meaningful and fulfilling life in marriage.

Studies have shown that emotional disturbance is both more frequent and more severe among prostitutes than among women who are merely promiscuous. A sizable percentage are mentally retarded, antisocial personalities, or ambulatory schizophrenics. In large cities many of them are primarily drug addicts who have resorted to prostitution as a means of supporting their habit. *See* PROMISCUTIY.

PSEUDOCONDITIONING (False conditioning). An increased response to a strong stimulus after it has been repeated several times. The process superficially resembles conditioning but is actually a form of "sensitization."

We have all experienced this type of response. If the fire siren sounds three times in one day, we usually react more violently the third time than the first. If we are repeatedly criticized, we are likely to become "allergic" to any hint of criticism.

At first sight these reactions look like conditioning, since we react or overreact to stimuli which did not produce this response before. This is what happens in classical conditioning when, for example, an experimenter repeatedly "pairs" a light with an electric shock, and finds that the animal or human being will make the same withdrawal response to the light that he originally made to the shock. However, closer analysis reveals that sensitization may occur when there is no pairing of a new stimulus with an old stimulus, but simply as a result of repetition of the same strong stimulus, such as the siren or the criticism. The repetition increases our sensitivity to a point where our reaction is readily tripped off. If this goes on long enough, we eventually become so sensitive that we overreact to almost any stimulus. *See* STIMULUS.

A similar effect takes place in so-called "backwards conditioning." In genuine conditioning, the neutral stimulus (the light) is presented first, and the natural stimulus (the shock) is presented immediately afterward—and eventually the neutral stimulus elicits the response by itself. In backwards conditioning, the natural stimulus is presented first, and then the neutral stimulus, and in some cases the neutral stimulus will elicit the response even though the usual order has been reversed. It has been found, however, that this occurs only when the neutral stimulus is strong (an intense shock, for example). Apparently the strong stimulus arouses the organism to a point where the second, or neutral stimulus, merely trip off the response. This means that backwards conditioning is also a case of pseudoconditioning. Here, too, no true learning is involved. It is simply another case of oversensitization to stimuli. *See* CONDITIONING, BEHAVIOR THERAPY.

PSEUDOPSYCHOLOGY. Questionable guidance and unscientific conclusions offered by self-styled experts or deliberate charlatans who pose as professional psychologists.

For a number of reasons psychology has proven a fertile field for the pseudoscientist. It frequently deals with problems that arouse not only interest but concern: emotional difficulties, personal relationships, vocational choice, the improvement of skills and abilities. It is one of the youngest sciences, and the great majority of the public are still so uninformed about its methods and its findings that they are unable to distinguish between the genuine and the false. It is concerned with many subjects that are surrounded with an aura of mystery and superstition—mental illness, the mind, the brain—and people therefore tend to accept any explanations if they are offered with confidence and assurance, no matter how farfetched or irrational they may be.

It is not surprising that a large segment of the public is an easy prey to the blandishments of the impostor and the promises of the enthusiast. Many people desperately want the kind of help these individuals offer them. They would like to have a tenacious memory, an engaging personality, an endless flood of energy. They want to discover latent abilities and release hidden potentials that will assure them success. They are aching to escape from feelings of inadequacy, self-doubts, anxieties or tensions that plague their lives. No wonder, then, that many people reach out for the help that is offered them, particularly when it is offered in the guise of newly discovered techniques by men or women who claim to be specialists in the science of behavior.

Pseudopsychologists have been closely studied by committees of the American Psychological Association, and individual surveys have been made of their methods and disguises. (See *Where Do People Take Their Troubles?* by Lee R. Steiner, 1945). By now there are a number of marks which distinguish these practitioners with fair accuracy. First, they make extravagant claims: "A new personality overnight," "Ten tested techniques for instant selling," "How to make everyone like you," "You'll never forget a name or face," "The autosuggestion way to a full and successful life." Second, these claims are widely and blatantly advertised not only in pulp publications but in many standard newspapers and magazines. Third, the practitioners frequently use fake titles and degrees, which they either create for themselves or obtain from "diploma mills" and questionable correspondence schools. Fourth, they offer their wares at bargain rates, and put a new personality or an improved memory in the class of commodities that can be bought in the market. Fifth, they offer short cuts to improvement: "Three easy steps," "A sure test you can take by yourself," "A quick way to peace of mind." Sixth, they often back their claims with anecdotes and testimonials, but never with controlled studies; and they refuse to submit to professional investigation. Finally, they build their claims on principles or techniques which have only limited and partial validity, and quite frequently depend upon procedures that have been completely discredited. *See* PHYSIOGNOMY, PHRENOLOGY, SALESMANSHIP, AUTOSUGGESTION, MEMORY IMPROVEMENT.

It must be recognized that some pseudoscientific approaches may bring limited results, though seldom for the reasons claimed. The person who takes a memory course may actually improve his memory for details, since he is strongly motivated (especially after paying good money) and since he will probably pay closer attention to what he sees and hears after attending the course. The salesman may find that learning some "magic sentences that sell" will give him the confidence if not the technique he needs. A depressed individual may feel relieved and encouraged by simply reading about the "miraculous" experiences of others, even though he may never practice the methods suggested by the author. These effects tend to be superficial and short-lived, since they are based primarily on suggestion. Even when the techniques appear relatively harmless, they have the unfortunate effect of substituting shoddy approaches for valid ones and are likely to keep troubled people from getting the kind of help they really need.

The prevalence of pseudopsychology is a serious matter, not only because it deludes and bilks the public with false promises and expectations, but because it undermines confidence in psychology as a whole. The American Psychological Association has undertaken to establish ethical standards for the profession, and its ethical code includes specific statements on responsibility, competence, misrepresentation, public statements, confidentiality, client relationships, remuneration, testing and research procedures, and promotion activities (Amer-ican Psychologist, 1963, 18). It has also established accreditation guidelines for approval of doctoral programs in clinical and counseling psychology, and has supported licensing and certification laws regulating the use of the title "psychologist." This campaign has been increasingly effective, and today most states with large numbers of psychologists either have such laws or are in the process of enacting them. This is a significant forward step, but it does not solve the problem completely, since the dubious practitioners dodge the issue by changing their titles. There is therefore a need for a widespread educational program that will alert the public to the dangers of pseudopsychology. *See* PSYCHOLOGIST.

PSEUDORETARDATION (Pseudofeeblemindedness). Retarded mental development due to adverse cultural or psychological conditions rather than congenital intellectual defect; also used for subnormal performance on intelligence tests due to temporary emotional upset, illness, unco-operative attitudes. This article will deal with the first type.

Pseudoretarded individuals sometimes escape identification and are therefore labeled retarded, feebleminded, or mentally deficient. As a result, many children have been confined to institutions for the retarded who do not belong in them, and therefore fail to receive the kind of treatment or special education that might bring them up to normal. This is less likely to happen today than in the past because of improved testing, diagnostic, and training procedures—nevertheless, it occurs more often than it should.

Cases of pseudoretardation are most commonly discovered through (a) test responses above the individual's general and customary level of intellectual, verbal or social functioning; (b) unexpected progress in educational and training programs; and (c) marked improvement in intellectual and social level during treatment for mental disorder. *See* WECHSLER INTELLIGENCE SCALES.

Pseudoretardation is attributed to three types of causes: early emotional deprivation, an extremely low level of stimulation, and severe emotional disturbance. Studies have shown that children who are deprived of mothering tend to be apathetic, unresponsive and detached, and as a result may become seriously retarded in personality development as well as intellectual growth. Children who are brought up in isolated communities, or in families in which there is little communication and stimulation, also tend to be retarded, especially in vocabulary level, reasoning ability, and imagination. Severe emotional disturbances which may lead to pseudoretardation are of two major types: childhood schizophrenia, and early infantile autism. Children with these disorders are frequently delayed in speech development and spotty in intellectual ability, in addition to their other symptoms, such as complete withdrawal, distractibility, negativism, compulsive behavior, and peculiar motor habits like walking on their toes. *See* SCHIZOPHRENIA (CHILDHOOD TYPE), EARLY INFANTILE AUTISM, MATERNAL DEPRIVATION, SOCIAL ISOLATION.

In addition to the types of pseudoretardation already mentioned, the term is sometimes applied to cases of limited development due to special disabilities rather than to a general lack of capacity. These include children with defective hearing, visual deficit, perceptual disability, motor or sensory aphasia, and motor handicaps that interfere with the learning of speech and manual skills. A large number of children with learning impairments have been classified in the past as "minimally brain damaged," but that label is now giving way to terms that do not necessarily imply organic defect, such as "children with brain (or cerebral) dysfunction," or "children with learning disorders." It should be noted that as the specific conditions associated with pseudoretardation have been identified, that term has also begun to drop out of use. *See* MINIMAL BRAIN DYSFUNCTION.

A distinction should be made between pseudoretardation and pseudodementia. In pseudoretardation the individual has never adequately developed his intellectual capacity, or functions temporarily at a low level as a result of emotional stress, illness, distractibility, hostility, etc. In pseudodementia, the individual has developed his capacities to a normal degree, but suddenly appears to deteriorate, without physical impairment, and acts as if he were retarded. The term is frequently applied to hysterical conditions in which the patient appears to be unable to answer the simplest questions or give a coherent account of himself. As with many hysterical, or conversion, symptoms, the disorder is likely to occur in situations in which it can be of great personal advantage. Henderson, Gillespie, and Batchelor (1962) make this comment on the condition: "In prisoners awaiting trial, for example, and in persons still at large who have committed some illegal act, a state *non compos mentis* may excuse, or be conceived to excuse, the misdoer from the immediate legal consequences of his act." The Ganser syndrome, or "syndrome of approximate answers" can probably be classified as hysterical pseudodementia. *See* GANSER SYNDROME.

A closely related disorder is *hysterical puerilism*, in which a patient reverts to behavior characteristic of early childhood, apparently in response to pressures and anxieties. McDougall (1926) cites the case of a soldier who regressed to earliest childhood after going through heavy bombardment. He was apparently unable to comprehend language or use ordinary utensils, walked with his feet far apart, had to be spoon-fed, enjoyed playing with a doll, and was afraid of ordinary animals. Nevertheless, he liked to smoke cigarettes, and made frequent passes at his nurse. He eventually recovered "to an approximately normal condition."

PSYCHASTHENIA (literally, "weakness of the mind"). A term introduced by Pierre Janet, who applied it to a neurotic disorder characterized by obsessions, compulsions, feelings of inadequacy, doubts, phobias, and anxieties. The term is now obsolescent.

Janet attributed these reactions to psychological weakness, which he defined as a decrease in the "psychic tension" or energy that ordinarily holds the stream of consciousness together. This decrease in energy was itself attributed to constitutional deficiency, fatigue, stress or internal conflict, and was believed to have a disintegrating effect on consciousness. As a result, the individual became prey to fear, obsessions and anxieties due to lack of conscious control.

Psychasthenia was one of three types of neuroses recognized by Emil Kraepelin, who considered this disorder purely psychological in origin. The other two categories were neurasthenia, or "weakness of the nerves," characterized by fatigue, aches and pains, and general debility; and hysteria, which took two forms—conversion hysteria, characterized by emotionally produced bodily symptoms, and hysterical dissociation, comprising such conditions as somnambulism, multiple personality, and amnesia. In today's classification, psychasthenia has been replaced primarily by phobic reaction and obsessive-compulsive reaction. *See* JANET, PHOBIC REACTION, OBSESSIVE-COMPULSIVE REACTION.

PSYCHIATRIC AIDE. A trained individual who attends to the nonmedical needs of psychiatric patients.

The attendant, or psychiatric aide, is generally in more direct and continuous contact with the mental patient than any other member of the psychiatric team. His function is a twofold one. First, he provides physical care to the small number of patients who need it —dressing, bathing and feeding—and performs other practical duties, such as looking after linens and keeping the premises in order. Second, he gives the patients companionship and understanding, helping to calm them if they become overwrought and to encourage them if they become depressed. In contrast to the practice of a few years ago, the attendant of today is not chosen for his strong arm but for his warm heart and his ability to make the patients comfortable when they need a helping hand.

The psychiatric aide, then, plays a crucial part in the "therapeutic community" of our time. He usually works in a mental hospital or psychiatric department of a general hospital under the direct supervision of a professional nurse or other mental health worker. As a result of his close contact with the patients, he can often contribute information of great value to the psychiatrist and other staff members in their efforts to understand the patients' needs and plan their therapeutic programs.

A high school diploma is desirable but not usually required for this occupation. However, special training is needed, either of the in-service or on-the-job variety. Many aides attend formal classes lasting from one week to three months, and some states have recently established experimental training schools associated with junior or community colleges. Sex, age, marital, race, and religious barriers are practically nonexistent. The major requirements are an interest in people, a sense of responsibility, ability to handle emergencies, good physical condition, and an understanding attitude toward people who may be irritable or disagreeable as a result of illness.

PSYCHIATRIC EXAMINATION. The psychiatric examination, or diagnostic evaluation, is a complex procedure involving a clinical interview, history-taking, medical examination and psychological tests—all aimed at securing a maximum amount of information about the patient. Its objectives are: (a) to clarify the symptom picture, (b) to obtain at least a tentative understanding of the development and dynamics of the disorder, (c) to classify the patient for treatment purposes, (d) to formulate a tentative treatment plan, and (e) to provide a tentative basis for prognosis.

The full psychiatric examination as applied to disturbed patients in clinics ordinated activity of a team of specialists consisting primarily of a psychiatrist, a clinical psychologist and a psychiatric social worker. In private office examinations, the psychiatrist may call in other sepcialists as needed. The various procedures will be briefly outlined under two headings, the medical examination and the psychological evaluation.

The medical examination is designed to evaluate the patient's general health and physical state, with special emphasis on symptoms, such as allergies, that may be associated with his disorder; and organic conditions, such as a possible tumor, that might be causative factors. It consists of a routine check of heart, lungs, glands, blood, etc., a general neurological examination of reflexes, sense organs, and the functioning of the central nervous system; and, where indicated, more specialized procedures such as electroencephalography (EEG), pneumoencephalography (skull X-ray), myelography (spinal X-ray), and various biochemical tests. *See* BRAIN WAVES.

The psychological evaluation is the most extensive part of the procedure, since it includes the clinical interview and psychiatric examination of the patient, observations of behavior, the case history as given by the patient and as gathered by the social worker, and psychological tests. The *interview* is designed to obtain significant information directly from the patient on his "presenting complaints" and difficulties, family and social relationships, and personal history or anamnesis. It also gives the examiner an opportunity to observe his general appearance, manner, attitudes, emotional tone, and ability to communicate. The effectiveness of the interview depends largely on the examiner's ability to put the patient at ease, show genuine interest, and establish rapport, since psychiatric patients tend to feel threatened and anxious, and may be hesitant about divulging their innermost thoughts and feelings to a stranger. It therefore depends on the interviewer's skill in eliciting information and attitudes without arousing the patient's resistances.

The *psychiatric history,* as gathered by the psychiatric social worker, psychiatrist, or others involved in the case, consists of information obtained both from members of the family and from the patient himself. It includes (1) details on the patient's age, sex, marital status, living arrangements, circumstances of consultation or commitment; (2) a detailed account of the general nature and development of the disorder, to determine so far as possible whether it was of insidious or acute onset, and whether it is related to sudden or gradual personality changes, physical illness, periods of stress, or other special circumstances; (3) the patient's conception of his illness, and his attitude toward his condition; (4) the family history, with details on hereditary illnesses or defects, methods and attitudes involved in child-rearing, sibling relationships, socioeconomic status, parental relationships, and special conditions that might have affected his life situation, such as death of a parent, divorce, mental illness in the family, occupational dissatisfaction, alcoholism, a slum environment, or suicide of a family member; (5) the personal history of the patient, showing his physical and emotional development from infancy to the present, with details on nature of birth, early illnesses, sleeping and elimination patterns, childhood attitudes and memories, emotional life, fantasy life, sexual development and experiences, disturbing events, adolescent changes, emotional and habit disturbances, etc.; and (6) description of the patient's personality in terms of outstanding traits, interpersonal relationships, activities, interests, and aspirations; patterns of hostility or affection, aggression or submission, perfectionism, suspicion, etc., as well as attitudes toward himself.

Observations of behavior are made by the psychiatrist during his examination and may be supplemented by the psychiatric social worker and hospital staff. In cases where the patient is amnesic or mute, material may be elicited under narcosis; in other cases of inaccessibility the examination may be restricted to observation of general appearance, bodily attitudes, obedience to commands, habits of eating and dressing, facial expression, and reactions to visits by members of the family. Noyes and Kolb (1963) list these observations under the following categories: (a) *general appearance, manner and attitude:* signs of tension and anxiety such as moist hands, strained voice and restlessness; gait, posture, gesture, dress; evasiveness, frankness, irritability, aggressiveness, arrogance; characteristics of the opposite sex; (b) *consciousness:* including the general sensorium and such states of consciousness as clouding, confusion, stupor; orientation as to time, place, and person; (c) *affectivity and mood:* prevailing feeling tone and emotional state; evidence of depression, euphoria, elation, apathy, panic, apprehensiveness, anger, silliness etc.; (d) *conation and expressive behavior:* general activity level as well as special drives and habits, such as stereotypy, mannerisms, grimacing, impulsiveness, combativeness, negativism, stupor, pres-

sure of activity, distractibility, preoccupation; (e) *associations and thought processes:* blocking, circumstantiality, incoherence, flight of ideas, retardation, irrelevance, neologisms, word salad, echolalia, etc.; (f) *thought content and mental trend:* fantasy and dream content; grandiose and persecutory delusions, ideas of reference, misinterpretations of reality, self-depreciation or self-accusation, hypochondriacal ideas, feelings of unreality, ideas of influence by others; (g) *perception:* illusions, distortions; auditory, visual and other hallucinations; (h) *memory:* general memory for details of life; evidence of confabulation, retrospective falsification, impaired memory for recent or past events, hiatus for a specific period of time; (i) *fund of information:* answers to questions about current events and matters of common knowledge as well as knowledge acquired in school; (g) *judgment:* intactness or impairment of judgment about external events, business affairs, etc.; (k) *insight:* extent of awareness of illness, and understanding of its nature and reasons for the psychiatric consultation; use of rationalization; (e) *personal maturity:* evaluation of the patient's stage of personality development through observations and questions dealing with his perspectives on life and work, psychosexual development, dependency and independence, etc.

Since the use of *psychological tests* is described under the topic CLINICAL PSYCHOLOGY, we will only note here that various tests are administered as needed, to determine intellectual capacity, motivation, conflicts, ego defenses, self-evaluation, and the general organization of the personality. They include intelligence tests, personality inventories, rating scales, projective tests, mental impairment tests, and special tests of interests, aptitudes, anxiety level, etc.

When all this material has been gathered, and usually recorded on a case-history form, the next step is to make a total, integrated evaluation or "diagnostic formulation." This may be done by the psychiatrist alone if he works in private practice, or in a staff conference attended by all members of the clinical team. The formulation includes a summary of the patient's behavioral, emotional and physiological disturbances; the outstanding features of his total history; results of medical and psychological examinations; an attempt to explain the origin and development of his illness; diagnostic classification of his disorder; a therapeutic plan, including basic and adjunctive treatments, whether inpatient or outpatient; and a prognostic evaluation based on application of the recommended treatment plan. See CLINICAL PSYCHOLOGY, ANAMNESIS, PSYCHOPATHOLOGY, DIFFERENTIAL DIAGNOSIS, PSYCHOLOGICAL TESTING.

PSYCHIATRIC NURSING. A specialized form of nursing devoted to the care of mentally and emotionally disturbed patients.

The psychiatric nurse plays an essential role in the treatment of mental patients. She is responsible for giving medications, and helps the psychiatrist apply electroshock or other treatments. Equally important is the part she plays in creating an atmosphere conducive to recovery, and in meeting the complex emotional needs of different types of patients. A good psychiatric nurse must therefore possess not only a technical knowledge of nursing and psychiatry—including all types of mental illness, diagnostic procedures and treatment methods—but personal qualities of patience, understanding, stamina and kindness. As the most constant observer of changes in the patient's condition, she serves as an important bridge between the psychiatrist and the patient, and is frequently called upon to participate in staff conferences in which the progress of patients is evaluated and plans for further therapy are made.

Psychiatric nurses are employed not only in mental hospitals, but in health departments, psychiatric sections of general hospitals, homes for disturbed children, nursing centers for the aged, and community clinics. They may also serve as public health or visiting nurses. Some psychiatric nurses teach in schools of nursing or help to carry out research projects on mental illness.

Educational requirements usually include a college preparatory course in high school with special emphasis on chemistry and biology, plus professional training consisting of a three-year diploma program conducted by a hospital school of nursing. A candidate may also take a baccalaureate degree program consisting of a four-year college course leading to a bachelor's degree with a major in nursing, or an associate degree program in a junior or community college lasting approximately two years. These programs must include a course in psychiatric nursing. In addition, a state board examination must be passed to obtain a license as a registered nurse.

Opportunities for promotion are especially good for those who take a B.S. degree in nursing. An increasing number are also working for the M.A. degree in order to obtain more responsible positions in clinical practice, supervision, teaching, administration, research, or consulting activities in the field of mental health. Though this is traditionally a woman's field, many men are now entering the profession. The need for graduate nurses is particularly urgent in the mental health field, and has been estimated at 75,000.

PSYCHIATRIC SOCIAL WORK. A field of social work concerned primarily with emotionally disturbed persons and their families.

Most psychiatric social workers carry on case work in mental hospitals and mental health clinics, although an increasing number serve in general hospitals, courts, health departments, rehabilitation centers, research institutes, and on the faculties of schools of social work and medicine. Training for this profession includes an academic high school program, preferably with extra-curricular and vacation jobs that develop skill in working with people; four years of college leading to a B.A. degree, with courses related to social work (especially biology, psychology, sociology, economics); and two years of graduate work leading to an M.A. degree from an accredited school of social work, followed by supervised work experience in the mental health field. There is a critical shortage of personnel at present, since the number of available psychiatric social workers is not keeping up with the rising demand for their services. Less than half of state mental hospitals meet the minimum standards set by the American Psychiatric Association, which call for one psychiatric social worker for every eighty admissions plus one for every sixty patients on convalescent status or family care.

The usefulness of the psychiatric social worker lies in his unique ability to co-ordinate a patient's treatment and rehabilitation with his environmental situation and needs. He is a link between the patient and his home and between the hospital and the community. He uses interview methods to investigate the patient's social and psychological background, and then contributes his findings to the psychiatric diagnosis and treatment plan. When the patient is admitted to the hospital, the case worker gives him direct help in adjusting to the hospital situation and in understanding the treatment facilities available to him. He also gives the family assistance in meeting problems created by the patient's absence, and helps them understand the patient's illness and the part they can play while he is being treated.

The psychiatric social worker participates fully in rehabilitation procedures and takes major responsibility in planning for discharge and follow-up care of hospitalized patients. He helps the patient find a foster home if that is required, and directs him to social agencies that will help him re-establish himself. Although he is often concerned with practical matters, such as jobs and living quarters, he has been trained to approach these problems with special sensitivity. His object is to keep the patient functioning effectively when he returns to his home and community.

The present expansion of day and night hospitals, outpatient care and foster-family care has added materially to the responsibilities of psychiatric social workers, since they are called upon to mobilize community services on behalf of patients in all these types of facilities. They also participate in the education and training of new personnel, including volunteers, for the social service department of clinics and hospitals. In addition, many psychiatric social workers participate directly in the treatment process under the supervision of the psychiatrist, by conducting individual and group psychotherapy with both children and adults.

In recent years psychiatric social work has greatly expanded in range and importance. As a result of their specialized knowledge of social welfare agencies, processes of referral and treatment procedures, leading psychiatric social workers have become increasingly active in community planning and in the functioning of outpatient mental health services. They may also represent a clinic in community councils, and help to organize special treatment centers for persons afflicted with convulsive seizures, brain injury, alcoholism, drug addiction, or mental retardation.

Many workers supplement their institutional activities with private practice, helping families and individuals in their social adjustment. Others have moved out of the hospital and clinic to develop and administer mental health programs for agencies or communities; such programs might involve mental health education or preventive social planning. In these capacities they work with public health authorities, judges, probation officers, wardens, teachers, nurses, physicians, clergymen, and industrial leaders. See COMMUNITY PSYCHIATRY, MENTAL HYGIENE.

PSYCHIATRIST. A physician who specializes in the diagnosis, treatment, and prevention of mental and emotional disorders.

The psychiatrist is equipped to treat the entire range of psychiatric disturbances, including transient conditions, personality disorders, psychoneuroses, and both functional and organic psychoses. Many psychiatrists also carry on research on the nature of mental disorder and the effectiveness of different therapies. Some administer or participate in programs designed to inform the public or maintain mental health in the community.

Psychiatrists work in many different settings: mental hospitals, psychiatric departments of general hospitals, outpatient clinics, and mental health centers, as well as in private practice. Many of them combine private practice with part-time service in hospitals, clinics for children and adults, health departments, public and private agencies, schools, industrial concerns, counseling services, and courts. Of the 19,000 psychiatrists practicing today, about 1250 are trained in psychoanalysis, a special form of psychotherapy which seeks to uncover the deeply buried roots of emotional disturbance and to modify the structure of the patient's personality. See PSYCHO-ANALYSIS (THERAPY).

In mental hospitals and community facilities, the psychiatrist functions as the leader of the treatment team, which usually includes clinical psychologists and psychiatric social workers as well as psychiatric nurses, occupational therapists, recreation specialists, and psychi-

atric aides. He directs and integrates the activities of other personnel through case conferences, and is equipped, through his medical training, to apply somatic treatments such as drug therapy and shock therapy. He holds the central responsibility for all forms of psychotherapy, individual and group, although clinical psychologists may carry out many of the therapeutic procedures, and psychiatric social workers may engage in counseling with the patients and their families. See CLINICAL PSYCHOLOGY, PSYCHIATRIC SOCIAL WORK.

Psychiatrists are the most highly trained of all professional workers in the field of mental health. Their education includes a broad college preparatory course in high school; premedical training in a college approved by the Council on Medical Education and Hospitals of the American Medical Association; a four-year course in a medical school, which generally includes courses in psychiatry; one year of hospital internship; three years of residency in an approved hospital or agency concerned with the diagnosis and treatment of mental and emotional disorders; and at least two additional years of experience, followed by an examination for certification by the American Board of Psychiatry and Neurology.

As the American Psychiatric Association points out, the acquisition of information and skill are only one part of psychiatric training: "The person interested in becoming a psychiatrist must first of all concentrate on becoming an educated person. This involves developing a trained, disciplined and open mind, the ability to work comfortably with many kinds of people, and an eagerness to experiment, explore and learn that makes the acquisition of knowledge a continuing, life-long adventure."

The standards for psychoanalytic training are determined by the American Psychoanalytic Association. Eligibility for training in the approved institutions of the Association depends upon the following: graduation from a class A medical school or its foreign equivalent; one year's internship in a hospital approved by the American Medical Association; three years of psychiatric training at an approved hospital, one year of which must be served before acceptance for training in psychoanalysis (unless it is part of the Institute's training program). Psychoanalytic training itself includes a preparatory analysis of at least 300 hours, with "the goal of freeing the candidate from emotionally conditioned attitudes which may interfere with psychoanalytic therapeutic work"; three years of assigned readings in the works of Freud and other psychoanalytic literature, correlated with courses dealing with the theory, clinical applications and technique of analysis; participation in continuous case seminars and at least 50 clinical conferences, with presentation of at least 3 cases; and a minimum of 150 hours of supervised clinical work in which the candidate analyzes no less than two adult cases. Additional lectures, clinical seminars, and supervision are required for specialization in child analysis. The training institute certifies the completion of a candidate's training, and after a two-year period he may apply for membership in the Association.

PSYCHICAL RESEARCH (Parapsychology). The object of psychical research is to conduct a systematic investigation of paranormal phenomena—that is, experiences, abilities, and events which appear to lie beyond the reach of natural science. These phenomena fall into the following major categories: (1) premonitory dreams, (2) mental telepathy, (3) divination, (4) mediumship, (5) apparitions, (6) materializations, (7) poltergeists. This article will report some of the highlights of the history of parapsychology.

The belief in psychical phenomena is probably as old as man. Practically all primitive people have been as convinced of the existence of a spirit world as of a material world. To them the whole of nature is alive, and all things are inhabited by either friendly gods or unfriendly demons. No line is drawn between inner fantasies and outer reality, and dreams are not only real but prophetic. They accept the claim of their priests or medicine men that by entering into a trance state they can not only read the future but cure disease, bring harm to enemies, and control the course of natural events.

Ideas of this kind have been prevalent not only among uncivilized tribes, but even in the most advanced civilizations. In ancient Greece and Rome men of the caliber of Aristotle and Cicero seriously discussed paranormal dreams and divination, despite the fact that the organized religion of the day sought to suppress these beliefs.

In the modern world a number of eminent men—among them, Ben Jonson, Linnaeus, Goethe—showed an interest in psychical phenomena and reported parapsychological events. Around 1850 the belief in spiritualism arose in the United States, and mediums soon appeared not only in all parts of this country but throughout the world. These individuals claimed to be able to communicate with the deceased, and even to "materialize" their spirits. A little later Sir William Crooke made experimental studies of these materializations, and in about 1880 Sir William Barrett became the first man in the scientific community to report successful experiments on telepathy.

The new interest in the scientific study of paranormal experiences gave rise to the Society for Psychical Research, founded by Cambridge scholars and others in London in 1882. Soon after, in 1885, William James helped to organize an American society, which later became a branch of the English organization. A number of international congresses have been held, starting in 1921; and by 1946 thirty parapsychology research centers were in operation. At least ten of these were in the United States, including laboratories at Stanford, Harvard, and the largest in the world at Duke University.

The early work of the London society was devoted to spontaneous claims of telepathy. Over 5000 persons were investigated through interviews and case-study techniques. The results of these studies were published in a two-volume work by Gurney, Myers, and Podmore under the title *Phantasms of the Living* in 1886. Among its major contents were dozens of cases of visions or dreams concerning accidents which were later found to have taken place. As a typical example, a woman awoke with the feeling of sadness and later had a vision of her brother tripping over a rope and being drowned. The next day she learned that her brother had actually been caught by the towline of a harbor boat, was thrown off the deck, and drowned. The authors presented statistics to show the probability that a specific dream of death and the actual death of the person dreamt of would fall within twelve hours of one another. It came to only 1/431,363, not to mention the even smaller likelihood that the specific details would match. They became convinced that these reported occurrences were not due to chance or coincidence, and attempted to explain them by the principles of dissociation and other processes which Pierre Janet and others were discussing at the time.

The experimental study of telepathy usually involved attempts to transmit impressions of drawings from an agent (the "transmitter") to a receiver (the "percipient"). Miles and Ramsden (1907, 1915) reported positive results on such experiments, and Usher and Burt claimed to have found evidence that dissociated states of mind are conducive to telepathy. In 1921 René Warcollier organized a group in Paris as well as "telepathic posts" in various parts of Europe to transmit and receive tele-

pathic messages. He also attempted transatlantic telepathy and studied the nature of the telepathic images and the effects of dissociated and relaxed states. In 1923 Bruck found that his subjects did not perform any better under hypnosis than in the normal state. However, he claimed that positive motivation and concentration on the task had a positive effect.

Beginning in 1919, Brugmans et al. conducted a series of tests in which a blindfolded subject attempted to identify specific squares on a forty-square checkerboard. This percipient participated in 187 trials and is said to have obtained a score of 60, which is several billion times chance expectation. GSR (galvanic skin response) recordings supported the subject's claim that he was relaxed and passive during the experiments. The investigators also claimed that alcohol improved the subject's scores because it helped to overcome normal inhibitions. In 1927, Estabrooks conducted experiments with a deck of twenty playing cards, and reported that the calls made by some of his subjects when they were shuffled and placed face down far exceeded chance for both suit and color. He also found that the first ten calls were significantly more accurate than later calls. This was evidence for a so-called "decline effect" which many others claimed to find in such experiments.

Closely related to telepathy is "psychometry," the reputed ability of some persons to hold an object in their hands and become aware of facts about its history or about people associated with it. Hettinger (1940) tested two subjects who claimed this ability, and found that their statements were significantly more accurate than statements made by control subjects. Murphy and Dale (1946) cite the case of a subject who read a sealed piece of paper found in a bottle washed up in the Azores. This "sensitive" described with fair accuracy the appearance of the writer, including a scar, and the sinking of a ship, although the events were unknown to anyone present in the room. The note was actually written by a man who went down with the *Lusitania*. It read, "The ship is sinking. Farewell my Luisa . . . your Ranson."

The "art" of mediumship dates back to Graeco-Roman times, but was revived in the middle of the nineteenth century. The medium claims to be able to get in touch with the deceased while in a hypnotic trance, and to serve as a "mediator" between the living and the dead. In theory, the deceased takes control of the medium's body and prompts the medium to utter his words, hear his voice, write his thoughts, or see his form. Some investigators claim to have found cases in which the medium gives facts that could not have been gained from past knowledge or logical inference. These cases are termed "evidential."

One of the most famous mediums was a Mrs. L. E. Piper, whose "communications" were closely studied and analyzed for a period of thirty years (1885–1915). According to the investigators, she reported material known to the sitter and not to herself, as well as material which could not have been known to either. Mrs. Piper was involved in a decade of attempts to contact one of the pioneers of the psychical research movement, F. W. H. Myers, after his death. Although she did not have a classical education, she was reputed to have answered questions on the classics through communication with Myers. In addition, he is supposed to have attempted a new method of communication called "cross-correspondence," in which different pieces of information were transmitted by Myers to different mediums and later put together to make sense. The object of this method was to reduce the possibility that a complete message given to one medium would be relayed to others by telepathy. Murphy (1946) rejects this technique as convincing proof of survival after death, since he holds that the mediums might still be drawing information from the minds of other living persons and might be *posing* as deceased communicators "at an unconscious level." Even though Murphy does not believe that survival after death has been proved, he apparently accepts telepathy as a fact.

A variation on traditional mediumship is the use of a "proxy sitter." In this case the seance is conducted by a note-taker, and the sitter and medium may be miles apart. The basic relationship, however, is the same, for the medium purports to get in contact with the deceased, and to transmit messages through the proxy. Mrs. Osborne Leonard was one of the most celebrated mediums used in proxy sitting, and her experiences have been reported in a book by J. F. Thomas entitled *Beyond Normal Cognition* (1937). Thomas worked out mathematical formulae to be applied to this type of mediumship, and believes that Mrs. Leonard's results greatly exceeded chance expectation. By removing the sitter to a distant place, the possibility of telepathy is minimized, though according to Murphy it is not ruled out entirely.

All in all, there is little agreement even among parapsychologists as to the possibility of communication with the dead. Some believe the deceased actually enters the medium's entranced body; others believe the deceased communicates with the sitter's mind on a subliminal level, and that the medium obtains the communication from the sitter by telepathy. Still others believe this type of paranormal phenomenon has yet to be proved.

Another type of psychical phenomenon, the poltergeist, has been reported ever since the seventeenth century. These "boisterous spirits" are said to throw stones, slam doors, rap on walls, upset furniture, and break crockery. Ordinarily these pranks last for only a few weeks, and most often occur in homes where there is a preadolescent child. Sir William Barrett investigated a number of cases, and though evidence of fraud and trickery was found in some of them, he attested to the fact that others were completely genuine and could not have been due to deception, hallucination, or any other known explanation. In one case his associate entered a "haunted house" and read passages from Scripture aloud. During the reading the clatter on the walls grew so loud that his words were scarcely audible—but when he repeated the Lord's Prayer, they abruptly ceased.

Finally, there are the reports of mediums who lift tables and move objects without physical contact, or who "materialize" faces or "ectoplasm" out of thin air. Time and again these claims have been exposed as fraudulent. Yet some parapsychologists are inclined to accept some of these phenomena as valid. Murphy and Dale (1966) cite reports of D. D. Home, who is said to have floated through an open window in broad daylight, and similar phenomena. They comment that "much fraud has been detected under loose conditions which permit it; but a very large mass of material remains unexplained."

In general, only a small percentage of American psychologists are acquainted with psychical research, and still fewer are engaged in this field. British and continental psychologists have expressed far greater interest in the subject, and are far less skeptical than the Americans—perhaps because American psychologists are more influenced by behavioristic procedures, and are inclined to base their judgments on repeatable experiments and statistical results. At any rate, the most recent survey of opinion among members of the American Psychological Association shows that only 4 per cent believe that mental telepathy is an established fact. *See* EXTRASENSORY PERCEPTION.

PSYCHOANALYSIS (THEORY). The theory of dynamic psychology developed by Sigmund Freud, based primarily on the influence of unconscious forces such as repressed impulses, internal conflicts, and early traumas on the mental life and adjustment of the individual. This article will be limited to outlining the historical development of psychoanalytic theory, since each of the major concepts is discussed as a separate topic. *See* list at end.

Actual neurosis versus psychoneurosis. Freud's original theory of neurosis, developed during the 1890s, divided nervous disorders into two types, both of which were sexually determined. The first type, *actual neuroses* (actual meaning "current" in German), included neurasthenia and anxiety states. Freud believed at this time that the neurasthenic suffers from debilitating weakness caused by excessive masturbation; and that anxiety neurosis is due to the reverse condition, a build-up of sexual tension resulting from a lack of sexual discharge.

The second group of disorders, the *psychoneuroses,* which became the center of attention in Freud's later writings, included obsessions, phobias, hysteria, paranoia, and hallucinatory psychoses. Freud attributed these disorders to past traumatic sexual experiences, and interpreted their symptoms as defenses against repressed mental conflicts produced by these experiences. He held that the character of the trauma determines the nature of the symptoms. He felt that the bodily symptoms of hysteria stem from a sexual trauma that has been passively experienced; he viewed obsessional states as an attempt to substitute harmless ideas for unacceptable thoughts associated with active seduction; he interpreted the delusions of paranoia in terms of the mechanism of projection, especially in attributing one's own sexual desires to others; and he explained the dynamics of phobia as a combination of displacement and substitution, as in substituting a fear of pointed objects for feelings associated with the male organ.

Freud's general psychology of 1895. During this period Freud attempted to explain mental processes in physiological terms, holding that the function of neural tissue is to reduce internal tension states. He based this assumption on the "principle of neuronic inertia." This physiological explanation later evolved into his "pleasure-unpleasure" principle —the theory that unpleasure is produced by an accumulation of *psychological* tension, while pleasure results from its discharge. At this time Freud's views on sexuality also differed from his later concepts, for he held that sexuality normally starts at puberty, although excessive stimulation during the early years can lead to precocious sexual impulses which might have harmful effects. This view was later superseded by his theory of infantile sexuality.

Between 1887 and 1902 Freud developed his concept of primary and secondary mental processes, which remained a cornerstone of psychoanalytic theory. The primary process consists of primitive biological instincts, wishes and desires that seek immediate gratification, or "cathectic discharge," without regard to logic or reality. The impulses and fantasies of the primary process dominate the mental life of the child and persist in the unconscious of adults, manifesting themselves in dreams, humor and disturbed behavior. The secondary process, on the other hand, consists of conscious thinking that obeys the laws of logic and enables us to postpone immediate gratification and adapt to the demands of reality.

As his theory developed, Freud applied the term "id" to the unconscious impulses of the primary process, and "ego" to the conscious self which inhibits the egocentric primary impulses and exercises the more highly developed processes of perception, memory, thinking, attention and judgment. The effi-

ciency of the ego is diminished during sleep, pathological reactions, and intense emotional experiences, and under these conditions, the individual regresses to the primitive, archaic primary process. This concept of regression is regarded as one of Freud's most important contributions. *See* PARALOGICAL THINKING.

The theory of instincts. Freud found considerable support for his early theories in clinical experience. Neurasthenia was frequently relieved when the patient stopped masturbating, anxiety neurosis subsided when the patient engaged in normal intercourse, and the disturbing effects of early traumas were reduced by reliving them and giving vent to the emotions they produced, a process he termed abreaction and catharsis. Nevertheless he was concerned that many of his patients left analysis before it was completed, and were often unable to distinguish between their childhood fantasies and what actually happened—for example, some patients became convinced, falsely, that they had been forced into perverse acts by their fathers. This concern led to a period of confusion on Freud's part, which only resolved itself when he undertook his own self-analysis.

Freud's self-analysis, based largely on the interpretation of dreams that occured after the death of his father, led to his discovery of the Oedipus situation and the concept of the libido. In the Oedipal situation, occurring between the ages of three and five, the child becomes sexually attracted to the parent of the opposite sex, and develops feelings of rivalry toward and a desire to displace the parent of the same sex. When he learns that sexual interest of this kind is forbidden, he develops intense feelings of guilt and anxiety. In the boy these feelings give rise to fear of punishment by castration, and in the girl to penis envy and feelings of inferiority arising from the belief that she has already been deprived of the penis. Freud held that this entire struggle, which he termed the Oedipus complex, is the crucial factor in the development of personality. The child who successfully renounces and represses his sexual feelings toward the parent of the opposite sex will usually develop a healthy personality. The child who cannot "work through" the conflict is likely to develop a serious personality disturbance.

The theory of the libido held that the sexual drive, broadly viewed as pleasurable experiences associated with bodily gratification, goes through a series of developmental phases in which libidinal energy is centered, or "invested," in one erogenous zone of the body after another, particularly the oral, anal, and phallic. Freud believed this process starts in infancy and used the term "polymorphous perverse" to describe the fluidity of the libido and its capacity to move from one bodily organ to another.

The theory of early sexuality helped to explain the fictitious seduction experiences mentioned above, for Freud concluded that even though they did not actually occur, the fantasies themselves exerted as much influence as the reality. The important fact was that these fantasies were manifestations of drives originating in the organism (endogenous drives). Starting with this observation, he developed the theory that our entire psychic life is determined by internal drives having the following four major features: (1) an impetuous *character*—the tendency to exert pressure for outlet; (2) an instinctual *source* in an organ of the body; (3) an *aim*, either in the form of internal discharge, as in fantasy, or in the form of external activity, as in sucking the thumb; and (4) an *object*, or the actual organ involved in expression, either autoerotic (the individual's own genitals, as in masturbation) or object-libidinal (the breasts or genitals of another person). According to his theory of psychosexual de-

velopment, the libidinal drive is autoerotic at first, since it focuses on the child's own body, but in time culminates in genital primacy and heterosexual love, which represent its most complete discharge.

At this stage in the development of his theories, Freud held that sexual perversions represent pregenital fixations (arrested development at the oral or anal stage) breaking through into behavior. He also held that activities such as artistic production and philosophic speculation are a "sublimation" of the original sexual aim and a channeling of the sexual drive into cultural expression. Moreover, many character traits develop out of earlier modes of sexual expression (for example, stubbornness may arise out of anal fixation due to refusal of the child to give up his feces). Likewise, he interpreted the symptoms of neurosis as a disguised eruption of severely repressed infantile impulses.

Transference neurosis and narcissistic neurosis. Between 1915 and 1917, Freud made a distinction between two types of neurosis. Patients suffering from *transference neuroses* are able to form a deep attachment to the therapist and make him the target of their neurotic impulses. This gives the therapist an opportunity to make the patient aware that his attitudes and behavior are actually repetitions of infantile drives, and that these drives are responsible for his problems.

The second type, *narcissistic neuroses*, include most of the psychoses, and are manifestations of what Freud termed secondary narcissism. In contrast to primary narcissism, which occurs in the early phases of infancy when the child is wholly concerned with his own gratifications and does not distinguish between the internal and the external world, secondary narcissism is a withdrawal of the libido from the object world (the world outside the individual) and a redirection of its energy toward the self. This occurs as a reaction to rejection, disappointment, or frustration suffered at the hands of external love objects, especially the parents. As a result, the individual may return to the stage of self-centered "magical thinking" which characterizes the thought processes of very young children and primitive people.

This theory brought schizophrenia within the scope of psychoanalysis, for, to Freud, this disorder represents a regression to a stage of life in which narcissistic impulses and the unrealistic fantasies of the primary process dominate the patient's mental life. *See* MAGICAL THINKING.

The Dual Instinct Theory. In 1921 Freud published a revision of his instinct theory, asserting that there are two basic drives, the libidinal and the aggressive. He described these two drives as psychological representations of two antagonistic processes: the libido, or life instinct, corresponds physiologically to the building up of the organism (anabolism); and the aggressive drive, or death instinct, corresponds to the breaking down of the organism (catabolism). Prior to this formulation he had held that aggression, while not an instinctive drive in itself "was a necessary part of all instinctual drives and that it played a role in neurosis, in dreams, and in symptomatic acts such as slips of the tongue (parapraxes)" (Ross and Abram, 1965). It was also closely related to the sex drive in that it first manifested itself during the anal phase of development. However, the aggressive drive began to occupy a prominent place in psychoanalytic theory only when Freud speculated that since the human being seeks to reduce his level of tension to a minimum (by gratifying his urges—the pleasure principle), he must be striving ultimately to attain a state of inertia or nothingness (the Nirvana principle). This meant that we are driven not only by a life instinct aimed at preserving the individual and the race, but by a death instinct, which Freud interpreted as basically destructive and self-destructive.

The philosophical theory relating aggression to a death instinct was supported by clinical data of various kinds: the high incidence of suicide (especially in Austria, where Freud lived), the intense need for self-punishment on the part of some of his patients, the prevalence of violent crime, the "negative therapeutic reaction" of patients who grew worse as they attained insight, the cruelty and aggression of World War I, and the general inhumanity of man toward man. These observations convinced Freud that aggression is a basic drive in itself and not merely a part of the libido. He did not trace its development systematically, however, as he did with the libido, and this entire portion of his theory has never been widely accepted. Nevertheless he succeeded in showing that many neurotic symptoms, perversions, and character traits are expressions of aggressive impulses, and that many of man's most heroic effects in overcoming such obstacles as the forces of nature may be interpreted as sublimations of the aggressive drive.

Dream Psychology. Freud's theory of dreams contributed greatly to clarifying his views on the dynamics of mental disorder. Since the principles of dream analysis are presented elsewhere, we will only summarize a few major points here: (1) the dream is not a random occurrence, but a disguised expression of unconscious wishes and impulses; (2) these wishes usually date back to the infantile period and the deepest levels of the psyche in which the primary process is dominant; (3) the distortions and disguises of the dream (such as symbolisms and condensations) are unconsciously designed to prevent the direct eruption of dangerous urges which would disturb sleep and threaten the sleeper; (4) a study of individual dreams throws light not only on the personal conflicts of the sleeper, but on the basic functioning of the psyche—especially the dynamic character of unconscious thoughts, the tendency to regress to infantile levels, the existence of primary process thinking in the present, and the repression of threatening impulses during waking life. All these concepts became cornerstones of psychoanalytic theory of practice.

The Topographic Model. In his first formulation of the structure of the psyche (1913), Freud divided the mind into three locales or systems: conscious, preconscious, and unconscious. The system unconscious (Ucs) is made up of (a) unconscious wishes, often mutually contradictory, which cluster together around a specific drive such as hunger, thirst, or sex; and (b) repressed childhood memories associated with these primitive urges. The system unconscious is characterized chiefly by dominance of the primary process and the urge for immediate gratification of desires. It is also characterized by "paleological thinking" which does not obey the laws of rationality, by absence of a distinction between psychic reality and external reality, and by the fact that it is not directed toward adaptation to the outside world.

The system conscious (Cs) develops out of the individual's need for adapting to society, and enables him to distinguish between inner and outer reality, to attend to both inward feelings and outward percepts, to delay gratification and cathectic discharge, and to take both future and past into account. Freud therefore described it as a survival system rather than a pleasure system, and held that in general it follows the secondary process, in which the rules of logic and conceptual organization are dominant.

The system preconscious (Pcs) stands between the Cs and Ucs systems and utilizes both the primary and secondary processes. It therefore contains logical,

realistic ideas intermingled with irrational, autistic images. These ideas can sometimes be summoned into consciousness at will, but at other times suddenly and mysteriously appear in the form of artistic intuition, scientific inspiration, or strange fantasies.

The Structural Point of View. Before outlining the structural point of view, which replaced the topographical model, it is necessary to review another aspect of Freud's earlier theory—the three basic principles which regulate all mental life: the repetition-compulsion principle, the pleasure principle, and the reality principle. The repetition-compulsion is an automatic drive, similar to the reflex arc, aimed at keeping the organism at a constant level of tension. It is the basic mechanism of habit and of what we now call homeostasis. It is also manifested in the drive to repeat childhood reactions and experiences later in life, as in the transference neurosis.

The pleasure principle is based on the theory that unsatisfied drives create tension which the psyche attempts to discharge when it increases above a certain level and produces a state of unpleasure. The discharge itself brings with it a state of pleasure.

The reality principle is a modification of the pleasure principle. It motivates the organism to adapt to the external world, control its tendency toward random discharge, and delay immediate gratification in the interest of future pleasure.

Freud began to restate the pleasure-reality relationship in 1911, when he made a distinction between two types of ego processes, a "pleasure ego" which acts on behalf of unconscious mental processes, and a "reality ego" which utilizes consciousness, reality testing, judgment and movement to "strive for what is useful and guard itself against damage." By 1923, when *The Ego and the Id* was published, these distinctions had crystallized into a new theory of psychic components—the ego, id, and superego—which constitute the structural point of view, replacing the topographical model.

The ego, which became Freud's major concern from 1926 on, has as its goal the harmonizing of the id (primitive impulses), the superego (conscience and the ideal self) and reality (the demands of the external world). In his original view, Freud identified the id with the whole of the unconscious, and described it as a primitive "seething caldron" of "instinctual impulses" which follows the primary process. Its energy is "free" and "unbound," and its object is to seek immediate discharge through various organs such as the mouth, anus, and genital organs. But, according to Freud, this free energy gradually becomes bound when it meets the demands of the environment—for example, when the parents force the child to eat or eliminate at certain times or in a certain way. As this occurs, the ego gradually emerges from the id functions and exerts control over behavior and adaptation.

The superego develops out of the ego but is partially activated by energy derived from the id. It functions as a judge, critic, and conscience, primarily on an unconscious level. In the course of development it probably stems from "sphincter morality" (Ferenczi, 1925), or social control of elimination, and from the oft-repeated "no" of the typical parent (Spitz, 1957). The superego does not attain structural form, however, until the period when the Oedipus situation is relived. (For this reason it has been called the "heir to the Oedipus complex"). During this process the child identifies primarily with the parent of his own sex and to a lesser extent with his other parent, gradually adopting many of their moral and social attitudes.

In the development of Freudian theory, the superego derived largely from Freud's concept of the "censor" which he utilized in 1900 to explain the disguises and distortions found in dreams, as well as from the "ego ideal," a term he introduced in 1914 "to designate the internalized precipitate of early parental reproaches, admonitions and threats, and the standards of moral and ethical perfection toward which the ego strives" (Ross and Abram, 1965). Today most psychoanalytic theorists ascribe three functions to the superego: self-criticism, setting up of ideal standards, and conscience.

All three concepts—the id, the ego, and superego—have a direct bearing on the development of Freud's later theories of neurosis and psychosis. Though he originally described the id as a caldron of unconscious drives, or "instinctual cathexes," he later included in this "region" innumerable fantasies, symbols, mechanisms and memories. These contents have two general effects on psychic life. First, they have an important place in ego functions such as imagination, intuition and creativity that at least in part follow the primary process; and second, they are a source of content for much of psychotic thinking, particularly the type that is modeled after the dream process, as in some forms of schizophrenia. See PARALOGICAL THINKING.

Freud's later concept of the ego, and the ego psychology that resulted, differed considerably from his earlier formulation. Originally (in 1898) he had held that anxiety neurosis resulted from a damming up of the libido, and particularly from an increase in tension due to inability to obtain sexual gratification. Later (around 1915) he made a distinction between two forms of anxiety: objective anxiety, which is an adaptive response to real danger, since it leads the individual to take steps to protect himself; and neurotic anxiety, which originates in unconscious conflict and is maladaptive in nature, since it produces disturbing effects on emotion and behavior, and also intensifies resistance during treatment. The prototype of neurotic anxiety was considered to be the reaction of the newborn to the birth experience, in which he is suddenly overwhelmed with stimulation that he cannot effectively handle.

The structural model, however, called for still another formulation. In the new view, the ego was conceived as the agency that produces and experiences anxiety, for it receives, interprets and co-ordinates stimulation from all sources and is the seat of all affects. When the stimuli are intense, the ego determines the limits of its tolerance, and when this limit is reached it experiences anxiety as a signal of the "awareness of danger in the quality or quantity of such stimuli" (Freud, 1926).

The basic danger situations manifest themselves in developmental sequence: (1) the newborn infant experiences a flooding by instinctual and external stimulation; (2) a little later, when he begins to recognize his dependence, he fears loss of the mother; and as he develops, (3) he begins to feel threatened by loss of control over his own drives and feelings; (4) when the Oedipal stage is reached, he experiences castration fear; and (5) during the latency period and afterward, he reacts to the warnings of conscience and experiences "moral anxiety." The first of these, overwhelming stimulation, leads to diffuse, primitive somatic reactions (a baby's kicking and wailing); the others gradually give rise to psychological reactions that characterize anxiety in later childhood and adulthood, and which can to some extent be prevented or controlled.

Anxiety, then, is an apprehensive reaction that occurs when the ego feels threatened. It may be either normal or pathological. Normal anxiety helps us recognize not only external dangers, but unacceptable feelings and urges that arise from internal sources. Freud described three forms which the more neurotic anxiety may take. First, vague, "free-floating" anxiety stemming from the individual's fear of his own id impulses—that is, the fear that his aggressive or sexual drives will overwhelm his ego controls. Second, phobic anxiety deriving from the same unconscious sources but displaced to objects or situations (elevators, insects, open areas) that represent the real fear but hold little if any actual danger in themselves. Third, panic anxiety, which assails the individual when unconscious impulses of a threatening nature are about to break through and be acted out in violent or impulsive behavior.

The recognition of the central importance of anxiety led Freud to a study of the defenses which the ego develops against id impulses and the anxiety they produce, and this gave rise to his final theory of neurosis. He concluded that the basic defense mechanism is repression, since it attempts to ward off anxiety by excluding the dangerous impulses from consciousness. But he also recognized many other mechanisms, such as rationalization, projection, reaction formation, regression, and denial of reality. He held that psychoneuroses develop out of failure of these defenses to control the unconscious impulses and the anxiety they produce. When this failure occurs, the individual may call upon more extreme measures, such as dissociative reactions (amnesia, for example) or bodily complaints, which operate on an unconscious level and constitute the symptoms of the various neuroses.

The new ego psychology brought with it revised interpretations of a number of psychological disorders. Mania came to be described in terms of an extreme and pathological harmony between the ego and the infantile narcissistic ego ideal, and melancholia was interpreted as an extreme disharmony between the two, since the patient is convinced that he has fallen far short of this ideal (Freud, 1921). Some types of criminal behavior were traced to lack of moral standards and an unduly lenient superego, as in the typical "psychopathic personality." Other types of criminal behavior were explained in terms of excessive superego pressures which produce feelings of guilt; Freud's follower Reik (1924) argued that the tendency to court punishment by leaving clues behind is evidence that crime may arise out of the need to be punished for real or fancied guilt. Freud also held that the oppression of a harsh superego plays a major role in the development of depressions and of obsessional neuroses that result from guilt feelings. On the other hand, he recognized that the superego plays an important part in the development of a coherent social organization, since it helps to control the individual's egocentric drives.

Metapsychology. This is not a metaphysical theory, as the term seems to imply, but an attempt to construct a total system of thought embracing all the postulates of psychoanalysis. In Freud's formulation of 1915, the system included three approaches: the dynamic (mental life described in terms of the action of forces differing in magnitude and direction); the topographical (three levels of awareness—conscious, preconscious, and unconscious); and the economic (based on the concept that psychic energy is subject to transformations following certain laws). (Though Freud included this topographical description in his last statement on metapsychology (1923), it had already been superseded by the structural model.)

Since Freud's time, other psychoanalytic theorists have dropped the topographical description and have added two others. One is the genetic approach, based on the fact that mental phenomena have a history and that psychological processes develop in a maturational sequence, with earlier forms influencing subsequent development, capable of being reactivated at a later time (Hartmann and Kris, 1945). The other is the adaptive approach, built around the idea that psychic phenomena must be viewed in their relationship to external reality, and emphasizing the principle that man and society must constantly adapt and readapt to each other in the interest of survival (Horney, Erikson, Rapaport). *See* METAPSYCHOLOGY, ID, EGO, SUPEREGO, EGO IDEAL, LIBIDO, CENSOR, PRIMARY PROCESS, SECONDARY PROCESS, OEDIPUS COMPLEX, CASTRATION COMPLEX, PENIS ENVY, UNCONSCIOUS, PRECONSCIOUS, ANXIETY, FREE-FLOATING ANXIETY, PSYCHOSEXUAL DEVELOPMENT, PREGENITAL, EROTOGENIC ZONE, AUTOEROTISM, ANAL EROTISM, ANAL CHARACTER, ORAL CHARACTER, FIXATION, OBJECT RELATIONSHIP, TALION LAW, DEATH INSTINCT, CATHARSIS, ABREACTION, TRANSFERENCE, EGO STRENGTH, CATHEXIS, DREAM INTERPRETATION (MODERN), PARAPRAXIS, DEFENSE MECHANISM, REPRESSION, REGRESSION, REACTION FORMATION, DISPLACEMENT, PROJECTION, RATIONALIZATION, INTROJECTION, ISOLATION, DISSOCIATION, DENIAL OF REALITY, SUBLIMATION, PLEASURE PRINCIPLE, REALITY PRINCIPLE, REPETITION COMPULSION, REALITY TESTING, WORKING THROUGH, NARCISSISM.

PSYCHOANALYSIS (THERAPY). A technique of psychotherapy developed by Sigmund Freud and modified by his successors, but in general designed to achieve a basic reconstruction of the personality through (a) eliciting and interpreting the patient's unconscious mental contents and processes; and (b) establishing a therapeutic relationship, or transference, with the analyst. The analytic process is based on the Freudian theory of the structure and development of personality; on the principle of determinism, which holds that all mental events have causes; and on the dynamic concept of the mind, which asserts that personality is primarily controlled by the interplay of unconscious forces, and that the only way to alter it fundamentally is to uncover the effect of these forces on behavior.

Freud did not offer a fixed and rigid therapeutic technique, but rather a general method which could be adapted to the needs of the specific case. As Bernstein (1965) points out, "It is true that the practice of psychoanalysis is governed by a set of general rules of procedure, but it is also a function of experience, the analyst's personality and ingenuity, the nature of the patient's illness, the particular requirements of the individual patient, reality considerations, the personal limitations of the analyst, intuition, inspiration, trial and error, and innumerable semantic, communicational, cultural and operational factors." Freud himself recognized the need for a flexible technique as early as 1913, when he compared the analytic process to a chess game in which only the opening moves could be spelled out, after which endless variations may develop.

Since the origins of the psychoanalytic approach have been summarized under the topic on Freud, we will devote this article to the major aspects of the technique: the patient, the analyst, the setting, the basic rules, interpretation, dream analysis, parapraxes and wit, resistance, transference, termination, and outcome.

The Patient. According to Freud, psychoanalysis is most effective between the ages of fifteen and fifty. Children younger than fifteen do not have sufficient intellectual maturity and reasoning power; adults over fifty do not have enough elasticity, and for this reason the process may be too prolonged. In any case the patient must be self-motivated and willing to co-operate with the therapist. It is usually inadvisable to attempt to analyze patients who are forced into therapy, whose life situation is too oppressive, who are in an acute or dangerous state, or who lack the ability to reason by virtue of psychosis, mental deficiency, mental confusion, or retarded depression. The patient must also be prepared to re-main in therapy for a lengthy period, since analysis takes an average of two years.

The classical technique has been most effective with relatively young, educated, intelligent patients afflicted with conversion hysteria, and—with only slight changes in method—with patients suffering from phobias and obsessive-compulsive reactions. According to Fenichel (1945) the following disorders require increasing modification in technique, in the order listed: character disorders, depressions, perversions, addictions, impulse disorders, and psychoses.

The Analyst. Freud held that medical training was not necessary for the practice of psychoanalysis. Today, however, relatively few candidates who do not possess a medical degree are accepted by the training centers approved by the American Psychoanalytic Association. In any case, psychoanalytic training must include a personal analysis, not only for didactic purposes but to free the candidate as far as possible from reactions that would interfere with the analytic process: "Every analyst's achievement is limited by what his own complexes and resistances permit" (Freud, 1910). This limitation arises from the fact that the analyst understands the patient through understanding *himself.* In the analytic process, he listens to his patient "without keeping in mind anything in particular," and the patient's free associations set up associations in his mind. He then attempts to decipher and understand these associations through a knowledge of his own psychic processes. In other words, the analyst uses the knowledge of unconscious dynamic processes which he has gained from his own analysis, as well as from other studies, in interpreting the unconscious of his patient. *See* PSYCHIATRIST.

Setting. Psychoanalytic sessions generally take place five times a week in a private office cut off as completely as possible from the outside world. To encourage the patient to direct his attention to his inward world of feeling and fantasy, and to say whatever comes to mind, the therapist asks him to recline on a couch. He then sits at the head of the couch completely out of the patient's sight. Throughout the process he remains as inconspicuous as possible, and keeps his patient in ignorance of the details of his own life. In this way he becomes a shadowy figure to whom the patient may attach, or "transfer," intense feelings arising from unconscious sources. Yet he can unobtrusively take notes at will, and observe gestures and facial or postural changes that give him clues to the patient's feelings and reactions.

Basic Rules. The "fundamental rule" of analysis is free association—that is, the patient is encouraged to report everything that comes to mind, however illogical or irrelevant it may appear. He frees himself as completely as possible from external stimuli and conscious control, and is encouraged to put all his spontaneous thoughts, feelings and memories into words. The object is to give free rein to the unconscious and bring repressed impulses, ideas and experiences to the surface where they may be subjected to interpretation. Free association also helps to discharge some of the energy which has given repressed experiences excessive control over the patient's attitudes and behavior.

Classical analysts also put in practice the "rule of abstinence." All gratifications which would tend to distract from the psychoanalytic process are, as far as possible, denied to the patient. He is therefore discouraged from pursuing pleasures, interests, and activities that give him satisfaction outside the therapeutic situation, and may be asked not to smoke or converse idly during the session itself. Freud believed such gratifications drain off basic instinctual energy that could be utilized in the therapeutic process, and that by elim-inating them, the drive toward health would be intensified. In addition, he felt that practice in deprivation would raise the patient's frustration tolerance and increase his ability to endure the frustrations that occur in actual life.

A third rule bars acting out feelings and events. This rule is imposed because patients who cannot call to mind crucial events and experiences may nevertheless express them in behavioral terms, a process that involves an automatic, inappropriate repetition of infantile behavior which tends to retard the therapeutic process. Acting out, according to Freud, replaces the impulse to remember with the compulsion to repeat, and this conflicts with the technique of psychoanalysis, which is based on the *verbal* revival of latent experiences. The object is to eliminate infantile behavior rather than to confirm it by repetition. As Bernstein points out, each time the patient replaces a self-defeating or destructive act with a thought he is moving toward better mental health. *See* ACTING OUT.

Interpretation. This is the analyst's attempt to discover the meaning that underlies the patient's productions—that is, in his free associations, dreams, behavior in and out of the sessions, relationships with other people, relationships with the analyst himself, symptoms, symptomatic acts like slips of the tongue, and his general character and style of life. The reasons for making interpretations are almost as varied as the material to be interpreted. Bernstein mentions the following: to develop insight, make the unconscious conscious, allay anxiety, provide emotional support, overcome resistance, facilitate free association, forestall acting out, produce behavior changes outside the session, arouse deeper interest in the treatment, and satisfy the therapist's urge to "do something" for the patient.

Interpretations can be given on deeper or more superficial levels, depending on the patient's needs at the time. Strachey (1934) applied the term "mutative" to interpretations directed toward impulses, feelings, and attitudes which are operative in the patient at the time they are given. In contrast to "dictionary interpretations," which interpret events remote in time, place and feeling, mutative interpretations are attempts to modify the ego and alter the personality structure of the patient. They must be given in minimal dosages since they require him to change the way he experiences his world. They must also be carefully "worked through" before they can be accepted and assimilated. See WORKING THROUGH.

Dream Analysis. Since free association is the basic tool of psychoanalysis, and the basic source of clues to the unconscious roots of the patient's difficulties, the therapist encourages this process as long as it is productive. However, Freud found that when the patient failed to produce material spontaneously—usually due to inner blocks —one way of breaking the deadlock was to ask him to recall his dreams and associate to them. It became apparent to him, largely through a study of his own dreams, that dream material could not be taken at face value. He saw it, rather, as a series of images that often represent or symbolize significant objects, events, and impulses in the patient's private world.

More specifically, Freud found that the true or latent content of the dream, as opposed to its manifest content (the images), tended to be material which had been repressed in waking life because it provoked anxiety. He further held that this material was more openly expressed during sleep because the patient's defenses were lowered at that time. However, he recognized that the defenses were not completely removed, and as a consequence the unconscious material had to be expressed in disguised, symbolic form—for example, the patient's father might be represented by a king, death by a journey, the penis by a necktie or sword. Some of these symbols were fairly common and transparent, others were more personal and individual. But in any case, they opened up a new avenue—a "royal road"— which free association could take to the unconscious. He found that by asking the patient not only to reveal his dreams but to associate freely to their content, he could frequently learn more about their hidden meaning and bring to light unconscious conflicts that were interfering with his relationships and producing the symptoms of his disorder. See DREAM INTERPRETATION (MODERN).

Parapraxes and Wit. Two lesser but still important paths to the unconscious are parapraxes and wit. Parapraxes are slips of the tongue, memory or limb that "accidentally on purpose" reveal repressed wishes and impulses. Forgetting to invite one's brother to a party may be an expression of sibling rivalry; tripping on the way to the analytic session may be an indication that threatening material is about to be touched upon, or perhaps it represents a desire to kick the analyst. Similarly, wit and humor may be a way of releasing some of the energy attached to repressed wishes—especially hostile or sexual wishes which would arouse feelings of guilt or condemnation by others if openly expressed. Both parapraxes and wit are regarded as symptomatic behavior which must be subjected to careful examination and interpretation. See PARAPRAXIS, HUMOR.

In its earlier form, psychoanalysis consisted primarily in bringing repressed material into consciousness by means of free association. This in itself was believed to have a therapeutic effect. Later, however, Freud realized that the effect was often slight or nonexistent, since the patient's ego was not prepared for these revelations. He therefore put more and more emphasis on the changes the ego itself must undergo in order to become capable of handling the repressed material and the interpretations of the analyst. As a result, the focus of the therapeutic process shifted to the patient's ego defenses, or resistances, which prevent him from becoming aware of the unconscious factors at work in his life; and the use of the transference, or relationship to the therapist, as a means of overcoming these resistances. The latter process is so important that psychoanalysis has been described as transference analysis.

Resistance. One of the major problems of analysis is that of removing the resistances invoked by the patient when his beliefs and attitudes are challenged by exposure to material or ideas that would give him greater self-knowledge. This is the reason why interpretations fall on deaf ears if they are not carefully prepared for and timed. As Bernstein points out, it is precisely the rigidity of personality brought about by resistances which has prevented the patient from letting his ordinary life experiences and education correct his faulty perceptions and attitudes—and therefore, paradoxically, the very resistances which bring him into therapy also interfere with the corrective process. However, in the analytic situation they serve the positive purpose of giving the therapist an understanding of the defensive stance of his patient. They also help him know when he is getting close to crucial material and therefore when the analytic process is striking fire.

Resistances are manifested in many ways—some obvious, some subtle. In general, they consist of any unwillingness or inability to co-operate, or any violation of the basic rules: lateness, broken or forgotten appointments, falling asleep during the session, silence, acting out, rationalizations or other defenses, sudden objection to the fee, "nothing to talk about," advance preparation of material, discussion with persons outside the analysis, an unending series of long and obscure dreams, preoccupation with senseless material and free association, inability to decide what to report, going over the same ground repeatedly, discussing only practical questions. In addition, patients may develop hostile feelings toward the analyst (negative transference) and attempt to discontinue or destroy the treatment. They may also develop erotic feelings (intense positive transference) and demand a love relationship rather than an analytic relationship. Some patients also show "epinosic" or secondary gain resistance arising from satisfactions derived from being ill and getting attention. Such patients wish to lose their suffering but not their neurosis.

All resistances, whatever form they take, are attempts to block the analyst's efforts to lift the patient's repressions and make him aware of feelings, impulses, and memories that are unacceptable to him. In dealing with resistances, the therapist must first make him aware that he *is* resisting and then help him understand what specific functions his resistance is performing. Since the patient resists even the discovery of his resistances, it takes great analytic skill and patience to help him recognize them, work through them, and give them up. *See* RESISTANCE, SECONDARY GAIN.

Transference. An important key to the analytic process—some say *the* key to it—is the establishment of a therapeutic relationship between patient and analyst. In essence, this relationship is not simply supportive, but is one that enables the patient to direct, or automatically "transfer," the attitudes, feelings and expectations he experienced in the past toward the therapist. The therapist, in effect, represents a parent or other significant figures in the patient's early life.

The transference process is based on Freud's theory of the repetition-compulsion, the tendency to repeat behavior patterns that originated in the distant past but still retain dynamic energy. The repetition permits the therapist to obtain a sampling of crucial feelings and impulses even when the patient cannot consciously recall the experiences that gave rise to them.

The analysts of today generally regard the handling of the transference as the main problem of the therapist. He allows the patient to give verbal expression to his faulty relationships, not as a form of catharsis or "getting them out of his system," but as a means of bringing them into the open where they can be analyzed and worked through. But before it is possible to refer the faulty behavior patterns back to past events, it is necessary to overcome the patient's resistance to reviving his repressed childhood experiences. This is where the analysis of resistances comes into the picture.

In handling the transference, the therapist must also become aware of the countertransference—that is, his tendency to direct his own neurotic behavior toward the patient or to respond in kind to the accusations or irrational demands which the patient directs at him. He must realize that the patient's criticisms and demands are only *transferred* to him, and that they actually express feelings toward the patient's parents or others in his past life, not feelings toward him as a person. In recent years, however, many analysts have taken the position that the therapist cannot avoid reacting entirely, and that his reactions may actually help him understand the patient's unconscious processes. The countertransference may therefore serve a positive purpose.

Transference is viewed as an artificial illness in which the patient manifests the same neurotic behavior in the analyst's chamber that he manifests in his everyday world. In working through this "transference neurosis," the patient not only becomes aware of the sources of his distorted feelings, but gradually frees himself from the destructive effects of past experience and adopts more appropriate attitudes and responses. The analytic process, then, is more than

analysis alone; it is a corrective emotional exerience in which the patient develops and tests more effective ways of dealing with the problems of life. *See* TRANSFERENCE, COUNTERTRANSFERENCE, REPETITION-COMPULSION.

Termination and Outcome. The termination of treatment is no simple matter. It involves not only recognition and evaluation of changes in the patient, but a resolution of the transference situation itself. After two or three years in which the patient has closeted himself with the analyst, has laid bare his deepest feelings, and has treated the analyst as a significant figure in his life, with all the positive, negative and ambivalent feelings that this involves, it takes time and skill to dissolve the relationship. But it must be done if the patient is to function on his own.

It is not easy to estimate the effectiveness of psychoanalytic therapy, since the criteria of success vary widely. Some analysts measure their treatment in terms of the patient's achievement of a thorough-going insight into infantile repressions and an equally thorough-going reconstruction of his personality. Others are satisfied with modifications of overt behavior and removal of symptoms. Bernstein suggests that if a patient's neurotic misery is reduced to normal unhappiness, and if his capacity to work and love has been raised to normal levels, the treatment may be considered successful. In terms of statistical results, estimates of full recovery are around 35 to 40 per cent, while estimates of improvement are in the neighborhood of 60 per cent. These are only rough figures, since the cases studied represent many different degrees of initial pathology, and many different types of disorders as well as different standards of improvement. There is a great need for definitive studies in this field.

Criticisms and Answers. Both during and after Freud's lifetime, psychoanalysis has been subjected to severe and often vitriolic attack. Some critics object to the "interminable" process, the patient's egocentric concern with his problems, the disruption of marital and family life resulting from the transference relationship, the high cost (fifteen to fifty dollars a session) and small number of patients treated (about 2 per cent of all psychiatric patients), and the amount of time and energy devoted to the patient's past experiences instead of present difficulties. Other critics claim that the process is built on dogmatic, unproven theories, an extremely limited number of cases, or a mythological account of the human personality (Oedipus complex, libido, etc.). Still others insist that the results are too precarious and meager to merit the time, effort, and money required.

Defenders of psychoanalysis argue that it took many years to acquire the faulty attitudes and distorted feelings that make therapy necessary, and that the human being is so complex that many months are required to root them out and reconstruct the personality along healthier lines. Even though this process calls for great effort, sacrifice, and single-minded devotion, it will ultimately—in many cases—lead to more constructive and fruitful relationships. They also contend that even those who cannot accept the theoretical structure of analysis in full must recognize the power of the unconscious and the necessity of understanding its operations if attitudes and behavior are to be changed in any fundamental way. Many specialists who take this position have been devoting themselves to making changes in the analytic process itself, often in the direction of shortening and simplifying the procedure, combining it with other techniques such as hypnosis or narcosis, placing greater stress on social and sociological factors, and focusing more fully on its re-educational aspects. See RECONSTRUCTIVE THERAPY, HYPNOTHERAPY, NARCOSYNTHESIS, NARCOTHERAPY, HORNEY, SULLIVAN, FROMM.

PSYCHOBIOLOGY. (Ergasiology). The broad, many-sided approach to personality developed by Adolf Meyer, who advocated a holistic point of view and a recognition of multiple determinants of behavior.

Psychobiology was formulated during the early nineteen hundreds when psychiatry was dominated by the classificatory or "nosological" approach. At that time patients were labeled and pigeonholed according to "verdicts of insanity," and their disorders were attributed to little-known causal factors such as organic conditions and sexual disturbances. In opposition to the prevailing opinion, Meyer (1951) pleaded for a holistic viewpoint recognizing that mental illness is the result of the interaction of many factors. He therefore proposed an eclectic, interdisciplinary approach that would co-ordinate the findings of sociology, psychology, and biology.

Meyer felt that the humanistic and natural sciences have been artificially separated, and must be brought together if we are to make an adequate study of the human being. In contrast to Emil Kraepelin and his followers, who believed that schizophrenia and other forms of mental disorder are due to organic pathology alone, he held that these illnesses are a function of "faulty reaction sets," a concept which allowed all possible causal factors to be recognized. This approach emphasized the fact that the therapist must deal with the pathological behavior itself instead of viewing it as a symptom of something else. Meyer also objected to forcing psychiatric disorders into a system of general medicine, a science that was developed to account for different kinds of problems. To be more specific, he proposed to start with that which is accessible in pathology—the patient's symptoms—and to view them as real, though distorted, attempts at adjustment. He believed we should not start out with the assumption that symptoms are a consequence of physical disorders or unconscious factors which are accessible only through especially devised methods and techniques. He did not rule out either of these possible causes —he simply opposed predetermined formulations of any kind.

To emphasize his opposition to the prevailing assumptions about mental illness, Meyer described his approach as "critical common sense." He held that we can understand an individual's behavior only by observing him in concrete everyday activity. He advocated a humanistic approach that would combat the tendency to "depersonalize" psychiatry and attach fixed labels to patients. Instead, each would be considered as an individual attempting to strike a balance between the demands made upon him and the adjustments he is capable of making. A study of the patient's complaints and symptoms would provide a positive guide to the attitudes and the behavior patterns which needed to be remedied. He applied the descriptive term "distributive analysis and synthesis" to this study to indicate that it involved both an investigation of all phases of the patient's past experience, and a discovery of assets on which a constructive synthesis could be built.

The processes of diagnosis and therapy were viewed as a joint search by the doctor and patient for a solution to the patient's problem. They included the following: (1) listening to the complaints of the patient; (2) compiling a biographical report, or anamnesis, based largely on the plain facts of the patient's life and behavior; (3) determining exactly what pathological reaction sets and childish patterns (timidity, self-hate, hostility, etc.) the patient has substituted for normal behavior; (4) avoiding any special frame of reference or classification that would eliminate possible biological, sociological, or psychological factors; (5) discovering normal aspects of behavior which the patient might still utilize; (6) building on these

assets in bringing about needed changes; (7) letting the goals and abilities of the patient rather than the views of the therapist set the general pace of therapy, though direct guidance and interpretation might be offered at times; (8) setting up the best conditions for realizing and developing the assets of each patient in a hospital or home environment.

Meyer's influence has been great in both psychology and psychiatry. His concept of symptoms as ineffectual attempts at adjustment is widely accepted. He is largely responsible for the viewpoint that underlies psychosomatic medicine. The biographical study, or anamnesis, has become an integral part of the psychiatric examination. Theorists, therapists and experimenters alike owe much to his pluralistic, holistic approach, and he is generally recognized as the Dean of American Psychiatry. *See* MEYER, ANAMNESIS, MENTAL HYGIENE, HOLISM.

PSYCHODRAMA. A technique of psychotherapy developed by J. L. Moreno, in which patients achieve insight and alter their behavior patterns through enactments of life situations. The method has been effectively used with child, adolescent, and adult patients, and is applied to a variety of functional disorders, both neurotic and psychotic, as well as to marriage and family problems.

Psychodrama is an outgrowth of the "Theater of Spontaneity" which Moreno founded in Vienna in 1921. In his early experiment he found that playing unrehearsed parts was not only excellent training for actors, but frequently had a salutary effect on their interpersonal relationships. He then began to develop this technique as a therapeutic tool that offered an alternative to strictly verbal approaches which operate wholly on a symbolic level. In contrast to the usual psychotherapy, psychodrama is based on a personal encounter between individuals involved in a situation. Even though the situation is simulated rather than real, it "comes alive" and elicits genuine emotions, generates new insights, and helps to establish healthier behavior patterns.

Moreno brought psychodrama to America in 1925, and since that time has introduced many modifications and variations in technique. In the basic method an actual stage setting is employed, with the therapist serving as director, the patient as protagonist, and a group of trained individuals called "auxiliary egos" playing different roles in the drama. The audience serves as a sounding board and a reservoir for auxiliary egos, and often experiences therapeutic reactions to the drama on the stage. The action itself may take two general forms: the protagonist-centered drama revolves around a personal problem of the patient; the group-centered drama deals with a problem (symbolic or real) involving all the participants. An example of the group approach is family psychodrama, in which members of the family group act out their difficulties in the presence of a therapist.

Moreno claims a number of advantages for the psychodramatic technique. It enables the individual to release his emotions through acting out in a setting that is emotionally safe and relatively controlled. It exposes attitudes and behavior tendencies that are readily repressed or camouflaged in real life or in other therapeutic situations. It evokes fuller and more salutary abreactions than is possible with purely verbal psychotherapy, since the protagonist lives out his traumatic experiences and the auxiliary egos stimulate him to handle them in a constructive way. It utilizes all dimensions of activity and expression instead of depending on the single, limited technique of free association. By emphasizing spontaneity in deed as well as word, it encourages the patient to adopt

a more flexible, creative and active approach to the solution of his problems.

In setting up a psychodrama, the patient is asked to choose a situation and indicate what types of auxiliary egos are needed. (If he is resistant, the director-therapist sets up the situation). A troubled individual may, for example, describe a family crisis that involves his wife, mother-in-law, and teen-age child. Or, to use one of Moreno's examples, a hallucinating patient might step on the stage and say, "I hear my father screaming." The director-therapist would then question him and discover, perhaps, that the father is reacting to the mother. He would then try to elicit more specific clues to their behavior and set up the action accordingly.

In the course of the drama, the auxiliary egos pick up further clues from the behavior of the protagonist, and shape their roles to suit. The therapist may merely serve as a catalyst, or he may be more directive, as his clinical judgment dictates. If he plays a directive role, he may suggest that one of the auxiliary egos exchange roles with the patient, or he may instruct one of them to resist when the patient makes him a target of sadistic behavior. But in any case the auxiliary ego must project himself as fully as possible into the action, and *live* his part instead of merely going through the motions.

Moreno has developed a large number of special techniques which the director may utilize for various therapeutic purposes, such as penetrating the patient's resistances, eliciting fantasies, or helping him to become more aware of his reactions. Among these techniques are: (1) *soliloquy:* if the protagonist refuses to act with other people, he may be asked to give a monologue; (2) *self-presentation:* he is asked to portray his mother, father, sister, wife, or some other significant member of his world; (3) *self-realization:* he enacts the plan of his life, with the aid of auxiliary egos; (4) *dream technique:* he lies on a bed to enable him to reconstruct a dream, then enacts it with the aid of auxiliary egos; (5) *role reversal:* he exchanges roles with an auxiliary in acting out an important interpersonal situation; (6) *double technique:* the auxiliary takes the part of the patient, so that the patient may interact with himself; (7) *mirror technique:* if the patient is unable to participate in the action, an auxiliary may copy his behavior patterns and thereby show him how other people perceive and react to him; (8) *hallucinatory technique:* the protagonist puts his delusions and hallucinations to the test by acting them out in the presence of normal auxiliary egos who react spontaneously to them; (9) *hypnodrama:* the protagonist is hypnotized on the stage and auxiliary egos help him portray his relationships. This technique is used to remove a patient's resistance to dramatizing his problems, and to stimulate the reproduction of traumatic incidents and emotional scenes in their full intensity (Moreno, 1959).

Psychodrama advances the therapeutic process in a number of ways. It brings troublesome feelings of guilt, fear, resentment or jealousy into the open, and drains off some of the tension they generate. It reveals a patient's typical motives, behavior patterns, and ego defenses, thus providing material for individual psychotherapy. It frees the patient from emotional blocks that stand in the way of expressing his true feelings. It gives him a new perspective on his attitudes and behavior by showing him the way other, more objective individuals react to him. It develops understanding and appreciation of the feelings and behavior of other people. It enhances his social skills and helps him achieve greater adequacy and confidence in his relationships. Finally, practice in meeting unpredictable situations in the drama helps him meet the real situations of life more spontaneously and effectively.

PSYCHOGENIC. A term applied to any disorder that is of psychological as opposed to organic origin, as well as any thought, feeling, reaction, or other psychic event that is believed to arise from other psychological activities and experiences. The development of a theory from previous observations and speculations could, in this sense, be called its "psychogenesis." This usage, however, is not common.

The term psychogenic is primarily used to characterize psychiatric symptoms and disorders in which there is no evidence of brain pathology, and which are believed to stem from psychological factors. Since there is no demonstrable organic or structural basis, these symptoms and disorders are also termed functional. Typical psychogenic, or functional, symptoms are hysterical blindness, amnesia due to emotional conflict, exhibitionism, claustrophobia, anxiety attacks, panic, emotionally produced asthma, nail-biting, and delusions of grandeur. Psychogenic disorders include all types of psychoneuroses, psychosomatic (psychophysiologic) disturbances, transient situational personality disorders, and the functional psychoses.

The psychological, or psychogenic, factors that produce these disorders are outlined under the separate topics, and an over-all review is given under ETIOLOGY. A few examples will indicate the general types and range of these factors. Among the significant predisposing factors are early frustrations and deprivations (for example, separation from the mother), faulty family patterns (rejection, overprotection, sibling rivalry, inconsistent discipline), traumatic experiences in childhood, inadequate preparation for adulthood, and faulty values. Precipitating factors include, among others, failures and losses that arouse intense feelings of guilt or inadequacy; severe conflicts between dependency and independence, sexual desire and restraint, avoiding and facing reality; and extreme pressure due to excessive competition, educational and occupational demands, racial discrimination, marital unhappiness, war experiences and civilian catastrophes. These stresses exploit personality weaknesses already established by the predisposing factors, and lead to the various symptoms of emotional disorder.

PSYCHOLOGICAL TESTING (GENERAL). The application of standardized objective instruments designed to measure the intelligence, personality, aptitudes, interests, or achievement of individuals or groups of individuals.

Psychological tests consist of a collection of items (questions, tasks, problems) that are carefully selected, pre-tested, and arranged in such a way that the responses of the subjects can be scored and the scores used in assessing individual differences. The information gained from a test or battery of tests may be used for a variety of purposes: to measure school achievement, guide students in their choice of courses, help men and women select occupations for which they are suited, assign personnel to training programs, hire people for specialized jobs, select and classify military personnel, place children for adoption, and diagnose psychological disorders. They may also be employed in making a thorough study of a single individual (the idiographic approach) and in attempting to discover general laws of behavior (the nomothetic approach). In the latter application they are used in measuring the difference between experimental and control groups in research on such problems as the impact of propaganda, the effect of improved ventilation on work output, or the psychological changes that occur with advancing age.

Psychological testing originated with the need for identifying and classifying the mentally deficient. It is interesting that as early as 1838, Jean Esquirol distinguished between various grades of the feeble-minded by their relative ability to use language, a criterion that is employed today; and at about the same time, Edouard Séguin developed a form board (resembling a jigsaw puzzle) for training the defective, a technique that is still used in performance tests of intelligence. The first experimental psychologists, such as Wilhelm Wundt, devoted themselves to exploration of visual, auditory, and other sensory phenomena rather than to measurement of individual differences. In the course of their work, however, they developed scientific techniques, such as the use of standardized conditions, that influenced the development of testing procedure. When the testing movement itself was launched by Francis Galton, the first traits to be measured were those investigated by Wundt: keenness of vision and hearing, muscular strength, reaction time. In measuring them, Galton developed not only various devices and apparatus, but questionnaires, rating scales, and statistical methods. *See* SEGUIN, WUNDT, GALTON.

The American psychologist James M. Cattell focused attention on individual differences in reaction time and other traits, and coined the term "mental test," though he applied it only to sensory and motor tests. Emil Kraepelin widened the scope of testing by measuring the perceptual, memory, and intellectual abilities of psychiatric patients; and Hermann Ebbinghaus applied arithmetic, memory, and sentence completion tests to school children.

In spite of these advances, the prevailing tendency at the end of the last century was to restrict testing to relatively simple and specialized abilities. But this trend began to change when Alfred Binet criticized this limitation in 1895 and developed the first broad-scale individual test of intelligence, published in 1905. The widespread use of group testing arose out of the practical needs of World War I, and since that time many types of tests, both group and individual, have been rapidly developed. *See* CATTELL, KRAEPELIN, EBBINGHAUS, BINET.

As Anastasi (1961) points out, "a psychological test is essentially an objective and standardized measure of a sample of behavior." If that sample is to have diagnostic and predictive value, it must be truly representative of the behavior in question, though it need not itself be identical with the behavior— that is, a French vocabulary test must contain French words but a vocational aptitude test may consist of individual tests of dexterity, co-ordination, etc. rather than work samples, and a personality test may be based on reactions to materials such as inkblots that have no direct resemblance to people or situations. The phrase "standardized measure," used in Anastasi's definition, means that a uniform procedure must be used in administering and scoring the test. Only if materials, time limits, instructions and other aspects of the situation are the same for different groups or individuals can we be sure of obtaining comparable scores. It is equally important to establish clear and definite norms or criteria for interpreting the results. These are not determined in advance of testing, but by giving the test to a representative group or "standardization sample" in order to discover not only the normal or average performance, but also the relative frequency of different degrees of deviation above and below the average. The empirically established norms then serve as an objective basis for comparing and scoring different subjects on the test.

If a psychological test is to have scientific value, it must meet two major requirements: reliability and validity. Reliability means that the test must be dependable, stable, and reproducible. The test items must mean the same thing to different subjects, yield the same results when administered by different examiners, and measure consistently whatever it may have set out to measure. Reliability can be measured by obtaining two independent scores for the same individual, either by repeating the same test, by giving him two equivalent forms, or by comparing scores on two halves of the test. If the two sets of scores are close—that is, if the coefficient of correlation or "reliability coefficient" between them proves to be .90 or above—the test is usually considered reliable.

An even more important requirement is validity: does the test measure what it is designed to measure? An examination in sociology may contain such abstruse questions that it is actually a test of logic or comprehension rather than a test of sociology. Such an examination might be highly reliable, but it would not be valid since it does not measure what it is supposed to measure. The validity of a test is measured by first setting up an independent criterion or criterion score, then determining whether the test score correlates highly with the criterion. If, for example, a typing aptitude test is being constructed, a certain number of words typed per minute with a minimum number of errors would be set up as a criterion. Then, in validating the test it would first be administered to a representative group of students before they took a typing course, and the scores would later be compared to the number of words and the number of errors they make after taking the course. The coefficient of correlation between the two scores is known as the "validity coefficient," and the higher it is, the more valid the test and the greater the confidence in it.

We might add that high validity coefficients are essential for tests designed to help an individual choose a vocation, as in stenography, while somewhat lower coefficients have proven useful for group testing of large numbers of individuals on a battery of tests, as in selection of air crew specialists. In either case, however, it is necessary to establish what are known as critical scores —that is, certain points on the scale of scores above which it is safe to accept candidates, and below which it is unsafe. These scores can be established by determining how well the test predicts success in school courses, training programs, or job performance. It has been found, for example, that it is risky to admit students to college who have an IQ of less than 112; on the other hand, the critical score for house painter is about 85.

Before enumerating the various types of psychological tests, we will briefly summarize a number of points regarding their use and misuse. First, the American Psychological Association has established a code of ethics which states, in substance, that (a) sale and distribution of tests should be restricted to qualified users; (b) scores should be released only to persons qualified to interpret them, and the examinee should have a clear understanding of how the results will be used; (c) tests should not be released prematurely for genneral use, and claims of merit should be based on objective evidence; (d) the items and norms should be revised often enough to prevent obsolescence; and (e) tests or parts of tests should not be published in newspapers, magazines, or popular books either for descriptive purposes or for self-administration.

The conditions under which tests are administered are highly important. The test situation must be as comfortable and relaxed as possible. All conditions producing tension and "test anxiety" should be carefully controlled, and the use of special incentives (exhortation, criticism, praise, group competition, etc.) should be avoided, since they have been shown to affect different subjects differently, and to have a distorting effect on results. It is important to establish rapport between examiner and subjects through a friendly, reassuring manner in order to encourage the subjects to try to do their best.

Another problem is the effect of practice and coaching on test performance. Research has amply demonstrated that coaching on specific types of items used on an intelligence test usually has a significant positive effect on scores, especially with subjects who have not had adequate educational opportunity. The College Entrance Examination Board, however, has found that gains due to intensive drill on types of material covered by the Scholastic Aptitude Test were not great enough to affect college admission decisions. Sheer repetition, or practice, also tends to raise scores, though the "practice effect" is greater on certain items than on others. Gains are more substantial on vocabulary, maze, block design, mechanical assembly, and tests involving precision of movement than on tests measuring speed of simple movements or auditory discrimination. As expected, repetition of identical tests has a greater effect than retesting with parallel forms, and tests repeated at short intervals have a greater effect than at longer intervals. In one study, for example, the median IQ of a group of 3500 school children increased from 102 to 113 when the same test was administered in successive years, but it dropped to 104 when another test was substituted (Dearborn and Rothney, 1941).

Finally, precautions must be taken against cheating by obtaining assistance from neighbors, starting before the signal or continuing after the signal to stop, or by obtaining correct answers beforehand. The problem of "faking good" by giving what the subject believes to be the right answer is especially acute on job applicant tests of the personality inventory variety, while "faking bad" may be attempted both on personality and ability tests, particularly in the military service. To avoid these pitfalls the purpose of the test may be disguised, and "malingering keys" may be used. One key, for example, is designed to detect individuals attempting to fake mental deficiency by showing that they score high on difficult items and fail easy items. Some tests, such as the MMPI, include specific items designed to detect faking. *See* MINNESOTA MULTIPHASIC PERSONALITY INVENTORY.

Tests are usually classified according to the aspects of behavior they sample. Since many of the major tests are discussed under separate topics, we will limit ourselves here to a bare outline. The usual division is into: (1) *Intelligence Tests,* designed to assess the general level of intellectual functioning (*see* INTELLIGENCE TESTS, STANFORD-BINET TEST, WECHSLER INTELLIGENCE SCALES, INFANT AND PRESCHOOL TESTS, SCHOLASTIC APTITUDE TESTS, INDIVIDUAL TEST, PERSONNEL TESTS, CULTURE-FAIR TESTS, MENTAL IMPAIRMENT TESTS, BENDER-GESTALT TEST, VIGOTSKY TEST); (2) *Aptitude Tests,* designed to measure either special skills and abilities, such as numerical or mechanical aptitude (*see* APTITUDE TESTS (SPECIAL), ART TESTS, MUSIC TESTS, CREATIVITY TESTS, COLOR BLINDNESS), or the individual's standing on a number of traits or "factors" such as numerical aptitude, verbal comprehension, and perceptual speed (*see* APTITUDE TESTS (MULTIPLE), SCHOLASTIC APTITUDE TESTS); (3) *Achievement Tests,* devised to assess the effect of training or instruction in school or industry (*see* ACHIEVEMENT TESTS, READINESS TESTS, DIAGNOSTIC TESTS IN EDUCATION, APTITUDE TESTS (PROFESSIONS), PERSONNEL TESTS); (4) *Personality Tests,* which seek to appraise nonintellectual aspects of behavior such as interests, attitudes, values, self-concepts, and emotional adjustment through such methods as self-report inventories, situational tests, and projective techniques (*see* MINNESOTA MULTIPHASIC PERSONALITY INVENTORY, PERSONNEL TESTS, PERSONALITY INVENTORIES, INTEREST TESTS, AT-TITUDE SCALES, PUBLIC OPINION SURVEYS, ALLPORT-VERNON-LINDZEY STUDY OF VALUES, PROJECTIVE TESTS, WORD ASSOCIATION TEST, RORSCHACH TEST, THEMATIC APPERCEPTION TEST, HOUSE-TREE-PERSON TECHNIQUE, MAKE A PICTURE STORY TEST, SENTENCE COMPLETION METHOD, ROSENZWEIG PICTURE FRUSTRATION STUDY, SZONDI TEST, TOMKINS-HORN PICTURE ARRANGEMENT TEST, FIGURE DRAWING TEST, PLAY, PLAY THERAPY, PSYCHODRAMA, OSS ASSESSMENT TESTS, SOCIOMETRY, SELF-CONCEPT TESTS, SOCIAL MATURITY TEST, MASCULINITY-FEMININITY TESTS, AND MARITAL ADJUSTMENT).

PSYCHOLOGIST. At the present time there are more than 27,000 psychologists in the United States, about 75 per cent men and 25 per cent women. The entire field is rapidly expanding, not only due to our growing population but to increasing recognition of the vital part psychology can play in education, industry, governmental agencies, and private institutions. Many clinics and mental hospitals are understaffed, and there are at least three positions available for every qualified psychologist in every subfield. *See* PSYCHOLOGY.

Today twenty-two states and four Canadian provinces require all psychologists to be licensed or certified before they can practice. A doctor's degree is usually required for responsible teaching, research, and clinical positions. The master's degree may be sufficient for psychological testing, market research, personnel work, and positions as school psychologist or instructor in some colleges. Requirements for the master's degree include a liberal undergraduate program with an emphasis on the biological and social sciences as well as basic psychology courses, plus a year's graduate work in all major fields, with individual specialization according to interest. An additional two to three years of study, research, and supervised training are required for a doctor's degree. About 150 universities in the United

States and Canada offer the doctor's degree. Many students are eligible for financial assistance in the form of part-time employment, scholarships, or fellowships granted by individual institutions or by such government agencies as the Veteran's Administration, the National Institute of Mental Health, the Vocational Rehabilitation Administration, the National Science Foundation, and the United States Office of Education.

Psychologists engage in a wide variety of activities in a broad range of settings. Over 35 per cent serve as professors, research scientists, and counselors in colleges and universities. About 25 per cent work for federal, state, and municipal government agencies, such as clinics, mental hospitals, health and rehabilitation services, education departments, defense and intelligence agencies, and space projects. About 20 per cent are employed in business, industry, and consultant organizations as specialists in personnel selection and training, systems design, human engineering, organization effectiveness, advertising, and public opinion surveying. About 10 per cent carry on their work in schools, where they function primarily as counselors and test specialists. The final 10 per cent are located in a variety of private organizations (clinics, hospitals, research foundations) or are self-employed as therapists and consultants.

PSYCHOLOGY. The scientific study of the behavior of man and other animals, behavior being understood to mean activities of the organism that can be directly or indirectly observed by others or recorded by instruments. Extreme behaviorists believe that private experiences, such as dreams, feelings, and unconscious processes have no place in scientific psychology, but all other investigators would include these activities on the ground that they are part of the real world and can be inferred from overt behavior, such as verbal reports of dreams and defensive reactions to latent anxieties.

Modern psychology is distinguished from earlier studies of men and animals by its strict adherence to scientific method. Aristotle sought to explain the relation between reason, will, and emotion; René Descartes postulated a close interaction between mind and body; Thomas Hobbes, John Locke, and David Hartley developed a doctrine of association to explain learning and thinking processes—but none of these thinkers based their views on systematic research procedures. The scientific era of psychology began when quantitative, experimental methods were introduced by Charles Bell and François Magendie in distinguishing between sensory and motor nerves, Pierre Flourens in localizing brain functions, Ernst Weber in measuring the relation between stimulus and sensation, and Francis Galton in testing individual differences. However, the field did not come fully into its own until Wilhelm Wundt, followed closely by G. Stanley Hall and William James, opened the first psychological laboratories, and Hermann Ebbinghaus made the first experimental studies of memory and Edward L. Thorndike of animal learning. (For details of these and other historical developments, see the biographies listed under History of Psychology, as well as the theories listed under Theories of Psychology, in the Category Index.)

Experimentation remains the primary method of psychological science. It is aimed at discovering systematic, lawful relationships between variables—for example, between learning ability and age, or between speed of reaction and consumption of coffee, or between productivity and background music. In a typical laboratory study, the experimenter controls one of the variables (called the independent variable—for example, the caffeine) to see if another variable (called the dependent variable—the reaction time) changes proportionately. At the same time other aspects of the situation must be held constant in order to rule out extraneous influences.

Several other methods are also widely used in psychological research. One of the oldest techniques, naturalistic observation, consists of a careful study of subjects, animal or human, carried out in their everyday environment—for example, observation of the social organization of bees or the play activities of children in a nursery school. To assure scientific validity, investigators are trained to avoid bias and to record their observations accurately. Devices such as cameras and tape recorders are frequently used to record the behavior of subjects for later study.

Another important technique is the compilation of a scientific biography, or case history, designed to give an organized account of the family background, type of birth, emotional experiences, health history, educational history, and social history of a single individual. Case histories are invaluable in studying the origins of emotional disturbances, delinquent behavior, and normal personality characteristics; they are also useful in investigating the effects of special conditions such as permissive versus strict upbringing, bottle versus breast feeding, or the early loss of a parent. In addition, the interview is a common psychological tool today, especially in market research, opinion surveys, and studies of voting behavior; and psychological tests are frequently utilized in gathering data on abilities, attitudes, interests, personality characteristics, and achievements of individuals and groups at work, at school, in the clinic, or in the hospital.

The subject matter of psychology can best be indicated by briefly describing its various branches and fields of specialization.

Experimental Psychology. Laboratory research on all the basic areas of behavior with the general aim of dis-

covering underlying principles: learning and retention, motivation, emotions, thinking, personality characteristics, sensory and perceptual processes, genetic and neurological factors. Also applied research in such areas as communication, detection devices, equipment design, work conditions, and training aids.

Physiological Psychology. Systematic and experimental study of the nervous system, glands, and sense organs, in their relation to such procedures as thinking, sensation, emotion, motor skills, and sex behavior; study of the role of different brain structures in attention, sleep, motivation, pleasure and pain, and memory storage.

Comparative Psychology. The study of lower organisms in their natural habitats and in the laboratory, with the double objective of understanding animal behavior in its own right, and of furthering the understanding of human behavior. Especially concerned with discrimination, learning, memory, instinct, imprinting, effects of drugs, localization of brain functions, and the evolution of behavior.

Developmental and Child Psychology. The study of the sequence of development from conception to maturity, including the roles of maturation and learning, heredity and environment, in motor, emotional, sexual, social, intellectual, and character development. Consideration of specific topics such as prenatal influences, the birth experience, prematurity, feeding and sleeping behavior, toilet training, discipline, handedness, rejection and overprotection, sibling rivalry, peer relationships, interest patterns, dreams and make-believe, underachievement and overachievement.

Social Psychology. The study, on both a theoretical and applied level, of the interactions between individuals in a social context: group processes, social norms and conformity, roles in society, class relationships, intergroup tensions, prejudice, stereotypes, crowd behavior, public opinion, propaganda analysis, attitude change, effects of mass media, brainwashing, language and communication; and the psychological aspects of important social issues such as poverty, industrial conflict, population control, disarmament, and civil rights.

Abnormal Psychology. The study of behavior disorders, including transient disturbances, neurotic and psychosomatic reactions, character disorders, psychotic reactions and mental retardation; diagnosis, etiology, therapy, and data on the incidence of the various conditions; study of the nature of mental health; prevention of mental and emotional disorder.

Clinical Psychology. The application of diagnostic techniques and psychotherapy to individuals with emotional disorders in mental hospitals, mental health centers, child guidance clinics, prisons, institutions for the mentally retarded, and in private practice; research on the accuracy of clinical tests and the effectiveness of different forms of therapy.

Counseling Psychology. The application of psychological insight—and, where indicated, tests and specific educational and vocational information—in helping normal individuals solve their problems. Includes vocational, educational, personal, pastoral, and marital counseling.

Industrial Psychology. The application of psychological knowledge to the work situation, particularly in job analysis, personnel selection and training, improvement of work conditions and morale, handling of interpersonal problems, and the design of machines and instruments to meet human requirements; advertising research, salesmanship, consumer psychology.

Educational and School Psychology. Educational psychologists apply psychological knowledge from the fields of learning, memory, motivation, personality, and intelligence to academic situations such as the teaching of reading or arithmetic, slow and fast learners, under- and overachievers, grouping of pupils, training of teachers; and the development and testing of teaching aids and programmed learning. School psychologists concern themselves primarily with supervising or administering intelligence and other psychological tests, identifying children with learning disabilities, guiding remedial work, dealing with adjustment problems, and making referrals to clinics and other social agencies.

Psychological Testing. The development, standardization, and administration of tests of intelligence, achievement, personality, interests, job performance, aptitudes, and sensory ability. Developing or assembling test batteries to be used in clinical diagnosis, personnel selection, vocational counseling, personality assessment, detection of learning disabilities, and specific needs such as selection of air force pilots or astronauts.

More specialized fields of activity include: *Geriatric Psychology,* the application of research methods to the study of aging; *Military Psychology,* the use of psychological testing in selection procedures, and the use of clinical and counseling techniques and experimental procedures in the armed services; *Engineering Psychology,* the study of equipment design, fatigue, work methods, and the working environment (illumination, ventilation, noise); *Consulting Psychology,* which is more a role than a distinct field, since the consultant provides expert guidance in the application of psychological knowledge and techniques to business and industry, federal and state agencies, the armed forces, and educational and scientific groups; *Public Service Psychology,* centering around problems encountered by psychologists employed full-time in federal, state, and local government agencies; *Medical Psychology,* which deals with the psychological aspects of physical illness, disability, and rehabilitation; the *Psychology of the Exceptional (or Special) Child,* which includes the assessment, treatment, and care of children with impaired speech, auditory or visual deficits, orthopedic disabilities, chronic disease, epilepsy, mental defect or retardation, as well as the characteristics and problems of gifted children; *Philosophical Psychology,* the study of philosophical issues relevant to psychology, such as the problem of knowledge (epistemology), the place of values in psychology, the mind-body relationship, and the nature of science; *Consumer Psychology,* the study of the characteristics of the consumer, advertising techniques, motivations to buy, and methods of testing advertising effectiveness and consumer reactions to products; *Esthetics,* comprising psychological research on such questions as reactions to music and painting, comparisons between judgments of connoisseurs and nonconnoisseurs, and the relation between creativity and personality characteristics; and, perhaps most recent of all, *Community Psychology,* the application of psychological methods (in collaboration with psychiatry, sociology, social work, etc.) to problems arising in a community setting and soluble only through a community-wide approach—particularly problems of mental health, social welfare, group relationships, education, and social action involving the well-being of all members of the community.

Finally, the subject of *General Psychology* provides an over-all view of the principles underlying the special fields. Its major divisions, as found in the numerous introductory and general texts, are the following: the nature and methods of scientific psychology, the physiological basis of behavior, human growth and development, motivation, emotion, the senses, attention and perception, learning principles and processes, remembering and forgetting, thinking and language, intelligence, psycho-

logical testing and measurement of individual differences, personality theories and appraisal, personal adjustment, behavior disorders, therapeutic techniques, social behavior, vocational adjustment, and efficiency.

Each of the fields just described is represented by one or more divisions of the American Psychological Association. A recent survey (1960), based on the National Register of Scientific and Technical Personnel, indicates that by far the largest field is Clinical Psychology (37 per cent of psychologists), followed by Educational and School Psychology (13 per cent); Experimental, Physiological, and Developmental taken together (13 per cent); Industrial, Personnel, and Measurements (12 per cent); Counseling (11 per cent); Social and Personality (8 per cent); General, Engineering, and other fields (6 per cent). *See* AMERICAN PSYCHOLOGICAL ASSOCIATION, PSYCHOLOGIST.

PSYCHOMOTOR EXCITEMENT. A general state of physical and psychological overactivity.

The excited patient is constantly on the move but totally unproductive because he constantly shifts from activity to activity and does not finish one task before starting another. His train of thought is equally rapid, and he shifts from one idea to another without warning. In this "flight of ideas" there is often little more than a superficial connection between one thought or one word and the next—for example, the sound of a word may introduce an entirely new idea (clang association). His flow of talk is therefore a continuous series of digressions and interruptions.

The patient's emotions are equally volatile, and he may reach a manic state in which he becomes excited, effervescent and irrepressible. He talks glibly, has a ready solution for every problem, and suggests the wildest schemes with complete confidence and assurance.

The most typical manifestations of psychomotor excitement can be found in the "pressure of speech" and "pressure of activity" that accompany the manic phase of manic-depressive psychosis. *See* MANIC-DEPRESSIVE REACTION (Manic Phase), FLIGHT OF IDEAS, CLANG ASSOCIATION, SCHIZOPHRENIA (CATATONIC TYPE).

PSYCHOMOTOR RETARDATION. A general slowing down of physical and psychological behavior due to psychiatric disorder.

The patient sits for hours with folded hands. Any action he takes is long delayed, then executed deliberately, as if with painful effort. He may claim that he often has the impulse to act, but feels as if a huge but indefinable burden is holding him back. His flow of thought is equally retarded, and he may report that ideas come slowly, or that he has difficulty in thinking and making decisions. He finds it hard or impossible to concentrate on reading or other intellectual activity, and the usual associations fail to come to mind. If he speaks at all it is usually in slow, halting, and low tones. His emotional life is just as sluggish, and he appears dull and unresponsive. In extreme cases patients become mute, motionless, and unable to initiate any activity.

Psychomotor retardation is most frequently found in the depressive psychoses (psychotic depressive reaction, depressive phases of manic-depressive reaction, involutional psychotic reaction), and in catatonic schizophrenia. *See* these topics; also, KINETIC DISTURBANCES.

PSYCHONEUROSIS (Neurosis). A functional personality disorder characterized by disturbing emotional symptoms such as morbid fears, obsessive thoughts, or depressive states, but without gross personality disorganization or loss of contact with reality. The terms neurosis and psychoneurosis are interchangeable.

Neurotic symptoms are generally viewed as exaggerated defense mechanisms arising out of unconscious attempts to cope with internal conflicts and the anxiety they produce—for example, one person screens out his difficulties by becoming preoccupied with repetitive thoughts (obsessions), while another may escape from an unbearable situation by forgetting who he is (amnesia). These faulty reactions weaken the individual's effectiveness and generate intense feelings of distress and unhappiness. The psychoneurotic therefore needs help in changing his basic reaction patterns so that he can deal more successfully with the problems and demands of life.

Many authorities of today believe it is theoretically possible to draw a continuous line from normal behavior through psychoneurosis to psychosis. A psychoneurosis is considered to be an exaggeration and distortion of ordinary human tendencies, such as keeping conflicting impulses apart or performing rituals as a means of feeling more secure. The normal individual uses such techniques sparingly and on a conscious level. With some people, however, they become automatic, standard, overworked methods of handling all problems and conflicts. These people may eventually arrive at a point where the faulty techniques have a controlling effect on their behavior and interfere with their evaluation of themselves, their efficiency in work, and their relationships to other people. In that case they may be described as neurotic.

Even though psychoneurosis may differ from psychosis in degree more than kind, a number of fairly definite distinctions can be made. In spite of the fact that he uses faulty adaptive patterns, the neurotic's personality remains relatively intact and he is fully in touch with everyday reality. He may show many psychological and somatic symptoms, yet he is still well oriented and not afflicted with delusions, hallucinations, emotional blunting, or bizarre behavior. Although his general efficiency may also be impaired, and he is apt to be a difficult person to get along with, he is not totally incapacitated for work or social life. He may be desperately in need of help, but he is unlikely to require institutionalization either for the treatment or for the protection of society.

Finally, the psychoneurotic knows he is ill, usually wants to get well, and has some insight into his behavior even though he is not aware of its underlying sources. In other words, his thinking processes are not seriously impaired. In contrast, the personality of the psychotic is disorganized; he rarely has any appreciable insight into his illness, frequently becomes disoriented, loses contact with reality, may sometimes engage in uncontrollable behavior that is dangerous to himself or others, cannot play an effective role in work or social life, and usually has to be treated in an institution.

It might, however, be stressed that these are not all-or-nothing characteristics, since there are many kinds and degrees of both psychoneurosis and psychosis. There are also many borderline cases which show a mixture of both types of reactions. On the other hand, it is interesting that only a few recognized neurotics, possibly less than 5 per cent, become psychotic. This fact lends itself to different interpretations. Some authorities argue that it means that the neurotic's defenses are usually strong enough to withstand the stresses he ordinarily faces, and that many more would become psychotic if the pressures were increased. Others take the low figure as evidence of a difference of kind as well as degree between neurosis and psychosis. *See* NEUROTIC PERSONALITY, BORDERLINE DISORDERS, PSYCHONEUROTIC DISORDERS (TYPES AND CAUSES).

PSYCHONEUROTIC DISORDERS (TREATMENT AND PROGNOSIS).

A wide variety of therapeutic approaches to psychoneurotic disorders is available today. We will make no attempt to summarize them all in this article, since they appear under separate topics in this encyclopedia, but will confine ourselves instead to the major current trends.

Drug therapy is an accepted part of the general therapeutic scheme at this time, and responsible for a marked alleviation of symptoms in at least 70 per cent of patients treated. Tranquilizers are effectively used to reduce anxiety and tension; antidepressants (sometimes combined with electroshock), in dealing with reactive depressions. In some cases these medications have the disadvantage of masking symptoms and making the patient feel he does not need treatment aimed at altering his personality patterns or life situation.

Three general types of psychological therapy are in use today. *Insight therapy* is based on the theory that deep and lasting personality changes cannot be brought about unless the patient understands the underlying sources of his distorted attitudes and defensive measures. Psychoanalysis is the general model for this approach, although many variations and modifications of orthodox analysis are now being employed. Briefer dynamic techniques, such as interviews under hypnosis or sodium pentothal are sometimes used as short cuts to the unconscious and are especially helpful in conversion reaction and in breaking through amnesias or other dissociative reactions.

The second general approach, *behavior therapy*, concentrates on the removal of symptoms. The theory here is that maladaptive responses, such as morbid fears, have been learned and therefore can be unlearned by deconditioning and desensitization procedures. Behavior therapists hold that when the disturbing symptoms have been eliminated, the patient will feel less anxious and will be able to deal more constructively with his problems.

The third approach, which is gathering force today (and which is sometimes considered a form of behavior therapy), shifts the emphasis from removal of symptoms to the modification of behavior patterns, and from insight by itself to re-education. It is important for the individual to understand his faulty ideas, assumptions, and defense measures—but this is only a preface to adopting new goals, new ways of living, and new techniques for handling problems. Therapy is therefore viewed as a profound *learning experience* during which the patient explores his feelings and attitudes, and acquires more effective ways of looking at himself and responding to his world. Although this process does not focus directly on the elimination of symptoms, it has been found that they automatically disappear as the individual becomes more mature and no longer has a need for them. The major emphasis is upon adopting adult attitudes and constructive behavior patterns, revising one's goals along more satisfying and fulfilling lines. (For various therapies, see the Category Index under Treatment).

The over-all prognosis for psychoneurotic individuals is highly favorable. Over 40 per cent improve greatly or recover fully without professional help. Several types of influence appear to play a major part in spontaneous recovery: contact with friendly individuals who serve as models, recognition and respect from significant persons, life situations that encourage more mature responses, and the opportunity to talk about and assimilate painful experiences (Stevenson, 1961). In cases where full treatment—including medical, psychological, and social approaches —is applied, the recovery or marked improvement rate approaches 90 per cent. The prognosis is best for anxiety and depressive reactions, with phobic cases not far behind. Psychoanalytic techniques are most effective with anxiety and phobic reactions. Obsessive pa-

tients are often resistant to all forms of psychotherapy since they involve the therapist in intellectual discussions instead of releasing emotion. Compulsives may be even more difficult, since they are accustomed to acting instead of facing their problems. However, exploration of unconscious sources plus re-educational measures is usually effective in all but the most severe obsessive-compulsive cases. In conversion and dissociative reactions the basic problem is not that of eliminating the symptoms, but of helping the patient to achieve a more balanced and mature personality in order to prevent the disorder from taking another form.

In general, the prognosis for all neurotic reactions is most favorable when the onset of the disorder has been recent and rapid, when the pre-illness personality was relatively stable, when external stresses played an important role in its development, and when the patient willingly tries to combat the disorder. Yet even where the prognosis is judged to be unfavorable, patients sometimes improve strikingly as a result of therapy.

PSYCHONEUROTIC DISORDERS (TYPES AND CAUSES). As stated under the topic Psychoneurosis, psychoneurotic disorders are persistent and relatively mild emotional disturbances arising out of faulty attempts to deal with conflicts and anxieties.

Types. The six major types—conversion, depressive, dissociative, obsessive-compulsive, phobic, and anxiety reactions—all appear to develop in the same general way: (1) the individual is subjected to damaging experiences and distorted relationships in childhood; (2) as a result of these influences, he acquires faulty attitudes and behavior patterns; (3) these personality weaknesses reduce his capacity for adjustment, and when he is faced with conflicts and problems he cannot cope with, he feels extremely anxious and threatened; (4) to ward off anxiety and gain a feeling of security, he falls back on infantile behavior and overuses various defense mechanisms; and (5) in time, these defensive measures develop into rigid, unconscious neurotic patterns with clearly defined symptoms.

Each of the six types of psychoneurotic disorders recognized in present-day psychiatry and psychology is based on the use of a different type of defense measure. They are discussed as separate topics in this encyclopedia, but can be briefly described as follows:

Conversion Reaction (also called *Hysteria*). In this reaction hidden wishes and impulses are converted into bodily disturbances in an unconscious attempt to divert anxiety and also to arouse sympathy or attract attention. Symptoms: hysterical paralysis, blindness, anesthesia, etc.

Depressive Reaction. The individual gives in to defeat, failure, or other setbacks because he is overwhelmed by anxiety when he tries to face his problems directly. Symptoms: despair, discouragement, resignation.

Dissociative Reaction. Anxiety-provoking impulses are kept out of consciousness but gain separate expression in pathological activities. Symptoms: amnesia, fugue states, somnambulistic behavior, multiple personality.

Obsessive-Compulsive Reaction. The individual unconsciously seeks to ward off dangerous impulses by becoming preoccupied with persistent irrational thoughts and actions which are symbolically related to these impulses. Symptoms: obsessive thoughts, compulsive acts.

Phobic Reaction. Anxieties stemming from inner conflicts are transferred to symbolic objects or situations which would not normally be threatening. Symptoms: specific, persistent, intense fears.

Anxiety Reaction. The individual is assailed with anxiety because he not only fails to resolve anxiety-producing difficulties on a conscious level, but also fails to protect himself from anxiety on an unconscious level through defensive maneuvers such as those employed in the other five types of neurosis. Symptoms: acute anxiety attacks.

Some authorities also include asthenic reaction (neurasthenia) among the psychoneurotic disorders, although the American Psychiatric Association places this reaction in the psychophysiologic or psychosomatic category. In asthenic reaction, anxiety-provoking conflicts and tensions produce feelings of weakness and fatigue and a variety of aches and pains.

More than ten million people are believed to suffer from psychoneurotic disorders in the United States today. Neuroses are found on all socioeconomic levels, but occur more frequently among women than men, and are most common in early adulthood. The incidence of the specific types of reactions has been found to vary materially in different historical periods. Hysterical reactions were particularly common in the medieval and romantic periods, but today anxiety reactions account for about one third of all cases, obsessive-compulsive and depressive reactions about one quarter each, with phobic reactions next in order of frequency, and conversion and dissociative reactions accounting for only about 5 per cent of the total. It must be recognized, however, that the various categories are not sharply defined; a great many neurotic patients show a mixture of symptoms, though one type of reaction is usually predominant.

Causes. Even though neurotic reaction patterns vary considerably, the personalities of neurotic individuals have much in common. Most of their characteristics stem from two general traits which are believed to constitute the "neurotic nucleus": a high vulnerability to stress, and an inability to cope with ordinary problems in effective ways. People so afflicted feel inadequate and tend either to lean on others or, to prove their adequacy, to go to the opposite extreme and obstinately refuse help. For them, life is either a long search for someone to depend upon or a long battle to prove their worth. They lack "ego strength"—that is, the capacity to tolerate frustration, stress, or defeat. As a consequence, many ordinary situations, such as taking a new job or competing on examinations, are highly threatening to them. They are therefore constantly beset with feelings of anxiety, which frequently become so acute that they develop many irrational fears, such as inordinate fear of illness, death, or breakdown. Their anxieties and insecurities also make them painfully aware of themselves and overconcerned with their own well-being. As a result, they overreact to minor setbacks and become irritable and hostile toward people who refuse their demands for help, approval, or sympathy. Most neurotics become so touchy and self-centered that it is extremely hard to live with them.

In attempting to cope with their difficulties and rid themselves of their anxiety, neurotics resort to many kinds of defenses. They close their eyes to problems, postpone decisions, dominate other people, become hypercritical and cynical, or hold themselves to rigid standards of perfection. Most of them have little or no insight into the reasons for their attitudes and behavior—and even those who realize they are using faulty methods of adjustment find themselves unable to change their ways. Their defenses, however, do help them ward off some anxiety and probably prevent them from becoming psychotic. For this reason, they overwork their "favorite" defenses until they crystallize into the specific symptoms of one or another neurotic disorder: phobias, obsessions, compulsions, etc. These disturbances are usually accompanied by the common physical symptoms of anxiety and "emotional overmobilization":

fatigue, indigestion, palpitation, headaches, insomnia, and assorted aches and pains. Although these symptoms, as well as the neurotic personality characteristics, express themselves differently in each individual, there is nevertheless a common denominator of tension, lack of zest, and general dissatisfaction running through all the six types of disorder. Neurotics are, as a whole, unhappy, unfulfilled, inadequate people who find it as hard to live themselves as it is for others to live with them.

How does this neurotic nucleus develop? What is the origin of the neurotic personality? Biological, psychological, and sociological determinants must all be considered. The role of biological factors has not been fully determined. The possibility of a hereditary predisposition exists but cannot be supported by clear-cut evidence. Several studies have shown a much higher than average incidence of neurotic disorders in families of neurotics, but this may be due primarily or wholly to the environment and upbringing rather than heredity. Some investigators, notably Eysenck, believe constitutional tendencies predispose individuals to one form of neurosis or another: "excitatory" personalities tend to become hysterics, and "inhibitory" personalities are more apt to become obsessive-compulsive or phobic. It is also possible that many people are born with a constitution that makes them especially sensitive to stress and therefore prone to anxiety reactions.

Biological factors are more clearly operative in another way. The anxieties and tensions of neurotics almost always produce somatic symptoms and these feed back into the neurotic anxiety. In other words, neurotics not only worry about their conflicts and inadequacies, but about their bodily symptoms as well. Moreover, constant emotionalism and physical symptoms may wear them down and lower their ability to meet the ordinary problems of life. This condition, sometimes termed "neurotic debility," probably creates a vicious cycle.

Sociological factors are even harder to pin down than biological factors. Neurotic disorders of one kind or another are found in all countries and among all economic and social groups, but the incidence of different types of neurotic reactions varies widely. Hysterical reactions are especially common on the lower economic and educational levels; anxiety and obsessive-compulsive reactions on the upper levels. An extensive New England study has shown that upper-level neurotics tend to have subjective symptoms such as anxiety, unhappiness, and dissatisfaction with themselves; those on the lowest level have more difficulties with other people and more bodily disturbances; middle-class neurotics have both types of symptoms (Freedman and Hollingshead, 1957). A few regional differences have also been found: a low incidence of neurotic disorders but a high incidence of emotional apathy and immaturity among Tennessee hill people, and a special "miner's syndrome" in Eastern countries, consisting of bodily complaints, lack of anxiety, and a passive attitude. Obsessive-compulsive reactions, which often arise out of feelings of guilt, are practically unknown in primitive societies in which there is no shame over sex and no individual responsibility because of the rigid social organization.

In the study of what causes people to develop neuroses psychological factors have received the greatest share of attention, neuroses being considered primarily a psychogenic phenomenon. Many theories have been developed, varying widely and attacking the problem from different angles. Since they are discussed more fully elsewhere in this encyclopedia, only the key emphases will be mentioned here. Some specialists maintain that faulty behavior patterns, such as morbid fears and compulsive cleanliness, are learned either through direct conditioning experiences at home (Eysenck) or through imitation of parental behavior (Bandura). Others emphasize factors that weaken the individual's ability to meet the stresses of life. Among these factors are conflicts between instinctual impulses—particularly sex and hostility—and the inhibitions of society (Freud); disturbing emotional experiences in childhood (Fenichel); reactions to rejecting or dominating parents (Horney); an inferiority complex which leads to overstriving or avoidance of competition (Adler); and feelings of failure and lack of self-acceptance arising out of unrealistic aspirations (Meyer). Some writers focus on difficult decisions and choices presented by life situations (Combs and Snygg, Miller and Dollard); conflicts between various selves (Shapiro) or incompatible "plans" of life (Miller); or an environment which threatens the individual's self-image and sense of worth (Rogers).

Many recent writers have stressed the failure of neurotics to build a meaningful, hopeful, and fulfilling life. To explain this, they have cited various basic reasons: disturbances and failures in interpersonal relationships, particularly with "significant others" (Sullivan); personality immaturity that leads to egocentrism, irresponsible behavior, and lack of ethical values in life (Mowrer); and failure to form a unique, independent, and meaningful self (Jung). Others have emphasized alienation from nature, fellow men, and the self due to the impersonal, dehumanized nature of our society (Fromm); failure to find guiding values in the struggle of life (Szasz); feelings of guilt, despair, and emptiness in immature individuals who lack the courage to shape their own existence and yield instead to a shallow life of group conformity (May).

Probably every one of these theories has some relevance to the problem of neurosis. Instead of simply choosing among them, they might well be used

20. Are you sure this is a depression, a crater? Turn the book upside down. The way we learn to interpret lights and shadows makes the difference. *See* DEPTH PERCEPTION.

21. The visual cliff experiment: how early can a child perceive depth? Will the baby venture over the "cliff" (which is actually covered with glass for protection)? *See* VISUAL CLIFF, DEPTH PERCEPTION.

HOW WE PERCEIVE OUR WORLD

Drawings by an artist under the influence of LSD. *See* LYSERGIC ACID.

22. Twenty minutes after the
first dose.

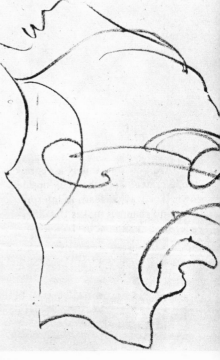

23. After two and
one half hours.

24. After two and
three quarter hours.

25. These two men are actually the same size. Why do they appear to be so different? *See* ILLUSION.

26. What emotion does this face express? Turn the page for the answer. *See* EXPRESSIVE BEHAVIOR.

27.

28. Perspective helps us perceive distance and know that near objects may be the same size as far objects. Compare the reproduced height of the near arches with the far arches under the roof. *See* DEPTH PERCEPTION, PERCEPTUAL CONSTANCY.

as guidelines in assessing the factors operative in any individual case. There is little doubt that neurotic life patterns are too complex to be explained by any single approach.

PSYCHOPATHOLOGY. The scientific study of disorders which have their origin primarily in psychological processes or in organic conditions that produce psychological effects. The aim of this study is to explore the causes, characteristics, and development of these disorders, which include all abnormal behavior and mental illness.

Historically, psychopathology stems from the first descriptions of disturbed behavior given by Hippocrates, Asclepiades, Aretaeus, and others in the ancient world. In the Renaissance, the study was furthered by the attempts of Johann Weyer (1515–88) and Felix Plater (1536–1614) not only to describe symptoms but to group disorders into recognizable types. During the eighteenth century many attempts were made to group mental disorders into classes, orders, and genera, just as Karl Linnaeus had done with plants. By the middle of the nineteenth century practically every symptom was considered a different disease, and labeled with a Latin or Greek term—for example, melancholia was divided into such types as erotica, fureus, misanthropica, religiosa, and oneirodynia (dreamlike). The effort at scientific classification reached a climax in the work of Emil Kraepelin, (1856–1926), who took not only symptoms but the course of illness into consideration, and formulated most of the diagnostic categories of psychotic syndromes in use today. Subsequent studies of abnormal behavior have elaborated the varied forms of psychoneurosis, mental deficiency, and personality disorder. *See* WEYER, KRAEPELIN, DESCRIPTIVE PSYCHIATRY, HIPPOCRATES, ASCLEPIADES, ARETAEUS.

Today the term psychopathology applies to a far wider range of study than the classification of symptoms into syndromes, or symptom-complexes. The major emphasis is on the inner nature and origin of the disorders, of which the symptoms are but the outer manifestation. Abnormal functioning is viewed as a total reaction to life and a total expression of the personality. It is not something that "happens" to a patient, like contracting a particular disease. Rather, it is due to the interaction of many factors in the patient's history, including constitutional characteristics, childhood experiences, personality-molding relationships with parents and peers, cultural and environmental circumstances, gradually acquired patterns of ego defense and anxiety reduction, stressful situations and traumatic events to which he may have been subjected, and organic defects or disorders that affect his adjustment to life. Some of these factors may be more influential than others in a particular case, but every one of them is likely to have some degree of relevance if the full story of any psychopathological disorder is to be told.

The study of psychopathology is therefore an extremely complex affair. Every phase of it presents basic and difficult problems. What criteria for mental illness should be used? What kinds of personality can be considered disordered or abnormal? What psychological attitudes and patterns of adjustment tend to be most harmful? What sociological and cultural circumstances contribute most heavily to susceptibility to mental disorder? What are the major types of stress? What kinds of physical illness or biological defect are likely to interfere with intellectual functioning and personality adjustment? What types of unconscious conflicts and stresses weaken the personality, and what is their source? What part do inherited and congenital tendencies play? Why are different sets of symptoms produced in different disorders, and what is their meaning and purpose? What types of questions must be asked, and what kinds of tests should be used, in making a thorough diagnosis? These are only some of the problems raised by the field of psychopathology today—but they are enough to indicate that this study is a multifaceted affair. *See* SYMPTOM, ETIOLOGY, PSYCHIATRIC EXAMINATION, ABNORMAL PSYCHOLOGY, ANAMNESIS.

PSYCHOPHYSICS. The quantitative study of the relation between psychological and physiological events, and specifically between changes in stimuli and changes in sensation.

A typical psychophysical problem is the detection of differences in stimuli. It is easier to detect the addition of one pound to a ten-pound weight than to a fifty-pound weight, and it is easier to perceive a one-inch increase in the height of a young child than the same increase when he is sixteen years of age. The aim of psychophysics is to determine the mathematical principles which govern such relationships.

Psychophysics was one of the first areas in which the experimental method was utilized in psychology. One reason attention was focused on these stimulus-sensation problems is that physiologists had assembled a respectable body of knowledge about the sense organs, and this made it easier to experiment on them. The second and probably the major reason is that early psychologists were vitally interested in philosophy, and one of the perennial questions in that field is how we obtain knowledge of the world through our senses. They felt that they would come closer to a solution of this epistemological problem if they could show that changes in the magnitude of the stimulus would produce systematic changes in sensation.

Ernst Weber was the first to use this approach. Between 1829 and 1834 he experimented on both tactile and visual discrimination. His studies showed, for example, that a weight of 29 or 31 ounces could be perceived as just noticeably different from a weight of 30 ounces, and that the fraction which represented the increase or decrease—1/30—was a constant that applied to other weights as well. In experimenting with different lengths of lines he discovered that the same principle held, except that the "Weber fraction" in this case was 1/100, indicating greater sensitivity in discriminating differences between lines than between weights. Since Weber fractions, or constants, were found for other sense modalities as well, it became possible to construct a single law, expressed in the following equation: $\frac{DR}{R} = C$, where R is the original, or standard, stimulus; DR is the increment by which R must be increased or decreased to produce a j.n.d. (just noticeable difference); and C is the constant, or Weber fraction. Thus, in the case of weights, if the standard weight is 600 grams, and the Weber fraction is 1/30, then

$$\frac{DR}{600} = \frac{1}{30},$$

and DR would be 20. This would mean that a weight of 620 or 580 would be judged just noticeably different from that of 600 75 per cent of the time. (The 75 per cent is an arbitrary figure set up by convention.) Weber, then, actually succeeded in discovering a mathematical relationship between stimulus and sensation.

Gustav Fechner introduced Weber's experimental method to the scientific community in his *Elements of Psychophysics* (1860). In this book he defined psychophysics as "an exact science of the functional relation or relations of dependency between body and mind." Again his interest was basically epistemological, although his ultimate purpose was to provide an empirical foundation for his mystical philosophy. He accepted the Weber equation as correct, but added two assumptions of his own. First, he claimed that even though the j.n.d.'s were different for different amounts (1 ounce for a weight of 30 and 20 for a weight of 600), the *sensation* produced by these increments was always identical. This prevented him from using the j.n.d. as a unit of sensation. Second, he held that a large sensation can be viewed as a sum of small sensations—for example, a 1200-ounce weight can be conceived as the sum of lesser weights (that is, smaller sensations). The effect of these assumptions was to model the psychological world after the physical world—but later research challenged both of them.

Fechner (1860), however, made a far more important contribution to psychophysics. After extensive experimentation, he restated Weber's law in terms of a functional relationship between physical stimuli and their corresponding intensities of sensation. The Fechner law reads $S = C \log R$, where S is sensation, R is stimulus, and C is a constant determined by the empirical manipulation of stimulus intensities and reports on the sensations produced. In essence, the law holds that sensations are proportional to the logs of their excitatory stimuli. This means that the stimulus must be increased by a constant *ratio* of its value (that is, ever increasing amounts), in order to yield an equal increment in sensation. In more specific terms, since the Weber fraction for weight is 1/30, a 300-ounce weight would have to be increased (or decreased) by 10 ounces to be judged barely different (1 j.n.d.). Now if we make 310 our standard weight and continue the process, we find that we must add not 10 ounces to get another j.n.d., but 1/30 of 310, or 10.3, yielding a total value of 320.3. Similarly, the next increase would be 10.7 ounces, so that our increases would be 10, 10.3, 10.7 to produce an equal increment in sensation (1 j.n.d.). Thus the stimuli must be increased in geometrical progression and the sensations in arithmetical progression—and this accounts for the log relationship.

The Weber and Fechner equations are attempts to formulate a general law which shows the relativity of our judgments. They actually hold fairly well, at least for the middle range of intensity in which most of our discriminations are made. They break down, however, at the extremes. Moreover, even in the middle range of sensations the j.n.d. is not a fixed unit, for the same observer requires a slightly different stimulus intensity at different times, probably because of the instability of the sense receptors themselves, due to such influences as fatigue, distraction, and sensory adaptation. But despite this variability, Fechner's log relationships have been useful in many fields. It has been found, for example, that his equation applies to the relationships between visual acuity and the brightness of the visual field, and to the relationship between loudness and physical intensity of sound. The decibel unit is actually based on the log scale. *See* HEARING, FECHNER, SENSORY ADAPTATION.

Psychophysical methods, then, are used today as tools in the study of sensory acuity. They have been applied to the problem of grading and comparing tobaccos, perfumes, and liquors. In addition, concepts derived from psychophysics have been utilized in constructing attitude scales and public opinion surveys. The development of achievement scales and intelligence tests, as well as the widespread use of statistical techniques in psychology, owes much to the quantitative, mathematical approach of Weber and Fechner.

The conditioning techniques introduced by Pavlov have also made use of psychophysical methods, particularly in experiments on the determination of auditory and visual discrimination in animals. Pavlov's technique was to reinforce the response to a certain stimulus by giving a reward, and then to present nonreinforced stimuli, gradually reducing the difference between them in order to see how far the animal could discriminate the difference. Finally, since all these psychophysical methods require decisions on the part of the subject, psychologists have recently tackled the problem of how we make these decisions. This has introduced another variable in the determination of the j.n.d., for experiments show that people adopt different criteria as to what constitutes a difference between stimuli. *See* DISCRIMINATION LEARNING, JUST NOTICEABLE DIFFERENCE, DETECTION THEORY, ATTITUDE SCALES, PUBLIC OPINION SURVEYS.

PSYCHOPHYSIOLOGIC DISORDERS (ETIOLOGY AND THERAPY). There are many ways of discharging tension, reacting to conflicts, and dealing with anxiety. The ordinary individual talks out his problems and releases his pent-up emotions through physical activity. The neurotic translates his difficulties into obsessions, compulsions, and symbolic physical complaints; he also escapes through forgetfulness or dissociation, or remains in the grip of depression or anxiety. The individual who is prone to psychosomatic disorders reacts in a somewhat different way. He unconsciously discharges his emotions through the autonomic nervous system and the visceral organs, and as a result develops a physical disorder. But why does he use this type of outlet instead of the others?

The answer to that question is still largely in the realm of theory, but there are some promising leads. We know that these individuals tend to overreact and remain "overmobilized" when they are faced with emotional difficulties. They are not the kind of people who respond by becoming apathetic or unconcerned or merely depressed, nor are they the kind who "do something about it." Instead, they worry, "stew," grit their teeth, and fume. External expression is blocked, and internal expression is all the more intense.

Background studies indicate that in many cases the mothers of these individuals have restricted their activities, discouraged the expression of emotion, and in the process aroused feelings of resentment and anger which they learned to suppress. The fathers were typically passive men who failed to show them how to assert themselves. As a result, they became insecure and unable to handle or express strong emotions, and developed feelings of acute inward tension whenever they were faced with problems. In time these inner tensions produced exaggerated and persistent physiological changes such as high blood pressure, which eventually led to physical disorders.

The problem at this point is why psychosomatic reactions are so specific for different individuals—that is, why A gets headaches, B colitis, and C eczema. One theory is that the specific responses are learned through imitation. This is supported by the fact that psychosomatic patients and close relatives tend to have the same type of reactions. Conditioning experiments have led to another theory. It has been found that near-asthmatic responses can be induced in some animals by rewarding certain breathing behavior. It is therefore quite possible that a mother who becomes especially disturbed when her child loses his breath while crying will give him the "reward" of extra attention, and the reward may help to fix the response. If this happens frequently, the child might acquire an unconscious tendency to wheeze in any anxiety-producing situation, and may eventually develop a case of psychosomatic asthma. (Turnbull, 1962)

Still another psychological factor is the nature of the stress situation itself—for example, the pressures and insecurities of the competitive business world of today are particularly hard to "stomach," and are therefore likely to produce gastrointestinal disorders. There is experimental evidence for this idea in the fact that when "executive monkeys" were required to make decisions under stress, many of them developed ulcers. (Brady, 1958 See PLATE 17.) Similarly, the particular stresses experienced by perfectionistic but resentful housewives seem to precipitate migraine headaches rather than stomach trouble. See PEPTIC ULCER, MIGRAINE, BODY LANGUAGE.

This theory still leaves open the question why a particular somatic reaction is associated with a particular form of stress. In some cases there seems to be at least a tentative rationale. A common complaint during the war was "my achin' back." Undoubtedly the basic cause was anxiety and a desire to escape from a dangerous situation—but perhaps the back was unconsciously chosen as the site of the complaint because it actually did ache quite frequently after carrying a thirty-pound pack on a long march. In other words, a predisposition to a particular response had already been established. Likewise, facial eczema might not only be a direct physical expression of anxiety over social problems, it might also serve as (a) a handicap that would excuse failure, (b) a conspicuous bid for attention and sympathy, and (c) self-punishment for failure or guilty behavior.

In addition to the psychological factors, there are many possible determinants of a biological and sociological nature. Basically, psychosomatic disorders are due to overmobilization of the nervous system and excessive physiological responses occurring in situations of stress. The perpetuation of the responses even after the acute situation has passed leads to a chronic somatic condition which sometimes results in organic, structural changes—for example, the excessive digestive juices secreted during periods of stress and strain may in time corrode the lining of the stomach and produce ulcers. See GENERAL ADAPTATION SYNDROME.

At one time it was thought that each psychosomatic disorder could be related to a clear-cut "personality profile," as suggested by Flanders Dunbar (1943, 1954). But recent investigations have failed to reveal specific ulcer, hypertensive, or other types. Yet, even though the early promise of specific profiles has not been fulfilled, the personality make-up cannot be ruled out altogether, since different people react to stress in different ways. Along these lines, Wolff (1950) has suggested that some people can be described as "nose reactors," others as "stomach reactors," or "pulse reactors." Each of these individuals reacts to *any* type of stress in his own particular manner—for example, the pulse reactor always responds with a rise in blood pressure but not a stomach ache. The question here is how these individual reactions develop. Three suggestions have been made. First, the weakness, such as a weak stomach, may be inherited or constitutional. Second, it may be acquired—for instance, a series of colds may lead to susceptibility to respiratory infection. Third, the individual may be conditioned through some early trauma, such as draining the sinuses.

Sociocultural factors also play a part in the etiology of psychophysiologic disorders. Since the general findings have been summarized in the following topic, only one example will be given here. The relation between peptic ulcers and the tensions of our times seems to be well established. Ours has been called the Age of Anxiety, and it is therefore not surprising that the incidence of ulcers has risen over 30 per cent in the past generation. It is indicative, too, that the rate is highest among "upward-striving" men whose fathers were less well educated than their occupational associates. Apparently such men put extra pressure on themselves to overcome the handicap. As this example shows, it is important to consider the family and social situation of the patient as well as the other factors we have been mentioning, such as constitutional tendencies, early conditioning, special stresses, physiological patterns, and personality characteristics. Only a holistic approach will give us a full picture of the causes of these disorders. In any individual case there is probably a collaboration of many factors.

Just as no single factor tells the whole story of causation, so no single approach can be adequate in treating the psychophysiologic disorders. Since they all involve physical symptoms, and since there is always a possibility of organic damage if the condition persists, early diagnosis and medical treatment are essential. Medication, diets, or surgery may be required to relieve the physical condition. But since many of the symptoms are due to anxiety and tension, tranquilizing drugs may also be administered to advantage. These drugs, however, relieve discomfort without going to the root of the disorder. See TRANQUILIZER.

Conditioning and other learning techniques have been effectively used in altering the reactions of the skin, colon, and other internal organs. But in many cases a deeper psychological approach is required. Psychotherapy may be needed to help the individual become aware of the relation between his physical complaints and his emotional tensions, as well as to help him revise immature personality patterns and faulty responses to stress. Sociotherapy can also be used to good effect in helping the patient change his life situation, or adapt to it if necessary, and to find practical ways of coping with specific problems.

In any case, the treatment program must be carefully adjusted to the individual's needs. If it is carefully worked out and the patient is fully co-operative, the prognosis is generally favorable. See PSYCHOTHERAPY, SOCIO-THERAPY, BEHAVIOR THERAPY.

Illustrative Case: PSYCHOPHYSIOLOGIC DISORDERS, CHEST PAIN

Mr. A.S., aged forty-two years, was referred because of an intractable pain over the heart from which he had suffered for two years. Studies in the clinic gave negative results. There was some local tenderness, but no signs of disease could be found. The patient was worried about his complaint, and feared it was heart trouble which would cause his death. The skin over the tender area had even been infiltrated with novocain, but no relief was obtained. The patient was a house painter of average intelligence. He worked during the day and at home in the evening, helped his wife with household tasks, and after reading the paper went to bed. He had no "bad habits," was very conscientious, serious-minded, and devoted to his family, made up of his wife and two children. Some five years ago, his two-year-old daughter had a broken leg which was followed by osteomyelitis. Treatment for this bone disease had drained his resources. Two years ago, his five-year-old son had had scarlet fever which "left bad kidneys," and the patient worried greatly because he had heard some neighbor remark that bad kidneys cause high blood pressure and strokes. Shortly after his son's illness, his wife became emotional and disturbed and the patient felt the burden of the entire family on his shoulders. He felt helpless and hopeless. One morning his wife complained of pain in her chest, and the patient immediately felt pain (identification) over his chest. The fear then entered that he might have heart trouble. The pain persisted. He became so weighed down by his troubles that he had thoughts of suicide and death; his thoughts were centered on physical ailments; and he literally "took things too much to heart." (Kraines, 1948)

PSYCHOPHYSIOLOGIC DISORDERS (GENERAL) (Psychosomatic Disorders). Disturbances in the function or structure of a bodily organ resulting from prolonged emotional stress. The symptoms are physical (somatic) and are produced in the main by overactivity of the autonomic nervous system, the system which controls the visceral and skeletal changes associated with emotions such as fear and anger.

The current interpretation of psychophysiologic disorders is based on the fact that when an individual has difficulty adapting to situations and solving his psychological problems, he may be thrown into a state of tension and emotional excitement. If this state is prolonged, the usual physical changes that accompany emotion—increased blood pressure, digestive upsets, rapid breathing, pale or flushed skin, etc.—become chronic and lead to definite organic symptoms. Different individuals tend to develop different disorders, such as peptic ulcers, migraine, or asthma.

These disorders have recently been reclassified by the American Psychiatric Association and brought under the heading "Psychophysiologic Autonomic and Visceral Disorders" instead of the broader designation "Psychosomatic Disorders." The term "psychophysiologic" is used because these disorders are physiological in nature but precipitated by psychological factors. The Association has grouped them according to the body system affected, and the following list contains the major reaction types, although it is not meant to imply that every case of hives, etc. is emotionally produced. Those discussed as separate topics in this book have been capitalized. Most of the others are listed in the Index and mentioned under other topics.

Skin Reaction: neurodermatitis, hives, acne, allergic eczema. *See* SKIN DISORDERS.

Musculoskeletal Reaction: Arthritis, Tension Headache, backache, muscle cramps, psychogenic rheumatism.

Respiratory Reaction: Asthma, Breath Holding, Common Cold, Hyperventilation Syndrome, tuberculosis, hay fever, sinusitis, recurring bronchitis.

Cardiovascular Reaction: Hypertension, Raynaud's Disease, Migraine, tachycardia (excessive heart action), vascular spasm, coronary disease, an-ginal syndrome. See Illustrative Case, PSYCHOPHYSIOLOGIC DISORDERS (ETIOLOGY AND THERAPY).

Hemic and Lymphatic Reaction: Disturbances in the blood and lymph systems, such as anemia.

Gastrointestinal Reaction: Anorexia Nervosa, Colitis, Peptic Ulcer, Bulimia, constipation, gastritis, hyperacidity, "heartburn."

Genitourinary Reaction: Frigidity, Impotence, Menstrual Disorders, Menopause, False Pregnancy, Infertility, painful urination, vaginismus, urethritis.

Endocrine Reaction: Diabetic Reactions, Obesity, hyperthyroidism.

Nervous System Reaction: Asthenic Reaction (Neurasthenia), Phantom Reaction, Anxiety Reaction, certain convulsive disorders, body image disturbance. *See* BODY IMAGE.

Organs of Special Sense: conjunctivitis, glaucoma, photophobia; disorders of hearing, taste, smell. *See* BLINDNESS, DEAFNESS, SENSITIVITY DISTURBANCES.

The recognition that mental and emotional factors can play a major role in organic illness has given rise to the psychosomatic approach. This is a comprehensive, "holistic" point of view which holds that the patient's tensions, life situation, and attitudes may be directly related to the symptom picture and the course of illness. It advocates treating "the person, not the disease," and maintains that it is often "more important to know what kind of patient has the disease than what kind of disease the patient has" (Dunbar, 1943). This approach applies not only to the specifically psychophysiologic disorders which are brought on by emotional factors, but to diseases which are primarily physical such as pneumonia and tuberculosis. The role played by emotions in the onset and course of these diseases will be discussed under the topic SOMATOPSYCHOLOGY. *See* HOLISM.

Psychophysiologic disorders are a major health problem in our society. Over half of all the people seeking medical assistance are said to be suffering from disorders produced or aggravated by emotional factors. Peptic ulcers alone account for an estimated five million cases in this country, arthritis for over seven million, and migraine headaches for over ten million. Psychophysiologic disorders as a whole may occur at any time of life, but they are most frequently observed in early and middle adulthood.

These disorders are not concentrated on any socioeconomic level, although the incidence for different types of disorder tends to vary widely with different environmental conditions. Migraine headaches, for example, are most common among city-dwellers. In a New York City study, arthritis and hypertension were most prevalent on the lower economic level, although in a Baltimore survey the highest incidence for hypertension was found on the middle and upper levels. Asthma seems to be most common at both economic extremes, and stomach ulcers occur most frequently among upward-striving individuals on any level. (Rennie and Srole, 1956)

In the Baltimore study, migraine, hay fever, and other allergies were more common among whites, and obesity, hypertension, and arthritis among nonwhites (Pasamanick et al., 1960, 1962). More than twice as many psychophysiologic disorders as a whole were found among whites than among nonwhites, but the actual difference was probably not so great, since nonwhites are likely to accept these ailments as a matter of course and therefore fail to report them to interviewers. (Pasamanick, 1963)

No generalization can be made on the sex ratio for these disorders as a whole except that they are common among both men and women. However, the individual disorders are not equally distributed: migraine, anorexia nervosa, and adult obesity are most common among women, and peptic ulcers among men.

The question of differentiating psychophysiologic disorders from conversion reactions frequently arises, since both involve physical symptoms produced by psychological factors. There are, however, a number of distinguishing characteristics. Psychophysiologic disorders usually involve the visceral organs, such as the heart or stomach, which are not under voluntary control. In each case a single organ system is usually affected, and if the tension persists long enough, it may result in dangerous structural damage. In contrast, most conversion reactions involve the cerebral-spinal system and affect organs, such as the arms, legs, and eyes, which are under voluntary control. The disorder may shift from one organ to another, and structural damage rarely occurs. In addition, it has been found that psychophysiologic reactions do not relieve anxiety but aggravate it, since the physical symptoms provoke additional apprehension. On the other hand, conversion reactions are quite effective in allaying or covering anxiety, and as a result the patient may display a *belle indifférence,* or happy unconcern. They may also produce more "secondary gains" in the form of attention and sympathy, domination over others, or avoidance of distasteful situations. *See* CONVERSION REACTION, BELLE INDIFFERENCE, SECONDARY GAIN.

PSYCHOSEXUAL DEVELOPMENT (Freud). The step-by-step growth of sexual life as it affects personality development.

In the Freudian theory, the impetus for psychosexual development stems from a single energy source, the libido, and for this reason the process is sometimes termed libidinal development. The successive stages through which the libido is expressed determine not only sexual growth in the narrower sense, but the entire course of personality formation; the experiences which the individual has at each stage are considered the major forces in shaping his character.

Oral Stage. During the first year of life, the mouth is the principal erogenous zone. In the initial, or "oral erotic" phase, from birth to eight months, sucking is the greatest source of gratification. In the second, or "oral sadistic" phase, from eight to twelve months, the child derives pleasure from aggressive biting. In this entire stage he is thoroughly self-centered and narcissistic.

Anal Stage. In the second and third year of life, the anal region becomes the center of satisfaction, and the child takes pleasure in both expelling and retaining feces and urine. During toilet training, he develops ambivalent attitudes toward his parents, consisting of acceptance and compliance on the one hand, anger and rebellion on the other. The way the child meets parental demands during toilet training helps to determine his later attitudes toward cleanliness, punctuality, orderliness, submissiveness, and defiance.

Phallic Stage. Between three and five or six, self-manipulation of the genitals becomes a major source of pleasurable stimulation, and serves the important purpose of focusing sexual feeling on these organs. In the oral and anal stages, the libido was directed toward self-preservation, but in the phallic stage it begins to be directed toward preservation of the race. During masturbation, the boy has sexual fantasies concerning his mother, and this leads to feelings of hostile rivalry toward his father (the Oedipus complex). Guilt aroused by these hostile feelings leads to castration anxiety, the fear that the father will retaliate by destroying his sexual organs. Castration anxiety causes the boy to give up masturbation and eventually enter the latency period.

The girl, on the other hand, discovers that boys have a penis, and blames her mother for the fact that she is deprived. She therefore turns to her father as the primary love object, and develops hostile rivalry feelings toward her mother. She has fantasies about obtaining a penis or a baby from her father, but slowly gives up these "Oedipal strivings" because of her fear that she will lose the love of both her parents.

Latency Stage. From the sixth to the twelfth year, overt sexual interest recedes, and the child's attention focuses on skills and activities, as well as the development of a set of values and standards (the superego). He now finds models for behavior beyond the family, in a gang or group of peers or among adults such as teachers and counselors. Boys seek the company of boys, and girls often have crushes on each other. This is the "natural homosexual period" which precedes the development of heterosexual interest.

Genital Stage. After puberty, the libidinal energy is increasingly concentrated on the genital organs ("genital primacy"), and the pleasure that can be derived from relations with the opposite sex. The girl learns to cope with menstruation, and the boy with nocturnal emissions. Both become self-conscious and concerned about changes in secondary sexual characteristics. They are torn between the comfortable satisfactions of previous stages and the responsibilities of adulthood, and for this reason their emotional life is characterized by frequent upsets, moodiness, sexual preoccupation, romantic infatuation, rebellion against authority, and lofty idealism. In Freudian terms, the id, the ego, and the superego are in constant conflict until equilibrium is reached and they are prepared for marriage, sexual relations with a loved mate, and child rearing. *See* ADOLESCENCE (THEORIES).

As each new stage in this process is reached, the satisfactions of the preceding stage are not abandoned. They may temporarily recede in importance, but they remain as permanent aspects of our personality. As we grow, however, they take disguised or "sublimated" forms, and exert greater or less influence upon our lives. The mouth remains a pleasure zone and a source of satisfaction in kissing, smoking, drinking, gum-chewing, talking, and oral sex contact. The anal zone continues to provide pleasurable stimulation, as evidenced by "anal humor" and the immense number of cathartic drugs sold each year.

Freud used the term "polymorphous perverse" to describe this capacity of the individual to derive erotic excitement from a wide variety of activities stemming from early expressions of sexuality—from rhythmic activities (swinging, dancing, caressing), exposing one's self (exhibitionism), looking (voyeurism), cruelty (sadism), organic processes (oral, anal, phallic), being hurt or shuddering with fear (masochism), stimulation by the same sex (homosexuality), and also "concentration of attention on an intellectual accomplishment." See SEXUAL DEVIATIONS.

Each stage also leaves its mark on our character and personality, determining our tendencies toward submissiveness or assertiveness, thriftiness or extravagance, stubbornness or pliability. The psychoanalyst, however, is less concerned with the normal expressions of the libido than he is with the personality disturbances that may stem from each stage of psychosexual development. In general, Freud found that disturbances arise when the child does not have an opportunity to work through one or another level satisfactorily. The development is then arrested or "fixated" at that level, and he persists in seeking inappropriate ways of making up for the original lack of satisfaction. A person who did not experience sufficient gratification in the oral period may later develop a compensatory drive to eat excessively. A

child who persistently rebelled against early and rigid toilet training may become an obstinate and stingy adult. The boy who failed to work through the Oedipal conflict may not succeed in developing heterosexual feelings, and may become a homosexual. See ORAL CHARACTER, ANAL CHARACTER, FIXATION, MASTURBATION, HOMOSEXUALITY, PENIS ENVY, CASTRATION COMPLEX, OEDIPUS COMPLEX, INCORPORATION, PSYCHOANALYSIS (THEORY).

PSYCHOSIS. A severe and disabling mental illness of organic and/or emotional origin characterized by loss of contact with reality, personality disorganization, and extreme deviation from normal patterns of thinking, feeling, and acting. See PSYCHOTIC DISORDERS.

Although there is no sharp dividing line between psychosis and neurosis, certain characteristics tend to be found exclusively among psychotic patients. They are frequently or totally disoriented—that is, confused about who and where they are. They are completely or almost completely lacking in insight into their behavior, the nature of their illness, or whether they are ill at all. They are so incapacitated that they are unable to work, study, or maintain relationships with other people. They often do not attend fully to their own physical needs, and their behavior may be uncontrolled and injurious to themselves, or, in a small minority of cases, to other people. They are so ill, and so incapable of meeting the ordinary demands of life, that they usually need institutional care and treatment. And finally, even though they may at times have obsessive-compulsive, phobic, or other neurotic manifestations, they always have severe symptoms that are rarely if ever found in psychoneurosis.

A recent analysis (Lorr, 1962) groups these symptoms into ten syndromes. They were found to occur in a greater or lesser degree in a large and representative group of psychotic patients, and constitute the basis for the In-patient Multidimensional Psychiatric Scale. It should be remembered, however, that each patient develops his own pattern of symptoms, and that in many cases they change considerably from time to time. Here are the ten groups:

Perceptual Distortion: hallucinatory voices that accuse, threaten, or order; visions; ideas change.

Conceptual Disorganization: irrelevant, incoherent rambling answers to questions; neologisms; stereotyped speech.

Motor Disturbance: rigid postures, overt tension, slovenly appearance, giggling, grimacing, repetitive movements, talks to self, startled glances.

Paranoid Projection: delusional beliefs; ideas of reference, persecution, conspiracy, or of people or forces controlling the patient; ideas of bodily destruction.

Disorientation: as to hospital, state, season, year, age; knows no one.

Excitement: unrestrained, hurried speech, elevated mood, attitude of superiority, self-dramatization, loud and boisterous, overactive, excessive speech; dominates interview.

Hostile Belligerence: verbal hostility, attitude of contempt, hostile attitude, irritability, blames others, bitter and resentful, complains and gripes, suspicious of other people.

Anxious Intropunitiveness: blames self, anxiety (specific), vaguely apprehensive, self-deprecating, depressed, guilt and remorse, shows insight, suicidal thoughts, recurring thoughts, morbid fears, ideas of sinfulness.

Retardation and Apathy: slowed speech, lack of goals, fixed expression, slowed movements, memory deficit, speech blocking, apathy, whispered speech, failure to answer.

Grandiose Expansiveness: attitude of superiority, voices extol, unusual powers, great person, divine message.

See HALLUCINATION, PERCEPTUAL DIS-TORTION, CONFUSION, NEOLOGISM, VER-BIGERATION, LOGORRHEA, STEREOTYPY, DELUSION, DISORIENTATION, ELATION, PSYCHOMOTOR EXCITEMENT, FLIGHT OF IDEAS, HOSTILITY, DEPRESSION, PERSEVERATION, ANXIETY, AGITATION, PERPLEXITY STATE, PSYCHOMOTOR RETARDATION, BLOCKING, GRANDIOSE DELUSIONS.

PSYCHOSURGERY (Lobotomy). A brain operation designed to control severe emotional and mental disturbance by severing the nerve pathways between centers for thinking processes in the prefrontal lobe and centers for emotion in the hypothalamus. The operation does not wholly eliminate faulty reactions, but reduces their intensity and domination over the patient's mental life.

Treatment of mental illness by brain surgery has a long history. There is considerable evidence that primitive trephining operations, in which the head was opened, were sometimes performed for the relief of symptoms rather than as a religious ceremony or magic ritual. Physicians of ancient Greece and Rome are known to have opened the skulls of patients to release vapors and humors thought to be responsible for insanity. Roger Frugardi, in the twelfth century, and Marcus Aurelius Severinus in the seventeenth sought to relieve mania and melancholy by cutting holes in the skull to permit poisons or other noxious substances to escape. In 1891 the Swiss psychiatrist Gottlieb Burckhardt successfully calmed a psychotic patient by removing portions of the cortex, though similar operations performed on other patients were less effective.

In 1935 John F. Fulton and C. E. Jacobsen found that surgery on the frontal lobes of two chimpanzees greatly altered their responses to frustrating situations. When faced with difficult experimental problems, they ordinarily screamed, raced about, defecated, and shook the bars of the cage—but after the operation they became indifferent and unconcerned. Egas Moniz, a Portuguese psychiatrist, heard a report of these experiments, and recommended a similar operation for the relief of mental disorders in human beings. The original technique, known as bilateral prefrontal lobotomy or leucotomy, was reported in 1936, and consisted in cutting through measured sections of brain fibers with an instrument introduced through two openings in the skull, one above each temple. Walter Freeman and James W. Watts (1942) introduced the operation in the United States, cutting the frontal white matter through two small burr holes, usually under local anesthetic. See DELAYED REACTION.

Several modifications were later made in order to reduce the undesirable personality changes which followed these operations. In *topectomy,* selected areas of the frontal cortex are removed, but convulsions frequently develop. In *thalamotomy,* or thalectomy, lesions are made in the thalamus by electrical means, a procedure known as thermo-coagulation. In the *Grantham lobotomy,* a variation on this technique, a needle electrode is inserted into the frontal lobe through a small hole drilled into the skull. In *cortical undercutting,* the skull is opened and long association fibers of the prefrontal cortex are severed. The object of these operations is to prevent frontal lobe damage, which affects thinking processes. In *transorbital lobotomy,* an instrument known as a leukotome is introduced through the socket above each eye, and swung carefully through a thirty-degree arch to sever connections between the frontal lobe and the thalamus. This operation was found to be quicker and easier to perform than other methods. It also produced fewer undesirable personality traits as well as fewer hemorrhages and seizures, since the skull was not penetrated. Many neurosurgeons, however, objected to it because it was a "blind" procedure.

A number of other techniques have also been developed. These include cut-

ting only the medial, or inside, portion of the lobes; *ultrasonic surgery,* in which high-frequency sound waves are focused on particular areas, making it possible to produce carefully controlled lesions without cutting through the skull; *cerebral injection;* in which small amounts of frontal lobe tissue are destroyed by injecting alcohol, formalin, procaine, or other solutions; and *radiosurgery,* in which a synchrocyclotron produces controlled lesions by beaming proton rays into the brain—an experimental technique which has been tried not only for mental illnesses but for Parkinson's disease and the relief of intractable pain.

In most cases psychosurgery is immediately followed by reduced nervous tension and anxiety, but the patient becomes confused or even stuporous for several days. During this period he cannot attend to any of his needs by himself. To hasten recovery he must be forced out of bed and made to bathe, dress, and feed himself as soon as possible. Active rehabilitation and retraining are instituted soon after to help him regain self-control and social behavior. The process of re-education may have to be continued for long periods.

In spite of these efforts, some patients remain at a passive, almost negative level of existence, and a few exhibit more marked symptoms than ever due to lack of cortical control. The majority, however, arrive at a point where they can function in everyday situations, although they can seldom work regularly. Generally speaking, they become cheerful, shy, immature personalities who live in the present, have little feeling for others, and cannot take much responsibility.

The effects of psychosurgery vary greatly with different types of disorders. Resistive, destructive schizophrenic patients frequently become manageable, even though the disease process itself is not basically altered. Although delusions and hallucinations do not usually disappear, they have less emotional effect on the personality. Habitual criminals remain relatively unchanged. Even when other techniques have failed, psychosurgery may relieve symptoms of depressive phases of manic-depressive reaction and the paranoid type of involutional psychosis. It has also been found effective in severe obsessive-compulsive reactions and agitated depression where tension is extreme and incapacitating.

When the operation has not been unduly postponed, about one third of all patients show considerable improvement and can be discharged, another third are improved and can usually live at home, but the remainder show no improvement. However, it takes from six months to a year before results can be fully evaluated.

There is no universally accepted explanation of the effectiveness of the operation, especially when it involves extensive damage to the brain. According to Freeman and Watts (1942), severing the pathways to the thalamus reduces the "sting" of the disorder by eliminating its "emotional nucleus." Cutting association pathways may also keep the stimuli from spreading to other cortical areas. Some authors, however, suggest that the operation forces a reintegration of present stimuli with past responses; others suggest that the unconscious threat of death involved in brain surgery may call upon the emergency resources of the organism; still others attribute improvement to the extra care and attention these patients receive.

In spite of favorable results, psychosurgery has been all but discarded in recent years. It is considered a last-resort therapy, to be employed only with severely and chronically disturbed patients who have failed to respond to tranquilizing drugs, insulin, and electroshock therapy. Even then most psychiatrists hesitate to recommend it because it permanently alters the organism

and there is a relatively high fatality rate (from 1 to 4 per cent). Moreover, there are undesirable postoperative effects in many cases, including convulsions, immature personality, and a degree of intellectual impairment. In any case, the results of the operation are highly unpredictable.

PSYCHOTHERAPY. Treatment of personality problems and maladjustments by the use of psychological techniques such as depth interviews, reconditioning, suggestion, reassurance, catharsis, and interpretation. The general nature, goals, and levels of psychotherapy will be considered here, and the specific techniques and systematic approaches will be discussed under separate topics (*see* the Category Index, under Treatment Techniques and Facilities).

Wolberg (1954) offers the following comprehensive definition: "Psychotherapy is a form of treatment for problems of an emotional nature in which a trained person deliberately establishes a professional relationship with a patient with the object of removing, modifying or retarding existing symptoms, of mediating disturbed patterns of behavior, and of promoting positive personality growth and development." Though the general components of this definition would probably be accepted by most psychotherapists, the various approaches and techniques of today vary widely not only in their emphasis on one or another of the objectives, but in the way they are to be achieved. Behavior therapists, for example, are almost exclusively concerned with the elimination of symptoms through modification of faulty behavior patterns, and do not focus directly on personality change. Psychoanalysts, client-centered therapists, and existentialists believe that lasting relief from emotional distress can be achieved only through basic personality growth—although they differ in the amount of emphasis they put on early emotional experience, self-realization, and the search for a meaningful existence.

There is also a wide range in types of "professional relationship" between therapist and patient. In general, the effectiveness of therapy is dependent on the establishment of friendly rapport, which encourages the patient to bring forth his innermost feelings freely and without fear of censure. This is so important that psychotherapy is often described as "relationship therapy." In addition to setting the stage for therapy, the relationship may be used as a therapeutic tool in a variety of ways. In supportive therapy, for example, it is used to give reassurance and encouragement, and to reinforce desirable behavior; in hypnotherapy, it paves the way to eliciting unconscious material or to the reinforcement of direct suggestions; in play therapy, it helps the child to express himself and test out new ways of acting; in psychoanalysis, it enables the patient to "transfer" his basic attitudes and feelings to the therapist so that they may be observed and analyzed.

Though different forms of psychotherapy differ on their *general* objectives, they differ even more on their more specific emphases. Coleman (1964) offers a representative list of goals, noting that psychotherapy involves the achievement of "one or more" of the following: "(a) increased insight into one's problems and behavior, (b) a better delineation of one's self-identity, (c) resolution of handicapping or disabling conflicts, (d) changing of undesirable habits or reaction patterns, (e) improved interpersonal or other competencies, (f) the modification of inaccurate assumptions about one's self and one's world, and (g) the opening of a pathway to a more meaningful and fulfilling existence." Any of these goals requires considerable time and effort, especially when they involve a change in attitudes and behavior patterns acquired during many years of life experience,

and therefore deeply rooted in the personality. But if the patient is willing to lend himself to the therapy, and can enter into a relationship with the therapist, there is a good chance that progress will be made toward the chosen goals.

The many goals and levels of psychotherapy can also be indicated by briefly describing three of its major "dimensions":

Surface versus depth. Surface therapy is directed at relieving the patient's symptoms and emotional distress through reassurance, reinforcement of present defenses, or direct attempts to modify attitudes and behavior patterns. It operates on a conscious level, focuses on the present, and is applied primarily where the patient has a good adjustive capacity, where there is no evidence of deep-seated pathology, or where uncovering therapy is not feasible because of crowded conditions, senile deterioration, etc. Examples of surface approaches are behavior therapy and supportive therapy—which includes such suppressive (or repressive) measures as persuasion, suggestion, and posthypnotic suggestion, all of which rely on a relatively authoritarian approach, and such "supportive" measures as encouragement and approval of desirable behavior, which rely primarily on warmth and friendship.

Depth therapy involves uncovering and working through unconscious conflicts or traumatic experiences that interfere with behavior and adjustment. In its shorter forms it is directed primarily at relief of symptoms and immediate improvement in attitudes and behavior; in its more extensive forms, as in psychoanalysis, it aims at a reconstruction of the total personality as well as modification of symptoms. *See* SUPPORTIVE THERAPY, RECONSTRUCTIVE THERAPY, BEHAVIOR THERAPY.

Brief versus long-term. Brief, or goal-limited, techniques are designed to make psychotherapy available to large numbers of people, and to provide assistance with emotional problems and maladjustments in cases where a long-range approach is considered unnecessary, undesirable, or impractical. The short-term approach may be applied on either a deeper level, as in hypnoanalysis and narcosynthesis, or on a more symptomatic level, as in the use of reconditioning techniques. It may also take the form of group therapy as well as individual therapy. See HYPNO-THERAPY, SECTOR THERAPY, BEHAVIOR THERAPY, NARCOTHERAPY, NARCOSYNTHE-SIS, REALITY THERAPY.

Long-term psychotherapy is available to a limited number of patients, since it usually requires a number of sessions per week over a period of many months. The most extended technique, psychoanalysis, takes two to three years, since it seeks to evoke unconscious material stemming from the patient's earliest experiences, and is directed at reorganizing his entire emotional life. Somewhat less extended are such approaches as client-centered therapy, existential therapy, and the analytic approaches of Horney, Sullivan, and Adler. See PSYCHOANALYSIS (THERAPY), HORNEY, SULLIVAN, ADLER, CLIENT-CEN-TERED THERAPY.

Directive versus nondirective. In directive therapy, the therapist takes the major responsibility by actively guiding the process as a whole. Instead of letting the patient take the lead, he uses various methods (hypnosis, narcosis, projective techniques, etc.) to uncover underlying conflicts and buried memories, and may suggest interpretations of the patient's dreams and other behavior. Some directive therapists are more authoritarian than others. The more authoritarian give specific advice and guidance, the less authoritarian give more subtle suggestions designed to nudge the patient in the direction of change.

In nondirective therapy, the entire course of the therapy is in the hands of the patient, on the theory that he has the seeds of change within him, and the therapist can only provide an opportunity for them to grow and flourish. This he does by inducing a warm and secure atmosphere, and by refraining from probing, interpreting, or offering advice. Instead, he helps the patient clarify his attitudes by repeating and "reflecting" his feelings, so that he will reveal them more fully to himself and arrive at greater self-understanding at his own pace.

Finally, psychotherapy may take place in a variety of settings—in clinics, mental hospitals, residential treatment centers, as well as private offices. It may be utilized with seriously disturbed patients in conjunction with drug therapy (tranquilizers, antidepressants), or when electroshock or insulin shock therapy renders them accessible to psychological approaches. It may be the sole technique, as it is with most maladjusted and neurotic patients, or it may be one aspect of a comprehensive treatment program in which the total environment or the entire family of the patient may be involved. In the hospital setting it may be part and parcel of a therapeutic community approach, which includes not only individual and group psychotherapy, but the activities of nurses, attendants, recreational and occupational specialists, all of whom combine to create a "total push" toward health. For the effectiveness of psychotherapy, see CLINICAL PSYCHOLOGY, PSYCHOANALYSIS THERAPY).

PSYCHOTIC DEPRESSIVE REACTION. A severe depression accompanied by gross distortion of reality, usually in the form of delusions of sin and unworthiness.

Most patients show a marked retardation of thought and activity, and many make suicidal threats or actual attempts. A few sink into a state of stupor and have to be tube-fed. The depth of the depression and the presence of psychotic symptoms distinguish the disorder from neurotic depressive reaction. The symptom picture is similar to that of the depressed phase in manic-depressive reaction, but there are two basic differences between the two disorders. First, in psychotic depression there is no history of recurrent depression or of cyclical swings from depression to elation. Second, the depression is generally precipitated by situational factors and for this reason can be described as *reactive* depression.

The situations which produce psychotic depressive reaction are as a rule acutely frustrating experiences that arouse intense guilt or remorse, or painful feelings of wounded pride. The disorder may also occur in elderly people who experience a series of personal losses and bereavements, or who are not philosophically prepared for their own death. The precipitating experiences and the patient's reactions to them must be given full attention during the therapeutic process, which generally consists of a course of electroshock treatments followed by psychotherapy.

Illustrative Case: PSYCHOTIC DEPRESSIVE REACTION

Virginia R., a sixty-one-year-old widowed mother, was placed in a private institution in a large Midwestern city by her only daughter.

Virginia was the youngest child in a close-knit family of seven. Her father, who had left a civil service job to become a prosperous businessman, died when she was in her early teens; however, this did not seem to cause any untoward reaction in Virginia, since they had never been close. While her father had been a happy, outgoing man, the mother tended to be reserved and secretive, and taught her children to keep to themselves. Virginia was most sympathetic to her only sister, who was but five years older than she, and the girls remained close friends throughout life. At the age of sixteen Virginia left high school after completing three years because, al-

though she had done well, she wanted a chance for some independence. She went to work as a bookkeeper in a large corporation, and held this job until her early thirties, when she met and married a junior executive in the company. Her only child was born when she was in her late thirties, and it proved to be a very difficult birth. Shortly afterward Virginia's mother died, but Virginia was able to bear this loss quite well.

The family was a close one, and enjoyed doing many things together. They were all devout Catholics, and regular churchgoers. Her husband and daughter enjoyed tennis and golf, and Virginia would go with them when they went to play. Basically a passive and dependent woman throughout her marriage, Virginia devoted much of her energy to her family. She entertained regularly, and she and her husband had many friends. She also derived pleasure from her collection of antiques.

About two years prior to admission, Virginia's husband died suddenly of a cerebral hemorrhage. She had a normal grief reaction, but seemed to respond gracefully to the loss. Her daughter, who had been planning to live at the dormitory on the campus of the nearby college she was attending, decided to continue with her plans, leaving her mother alone in their house. Following her graduation, Virginia's daughter decided to marry a classmate who had been her steady beau and who was about to enter the service. As soon as she could she moved to the West Coast to join her husband at his post of duty. Virginia continued to live alone until about ten months prior to admission when Virginia's closest friend came to live with her following the death of her own husband. They were both very happy with the arrangement and enjoyed a warm relationship. Five months before Virginia's admission the friend became ill, necessitating a series of costly operations and close personal care for which Virginia assumed the responsibility, financially and physically. During her friend's convalescence Virginia spent a short vacation with her daughter and son-in-law and disclosed to them that she was reluctant to return home and resume responsibility for the friend's care. One month prior to admission the friend died, and, although there was no striking grief reaction, this seemed to precipitate Virginia's symptomatology.

She was again alone in the large house, and now took to sleeping downstairs on the divan, rather than in her upstairs bedroom, because she was afraid to be there alone. She became seclusive and failed to answer either the phone or doorbell, although she was certainly physically capable of doing so. She stopped writing to her daughter and calling on her friends, and also began to neglect paying her bills.

At the suggestion of concerned relatives, she agreed, five weeks before admission, to attempt to sell her house, although she was skeptical about her ability to do so since she felt nobody would want a "decaying old house." To her surprise the sale was successfully completed within a two-week period. Shortly after the sale she began to claim that the house hadn't been sold, since the real estate man was a fast talker. Because she believed that the buyers had been duped with a false deed, she was afraid to spend any of the money from the sale, and began to complain about her financial state. At this time she had close to $75,000 in the bank and in sound stocks.

With the help of a sister-in-law Virginia reluctantly found an apartment into which she could move. She was becoming more seclusive and would only speak about her imagined depleted finances. She refused to drive her car, claiming that she was a bad driver. After the sale of the house her appetite decreased sharply, she began waking early in the morning, and she became constipated. Finally her sister-in-law called Virginia's daughter, who flew back to see her mother. Virginia told her that her in-laws would break up her marriage because she, Virginia, had done everything wrong. She felt that everything was going "down, down, down" and she was going along with it. She told her daughter: "I let myself go down through carelessness." The day before Virginia was to have moved into her new apartment, her daughter entered her in the local hospital.

Upon admission Virginia appeared depressed and was uncommunicative with the hospital staff. She left sentences unfinished, and did not (or would not) recall the answers to the questions of the interviewer. She frequently would answer "I don't know," or begin sentences only to trail off, leaving them incomplete. Her answers were all retarded, incomplete, and inadequate. She frequently interpersed "I've been careless" with the few responses she did make. She was able to say that she felt unreal, as though she were in a fog or in a dream.

Virginia was given a series of six electroconvulsive shock treatments, and this removed the depression, although she remained confused. After a period of two weeks the confusion lifted and she was released for out-patient psychotherapeutic treatment. (Zax and Stricker, 1963)

PSYCHOTIC DISORDERS. Psychotic disorders fall into two general categories, functional and organic. Functional, or psychogenic, psychoses originate primarily from psychological factors; no brain pathology can be demonstrated, although there may be a hereditary or constitutional predisposition in some cases. These disorders constitute about one fourth of first admissions to public mental hospitals, according to the 1965 United States Public Health Service figures, and include schizophrenic (18 per cent of first admissions), involutional psychotic (3.1), manic-depressive (1.1), psychotic depressive (2.0), and paranoid (.4) reactions.

Organic psychoses are of two types: acute brain disorders due to temporary brain impairment; and chronic brain disorders, due to lasting brain damage. They comprise slightly over one fourth of all first admissions to mental hospitals. The acute brain syndromes include disorders associated with alcoholic intoxication (2.6 per cent), drug or poison intoxication (.4), and other conditions, such as vitamin deficiency, high fever, hyperthyroidism (.5). The chronic brain syndromes consist of disorders associated with cerebral arteriosclerosis (11.6), other circulatory disturbance (.9), senile brain disease (4.4), alcoholic intoxication (2.0), convulsive disorder (1.3), syphilis of central nervous system (.15), trauma other than birth (.5), epidemic encephalitis and intracranial infections (.15), and other conditions

(2.0). The other half of first admissions consists primarily of severe personality and psychoneurotic disorders, as well as undiagnosed cases.

The total number of individuals affected with psychotic disorders at any one time in the United States is estimated at one million. Of these, about two thirds are hospitalized, with approximately 98 per cent in public institutions. The present trend is to treat as many cases as possible within the community, and a growing number are now receiving treatment in day hospitals, night hospitals, general hospitals, and mental health centers. Many thousands, however, are kept at home untreated. Almost half the hospital beds in the United States are occupied by mental patients (mostly psychotics), but their length of stay has, at least until recently, been measured in months and years, while that of physical patients averages only two weeks.

The new drug treatments have materially shortened treatment for the functional patients and have helped to bring about a substantial decline in the resident mental hospital population in the last few years. At the same time the number treated has increased due to the fact that the length of stay for new patients has declined. As for the over-all trend, the rate of hospitalization for schizophrenia seems to be fairly constant, but the rate for manic-depressive reaction, involutional psychotic reaction, and paresis has declined. These decreases, however, have been offset by increases in the mental disorders of old age: cerebral arteriosclerosis, senile brain disease, etc., due to the increasing span of life. See MENTAL HOSPITAL.

The specific causal factors associated with each of the functional and organic psychoses will be considered under the separate disorders, but certain generalizations can be made about the entire group taken together. Statistical studies have shown that the median age for all first admissions to mental hospitals is forty-four years, with schizophrenic reactions concentrated in early adulthood balancing senile psychoses occurring late in life. Males outnumber females by four to three, but in manic-depressive, involutional, and senile psychoses females outnumber males. The distribution of intelligence and education is about the same as for the general population, although paranoids tend to be higher and paretics lower on both counts than the other reaction types, but with many exceptions. Married people as a whole are considerably less subject to psychosis than the divorced, single, separated, or widowed—but the quality of the marriage must be considered: good marriages have a stabilizing influence, while poor marriages lower resistance to stress.

The rate of admissions from urban areas is double that from rural areas, but this finding is qualified by the fact that the mentally ill are more likely to be cared for by their families in the country, and more of them can keep working at the less stressful work of nonindustrialized areas. Occupational differences have not been sufficiently explored, but some studies indicate that schizophrenia is more prevalent in lower level occupations and manic-depressive in upper, especially for males. Studies conducted in the armed forces show that the incidence of major mental disorders was over twice as high in the lowest socioeconomic level as in the highest, and an intensive survey in New York City (Rennie et al., 1957) revealed that psychotic disorders were found in 13 per cent of individuals in the lower social strata and only 3.6 per cent in the upper. There probably is no simple cause and effect relationship here, since these disorders themselves often reduce fitness for high-level work.

The incidence and type of psychosis varies considerably in different ethnic, cultural, and religious groups. The determining factors, where they can be found, seem to be customs, values, or socioeconomic situation rather than biological differences. Various studies have shown that the rate for psychotic reactions is higher among Protestants than among Catholics and Jews. Alcoholic psychoses are rare among Jews and practically nonexistent among other groups, such as the Hutterites, who have even stronger conventions against excessive drinking.

The rate of hospital admissions for Negroes is higher than for whites; but this is probably a reflection of the stresses of life and inability to care for disturbed individuals at home, since no significant difference was found when both hospitalized and nonhospitalized cases were included in a survey in Baltimore (Pasamanick, 1962). The rate of psychoses for nonindustrial societies seems to be considerably less than for industrial societies—probably as a reflection of a simpler, more conventional life. In Kenya, for example, it has been estimated at 37 as compared with 880 per 100,000 in the United States. The content of delusions and hallucinations, and the form of certain psychoses, also differ widely from society to society. Ideas associated with magic, witches, and appeasement of gods play a large part in psychoses found in folk societies (Carothers, 1953). *See* EXOTIC PSYCHOSES.

Physiological factors, as can be expected, predominate in producing organic psychoses, although in many cases the patient's attitude and life situation may either aggravate or mitigate the disorder. This is particularly true of chronic brain syndromes resulting from cerebral arteriosclerosis, syphilis, and epilepsy. Psychological and sociological factors collaborate in the etiology of functional psychoses, but may interact with biological factors. Even though there is no known organic pathology, and no simple dominant or recessive genetic pattern, there is some evidence for the theory of constitutional predisposition to certain types of functional psychotic reactions, particularly in the manic-depressive and schizophrenic as opposed to the paranoid reaction types. The exact mechanism is not known, but there is a good possibility that subtle defects in brain chemistry or structure may interfere with the ability to meet certain types of stress. This would help to account for the fact that some individuals can adapt themselves to disturbing experiences while others cannot.

The psychological factors appear to assume different patterns for different psychoses, but in general they are of two types: family relationships and traumatic experiences which interfere with healthy personality development during childhood; and special pressures and conflicts which exploit these faulty personality tendencies. In some instances the psychosis develops slowly and insidiously, but in others precipitating stresses may produce an acute onset. In either case the patient's specific defense mechanisms become exaggerated, his attitudes toward reality and relationships to other people become distorted, and rational control over behavior is diminished and may eventually reach a point where complete disintegration of the personality takes place. It may well be that this disintegration is partly due to physiological changes caused by severe and prolonged emotional stress and consequent overloading of the nervous system. *See* ETIOLOGY.

In recent years the application of full-scale intensive treatment, as contrasted with mere custodial care, has materially improved the general prognosis of the psychotic disorders. About 80 per cent of all first admissions are discharged as improved or recovered, over one half within one or two months and most of the others within a year. Manic-depressives show a somewhat higher recovery rate than schizophrenics, and the prognosis for organic disorders is somewhat lower than for functional disorders as a whole, since they include not only acute but chronic and senile cases in which there is often irreversible brain damage.

Early detection and treatment are extremely important in all types of psychoses, although some patients are now able to make social recoveries after many years in the hospital. The outcome is most promising where the onset of the illness is acute and where the premorbid personality has been fairly well integrated. Recovery is most likely to be lasting where the hospital provides psychotherapy and sociotherapy, and prepares the patient for returning to an active and productive life. It is also dependent on acceptance by the family and the community, and the regular use of prescribed medication after returning home. With all these factors working for them, many patients make a better adjustment after their illness than before.

PUBLIC OPINION SURVEYS. A form of attitude testing in which a cross section of a given population answers a carefully prepared set of questions on a specific topic.

Surveys, or polls, have three primary uses: (a) to inform the public about opinion trends on current issues; (b) to provide government agencies, political candidates, business and social welfare organizations, and the like, with confidential reports that will help them with plans and policies; and (c) to further the research efforts of sociologists, psychologists, and other social scientists. Modern methods of polling are now employed in every important democracy in the world, and twenty nations have research organizations which sound out public opinion on a regular basis.

The first survey that can be called a public opinion poll was a straw vote conducted by the Harrisburg *Pennsyl-*

vanian, which wrongly predicted the election of Andrew Jackson over John' Quincy Adams in 1824. Newspapers and magazines continued to conduct most of the polls until the *Literary Digest* mistakenly predicted Roosevelt's defeat by Landon in 1936—primarily because ballots had been sent to telephone and car owners, ignoring the third of the population who did not have these facilities and who tended to favor the candidate of the "common man." This failure had the effect of spurring the development of scientific polling methods, which had already started with a series of market surveys known as the "psychological barometer." These surveys were of the personal interview type and were conducted periodically by The Psychological Corporation in fifteen cities and towns.

Between 1934 and 1935 Paul Cherrington, Elmo Roper, George Gallup, and Archibald M. Crossley began to experiment with personal interviews on a nationwide basis. They also used a "quota sampling" technique (see below) and, in contrast to the *Literary Digest* failure, succeeded in correctly forecasting Roosevelt's re-election in 1936. From then on the polls were further refined, and their accuracy improved to a point where the American Institute of Public Opinion (Gallup Poll) achieved an average error rate of less than 3 per cent in hundreds of elections over a twenty-five year period.

In 1948, election surveys met a setback in the public eye when all the leading polls wrongly predicted a Dewey victory over Truman. However, analysis showed that the error was not due to the basic technique itself but to mistakes in interpreting the trends, as well as the fact that the interviewing was terminated too soon, since a last-minute drop in farm prices swung the farm vote toward Truman. As a result, the procedures were modified and the predictions made during the following four elections, between 1952 and 1964, were highly accurate.

Public opinion polling is a six-step affair. First, *the definition of objectives:* each poll must be designed with a particular purpose in mind—for example, to determine what people think about an issue or product, why they think as they do, how strongly, how well they are informed, or how their views affect their behavior. Second, *formulation of questions:* the wording must suit the subject matter and objectives of the survey. Some polls use a simple "yes—no—don't know" form, others a multiple choice format; and occasionally open or free-answer questions are employed. In any case the questions must be clear, understandable, unambiguous, and unbiased. Experience has shown that negative wording, and especially double negatives, should be avoided. Third, *pretesting of questions:* interviewers try the questions on representative respondents to test not only the wording but the order in which they are presented. As an example, it was found that the question "Do you agree with Roosevelt that Thanksgiving should be moved a week earlier"? elicited far more affirmative responses than a similar question that did not refer to the President.

Fourth, *selection of the sample:* according to one of two techniques, (a) quota or judgment sampling, which divides the population into subgroups, or "controls," based on geographic location, size of community, socioeconomic level, sex, and age, with the sample containing the same proportions of each of these categories that exist in the population as a whole; and (b) random or probability sampling, which attempts to be even more representative by using random selection. In either case the mere size of the sample is less important than its ability to mirror the entire population. In nationwide surveys from 1500 to 5000 persons are polled, with an accuracy within 2 per cent. The *Literary Digest* Poll of 1936,

though based on 2,375,000 mail ballots, had an error of 19 percentage points, yet the chances are overwhelming that it would have correctly forecast the results if a pure random sample of only 500 persons had been polled!

Fifth, *interviewing the sample.* Early methods in which questionnaires were mailed or printed in newspapers have been abandoned because the people who send in their answers are not necessarily representative of the entire "universe" under test. Personal interviewing is far more reliable since everyone in the sample can express his views and the interviewer can make sure the question is understood and the answer relevant. Interviewers must be carefully selected and trained to eliminate bias in asking the questions and reporting the answers. Sixth, *tabulating and analyzing the results.* Machine tabulation can be readily used for the yes-no and multiple choice questions, but with open questions the answers must be grouped and coded before being counted. This is a fairly complicated procedure because of shades of meaning, but once the coding is done, a tabulation count can be made either by hand or by a card-punching and -sorting machine. *See* CONSUMER RESEARCH.

PUERPERAL PSYCHOSIS (literally "Childbirth Psychosis"). Psychotic reactions occurring in the period following childbirth, which is technically known as the puerperium. This period extends from the termination of labor to the return of the uterus to its normal condition.

The majority of these reactions are schizophrenic and depressive, but occasionally there are delirious episodes precipitated by infection, hemorrhage, exhaustion, or toxemia (blood poisoning). These episodes are most likely to occur in poorly adjusted women. Manic reactions are also found, but infrequently. The term puerperal psychosis has been replaced by postpartum psychosis. *See* POSTPARTUM PSYCHOSIS.

PYROMANIA. The compulsive urge to set fires.

Pyromania is classed by most authorities as an obsessive-compulsive reaction, but some consider it a manifestation of an antisocial or psychopathic personality, while others describe it as an impulsive form of neurotic behavior. In any case, the disorder is characterized by preoccupation with the idea of fire and an uncontrollable impulse to set fires even though the consequences are likely to be disastrous. Examples are not hard to find. One arsonist set over nineteen fires, causing damage in excess of $2,000,000; another set fire to 130 factories and warehouses over a period of four years; a third—a fourteen-year-old boy—admitted setting innumerable fires, one of which resulted in the death of two children and damage estimated at a quarter of a million dollars. Characteristically, individuals of this kind cannot explain or justify their behavior, but claim that they have responded to an overwhelming urge which they are powerless to resist.

The psychodynamics of pyromania appear to vary from case to case. Three of the more common types of motivation—all operating largely or wholly on an unconscious level—are defiance of authority, the expression of hostility and aggression, and the attempt to resolve a deep-seated sexual conflict. Rebellion against authority may take either a specific or a general form—that is, the fire-setter may attempt to burn a building, such as his father's house, which directly represents his defiant attitude, or he may set fire to any buildings indiscriminately as an act of rebellion against law and order in general. In the latter case the defiance is usually directed at the police in their role of father image. Fire setting as an aggressive act, on the other hand, is believed to be a response to feelings of hostility that frequently originate in rejection or deprivation during childhood. The pyromaniac attempts to satisfy his aggressive and often sadistic urges by setting fires that not only destroy property but endanger the lives of others.

Many cases of pyromania are associated with deviant sexual drives. Fire is one of the most common erotic symbols in poetry, song, and everyday language, as witness such expressions as "playing with fire," "the flame of passion," "she was an old flame of mine," and "on fire" or "hot" as applied to sexual excitement. As Gold (1962) and others have pointed out, a study of pyromaniacs frequently reveals a strong early association between fire and sexual stimulation in addition to inability to approach members of the opposite sex due to feelings of fear and inadequacy. This pattern leads to the pyromaniac's deviant sexual response: typically he feels forced to watch the fire he starts and, while doing so, becomes sexually excited to the point of orgasm. The achievement of gratification is often followed by intense guilt feelings which he may seek to relieve by actually helping to put out the blaze. More than one arsonist has been apprehended when he lingered on the scene or volunteered his help in fire after fire.

These appear to be the major motivations found in neurotic incendiarism. It should be added that repeated firesetting may also be associated with certain brain syndromes which reduce the individual's ability to control his impulses. Redlich and Freedman (1966), for example, note that various types of impulsive behavior—including kleptomania, poriomania (running away), and gambling as well as pyromania—may occasionally be observed in postencephalitic, epileptic, or mentally deficient patients. *See* KLEPTOMANIA, EPIDEMIC ENCEPHALITIS, GAMBLING, FUGUE STATE.

R

RACE DIFFERENCES. Most of the psychological studies of race differences have dealt with the comparative intelligence of Negroes and whites. The results of these investigations can be readily summarized, but interpretation is quite another matter. The many studies—over 170 in all—have shown small but consistent differences in favor of the whites. These differences are not considered substantial, and they are far smaller than the differences found within each of the groups. In fact, the range of IQs overlaps completely, since both Negroes and whites are found in all categories of intelligence from the lowest to the highest.

Some investigators attribute these differences to heredity, others to environment. Those who believe there is a basic inborn difference argue that the scores show a difference on all educational levels, on nonverbal as well as verbal tests, in Northern as well as Southern areas, and in areas where the cultural environments of Negro and white appear to be closely alike (Shuey, 1958). On the other hand, those who believe that the differences are largely if not wholly due to environmental factors offer a different interpretation of many of these findings and point to specific investigations that call them into question. They point out that the most widely used intelligence tests probably favor whites because the items are largely based on middleclass experience. They cite studies that show no significant differences between white and Negro children on the infant and preschool levels (Pasamanick, 1946), and studies which indicate that the differences in IQ tend to decrease in size when Negroes and whites have

approximately the same socioeconomic status and educational opportunity. They point out that the IQ scores of Southern children who have migrated north tend to increase regularly as they go through the Northern schools, until they closely approximate the scores of their white classmates (Klineberg, 1935; Lee, 1951).

There is, then, a fairly sharp division of opinion on this question at the present time. Berelson and Steiner (1964) summarize the controversy in these words: "It is probably fair to say that many specialists acknowledge a consistent difference in test scores in favor of the whites, but then disagree on how the difference is to be interpreted: whether it is to be assigned to hereditary origin or to socioeconomic factors that characterize the disadvantaged position of the Negroes. Certainly the large majority of social scientists . . . believes that differences in intelligence scores between Negroes and whites in the United States are directly attributable to such environmental differences as educational opportunity and class position."

It is hard to make a fair comparison between races in the United States, since socioeconomic differences pose a major problem—but it is even more difficult where there are both language and cultural barriers. People in Asia and Africa are rarely accustomed to the idea of being tested, usually have little or no experience with the type of items given on the verbal or even the performance tests—and so far no truly culture-free or culture-fair tests have been devised. However, an objective evaluation of Oriental culture would certainly argue against any notion of the inferiority of the Mongoloid race. Moreover, Japanese and Chinese children who have been educated in the United States make the same scores, on the average, as white Americans; and as Garth (1935) has shown, American Indian children who are raised in foster homes under the same conditions as white children score considerably higher than their own brothers and sisters living on the reservation: 102 IQ as compared with 87.5. In the light of present knowledge, then, the majority of psychologists would probably agree that inborn differences between the races have not been proved to exist. *See* CULTURE-FAIR TESTS.

A few studies have been made of temperament. There is no evidence that such characteristics as the proverbial stolidity of the American Indian or the tranquillity of the Oriental are universal among these groups, or that they are due to hereditary tendencies. Simpson and Yinger (1953) have concluded that at present "no objective generalizations can be made on the question of race and temperament," and Klineberg (1957) has stated that "the correlations between traits of intelligence or temperament, on the one hand, and anatomical characteristics (stature, skin color, shape of head, size of head, height of forehead, and so on), on the other, have almost invariably yielded results of no predictive value."

Studies of the sensory characteristics among different racial and social groups have led to the same conclusion. There is a widespread opinion on the basis of hearsay and anecdote that primitive people have keener senses than people from more advanced cultures. It cannot be denied that some groups do develop their sense of smell or vision or hearing more fully than others when they are especially dependent on them for survival—but this does not mean that there are basic inborn differences. Woodworth gave extensive sensory acuity tests to a group of three hundred

Negritos, Eskimos, Ainus, Philippinos, Patagonians, and American Indians at the St. Louis World's Fair in 1904, and concluded that there was no significant difference between one group and another, although there were wide individual differences. *See* TEMPERAMENT.

RANK, OTTO (1884–1939). A Viennese by birth, Rank was a brilliant member of Freud's coterie, but Freud broke with him over his "one-sided" emphasis on the birth trauma and his innovations in therapy. In this country he had an influence on the development of short-term techniques, but a far greater effect in the field of social work than in psychiatry. The functional school of social work, with its emphasis on inner change rather than social adaptation, is largely due to him.

Rank stated his basic views in *The Trauma of Birth*, published in 1924. In it he argued that terror experienced during the birth process affects our later course of development and may establish a susceptibility to neurosis. He believed that all of us have a lasting urge to return to the serenity of the womb, as evidenced not only in the child's struggle against separation from his mother, but in the satisfaction achieved through sexual intercourse. We also have an instinct, however, to break away and develop ourselves as independent beings. Rank termed these two contradictory impulses "life fear" and "death fear," and viewed human existence as a battle between them. *See* BIRTH TRAUMA, ADOLESCENCE (THEORIES).

As the individual grows, he develops a healthy "counterwill," or will to independence, directed originally against his parents and generated by the death fear. This drive is always opposed by a desire to conform and unite with others, a drive that originated in the impulse to return to the womb (life fear). The individual who can successfully resolve the conflict between these two fears, and achieve genuine creative independence, Rank termed an "artist."

29. *(Above)* A clue to suicide. In analyzing this painting, the therapist detected a suicidal urge—not in the macabre figures, which are common in the work of mental patients, but in the white bird ascending to heaven to escape them. *See* ART THERAPY.   **30.** and **31.** *(Below)* Symbolic paintings of a schizophrenic girl. The one on the left was produced at the start of therapy, the one on the right at the end when she was on the road to recovery. *See* ART THERAPY.

32. A group therapy session in a mental hospital. *See* GROUP PSYCHO-THERAPY.

33. Hypnotic regression, used in recapturing repressed experiences. In returning to an earlier age through suggestion, this nineteen-year-old girl wrote exactly as she did at ten and six, then scribbled like a preschool child. *See* HYPNOTHERAPY.

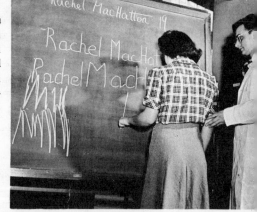

34. Occupational therapy in a mental health clinic. *See* OCCUPATIONAL THERAPY.

THERE ARE MANY APPROACHES TO THERAPY

35. Patients in crumbling attic quarters of an outdated custodial institution with nothing to occupy their time and little chance for treatment. *See* MENTAL HOSPITAL.

36. A modern mental hospital ward, with its comfortable, morale-building living quarters. Compare this with the bleak surroundings of the older custodial institution. *See* MENTAL HOSPITAL.

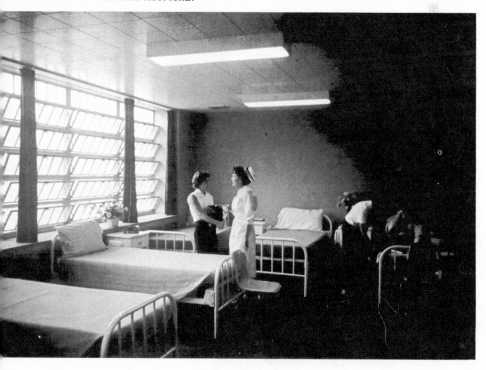

37. Typical posture of an autistic child, withdrawn and unresponsive. *See* AUTISM, AUTISTIC CHILD, WITHDRAWAL.

38. A withdrawn schizophrenic child is rewarded for making progress toward reality by receiving tokens that enable her to obtain candy, trinkets, and a motorboat ride. *See* BEHAVIOR THERAPY, REINFORCEMENT, SCHIZOPHRENIC REACTIONS (Therapy).

39. Play therapy in a child guidance center. The little girl projects her feelings into the dolls and other materials. *See* PLAY THERAPY.

The "average man," however, can do little more than adapt himself to the conventions of society, and will inevitably find himself confused when social change is rapid.

In Rank's theory, a neurotic is a "frustrated artist," a man or woman who tries to live his own life but is unable to function effectively. There are two principal sources for this incapacity. The individual may suffer from an excessive life fear (inability to handle separation from the mother), and react by becoming overly aggressive or overly submissive toward other people. Or he may suffer from an excessive death fear (fear of losing himself in union with other people) and become withdrawn and detached from life. In either case he is assailed by anxiety and needs help.

The object of Rankian therapy is to enable the patient to accept himself as a separate, independent human being without feeling guilty or anxious. The therapist does not use the Freudian technique of free association, but depends heavily on the process of transference—that is, he uses the patient's relation to himself as the therapeutic instrument. His attitude is friendly and accepting, and he serves as a sympathetic sounding board and critic throughout. He also keeps the therapy focused on concrete experiences in the patient's daily life, past and present, constantly encouraging him to move in the direction of creative independence by trying out more constructive and trusting relationships with other people, at the same time avoiding the two extremes of aggressiveness and submissiveness. As a further impetus toward independence, the patient is given the responsibility of setting a time limit for the therapy, and of deciding when he is ready to navigate on his own.

RAPE. A sexual deviation in which sexual relations are forced upon another person.

Forceable rape is distinguished from statutory rape, which consists of sexual relations outside of marriage with a female under the legal age of consent (usually eighteen) even if she participates voluntarily. Over 16,000 cases of forceable rape were reported in 1962, according to the FBI. The offenders are practically always males, most often in their early twenties. Over half of them are married and living with their wives at the time of the offense.

Extensive studies indicate that most rapists are antisocial personalities, many of them with police records for aggressive offenses. One investigator, Kopp (1962), has described the rapist in these words: "This antisocial psychopath is a cold, seemingly unfeeling man who has always taken what he wanted from others without apparent concern for the feelings of his victims or for the consequences of his act. For him, rape is just another instance of aggressive taking, except that in this case he steals sexual satisfaction rather than money or property. When questioned about his offense, he often responds with callous sarcasm, completely devoid of guilt or concern. He may well simply respond with the statement, 'I wanted it so I took it.' The rape fits so well with his character structure and is so typical of his general behavior pattern that he can see nothing wrong with the act, and often goes on to rationalize that the victim probably enjoyed it. He wants no part of therapy unless he sees it as a means of manipulating his way out of incarceration. Needless to say, he is just as difficult to treat as those psychopaths who commit nonsexual offenses." Rapists, then, appear to act almost completely on impulse. Many of them suddenly decide to rape the next possible woman, and a seventy- or eighty-year-old is as likely to be the victim as a younger woman.

There are other, less common types of rapists. One group appear to be passive-aggressive personalities—sullen,

stubborn, spiteful individuals who ac-
cumulate feelings of tension and hostility until they commit a hostile act,
and afterward feel guilty and concerned
about their victims. A few offenders
are psychotic individuals who lose control of themselves during manic states
or schizophrenic excitement.

Rapists frequently inflict serious injuries, and in some cases murder their
victims to prevent discovery. The psychological damage to the victims who
survive is likely to be severe, and if
the woman is married, the experience
may be as disturbing to her husband as
to herself. This is particularly the case
if the husband is forced to watch his
wife being raped. Both psychological
and physical injury are likely to be
severe in cases of group rape—that is,
when several men or a juvenile gang
attack and rape the same woman con-
secutively.

The psychological explanation of rape
is far from complete. With the passive-
aggressive offender it seems to be primarily an expression of aggression
against society, and the sexual nature
of the act is probably secondary. With
psychopathic personalities, rape is only
another variation of their dominant
theme of getting what they want when
they want it—but the origin of that
motive is in considerable doubt. A
study of the wives and mothers of
rapists suggests a possible clue to some
cases. Frequently they were both found
to be sexually seductive but at the same
time rejecting. On this theory, the act
of rape has the unconscious meaning
of forcing both the wife and the mother
into submission.

Because of the severity of the offense
and the danger of repetition, rapists
are usually given long prison sentences.
As yet there have not been enough
attempts at rehabilitation of offenders
to draw any conclusions about either
treatment procedures or prognosis. See
ANTISOCIAL REACTION, PASSIVE-AGGRES-
SIVE PERSONALITY.

RAPPORT. In general, a spirit of harmony, accord, and mutual confidence
between two or more people, as in the
relationship between the members of a
group or between a leader and a group.

In psychiatry and clinical psychology
the term is frequently used in describing
the most effective relationship between
therapist and patient. Rapport occurs
largely on a conscious level, as contrasted with transference, a close relationship in which the patient focuses
unconscious feelings on the therapist.
A strong sense of rapport contributes
to the patient's trust in the therapist
and his willingness to work co-operatively with him. It is an important factor in the therapeutic procedure, since
the patient must feel that the therapist
is interested in him, sympathetic toward
him, and will be able to understand
him. Moreover, good rapport will make
him feel comfortable and reassured, and
he will therefore not hesitate to express
his innermost thoughts and feelings. This
is a prerequisite to success in any type
of psychotherapy.

The therapist does whatever he can
to establish rapport during the first
meeting with the patient. He shows a
warm, friendly, accepting attitude, expresses his interest, encourages the patient to express himself, and helps him
to feel as relaxed as possible. He is
prepared, however, to find that full
rapport cannot always be established
immediately, and in some cases not at
all. This relationship is of such vital
importance that it is probably useless
to proceed with a given therapist if it
is wholly lacking. In this case the therapist usually suggests a colleague who
may be more congenial to the patient.
See TRANSFERENCE, LEADERSHIP.

RATIONALIZATION. The unconscious
defense mechanism of giving questionable reasons to justify behavior or relieve disappointment.

The behavior itself is likely to be
unacceptable or dubious in some re-

spect, and the situation that gave rise to the disappointment usually reflects on the individual's ability or worth. The basic purpose of the mechanism is therefore to ward off feelings of guilt, anxiety, or discouragement. If it proves effective, the individual can then do what he wants to do, think what he wants to think, and continue acting in the face of disappointment without losing his self-respect or feeling too uncomfortable.

Examples of rationalization are not hard to find, since it is one of the most frequently used of all defense mechanisms. The salesman who overcharges his customer and neglects to correct the error justifies himself with such remarks as "He can afford it better than I'" or "Serves him right for not checking the price." The wife who wants to take an extravagant vacation may argue that "We haven't had a *real* vacation in years," "It's the only way to meet the right people and you never know what that can lead to"—and if all else fails, "Anyway, you only live once." The man who wants to buy an expensive car may argue that it is bound to save money in the end, or improve his "image" and open the way to new business. If, however, he is opposed to buying a new car, he can find equally good reasons to prove that it is not necessary (the "sour grapes mechanism"), and he will suddenly think of excellent reasons why his present car will last another year or two (the "sweet lemon mechanism").

The habit of rationalization is readily acquired because our motives are generally so complex and mixed that it is quite easy to select the one which suits our purpose best. It is often hard to tell where objectivity ends and distortion begins. There are, however, some fairly certain signs. If one "reason" falls short, the rationalizer will always come up with another. He will invariably give the faulty reason more weight and attention than is justified. He will

offer it and defend it with undue emotional intensity. And, most important, he will be taken in by his own false reasoning and have little or no idea that he is using a defense mechanism.

The last point is of special psychological significance. When we fall into the pattern of rationalization, we may succeed in feeling more comfortable, but we do so at the expense of deceiving ourselves. This is a tendency that can lead to both social and personal harm. Many people spend their time justifying their mistakes and misdeeds instead of correcting them. Even the one who uses the sour grapes or sweet lemon mechanisms to make himself more satisfied with his lot may at the same time be accepting inaction and inertia instead of trying to improve himself.

Some people carry rationalization so far that they actually feel righteous about attitudes and behavior for which they ought to feel ashamed and disgusted—for example, the brutal father who beats his three-year-old son to "toughen him up," or the promiscuous girl who is "just being kind to the boys." And finally, in some types of mental illness—particularly where the personality has disintegrated and the patient has lost touch with reality—the mechanism of self-deception can gain full supremacy and take the form of impenetrable delusions. *See* PARANOIA, SCHIZOPHRENIA (PARANOID TYPE).

RATIONAL PSYCHOTHERAPY. A therapeutic approach developed primarily by Albert Ellis, based on the view that emotional difficulties are due to faulty, illogical attitudes which can be altered by controlling one's thought processes.

Ellis rejects the classical analytic approach with its emphasis on unconscious biological urges. Like Alfred Adler, he holds that men are naturally helpful and loving, but in some cases adopt irrational, self-defeating thoughts.

These thoughts take the form of verbalizations, or "self-talk," which have a distorting and disturbing effect on feelings and reactions. Ellis maintains that when we are angry or afraid, we are producing some form of the sentence "This is terrible" on a surface or deeper thought level. This type of self-dialogue has the effect of confirming and reinforcing faulty beliefs which we have acquired from parents, teachers, companions, the mass media, or other contacts with our general culture. Here is an example: "It is a dire necessity for an adult to be approved or loved by almost everyone for almost everything he does. It is most important what others think of me." A more reasonable, and less self-defeating, attitude would be: "It is pleasant, but not necessary, for an adult to be approved or loved by others. It is better to win one's own respect than others' approval."

According to Ellis, we are all prone to these "internalized sentences," though we are seldom aware of them. Most of us keep them under reasonable control, but if they come to dominate our life and create disturbing emotions, we become neurotic: "Neurosis, in other words, consists of stupid behavior by a non-stupid person" (Ellis, 1958). Such a person behaves stupidly because he is constantly telling himself "It is tragic not to be highly successful," or "You have to be self-confident and competent in every situation," or "Other people should make things easier for me," or "It is better to avoid than to face difficulties and responsibilities."

The task of the therapist is, first, to establish an emotional, supportive relationship with the patient; second, to unmask these unrealistic ideas and make the patient fully aware of them; third, to show him how they are producing his problems; fourth, to help him change his faulty assumptions and speak to himself in a more constructive fashion; and fifth, to encourage him to put his new approaches into action even though the process may be strenuous and painful.

In carrying out his task, the therapist focuses his attention on current modes of behavior. He spends little if any time on delving into the past, for he holds that even if a "primary" difficulty can be uncovered, insight into it does not automatically remove the symptoms. Instead, Ellis makes a forceful counterattack against the irrationalities of his patient, aimed at making him understand the self-defeating character of his ideas. He then utilizes whatever methods he finds effective, from encouraging and cajoling to outright command, to induce him to rectify his warped attitudes.

In essence, this is a process of relearning a more rational philosophy of life through an "internalization" of new values: "The rational therapist, then, is a frank propagandist who believes wholeheartedly in a most rigorous application of the rules of logic, of straight thinking and of scientific method to everyday life, and who ruthlessly uncovers every vestige of irrational thinking in the client's experience and energetically urges him into more rational channels" (Ellis, 1958). The originator of this approach recognizes that it is most successful with patients who seek direction from the therapist, and who have considerable flexibility, intellectual curiosity, and a willingness to work.

RAY, ISAAC (1807–81). After receiving his medical degree from Bowdoin College in 1827, Ray entered upon a career that was to make him one of the most influential psychiatrists of his time. Energetic and versatile, he became almost equally renowned in Europe and America as an author of over a hundred books and articles, a leader in hospital administration, a pioneer in the study of criminal behavior, and one of the founders of the first psychiatric organization in America.

In 1841 Ray was appointed medical superintendent of the State Hospital for the Insane in Augusta, Maine. By 1844 he had achieved sufficient stature to help create the Association of Medical Superintendents of American Institutions for the Insane, which later became the American Psychiatric Association. In 1845 he accepted a position as head of the Butler Hospital in Providence, Rhode Island, one of the most progressive private mental institutions in this country. Within a short time he was commissioned by the trustees to travel to Europe to study architectural innovations in the asylums of Great Britain, France, and Germany. Upon his return he wrote a paper which led to the construction of a new building of advanced design.

Some years later Ray collaborated with Thomas Kirkbride in compiling a list of basic tenets for mental hospitals, based on resolutions voted by the Association of Medical Superintendents. These tenets emphasized the evils of overcrowding and unnecessary restraint, and the need for well-built, well-arranged, well-managed, and well-ventilated institutions in which patients would have "abundant means for occupation and amusement." See KIRKBRIDE, MENTAL HOSPITAL.

Ray was a major contributor to the field of forensic psychiatry. He was frequently called upon as an expert witness, and his *Treatise on the Medical Jurisprudence of Insanity*, written in 1838, was the first book on the subject in the English language, serving as an authoritative text for over fifty years. Among his other works were *Mental Hygiene* (1863) and *Contributions to Mental Pathology* (1873), which contained, among other articles, essays on portrayals of insanity by Shakespeare and other writers. His *Ideal Character of the Officers of a Hospital for the Insane* (1873) delineated the personality traits most needed by the head of a mental institution. See LEGAL PSYCHIATRY.

Ray's approach was generally an enlightened one. At a time when many others were attributing mental illness to sexual excess, lack of physical hygiene, or even "politics" and "chagrin," he pointed out that "Many emotions set down as causes, such as religious doubts and anxiety, would often be more justly regarded as its effects." In spite of the fact that he showed insight of this kind, and was a strong advocate of institutional and legal reform, he did not free himself from belief in the practice of physical restraint which most superintendents considered the backbone of the asylum system. He repeatedly engaged in heated debate on the subject, often advancing emotionally illogical arguments in favor of restraint. It did not seem to occur to him that most patients actually did not need mechanical restraint, as Philippe Pinel in France and William Tuke in England had already shown. See PINEL, TUKE.

Ray's position on another important issue was more defensible. At the start of the nineteenth century practically all physicians believed that mental illness could rarely if ever be cured, but around 1820 superintendents of asylums began to "prove" their own efficiency by reporting higher and higher rates of recovery. The movement began with a claim of 60 per cent cure by a Dr. Willis, head of a private institution, and before long reports of 80 to 100 per cent recovery rates for "recent cases" were commonplace. Ray was one of the first to question these results, pointing out that no adequate criteria had been set up on what constituted either recovery or recent cases. He also questioned the validity of medical statistics in general, pointing out that some illnesses were periodic, so that one patient could show many recoveries. (Another psychiatrist of the time, Pliny Earle, reported a case where one woman recovered forty-six times!) This critical approach helped to swing the pendulum back to a more realistic attitude toward curability, and in 1867 a distinguished group of physicians was appointed by the International Congress of Alienists to devise more adequate methods of dealing with psychiatric statistics.

RAYNAUD'S DISEASE. A psychophysiologic disorder of the circulatory system involving blanching, swelling and /or cyanosis (blue appearance due to a lack of oxygen) of the fingers and, less often, the toes. The condition is due to spasmodic constriction of blood vessels, which interrupts the flow of blood to the extremities.

The disease was first described by the French physician Maurice Raynaud, in 1862. It occurs primarily in tense, underweight women and only rarely in men. The attacks are most commonly precipitated by cold, but emotional stress is believed to play a decisive role in many instances—and for this reason the condition is included among the psychophysiologic disorders. Experiments have shown that if patients are placed in a room at moderately low temperature, discussion of a stressful life situation will induce a drop in finger temperature and a characteristic Raynaud attack (Mittelmann and Wolff, 1939).

Attacks may sometimes be prevented if the patient wears extra clothing in cold weather (or moves to a warmer climate), avoids emotional stress and exhaustion, and eliminates the use of tobacco, since it interferes with circulation in the extremities. Many patients respond well to psychotherapy or hypnotherapy, but in severe cases it may also be necessary to sever the nerves that control the contraction of the blood vessels in the affected parts (sympathectomy) to avoid the danger of gangrene.

REACTION FORMATION. The unconscious defense mechanism of going to the opposite extreme.

This is the common human tendency to protect ourselves from our own unacceptable impulses through behavior that is the very reverse of our actual feelings. To conceal indifference, we become oversolicitous; to deny ingratitude, we become effusive; to resist hostile impulses, we become overfriendly. The overindulgent mother may be reacting to feelings of rejection. The crusader against salacious literature, alcohol, or homosexuality may be inwardly fighting his own urges.

This is not to say that all concern for others and all zeal for the right should be interpreted as a reaction against the reverse tendency. The line may sometimes be hard to draw, but the marks of reaction formation are usually fairly clear: the behavior is generally exaggerated, uncompromising, and even inappropriate. We are not just solicitous but oversolicitous, not just brave but reckless. Moreover, the outward behavior may, at least in some cases, provide a disguise or vicarious outlet for the very tendencies it seems to oppose. The professional defender of public morals may get a good deal of satisfaction from reading the literature or seeing the shows he so roundly condemns.

Reaction formation leads not only to a distorted conception of one's self but to behavior that interferes with relationships to others. The ingratiating, overpolite individual is bound to irritate other people because he "protests too much." The straitlaced, overzealous reformer almost inevitably arouses suspicion of hypocrisy. Such behavior is usually within the realm of normality, but in some individuals it may reach obsessive proportions indicative of a neurosis. *See* OBSESSIVE-COMPULSIVE REACTION, COMPULSIVE PERSONALITY, OBSESSIVE PERSONALITY.

REACTION TIME (Response Latency).
The time between the onset of a stimulus and the start of an overt response.

Reaction time, or RT, is a measurement of the speed of response. As the definition states, it is the interval between the *onset* of the stimulus and the *start* of the response rather than its conclusion. These distinctions are important in such activities as driving a car. It takes about .55 seconds to put on the brakes when the light changes to red, and in this time a car traveling at sixty miles per hour covers forty-eight feet. Then it takes, on the average, a full two seconds to bring the car to a stop, and in that time it travels an additional two hundred feet. The reaction time is the first figure, since it measures the behavior of the driver and not the behavior of the car.

The first RT experiments were performed by the German physiologist Hermann Helmholtz in 1850 during his investigation of the speed of the nerve impulse. By applying an electric shock to the skin at various points, he discovered that the interval between stimulus and response varied with the distance from the brain. He carefully measured both the distance and the reaction time, and discovered that the nerve impulse travels at approximately 90 meters per second. He also found that the reaction time was longer for complex reactions involving choice than for simple reflex activities. This suggested—and subsequent experiments have proven—that most of the time taken by complex responses is consumed by brain activity. *See* HELMHOLTZ.

Since these early experiments, a vast number of reaction time experiments have been performed. The research literature can best be summarized under separate headings:

Sense modalities. The reaction time of any individual varies somewhat from moment to moment since it is affected by changes in attention, emotion, receptor sensitivity, and readiness for muscular response. Nevertheless, fairly stable averages for each sense have been obtained by subjecting large numbers of subjects to repeated trials. Simple withdrawal of the finger was used in response to all the following stimuli; electric shock, .143 sec.; sound, .140; touch, .140; light, .180; odor, .210; taste (salt), .308; rotation, .400; pain, .888; warmth and cold, .300 to 1.60. The relatively long reaction time for pain may be surprising since it does not seem to be helpful for survival, but it is due to the fact that the sensation depends on injury to tissue, and it takes longer for tissue to break down than merely to respond to warmth or pressure. The superiority of sound over light may also be unexpected, but it is demonstrated by the fact that we react more quickly to an automobile horn than to a red light. The reason for the slower reaction to light is that it involves a chemical change in the retina, while sound only requires a mechanical change in the ear.

The reaction times just given have all been classed as simple responses to stimuli. Many of our reactions, however, involve decision—that is, we have to make different responses to different stimuli. The ball player reacts one way to one signal from his coach and a different way to another signal; and in a tight situation the driver has to decide quickly whether to step on the accelerator or the brake. In an early series of experiments, a subject was required to react with individual fingers of the right hand when the Arabic numerals 1 to 5 were presented, and with the left hand when the Roman numerals I to V were presented. The reaction times for these "disjunctive reactions," as they are called, were about three times as long as for simple reactions. Also it has been found that the more alike the stimuli, the longer the reaction time—for instance, it takes more time to discriminate between red and green than between black and white. Even the factor of preference makes a difference. Subjects were found to react more quickly when one color was greatly preferred to the other than when they were liked equally (Shipley et al., 1945, 1946). These findings are useful in constructing highway signs and signals.

Strength of stimulus. Intense stimuli produce quicker reactions than faint stimuli. In the case of sound, there is a continuous drop in speed of reaction from loud sound (.110 sec.) to faint sounds (.400 sec.), according to Chocholle, (1945). This is why we shout or blow a loud blast on the car horn in warning people of danger. Similarly, we are careful to touch a strange dog lightly and move our hands slowly, since more intense stimulation would quickly evoke defensive responses.

Motivation. The speed of response is usually increased when motivation is intensified. If a team is behind, its members are likely to be more alert and react more quickly than when they have a comfortable lead. Since employees rarely work close to their physiological limits, incentives such as bonuses are frequently used to increase their working speed.

Group differences. Men, on the average, react about 10 per cent faster than women, although there are wide individual differences. Age is also a factor: the RT decreases steadily until we reach the age of twenty-five, remains relatively unchanged until about sixty, and then slowly increases. Here, too, there are large individual differences, probably because people age at different rates. (Miles, 1942)

Specific influences. Moderate amounts of alcohol have been found to lengthen the reaction time only slightly, but large amounts slow us down considerably. Small quantities of caffeine have little effect, but large doses quicken our responses, especially when a choice is involved (Hollingworth, 1912). Nutri-

tional deficiencies and insufficient oxygen tend to slow down reactions. Increased gravitational forces (the G factor) also decrease the speed of response, particularly in airplanes and satellites, since these forces reduce the amount of blood that feeds the brain (Canfield, Comrey, and Wilson, 1949). Tight-fitting pressure suits are now worn by pilots and astronauts to keep the blood from rushing to or from the brain, for either increased or decreased reaction time can be disastrous in flying situations. *See* AIR HUNGER.

Set. An individual's set, or readiness for response, has a considerable effect on reaction time. The standard practice in experiments is to signal the subject during a "foreperiod" that a stimulus will soon be presented, just as we say to a runner, "On your mark, get set." The foreperiod is varied so that the subject will not react to a constant interval. Experiments indicate that the optimal foreperiod is from two to four seconds in most modalities, although it appears to be a little shorter (1.5 seconds) for a foot race, probably because the contestants are keyed up (Kobayashi and Matsui, 1938). Other studies have shown that in starting a race and in other simple reactions, we respond more quickly if we concentrate on the reaction we are to make (motor set), but in choice or "disjunctive" reactions, it is best to attend to the stimulus (sensory set). *See* SET.

Applications. The determination of reaction time has been put to use in a number of psychological fields. Safety studies have revealed that unusually rapid responses are as dangerous as slow responses, since accidents are frequently caused by impulsive, thoughtless behavior. In driving, the fast reactor tends to get hit in the rear, while the slow reactor collides with the car ahead. The time it takes to respond on word association tests is often measured, and it has been found that quick responses indicate freedom from conflict, while hesitation (among other responses) indicates that a stimulus word has touched upon an area of emotional difficulty. In learning tests, such as naming state capitals, rapid responses are taken as an indication of a higher learning level than slower responses. A long RT is also used as an indicator of possible neurological defect, especially on the pupil dilation test. *See* WORD ASSOCIATION TEST.

READABILITY RESEARCH. The analysis or measurement of written material in terms of level of difficulty or other characteristics such as human interest.

The major object of readability research is to simplify the reader's task. This can be accomplished in part by improving the layout and legibility of the printed page, but the major emphasis of psychologists and reading specialists has been on the content and form of the language used. The choice of words is very important, since vocabulary is one of the major factors in reading ease. Copywriters and others concerned with communication sometimes consult the Teachers Wordbook of 30,000 Words compiled by Thorndike and Lorge. It contains an alphabetical list of the more common English words with their frequency of use; the list is based on exhaustive word counts of different types of material ranging from cookbooks to classics, from postal regulations to newspapers, textbooks, and magazines. Needless to say, a word with a frequency of 100 times per million will be more likely to be understood than a word with a one in a million frequency. The wordbook also contains lists of rare words with even smaller frequencies as well as lists of the 511,000 most common words.

Another method used to determine readability is to devise and apply a "readability formula" to measure reading ease. Various formulas have been suggested based on characteristics which have proved to be most closely associated with reading ease; for example, word length, number of abstract words, and sentence structure. The formula in widest use today was developed by Rudolf Flesch (1948, 1949). It takes into account average word length in syllables (wl) and average sentence length in words (sl). These elements are combined to give a reading ease (RE) index based on analysis of 100-word passages: $RE = 206.835 - 846$ wl $- 1.015$ sl. An RE score of 0 to 30 is rated very difficult since there are 192 or more syllables per 100 words, and an average sentence length of 29 words or more. The typical magazine presenting such material is described as scientific, and the reader usually has to be a college graduate. An RE score of 70 to 80 is rated fairly easy, since the material contains only 139 syllables per 100 words and fourteen words per sentence. Such material is found in slick-fiction magazines which can be easily read by a seventh grader.

Flesch has also devised a human interest score (HI), based on the percentage of personal words (pw) in the passages analyzed—that is, proper names, personal nouns, and personal sentences (ps), which include spoken sentences, questions, and exclamations. The formula is $HI = 3.635$ pw $+ .314$ ps. In applying this formula anything which produces a 60 to 100 HI score is described as dramatic; such material is typically found in fiction magazines. A 0 to 10 HI score, produced by the kind of material in scientific magazines, is rated dull.

The Flesch formulas have focused attention on the importance of readability, and have probably contributed to a simplification of style among many journalists, copywriters, and others who write for mass audiences. They have also been utilized in a number of investigations of industrial communications, advertising, and magazine content. Lauer and Paterson (1951) showed that a typical management-union contract had a reading ease score in the very difficult range, requiring a college education. Tiffin and Walsh (1951) analyzed fifty-nine union-management agreements and found that the language was far above the educational level of about 70 per cent of those who were expected to read them.

A study of issues of *Time* and *Newsweek* made by Trencherd and Crissy (1952) suggests that advertisers are attempting to adapt the level and style of their material to the editorial content. Although they found that the advertising copy was in general easier to read than the editorial copy, a comparison of issues published before and after World War II revealed that the two kinds of copy are coming closer together, with the advertising getting more difficult and the editorial material easier. In another study, Haskins (1960) scored the articles in a single issue of *The Saturday Evening Post* according to another Flesch formula, the Abstraction Index, and found a high negative correlation between abstraction and a "finishing index"—that is, the more abstract the article, the less likelihood that the reader would finish it—although those who did finish the more abstract articles were likely to rate them "excellent." Split-run tests using easy and hard versions of the same articles have reported changes in the volume of readers for the simpler versions ranging all the way from a slight loss to a 66 per cent gain. The higher gains are somewhat questionable, however, because the more difficult material tended to be stilted and less clearly organized.

Readability formulas are not universally accepted. While some specialists regard them as a sure guide to better writing, others claim that the "computer" approach makes writing a mechanical affair and completely ignores the esthetic values implicit in figures of speech and unusual vocabulary. Moreover, scientific and literary material should not be rated on the same scale, especially a scale that overlooks the purpose of the material. Can we really call scientific writing "dull" simply because it lacks *human* interest? It would seem, therefore, that Flesch's approach has a limited application. As Anastasi (1964) concludes: "Readability formulas are appropriate when the object is to measure the communication of simple messages. This is the purpose of advertising copy, cookbooks, instruction sheets, training manuals government bulletins, and similar forms of writing designed for mass audiences."

READINESS TESTS. Tests designed to predict how well an individual is prepared to profit from instruction in a particular field.

Readiness tests are confined largely to reading and mathematics. Both types are basically aptitude tests but can also be viewed in terms of achievement, since they reflect the skills and information required for successful study. Where possible they should be administered by specialists who are not only thoroughly acquainted with the capacities of small children, but who are alert to difficulties that might require a thorough clinical study. *See* READING DISABILITY. The following tests are in wide use today:

Metropolitan Readiness Tests (Kindergarten and grade 1) (*Fig. 43 and Fig. 44*). Six tests are included: (1) word meaning (selecting pictures that correspond to words given by the examiner), (2) sentences (same as above, except that sentences and phrases are used), (3) information (same, except that the oral descriptions are more complex—for example, "Mark the one you can take pictures with"), (4) matching (selection of pairs of identical words or pictures of common objects), (5) numbers (concepts and operations similar to those on IQ tests), (6) copying (geometrical forms, numbers, capital letters). Percentile norms are provided

Fig. 43. The child chooses the picture that corresponds to a word given by the examiner.

for reading readiness (the first four subtests given above), number readiness (test 5), and total readiness for first-grade work.

American School Reading Readiness Test (grade 1). Includes eight subtests: vocabulary, discrimination of letter forms, discrimination of letter combination, word selection, word matching, discrimination of geometric forms, following directions, memory for geometric form.

Gates Reading Readiness Test (Kindergarten, grade 1). Consists of five subtests: following directions in marking pictures, word matching, word perception (selecting one word from among four), rhyming (auditory perception), naming letters and numbers.

Harrison-Stroud Reading Readiness Tests (Kindergarten and grade 1). Six subtests are included: making visual discriminations, using contexts, making auditory discriminations, using auditory clues in identifying items, using symbols, giving names of letters.

New York Test of Arithmetical Meanings. This is a representative example of tests designed to assess arithmetic achievement in the primary grades, and readiness for further instruction. It is based on teaching objectives and curricular analysis, and covers concepts of size, weight, time, distance, symbols and terms, fractional parts, and simple computations. Percentile norms for the beginning of the second and the beginning of the third grades are provided, based on large nationwide samples.

The Iowa Algebra Aptitude Test is based upon previously learned skills, including arithmetic problems involving numerical manipulations, verbal problems using arithmetic and simple algebraic procedures, number-series exercises requiring identification of the principle in each case, and equation

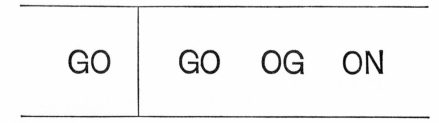

Fig. 44. The child matches the word at the left with one of the three sets of letters at the right.

problems in which one value is varied to produce a change in the other.

The Orleans Algebra Prognosis Test, and Orleans Geometry Prognosis Test. Prediction of future performance is based on the child's ability to handle *new* tasks. The tests are actually work samples, presenting simple material to be learned and applied in actual "lessons." The algebra test, for example, includes the use of symbols representing numbers, substitution of values for symbols, and expression of relationships by means of symbols.

The Modern Language Aptitude Test is designed to measure the student's capacity for learning any foreign language. It is given by means of tape-recorded and paper-pencil materials, and tests ability to learn orally presented numbers and visually presented words of an artificial language. It also measures sensitivity to English grammatical structure, the use of spelling clues, word recognition, and rote memory. Studies indicate that the test is effective in predicting success in actual courses.

The Anton Brenner Developmental Gestalt Test of School Readiness. Based on research employing Gestalt and developmental principles, this test is easily administered, scored, and interpreted. It is used in many schools primarily for rapid identification of school readiness, but can also be employed as a diagnostic instrument.

READING DISABILITY (Paralexia, Dyslexia). A general term applying to all cases in which a child's reading skill is one or more years behind his intellectual development.

Children with reading disability are not to be confused with "retarded readers," who fall behind because of low intelligence. Instead, they have special difficulties of a psychological, physical, or social nature that interfere with their performance. A careful diagnosis must be made in each individual case before

an effective remedial program can be undertaken.

Between 10 and 15 per cent of elementary school children show mild or severe reading disability. The boys outnumber the girls by about three to one. In spite of the fact that there are many kinds of disability, these children have two things in common: their failure to read well is bound to interfere with almost all academic work, since reading is the one indispensable tool for learning; and their shortcoming will almost inevitably lead to feelings of inadequacy and discouragement. (Goldenson, 1957)

The diagnosis of reading disability is a two-stage affair. First it is necessary to make a full evaluation of the child's reading skills in order to locate his special weaknesses. The grade teacher or reading specialist uses informal procedures, trial lessons, and standardized tests of both oral and silent reading to determine the general reading level and to reveal such difficulties as poor comprehension, inadequate word recognition or word analysis skills, significant mispronunciation, lack of fluency in oral reading, slowness in silent reading, deficient vocabulary, consistent spelling errors, and faulty habit patterns such as mouthing words or backtracking. More severe disabilities require further diagnosis in which special tests and case studies are carried out by a psychologist or remedial specialist. The purpose is to isolate basic causes of the disability so that an effective remedial program can be planned. *See* ALEXIA, HANDEDNESS, STREPHOSYMBOLIA, APHASIA.

A thorough diagnosis of reading disability requires several steps. An individual intelligence test must be given to determine the discrepancy between the child's reading level and his intellectual capacity. After that, five sets of factors which represent common causes of reading disability must be examined and assessed. These are: *phys-*

iological immaturity ("developmental lag") producing such deficiencies as poor auditory or visual discrimination and "directional confusion" (reading from right to left); *physical handicaps,* such as low vitality, frequent illness, impaired vision or hearing, and in some cases, brain damage; *emotional handicaps,* such as tensions, anxieties, and feelings of inferiority or discouragement; *environmental conditions,* particularly a deprived home in which intellectual stimulation is lacking or a foreign language is spoken exclusively; and *educational factors,* which may include ineffective teaching, inappropriate reading materials, or a classroom climate unsuited to learning. In most cases of severe reading disability several of these factors are operative at once. *See* DIRECTIONAL CONFUSION, PSEUDORETARDATION.

After a full diagnostic study is made, the next step is to make and carry out a plan for reading improvement based upon the needs of the individual child. Simpler difficulties are handled by a *corrective* reading program, in the regular class. It consists of direct teaching of missing skills through word games, extra practice in phonics, and special attention to prefixes and suffixes, exercises that counteract regression, etc. A program of *remedial* reading, however, is required in cases of more severe disability. Individual children or small groups meet either with the class teacher during special periods, or with a reading specialist in the school or clinic or on a private basis. In many cases, consultants are called upon to deal with special difficulties that interfere with learning, such as visual and auditory handicaps or emotional problems. In all cases, however, the co-operation of the parents is sought, not only to provide additional reading practice and reading materials at home, but to modify faulty attitudes toward the child and improve the general atmosphere in the home.

Remedial reading is a concentrated training procedure designed to overcome a child's particular defects. Basic word analysis skills often have to be developed through special study of sight words, consonants and consonant combinations, short and long vowels, and division into syllables. Sight, sound, motor, and game techniques are used according to the child's needs. Some children require special attention to root words, context clues, reversal errors (reading "no" for "on"), or spelling. Others need practice in oral reading to develop better comprehension, phrasing, and expression; while still others may require training that will expand vocabulary and improve study skills.

There is considerable confusion today about the use of the term dyslexia. Many specialists accept the position of the 1961 Johns Hopkins Conference on Dyslexia, where it was defined as a genetic, neurological dysfunction uncomplicated by other factors. Many others would agree that there is a malfunctioning of the nervous system, but would broaden the term to include not only cases in which the child appears to have a genetic neurological defect that makes reading difficult, but also cases in which there is evidence of birth injury, early disease, or developmental disorder, as discussed under the topic MINIMAL BRAIN DYSFUNCTION.

In educational circles the term dyslexia is being replaced by "specific language disability" (SLD). This term is applied to an estimated two to three million children who have a basic inability to perceive or record the world of symbols without distortion. These children have a persistent tendency to reverse letters, words, and numbers, and often fail to distinguish figure from ground, to see words as totalities, or to recognize the same word in different contexts or even in different colors. They may also show confusion in the sounds they hear—for example, they may pronounce T, A, and P correctly but will read "Pat" instead of "Tap." Not infrequently they react to their disability by becoming aggressive, withdrawn, or despondent over their failure to understand or communicate. Unfortunately many cases are undiagnosed, especially bright children with mild disabilities which they can partially overcome through extra effort.

When the specific perceptual disabilities of these children are carefully identified, and when intensive, individualized training is applied, they usually show great improvement. However, very few public schools and only a limited number of private schools now offer the kind of analysis and training that will help the perceptually impaired child to overcome his handicap. There is a crying need for techniques which can be applied in regular classrooms, or at least in regular schools.

The problem is being attacked in a number of centers, among them the McGlannan School in Miami, Florida. At that school work is being done on a screening test that will identify perceptual impairment in its early stages, since the difficulty becomes aggravated as the child grows older. At the same time, techniques are being developed in which tactile-kinesthetic experiences are used to supplement and reinforce visual-auditory perception of symbols. In one set of exercises the child starts by feeling, matching, tracing, and cutting out simple geometric forms in cardboard. He then goes on to identifying letters by handling cutouts and tracing grooved letters with his finger. After that he matches the cut-out letters with the symbols on a printed page, and then combines the letters to form words. Another set of exercises utilizes an "Alpha-Sound-Box," which consists of a cabinet containing small drawers, one for each letter. Each drawer contains familiar, minute objects whose names begin with the sound of the letter pictured on the front of the drawer—for example, a small fish

is found in the F drawer. When a certain sound is given, the child identifies the drawer and associates the objects it contains with that sound. This serves to strengthen his memory and increase his ability to identify the letters. Still later, the child learns to "slide" the individual sounds together to form words.

The following case illustrates many of the factors to be explored in diagnosing a reading difficulty and planning a remedial program.

Illustrative Case: READING DISABILITY

Jimmy was an attractive nine-year-old in the high third grade. He had failed to make progress in the remedial reading group, and had been referred to the City College Educational Clinic by a mental health clinic which had been working with him and his family. During his first visit he became nauseous and vomited, an indication of emotional upset; later on he was more relaxed and responsive. His speech was flat, indistinct, and nasal, with a marked lisp and difficulty in pronouncing the letters l, r, j, g, and sh. Movement of his tongue was somewhat restricted by a tongue-tie condition, for which he had been operated on three times. Jimmy had a long history of illness: pneumonia at three months, removal of infected tonsils and adenoids at fourteen months, frequent colds and digestive upsets, a broken bone requiring many hospital visits.

Intelligence tests revealed an IQ of 117, but reading tests placed him at a beginning second grade level. His oral reading was slow, inaccurate, full of mispronunciations, and his knowledge of phonics was meager. He confused m and n, n and v, b and d, and tended to pronounce all vowels as uh. In both classroom and remedial work, he had been taught by a completely visual method. His spelling was on high first grade level, but his arithmetic was high fourth grade. Because of illness he had attended kindergarten only eleven days, and when he entered first grade he showed no interest in reading but only wanted to play.

Conditions in Jimmy's home were poor. His parents had quarreled for years, and had separated when the boy was three. His mother was nervous, sickly, and hard-pressed for food and clothing. Jimmy keenly felt the lack of a regular father, and could not get along with his older brothers and sisters. His mother frequently criticized him and threatened to give him away, but when he cried, sulked, or had temper tantrums, she would let him have his way. A psychiatrist at the mental health clinic concluded that his behavior difficulties were entirely due to feelings of rejection and disturbing experiences in the family. As a result of this investigation, arrangements were made for Jimmy to attend the Remedial Reading Service twice a week, and to receive medical help for his hearing loss and tongue-tie. He was also to continue visiting the clinic.

At the Remedial Reading Service, Jimmy was assigned to men because it was felt that he would more willingly accept instruction from men than from women. He received twenty-seven lessons over a period of five months. Reading material consisted of pre-primers, primers, first and second readers, and selected workbook exercises. To develop phonics ability, he was taken through reading drills which emphasized letter-by-letter sounding and blending, with particular attention to hearing and pronouncing words correctly. He soon learned to analyze new words and build word families from them. Each new word was printed on a card and put in an envelope marked either "do know" or "do not know," and treated as a game. Because of his speech and hearing defects, considerable time was spent in oral reading. The tutor spoke with exaggerated distinctness and encouraged Jimmy to do likewise. He willingly took books home, and a progress chart was used as an incentive for extra silent reading.

Since Jimmy had a mental age of eleven years, his ability to understand was well advanced, and comprehension exercises at a second-grade level were soon introduced. No attention was given to speed, except near the end of the tutoring, when he was encouraged to give up pointing with his finger and received special practice in phrase reading. At his own request he was also given instruction in spelling. A visual-motor method was used, in which he printed each word on a card, looked at it, said it, then closed his eyes and printed it from memory. The tutors who worked with Jimmy shared his interest in sports and evoked his com-

petitive spirit by keeping score on his progress. They also showed respect for his intelligence and gave him generous praise. They tried to change his mother's critical attitude toward him by repeatedly expressing confidence in his ability when she called for him.

At the end of the five-month period, Jimmy had advanced to a third-grade level in spelling, high third grade in paragraph reading and vocabulary, and fourth-grade level on silent reading tests. He had developed an efficient method of attack on new words, and his general progress was reflected in an air of confidence, marked improvement in conduct and personality ratings, and average grades of B plus for the following two years. (Harris, 1961)

REALITY PRINCIPLE. In psychoanalytic theory, the regulatory mechanism that represents the demands of the outer world on the individual. These demands set limits to the blind operation of the pleasure principle, which represents our internal needs and desires.

In the course of normal development, the pleasure principle appears first, but as the child grows the reality principle forces him to recognize the requirements of the outside world of people, things, and events. He must therefore learn to forgo or postpone many of his satisfactions. As Hendrick (1963) points out, "The reality principle is the capacity of human beings to dispense with immediate pleasure in order to ensure pleasure, or avoid pain, at some future time. This function is the hallmark of mature behavior and is negligible in the infant. It is not innate but develops as the child gradually learns by experience that immediate pleasure may incur subsequent pain, most often the pain of punishment or loss of love by a parent. Thus a child may derive pleasure from sucking his thumb. In accordance with the pleasure principle, he will perform this agreeable act on every occasion when the instinct urges. If, however, he learns that mother slaps him, or that mother withholds a kiss when he sucks, he will eventually adopt the reality principle, and deny himself immediate sucking pleasure in order to ensure the greater pleasure of mother's affection in the future. The reality principle, therefore, is not opposed to the pleasure principle, but is a modification, learned by experience and characterizing emotional maturity, of the inborn pleasure principle." (*See* PSYCHOANALYSIS (THEORY), PLEASURE PRINCIPLE.

REALITY TESTING. The process of exploring and experimenting with the environment in order to discover the nature of things, people, and events, and the difference between reality and fantasy.

Reality testing is a basic, essential process which begins in the early years of life when the child actively tries to find out what the world is like and what he can do with it. It also includes the process of discovering his own abilities and limitations. The baby puts objects in his mouth, bangs them on the floor, stretches his arms, and examines his toes. The toddler pokes and prods people as well as things in an attempt to discover how they react. In the process he discovers the difference between the animate and the inanimate, and the limits imposed by the environment on his own behavior. Gradually, too, he learns to distinguish between himself and external reality, and ceases to confuse his fantasies and dreams with events in the actual world.

Psychosis, particularly schizophrenia and paranoia, is sometimes defined as an impairment of reality testing. Loss of contact with reality means that the patient has ceased to test his ideas against the outer world. He has retreated to an inner, autistic realm of fantasies, delusions, and hallucinations. It may well be that one of the factors in the background of some of these cases is a failure to learn the techniques of reality testing early in life. The child

who is constantly confronted with a discordant, disorganized family life may have trouble distinguishing not only between right and wrong, but between reality and unreality. In their study of the families of schizophrenic patients, Lidz and others (1957, 1963) found that they "virtually always emerge from homes marked by serious parental strife and eccentricity," where the parents' attempts to hide their difficulties have "created a strange emotional environment that was perplexing to the child." Therefore, as R. W. White (1964) suggests, "The future patient is thus seen as growing up in a situation filled with irrationality, emotional distortion, and faulty reality testing, all of which tend to hinder the growth of a strong ego. . . . The patient's weak hold on rationality is attributed to the irrationality amidst which he is brought up."

REALITY THERAPY. A treatment technique in which the psychotherapist focuses the patient's attention on his conscious behavior, helping him to assume greater responsibility for his own actions and to find better ways of handling the situations of life.

Reality therapy was developed by William Glasser (1965a, b) as an alternative to the psychoanalytic approach, which, he holds, tends to weaken the patient's responsibility for himself. It challenges "conventional psychiatry" at several key points. First, it denies the concept of mental illness, which encourages the patient to see himself as a sick person to be treated by the therapist according to a fixed diagnostic classification. According to Glasser, the analytic process concentrates primarily on the unhappy experiences which have caused the individual's illness, in the belief that when these experiences are exposed, "the mentally ill person will recover in much the same way that the physically ill person recovers from a strep throat when the penicillin kills the streptococcus."

In contrast, reality therapy views the patient as weak rather than ill, and seeks to cure him by strengthening his ability to cope with the stresses of life and take fuller responsibility for the satisfactory fulfillment of his needs. It therefore dispenses with any extensive inquiry into the patient's history: "Treatment, therefore, is not to give him understanding of past misfortunes which caused his illness, but to help him to function in a better way now." To accomplish this goal, the patient is encouraged to view himself not as a recipient of help but as a person who can change his own current attitudes and behavior regardless of what has happened to him in the past: "Once we become involved with the patient and teach him new ways of behavior his attitude will change regardless of whether or not he understands his old ways. What starts the process is *an initial change in behavior,* and it is toward this that the therapist must work."

Second, the psychoanalytic approach is based on the theory that the patient develops insight most effectively through the transference—that is, he relives and re-experiences his early attitudes and relationships by focusing them on the therapist, whom he treats as a father, mother, brother, or other significant person in his life. This brings his faulty attitudes into the open where they can be studied. In this process, the therapist is an impersonal, detached figure who can assume any of these roles as they are needed. Glasser rejects this "halfway" involvement with the patient, which again puts the emphasis on the past, and advocates a close personal relationship in which the therapist becomes an important figure in the patient's life, acting and reacting as himself and not as someone else. He holds that involvement of this kind is "absolutely essential" to his form of therapy.

Third, conventional psychiatry seeks to make the patient aware of the unconscious reasons for his behavior. Reality therapy does not deny the existence of unconscious motivation, but holds that discovering why we act the way we do does not in itself bring about change or fulfillment. Glasser states that "what is really below the level of consciousness is what the patient is doing now"—that is, he is not fully aware of the nature and consequences of his *present* behavior and must be made to face these facts.

Fourth, conventional psychiatry does not concern itself with right and wrong, with morality, and simply assumes that once the patient resolves his conflicts he will be able to improve his behavior. Reality therapy points out that society is based on morality and that "if the important people in the patient's life, especially the therapist, do not discuss whether his behavior is right or wrong, reality cannot be brought home to him." The object, however, is not to legislate for the patient, but to get him to judge the morality of his behavior: "We have found that unless they judge their own behavior, they will not change." As a guideline "for the purpose of therapy," Glasser has found the following definition "extremely useful": "When a man acts in such a way that he gives and receives love, and feels worthwhile to himself and others, his behavior is right or moral."

Finally, Glasser holds that conventional therapy is limited to helping the patient gain insight into the causes of his behavior, while in reality therapy, "We spend much time painstakingly examining the patient's daily activity and suggesting better ways for him to behave. . . . Patients who have not been able to fulfill their needs must learn both how to approach people so that they can become more involved and how to accomplish enough so that they can gain an increased feeling of self-worth. Once involvement is gained and reality is faced, therapy becomes a special kind of education, a learning to live more effectively that is better and more quickly achieved if the therapist accepts the role of teacher." *See* RE-EDUCATION, DIRECT THERAPY.

Reality therapy has been criticized on a number of counts. Moravec (1965) holds that the Freudian approach can actually strengthen rather than weaken responsibility, and takes Glasser to task for not showing where psychoanalysis can be usefully applied. He also objects to his introduction of the moral concept of "right and wrong" and suggests that the emphasis should be on "appropriate behavior" instead. Wahler (1965) suggests that "with broader knowledge, a therapist would not have to prescribe 'better ways of behaving' but rather would help the sufferer discover better ways of *perceiving* and *thinking* so that his own intrinsic motivation would lead him to better ways of behaving."

RECEPTOR. A specialized biological structure which receives particular kinds of physical stimuli and converts them into impulses to be transmitted through sensory nerve fibers. An example is the retina of the eye. The term is also used more loosely for the organ itself, such as the eye, which contains the sensitive structures.

In the course of evolution, receptor cells developed after effector cells. In animals like the sponge, the effectors served the double purpose of receiving and reacting to stimuli, since they were both irritable and contractile. Later on, separate receptor cells developed, and their function was to be excited by external stimuli and transmit the excitation to effectors. Still later adjustor or connector neurons came into the picture to conduct impulses from the receptors to the effectors. The co-ordination of these three types of nerve cells constitutes the nervous system.

Receptors reach their highest development in mammals, and especially in man. In these organisms they are specialized to receive four different types of stimuli: thermal (cold and warm receptors in the skin), mechanical (hearing, balance, and touch), chemical (taste, smell, and chemical sensitivity of the skin), and light (vision). This division is not rigid, since light receptors in the eye respond to intense thermal and chemical stimuli, mechanical receptors are sensitive to strong chemical stimuli, and all types of receptors are capable of responding to electrical energy—a fact that is highly useful for experimental purposes.

The different types of receptors are described in the articles dealing with the individual senses, but here it may be useful to catalogue them in terms of the bodily organ or tissue involved, the location and type of sensitive structure, and the sensory experience which they ultimately arouse.

Eye: rods and cones in the retina—for black, white, color, and visual perception of objects, space, and motion (Vision).

Inner Ear: (a) nerve endings attached to the organ of Corti in the cochlea—for tones, noises, speech, music, location of sounds in space (Hearing, Audition); (b) nerve endings attached to otoliths in saccule and utricle—for static position of the body, straight-line motion, sense of balance (Static Sense; Equilibrium); (c) nerve endings attached to hairs in the semicircular canals—for rotation of the head, sense of balance (Equilibrium).

Tongue, Mouth, Throat: nerve endings in taste buds—for sweet, salt, sour, and bitter tastes (Taste, Gustation).

Nose: endings in olfactory epithelium in upper nasal cavities—for smell (Smell, Olfaction).

Skin: various cells in the superficial and deeper layers (Ruffini corpuscles, Krause end bulbs, Meissner corpuscles, Merkel's corpuscles, Pacinian corpuscles, basket nerve endings and free nerve endings)—for light touch, deep pressure, warmth, cold, pain (Skin Senses, Cutaneous Senses, Touch).

Internal Organs: various cells, probably like the skin cells, in the stomach, intestines, esophagus, etc.—for distention and pressure, warmth, cold, pain (Organic Senses).

Muscles, Tendons, Joints: nerve endings in muscle spindles, for stretching; in tendons, for contraction; and pressure sensitivity endings in tissue around joints—for position and movement of parts of the body (Kinesthetic Sense).

See Category Index for topics on individual senses, under SENSATION AND PERCEPTION.

RECONSTRUCTIVE THERAPY. A general term for psychiatric treatment methods aimed at relieving emotional disturbance by altering the patient's basic personality structure.

Reconstructive therapy is contrasted with supportive therapy, which aims at relieving symptoms through the use of reassurance, persuasion, suggestion, milieu therapy, and recreational or occupational activities without attempting to change the basic personality. It is also distinguished from re-educative therapy, which is designed to modify the patient's attitudes and behavior patterns as a means to better adjustment. However, the line between the three approaches is not a sharp one, since supportive and re-educative therapy may have a reconstructive effect, and the reconstructive approach always contains supportive and re-educative components. *See* SUPPORTIVE THERAPY, RE-EDUCATION.

In reconstructive therapy the relief of symptoms is indirectly achieved, since it comes about through a revision or reorganization of the patient's basic attitudes toward himself as well as his relationships with other people. There are many ways of accomplishing these purposes, but most of them have two major features in common. First, they are usually carried out through a close interpersonal relationship with a therapist; and second, the process usually involves an increase in insight on the part of the patient. There is difference of opinion, however, as to the function of insight. Some therapists consider it the major instrument of personality change, but others regard it as a result or an indicator of progress in personality growth.

The following are representative reconstructive therapies. Since they are described elsewhere in this book, they will merely be listed here: (1) psychoanalysis; (2) modifications and variations of psychoanalytic theory: (a) Sullivan's interpersonal theory, (b) Fromm's theory of social character, (c) Horney's cultural theory, (d) Stekel's active analytic therapy, (e) Ferenczi's active techniques, (f) brief psychoanalytic therapy, (g) Karpman's objective psychotherapy, (h) Deutsch's sector analysis, (i) Mowrer's learning theory approach, (j) Reich's character analysis and vegetotherapy, (k) Federn's ego psychology, (l) Dollard and Miller's integration of psychoanalysis and learning theory; (3) Jung's analytical psychology; (4) Rank's will therapy; (5) Allen and Taft's relationship therapy; (6) Rogers' client-centered (nondirective) therapy; (7) Whitaker and Malone's experiential psychotherapy; (8) Adler's individual psychology; (9) Meyer's psychobiology; (10) hypnoanalysis; (11) hypnoidal psychotherapy; (12) therapy under drug-induced narcosis: Grinker and Spiegel's narcosynthesis, Horsley's narcoanalysis; (13) play therapies; (14) Levy's release therapy; (15) Moreno's psychodrama; (16) reconstructive group therapies; (17) projective psychotherapy; (18) Herzberg's active psychotherapy; (19) general semantics; (20) existential analysis; (21) Szondi's fate analysis; (22) Zen. *See* the Category Index, under Treatment Techniques and Facilities.

RECREATIONAL THERAPY. Recreational pursuits, both active and passive, used as supportive therapeutic measures.

A well-planned program in a mental institution offers a wide variety of activities designed to suit the needs and interests of every type of patient. These include not only many kinds of sports and games, but handcrafts of all types, dramatics, movies, music (concerts, practice, participation in choir or band), dancing (ballroom, square, folk, rhythmic exercises), gardening, and other hobbies. In addition, the program usually includes many special events, such as picnics, birthday parties, and trips to ball games, museums, zoos, or historical sites, as well as social events in nearby communities. An increasing number of mental institutions are now giving patients the opportunity to spend a two- or three-week period at a summer camp.

The program is the responsibility of the recreation specialist, who works under the general direction of the hospital's medical staff. Its objective is not only to keep the patients occupied and provide pastimes for lonely hours, but to serve dynamic therapeutic purposes such as building self-esteem, establishing social contact, preventing them from lapsing into inertia, and giving them an opportunity to participate in everyday activities as individuals rather than as patients in an institution. The specialist often collaborates with the psychiatrist in recommending activities that will meet the special needs of individual patients—for example, a bridge or canasta tournament to awaken the apathetic; a gardening project for the withdrawn, who can relate to things but not to people; charades for those who cannot communicate in words; volleyball to give the excited a chance to drain off emotional energy. In the course of these activities the recreation specialist frequently makes observations which are helpful to the psychotherapist in his own work with the patients.

Today recreation specialists are employed in practically all state mental hospitals and Veterans Administration hospitals, as well as in many Armed Forces hospitals throughout the United States and overseas. They also work in special facilities for mentally disturbed or mentally retarded children, and in some cases in private hospitals and homes for the aged. The larger hospitals usually have a recreation department headed by a recreation director, who is assisted by recreation leaders, recreation aides, and a corps of volunteers from the community. There is also a growing trend toward extending recreational services beyond the hospital stay, and they are becoming an integral part of the aftercare and rehabilitation programs for patients who have returned to their homes or communities. For this reason an increasing number of recreation specialists are now working in community centers, settlement houses, and other facilities which offer aftercare programs.

A promising development in this connection is recreation counseling, a service which originated in the Veterans Administration hospital in Kansas City, Missouri. In that hospital a counseling team consisting of a psychiatrist, psychologist, hospital recreation worker, and city recreation group leader provides individual recreational guidance to former mental patients. The object is to help them re-establish their affiliations with social and civic organizations, and to show them how to make full use of community recreation resources. There is evidence that such counseling not only makes the ex-patient more comfortable in the community, but actually prevents relapse and readmission to the hospital.

The field of therapeutic recreation is open to men and women who enjoy varied activities and have leadership and organizing ability, a pleasing and outgoing personality, a genuine understanding of people, and an interest in helping the sick and handicapped live fuller and more satisfying lives. Preparation for a career in this field should begin in the high school years and include such activities as dramatics, sports, music, public speaking, working on school publications, and part-time or summer experience in recreational work in playgrounds, summer camps, or community agencies. Minimal standards for the profession of recreation specialist, as outlined by the National Recreation Association, are as follows: (1) *hospital recreation aide:* a high school diploma plus three years of successful full-time paid hospital recreation experience under a qualified recreation director or leader, or four hundred hours of approved in-service training; (2) *hospital recreation leader:* a B.A. degree from an accredited college or university with a major in recreation or related fields such as music, dramatics, sports, or dance; (3) *hospital recreation director:* an M.A. degree from an accredited college or university with a major in hospital recreation, recreation in rehabilitation, or recreational therapy, plus one year of successful full-time paid experience in recreation for the handicapped in a medical setting; or an M.A. with a major in recreation plus two years of full-time experience; or an M.A. with a major in a professional field closely allied to recreation and applicable to recreation for the handicapped in a medical setting, plus an undergraduate major in recreation and two years of full-time experience. *See* DANCE THERAPY, MUSIC THERAPY, ART THERAPY.

RE-EDUCATION. A form or stage of psychologial treatment in which the patient is taught—or, better, given an opportunity to learn for himself—more effective ways of dealing with problems and relationships.

The term is a broad one that arises out of the fact that the goal of therapy is not merely to eliminate disturbing reactions or faulty modes of adjust-ment, but to replace them with more successful behavior. Most therapists view this process as "emotional re-education," or "corrective emotional experience," and not as a simple learning process. The reason for the emphasis on emotion is that psychotherapy is rarely viewed as an intellectual procedure. It can be effective only through modification of the patient's feelings and reactions.

There are many ways to approach re-education, and many levels of achievement. Probably the deepest and most difficult level is the one on which psychoanalysts operate. Their aim is to effect a fundamental change in the structure of the patient's personality, so that changes in attitude and outward behavior will stem from inner sources. In the course of treatment, the patient gradually learns how to handle emotional situations, such as marital, social, or occupational problems, that have caused great anxiety in the past. If he finds his new patterns of adjustment rewarding and satisfying, he will become more capable of navigating on his own, without support from a therapist.

Re-education is an essential aspect of treatment in most modern mental institutions. Patients are encouraged to adopt new attitudes toward themselves and new patterns of adjustment toward other people through such techniques as group therapy and occupational, social, and recreational activities. In the "total push," milieu, and therapeutic community aproaches, the entire institutional life is viewed as a re-educational force. As institutionalized patients improve and approach discharge, they generally participate in classes and discussion groups which are designed to prepare them to find suitable jobs and meet the demands of everyday life in the community.

Today a number of therapists are focusing directly on re-educational methods designed to bring about behavioral changes in neurotic patients. They believe it is possible to foreshorten or sweep away entirely the groundwork which psychoanalysts find so necessary —that is, the lengthy process of interpreting dreams and free associations, breaking through resistances, and analyzing the transference. Instead, they get down to the business of re-education at once, using whatever technique of behavior change they believe to be most effective. In *persuasion treatment,* the therapist first explores the patient's difficulties, points out faulty reactions, such as a pattern of evading issues, and then encourages him to try different ways of meeting his problems. In *directive psychotherapy,* the therapist charges the patient with the responsibility of making definite changes in his behavior—for example, by asking a hypochondriac patient to refrain entirely from referring to his illnesses. In *conditioned response treatment* (behavior therapy), rewards may be used to reinforce new reaction patterns; or distasteful stimuli, such as electric shocks or nauseating drugs, may be used to eliminate undesirable behavior. Some therapists use *hypnotic suggestion* in combating insomnia, smoking, and overeating; a combination of hypnosis and relaxation techniques is occasionally applied to reduce anxiety and prepare an expectant mother to go through the birth process with a minimum of stress.

All these methods have proved valuable in removing symptoms or bringing about desirable behavior changes. Their effectiveness, however, seems to be limited largely to the milder and less fixed conditions, such as habit disturbances, traumatic neuroses, phobias, and hysterical reactions of recent origin. The therapist must always be prepared for the possibility of relapse, which usually indicates that the patient's problem is on a deeper level than behavior techniques can touch. Moreover, these techniques are not so simple and mechanical as they are sometimes pictured. They

work best when the therapist establishes rapport with his patient, shows interest in his problems and concern for his welfare, and gains his confidence and trust. R. W. White (1964) sums up the case for and against the more rapid methods of re-education in these words: "We must accept the long-accumulating evidence that symptomatic treatment can be successful, but must not overlook the equally long-accumulating evidence that symptoms are in many cases the surface phenomena of more complex emotional difficulties." *See* PERSUASION THERAPY, BEHAVIOR THERAPY, DIRECTIVE PSYCHOTHERAPY, HYPNOTHERAPY, RELAXATION THERAPY, MILIEU THERAPY, SOCIOTHERAPY, TOTAL PUSH THERAPY.

REFLEX. An automatic, unlearned response to a specific stimulus involving relatively simple and fixed nerve connections.

Reflexes are classified in several ways. One important distinction is between the brief, specific *phasic* reflexes such as blinking the eye when a light is flashed, and the longer-lasting, sustained *postural reflexes* which keep the head up and the trunk erect when we stand or sit. A second distinction is between *flexion reflexes,* as in withdrawing our hand from a hot stove, and *extension reflexes,* as in stretching our leg to support our weight. If we are standing, the stretch reflex in our leg is primarily postural, but if we are walking it is a phasic reaction that alternates with a flexion reaction—that is, extending one leg while bending the other and vice versa.

Reflexes can also be classified according to the level of the nervous system involved. The flexion and extension reflexes just mentioned are *segmental reflexes,* since they take place over pathways of a single spinal segment. These pathways form a "reflex arc," which consists of a sensory, or afferent, neuron conducting an impulse

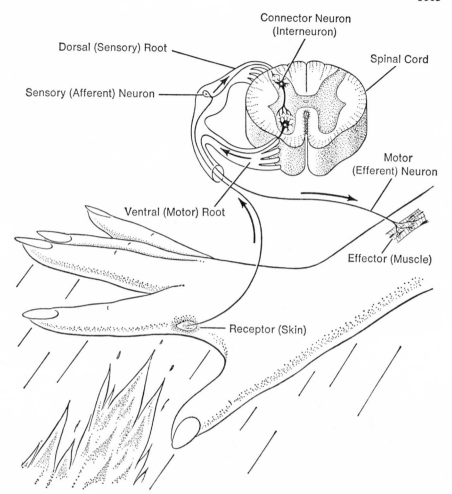

Fig. 45. A simplified representation of a reflex arc, showing connections in a cross section of the spinal cord.

to the spinal cord, a motor, or efferent, neuron carrying the impulse to a muscle, and usually an intervening association neuron between the two (*Fig. 45*). This account, however, is oversimplified, since *groups* of neurons are always involved, as well as connections to higher brain centers which may exert a measure of control over the response.

The reflexes that involve more than one part of the spinal cord—*intersegmental reflexes*—are of two types: the autonomic reflexes, which control such functions as heartbeat, salivation, per-

spiration, stomach movements, as well as contractions of the bladder and rectum; and the somatic reflexes, which consist of fairly complex patterns enabling us to make the rhythmic movements involved in walking or scratching ourselves. Finally, there are *suprasegmental reflexes,* which depend not only on the spinal cord but on centers and pathways in the brain. These consist of complex patterns of segmental and intersegmental reflexes organized and controlled by the higher centers. The most important are various postural reactions, which usually involve motor areas in the frontal lobes, and in some cases visual and somesthetic areas. Among them are the supporting reactions (stiffening and relaxing) of the legs which are necessary in walking, tonic or attitudinal reflexes which prepare the organism to pounce on a victim, the grasp reflex which is present in most human infants at birth, and the shifting, righting, and hopping movements which occur when an animal or person is thrown off balance. See BABINSKI REFLEX.

REFRACTORY PERIOD. A brief interval following the discharge of a nerve impulse, during which the cell is absolutely or relatively insensitive to stimulation.

The nerve impulse consists of an electrochemical change occurring along the membrane or outer layer of the neuron. This change, which takes as little as a thousandth of a second, temporarily depletes the neuron, and it must go through a series of chemical changes before it can be activated again. This recovery phase, or refractory period, is a two-stage affair. In the first phase, or absolute refractory period, no stimulus, no matter how intense, will produce a nerve impulse. During the second phase, or relative refractory period, the fiber gradually returns to normal sensitivity and a relatively intense stimulus will activate it. The two phases may be compared to our reactions after engaging in extremely heavy work. For a while we are so "dead tired" that nothing can move us; but after a period of time we recover to a point where we can be aroused by events that are especially stimulating or interesting.

The refractory period helps to explain the immense variations in both sensation and response to sensation. At any given time some neurons in our skin, eyes, or other sense organs are ready to discharge while others are in the recovery phase, and the same holds

for the nerve fibers that control our muscles. This phenomenon also helps to explain the "selection of pathways," that is, the reason why an impulse takes one path rather than another when it reaches a junction in the extremely complex network of the nervous system.

Some newer findings have thrown further light on this phase of neural activity. It has been found that neurons do not all show the same rate of recovery. Larger fibers go through the two phases within approximately a thousandth of a second and can theoretically produce about one thousand nerve impulses per second. Smaller nerve cells recover at a much slower rate and some of them can transmit only a few impulses per second. Moreover, the return to normal is not a smooth process. Immediately after the relative refractory period the nerve fiber goes through a so-called supernormal period in which it is more sensitive than usual, and this is followed by a subnormal period when it is less excitable than usual. After these intervals, which take fifteen to twenty thousandths of a second, the cell returns to its normal state. The whole process is therefore highly complicated, but the new information brings us closer to an explanation of the nuances of sensory experience and motor activity. See NERVE CONDUCTION.

REGRESSION. The unconscious defense mechanism of reverting to immature behavior.

When threatened with external problems or internal conflicts which they cannot cope with, some individuals return to reaction patterns which gave them comfort or relief at an earlier period in their lives. This tendency can be observed at any age from childhood to old age. When a new brother or sister arrives, the older boy or girl in the family sometimes reverts to bedwetting, thumb sucking, or baby talk in an unconscious effort to recapture the parental attention these activities elicited at an earlier age. Adolescents who cannot resolve their emotional problems sometimes regress to sulking, weeping, or temper tantrums as a means of getting what they want. Adults may become so helpless and indecisive that others have to solve their problems for them, just as their father or mother used to do. Many older people revive childhood memories and live in the past, in an unconscious effort to regain the satisfactions of their youth.

Frequently, the tendency to regress is found in individuals who have "gotten away with" infantile behavior as they were growing up. The parent who gives in every time the child cries or pouts may be setting a pattern which will be revived every time the child meets problems later on. Similarly, regressive behavior patterns are often found in people who have failed to grow up in all respects—usually because their parents have been overprotective. They have been partially arrested, or "fixated," at one or another stage of development, and return to that stage when they encounter difficulties they find hard to handle. Psychoanalysts believe that some people also tend to reactivate impulses which were denied sufficient expression early in life. According to this theory, an individual might regress, under stress, to thumb sucking if he did not have enough "sucking satisfaction" as an infant, perhaps as a result of hasty feeding or a large-holed bottle.

We are all tempted to retreat to immaturity at times, and there are situations where it does no harm to yield to that temptation. The businessman who has been "thrown for a loss" may need to be babied by his wife for a while; and the wife herself may benefit from an extra dose of t.l.c. (tender loving care) when she has suffered a disappointment. But generally speaking, regression is an attempt to evade rather than solve problems, and immature behavior almost inevitably leads to greater difficulties than ever.

The mechanism of regression can reach extreme proportions. Under the stress of the concentration camp, where all normal satisfactions were denied, some prisoners reverted to childish reactions:

"The prisoners lived, like children, only in the immediate present. . . . They became unable to plan for the future or to give up immediate pleasure satisfactions to gain greater ones in the near future. . . . They were boastful, telling tales of what they had accomplished in their former lives. . . . Like children they felt not at all set back or ashamed when it became known that they had lied about their prowess" (Bettelheim, 1943). The term "hysterical puerilism" is sometimes applied to cases of temporary infantile behavior resulting from prolonged combat or other extreme stresses. For an example, see PSEUDORETARDATION.

The most striking and pathological examples of regression, however, are found in cases of severe personality disorganization. In chronic schizophrenia some patients return to a completely infantile level where they have to be washed, diapered, dressed, and fed. This process may even go so far that they curl up into a fetal position and remain in that position for months.

Illustrative Case: REGRESSION (Infantilism in a seventeen-year-old)

A seventeen-year-old girl was brought to a psychiatric clinic by her mother with the complaint that for the preceding five months her behavior had become increasingly irrational and destructive. The history revealed that after the patient was about four years old her parents had begun to quarrel violently, making her early environment extremely contentious and unstable. At about this age she first developed various neurotic traits: nail biting, temper tantrums, enuresis, and numerous phobias. When the patient was seven the mother refused further sexual relations with the father and left the marital bed, but the patient continued to sleep with the father until she was thirteen. At this time the mother suspected that the patient was being incestuously seduced, obtained legal custody of the girl, and moved away with her to a separate home. The patient resented this, quarreled frequently with her mother, became a disciplinary problem at home and at school, and acquired a police record for various delinquencies. Three years later, at the patient's insistence, she and her mother paid an unexpected visit to the father, and found him living with another girl in questionable circumstances. In a violent scene, the mother denounced the father for unfaithfulness and, again contrary to the patient's wishes, took her home. There the patient refused to attend school and rapidly became sullen, withdrawn, and noncommunicative. During her mother's absence at work she would keep the house in disorder, destroy clothes her mother had made for her, and throw her mother's effects out the window. During one of these forays she discovered a photograph of herself at the age of five which, incidentally, was so poorly lighted and faded that, for one detail, it did not show her eyebrows. Using this as a pattern, she shaved off her own eyebrows, cut her hair to the same baby bob, and began to affect the facial expression and sitting posture of the pictured child. When brought to the hospital her general behavior was correspondingly childish; she was untidy and enuretic, giggled incessantly or spoke in simple monosyllabic sentences, spent most of her time on the floor playing with blocks or paper dolls, and had to be fed, cleaned, and supervised as though she were an infant. In effect, she appeared to have regressed to a relatively desirable period in life antedating disruptive jealousies and other conflicts; moreover, she acted out this regression in unconsciously determined but strikingly symbolic patterns of eliminating the mother as a rival and regaining the father she had lost in her childhood. (Masserman, 1961)

Illustrative Case: REGRESSION (Total regression in a sixty-one-year-old)

This woman was born shortly after the Civil War of a rather healthy family. She had been petted, spoiled, admired, waited upon, and had attained a fair education. From this sheltered unmarried life she had been lovingly transferred into the strong, protective arms of an adoring husband. He was a corporation official, intelligent, efficient, alert, but at the same time exceedingly gentle toward and proud of his rather fragile and beautiful young wife.

Her husband provided for her a house, servants, comforts, and what luxuries he could afford. He relieved her from all responsibilities, smoothed out her annoyances, and managed her personal affairs even to details. She never made a move without her husband. He escorted her on all the trips she made, and he assisted her in picking out her hats and dresses.

While still in his prime her husband died and she was faced with problems of handling the estate and the upbringing of three adolescent children.

This situation seemed appalling to her although the estate was ample. She began to feel that she should be younger in order better to understand the children and to be more companionable with them. When the usual period of mourning was over she dressed and decorated herself as a younger woman would. She sought the companionship of young married couples and attempted to take up their activities.

But finding that this still did not blend with the life of her children, she entered her children's lives with even greater zest. She went out with them, adopted their friends, and dressed as her daughters dressed. . . .

It was not long before she gave the children considerable anxiety by becoming adolescent. They had to direct her goings out and comings in, to try to persuade her that her clothes were entirely too youthful for her and to induce her to converse less flippantly. But the mother continued to act younger at the rate of a year or so every few months.

At the age of sixty-one she acted like a girl of seven. She behaved like a little girl in short dresses. She read simple things rather badly; she craved attention; she laughed sometimes and at other times she would cry a little. She talked with childish glee, or was mischievous and delighted in trying to play jokes or fool the doctors and nurses. She would play with objects as if they were toys. When her children came to see her she would act as if she were their child.

A few months later she began to act as if she were four years of age. Her enunciation became less distinct, she was careless with her spoon, spilling food, and had to be assisted with her feeding. She would prattle at times and occasionally soil herself. She had ceased to read and would have crawled around on the floor had the nurses so permitted.

In several months she was in bed moving her hands and feet aimlessly, often whining and crying like a very young child. The only articulation one could understand was her frequent crying for "mamma," although her mother had died thirty years before. She would take a towel or any cloth, roll it up and hug it to her as if it were a rag doll. She now required liquid nourishment because she would not chew, and soon had to be fed liquids with a spoon, taking them with a sucking movement. She also would suck the corner of her gown or a bed sheet. She began to soil herself regularly and had to be changed without giving any assitance, the nurse using large cloths in the manner of diapers. She would eat, sleep, make peculiar noises, and cry. She liked to be fondled and handled by almost anyone. Her only recognition of her family was an expression of delight when they came to see her.

She continued to regress until she assumed the fetal position, breathing gently being her only movement. She lived for a few months in this state and died. (Podolsky, 1953)

REHABILITATION (Psychiatric).

Rehabilitation may be defined as the process of helping an individual who has had a physical or mental disorder to participate in society to the fullest extent of his capacities. It is often described as the fourth phase of medical practice, the others being prevention, diagnosis and treatment.

In general medicine rehabilitation usually designates "that phase of care during which the patient is helped toward an independent role in competitive society. Rehabilitation follows the cura-

tive and restorative medical program and the period of convalescence. Rehabilitation seeks to overcome and compensate for an existing physical handicap and for the emotional blocks that prevent the patient from doing his best. The major emphasis is on occupational self-sufficiency" (Braceland, 1966). In psychiatry—and to a growing extent in physical medicine—the emphasis is not only on vocational performance, but on social adjustment as well: "The successfully rehabilitated patient is one who is able to live in a nonmedical setting at a level of occupational performance comparable with other adults in the community" (Freeman and Simmons, 1963). The term implies that residuals of psychiatric disorder may remain after treatment; the rehabilitative process is designed to cope with them and keep them from interfering with social and occupational activities.

Historically speaking, the "moral treatment" applied in the mental hospitals of a century ago was essentially a form of rehabilitation, since it emphasized the value of occupational, educational, and social activities carried out in an optimistic environment. This approach, however, was abandoned when the view that mental illness was due to incurable brain disorder became dominant, and as a result mental hospitals became largely custodial institutions. But in the last thirty years, effective treatment techniques have been developed, and it has become an accepted fact that if they are fully applied, most patients can recover sufficiently to lead an active and constructive life in the community. At the same time it has also become apparent that rehabilitative measures should not be postponed until the patient is out of the hospital, but should be an integral part of the treatment process itself. *See* MENTAL HOSPITAL, RAY, KIRKBRIDE.

Since specific rehabilitative activities and facilities are discussed under separate topics, we will do little more than enumerate them here, following Braceland's classification into in-patient and community rehabilitation. The in-patient process has the double aim of preventing the development of a "disability syndrome" or "institutional neurosis" characterized by apathy, withdrawal, and resignation; and of preparing the patient for social and occupational participation in the community when he leaves the hospital. The institution as a whole is organized as a "therapeutic community" directed toward the recovery and the rehabilitation of the patient. Every member of the staff is viewed as a contributor to this process, and free and open communication is encouraged at all levels. The patients themselves participate in discussion groups, committee activities and self-government. Even the physical arrangements are designed to stimulate socialization: large wards are broken up into small units and many individual rooms are available for the various patient activities. The scope of the activity program has been widened to include practically every conceivable way of broadening the patients' interests, helping them to use their time constructively, and increasing their confidence and skill. Among the activities are handcrafts, dramatics, art classes, music therapy, dance therapy, occupational therapy, industrial therapy (paid work), patient clubs, recreational therapy, and outside employment as a transitional step to the community. See MILIEU THERAPY, RECREATIONAL THERAPY, OCCUPATIONAL THERAPY, ART THERAPY, DANCE THERAPY, MUSIC THERAPY.

The goal of community rehabilitation is to provide a bridge to normal life for the patient who has been released from residential treatment. Transitional facilities and after-care programs have multiplied in recent years, though they are still unavailable in many localities. They include: day hospitals, providing all types of psychiatric treatment and all rehabilitative activities on a day basis; halfway houses, where patients may live during the readjustment period, including not only group residential centers but subsidized apartments supervised by social workers, such as Horizon House in Philadelphia and Quarters House in San Jose; occupational rehabilitation under the Federal-State rehabilitation system and private organizations, providing vocational counseling, job-finding, and placement in industry or in sheltered workships; ex-patient clubs for social and therapeutic purposes, run by either the patients themselves or the hospital as part of its after-care program; foster-family care in carefully selected families under the supervision of a social worker and visiting psychiatric nurse; family care in the patient's own family, with the assistance of psychiatric or public health nurses and social workers who work with the family as well as the patient. See DAY HOSPITAL, NIGHT HOSPITAL, HALFWAY HOUSE, SHELTERED WORKSHOP, FAMILY CARE, MENTAL PATIENT ORGANIZATIONS, HEAD INJURY (CHRONIC TRAUMATIC DISORDERS), NURSERY SCHOOL EXPERIENCE, SOCIAL BREAKDOWN SYNDROME.

REINFORCEMENT (Reward and Punishment). Any procedure that increases the strength of a conditioning or other learning process.

The concept of reinforcement has different meanings in classical and operant conditioning. In the classical type, it refers to the repeated association of the conditioned stimulus (the sound of a bell, for instance) with the unconditioned stimulus (the sight of food). After the two occur together a number of times, the connection between the bell and salivation (the conditioned response) will be strengthened, and salivation will occur when the bell is sounded alone. If the conditioned stimulus is repeatedly presented without being reinforced by the unconditioned stimulus, the response will be weakened and eventually "extinguished."

In operant conditioning, reinforcement refers to the reward that is given after a correct response, or the punishment that follows an incorrect response. In training procedures it is important to apply a carefully worked out "schedule of reinforcement" instead of giving rewards or punishments haphazardly. Here, too, a weakening and eventual extinction of the response occurs if reinforcement is consistently withheld— that is, if the animal being trained is not rewarded with food.

Whether we recognize it or not, most of our time is spent in doing things that give us some type of reward or keep us from receiving some kind of punishment. We are constantly striving to elicit praise and encouragement from the people we respect, and we are equally eager to avoid their disapproval. Few people work "just for the fun of it"; they expect to receive a definite reward for their efforts. In one experiment, four groups of boys were required to learn a maze. One group was paid twenty-five cents for mastering the task; the others received much smaller rewards. The first group did the best by far. Yet material rewards are by no means the only effective kinds. A gold star or a pat on the back, especially when given by an important person, can be as potent as a chocolate bar, and the feeling that we are improving can be as great a satisfaction as an increase in salary.

Rewards must be appropriate to the situation. We do not give an adult a gold star when he does a job well, nor do we give a first grader a dollar bill for learning the alphabet. High scholastic standing may be a reward to one student, but a sure sign of a "greasy grind" to another. Some situations that appear to be punishing are on closer examination actually rewarding. A beginning medical student may be nauseated at the thought of cutting up a human cadaver, but this negative reaction is soon banished when he begins to reap the rewards of knowledge.

In general, reward is superior to punishment as an incentive to learning. Reward reinforces positive performance; punishment only indicates what is objectionable. Punishment does not by itself modify attitudes and skills, and it frequently produces tension and resentment. Since it is a cue as to what not to do, its chief value lies in suppressing the undesired response until the correct response can be learned.

Sometimes punishment or the prospect of it actually interferes with learning the desired response. It may produce so much anxiety that the individual comes to fear the entire situation and tries to avoid it altogether. If a child is continually punished for playing with a certain toy in a particular room, after a time he may rebel at going near the room. In socializing a child, or in reforming an antisocial person, the purpose is to induce him to adopt acceptable behavior and avoid unacceptable behavior. Attempts to restrain antisocial acts merely by threats that provoke anxiety are usually ineffective. What often happens is that the person avoids the situation in which he is threatened with punishment, but acts in an antisocial fashion in a different situation. Punishment therefore fails to educate or re-educate the offender. This is one reason why reform schools and prisons do not succeed in rehabilitating the majority of their inmates.

One of the most important findings in the entire field of learning is that reinforcement is most effective when it is intermittent. Both reward and punishment tend to lose their force when they are constantly applied. This is particularly true with children who are overrewarded or overpunished. Fortunately a single reinforcement may persist and have an effect for a long period of time. In a classic experiment

(Skinner, 1950), a pigeon pecked at a rate of six thousand times per hour for several hours even though it was only rewarded at five-minute intervals (an intermittent schedule of reinforcement). Running a gambling house is a successful operation because it takes only a few small wins to keep people in the game until they lose their whole bankroll. Unfortunately a few small losses rarely have an equally strong deterrent effect.

The lasting effects of partial reinforcement are especially evident in child-rearing. If rewards and punishments are few but consistent, they will usually make a lasting impression. The mother who repeatedly reminds her child to look both ways when crossing the street can usually count on him to take this precaution when he is alone. He will, however, need occasional reminders or rebukes—that is, intermittent reinforcement. This principle can also work negatively. Many young children cry when they are put to bed in order to get extra attention and stay up longer. If the parents "reward" this behavior by giving in even once or twice, the child will try it again and again.

Many superstitions are based on partial reinforcement. Indian rain dances are only occasionally followed by rain, yet this is enough to maintain belief. A superstitious person will remember the one case when he had bad luck after a black cat crossed his path, but will forget all the "negative instances" when nothing happened to him. Athletes are notoriously superstitious. After winning a game they sometimes think over every action they performed and try to repeat the same routine the next time they play. A baseball player, for example, may take the same number of steps to get to his position in the outfield, or take a drink of water at exactly the same time during every game. These are all examples of partial reinforcement.

Reinforcements are frequently divided into two types. *Primary reinforcements* directly satisfy basic needs or punish unacceptable behavior. Examples are material rewards or expressions of approval, and punishments like a slap or a reproach (PLATE 37). *Secondary reinforcements,* on the other hand, are merely associated with direct reinforcements—nevertheless they can be extremely effective. In animal training, the sight of food, as opposed to the actual taste, may become a reinforcer. Restaurateurs know that good meals are their best advertisement, but they also know that a meal tastes best in an atmosphere of comfort and relaxation. The meals are the primary reinforcement, the atmosphere a secondary reinforcement. Similarly, many teachers find that the learning process can be enhanced by an occasional digression or dash of humor. As we become more sophisticated, these secondary reinforcements play a greater and greater role in our lives. A man who has long ago made enough money to satisfy all his family's physical needs will continue to work for humanitarian causes or for such status symbols as titles and honorary degrees. Likewise, the person who does not respond to physical punishment may be deterred from bad behavior by fear of criticism or loss of face. *See* CONDITIONING, DISCIPLINE.

REJECTION. Denial of recognition, approval, or affection by an emotionally significant individual or group—particularly, a parent's refusal of the love or care needed by his child.

There are many forms and degrees of rejection, but they all have the common denominator of depriving the child of what he needs more than anything else, the love and approval of his parents. No parent can be expected to accept everything the child does or to meet all his demands, but the truly rejecting parent consistently treats the child as if he were unwanted or unworthy. The more common forms of rejection include ignoring the child, neglecting his welfare, constant criticism, unfavorable comparisons with others, and nagging or spanking for the slightest misbehavior. Some parents go so far as to lock up the child, threaten to evict him, deliberately frighten him, put him in an institution, or beat him unmercifully. *See* CHILD ABUSE.

Rejection may also take indirect and disguised forms. A parent may show no interest in the child's inner feelings and fears, or turn a deaf ear to his difficulties at school, or promise him love only if he obeys or brings home good grades. Many parents go to the opposite extreme to conceal or deny feelings of rejection, and overindulge or overprotect the child. They give him everything he desires in order to keep him "out of their hair," or show their lack of confidence by constantly hovering over him and refusing to let him venture on his own. *See* OVERPROTECTION.

Studies of rejecting mothers show that they are likely to be dissatisfied with their marriage, to have an unsatisfactory sex life, or to resent the responsibility of raising children. The fathers, and sometimes the mothers as well, were usually spoiled in their childhood, dominated by their mothers, or subjected to harsh and inconsistent discipline. In many cases their own parents were poorly mated and there was excessive friction in the home. (Koppitz, 1957)

Parental rejection inevitably has a damaging effect on the child's personality. Constant disapproval or punishment undermines self-esteem, corrodes self-confidence, and gives rise to feelings of frustration, helplessness, and insecurity. The child who has failed to receive affection will almost inevitably have difficulty bestowing affection on others. He is apt to feel that the world is a hostile place and will not expect other people to be friendly—and when they try to show him affection, his guard will immediately go up, and he will become reserved or mistrustful. He will also be prone to develop symptoms of emotional disturbance: enuresis, feeding problems, nail biting, stuttering, and in some cases aggressive or antisocial behavior (MacFarlane et al., 1954). *See* ETIOLOGY.

Rejected children, then, suffer many handicaps. Yet it should not be assumed that they are totally lost. Some are resilient enough to develop compensatory qualities such as independence, shrewdness, realism, and early maturity (Mead, 1949). Others become more confident and responsive by virtue of contact with teachers or other adults who give them the approval and understanding they need. As Jersild (1960) reminds us, in language that is refreshing to find in a psychological treatise, "Even a child who seems beyond repair may possess potentialities for health and growth. A child who has suffered rejection may still retain, within the desert of his life, a small green patch that can be cultivated." For social rejection, *see* PREJUDICE.

RELATIONSHIP THERAPY. In its broadest sense, this term can be applied to any form of psychological treatment in which the relationship between the patient and therapist is a key factor in the therapeutic process. This includes techniques as diverse as direct guidance, suggestion, hypnotherapy, client-centered therapy, and psychoanalysis. The relationship, however, is utilized for many different purposes in these procedures. In techniques involving direct advice or suggestion it is used to establish faith in the therapist and to provide emotional support; in the nondirective approach it is the essential means of creating a warm, accepting atmosphere that will foster personality growth; in psychoanalysis, it serves many purposes—to lend the patient indirect emotional support, to encourage the spontaneous expression of feelings and associations, and especially to establish a "transference" situation in which the patient focuses his basic attitudes and feelings onto the therapist so that they may be brought out in the open and subjected to analysis. *See* RAPPORT.

In a more specialized sense, the term relationship therapy has been applied by F. H. Allen and Jessie Taft to a form of psychotherapy developed at the Philadelphia Child Guidance Clinic. According to Allen (1942), relationship therapy is not a form of manipulation in which the patient is changed by a specialist's skill, but rather a process in which the patient himself participates. This process "begins when the therapist is brought into a relationship as a supporting and clarifying influence around the patient's need and desire to gain or regain a sense of his own worth," and is therefore "rooted in a philosophy of responsibility, a belief that people have within themselves, irrespective of what has gone before, capacities which can be utilized creatively to effect harmonious relations with the realities of their living."

The treatment process is focused on the present, not on the past, and seeks to utilize the immediate experience and relationship as a means of accelerating the patient's capacity to change: "The patient is . . . a human being who must find new values in himself, not in isolation, but in a relation with another human being. . . . It is the heightened and deepened experience in living that constitutes the heart of therapy." As an example, Allen cites the case of a boy of five who was so strongly attached to his overprotective and overanxious mother that he was unable to function independently. For this child, the experience of spending time alone with the therapist was itself a major step toward emotional separation from the mother. Though hesitant and anxious at first, he became intrigued

with the play materials in the office, and while playing with them gradually developed a constructive relationship with the therapist.

This relationship enabled him to discover and to release his own inner strength, and gave him an opportunity to prove to himself that he was a "big boy." Interestingly, the boy expressed his desire to be mature by assuming the role of doctor in his play and by offering the therapist paint for medicine to cure his "badness." By projecting his own desire to be bad onto the therapist, and by applying a remedy for it, he was testing his ability to assert himself. This was followed by sessions in which he released further aggressiveness by "making a mess" with the clay and paint. After a time, he was able to accept the limits on this type of activity which were set by the therapist, and finally devoted himself to constructive play activities.

In the course of the later sessions, the boy talked increasingly about growing up—for example, remarking, "A long time ago I was a baby and now I am a big boy." This indicated that the therapy was reaching its conclusion, and in the last hour the child accepted the idea that he was to be on his own. In spite of some feeling of anxiety, he signified his readiness to terminate by handing the therapist a slip of paper, saying, "Here is your ticket. You go on the steam train." Then, taking a piece of paper for himself, he remarked, "This is for home." Allen comments: "With the poignant simplicity of a five-year-old child, George thus brought to an end this intensified growth experience."

RELAXATION THERAPY. The use of muscular relaxation techniques as an aid in the treatment of disorders involving persistent tension.

Therapeutic relaxation is advocated by many psychiatrists as a means of reducing emotional tensions associated with such conditions as stuttering, asthma, peptic ulcer, spastic colitis, uncontrolled vomiting, and paroxysmal tachycardia (rapid heart). It has also proved effective in overcoming recently acquired fear reactions, as in combat disturbances, and in the relief of insomnia, pain, and anorexia (loss of appetite).

Most individuals afflicted with these disorders generate excessive energy which tends to aggravate the underlying condition. Typically they engage in many "nervous" activities such as drumming their fingers, talking loudly, bracing themselves when sitting in a chair or lying in bed, holding a pencil tightly, or tensing their entire body while performing any activity. In addition, many individuals who are not afflicted by any specific psychosomatic or psychoneurotic disorder manifest similar behavior, especially when under stress; and frequently they find themselves too tense to sleep well or too irritable to live harmoniously with others. These states of muscular hypertension can often be relieved to some extent by the use of systematic relaxation.

There appear to be two general approaches to therapeutic relaxation: relaxing the "mind" and relaxing the muscles. Kraines (1948) holds that mental relaxation and attitude change are the key to the process. This takes the form of teaching the patient "(1) to understand the mechanism of his tension, (2) to see his problems and himself in a true perspective, (3) to realize that anger and impatience retard rather than facilitate his plans, (4) to cultivate an attitude of self-tolerance, and (5) to substitute reasonable planning for emotional demanding." He also suggests that tension may be reduced by helping the patient set goals which are realistic and within his capacity. After discussion with a therapist along the lines just outlined, a light hypnotic state may be induced to help relax the muscular system. When the patient has reached a suggestive state, he is repeatedly told that he is no longer tense, that he will approach all his difficulties with composure, and will be able to relax both his body and his mind at will. *See* HYPNOTHERAPY.

Jacobson (1942) and Fink (1943) place the primary emphasis on muscular rather than mental relaxation. They point out that even when the average individual believes he is thoroughly relaxed there generally remain residual tensions in the form of stiffness, reflex swallowing, or tremors. The aim of their techniques is to teach the individual to eliminate these residual tensions and reach a completely flaccid state which he usually experiences as pleasant and restful. In Jacobson's system of "progressive relaxation," the subject is first made aware of the feelings involved in muscular tension by deliberately contracting one muscle group at a time. He starts with the large muscles first, since they generate the most conspicuous sensations—proceeding from the arms to the legs, the trunk, the neck, the mouth, and finally the eyes.

Fink's technique is similar, though he places pillows underneath the neck, knees, and chest, and starts the relaxation process with the jaws, proceeding then to the eyes, breathing apparatus, legs, etc. He also suggests that the patient "talk to" the various muscle groups, telling them to "let go, let go" more and more. This procedure is to be repeated once or twice a day until the patient feels less tense and more comfortable. He is also advised to practice "differential relaxation" during work or other activities—that is, to reduce contraction of muscles directly employed in an action and at the same time relax the muscles that are not involved, such as relaxing the left arm while writing with the right.

Therapists who recommend relaxation techniques usually employ them as a supplement to interview and other forms of psychotherapy. They are therefore viewed as a supportive or adjunctive approach, not as the primary therapy. As Thorpe, Katz, and Lewis (1961) point out, "Relaxation is believed to have advantages therapeutically over sedatives, change of scene, entertainment, or any of the other methods of distraction or inhibition whose aim is to relieve muscular tensions for the reason that it represents a planned scientific approach to the problem. The individual is taught how to relax instead of simply being told to do so." The technique also has a place in some forms of behavior therapy. *See* this topic.

RELEASE THERAPY. A form of play therapy in which young children act out their emotional problems in the presence of a permissive and sympathetic therapist.

The method was developed by David M. Levy, who limited it to cases in which definite anxiety symptoms were precipitated by specific events in the child's recent past—such as a frightening experience, divorce of the parents, or the birth of a brother or sister. The parents provide this information, and the therapist chooses toys such as doll figures, weapons, animals, and water guns which will encourage the child to re-enact the disturbing situation. No attempt is made to offer him any interpretation or to suggest new ways of meeting his problem. He works out, or rather *plays* out, his solution by himself.

Levy (1939) has described the case of a seven-year-old boy who had repeated nightmares in which he was bound and tortured. The precipitating event was a story read at school about two knights who nailed an innkeeper's hands to the door of his inn. When the boy heard this story, it called to mind an actual incident in which some boys had bound him to a tree and pretended to torture him. Both the story and the incident aroused anxiety

because of their similarity to a hospital experience during which he had been wrapped in blankets while his eardrums were punctured without the use of an anesthetic. In the play sessions he was given toys that represented knights and an inn, boys, ropes and a tree, as well as blankets and a doctor. It took only four sessions of active play to eliminate the nightmares.

The effectiveness of release therapy is due to the fact that it enables the child not only to discharge pent-up feelings, but to reduce his sensitivity to the threatening situation. By re-enacting an alarming event or disturbing relationship, such as sibling rivalry, he comes to see it in a new light, gains some understanding of his reactions, and thereby achieves a degree of mastery over the fear, antagonism, or guilt that has been causing him anxiety. As Thorpe, Katz, and Lewis (1961) point out, "If adequately carried out, release therapy may bring about aeration of the thought processes of the child, the relief of repressed hate, the alleviation of guilt feelings through self-punishment, and sufficient catharsis to enable the child to redirect his energies into constructive channels." The technique bears a resemblance to the use of drugs and hypnosis in bringing about an "abreaction" of traumatic experiences undergone by adult patients. With children, however, play is a strong enough stimulus to produce this effect because their imagination is so active and the traumatic events are not deeply repressed. *See* ABREACTION, CATHARSIS, PLAY THERAPY, POSTOPERATIVE DISORDERS.

REMEMBERING. The process of retaining previous experience; also the process of bringing to awareness, or reviving, retained material.

Remembering, in the sense of retention, is essential to learning; without it we would not profit from training, practice, or past experiences—for if nothing were left over from these processes, nothing would be learned. It is also an indispensable foundation for thinking and reasoning, since remembered facts and procedures are constantly employed in carrying out these activities. Without memory we would have little if any sense of time, and no ability to relate the future to the past; nor would we have any sense of personal identity, since we would not know that we are the same person we were last week and last year.

Remembering takes four major forms: recollection, recall, recognition, and relearning. In *recollection* we conjure up, or reconstruct, memories from our own past experience—for example, a present event may remind us of the day we started on our first job. The term "redintegrative memory" is sometimes used for this process, since we bring together or "re-integrate" (the "d" is added for euphony) an earlier experience on the basis of a partial cue, a reminder.

Only a few investigations have been made of this type of memory. Reiff and Scheerer (1959) have shown that memories of schoolroom experiences at ages seven and ten can be more accurately recovered by adults when under hypnosis than in the waking state; and some investigators have been able to authenticate personal memories dating from the first year of life, although most people cannot recollect events before the third or fourth year at most (Dudycha and Dudycha, 1941). Experiments on testimony in which students are asked to report staged events which they have witnessed in the classroom indicate that reconstruction of dramatic situations is subject to many kinds of distortion. Redintegrative memory also plays an important role in psychoanalysis, since this process depends in large part on the resurrection of personal experiences from early childhood. *See* LEGAL PSYCHOLOGY.

In *recall*—the second type of memory process—we remember events, data, or skills without reference to the past. Thus we may recall a song or date or quotation without remembering the circumstances under which we learned it. This also applies to remembered skills such as riding a bicycle or sewing on a button. This kind of remembering is more easily studied in the laboratory than redintegrative memory and is involved in the standard experiments on memorization, such as those using the serial method (memorizing lines of a poem, or a series of nonsense words) and the paired associates method (learning words in pairs, such as the states with their capitals). The words are usually exposed briefly on a memory drum (PLATE 32). *See* PAIRED ASSOCIATES LEARNING.

In *recognition* we experience a sense of familiarity when we come upon someone or something we have encountered before. We often recognize people whom we cannot call by name, and students frequently recognize the right answer on a multiple-choice question even though they would have been unable to give it if they had been asked a direct question. Sometimes the sense of familiarity is deceptive, as in the déjà vu experience. *See* PARAMNESIA. In a typical laboratory test of recognition, a group of subjects are required to study a series of photographs of different people, and after an interval are asked to select them from a much larger group.

In the *relearning* method, retention is demonstrated by showing that material learned in the past and apparently forgotten can be relearned more rapidly than new material. A standard laboratory method consists of having subjects learn a list of words by repeating them over and over until they can be recited once perfectly, then allowing a week to elapse, after which they study the list again until they can repeat the words perfectly. The number of trials required for the relearning as compared with the number originally required yields a "saving score": if the entire list can be repeated perfectly after one trial, the score is 100 per cent; if only 25 per cent of the trials are required as in the original learning, the saving would be 75 per cent. This general method was used in a celebrated experiment in which Burtt (1941) read a number of Greek passages on a daily schedule to a boy from his fifteenth month to his third year. The boy was later tested by the relearning method without having studied Greek in the meantime. At eight years of age he was found to require 27 per cent fewer repetitions in learning some of the original material than in learning equivalent new material (that is, the saving score was 27 per cent). At fourteen, when he was tested on another set of passages, there was still an 8 per cent saving, but by eighteen years of age no saving could be detected. The experiment dramatically demonstrated that the boy retained a substantial amount of the original material at ages eight and fourteen even though the passages were totally meaningless to him. *See* MEMORY STORAGE, MEMORY IMPROVEMENT, FORGETTING.

Two other phenomena of memory deserve special attention: reminiscence, and the tip-of-the-tongue state. As mentioned under FORGETTING, it has been found that we tend to forget at an especially rapid rate immediately after learning, and after that the "retention curve" drops more gradually. However, it has also been noted that in some cases the curve goes up instead of down after an interval, and begins to decrease later on. It has even been found that incompletely learned material can be recalled more fully after a rest period than immediately after learning—for example, Ward (1937) found that a subject who recalled an average of 9.5 nonsense syllables immediately after practice might recall 10.5 after

two minutes. This phenomenon, which applies to motor as well as verbal skills, is termed reminiscence. Several explanations have been suggested but none is universally accepted. Some investigators claim it is due to rehearsing the material during the interval, although experiments show that it occurs when other activities interfere with rehearsal. Others believe it is due to the tendency for incorrect associations to drop out during a rest period. Still others attribute it to the "consolidation of the memory trace," the idea that it takes time for memories to get "set" in the nervous system. *See* FORGETTING, MEMORY STORAGE.

The tip-of-the-tongue (TOT) state—the feeling that a particular fact or word is on the tip of the tongue even though we cannot recall it at the moment—has recently been investigated by Brown and McNeill (1966). They have demonstrated that the words which come to mind have something in common with the "target word" we are searching for. In their experiments they selected unusual words (sampan, cloaca, ambergris, etc.) which were likely to be in the subject's recognition or passive vocabulary but not in their active-recall vocabulary. Definitions of these words were read aloud, and when the subjects felt they knew the word corresponding to one of the definitions (that is, when they were in the TOT state), they were asked questions about it. The answers to these questions showed that they actually had information about the target word, and the closer they were to recognizing it, the more accurate that information proved to be. The similarity between the suggested words and the target word had to do with sound more often than meaning —for example, if the target word was sampan the subjects often thought of like-sounding words such as Siam and Saipan rather than words with similar meaning such as barge or junk. Often, too, they were able to give the initial letters and the number of syllables of the target word, and in some cases the final sound and stressed syllable as well.

REPETITION-COMPULSION. A psychoanalytic term for the tendency to repeat past behavior and, more narrowly, to relive disturbing experiences.

Freud viewed repetition-compulsion as an unconscious, instinctual impulse that is "more fundamental than the pleasure-pain principle and differing widely from it," since the experience that is repeated is usually a painful one that contributes "no potentiality of pleasure." His English disciple, Ernest Jones (1938), described it as "the blind impulse to repeat earlier experiences and situations quite irrespective of any advantage that doing so might bring from a pleasure-pain point of view."

This tendency is clearly expressed in children who repeat mischievous behavior or disagreeable habits even though they may be punished for them. Freud came to believe that the repetition impulse is the core of neurosis, since the neurotic individual persists in using behavior patterns that are clearly irrational and maladaptive—for example, blaming others for his errors (projection), becoming sick in order to escape problems (conversion), or acting childishly when faced with difficulties (regression). Another example given by Freud is the tendency of divorced people to choose a new mate who has the same faults as the original mate. This tendency may be an expression of what he called a "destiny neurosis," the compulsive unconscious need to arrange life experiences in such a way that one is bound to suffer failure and defeat. Neurotics of this type invariably blame an unkind fate for their continual reverses, and are unaware that they are themselves responsible—or that they are "paying the piper" for deep-seated feelings of guilt.

Repetition-compulsion is put to positive use in the psychoanalytic process.

Freud found that his patients had a compulsion to re-experience their childhood difficulties during analysis, and they also tended to repeat basic relationships by putting the therapist in the place of one or the other parent. This process, called transference, enables the patient to bring his feelings and attitudes into the open. With the aid of the analyst, he becomes more aware of them, and learns to understand and cope with them. During this process he also finds new ways of approaching his difficulties, and practices them repeatedly during the analytic sessions.

The tendency to relive traumatic experiences is another form of repetition-compulsion. The clearest examples are nightmares, terror dreams, and daytime fantasies in which we rehearse events which have been deeply disturbing or damaging to our ego. Many soldiers are "haunted" by battle dreams for months or even years after their war experiences, and almost everyone is afflicted by recurrent nightmares after an accident or near-accident. Very few specialists today would characterize this tendency as instinctual, as Freud did. Rather, they usually explain such dreams as either an attempt to master our anxiety or to get it out of our system. They would also hesitate to ascribe neurotic patterns to "blind impulse" but would explain them as unconscious attempts to overcome anxiety. Freud himself preferred this type of explanation in his later thinking. *See* NIGHTMARE, PSYCHONEUROSIS, DEATH INSTINCT, PSYCHOANALYSIS (THEORY).

REPRESSION. The defense mechanism in which painful or threatening experiences and impulses are automatically excluded from consciousness. Repression is not to be confused with suppression, which is a deliberate attempt to keep unpleasant ideas out of mind.

The concept of repression was originally developed by Freud to account for the fact that his patients often failed to recall the events that produced their symptoms. At first he felt that repression produced anxiety, but he later reversed this order and came to believe that anxiety produced repression—that is, traumatic events and disturbing experiences are pushed into the unconscious because the individual cannot tolerate the anxiety they generate. In time, the interpretation of repression as a defense against anxiety became "the cornerstone of dynamic psychiatry" (Noyes and Kolb, 1963), and was used not only to explain lapses of memory, but our tendency to expel from consciousness unacceptable sexual desires, dangerous feelings of hostility, and ego-threatening impulses of all kinds.

Even though repression may banish objectionable memories or impulses from consciousness, it does not deprive them of their dynamic force. "They continue to lead a subterranean life beneath the conventional surface, yet they are liable to manifest their influence in the roots of personality, in special interests, in some system of beliefs or code of values, or in more marked form as neurotic, psychosomatic, or psychotic symptoms" (Noyes and Kolb). In addition, repressed or half-repressed impulses may express themselves in many indirect ways, as in dreams, fantasies, jokes, and slips of the tongue. They may also produce vague feelings of guilt, insecurity, and uneasiness—and if they rise close to the surface and gather force, they may arouse intense feelings of anxiety. *See* ANXIETY REACTION.

Repression is probably the basic defense mechanism, the one most frequently called upon to protect the ego. Moreover, it appears to be involved in most of our other defenses. It comes into play, for example, when we fail to perceive unpleasant realities (denial of reality), when we conceal objectionable impulses by going to the opposite extreme (reaction formation), and when

we protect ourselves from hurt by withdrawing into passivity or intellectuality (emotional insulation and intellectualization). *See* these topics.

Like other defense mechanisms, repression has both advantages and disadvantages. It may help us control impulses that arouse guilt feelings or run counter to the moral code, and it may —through temporary amnesia—protect us against traumatic experiences until we are better prepared to assimilate them. But repression is also a form of escape, and it is usually better to face our problems than to evade them. We cannot merely say, "Don't repress," because this mechanism operates on an automatic unconscious level. To keep it in check, we have to approach it indirectly by getting in the habit of airing our feelings openly and by encouraging our children to express their feelings freely, so that they will not feel guilty about their thoughts and impulses. Moreover, if we create an accepting and secure atmosphere, feelings of anxiety are unlikely to arise, and there will therefore be no need to drive any thoughts, impulses, or experiences underground where they can damage the personality.

If repression has already taken place, it is often possible to break through it and bring the original events into consciousness where they can be understood and overcome. This is one of the major functions of "uncovering" techniques such as hypnotherapy, sodium pentothal interviews, and, on a more comprehensive level, psychoanalysis. *See* SCREEN MEMORY, SUPPRESSION, FORGETTING.

Illustrative Case: REPRESSION

A young man who had recently become engaged was walking along the street with his fiancée. Another man greeted him and began to chat in a friendly fashion. The young man realized that he must know this apparent stranger, and that both courtesy and pride required that he introduce the visitor to his fiancée. The name of the other man, however, eluded him completely; indeed, he had not even a fleeting recognition of his identity. When in his confusion he attempted at least to present his fiancée, he found that he had also forgotten her name.

Only a brief behavior analysis was necessary to make this incident comprehensible as an example of normal generalized repression. The apparent stranger was in fact a former friend of the young man; but the friendship had eventually brought frustation and disappointment in a situation identical with the one described. Some years before, our subject had become engaged to another young woman, and in his pride and happiness he had at once sought out this friend and introduced the two. Unfortunately the girl had become strongly attached to the friend and he to her; at length she broke her engagement and married the friend. The two men had not seen each other until this meeting, which repeated exactly the earlier frustrating situation. It is hardly surprising that the newly engaged man repressed all recognition of his former friend, all hints as to his identity, and even the name of the fiancée. (Cameron and Magaret, 1951)

RESISTANCE. In psychotherapy, the patient's tendency to use various devices to avoid bringing repressed material into awareness. The material is opposed and resisted because of its painful nature.

The resistance process goes on completely or almost completely beneath the level of consciousness. Just as healthy individuals avoid unpleasant subjects of conversation, the patient in therapy may automatically use any number of techniques to keep disturbing memories or insights out of awareness. He may forget his appointments, divert the discussion to irrelevant topics, insist that certain ideas are too "ridiculous" to discuss, lapse into complete silence, or flare up at the therapist and walk out in a huff. *See* SCREEN MEMORY, SCOTOMA.

Manifestations of resistance are particularly apt to occur in psychoanalytic therapy, but may be observed in other procedures as well. The therapist uses

them as a clue to the repressed material itself, and as a sign that he is getting close to the core of the neurosis. If the resistance does not dissolve of its own accord, the therapist will usually focus attention on it and enlist the patient's aid in searching for an explanation, a process that is termed "analysis of the resistance." If it is successful it can contribute materially to the therapy. *See* PSYCHOANALYSIS (THERAPY).

RESTITUTION. The unconscious defense mechanism of making amends for guilty thoughts or behavior.

In psychiatry restitution is classed as a defense mechanism because it is aimed at relieving a deeply embedded sense of guilt and not merely at making reparation for actual damage done. Generally the individual's extreme sense of guilt stems from minor or imaginary wrongdoing and therefore seems exaggerated and uncalled-for. In some cases the need to "make amends" produces a persistent, highly compulsive drive that dominates the individual's entire life. He becomes the kind of person who is constantly "doing for others," sacrificing himself, and unnecessarily acting the martyr. This behavior interferes with his relationships, since by forcing his attentions on other people he puts them in debt for unwanted services and inevitably arouses resentment.

RETICULAR FORMATION (Reticular Activating System, RAS). A network of nerve cells deep in the middle of the brain (PLATE 1), extending from lower to higher centers; a structure involved in arousing and alerting the organism.

The RAS is made up of nerve cells in the lower brain stem, a structure about the size of the little finger. It is located in a strategic position since all incoming and outgoing sensory and motor impulses pass near it and may stimulate it. The portion of the structure which sends impulses to the cortex, the ascending RAS, helps to bring about and maintain attention; the part which sends impulses to the spinal cord, the descending RAS, affects the musculature and the autonomic nervous system.

The reticular formation plays two interrelated roles. It serves a general arousal function which differentiates wakefulness from sleep (Samuels, 1959), keeping the organism alert to sensory signals; and it regulates the level of attention to specific stimuli. The cortex becomes receptive to stimulation only after it has been aroused by the RAS—for example, input from the visceral and surface receptors (stomach, eye, ear, etc.) stimulate the RAS, which in turn activates the cortex (Lindsley, 1951). Its functions have been tested by direct stimulation, which has been found to produce a waking EEG pattern known as alpha blocking. Experiments have also shown that sleeping animals, such as the monkey, are awakened by such stimulation, and the RAS has therefore been designated the "waking center" (Segundo et al., 1955). On the other hand, injury to the RAS results in apathy, lethargy, or drowsiness (Lindsley, 1951). *See* BRAIN WAVES.

Experiments also indicate that when an individual is asleep, tactile or other stimuli actually reach the cortex, but since the RAS is not active, the arousal state is low and the signals are not appreciated, or "encoded," by the brain. Similarly, neural activity can be recorded from the brain during deep anesthesia, but the message cannot be detected and understood because of low RAS activity. It is believed that drugs which produce sleep (barbiturates) or alertness (amphetamines) act upon this area of the brain. Other experiments have shown that monkeys will perform discrimination tasks more quickly and accurately than usual during electrical stimulation of the RAS. Also, when human beings are given the tranquilizer chlorpromazine to cut down on RAS

arousal, they show impaired discrimination ability (Primac, Mirsky, and Rosvold, 1957).

Sensory deprivation experiments indicate that the loss of normal functions which occurs in this state is due to a low level of RAS activity. Some investigators believe the RAS is involved in pain arousal, and that general anesthetics produce their effects through this structure. It is also believed to account for the ability of the mother to awaken when her baby cries, and to remain asleep through much louder sounds, although the exact mechanism is still unknown. Hernández-Peón, Sherrer, and Jouvet (1956) have recorded the neural activity in a cat's ear, and have shown that a continuously sounding click ceases to be registered as soon as the cat is shown a mouse, or smells the odor of fish, or is given an electrical shock. Apparently the RAS cuts off the auditory responses when the situation changes so that other stimuli become more important than the task at hand. Experiments of this kind have led to the theory that RAS is a "gating" or "shunting" mechanism which makes it possible for impulses significant for survival to gain dominance over less important stimuli. *See* SENSORY DEPRIVATION, NARCOLEPSY.

RITUAL. A complex series of compulsive acts carried out repeatedly as a defense against anxiety or as a release of tension.

A long or involved ritual may be a kind of magic ceremonial unconsciously created to ward off punishment for forbidden wishes and urges. It may at the same time serve as penance and atonement for guilty thoughts or actions (fancied or real), or as a means of screening out distasteful or threatening emotions attached to them. The acts themselves are usually symbolic in nature, and the major defense mechanisms involved are undoing and isolation. *See* UNDOING, ISOLATION.

Rituals are fairly common neurotic symptoms in children and adolescents as well as adults. Among children they may subside without treatment if adequate opportunity is given to voice fears, release tensions in healthy activity, and establish more satisfactory relationships with others. Among adults, rituals are usually indicative of an obsessive-compulsive trend that requires intensive psychotherapy. In one of his earliest papers, "The Neuro-Psychoses of Defense" (1894), Freud cited the following case:

"An eleven-year-old boy had instituted the following obsessive ceremonial before going to bed. He did not sleep until he had told his mother in the minutest detail all the events of the day; there must be no scraps of paper or other rubbish on the carpet of the bedroom; the bed must be pushed right to the wall; three chairs must stand by it and pillows must lie in a particular way. In order to get to sleep he must first kick out a certain number of times with both legs and then lie on his side." For the dynamics of compulsive rituals and an illustrative case, see OBSESSIVE-COMPULSIVE REACTION.

ROLE PLAYING (Sociodrama). A technique of human relations training and psychotherapy in which the individual acts out social roles of other people, or tries out new roles for himself.

Role playing was originally developed as a technique to be used in psychodrama, but it is now widely practiced in industrial, educational, and clinical settings. Unlike psychodrama, it is a highly informal procedure that does not require a stage or specially chosen personnel. As a training device, it is frequently employed in developing the ability to meet practical situations such as making a speech, conducting an interview, handling sales problems, or applying for a job. In most cases the individual not only practices his own role, but takes the roles of others in order to see the situation from their standpoint and gain a more objective view of himself. As a treatment technique, it may be used either in individual or group therapy, though it is more often applied in the latter type of situation. Playing various parts in realistic but "safe" situations gives the patient new insight into himself and other people. It also provides him with an opportunity to rehearse and test out new attitudes, relationships, and ways of coping with conflicts and stresses.

Role playing has proved highly effective in family group therapy. By playing each other's roles in facing troublesome situations the various members of the family bring their deeper feelings to the surface, achieve a new understanding of each other's point of view, and gain a different perspective on their own place in the family picture. This process often leads them to approach their problems on a new plane and reach a resolution that is acceptable to every member of the family.

The technique is also employed for a variety of purposes in hospital and clinic settings. As part of her training, a nurse might act out an encounter with an irritable or resistant patient, then switch roles and play the part of the patient himself. To increase their understanding and acceptance of the staff, patients are asked to show how they themselves would handle typical hospital situations. To provide the patient with a chance to release pent-up emotions, he might be requested to dramatize the last quarrel he had with his wife, or act out what he really wanted to say to the doctor who refused him a special privilege. To prepare mental patients for discharge from the hospital, it is common practice to have them act out some of the situations they are likely to meet, such as answering questions about their illness or applying for a job. In all these cases, the role playing not only brings troublesome feelings to the surface, but paves the way for free and open discussion.

See PSYCHODRAMA, MANAGEMENT DEVEL-
OPMENT.

RORSCHACH TEST. A projective technique in which responses to standard inkblots are professionally interpreted.

The Rorschach test is based on the common human tendency to react emotionally to ambiguous stimuli such as cloud formations or shadowy shapes in a forest at night. We read, or "project," our own interpretations and feelings into these objects, usually in a highly individual way. From this cue, Hermann Rorschach (1884–1922), a Swiss psychiatrist reasoned that deeper trends of the personality could be revealed through reactions to a series of ordinary inkblots. After extensive trial and study, he narrowed these blots down to ten which appeared to elicit the most telling responses. (Rorschach, 1921)

The standard inkblots are all symmetrical, but so irregular in form that innumerable interpretations are possible (*Fig. 46*). Some are black, some gray,

Fig. 46. An inkblot of the type used on the Rorschach Test.

and some contain patches of color. The subject is asked to examine one blot at a time and answer the question "What might this be?" The average individual gives more than one response to many of the blots; the total for the series of ten is in the neighborhood of 30 or 40. These responses are taken down by the examiner and usually scored according to a set of rules.

The first step in the scoring process is to put the responses into three major categories. *Location scores* tell what part of the blot is used: (W) stands for the whole blot, (D) for a part of the blot, and (Dd) for an unusual detail. The *determinant score* indicates what aspects of the blot were utilized: if form was more important than color, the response is designated (FC), and the reverse if color was the controlling factor; if the object was seen as moving, the score (M) is used; if the response fits the objective form of the blot, it is rated (F plus), and if the form quality is poor it is rated (F minus). The *content score* indicates the category in which the response falls: (H) for human being, (Cg) for clothing, (A) for animal, and so on. All these scores are tallied, and a total profile is obtained.

The next step is to interpret the scores. This is often done by comparing certain "response indicators" to norms obtained from large samples of the population. Rorschach theory suggests, for example, that too many original, non-popular responses indicate a disturbance of a schizophrenic nature; human movement responses are believed to represent imagination and creative impulses; and color responses are associated with emotionality. If the subject avoids using the colored portions of the blots, or gets extremely upset when he first looks at a blot containing color, his reaction is termed "color shock" and taken as evidence of difficulty in controlling emotion. If he does not respond to the shaded areas, he is probably a "black-and-white" kind of individual.

The test is also believed to reveal general personality trends. Compulsive persons, for example, have a need to do everything "right," and to maintain tight, rigid control over themselves and their world. On the Rorschach test, these people tend to respond to the details instead of to entire figures at once. The theory states that they must account for every part of the blots, just as they would feel compelled to do in a real life situation.

Studies of Rorschach interpretations have shown that these indices vary greatly in validity. Single quantitative scores have proved practically worthless as indicators of specific personality traits and as predictors of future behavior. Many psychologists have therefore abandoned the usual scoring procedures and use the test only to obtain an over-all "global" impression of the dynamics of the individual. This impression is then checked against the results of a battery of other personality and intelligence tests. In this way the therapist works with the responses in much the same way that a psychoanalyst deals with the free associations of his patient. He notes the sequence of responses and tries to find the internal forces that brought them about. He forms hypotheses about the individual from his reactions to the first figure—for example, "bat, butterfly, moth, people facing each other," or "reminds me of a bat, the whole thing" —then he looks for verification of his hypothesis in the responses to the remaining figures. The difficulty with this approach is that it depends almost wholly on the examiner's own knowledge of personality dynamics, and his interpretations are often private and unverifiable. Furthermore, the examiner runs the risk of fitting new data into pet theories which may tell more about his own personality than that of his subject.

The Rorschach technique has been tested in many areas of human behavior, and its strengths and limitations are now fairly apparent. When it is applied in conjunction with other evaluative tests it frequently yields information that other instruments are not geared to tap. The unstructured character of the blots seems to elicit deep-seated aspects of the personality. At times, however, the test merely documents the obvious by showing that blatantly ill people give bizarre responses.

On the other hand, it has uses which were not originally anticipated. Recent studies show that it gives significant information about the way people feel about their bodies—that is, their body image. A new interpretation called a "barrier score" has been developed which indicates the sharpness of distinction between the body and its surroundings. Responses like "alligator" and "armadillo" contribute to a high barrier score since the skin of these animals has unusual qualities. These responses have been found among people with symptoms that lie in or near the surface of their bodies, such as dermatitis, rheumatoid arthritis, and conversion reaction. They are not usually given by people who suffer from internal conditions such as stomach disturbances and ulcerative colitis.

The Rorschach test has not proven to be a valid tool for predicting vocational success. But, more important, newer investigations seriously question its validity in both diagnosis and prognosis, the two areas where it has been most frequently used. Cronbach (1960), for example, has severely criticized the assumptions on which it is built, as well as the statistical handling of data. He has estimated that 90 per cent of the conclusions based on Rorschach findings are unsubstantiated. Attacks of this kind, plus the development of newer techniques such as the Thematic Aperception Test, have resulted in a more limited use of the Rorschach in clinical work.

In addition to the Rorschach, there are other important inkblot tests. The Holtzman Inkblot Technique, designed to achieve greater objectivity than the Rorschach without sacrifice of sensitivity, consists of ninety inkblots in parallel forms of forty-five each so that progress in therapy may be evaluated. The blots vary in symmetry, color, and texture, and a smaller number can be selected for intensive exploration of a particular area. One response is given to each blot and analysis of protocols by computer processes has resulted in an objective, reproducible scoring guide giving percentile norms for twenty-two response variables based on eight normal and pathological groups of individuals ranging from five years of age to adult. The newly developed Harrower Psychodiagnostic Inkblot Test is particularly well adapted to group testing, since the inkblots are expendable and subjects write their responses in private. The manual contains extensive research data, case studies, tables of frequency of response, and comparisons between normal and hospital populations.

ROSENZWEIG PICTURE-FRUSTRATION STUDY (P-F). A projective test which assesses patterns of reaction to typical stress situations.

It is an all-too-obvious fact that frustrating experiences are a common feature of everyday life, and it is equally apparent that they provoke emotional responses. Building on these two facts, S. Rosenzweig (1947–49) has constructed a test which presents the subject with frustrating situations on the theory that the way they are handled will be a significant index of emotional adjustment.

The test consists of a series of cartoon situations which depict frustrating circumstances experienced in everyday life. In one of these cartoons, a car splashes a pedestrian and the driver says, "I am very sorry we splashed you. I tried to avoid the puddle"; in another, a woman had just knocked over a vase, and the hostess says, "How awful! That was my mother's favorite vase." The characters are shown without facial expressions or special posture that might suggest the nature of their reactions, and the subject is asked to indicate what the second person in the situation would reply, writing down the first words that come to his mind. It is assumed that he identifies with the frus-

trated character and that his replies are a projection of his own typical reactions. After the twenty-four situations are presented he is asked to read aloud both the printed speeches of the frustrating character and his own responses. The examiner takes note of any significant omissions or inflections in his voice during the reading.

The responses are basically interpreted in terms of three types of aggression. First, "extrapunitive" responses are directed outward, at people or things. In the first situation above, the pedestrian might swear at the driver or demand that he pay his cleaning bill. Second, "intropunitive" responses are directed inward, toward himself; the pedestrian might say, "It was my fault. I should have stood farther away from the curb," or "I guess I didn't look where I was going—as usual I did a stupid thing." Third, "impunitive" responses make light of the problem and are usually delivered in a conciliatory tone; "It was an accident. It could have happened to anyone," or "Don't worry, it was an old suit."

The examiner is also alert to three other kinds of reactions to frustration: "obstacle-dominated" responses, in which the problem created by the experience is emphasized; "ego-defensive" responses, in which a defense mechanism is used; and "need-persistent" responses, which focus on the solution of the problem. In scoring the test these three possible reactions are combined with each of the three aggressive reactions described above, to give a total of nine possible responses. To illustrate, the following replies in the splash situation are all extrapunitive, but the first is obstacle-dominated, the second is ego-defensive, and the third need-persistent: "I am sorry too, the suit is new," "Why don't you watch where you're going?", and "What about cleaning the suit?"

Responses to this test have been thoroughly analyzed, and norms are available. Two of the most important considerations are the consistency of the responses and the general trend throughout the entire series of situations. A subject who says, "I'm sorry," in all situations is bound to be responding in an inadequate and inappropriate way on some of them—for example, this remark is more appropriate in the broken vase situation than in the splash situation. Inadequate responses of this kind often indicate low frustration tolerance, a sign of immaturity. The test itself presents so many situations that it is important to note changes in the mode of response while it is being given. This would be an important indicator of the way the subject would handle a long series of frustrating situations.

There is also a children's form of the P-F test designed for ages four to fourteen, presenting situations that might occur in any child's life. This test is handled in the same way as the adult form except that the examiner makes an additional analysis of responses, noting what special needs are being thwarted and whether the frustrating person is another child, a parent figure, or other individual. Both forms are usually administered in conjunction with a battery of projective tests.

Although the P-F test is primarily used in assessing personality and adjustment, it has also been employed in studying the way different racial and nationality groups react to frustration. In addition, a similar technique has been applied in studying attitudes toward minority groups and opinions on social issues such as the prevention of war.

RUMOR. An unverified report or account that circulates primarily by word of mouth.

Rumors may be wholly false or may contain an element of truth that is usually distorted or exaggerated. Though they often circulate in the form of gossip and may be deliberately "planted" at any time, they tend to occur in greatest profusion during periods of public crisis when reliable information is hard to obtain. As Allport and Post-

man (1945) have pointed out, the bombing of Pearl Harbor created a perfect setting for the circulation of rumors: "The affair was important because of the potential danger it represented to all of us, and because its aftermath of mobilization affected every life. It was ambiguous because no one seemed certain of the extent or reasons for, or consequences of the attack. Since the two conditions of rumor—importance and ambiguity—were at a maximum, we had an unprecedented flood of what became known as 'Pearl Harbor rumors.' It was said that our fleet was 'wiped out,' that Washington did not dare to tell the extent of the damage, that Hawaii was in the hands of the Japanese. So widespread and so demoralizing were these tales that, on February 29th, 1942, President Roosevelt broadcast a speech devoted entirely to the harmful rumors and to reiterating the official report on the losses."

Allport and Postman (1947) have conducted a number of studies of rumor under controlled conditions. The most striking was a "chain reproduction" experiment in which pictures were projected on a screen before an audience. A first subject was brought in, placed behind a partition out of sight of the screen, and asked to listen as a selected member of the audience described the picture in detail. After this, several other subjects were admitted in turn, each one relaying the account to the next without seeing the picture. Analysis of these accounts showed that, with each succeeding description, the story became less detailed and more inaccurate. From this study the experimenters derived three principles (based on Wulf, 1922) which they believed to apply to rumors in general: first, leveling—simplification by eliminating details; second, sharpening—increased emphasis on certain details as leveling takes place; and third, assimilation—the tendency of the transmitters to fit their accounts into a context based on their own attitudes and expectations.

To cite a concrete example, one of the pictures showed a subway car with a number of seated passengers and two men standing up facing each other, one a Negro and the other a white man with an open straight-edge razor in his hand. In this case, leveling was illustrated by the fact that the first report was only half as long as the original account, and the fifth read, quite simply, "This is a trolley car with seven persons on it. There is a woman with a baby. Somebody is flashing a razor. There are some signs and some colored people." The emphasis on the razor, the adjective "flashing," and the highlighting of color ("*some* colored people") are examples of sharpening. In repeating this experiment with different subjects it was found that many individuals shifted the razor to the Negro and said he was threatening the white man with it—an illustration of assimilation to prejudice.

In discussing these experiments, Munn (1966) points out that the three processes also apply to the transmission of legends, since the original details become simplified (leveling), certain details are accentuated (sharpening), and the story itself persists because it expresses fears, wishes, or values which society seeks to perpetuate (assimilation). The same principles also apply to gossip, hearsay, distortions of memory, and explain many of the inaccuracies found in testimony. See FOR-GETTING, LEGAL PSYCHOLOGY, PARAMNESIA, SUGGESTION, PERCEPTUAL DISTORTION, STEREOTYPE, PREJUDICE.

RUSH, BENJAMIN (1746–1813). Rush, the first American psychiatrist, was born in Pennsylvania and graduated from the College of New Jersey (now Princeton). He then went on to receive his medical degree from Edinburgh University. During his distinguished career he became equally eminent in politics and social affairs, chemistry, general medicine, and psychiatry. As a member of the Continental Congress he was one of the signers of the Declaration of Independence. He also took a strong stand against slavery, capital punishment, and excessive use of alcohol, and helped organize the first Negro church in Philadelphia. During the Revolutionary War, Rush served as Physician-General in charge of hospital patients and wrote a pioneer work on mental hygiene entitled "Directions for Preserving the Health of Soldiers." He also played an active role during a yellow fever epidemic in Philadelphia, employing the drastic technique of bloodletting and mercury intake, on the theory that debilitation would weaken the fever. Although bitterly attacked for both his medical and political views, his reputation grew to such proportions that he became known as the "Hippocrates of Pennsylvania."

During the first twenty years of his professional life, from 1769 to 1789, Rush held the first professorship of chemistry in America, at Dickinson College; but from that point until his death he turned his attention almost entirely to psychiatry. In 1792 he was instrumental in establishing a separate wing of the Pennsylvania Hospital for active treatment and intensive study of the insane, who had previously been confined to basement cells. During the years that followed, he sought to convince his medical colleagues that insanity was a disease that is essentially treatable. In support of his thesis he published a book, *Medical Inquiries and Observations Upon the Disease of the Mind,* which became a standard authority in America and Europe for the next seventy years.

In his general approach to mental illness Rush was well in advance of his associates, but his specific techniques present quite another story. His basic theory was that "the cause of madness is seated primarily in the blood vessels of the brain," and his treatments were largely aimed at restoring the blood supply to its proper balance. He held, however, that the two major types of disorder, maniacal states and torpid states, require different types of treatment because one is due to an oversupply and the other an undersupply of blood in the brain.

Since he believed that people become maniacal if their brains become "overcharged" with blood, Rush recommended the same general type of treatment he had applied to yellow fever. He attempted to relieve the saturation of the blood in the brain by bloodletting to the point of fainting, and produced a state of debility primarily through purges and emetics. These techniques were often combined with other methods of quieting the patient. One of his procedures was to keep him awake and on foot for twenty-four-hour periods so that "the debility thus induced in those muscles would attract morbid excitement from the brain, and thereby relieve the disease." He also advocated a psychological approach, and sought to calm the patient through kindness. However, if this did not work, he felt it necessary to employ intimidation, just as one would do with an "unruly animal." He therefore advised the physician to speak to the patient in a stern, authoritarian voice, and if necessary to apply a kind of "shock" treatment by threatening him with death. If these methods also failed he prescribed punishment, such as pouring cold water down the patient's sleeve, or the use of his "tranquilizer chair." This was a heavy wooden affair in which the patient was strapped at the chest, abdomen, ankles, and knees, with his head inserted in a wooden box. Rush preferred this method of restraint to the strait jacket because it did not interfere with the bloodletting. He also believed it served a therapeutic purpose in itself by reducing the flow of blood to the patient's head.

Torpid and melancholic states were treated quite differently, since these conditions were attributed to a depletion of blood in the brain. Rush believed that these patients should be handled gently and leniently. Nevertheless, he devised a piece of apparatus that appears to be anything but gentle. He placed his patients in a mechanical cage, or gyrator, which could be rotated with a crank. The object was to drive out the illness by producing vertigo, perspiration, and nausea, and to employ centrifugal force to move the blood back into the brain and thereby stimulate it to normal activity.

As these methods indicate, Rush did little if anything to advance psychiatric treatment. Most of the techniques he used were on the level of the European psychiatry of the time. However, he did much to bring mental illness into the general field of medicine by advocating treatment as opposed to incarceration. And the fact that a leading physician of the day devoted himself wholeheartedly to the problem of mental illness was undoubtedly a stimulus to others. In the opinions of many historians these contributions were sufficient to earn him the title of "Father of American psychiatry."

S

SADISM. A sexual deviation in which gratification is obtained by the infliction of pain on others. The term has also been broadened to include any type of extreme cruelty.

The word sadism derives from the

name of the Marquis de Sade (1740–1814), who described a variety of sexual perversions in his novel *Justine and Juliette, or The Curse of Virtue and the Blessing of Vice.* The Marquis himself is said to have engaged in such cruel sexual practices that he was committed as insane.

Sadistic pain may be either mental or physical, although physical pain is more often associated with sexual deviation. Mental pain is usually inflicted by humiliating, derogatory remarks made in the presence of others. Physical pain may be inflicted in a great variety of ways: whipping, biting, pinching, sticking with needles, choking, branding. Whipping is such a classic form of sadism (and masochism) that it has a special name, flagellantism. Some individuals can achieve sexual satisfaction only from the sight of blood. They are likely to inflict injury on parts of the body such as the neck and abdomen where bleeding is most profuse. In the most extreme cases, the sadist may torture his victim to death or commit "lust murder" and mutilate the body afterward. In its milder forms, the sadistic impulse may be expressed through fantasies of injuring women, slashing their pictures, or collecting and cutting up shoes or other articles associated with them.

Sadistic behavior is most frequent in males, but is occasionally found in females who become involved with masochistic men. In some cases the infliction of pain is a preface to actual sexual relations, but in others it yields full sexual gratification by itself. In lust murder, as distinguished from necrophilia, the deviate does not attempt coitus with the corpse because the act of killing itself produces orgasm. (Rapists and other criminals who kill their victims have been known to mutilate the bodies in order to suggest that they were the victims of sadists or other mentally ill persons.) Sadistic practices are relatively rare in our culture, comprising an estimated 5 per cent of all sexual offenses. *See* NECROPHILIA.

Sadistic individuals not only derive gratification from inflicting pain on others, but are believed to harbor masochistic impulses as well—that is, they obtain pleasure from receiving as well as giving pain. The simultaneous existence of the two tendencies is termed sadomasochism; some individuals shift abruptly from one to the other. Many authorities believe sadism and masochism are manifestations of the same drive. The sadism is sometimes interpreted as a reaction-formation against masochism—that is, an attempt to deny the desire to be injured by going to the opposite extreme of inflicting injury on others. Masochism, on the other hand, may be a turning of sadistic impulses against the self as a result of guilt and an unconscious need for punishment. *See* MASOCHISM.

A variety of explanations has been offered for sexual sadism, and in some cases several factors may be operative at once. The following have been emphasized by J. C. Coleman in his comprehensive volume *Abnormal Psychology and Modern Life* (1964). First, it may be an expression of a more generalized hatred and hostility experienced by individuals who have been rejected or frustrated. In some instances men have displaced their anger against their wives by attacking other women. In these cases the sexual element appears to be secondary to the impulse to retaliate.

Second, sadistic behavior may be associated with a feeling that sex is ugly, sinful, or degrading. The individual achieves sexual satisfaction in hurting others, but rationalizes his behavior by asserting that it is simply a means of punishing them for their sexual desire, or of showing his contempt for sexual activity. Wertham (1949) cites the extreme case of a man who castrated boys and killed young girls to "save" them from later immoral behavior.

Third, the sadistic impulse may result from early experiences in which sexual stimulation has been associated with the infliction of pain. In their fantasy life, children frequently picture sexual relations in terms of a violent attack. Later on these ideas may be reinforced by stories and articles dealing with "assaults" upon women, and by personal experiences in which the infliction of pain on animals or people gives rise to strong emotion that is frequently accompanied by sexual stimulation. The connection between sexual arousal and intensely emotional situations of any kind is particularly close during adolescence. For reasons that are largely unknown, experiences involving fear or pain—accidents, watching a large fire, driving rapidly—are often erotically stimulating to young people.

A fourth motivation arises out of the fact that many sadists are timid, effeminate individuals who are trying to bolster their potency. In some cases the impotence may be actual, in others it is merely feared. They may also be motivated by fear of failure and humiliation in approaching the opposite sex. Some of them believe they can arouse greater response in their sex partners through cruelty, and thereby increase their own excitement to the point of orgasm. In this way they achieve sexual gratification and "prove" they are both potent and powerful. In many cases they even demand that their victims act as if they enjoyed being beaten or lashed, for this kind of sadist obtains little or no gratification if the victim remains unresponsive.

According to psychoanalytic theory the sadistic impulse is first expressed in the oral and anal stages of psychosexual development when the child discovers that he can derive pleasure from biting, and that he can express power and resentment by withholding his feces.

Freud held that these are the earliest manifestations of the aggressive instinct, and that some individuals become "fixated" due to emotional difficulties occurring at these stages, and continue to seek pleasure in sadistic behavior.

In psychoanalytic theory the fear of impotence, which we noted above, is associated with castration anxiety. This form of anxiety is believed to arise during the Oedipal stage of development when the boy desires his mother and fears that the father will castrate him as punishment. In this interpretation, sadism enables the man to perform sexually and thus assures him that his organ is intact. At the same time the sadistic act gives him the added satisfaction of feeling that he is the castrator instead of the one castrated.

Finally sadistic behavior may be a symptom of certain severe forms of emotional disturbance, particularly schizophrenic reactions and manic states. In these cases it appears to be associated with distorted thought processes and reduced control over behavior stemming from mental and emotional disorganization. Antisocial personalities may also become sexually sadistic as an expression of their habitually violent behavior, uninhibited gratification of impulse, and lack of moral restraint. See ANTISOCIAL REACTION, RAPE, PSYCHOSEXUAL DEVELOPMENT, FIXATION, CASTRATION COMPLEX.

Illustrative Case: SADISM

A seventeen-year-old student was found guilty of three brutal murders and a large number of burglaries. On the wall of one apartment, in which he killed a young woman, was found written with lipstick, "For heaven's sake catch me before I kill more; I cannot control myself." Sexually deviant behavior began in his case at the age of nine and took the form of fetishism. He repeatedly stole women's underclothing, took it to his room, and dressed himself in it with great sexual excitement. At thirteen he began securing the desired objects by going into houses through windows.

Sexual excitement gradually became concentrated on this act. He often struggled to prevent himself from leaving home at night, but sometimes desire would break down his resolutions. At the sight of an open window at a place that might be burglarized, he experienced sexual excitement with erection. Usually as he passed through the window he experienced orgasm. If so, he generally left without taking anything. The impulse to kill came only if he was startled in the act of burglary. On one occasion, however, he experienced orgasm when he hit a woman who interrupted him, and he left at once without hitting her again.

Reports on this case do not disclose the sequence of events and fantasies that led the sexual need into such peculiar channels. They do show, however, that there were severe blocks on normal channels. At first he indignantly denied that he had ever practiced masturbation, but he later admitted having tried it twice without being able to secure any sexual excitement. With equal reluctance he admitted occasional petting with girls, but reported the experience to be so upsetting and repulsive that he usually burst into tears. The pattern of guilt feeling could hardly be stranger. He was much less upset in speaking of his brutal murders than he was when questioned about normal sexual behavior. (White, 1964)

SAFETY PSYCHOLOGY. The study of the human factors involved in accidents and accident prevention.

Accidents are a matter of general concern, since they rank second as a cause of death in America, produce inestimable hardship, and account for a loss of millions of man-hours of work each year. Some investigators have claimed that a few "repeaters" who have one accident after another are responsible for the great majority of accidents. More recent studies have not denied the existence of repeaters, but have indicated that "the majority of accidents may be attributed to the majority of the population." (Brody, 1959)

The huge number of accidents can be reduced only by approaching the problem comprehensively. Both human and environmental factors must be taken into account. The environmental approach focuses attention on such measures as seat belts, safety shoes, goggles, safe placement of machines, careful highway construction, and regulation of general work conditions to reduce noise, fatigue, and overcrowding. The human approach is clearly more complex. It includes a study of safe and unsafe attitudes, stress conditions, safety habits, accident-proneness, physiological factors, and the techniques of safety education. Both approaches must not lose sight of the fact that chance occurrences—an animal on the roadway, a temporary condition of stress—may play an important role in producing any particular accident.

The psychological study of accidents has been particularly fruitful in explaining why accidents occur in spite of caution signs and safe conditions. In industry an estimated 88 per cent of accidents are caused by human factors, including unsafe operating procedures, faulty attitudes, and emotional stress (Heinrich, 1959). Younger workers have a consistently higher accident rate than older workers (Van Zelst, 1954). Studies of traffic accidents show that a great many people have dangerous attitudes which increase the probability of an accident: overconfidence about their driving ability, a tendency to blame the other fellow, lack of moral responsibility, a feeling that accidents are inevitable, and the conviction that "it can't happen to me," or that "every man has to look out for himself." It has also been found that many people share one or more of the attitudes which characterize accident-repeaters: impulsiveness, intolerance of authority, aggressiveness, and fatalism. Tests, such as the Siebrecht and Hannaford Scales, have been developed to elicit such attitudes, and much of today's safety education is directed toward modifying them.

A study of hot-rod drivers conducted by Neazles and Winokur at the

Menninger Clinic in 1957 has brought some of these dangerous attitudes into sharp relief. Their report concludes, in part: "The usual hot-rod driver, then, is a precocious physically strong boy. He is aggressive of temperament and his early history shows evidence of emotional deprivation. His relationship with his mother is usually a very ambivalent one ('Yuh gotta have mothers, but I can't stand 'em. They're bossy.') . . . Athletics, at least in these thirty cases, were no source of release (for their aggressiveness) . . . They could not face the complicated team cooperation that goes into a good baseball game."

The factor of stress has also received much attention. It is now recognized that people can become temporarily accident-prone under such conditions as infection, menstruation, lack of sleep, malnutrition, intoxication, and a physically uncomfortable work environment, as well as emotional tensions arising out of job difficulties and family problems. People under stress are likely to become preoccupied, less alert, and less able to call upon their knowledge and skill. As a result, they may not be able to cope with the chance emergencies that are constantly occurring in driving a car, operating a factory machine, or even walking across a slippery street.

It is now recognized that safe behavior should not be solely the concern of safety educators. Parents should begin very early in a child's life to help him cultivate responsible attitudes and develop an ability to endure or avoid stress, handle emergencies, and recognize the rights of others. Teachers and school administrators must continue this kind of instruction in school, where special techniques have been developed to impart the information and develop the skill and attitudes so urgently needed for safety.

Among the most effective educational techniques are: (1) *group discussion* of concrete safety problems and actual experiences, conducted in a democratic, informal atmosphere; (2) *group decision* methods, in which a student safety council or other group not only discusses problems but sets goals, makes practical recommendations, and even assumes responsibility for carrying out a safety program; and (3) *role-playing* (sociodrama) in which participants act out realistic safety situations, usually rotating and reversing roles. These methods, however, do not dispense with the need for individual counseling of accident-repeaters, as well as intelligent discipline through a school safety court or a state point system for driver improvement. *See* ACCIDENT PRONENESS, ROLE PLAYING, FATIGUE.

SALESMANSHIP. Salesmanship is viewed as a form of advertising, since its object is to show that a particular product or service will satisfy the consumer's wants. The face-to-face situation differs from the more impersonal forms of advertising, however, since it permits the salesman to determine the customer's special needs and observe his reactions as the sales talk proceeds. Then he can adapt his approach and selling points to the individual prospect; and if he has a variety of products to offer, he will be able to select the one best suited to the customer's individual requirements.

This concept of salesmanship differs greatly from the older (but still prevalent) approach in which the salesman sought to overpower the prospect with his "personality" and to pressure him into purchasing by enthusiastic but empty phrases. Today it is not enough to tell the customer that the product is a great buy and that he will be missing the opportunity of a lifetime if he doesn't snap it up. Rather, the sales process must be a two-way affair in which the salesman not only talks but asks questions and listens—and he must be able to think more in terms of serving than selling. In a word, the newer approach is customer-oriented, not sales-oriented, and there is evidence that it leads to greater success in the long run since its object is not merely to sell but to suit the product to the buyer.

This point of view has been accompanied by a radical change in the concept of the "sales personality" as well as in the selection of salesmen, sales training, and especially sales techniques. These aspects of the subject will now be reviewed.

Sales Personality. Older treatises as well as popular books offer inventories of salesman traits such as aggressiveness, self-confidence, enthusiasm, verbal fluency, extraversion, emotional stability, sense of humor, and so on. Different authors suggest different sets of traits, and little evidence is given to support their choices. Moreover, this approach breaks down when we recognize that different types of selling require different approaches. Selling computers differs from selling shirts, and door-to-door selling is not the same as wholesale selling. Aggressiveness and overconfidence would be a hindrance to a man selling scientific equipment, and an emotional, overenthusiastic approach would be highly suspect. On the other hand, a thoughtful, well-informed explanation with special attention to features that meet the specific requirements of the company would probably be highly effective.

Salesman Selection. Most companies, then, are not looking for "sales personalities" in general, but for men or women who can sell their particular product to a particular market. For this purpose the most useful single selection method appears to be a carefully devised, weighted application blank based upon studies of salesmen who have been successful and unsuccessful with the specific product or service. For high-level sales personnel it is helpful to include an intensive interview and a battery of selected tests. Some investigators maintain that general sales aptitude tests are of little or no use since different sales jobs have different requirements.

Sales Training. On-the-job training and role playing are both highly effective. The optimum amount of training varies considerably from individual to individual and job to job. Technical selling often requires long-term preparation and special classes, as well as refresher courses and frequent sales conferences designed to keep the salesman up to date. Most of the sales training today focuses on information more than on techniques, since the salesman must be prepared to answer his prospect's questions, and must know the details about the competitor's product as well as his own.

Sales Methods. As Anastasi points out (1964), field research on the sales process is meager, and studies based on simulated sales interviews conducted in the laboratory are limited and artificial. However, she cites two investigations which have yielded significant results. The first study compared effective with ineffective saleswomen engaged in door-to-door selling for a nationwide organization. An interviewer who had no knowledge of their sales records evaluated them on certain aspects of oral communication, such as use of voice and language, listening behavior, and dramatic appeals. The differences between the two groups were substantial enough to suggest the importance of stressing communication skills in selection and training programs for this type of selling (Pace, 1962).

The second investigation was a field study of driver-salesmen for a large company. The sales records of the men were found to be unrelated to their personalities—for example, the men who were described as "negative, colorless, weak, and drab" did as well as those described as "genial, cordial, familiar, easygoing, backslapping." On the other hand, those who took the trouble to count the dealer's stock of the company's products received orders that were on the average two and a half times as large as those obtained by salesmen who neglected this step; and those who informed the dealer about the week's special offer before taking the regular order averaged 27 per cent more sales per call than those who took the regular order first (White, 1940). This study provides further evidence for the point made earlier, that the methods of the salesman are in general more important than his personality. As Anastasi comments, "With regard to 'sales personality,' there seems to be room for wide individual differences in successful selling. Each individual should try to utilize his unique pattern of traits to his best advantage, rather than trying to follow someone else's rules for getting along with people." See APTITUDE TESTS (SPECIAL).

SATYRIASIS (Satyrism). A sexual deviation in males consisting of an excessive or insatiable desire for gratification.

The terms "excessive" and "insatiable" are difficult to define since there are wide variations in the intensity and frequency of the sex urge among normal people. Most men have a strong desire for intercourse between one and six times a week, but there are men who engage in sexual relations as much as several times a day for long periods without appearing to be abnormal. The criteria for satyriasis can therefore not be based merely on frequency of sexual activity. More important is the urgency of the impulse. In a true case, the man appears to be in the grip of a continuous, uncontrollable drive, and centers his whole life around this one form of gratification. The term priapism has been used as the equivalent of satyriasis, though it is now more often applied to a persistent erection due to organic disease rather than sexual de-

sire. (Priapism derives from Priapus, the Greek god of procreation.)

The question is why this excessive impulse occurs. The answer appears to be that the satyriast is not physiologically "oversexed," but uses this activity to satisfy intense emotional needs. These needs are usually on an unconscious level and vary considerably from individual to individual. One man may need constant reassurance of potency because of inner doubts about his adequacy. Another may engage in excessive heterosexual activity as an unconscious attempt to deny a latent homosexual trend. (This is frequently the case with the "Don Juan" type.) Still another may carry on a dozen affairs at once as a means of warding off anxiety stemming from emotional conflict, or as an escape from threatening home or business problems. A fourth may be compensating for feelings of failure, disappointment, or frustration. Others must keep proving that they are attractive to women because they believe they are undersized, homely, or socially inept. And, according to some psychoanalysts, men who seek conquest after conquest may be unconsciously avenging themselves against all women for disappointment experienced with their mother in early life.

Many of these men not only engage in excessive sexual activity, but become obsessed with the subject of sex to a point where it dominates their entire thinking and conversation. It may even displace all other interests and interfere with their pursuit of a living. Such men are urgently in need of psychological treatment directed toward readjustment of the entire personality. Interview therapy and psychoanalytic techniques are generally employed in discovering the roots of the problem and helping the patient to resolve his conflicts and achieve greater emotional security. See EROTOMANIA.

Recent research has disclosed a specific control center for the sexual drive at the base of the brain, in a structure called the amygdala. If this center is destroyed by disease or blocked off by surgery, the result is an abnormal sex drive. It is possible that damage to the amygdala is a causal factor in some cases of satyriasis, but so far there has not been sufficient medical evidence to draw any positive conclusions. *See* AMYGDALA, NYMPHOMANIA.

Illustrative Case: SATYRIASIS

George S., age thirty-two, salesman, divorced, sought psychological treatment for his constant desire for sexual relations. He gave his psychotherapist the following information about himself.

The primary reason he came for help was that he was unable to continue to carry on his work satisfactorily. Because he was so preoccupied with getting sexual satisfaction, he could not concentrate on his job. In the past two years he has had at least ten different sales jobs. Two months ago he found a job that he liked extremely well. It was his fear of not being able to hold his present job that caused him to seek treatment.

The family history indicated that George grew up in a divided home. His parents never got along well. There were times when the scenes between them were so violent that George was terrified. On several occasions there were temporary separations. His father was an exacting and demanding person with perfectionistic tendencies. He often was moody and wanted to be left alone. There was never any closeness or companionship with his father. His mother was a very emotional person and had frequent crying spells. She felt sorry for herself and let George and the father know about it. Both parents disciplined George— his father would switch him, whereas his mother would send him to his room, sometimes for a whole day.

A personal history showed that George was a hyperactive and restless child. He was a fitful sleeper and used to grind his teeth at night. He was enuretic until he was twelve. He remembers engaging in masturbation when he was about eight years old. He had a brother who was almost two years older with whom he frequently engaged in mutual masturbation. At thirteen he was a compulsive masturbator, engaging in the practice several times a day. He states that he had his first experience in sexual relations with a girl when he was fourteen. During his adolescence there were only occasional sexual relations. At nineteen he went into the service and during his stay for two years had numerous affairs with women who were usually older than he was. He married when he was twenty-four and was divorced four years later. He had one child, a son who is with his mother.

His strong sexual desires have never subsided. Masturbation still continues on a daily basis. He has learned that it is not harmful, so he isn't bothered by any fear of what will happen to him. His concern is primarily with his preoccupation with sex, and he is seeking psychological treatment for that reason. (Thorpe, Katz, and Lewis, 1961)

SCHILDER, PAUL FERDINAND (1886–1940). Schilder, noted chiefly for his studies of schizophrenia and the body image, was born in Vienna and received his medical degree at the city's university. In his first position, as assistant physician at the University Hospital in Halle, he studied different types of personality disintegration, such as depersonalization and double consciousness, and also investigated pathological conditions of the nervous system. Among his contributions in the latter field was a classic description of encephalitis periaxalis diffusia, now called Schilder's disease. *See* DEMYELINATING DISORDERS.

During the latter part of this period, he turned his attention to the Freudian theory and to the subject of schizophrenia. These two interests came together when he made an attempt to discover the form and content of schizophrenic thought by applying his extraordinary ability to communicate with deeply psychotic patients. The results of these observations were reported in *Wann und Erkenntnis* (Delusion and Knowledge), which contains a comparative analysis of the dynamics of schizophrenia and primitive thought processes.

Other books published in this period were *Symbols in Schizophrenics* and *Consciousness of One's Self and One's Personality*.

After serving in the Austrian Army during World War I, Schilder worked at hospitals and taught at the University of Vienna for ten years. In 1928 Adolf Meyer invited him to work and lecture at the Henry Phipps Psychiatric Clinic, and in the following year he was appointed Clinical Director of the Psychopathic Division of Bellevue Hospital in New York. While at Bellevue he married Dr. Loretta Bender, with whom he collaborated on many outstanding research projects in the fields of neurology, psychiatry, and psychopathology. His brilliant career was suddenly brought to an end when he was killed in an automobile accident at the age of fifty-four.

Schilder made significant contributions in many areas and exerted a strong and lasting influence on his disciples in Vienna and in this country. The titles of his later works indicate the scope of his activities: *Soul and Life* (1923), *Medical Psychology* (1924), *Hypnosis* (1927), *Introduction to a Psychoanalytic Psychiatry* (1928), *Brain and Personality* (1931), *The Image and Appearance of the Human Body* (1935), and *Psychotherapy* (1938). Three other volumes were published posthumously, *Contributions to Developmental Neuropsychiatry, Mind: Perception and Thought in Their Constructive Aspects* (1942), and *Goals and Desires of Man* (1942).

More specifically, Schilder developed the important but neglected concept of body image, and made it the center of a psychology of the human personality, linking it to the Freudian concept of the ego, narcissism, and libido. In his writings he also presented a penetrating criticism of Freud's concept of the death instinct; analyzed the dreams of epileptics, showing that they contained a rebirth theme; and explained the psychology of mania. Although he recognized and utilized psychoanalytic concepts, his general approach can be described as holistic, since he maintained that the organic and psychological viewpoints must both be recognized, and that an overevaluation of either of them would lead to useless argument. One of the best illustrations of this approach is found in his attempts to interpret organic psychoses along psychoanalytic lines.

In his views on therapy, Schilder also departed from the orthodox Freudian approach. He joined forces with Adler, Sullivan, Horney, and others who recognized the importance of the social milieu in both the etiology and treatment of neurosis. He therefore put less emphasis on the analysis of instinctual drives and the process of bringing unconscious material into consciousness, and more on the social and cultural origin of neurotic symptoms. His recognition of social factors also led to an interest in group therapy. He found that group treatment brought many problems to light that were not illuminated by individual therapy, especially attitudes toward family ideals, ideologies, and body concepts. To further this process, he made two innovations: he asked each group patient to answer questionnaires and to write a "free association" autobiography. These procedures provided material which could be used in stimulating discussion and in guiding the therapist's interpretation.

These are but samples of the creative work of this remarkable man, whom Fritz Wittels described in these terms: "A veritable Faustian man, he worked without rest and apparently without strain in many fields. There are few neurological or psychiatric problems which did not interest him at one time or other and which were not enriched by his approach" (1941). *See* BODY IMAGE, DEPERSONALIZATION, GROUP PSYCHOTHERAPY.

SCHIZOID PERSONALITY (Schizo-thymic Personality). A personality pattern disturbance characterized by shyness, introversion, and a tendency to avoid social contact and close relationships.

The schizoid individual usually appears aloof, detached, and somewhat eccentric. He is likely to prefer books or solitary hobbies to social activity and companionship. The more sensitive schizoids suffer from feelings of loneliness and inadequacy, but may find solace and satisfaction in poetry, philosophy, or nature. They are unable to express anger or endure competition, and frequently retreat into an inner world of fantasies and daydreams. Those who lack imagination and finer sensibilities tend to be conscientious, hard-working, and dull; in some cases they may be cold, moody, ill-tempered, and mistrustful. These individuals also tend to develop fantasies, but instead of being absorbed in idealistic or poetic visions, they are likely to daydream about retaliating against their enemies.

Case histories show that schizoid individuals were timid and withdrawn in childhood, and became increasingly seclusive, detached, and "shut-in" after puberty. If they find work and living arrangements that require only a minimum of contact with other people, they may reach a fairly stable adjustment. But if they are faced with threatening or overwhelming situations, they may retreat further from the world and develop schizophrenic reactions. *See* PERSONALITY PATTERN DISTURBANCE.

Illustrative Case: SCHIZOID PERSONALITY

Raymond A., a twenty-two-year-old unmarried man, was admitted for the first time to the psychiatric unit of a county hospital after having been arrested for disturbing the peace. Unemployed, he was living in the suburban middle-class home of his parents when he was arrested.

Raymond was the only child of a couple whose marriage was generally marked by an undercurrent of dissatisfaction. His fa-

ther was a retiring, passive, almost withdrawn person who took pride in the fact that he had no close friends and did not feel the need for any. This aloofness characterized his manner with his wife and son as much as it did his relations with outsiders. He was a man content to do his daily work as a bookkeeper for a large hardware business and then return home to the life of a recluse. He assiduously avoided the job of disciplining his son and seemed to assume that matters would take care of themselves if ignored long enough. This general attitude toward life was one which upset Raymond's mother, an active, more gregarious person who would have liked to have a wider circle of friends and a husband who could be more of a companion. To meet some of these needs she had chosen to work throughout her marriage as a receptionist for a physician and to leave the rearing of Raymond to sundry relatives, baby sitters, and nursery schools.

Raymond's early years were uneventful, except that it was noted that he never displayed much emotion, even when it seemed evident to outsiders that he must be heartbroken. He made a good school adjustment, becoming an early favorite of teachers because of his quick mind. Socially, however, he chose to remain a lone wolf. An early interest in and talent for playing the trumpet earned him a place in the high school band, but he failed to capitalize on this activity to make friends with fellow band members or with young people who came to the various functions at which the band performed. Despite his apparent disinterest in other people, he went through a stage in early adolescence in which he was unusually meticulous about the way his hair was combed and would literally spend hours arranging and rearranging his hair. He never displayed any interest in the opposite sex and once confided in his mother that he feared that females might be sexually aggressive if he dated them.

After being graduated from high school, Raymond decided to enroll at a small school of music in a large eastern city. He attended this school for only one term before becoming discouraged, feeling that he lacked the talent to succeed as a musician. Upon his return home he attempted to find work with which he would be happy but seemed to drift aimlessly from one job to another.

Eventually he began seeing himself as a nonconformist and began identifying with the existentialist movement.

About three months before his hospital admission Raymond gave up any attempt to find work and began saying that anyone who had to work to earn his own living was a failure in life. He became personally untidy and unkempt. The same clothes were worn for days on end, and most of his time was spent alone in his room, where he practiced his trumpet-playing and wrote long essays to express his philosophy of life. He refused to alter these habits and resented any attempt by his mother to clean his room or to persuade him to change his clothes and to be neater. He spoke of wanting to remain by himself forever in his own room and began refusing his mother admittance.

On Christmas Eve, Raymond was repeatedly invited to participate in the family celebration that was taking place in his house, but he refused. Finally, harried by his mother's persistence, he slipped out his bedroom window and was later arrested by police on the complaint of neighbors that he was parading down the middle of the street playing his trumpet. Raymond's mother convinced the police that he should be placed in a hospital where he might be observed for a psychiatric disorder.

During the thirty days that he was hospitalized Raymond was as indecisive as ever about the course his life should take. He offered various unrealistic plans which would take him out of his home town, the state, and even the country. Although he felt he should spend much of his time writing, he eschewed the idea of attempting to sell what he wrote and seemed to have no idea how he could support himself—nor was he greatly concerned. After a thirty-day period of observation he was released from the hospital on the grounds that he did not display a severe enough disorder to warrant his remaining. (Zax and Stricker, 1963)

SCHIZOPHRENIA   (CATATONIC TYPE). A psychotic disorder which takes the form of either generalized inhibition or excessive, disorganized activity. These two states, known as catatonic stupor and catatonic excitement, usually al-

ternate, but in some cases there may be repeated episodes of one or the other type. Each of the phases may last from several hours to several days or weeks, and the patient may shift from one to the other without warning or apparent reason. Sometimes there is a period of relative normality between episodes.

Catatonic stupor often comes on suddenly, although it may be preceded by a short period of depression, loss of interest, and preoccupation. The patient becomes mute, stares blankly at the floor, and assumes a fixed, stereotyped posture which he may maintain for days or weeks. Some patients sit motionless on the edge of a chair, others crouch on the floor, or sit in one position until their joints swell and their feet turn blue. They not only obstinately resist every effort to move them, but refuse to dress, eat, or comply with the slightest request. Nurses or attendants have to dress and wash them, and even take care of their eliminative needs. Some patients, however, fall into a state of automatism in which they imitate any action of another person, repeat any phrase he utters, or obey any command, no matter how absurd it may be. They may also lapse into a state of catalepsy, or "waxy flexibility": if another person places the patient's arm or leg in any position whatever, no matter how uncomfortable or awkward it may be, he will maintain that position for many minutes or even hours.

Although the stuporous patient gives little or no indication that he is aware of the outside world, and may even curl up as if in the womb (a form of "claustrophilia," the desire to withdraw into a closed space), he actually registers what is going on around him and may later give a detailed account of everything that occurred. Moreover, behind his vacant, masklike face he may be experiencing the most vivid hallucinations and delusions. These may later provide clues to his strange postures and behavior. They sometimes suggest that the stupor is a protective withdrawal from threatening situations, comparable to the state of shock or panic which normal individuals sometimes experience after an overwhelming catastrophe.

Catatonic excitement is a state of frenzied motor activity. The patient may talk incoherently at the top of his voice, rush frantically back and forth, tear off his clothing, and without warning break up furniture or attack the nearest bystander. He may strike one bizarre attitude after another, make a series of strange grimaces, masturbate openly, soil his clothing, mutilate himself, and even commit suicide. Here, too, there is evidence of vivid fantasies and terrifying or ecstatic hallucinations—but in the excited as distinguished from the stuporous state he reacts in a completely overt manner. Before modern methods of treatment were developed, many of these patients maintained their state of excitement until they collapsed and even died of exhaustion. Others, however, passed into the stuporous phase or into a period of normal behavior.

Catatonia appears most often between the ages fifteen and twenty-five. The onset is usually more sudden than in other forms of schizophrenia. The acute reaction is frequently preceded by a profoundly disturbing experience, although the patient's history usually reveals the typical schizophrenic pattern of gradual withdrawal with some degree of apathy. The prognosis is considerably more favorable than in other schizophrenic reactions; the more acute the onset, the better the prospects for recovery. See ECHOLALIA, ECHOPRAXIA, CEREA FLEXIBILITAS, CATALEPSY, STEREOTYPY, STUPOR, PSYCHOMOTOR RETARDATION, PSYCHOMOTOR EXCITEMENT.

Illustrative Case: SCHIZOPHRENIC REACTION, CATATONIC TYPE

There was no family history of mental illness in the case of F.C. He had been an average scholar but introspective and solitary at school, with no liking for games and no hobbies. He became a millworker at the age of fifteen and was "more a boy for home, never keen on girls." He served in the Army during the Second World War and had some sort of transient mental breakdown, of which no records are available. After demobilization he was idle for six months: he appeared depressed and mixed up, seemed to take no interest in things around him and did not even respond to questioning. Then he had a job for six months, but was dismissed and again hung around the house, making no attempt to seek further employment. Thereafter he became even more dull and apathetic, looked vacant and faraway, refused to get out of bed or take food. He declared that people were trying to take a rise out of him, that some unknown individual was "making him think about things," and that he himself was a "riddle of bones." In the year following his demobilization from the Army he was admitted to a mental hospital, aged twenty-three.

In hospital at first he lay in bed with an occasional vacant smile, and refused food. He was correctly orientated and could give his history with reasonable accuracy, but he had little insight, saying that he had been sent to hospital on account of fits of bad temper. He was both auditorily and visually hallucinated: he complained of hearing buzzing noises, sounds like someone squealing and voices which he could sometimes understand but whose messages he could not remember, and he described flashes of light and shadows in the middle of the room. He expressed the belief that the doctors and nurses could manipulate their shadows, and that there was another person in the bed. Later he complained of tasting soap in his mouth and of receiving poison from the post beside his bed.

Treated initially with E.C.T. and then with reserpine, he remained withdrawn and apathetic, often could not be engaged in conversation, sat vacantly by the hour, and had to be taken to his meals and pressed to eat. At times he was incontinent, chewed the end of his tie, and hoarded rubbish. For weeks on end he would be in a state of stupor or near to it, showing catalepsy and flexibilitas cerea. Then a period of excitement would intervene, when for days or weeks on end he would be hyperactive and talk a great deal in a disjointed and usually incoherent way. At these times he would strike out impulsively at the nursing staff. On occasion he clowned in a crude way and would walk on his hands.

Repeated courses of E.C.T., various tranquilizing drugs, and treatment in occupational and social groups have had no effect, and he has become grossly demented. (Henderson, Gillespie, and Batchelor, 1962)

SCHIZOPHRENIA (CHILDHOOD TYPE). Childhood schizophrenia is a broad and loosely used term applied to reactions of a general schizophrenic character appearing early in life. These reactions are varied and there is no single clearcut syndrome. The symptoms most commonly noted are: failure to relate to other people, inability to respond emotionally, extremely narrow interests, retarded or disturbed language functions, low frustration tolerance, distorted thinking, and disordered motor activity.

Each of these symptoms may be expressed in many ways. The language disturbance may take the form of a very late start in learning to speak, mutism, garbled use of words, or grunting instead of speaking. The disordered motor activity may consist of extreme restlessness, complete immobility or repetitious, stereotyped behavior, such as facial grimaces, strange gestures, rocking back and forth, toe-walking, or sudden whirling movements. The low frustration tolerance may lead to violent temper tantrums, extreme destructiveness, or banging the head against a wall whenever the child is interfered with and does not get his way. In many cases basic habit patterns are deeply disturbed; these children sleep and eat irregularly and cannot be easily toilet-trained. Moreover, they are frequently so uncommunicative, unresponsive, and infantile that they are apt to be considered mentally defective, although tests and observations of behavior usually show they are in the average or su-

perior IQ range. *See* PSEUDORETARDATION.

Bender (1947) cites the following example of deeply distorted impulses and thought processes in a nine-year-old schizophrenic child, who said, "I want a hammer to kill my bed. I am mad at it. It won't come to me at night, and I have to go and find it. I am mad at my mother, too. She takes food to bed and eats it in bed. . . . I got a gun to shoot somebody's head off and a razor to cut my fingers off. . . . Is that a lady or a man doll? . . . It must be a skeleton. They kill people, jump on your back, and bite you all to pieces. . . . I dreamed a fox was after me. I jumped off the roof, I landed right on my head and got hurt. I like that. When you get hurt and wake up it is beautiful. . . . My mother doesn't love me. She shouldn't have had me. I should have stayed in her guts. I am in my own gizzard. I think I will go back to heaven where I came from."

Schizophrenia in children varies both in initial symptoms and in age of onset, though it is often not possible to specify when it starts since the onset is insidious. The child gradually withdraws, loses interest in play and other activities, refuses to eat or communicate with others. In some cases, however, there may be a sudden change in personality and appearance. Typically, the child's face takes on a waxy tone. At times he will not look at other people, and may gaze into space for hours on end. At other times he will assume an odd posture, examine a single object for a long period, or endlessly put together and take apart the same toy. At still other times he may become extremely restless and there may be frequent, uncalled-for episodes of kicking and screaming. Among older children the clinical picture usually resembles adult schizophrenia more closely—they may, for example, develop hallucinations and delusions.

The causes of childhood schizophrenia

are still obscure. Some theorists believe it is rooted in a disturbed relationship between mother and child, but in most cases there is insufficient evidence to support this hypothesis. Others maintain that these children have been subjected to an extremely frightening experience which has convinced them that the world is a dangerous place. They therefore become acutely anxious, withdraw into their shell, and seek security in simple, repetitive, nonthreatening activities.

Many authorities believe child schizophrenics show evidence of constitutional defect. Bender (1953, 1955) found so many cases of retarded and irregular development that she has suggested the possibility of diffuse brain pathology. This condition might account for many of the physical symptoms she found, such as motor awkwardness, EEG abnormalities and disturbances in eating, sleeping, and elimination patterns. Brain pathology might also explain the fact that these children have difficulty in developing an accurate image of themselves, constructive relationships with their parents and other people, and an organized picture of reality. The net result is that reality eludes their grasp, the world becomes a strange, frustrating place, and they become overwhelmed with intense anxiety and uneasiness. In attempting to cope with these painful feelings, they adopt defenses in the form of such symptoms as withdrawal, indifference, rigid behavior, and occasional outbursts of temper and destructiveness. In a word, this type of schizophrenia can be understood as the reaction of a disturbed child to a world he is not equipped to face.

Recent investigations indicate that childhood schizophrenia is not a single illness but a group of disorders, some due predominantly to constitutional factors, others to psychological influences, and still others to an interaction between the two. Goldfarb (1961) has found that these reactions cluster around

two poles, with numerous cases in between. In one cluster there is considerable evidence of neurological disturbance but little or no evidence of faulty family relationships. In these cases the parents offer good models for identification and provide practice in communication and social awareness—yet the children are confused about their own identity and body image and have trouble with time and space concepts. They tend to depend on the contact receptors of touch, taste, and smell instead of the distance receptors of sight and vision. Noyes and Kolb (1963) comment, "It is probable, then, that a goodly proportion of the small children classified as schizophrenic might more properly be considered to be suffering from personality disorders associated with organic brain damage."

The second major group show little evidence of brain damage, but have been reared in disturbing family situations—especially in families where the parents are cold, unresponsive, or preoccupied, fail to encourage their children to develop themselves as persons, and offer too little help in teaching them to talk, play, and form the basic concepts necessary for feeling at home in the world. Since these children have been discouraged from feeling close to their parents, they fail to form attachments of any kind; and since they have not learned how to grasp reality, they retreat into a simplified, self-enclosed world of their own. See SCHIZOPHRENIC REACTIONS (THERAPY).

Illustrative Case: SCHIZOPHRENIC REACTION, CHILDHOOD TYPE

Tommy M. is a twenty-four-year-old patient whose psychotic behavior first was observed when he was about six years old. He was an extremely hyperactive and restless youngster who was easily distracted, and who sometimes refused to talk. When he did speak, he repeated such phrases as, "Tony Macaroni, Tony Macaroni, Tony Macaroni," or began counting without being asked, "One, two, three, vanilla pudding; one, two, three, vanilla pudding."

When Tommy was ten years old, he was sent to a special school. His motor coordination and posture were good, and he was able to use his hands and feet very well. The school reported that his response to music and literature was extraordinary. He loved to listen to stories and could relate parts of them from memory. He was also fond of music, and could reproduce a melody correctly after hearing it once. It was reported that his enunciation and pronunciation of words were perfect, although sometimes he said things that made no sense. On occasion, he used advanced words like "confidentially" and "necessary."

His teacher reported: "This youngster's behavior is his greatest problem. He is definitely disturbed. If one could get him to cooperate, one might really be surprised how intelligent he really is. His behavior improved considerably throughout the year. Earlier in the year he refused to come inside the classroom, and ran away. At the end of the school year, this behavior had reversed and he was refusing to leave the classroom."

Tommy was seen by a diagnostic center when he was twelve years old. During his stay at the center, he was observed in many different situations. Negativism was present during all the examinations. He often became restive, twisted and turned in his chair, giggled at the examiner while watching his face very closely, and rambled off into disconnected associations triggered by the question. It was observed that he used words at a much higher level than he was able or willing to define on a vocabulary test.

Tommy was admitted to the psychiatric hospital when he was fourteen years old. At that time he was in poor contact with his surroundings. He withdrew from the examiner, and faced the other way during the initial interview. He showed anxiety in the form of quick nervous movements, but there were no truly bizarre actions. Most of the time he seemed preoccupied in fantasy. His speech was frequently irrelevant and often incoherent. His mood was sometimes inappropriate, with his thought content limited to a few perseverated comments about his father's car, a swim suit, and a vague story about a relative he liked.

When seen ten years later, when the patient was twenty-four years old, he was overactive, paced back and forth, stooped down to pick things off the floor, and gazed at the ceiling. Most of the time he avoided looking at the examiner although he would do so if a direct command were given. He said he was born in 1953, and that he was ten years old. He said he heard voices and pointed to the corner of the room where he said some boys were standing. (Kisker, 1964)

SCHIZOPHRENIA (HEBEPHRENIC TYPE).

Hebephrenia is characterized by severe disintegration rather than mere impoverishment of personality, as in simple schizophrenia. The patient loses touch with reality, and all major functions—thought, speech, behavior, and affect—become increasingly disorganized and distorted.

The hebephrenic patient wears a silly grin, giggles and laughs without provocation, makes strange faces and bizarre gestures. Speech is often incoherent, scattered, and replete with neologisms and verbigeration (invented words and meaningless, repetitive phrases). Thinking may be dominated by transient and usually fragmentary delusions involving strange sexual fantasies such as sex change, religious obsessions, concern over dread diseases, or ideas of persecution, rebirth, or cosmic identification (belief that one is the universe). One patient may insist that he is nine hundred years old; another, that his left arm has been stolen. In rare cases, patients come to believe that they are a dog ("cynanthropy"), a cat ("galeanthropy)" or a horse ("hippanthropy"). *See* NEOLOGISM, VERBIGERATION.

Auditory hallucinations are also common. Voices accuse the patient of heinous sins, call him vile names, or "pour filth" into his mind. An occasional patient may strike out at his imaginary enemies and injure other people—but most hebephrenics are too withdrawn and introverted to be dangerous to others. If untreated, they may regress to a point where they lose all sense of shame, smear feces on the wall, eat in a ravenous manner, and babble incoherently to themselves like infants. The ultimate disintegration of the personality is greater than in other types of schizophrenia.

Hebephrenic reactions usually develop gradually during adolescence. Typically there is a history of eccentric behavior, overconcern about trivia, and preoccupation with insoluble religious and philosophic problems. Often there is a strong inclination to brood about minor moral infractions and the dire effects of masturbation. The patient becomes increasingly seclusive, retreats into his own fantasy world, and gradually regresses to a silly, childish level of behavior. In so doing, he abandons all efforts to solve his problems, protects himself with an armor of indifference toward the outer world, and loses touch with the ordinary rules and regulations of life. As he ceases to test reality and lapses into a dream world, his thoughts, feelings, and behavior become more and more distorted.

Many authorities interpret hebephrenic reactions as a desperate, unconscious attempt to escape from the stresses and tensions of life. Some attribute this attempt to constitutional weaknesses, others to threatening experiences in childhood or a combination of these factors. *See* SCHIZOPHRENIC RE-ACTIONS (ETIOLOGY).

Illustrative Case: SCHIZOPHRENIC REAC-TION, HEBEPHRENIC TYPE

The patient was a divorcée, thirty-two years of age, who had come to the hospital with bizarre delusions, hallucinations, and severe personality disintegration and with a record of alcoholism, promiscuity, and possible incestuous relations with a brother. The following conversation shows typical hebephrenic responses to questioning.

DR: How do you feel today?

PT: Fine.

DR: When did you come here?

PT: 1416, you remember, doctor (silly giggle).

DR: Do you know why you are here?

PT: Well, in 1951 I changed into two

men. President Truman was judge at my trial. I was convicted and hung (silly giggle). My brother and I were given back our normal bodies five years ago. I am a policewoman. I keep a dictaphone concealed on my person.

DR: Can you tell me the name of this place?

PT: I have not been a drinker for sixteen years. I am taking a mental rest after a "carter" assignment or "quill." You know, a "penwrap." I had contracts with Warner Brothers Studios and Eugene broke phonograph records but Mike protested. I have been with the police department for thirty-five years. I am made of flesh and blood—see, doctor (pulling up her dress).

DR: Are you married?

PT: No. I am not attracted to men (silly giggle). I have a companionship arrangement with my brother. I am a "looner" . . . a bachelor. (Coleman, 1964)

SCHIZOPHRENIA (OTHER TYPES). Many cases of schizophrenia cannot be classified into the four primary types (simple, paranoid, catatonic, hebephrenic) because the symptom picture is so mixed. Also, some cases have unique features which call for special descriptive terms. These additional types of schizophrenia have been receiving increasing emphasis in recent years. They fall into the following major categories:

Acute Undifferentiated Type. Cases with a wide variety of symptoms that cut across the four major types. The symptoms manifest themselves suddenly and do not appear to be precipitated by external stress. During an attack the patient is thrown into a state of mental and emotional turmoil, and becomes confused and bewildered by what is happening to him. These cases may clear up in a few weeks, but frequently recur or progress to one of the other reaction types.

Chronic Undifferentiated Type. Here, too, the clinical picture is mixed, but symptoms develop insidiously and there is no acute attack. The patient grows apathetic and appears to accept and "settle down" with his disorder. The category includes so-called "latent," "incipient," and "pre-psychotic" schizophrenic reactions in which there are relatively mild changes in thought, behavior, and affect. The condition is persistent, but many individuals succeed in living with it, although they are poorly adjusted.

Schizo-Affective Type. This is a mixed reaction with both schizophrenic and manic-depressive features. The episodes are recurrent and of two general kinds: predominantly schizophrenic but accompanied by pronounced elation or depression; and predominantly affective but accompanied by schizophrenic thinking and bizarre behavior. The schizophrenic symptoms are usually of the paranoid type: the patient may have delusions, ideas of reference (others talking about him), and hallucinations, and yet at the same time manifest a depressed mood with ideas of guilt and self-accusation. Less frequently the delusions and hallucinations are accompanied by an elevated mood with grandiose overtones. The manic-depressive characteristics are usually more prominent at the beginning of the illness, but if the condition is not arrested, each new attack tends to be more schizophrenic until one of the classic forms is reached.

Some authorities, notably Stanley Cobb, cite these mixed reactions as evidence that there is actually only one serious mental disease with many variations. They contend that the more schizophrenic disorders are at one end of a continuum, with the affective disorders at the other end, and the schizoaffective in between. Others claim that instead of being variables of one "disease," these are simply different types of reactions or personality patterns.

Residual Schizophrenia. This term is applied to patients who have suffered from any of the types of schizophrenia but show sufficient improvement to be discharged from the hospital and get along in the community, even though they continue to manifest mild schizophrenic disturbances of thought, affect, or behavior.

Ambulatory Schizophrenia. As with residual schizophrenia, this is not a separate type in the sense of a special set of symptoms. The term refers, rather, to individuals who "walk around with" schizophrenia. They are usually untreated or insufficiently treated patients who are schizophrenic in their thinking, behavior, and emotional life but manage to stay out of the hospital and live in the community. They are marginally adjusted and often put an extreme burden on their families and associates. Some of them withdraw from practically all activities and social life, spending their time wandering aimlessly about. Others make peculiar grimaces, talk to themselves, and behave in a generally eccentric manner. Still others are hypersensitive and therefore easily hurt by the slightest criticism. Out of this sensitivity they may develop suspicious attitudes which may occasionally lead to destructive actions.

Pseudoneurotic Schizophrenia. These patients are apparently afflicted with a severe, mixed neurosis, but careful examination reveals the presence of serious and disabling thought disturbances of a schizophrenic nature. According to Hoch and Polatin (1949), they suffer from "pan-anxiety," "an all-pervading anxiety structure (that) does not leave any life-approach of the person free of tension," and "pan-neurosis," in which "all symptoms known in neurotic illness are often present at the same time." The symptoms shift constantly and include hysterical disturbances, phobias, obsessions, compulsions, depression, and such psychosomatic symptoms as loss of appetite, poor sleep, vomiting, and palpitation. A latent or incipient psychosis lurks beneath this neurotic façade and first makes its appearance in the form of short psychotic episodes. About one third of these patients later develop frank schizophrenia, although it is not usually of an extreme character.

Pseudopsychopathic Schizophrenia. In some patients the schizophrenic tendencies are masked or overlaid by delinquent or antisocial behavior. They exhibit typical and pervasive psychopathic (antisocial) personality traits, such as pathological lying, violent and uninhibited behavior, and sexual deviations. The existence of the pseudopsychopathic type of schizophrenia suggests that no strict line can be drawn between schizophrenia and character disorder, just as the pseudoneurotic type appears to bridge the gap between psychotic and psychoneurotic disturbances.

Propfschizophrenia. A form of schizophrenia found in a small minority of metal retardates, generally at the mild or borderline level. "Propf" comes from the German word for "to graft" (propfen); the disorder is therefore conceived to be engrafted, or superimposed, on the mental deficiency. It takes the form of paranoid episodes with delusions and hallucinations, which may be followed by gradual regression to infantile, deteriorated behavior.

A distinction is frequently made between two general classes of schizophrenia which cut across both the major and minor types. The term *process* (or nuclear) *schizophrenia* is used to designate cases that begin early in life, develop gradually, and have a poor prognosis. These patients are withdrawn, socially inadequate, and indulge in excessive fantasies even though they have never been subjected to any special situations of stress. Some therapists view process schizophrenia as the basic or "true" form of the disorder, and believe it stems from a biological, constitutional predisposition. Many authorities, however, believe there is no concrete evidence for a constitutional basis. In *reactive schizophrenia,* on the other hand, the individual has a history of better adjustment and socialization in childhood. He has not been particularly isolated or introverted, has not experienced any special difficulties at school,

and has usually shown an interest in the opposite sex during adolescence. Here the onset of the disorder is acute and appears to be a response to precipitating stress. The degree of regression is lower than in process schizophrenia and the prognosis is considerably more favorable. Some specialists apply the adjective "schizophreniform" to this illness, to indicate that it is not basically schizophrenic. Reactive schizophrenia is considered to be functional and environmental in origin, with no constitutional basis. *See* SCHIZOPHRENIA (CHILDHOOD TYPE).

Illustrative Case: SCHIZOPHRENIC REACTION (SCHIZO-AFFECTIVE TYPE)

Jane S. is a thirty-eight-year-old married woman who developed a sudden episode of violence in her home. She became so abusive and destructive that it became necessary to call the police. The patient barricaded herself in a room, and it required six police officers to subdue her after the door was broken open. The patient was brought to the hospital in a wildly excited state in which she hurled verbal abuse at the two officers who were accompanying her. When she arrived at the hospital she broke loose and tore up the admitting office, threatening to kill anyone who came near her. It was necessary to bring psychiatric aides from nearby wards to place her in restraint. The patient literally roared in a most frightening manner. It was necessary to keep her in mechanical restraint until the calming drugs took effect. She was intermittently hostile, euphoric, tearful, and depressed. (Kisker, 1964)

Illustrative Case: SCHIZOPRHENIC REACTION (CHRONIC UNDIFFERENTIATED TYPE)

Sylvia M. is a forty-five-year-old single woman who was admitted to the psychiatric hospital after a series of complaints by neighbors, the fire department, and the Board of Health. The patient's psychotic condition existed for at least four years, during which time she had been living alone. She hallucinated actively, talked to herself, and screamed at night. Neighbors reported she would scream from the window, "Get out of here, or I'll kill you if you take the children." The patient has never been married and has no children. Her apartment was filthy, with thirty-seven large bags of garbage found in her apartment when she was hospitalized.

The patient was an excellent student in school, and graduated from the university with honors in sociology. She was an active and well-liked member of a sorority, and following her graduation she took a position in the field of social work. She enjoyed a secure financial position, and was considered an attractive and well-dressed woman. Several young men wanted to marry her, but her father interfered each time.

Sylvia's mother died soon after the child was born, and the father became an alcoholic. The patient was adopted by relatives, although she did not know of her adoption until her adoptive mother died while the patient was in her late twenties. At that time she had an emotional disturbance which required hospitalization. Upon her recovery she returned home and took care of her father until his death a few years ago. Since that time she has been living alone, showing a steady deterioration of her personality.

When seen at the hospital, the patient appeared somewhat older than her age of forty-five years. She was unkempt, disheveled, and gray-haired. When she entered the interview room she was suspicious, looked carefully at the walls and into the corners. She was tense and agitated, frequently rubbing her hands, and sometimes giggling and laughing inappropriately. She commented, "There doesn't seem to be much the matter with me, just my nerves." When asked why she was in the hospital, she replied that she had no idea except that the police brought her. At times she appeared puzzled and bewildered. She was oriented for time, place, and person, although her remote and recent memory were impaired. She showed much delusional material centering around her practice of "standing" as a part of some type of legal action involving her nonexistent children. She admitted that she did not understand it very well, but knew that the situation required that she stand up for long intervals, sometimes throughout the night. (Kisker, 1964)

SCHIZOPHRENIA (PARANOID TYPE). The major symptoms of this

reaction type are poorly organized, internally illogical, changeable delusions, often accompanied by vivid hallucinations.

Delusions of persecution are the most common type. The patient may insist that his relatives or associates are talking about him, watching him, or conspiring against him, or he may complain that he is being followed, poisoned, or subjected to lethal rays by unknown enemies. He may conclude that since he is the center of so much attention, he must be an extremely important person. As a consequence, he may develop delusions of grandeur such as the belief that he is a saint, the president, Caesar, or Napoleon. These delusions are frequently reinforced with auditory, visual, or tactile hallucinations. The patient may hear a heavenly choir sing his praises or a tribunal denouncing him for overthrowing the government; he may watch his enemies slowly close in on him, or feel "molecular missiles" penetrating his brain.

Paranoid reactions are the most common form of schizophrenia, comprising over half of all cases admitted to mental hospitals. The disorder develops later than the other types, most commonly between the ages of twenty-five and forty, and is usually preceded by a long history of poor relationships with other people. During the prepsychotic period the paranoid patient has generally been cold, mistrustful, and suspicious; and in many cases he has been argumentative, bitterly aloof, or hostile toward practically everyone.

The first clear sign of psychosis usually consists of ideas of reference— that is, the patient feels that other people are whispering or talking about him. As his grasp on reality loosens still further, limited delusions begin to appear. The onset can frequently be traced to some precipitating stress, and in the early stages it is often possible to relate the character and content of the delusions to gnawing anxieties and disturbing experiences.

As the psychosis develops, the patient may suddenly attack people he thinks are persecuting him, or respond to inner voices that order him to commit acts of violence. As his personality disintegrates, his delusions and hallucinations become less systematized and logical, growing in time more and more fantastic, absurd, and changeable. If the patient is asked to talk about them, his explanations become extremely vague, incoherent, and full of neologisms. He now becomes increasingly "flat" and apathetic emotionally, except for periods of irritability and occasional surges of uncontrollable rage. If he remains untreated, he may eventually regress to childish behavior, such as hoarding objects of no value or performing ritual acts.

The most prominent mechanisms of paranoid schizophrenia are projection and displacement. The patient reacts to inner tensions by blaming others and transferring his feelings of hostility and his unacceptable impulses to them: *he* is not aggressive, his enemies are, and he is only defending himself against their machinations; *he* is not unethical —rather, others are making false accusations against him or suggesting illicit behavior—which is often of a homosexual nature. This fact led Freud to maintain that homosexual conflicts are a major source of anxiety and hostility in these cases. Some recent investigations (Klaf and Davis, 1960; Moore and Selzer, 1963) appear to have supported this hypothesis. Their studies have revealed a far greater preoccupation with homosexuality, more latent homosexual trends, and more homosexual experiences among paranoid patients than in other groups of disturbed persons. Interesting, too, is the fact that the "persecutors" of these paranoid patients were found to be male in practically all cases. Studies of female paranoid schizophrenics, however, failed to reveal similar conflicts. The exact connection

between homosexual tendencies and the disorder is therefore still unclear.

Most paranoid schizophrenic reactions are of the acute type and respond to treatment within several weeks or months. In cases where the disorder has developed gradually and there is no evidence of precipitating stress, it is more likely to become chronic and incurable. See SCHIZOPHRENIC REACTIONS (THERAPY).

Illustrative Case: SCHIZOPHRENIC REACTION, PARANOID TYPE

An ex-college student, after years of unshared pondering, fantasying, watching, and cautious questioning, came to the wholly unfounded conclusion that acquaintances of his had been involved in crimes of rape and incest. On the basis of bizarre misinterpretations of ordinary city street scenes, such as the exchange of greetings between pedestrians and shouts or laughter from people in passing automobiles, he organized an extravagant pseudocommunity of plotters and counterplotters. This pseudocommunity he peopled with the acquaintances whom he suspected, and with imagined persons who talked to him at night. In his preoccupations —which were deep enough to make him lose one job after another for inattention to duty —the patient fixed upon first one and then another person as the ringleader of the criminals. Finally he "realized the truth," heard the same night that his discovery would cost him his life, sought out the man who he "knew" was the mastermind, and assaulted him with almost fatal results. (Cameron, 1947)

SCHIZOPHRENIA (SIMPLE TYPE). Simple schizophrenia can be described as a pervasive impoverishment of personality. The patient's life contracts to a point where he manifests little or no interest, ambition, emotional response, or spontaneous activity. He withdraws from society, hardly talks to other people, shows practically no sexual drive, and neglects personal appearance and hygiene. Although he is generally timid and unaggressive in all his dealings, he may occasionally become irritable or even explosive. Efforts to arouse him from his lethargy are useless and may lead to obstinacy or negativistic behavior.

The onset of the disorder tends to be gradual and insidious, often taking the form of a growing indifference, moodiness, and indolence. In many instances the psychosis first appears in adolescence. A young man or woman who has shown promise at school or on the job loses his drive, makes no effort to work, and isolates himself from others. Although he may become more and more involved in his private world of fantasy, he does not usually experience hallucinations or delusions. There is little evidence of intellectual impairment or disorganization, at least in the early stages—rather, the patient simply stops using his mentality for any constructive purpose.

Simple schizophrenics often appear to be content to live idly at home and be cared for by others. They are therefore unlikely to be committed to a mental hospital. At most they engage in repetitive, routine occupations; but they are more likely to become neighborhood eccentrics, and in some cases lapse into vagrancy, petty crime, or prostitution. In general they remain colorless, ineffectual, shallow, "shut-in" persons who drift through life without serious loss of contact with reality.

Illustrative Case: SCHIZOPHRENIC REACTION, SIMPLE TYPE

An unmarried woman was admitted to a state hospital at the age of twenty-eight. Her mother and sister reported that during the previous five years she had gradually become inactive and withdrawn. She refused to go outdoors and spent much of her time lying in bed. She became very careless of her appearance, often did not answer questions that were put to her, and sometimes talked aloud to herself. Occasionally she would become very tense, her face would turn red, and she would bite herself on the arm.

The patient came from a family characterized by isolation and social nonparticipa-tion. She was the third of four children, none of whom had married when she was hospitalized. Her mother was thirty-eight and father forty-four when she was born. The parents had few friends. The mother was quiet, inactive, and overcontrolled. The father had been incapacitated by a neurological disorder for five years prior to the patient's hospitalization.

The patient had been sickly as a child. She attended school until the age of eighteen, stayed home with her mother until she was twenty-one, and left to work as a stenographer. After one year she returned home where she remained until hospitalized. For a brief period during adolescence, she had been fairly active in girls' clubs, but she had never had a boy friend or been out on a date.

On arrival in the hospital she was unattractive and appeared unconcerned. Her clothes hung loosely, she wore no makeup, and her behavior was self-effacing. Her voice was colorless and flat. She lacked insight into her condition. "I really don't know why they sent me here," she said. "I know I have a bad heart, but otherwise I don't know." Asked how her heart bothered her, she replied, "Just weakness. I just haven't as much life in me as most people have." Her perception of her mother, a markedly quiet and passive person, was very ambivalent and idiosyncratic. "I guess Mother and I don't get along as well as we might," she stated. "She tells people everything she knows. She can't seem to sit down. She's on the go all the time."

In the hospital the patient was completely disinterested in ward activities. She never became excited or otherwise evidenced affect and never initiated interactions with other patients. In group therapy she was an apathetic nonparticipant with nothing to say. She seemed to be devoid of ideas, yet an intelligence test revealed an IQ of 110; she was autistically preoccupied rather than mentally defective. On the Rorschach ink blots she manifested strong feelings of insignificance and inferiority.

She was treated with tranquilizers, ECT, and insulin therapy; none of these helped much and she remained withdrawn and apathetic. Eventually she was able to return home, but only to resume her earlier dependency on her family. (Rosen and Gregory, 1965)

SCHIZOPHRENIC REACTIONS (ETI-OLOGY). More research has been devoted to schizophrenia than to any other mental disorder. Scores of clues have been investigated, dozens of theories have been propounded—yet it still remains the most baffling of all psychiatric conditions.

As the discussions of the different types of schizophrenia suggest, there has been a growing conviction in recent years that schizophrenia is not a single disease process. Rather, it appears to comprise several kinds of faulty reactions which have one general factor in common, namely a disorganization of the personality leading to misinterpretation or distortion of reality. There is also an increasing conviction that the varied reactions may be due to different combinations of causal factors, some biological, others psychological, and still others sociological or sociocultural in nature. With this point of view in mind we will summarize a number of outstanding research findings on each of these causal factors.

1. *Biological Factors.* Biological factors include hereditary predisposition, constitutional tendencies, and various glandular, biochemical, and neurological conditions. Studies of the family background of schizophrenics as well as the concordance rate among twins present strong evidence for hereditary predisposition. Where one parent is found to have the disorder, the probability that the children will also develop it is nineteen times that of the general population; and where both parents are afflicted, it is eighty times the average expectancy rate. The rates are also closely related to the degree of blood relationship. If one sibling has this disorder, there is a 7 per cent likelihood that his half-sibling will get it. This percentage doubles if the two children are full siblings, and rises to about 85 per cent if they are identical twins.

Rosen and Gregory (1965) have summarized the results of six major studies of twins which show that the average concordance rate (if one twin has the disorder, the other will also have it) is four to six times higher among identical twins than among fraternal twins, "indicating a very sizable hereditary contribution." They cite evidence, however, that the disorder is not due to a single dominant or recessive gene, but to a combination of recessive genes. This argues for the theory that schizophrenia may not itself be inherited, but may be due to an inherited weakness or predisposition which can be exploited by stressful situations. Even Kallmann (1953, 1958), who has been the major champion of the hereditarian point of view, has said, "From a genetic standpoint, unusual behavior of any kind is viewed as an extremely complex and continuous chain of events in the individual's adaptive history and not as some inevitable manifestation of an inborn error of the metabolism."

Many other investigators point out that since 30 per cent of children of schizophrenics do *not* develop the disorder, there may be two general types of schizophrenia. In one of them hereditary predisposition would play a major role, and in the other environmental and internal stress would be wholly or almost wholly responsible. This ties up with the distinction between process and reactive schizophrenia. Some of the observers, however, minimize the role of heredity altogether and believe that psychological environmental factors are the basic if not the exclusive causes in all cases. At the moment it can probably be said that most authorities believe that heredity plays some role in schizophrenia as a whole, but exactly what it is remains to be determined.

It is also possible that constitutional factors having little or nothing to do with heredity play a part in the etiology of this disorder. Sheldon and others have found that schizophrenics tend to be frail and slender (ectomorphic), and in some cases it can be shown that poor muscular development arouses anxiety or causes a child to withdraw from social contacts. Physique may therefore be a contributing factor, but probably cannot be classed as a major determinant. Other investigators (Bender, 1953, 1955, 1961; Escalona, 1948) emphasize irregular development, physical immaturity, and imbalance between the various bodily systems during early childhood. Doust (1952a; 1952b) has also found a high rate of childhood illness as well as lack of maturity in bodily development. All of these conditions are believed to make them hypersensitive, anxious, and incapable of developing an acceptable view of themselves and the world. They also foster negativistic, overactive, or lethargic behavior, which makes them hard to manage and live with. This in turn interferes with their relationship to their parents and gives rise to an unfavorable psychological atmosphere in the home. These factors are probably more significant in childhood schizophrenia than the adult type, since a history of developmental disturbances cannot be discovered in most of the adult cases. See CONSTITUTIONAL TYPES.

A number of other physical factors have also been investigated. Beckett and others (1960, 1963) have found evidence for biochemical and metabolic defects that lower the individual's "adaptive energy." They theorize that this deficiency makes it so difficult for him to cope with stresses that he gradually retreats from reality. Others ascribe the apparent lack of adaptive energy to failure of the adrenal glands, and describe the course of the illness in terms of the "general adaptation syndrome," which develops as follows: the individual meets a stressful situation, is thrown into a state of alarm, cannot mobilize sufficient energy to put up adequate resistance because of adrenal deficiency, and finally becomes exhausted and disorganized. The difficulty with this theory is that most schizophrenics have a normal supply of adrenal hormones—and even where that supply is inadequate, the deficiency may be the result rather than the cause of the psychosis.

A great deal of recent research has been devoted to disturbances in brain functioning. The discovery that mescaline and LSD produce psychotic-like symptoms has spurred the search for chemical substances within the body that might account for schizophrenia. For a time it was thought that disturbed levels of ceruloplasmin or serotonin resulting from stressful conditions are responsible for this mental disorder. Subsequent studies failed to support either hypothesis. Heath et al. (1957) extracted a substance they called taraxein from the blood of schizophrenic patients and injected it into volunteer subjects. Within about a half hour they developed schizophrenic symptoms of one kind or another, but soon regained their normal state. Although several investigators in this country failed to reproduce these findings, at least five laboratories claim to have found a blood factor in schizophrenia, and positive results with the Heath test have been reported from Sweden and Russia.

The taraxein hypothesis has been further developed in recent research projects. Heath and his colleagues (1966, 1967) have taken tissue from the septal and caudate nucleus regions of the brains of schizophrenic patients after death, and have inoculated sheep with this tissue in order to obtain antibodies. Serum from the sheep was then injected into the cerebral ventricles of live monkeys, and was found to produce EEG waves associated with catatonic behavior. The recordings also resembled the brain waves of monkeys that had received taraxein from schizophrenic patients, as well as those of schizophrenic patients during psychotic episodes. Fluorescent studies indicated that the antibodies combined chiefly with the nerve cells of the septal region and basal caudate nucleus in the monkeys.

On the basis of these experiments the investigators have hypothesized that the symptoms of schizophrenia are the result of an immune process, and that the disease may therefore be described as basically immunologic. In their view, taraxein may be an antibrain antibody which is created to work against a "unique antigen" contained in the septal-basal caudate region of the brain. This antigen, which resembles histamine, may itself be produced either by stress or by inborn constitutional defect. The investigators suggest that this hypothesis may provide "a framework for future studies that may prove or disprove the concept."

Another interesting lead is the possibility of an imbalance between "excitatory and inhibitory processes" in the brain, due to subtle defects in its structure and functioning (Voronin, 1962; Wortis, 1962). The theory, which stems from Pavlov's early work, suggests that when the schizophrenic is faced with difficult situations, his brain overreacts to every kind of stimulus, and fears, fantasies, and vague impressions have the same effect as directly perceived reality. This throws him into a state of confusion and his behavior becomes disorganized.

Many workers in the field of brain research are trying to find specific centers that regulate specific aspects of our behavior and emotional life, and we may soon know whether excitatory and inhibitory processes are actually out of gear in schizophrenia.

Other current investigations are concerned with the disorganizing effects of extreme loss of sleep, and the presence of abnormal amounts of protein and other substances in the cerebral spinal fluid of many schizophrenic patients. These studies are mentioned to show that a great variety of biological leads are being followed, and that the entire field of research is in ferment. It may

well be that schizophrenic reactions are so diverse that many of these factors are involved to a greater or lesser degree. And it may be that many if not all of them are the result of the internal stress which accompanies schizophrenia rather than the cause of the disorder.

These, then, are the major biological factors under consideration at this time. But even if hereditary predisposition, constitutional defects, or biochemical disturbances are involved in schizophrenia, they appear to most observers to be contributing or limiting factors rather than causes operating by themselves—that is, they may establish a predisposition which develops into schizophrenia only if the individual is subjected to certain adverse psychological or sociocultural conditions.

2. *Psychological Factors.* So many psychological factors have been investigated that it is extremely hard to assess their relative importance, but future research will probably show that (a) several of these factors usually collaborate in producing the personality disorganization and retreat from reality that characterize schizophrenics; and (b) though "multiple causation" is the rule, one or more factors will generally be dominant, and will help to account for the particular form the disorder takes in a given case. At this point we can only present a résumé of the psychological factors most frequently cited today.

a. *Defective Family Patterns.* These are disturbed relationships that produce extreme anxiety, foster faulty response patterns, interfere with the development of the child's ego and self-esteem, and in general render him psychologically unfit to face the world. Many studies have focused on the "schizophrenogenic mother," particularly the mother of the male patient. Typically she is herself emotionally disturbed and tends to be rejecting, dominating, overprotective, perfectionistic, cold, and insensitive to the feelings and needs of others. By keeping the boy in a dependent state, she arrests his development; and by adopting a seductive attitude accompanied by rigid moralism, she intensifies his sexual conflicts. The result is an immature, helpless, anxious youth who withdraws into himself because he lacks personal identity, a sense of adequacy, and social competence.

Investigations of the fathers of schizophrenic patients have shown that they also tend to be emotionally disturbed, but instead of being dominating, they are usually weak, passive, detached, and even autistic (Eisenberg, 1957; Lidz et al., 1957; Kaufman et al., 1960). They are more likely to be rejecting than overprotective, especially toward the son; and in families where a daughter becomes schizophrenic, are generally contemptuous toward the mother and seductive toward the daughter. These attitudes have the effect of depriving the son of an adequate masculine model and the daughter of a feminine model. The daughter is also pitted against her mother and encouraged to form a pathological attachment to the father, which will later create severe internal conflict.

Disturbed parent-child relationships tend to occur most often on the lower socioeconomic levels where the bulk of schizophrenic patients are found. On the other hand, they have also been observed in families where schizophrenia does not occur—and conversely, schizophrenia may occur where parent-child relations appear to be normal (Block et al., 1958). In the latter case, constitutional factors or traumatic experiences (or a combination of the two) may have been the major determinants (Goldfarb, 1962). Constitutional factors may also help to explain why one child in a pathological family becomes schizophrenic and another does not, although Lidz et al. (1963) found evidence that the children who remained normal tend to utilize defensive strategies such as "flight from the family"

to protect themselves from its injurious effects.

Considerable research has been carried out on the total organization of the families of schizophrenics. First, several investigators have found that the roles played by the members tend to be so rigid and stereotyped that they do not allow the child room for personality growth (Wynne et al., 1958; Rychoff et al., 1959; Rosenbaum, 1961). Second, in many of these families communication between the members is so confusing that the child may be torn between conflicting feelings and demands. As an example, the mother may tell him he is getting too fat, yet offer him sweets as a reward for good behavior; or she may complain that he is not affectionate, yet freeze up when he tries to put his arm around her. The confusion is compounded by the fact that the father is usually too weak to act as a guide to the mother's conflicting messages. The term "double-bind" has been applied by Bateson (1960) to this type of situation. It may have the effect not only of generating insoluble conflicts, but of disorganizing the child's thought processes—both of which are characteristic of schizophrenic reactions. *See* AMBIVALENCE.

Third, numerous studies have revealed a far higher than average percentage of marital incompatibility, open discord ("marital schism"), undermining of one parent by the other, acceptance of the pathological behavior of the dominant parent by the other parent ("marital skew"), social isolation, and incestuous entanglements. Although the deviant pattern of the schizophrenic cannot be attributed completely to these pathogenic family patterns, Rosenbaum (1961) has commented that "All the qualities of disordered thinking and interpersonal relations which have been described for the individual schizophrenic have recognized counterparts in his family."

b. Early Traumatic Experiences. In a

large-scale study, Wahl (1956) found that four times as many male schizophrenics as nonschizophrenics had lost one or both parents by age fifteen. There is also evidence that a disproportionate number of schizophrenics suffered severe beatings, sexual traumas, painful illnesses and injuries, and separation from their family in orphanages or hospitals when they were children. The following account, quoted from a study of fifty-six psychotic children by Yerbury and Newell (1943), describes the kind of experiences to which many of these children have been subjected:

"Ten of them had been shocked by the deaths of parents to whom they had retained infantile attachments. Four children were so disoriented upon learning of their adoption that they could not reconcile themselves to the true situation. Four children had lived with mentally ill mothers who were finally hospitalized. Sex traumas were reported in fourteen cases of children who were overwhelmed with guilt and fear regarding masturbation. Four boys had been seduced and exploited by homosexuals. Three children were horrified by incest in the home, and three girls had become pregnant. Five girls were obsessed with imaginary pregnancy, having had no sex instruction except from other girls. Six children had been tormented, beaten, tied, and confined by their companions so that they were terrified in the company of children, and felt safe only with adults."

Experiences of this kind, often coupled with the disturbed home life described above, indicate that schizophrenic symptoms of seclusiveness and emotional flatness may be unconscious attempts to protect the self from a dangerous and threatening world. Withdrawal, however, has three highly significant effects. First, it opens the way to a life of fantasy as a substitute for the satisfactions of real life. Second, it curtails the individual's experience, so that his thoughts, fantasies, and impulses are insufficiently checked against reality and therefore become increasingly distorted, bizarre, and dreamlike. And third, as the individual's mental processes lose touch with the outside world, they become more and more responsive to the inside world of his own emotions and problems, and take the form either of strange, fragmented thoughts—due to the fact that his personality is torn by conflicts—or hallucinations and delusions that represent a more systematized expression of his wishes and feelings. If this process continues, the patient loses control of his thoughts, and they appear to take on a life of their own. This produces a terrifying sense of bewilderment, since he now feels alienated not only from outer reality but from inner reality as well. See WITHDRAWAL, TRAUMA, DEPERSONALIZATION, PERPLEXITY STATE.

c. Precipitating Stresses. Schizophrenic reactions may develop imperceptibly and insidiously out of schizoid tendencies—that is, out of the tendency to isolate one's self, retreat into fantasy, and avoid involvements of any kind—a behavior pattern that has been called "aversive motivation" (Garmezy and Rodnick, 1959). In some cases, however, the actual break may be precipitated by a specific stress experience which overwhelms a personality already weakened by pathogenic experiences and relationships. The most common precipitants are new situations and problems that arouse latent conflicts and anxieties over sex, hostility, independence, and the assumption of responsibility. Among these stresses are marriage, parenthood, transfer to a new job, or working with a person who resembles a threatening childhood figure. See SCHIZOID PERSONALITY.

Other people can usually take such situations in stride, but the schizoid individual is not equipped to cope with them. If he has been overprotected and dominated by his parents—as is often the case—he will be too submissive, inhibited, and insecure to handle normal competition. If he has developed highly rigid and moralistic attitudes toward sex, if he has failed to identify with his own sex role, or if he harbors latent incestuous impulses—also common in these patients—the normal relationships of dating and marriage will produce disabling conflicts. If he has never been able to form satisfying relationships with significant persons and has failed to develop meaningful interests and goals, he will be unable to find a place for himself in life and will feel constantly alone and estranged from other people and the world at large. As a result he will retreat further and further from an existence that has no meaning or hope for him.

The schizophrenic's reactions to precipitating stresses constitute the major symptoms of his disorder. In general, these reactions are believed to represent a complex defensive strategy unconsciously designed to protect him from feelings of anxiety, helplessness, and worthlessness. Among them are emotional blunting and flatness, wish-fulfilling fantasies, projection of blame on others, symbolic gestures and rituals, magical thinking, reorganization of thought into hallucinations and delusions, and regression to childhood as a means of avoiding problems and eliciting the assistance of others. Many investigators, particularly those of the psychoanalytic school, regard regression as the basic mechanism in schizophrenia. They hold that the patient is reliving infantile conflicts and falling back on the "primary process" thinking of early childhood in dealing with them. His hallucinations are regarded as projected images of his parents, his delusions represent primitive id impulses, and his paralogical thinking is a reversion to the confusion of reality and fantasy that characterizes the thought processes of the young child. Examples of this type of thinking are ideas of omnipotence, the belief that others can read his thoughts, and attributing supernatural

powers to electronic devices. This point of view has received some research support from the studies of Goldman (1962) and others, but it fails to explain many other symptoms common in schizophrenic patients, such as emotional unresponsiveness. For the rationale of the specific types of schizophrenic reactions—simple, paranoid, etc. —see topics listed in Category Index. See also PARALOGICAL THINKING, DEREISTIC THINKING, PRIMARY PROCESS, MAGICAL THINKING, STEREOTYPY, REGRESSION, HALLUCINATION, DELUSION.

3. *Sociocultural Factors.* All forms of schizophrenia are found in every known society, but there is considerable variation in their incidence from culture to culture. The paranoid form is most prevalent in the United States but uncommon in Africa; hebephrenic reactions are more common in Africa than here. In primitive societies as a whole, catatonic excitement and homicidal behavior are reported far more often than depressive symptoms, perhaps because in these cultures hostility tends to be directed outward rather than inward (Benedict and Jacks, 1954). In our own society the schizophrenic rate is eight times as great on the lowest socioeconomic level as on the highest —probably a reflection of both the disorganized, stressful conditions in the neighborhood and faulty relationships in the home. The higher rate may also reflect the poorer quality of treatment received by the lower economic groups, which leads to a greater percentage of chronic cases. When only newly diagnosed cases are counted, the figure drops from eight to two and a half times as many.

Studies also show that the incidence of schizophrenia varies considerably for different groups in the population. Recent immigrants, Negroes, and the undereducated show relatively high rates. These rates are attributed to adverse socioeconomic conditions and inability to obtain good medical care rather than to nationality or race. The incidence in urban centers is considerably higher than in rural areas, and highest in disorganized neighborhoods. It is also high among single, separated, and divorced men—partly because they lead lonely, alienated lives, and partly because they tend to live in the disorganized areas of the city. A Texas study has shown a relatively low rate among professional men and a relatively high rate among women in professional and semiprofessional occupations (Jaco, 1960). See ECOLOGICAL STUDIES.

Although increasing attention is being paid to sociological factors, their full and precise role in the etiology of schizophrenia is yet to be determined. At present there is far more emphasis on constitutional predisposition, traumatic experiences, pathogenic relationships, and precipitating stresses.

SCHIZOPHRENIC   REACTIONS (GENERAL). A group of severe mental disorders primarily characterized by general disorganization of the personality and marked distortion of reality. The individual's emotional life, thought processes, and behavior are all grossly disturbed, and consequently every phase of the personality is affected.

Although the term schizophrenia literally means "splitting of the mind," the disorder should not be confused with split or multiple personality, a rare neurotic disorder characterized by the development of two or more independent personalities in the same individual. In contrast, the split in schizophrenia is among the various psychological processes within the personality. It takes many forms, including a split between an inner fantasy life and outer reality; disconnected, illogical thought and speech; inappropriate or blunted emotions; and breakdown in control over behavior. In extreme cases of chronic schizophrenia a pervasive disintegration of all functions takes place. Here the personality is quite literally

"split up," and the individual "breaks up" or "goes to pieces." The term schizophrenia is therefore quite an apt one.

This term is only about fifty years old. In 1857 the Belgian psychiatrist Francis Morel applied the phrase *démence précoce* to the "early deterioration of the mind" which he had observed in a fourteen-year-old boy. In 1896 Kraepelin introduced a Latin translation of this term, dementia praecox, and applied it to a number of different conditions which appeared to develop early in life. The Swiss psychiatrist Eugen Bleuler advocated a change of name, since he had observed that these disorders did not necessarily develop in childhood and rarely if ever led to permanent mental deterioration. He found, however, that they all involved a disintegration or splitting of the personality, and in 1911 suggested the term schizophrenia. See KRAEPELIN, BLEULER.

Schizophrenic reactions comprise four major types which both Kraepelin and Bleuler recognized, plus a number of minor variations. The four are: (1) *simple schizophrenia:* characterized primarily by gradual withdrawal from social contact, lack of initiative, and emotional apathy; (2) *hebephrenia:* shallow and distorted emotions, silly and bizarre behavior; (3) *catatonia:* alternate states of profound stupor and frenzied excitement; (4) *paranoid:* transient, poorly systematized delusions of grandeur and/or persecution, usually with hallucinations. The other types include childhood schizophrenia and the acute undifferentiated, schizo-affective, and residual types.

Schizophrenic reactions constitute the largest single group of psychotic disorders. According to the United States Public Health Service statistics for the year 1965, they accounted for 18 per cent of first admissions and 49.7 per cent of resident patients (224,978 individuals) in public mental hospitals.

The median age for first admissions was about 33 years, and for resident patients, about 50 years. The number of males and females was about the same, but the rates for single and divorced persons were far higher than for married persons, especially for males. An estimated 1 per cent of the population in both America and Europe will be affected by schizophrenia in the course of their lives. The cases are found on all intellectual and educational levels, but the incidence is highest on the lowest socioeconomic level.

The clinical picture in schizophrenia varies widely from case to case. Nevertheless certain types of symptoms tend to predominate. The most important are:

(1) *Withdrawal from Reality.* The first sign of schizophrenia is frequently a loss of interest in the environment. People and events lose their meaning, and the patient becomes apathetic and indifferent to everything outside himself. He may complain that a wall of glass has been erected between himself and the world; he can see what is happening but cannot feel anything. This sense of unreality or "depersonalization" may later extend to his own body and mind. *See* DEPERSONALIZATION, WITHDRAWAL.

(2) *Autism.* As he loses touch with the outside world, the patient becomes increasingly absorbed in his private thoughts. His own wishes, fears, and fantasies dominate his thinking, speech, emotional reactions, and behavior. He becomes "encapsulated" in a dreamlike microcosm and is likely to misinterpret and distort whatever filters through to him from the outside world. The faces of other people may appear to be scowling at him; innocuous comments may be taken as severe criticisms. Some schizophrenics live their entire life within their minds; they may even become inwardly involved in a life-and-death struggle upon which they feel the entire fate of the world depends. *See* AUTISM, DEREISTIC THINKING.

(3) *Thought Disturbances.* The more the schizophrenic withdraws into his inner world, the more disturbed his thinking processes become, perhaps because they are not checked against fact and observation. Some of these thought disturbances are: (a) "loosening of associations": thinking is disconnected, fragmented, and perverted ("paralogia"); it does not follow the usual lines of connection and association but jumps from one idea to a totally unrelated and irrelevant idea; (b) "poverty of ideas": repetition of a few simple or meaningless phrases or sentences, a symptom known as verbigeration; (c) "concrete thinking": inability to deal with abstract concepts—for example, if he is asked what is meant by the saying "A rolling stone gathers no moss," the patient may say, "It won't grow any grass."

Accompanying these thought disturbances are various speech disturbances: vague, bizarre, stilted expressions, and use of inappropriate words ("acataphasia"), with frequent neologisms and a fascination with the mere sound of words—a typical example is "the religionation of the actionation is joy awoy." These tendencies reach their extreme in the garbled speech often described as word hash or word salad, and in the involuntary production of animal-like sounds, which has been termed "aboiement." Neologisms and distortions are also observed in schizophrenic writing, a symptom known as "paragraphia." *See* PARALOGICAL THINKING, VERBIGERATION, NEOLOGISM, WORD SALAD, CLANG ASSOCIATION.

(4) *Emotional Disturbances.* The original apathy develops into a generalized "shallowness of affect" and "inappropriateness of affect." The schizophrenic becomes so emotionally "flat" that he does not react or change his expression at all, even in response to the most startling events—or he may react in a

completely inappropriate way, such as smiling when he is told his best friend has died. He also suffers from "anhedonia," the inability to experience pleasure. He has little capacity to feel or reciprocate affection, and he is usually sexually unresponsive. Some recent theorists believe the schizophrenic does have a feeling life, but it is dominated by an intense, pervasive anxiety. They maintain that he cultivates indifference and withdrawal as a means of warding off this painful state of mind. *See* ANHEDONIA, WITHDRAWAL, AFFECT.

(5) *Disturbances of Activity and Behavior.* There is a progressive loss of control by the higher, rational brain centers, and behavior becomes infantile, primitive, and disorganized. The disturbances in activity take many forms: lack of initiative and spontaneous activity (anergia, abulia), incapacity for sustained activity toward any goal, bizarre grimaces, silly giggling, stereotyped gestures and postures which may, at least at the start, have an inner autistic meaning for the patient. Other behavior disturbances are: automatic imitation of the movements or utterances of others (echopraxia, echolalia), extreme excitement and overactivity, stuporous inactivity, and impulsive violence. Ambivalent behavior is common in severe cases—for example, laughing and crying at once, or tearing off clothing while berating one's self for immodesty. Some chronic patients lose control over their behavior and regress to such an extent that they masturbate in public, become completely dilapidated in appearance, and pay no attention whatever to bowel and bladder functions. *See* ABULIA, STEREOTYPY, CEREA FLEXIBILITAS, ECHOLALIA, ECHOPRAXIA, STUPOR, PSYCHOMOTOR EXCITEMENT, PSYCHOMOTOR RETARDATION, AMBIVALENCE, DETERIORATION, SYMBOLIZATION.

(6) *Delusions and Hallucinations.* Many but not all schizophrenic patients experience delusions and hallucinations. Though often fantastic and disguised by symbolism, these symptoms are believed to be directly related to their emotional needs and life experiences. All types of delusions occur: reference, active or passive influence, persecution, grandeur, somatic, and hypochondriacal. Many patients believe they are being pursued by nameless spies and conspirators, or influenced by strange electronic devices, that they are the Chosen Ones or reincarnations of Adam, or that their body is dead, their genitals removed, their strength drained away by some secret process. Hallucinations also take different forms: visual, tactile, gustatory, and particularly auditory. The patient hears imaginary voices cursing, threatening, or in some cases praising him; he sees vague images of angels and devils, smells foul odors, tastes poison in his food, or feels electric currents coursing through his body. *See* DELUSION, HALLUCINATION.

Schizophrenia does not run a single course. It ranges all the way from an acute attack lasting a few hours, days, or weeks to chronic, lifelong illness. Some chronic patients become stabilized and show little change in symptoms; others undergo continuous disintegration in all phases of the personality. Most patients, however, fall into a three-stage pattern. In the first or breakdown stage, they become anxious and bewildered by their loss of contact with other people, inability to react, feelings of unreality, and strange disturbances. Later in this stage scattered delusions and hallucinations begin to appear, and they wonder whether the ideas they entertain and the voices they hear are real. As these symptoms develop, they grow increasingly confused, and pathetically ask others what is happening to them.

In the second stage the symptoms gradually form a fairly clear constellation. The patient now accepts his disturbances of thought and behavior, no matter how strange they may appear to others. In this phase it is usually possible to classify his disorder as one or another of the recognized schizophrenic reaction types.

If these patients are untreated or ineffectively treated, they eventually enter a third stage in which many of their acute symptoms "burn out," and they sink into a state of profound apathy. Some patients regress to a primitive level of existence, wolfing down their food, talking childishly and often incoherently, neglecting their appearance and bodily functions, and finally isolating themselves completely from their environment. *See* REGRESSION, CONFUSION, PERPLEXITY STATE, VEGETATIVE STATE.

SCHIZOPHRENIC REACTIONS (THERAPY). The treatment of schizophrenic reactions has undergone a drastic change in the past fifteen years. Insulin coma therapy, widely accepted in the 1940s, has now been almost completely superseded by methods that are more effective and less risky, primarily electroshock therapy and psychotropic drugs. Psychosurgery is also rarely used except as a last resort in chronic regressed patients who appear to be hopeless. Studies show, however, that a substantial number of these patients can be returned to the community, and as many as 25 per cent can become self-supporting. In addition to the use of somatic therapies, there has been a considerable advance through the use of individual and group psychotherapy, milieu therapy, aftercare, and rehabilitation techniques, and the experimental use of behavior therapy.

The two most widely applied techniques, electroshock (ECT) and drug therapy, vary in effectiveness with different types of schizophrenic reactions and different stages of the illness. ECT is particularly helpful in controlling the symptoms of catatonic excitement or stupor, somewhat less effective with paranoid patients, and least successful with patients of the hebephrenic and simple type. The most commonly used drugs are (a) the phenothiazines, such as chlorpromazine, used to control excitement, agitation, and thought disorders such as hallucinations, delusions, and paralogical thinking; (b) antidepressants or energizers, aimed at elevating mood and increasing interest and alertness; and (c) antianxiety drugs prescribed to reduce tension and apprehension and promote sleep. These drugs may be used in combination with each other or together with electroshock therapy.

Phenothiazines may be administered for months or even years, but the antidepressants and antianxiety drugs are usually prescribed only for a short time or during periods of stress. In general, the tranquilizing drugs are more effective with schizophrenics than the energizers, and both types are more successful with acutely ill patients than with the chronically ill. One of their major values is that they render many patients accessible to psychotherapy. Another is that they enable a substantial portion of patients—possibly 50 per cent or more—to be treated in outpatient clinics or day hospitals; in some cases even acute psychotic episodes can be managed by medication without the necessity of hospitalization. *See* ELECTROSHOCK THERAPY, CHEMOTHERAPY, ENERGIZER, TRANQUILIZER, PSYCHOSURGERY, INSULIN SHOCK THERAPY.

Electroshock therapy is seldom used with schizophrenic children, although it is sometimes administered to adolescents. The same applies to drug therapy. Some of the more widely applied techniques are play therapy, relationship therapy, and activity group therapy in hospitals or residential treatment centers. Reinforcements (rewards) are sometimes used to overcome tendencies toward apathy and withdrawal (PLATE 38). *See* PLAY THERAPY, RELATIONSHIP THERAPY, ACTIVITY GROUP THERAPY.

Many attempts have been made to treat schizophrenics through individual and group psychotherapy. The results vary considerably from patient to patient as well as from therapist to therapist. The assumption is, as Arieti (1959) puts it, that the schizophrenic "is not happy with his withdrawal, as some psychiatrists used to believe, and he is ready to resume interpersonal relations, provided he finds a person he trusts, a person who is capable of removing that suspiciousness and distrust which originated with the first interpersonal relations."

Therapists who agree with this position adopt an accepting, understanding attitude toward the patient, though some therapists treat him as a mature adult when he behaves in an infantile way, while others assume the role of a benevolent and loving parent. In either case they realize that the schizophrenic is easily hurt and therefore tolerate his hostility while avoiding any show of anger. Many of them find it is best to proceed slowly, even by sitting and smoking in silence with the patient, or by bringing him presents such as food as a means of establishing a trusting relationship. The couch is usually avoided since a prone position encourages the patient to live in his fantasy world instead of relating to reality. His delusions and hallucinations are rarely directly challenged by the therapist; instead, he encourages the patient to question them himself. He may also attempt to bring the patient closer to reality by direct support and guidance in the regulation of his life, as opposed to attempting to increase his insight, since this often has the effect of arousing conflicts rather than diminishing them.

Finally there is increasing emphasis on sociotherapeutic techniques. Where psychotherapy is applied, the group approach is often preferred to the individual, since it encourages the establishment of normal social relationships and group members tend to correct one another's fantasies and bring one another closer to external reality. Socialization is also advanced by organizing the hospital as a therapeutic community offering not only occupational and recreational therapy, but discussion groups and patient government.

While most of these techniques are applied to patients on the road to recovery, there has also been progress in bringing chronic, withdrawn patients into closer touch with everyday reality. One approach, termed remotivation, utilizes planned conversational groups conducted by psychiatric aides or other nonmedical personnel. In a typical session, the leader creates a "climate of acceptance" by warmly greeting and complimenting each patient, then establishes a "bridge to reality" by reading and having patients read familiar poetry and other material. This is followed by a discussion of a special topic, such as space flight, that arouses interest without touching on personal problems. After this the discussion is focused on the "work of the world," during which the leader notes references made to former hobbies and occupations—and later sees that the patients have an opportunity to pursue them in the hospital. At the end of the session a plan is outlined for the next meeting, and each patient is thanked for his participation.

In the past few years social psychiatry has extended beyond the hospital and now includes such approaches as involving the patient's family, the planning of a rehabilitation program, halfway houses, ex-patient organizations, and aftercare in the community. See SOCIO-THERAPY, PSYCHIATRIC SOCIAL WORK, REHABILITATION, MENTAL PATIENT ORGANIZATIONS, FAMILY CARE, MILIEU THERAPY, GROUP PSYCHOTHERAPY.

All these advances in therapy and care have had a substantial effect on the prognosis in schizophrenia. In general, the rate of discharge before modern treatment methods were introduced was approximately 30 per cent; today about one half of all first admissions are discharged within four months (with fewer than 20 per cent readmitted), two thirds within six months, and 90 per cent within one year. However, the prognosis is different for different types of schizophrenia. Cases of early and insidious onset (process schizophrenia) require a longer hospital stay than cases of recent and acute onset (reactive schizophrenia). The prognosis is better for the catatonic, schizoaffective and undifferentiated types than for the hebephrenic, simple, and childhood types, with paranoid patients somewhere in between. In addition, the prognosis is considerably less favorable for patients coming from a severely pathological background and patients who have a long history of adjustment difficulties or repeated schizophrenic episodes than it is for patients whose home situation is favorable, and whose family shows an interest, accepts the patient after his discharge, and encourages him to continue his prescribed medication.

SCHOLASTIC APTITUDE TESTS. Tests designed to appraise the abilities required for academic work, particularly in liberal arts colleges, teachers' colleges, and engineering schools.

Before scholastic aptitude tests were developed, students were chosen for higher education largely on the basis of high school grades and scores on intelligence tests. Both of these methods had distinct limitations. It was found that the differences in curriculum, marking norms, and student body among different secondary schools were so great that the student's grades were often an inadequate criterion of success in college. Studies by Harris (1940) and others showed that the correlation with college marks was considerably higher (.60 to .70) when the high school grades were combined with scores on group intelligence tests. However, this was only an *average* result, and further investigation showed that the predictive

value of this combination varied greatly from institution to institution due to differences in admissions criteria, scholastic standards, and curriculum. As a result, a number of psychologists turned their attention to the construction of a single standardized test of scholastic ability based upon the specific abilities required for academic success in institutions of higher learning.

All scholastic aptitude tests are alike in certain respects. They all attempt to measure abstract ability; and there is also a basic similarity in content since they utilize items which have survived years of research and experimentation. There are, however, certain differences: the items on some of the tests are more closely related to school learning than on others; and certain tests have been standardized on very few institutions and are not representative of the nation's colleges as a whole. For this reason it is important for the guidance counselor to determine how well a particular instrument applies to the institutions under consideration. The major scholastic aptitude tests will be briefly described.

American Council on Education Psychological Examination for College Freshmen (ACE). A widely used test originally developed by L. L. and T. G. Thurstone in 1924. Both high school and college forms are available. Each of them yields two separate scores: an L (linguistic) score based on verbal analogies, same-opposite and vocabulary completion items; and a Q (quantitative) score based on figure analogies, arithmetic reasoning, and number sequences. The items are similar to those given at lower levels of education, but more difficult.

This test has been displaced by others for several reasons. The administration of many of the subtests is awkward, the part scores are of little practical value, and it has been shown that the L and Q scores do not accurately predict verbal and scientific success (Berdie et al., 1951). A total score can also be computed, but it predicts grade averages with a validity of only .45 (Cronbach, 1960).

Ohio State Psychological Examination (OSPE), originally developed by H. A. Toops in 1919, but frequently revised. This is an entirely verbal scale standardized for grades nine to twelve and intended for selection of college freshmen without regard to their future area of specialization. Critics recommend supplementing its same-opposite reading comprehension and word analysis sections with quantitative items, especially for prospective technical and science students. The test predicts college marks with substantial accuracy; .60 correlations are often obtained (Cronbach, 1960). A shortened version of this test, called the Minnesota Scholastic Aptitude Test, is also available.

Scholastic Aptitude Test (SAT). In use since 1926, the SAT is considered a highly effective instrument in determining whether high school seniors of upper ability level are "college material." The scale is valid enough to detect fine differences even in this rather homogeneous population, but it is considerably more accurate in predicting success in the liberal arts than in technical subjects. There are separate norms for public and private schools, for boys and girls, for all schools combined, and for students in different curricula such as liberal arts and engineering. The items are primarily designed to measure "abstract intelligence." A mathematics score is computed on the basis of answers to geometry, arithmetic, and algebra problems on the high school level, while the verbal score is based on completion, analogies, opposites, and paragraph meaning problems. French (1958) found that the verbal scores correlate fairly well (.43) with the grade average of a typical college, but quantitative scores show a fairly low correlation (.27) for students in the fourth year of college.

College Qualifications Test (CQT). Developed by E. K. Bennett et al., in 1957, this test is also designed to select college freshmen and to predict their degree of academic success. Like most other tests in the field it yields a verbal, numerical, and total score, but it is unique in presenting seventy-five items as a test of information which reflects prior learning opportunities. These items consist of a broad range of questions in social, physical, and biological sciences. Separate scores are calculated for the social area and science area, as well as for over-all information. This information subtest arises out of the conviction that the educational background which the student brings to college is a good indicator of future learning. Implicit in this rationale is the idea that a high information score reflects good study habits and general ability to grasp concepts, both of which are considered essential for college success. Moreover, studies have shown that scores on general information tests correlate highly with scores on general intelligence.

Cooperative School and College Ability Tests (SCAT). These tests were developed by the Educational Testing Service in 1955, primarily as a replacement for the ACE. The tests cover all grades from the fourth to the college sophomore level, and are designed to estimate the student's capacity for additional schooling. The entire series is based on a measurement of "school-learned abilities," and can be administered by educators who have not been trained in psychology. It consists of two types of items: vocabulary and reading comprehension subtests, from which a verbal score is obtained; and arithmetic reasoning and understanding, yielding a quantitative score. A single over-all score can also be computed. Although the test was created to measure school-learned abilities, the actual items are similar to those in other instruments.

Illinois Index of Scholastic Aptitude. Constructed by B. E. Blanchard, this twenty-five-minute test is designed for grades nine to twelve, inclusive. Although its primary purpose is to provide an objective evaluation of the subject's prospects for success in high school, it can also be used in identifying students who need special assistance.

Kuhlmann-Anderson Measure of Academic Potential. This well-established test, now in its seventh edition, measures general learning ability in children from kindergarten through grade twelve. The tests for grades seven to twelve yield separate verbal and quantitative scores as well as a total score, and may be used as a measure of intelligence.

Academic Promise Tests. A battery of tests for grades eight to twelve, designed to identify superior students, locate those who need special programs, and serve as an aid in grouping students and planning the transition from elementary grades to junior and senior high school. The Verbal Test measures ability to understand word meanings and to reason with words; the Numerical Test measures basic numerical skills and ability to think; the Abstract Reasoning Test measures ability to reason and form concepts from nonverbal problem figures; and the Language Usage Test measures such communication skills as grammar, usage, and spelling.

SCHOOL PHOBIA. A neurotic reaction occurring in children in the primary grades, characterized by a persistent resistance to attending school accompanied by acute anxiety that may attain panic proportions.

School phobia is found in about three out of a thousand children, particularly when they are taken to school for the first time. It may also take the form of sudden and adamant refusal to go to school among older children who have made a good school adjustment. These cases can usually be traced to a stressful or pathological home situation. If the older children are forced to go to school, they may become violent, refuse to do any work or participate in any activity. The younger children react by becoming frightened, tense, apprehensive, and by crying convulsively and trying to run out. Many of these children wake up in the morning with headaches and nausea, and may vomit before going to school or just after arriving. They may also attach their fear to anything or anyone associated with the school: the teacher, the janitor, the other children, the lunch room. If they succeed in staying at school at all, the phobia may be reinforced by traumatic experiences such as ridicule by other children or beatings administered by the school bully.

If the mother stays by the young child's side, school phobia does not usually develop. This indicates that the reaction is a form of "separation anxiety." It has been found to occur in deeply dependent children whose mothers are overprotective and constantly wait on them. Typically, this kind of mother lacks confidence in herself and is almost as dependent on her child as the child is upon her. When she takes her child to school for the first time, she feels anxious about "losing her baby" and communicates this anxiety to the child through her tense manner and quavering voice. *See* SEPARATION ANXIETY.

In some cases the situation is complicated by the fact that the mother feels an unspoken resentment toward the child for clinging to her and holding her down. The child senses this feeling and reacts to school as a form of rejection. This increases his panic and makes him cling all the more to his mother. The entire situation has been compared to folie à deux, in which two closely related people feed each other's weaknesses and develop a joint disorder. This is most likely to occur in extreme form where the father is not in the picture and the mother and child form a symbiotic relationship of mutual dependence and isolation from other people. *See* FOLIE À DEUX, SYMBIOSIS.

If the child is panic-stricken when he is brought to school, and all efforts to distract him and make him feel comfortable prove ineffective, his entrance to school will usually have to be postponed. But if the home situation is as extreme as the one just described, postponement may not solve the problem. The mother will need psychological guidance and in some cases extended psychotherapy to enable her to let go of the child. The therapist may also suggest a graduated series of experiences through which the child may be conditioned to accept and tolerate separation from the mother. *See* BEHAVIOR THERAPY.

School phobia can be prevented by encouraging young mothers to develop their own skills and confidence in dealing with their children, and by reminding them to maintain other interests which will prevent them from making too great an emotional investment in their children. On his part, the young child needs practice in playing with other children, in relating to adults outside the family, and in relying upon himself. Overnight visits to relatives can also be helpful. In addition the child should have an opportunity to spend a few hours at the school several weeks before entering. This is unlikely to arouse anxiety, because he will only be a visitor. Such visits will usually make him look forward to entering the school, and help him feel at home when he does.

School phobia in older children is also interpreted as a form of separation anxiety. Rosen and Gregory (1965) make this comment: "Years of experience in exploring and treating this syndrome have indicated that while some reality factors may exist in the child's distaste for school (such as, for example, an overly strict or poorly prepared teacher, poor achievement, or unrealistic demands on the child), the actual source of his anxiety is often related to his fears of leaving home and being separated from a parent, usually the mother. The fear is displaced from the parental relationship to the school. In some cases that were diagnosed and treated, the child was afraid to leave his mother for fear she would be beaten by his alcoholic father, or he did not wish to leave her alone with a younger child, perhaps a newborn infant, who, he feared, would get all her affection." In the following case, the child's refusal to attend school arose out of a pathological relationship which she developed toward her father after the death of her mother.

Illustrative Case: SCHOOL PHOBIA

The patient, a ten-year-old girl, was brought to a child guidance clinic because of her refusal to attend school. About five months earlier, her mother had died following a lingering illness and hospitalization. Although the child had completed the remaining six weeks of third grade without apparent problems, she refused to attend school after the summer vacation. She went to her fourth grade room the first morning with some reluctance but came home at noon and would not return. Sometimes she used physical symptoms as an excuse and at other times was slow to get ready. When urged to go she became very anxious, cried, refused to move from her chair, and said she hated school. She remained home with only a neighbor to come in occasionally, and her father made arrangements at work for an extended noon hour to have lunch with her. The one other child in the family was a boy of eighteen.

Physical examination revealed an attractive but obese youngster who was otherwise in good health. She scored an IQ of 109 on the Stanford-Binet, Form L. Her school adjustment had been considered good, although she was unusually conscientious and perhaps an overachiever. Her relations with other children were thought to be rather superficial; she was sweet to everyone, was accepted by others, but had no close friends and rarely brought other children home. Although her weight, a problem since she had been four years old, caused her some minimal concern, her father always assured her that good behavior was more important and that her behavior was just like her mother's.

The father stated that the patient had always been a conforming, rather quiet child, especially with people outside the family. Her reaction to her mother's illness and death had been amazingly adult-like, he considered, despite what he termed a close mother-daughter relationship. What many girls shared with friends, she had shared with her mother and had always shown an interest in helping with household chores, such as cooking and cleaning.

Following her mother's death, however, the patient did little but sit around the house and look at books and magazines. Her interest in toys was minimal and she took no initiative in helping with household tasks, even those she had performed during her mother's hospitalization. She became dependent upon her father for everything, and he, out of sympathy and concern, complied by doing all the chores and, in addition, planning joint excursions. She particularly enjoyed expeditions to buy clothes for her and to attend movies. At no time did the father question her changed mood and behavior except to suggest that she return to school. He also urged his son not to tease her for laziness.

She talked and laughed at home as much as usual and showed no signs of depression other than inactivity. About two weeks before the beginning of school she decided to give up her own room and sleep with her father. He thought the move inadvisable, but, again, complied when she rebelled against his objections. He reassured himself that the move was only temporary.

The girl was assigned to a female therapist and for many weeks related only superficially. She was very polite, answered questions, accepted and followed all suggestions for activities, and displayed little initiative. As time went on, however, she became less inhibited and volunteered information about her family and feelings more freely. On one occasion, when cleaning up after painting,

she commented that she used to pick up her things and help her mother but that now she did nothing because the amount of work to be done discouraged her. Since she tended to be a perfectionist, she chose to do nothing rather than attempt to do things she felt she could not do well. She had tried to take over her mother's role but felt guilty because she had failed at keeping house. As therapy progressed, it became evident that she tried to make up for this failure by doing other things her mother had done, such as sleeping with her father, accompanying him on activities that he enjoyed, and staying at home while he was at work.

The disturbance in the child and in the parent-child relationship turned out to be less severe than had initially appeared. The father was able to see how he had permitted the problem to develop and continue, and was able to take some immediate steps to change the situation.

He hired a woman to help with the household chores and made arrangements for a neighbor, who appeared to be interested in the girl, to shop for clothes with her and help fix her hair. These acts not only relieved him of unwelcome responsibilities but helped change the nature of the relationship that had developed between him and the girl after the mother's death. He joined a bowling league that met one night a week and encouraged the girl to bring friends to the house. When she became concerned about her weight problem and was able to follow the doctor's prescribed diet, he was able to give her much more encouragement than in the past.

About eight weeks after the beginning of therapy, the child returned to school and, at the father's suggestion, willingly gave up sleeping with him. She also began to take a little more responsibility at home, but never regained her earlier interest. The family itself decided to share cooking responsibilities, although the father actually did most of it.

The girl completed the fourth grade satisfactorily. Both she and her father remained in treatment for about fourteen months and she developed an increasingly good relationship with the therapist. She confided in the therapist more and more and looked to her for guidance. The therapist, apparently, served as a mother substitute. The father needed support during this period for his new firmness with his daughter.

Follow-up evaluation two years after the case was closed revealed that the improved family relations were maintained: the child was active in school and attended freely; the brother was married to a young woman who took a great interest in the girl; and the changes made in the father's life pattern during treatment had become fairly permanent. (Rosen and Gregory, 1965)

SCHOOL PSYCHOLOGY. A psychological specialization concerned with the development and adjustment of the child in the school situation.

The school psychologist has many functions. He selects and supervises the administration of group intelligence examinations, as well as special achievement tests such as in reading or arithmetic. In conference with teachers and the principal he advises on pupil grouping and curriculum problems based on his knowledge of the psychology of learning. In high schools he administers aptitude and interest tests when they are needed for the selection of courses or in vocational counseling. Above all, he devotes himself to individual children who need psychological help.

The school psychologist works on the staff of a school or school system but is not directly involved in administration or teaching. He is therefore in a unique position to make an objective and many-sided study of children who are beset with academic, interpersonal, or emotional difficulties. He plays a key role in the entire mental health picture, since the school is the only institution outside the family to which every child belongs—and it is an institution that involves the total personality of the child. For this reason, if a schoolchild has any special psychological needs, they are almost certain to come to the surface; and if these needs are met during the school years while his personality is still plastic, permanent damage can often be prevented.

In most cases it is the teacher who detects these needs and brings them to the attention of the psychologist. They cover such a wide range that the psychologist must, in most cases, be a Ph.D. with training and experience in diagnostic methods, learning problems, educational testing, and interviewing and group techniques used with both adults and children. He must also be well-versed in the work of social welfare agencies, clinics, and other community institutions in case the child or his family must be referred for special help.

Here is a sampling of problems that confront school psychologists. Eight-year-old Jimmy, in his second grade, is inattentive, restless, uncontrollable, and distracts the other children. The psychologist must determine whether he is a spoiled child, emotionally immature, or suffering from anxiety . . . Helen, a fourth-grader, reads so haltingly that she cannot understand the simplest material. She also mispronounces a great many words and has a marked lisp. Can a remedial reading teacher handle her problem? Does she need speech correction? Is her hearing defective? . . . Thirteen-year-old Jeanne is described by her teacher as "completely negative, a wet blanket," and her record shows that she has been apathetic, indifferent, and unco-operative ever since she has been in school. Is she emotionally shallow, mildly retarded, or lacking in confidence? What is the home situation like?

To find an answer to questions of this kind, the psychologist calls upon a variety of techniques. He observes the child unobtrusively in the classroom or in other school activities, then discusses his findings with the teacher. He has a friendly, informal interview with the child himself, and gives him individual intelligence tests, personality tests, or diagnostic tests for specific defects, such as hearing or vision or reading disability.

The next step is to work out a plan of attack. This may involve sending the child to a clinic or private therapist. The school psychologist may also undertake therapy himself if the school system provides this service. In any case, he will act as a liaison between the therapeutic process and the classroom. It is usually his duty to interpret clinical findings to the teacher, and to work with her in finding a practical solution to the child's problem. A shy child may need more encouragement, a culturally deprived child may need special experiences, a child who lacks self-confidence may profit from classroom jobs, and a slow-learner may need to be regrouped.

In many instances, too, the parents will be asked to come in for an informal conference in which the psychologist finds out about the child's life at home, difficulties the family may be encountering, and the feelings and attitudes of the parents toward the child. The individual interviews are often supplemented by parent group discussions or "workshops" which deal with selected topics on child guidance and family life. These may be planned or conducted by the school psychologist.

The school psychologist of today makes a special study of the cultural milieu of his school, and realizes that special problems arise in a middle-class urban environment, a suburban community, a deprived area, or a neighborhood in which prejudice and discrimination are frequently encountered. Many school psychologists specialize in the problems of the "exceptional" child —that is, the child who deviates from the average in one respect or another. They may test and evaluate retarded children and slow learners, and develop special educational approaches with their teachers. They may make a study of intellectually gifted children and children with special talents, devising methods for discovering high ability, and developing programs that will help these children make the most of themselves. Others specialize in educational techniques which will help to rehabilitate children with delinquent tendencies,

while still others engage in educational research and experimentation on such subjects as school dropouts and college admission procedures. (Gottsegen and Gottsegen, 1960, 1963; White and Harris, 1961)

SCOTOMA (literally, "dimness of vision"). In psychiatry, a scotoma is, figuratively, a "mental blind spot." This usage derives from the medical term for a blind or partially blind area in the visual field due to damage in the retina caused by disease or injury. The term is applied to a persistent lack of insight or awareness, such as the inability to recognize one's true motives or to consider interpretations that conflict with preconceived ideas about one's self or one's relationships with other people. "Scotomatization" may therefore be viewed as a defense mechanism or a form of resistance on the part of the patient to the recognition of the truth about himself. In psychoanalysis, such resistance is interpreted as an unconscious attempt to prevent disclosure of repressed impulses or memories that would threaten the patient's ego. See RESISTANCE.

SCREEN MEMORY (Cover Memory). A consciously acceptable memory unwittingly used to cover or screen out an associated experience which would be painful or unacceptable if called to mind.

The term is used primarily in psychoanalysis for the tendency of the patient to recall trivial and innocuous childhood incidents in order to keep from revealing more significant events. It is one of the many kinds of "resistance" encountered by the therapist. A patient might recall and describe in detail everything that happened in a barn or basement except the guilty sexual activity in which he was involved. Or he might concentrate on the happy incidents that occurred in school in order to screen out the fact that he was actually rejected by his class-mates. This process occurs on an un-conscious level and is regarded as a form of repression. *See* RESISTANCE.

SECONDARY GAIN (Epinosic Gain). Advantages and benefits derived from neurotic or other illness. Among these gains are sympathy, personal service, extra attention, financial disability bene-fits, and domination over others.

The patient does not consciously and deliberately seek these benefits, although he may enjoy them when they occur. Unlike primary gains, they are not the original source of the illness; that is, the patient does not become sick in order to obtain these advantages. Rather, they are the *result* of being ill, and for this reason Freud termed them "secondary" or "epinosic," which means "on, or over, disease."

Nevertheless, the line between pri-mary and secondary gains is often hard to draw, and there is little doubt that in some cases a dim anticipation of the "strategic value" of symptoms may have something to do with their forma-tion. This probably occurs most often in hysterical, or conversion, reactions. An example might be the worker who has a particularly tough boss, a "pain in the neck." In time this man develops a severe neck pain, presumably from the heavy work, and has to be trans-ferred to a lighter job. He does not deliberately plan to have the pain; rather, he unconsciously develops the symptom primarily as a result of the burden of resentment he is carrying— yet at the same time he may also have had a "secondary," half-unconscious hope that he might develop some kind of disability which would necessitate the transfer. *See* PRIMARY GAIN, COMPENSA-TION NEUROSIS, CONVERSION REACTION.

SECONDARY PROCESS. In psycho-analytic theory this term is applied to mental activity which is characteristic of the ego and guided by reality. It includes all the thought processes that enable us to meet the demands of the environment, such as systematic think-ing, logic, scientific method, and prob-lem-solving.

Secondary process thinking contrasts with primary process thinking, which is dominated by the id and its instinctual drives, and consists mainly of wishes and fantasies entertained without regard to objective reality. According to the theory, the ego is the component of the psyche, or mental apparatus, that exerts control over the instinctual drives arising from the id, deciding whether its demands should be satisfied, post-poned, or suppressed. It also enables the individual to adapt to the demands of the external world in a way that will avoid danger and achieve self-preservation. In carrying out both of these functions, it utilizes the secondary process—that is, intelligence, judgment, reality testing, and foresight: "After con-sidering the present state of things and weighing up earlier experiences, [the secondary process] endeavors by means of experimental actions to calculate the consequences of the proposed line of conduct" (Freud, 1949). *See* PSYCHO-ANALYSIS (THEORY).

SECTOR THERAPY. A therapeutic procedure developed by Felix Deutsch (1884–1964), in which chains of as-sociations that have produced emotional difficulties are broken up and replaced with more realistic and constructive pat-terns.

Sector therapy deviates from ortho-dox psychoanalysis in several ways. First, it does not attempt to reconstruct the patient's personality, but concen-trates on specific "sectors" that appear to be producing symptoms. Deutsch therefore describes it as "goal-limited adjustment therapy." Second, Deutsch recognizes the value of free association but believes the patient is too apt to alter his responses in that process; he has therefore devised an interview-free association technique aimed at eliciting thoughts and feelings which are less guarded and less influenced by conscious control. Third, the therapist actively responds to the patient's associations and attempts to guide them along new lines.

The interview technique, termed "associative anamnesis," was first developed in dealing with psychosomatic disorders, but has subsequently been applied to other neurotic conditions such as anxiety reactions, phobic reactions, and obsessive-compulsive reactions. The therapist first listens without interruption to the patient's autobiographical account of his history and difficulties (the anamnesis). As he does so, he identifies words and sentences which appear to be directly related to the area and stratum of the patient's personality, conscious or unconscious, which is most closely associated with his emotional problems. He then incorporates these verbal expressions into sentences of his own and observes the patient's reactions. These reactions carry the therapist, by "associative linkages," closer to the repressed or suppressed material that lies at the root of the disturbance. If the patient claims that the associations have little or nothing to do with his problems, the therapist confronts him with "key words" that establish the connection. In this way underlying conflicts and their expression in the past are linked up with current problems and symptoms.

The principal focus of this procedure is not on the past but on the present. The therapist encourages the patient to look back through free association only as a means of directing his attention to early attitudes and experiences that account for his present infantile behavior. If he wanders away from the emotional material, the therapist breaks through this defense by interrupting him and guiding him back to the key words and phrases. But as the chain of associations is elicited, and the repressed or distorted memories are brought into the open, the therapist attempts to loosen the associative links to old experiences and to establish new connections: "The dissolution of these chains and replacement by new ones is, in fact, the therapeutic process" (Deutsch, 1949).

As Deutsch describes the process, the old words are placed in a new environment of thought and feeling and become linked with a new context or "Gestalt." The therapist stimulates this relearning of associations to key neurotic words and expressions by incorporating them in his own sentences. The patient follows suit and begins to use them in the new context both because he has a good rapport (transference) with the therapist, and because he has discharged the emotions connected with the old linkages while describing his early experiences. Deutsch warns, however, that confrontation with earlier words and associations, which is the key to the process, must be carefully timed, otherwise the patient may become hostile or lapse into defensive silence. But if the timing is right, the faulty associations will disappear and new associations as well as new attitudes will be formed. *See* ANAMNESIS.

SEGUIN, EDOUARD (1812–1880). A psychologist as well as physician, Seguin was a pupil of the Parisian doctor Jean Itard, who became famous for his work on mental retardation and his attempts to educate a boy who had apparently lived nearly all of his eleven or twelve years in the woods of central France. Although Itard considered these attempts a failure because the boy learned only a few words, Seguin was impressed with the fact that he was able to master a number of useful habits. This led him to the realization that even though mentally defective children could not be brought up to normal, they still possessed capacities which could be trained and developed. *See* SOCIAL ISOLATION.

Itard's educational methods were based on principles of the associationist school, which holds that an accumulation of sensory experience is the basis of all mental growth. Seguin built on this approach by applying what he called the "physiological method" of developing the motor and sensory capacities of the mentally deficient. His procedures included various activities designed to promote motor co-ordination, such as climbing ladders or walking along lines, and a wide range of experiences aimed at educating the senses, including exposure to bright colors, varied sounds, and objects of different shapes. These techniques influenced the Italian educator Maria Montessori, who developed materials and procedures which are now being applied not only to defective but to normal children.

Seguin's work had a profound effect on the treatment of the mentally retarded. The accepted approach at his time was merely custodial, but as a result of his discoveries, constructive educational programs were introduced, and the defective were treated with greater understanding and humanity. Patients who had ordinarily been classified as hopeless showed great improvement, and the attitude of the public as well as the institutions began to change for the better.

In 1842 Seguin became the director of an institution for the feeble-minded in Paris, but in 1848 he had to leave the country because of his Christian Socialist political views. He accepted an invitation to the United States, sent by professional people who wanted to see his methods adopted in this country. He remained here for the rest of his life, establishing constructive educational programs in a large number of institutions.

Seguin's most important works were *Traitement Morale; Hygiène et Education des Idiots* (1848) and *Idiocy, Its Treatment by the Physiological Method* (1866). Though these books are rarely read today, one of his tests is still in use: the Seguin formboard test, which presents blocks of various shapes to be fitted into cutouts on a wooden board.

In assessing Seguin's contributions, Murphy (1949) calls him "the greatest figure in the century in the training of mental defectives."

SELF-CONCEPT TESTS. Personality tests designed to determine how the individual views himself—that is, the pattern of attitudes he entertains or assumes concerning his values, goals, abilities, and personal worth.

An individual's self-image, or self-concept, is considered one of the most basic and crucial components of his personality. It deeply affects not only his relationship to himself but his relations to other people and the world at large. A realistic self-evaluation and a full measure of self-acceptance and self-esteem are regarded as foundation stones of healthy adjustment. A consistent, well-organized conception of his ideals, abilities, and possibilities gives him a sense of personal identity and a point of departure for developing a life style of his own. On the other hand, the individual who entertains a deep doubt about who or what he is tends to feel lost, confused, and alienated from himself and from other people. And if he lacks self-acceptance or sets unrealistic goals for himself, he is apt to develop feelings of inferiority which cause him either to avoid competition or to overcompensate by attempting to prove his superiority over others. One of the major aims of psychotherapy is to help the patient eliminate such defensive maneuvers and achieve a more adequate, realistic, and unified conception of himself.

A number of tests have been developed to elicit and define the individual's conception of himself. They are used as a research tool in studying the nature of personality, with emphasis on the uniqueness of each individual; and also as a clinical instrument in assessing individuals who need therapeutic help. One device is the Adjective Check List (Gough, 1952), consisting of three hundred adjectives, from "absent-minded" to "zany." The subject is asked to check all items that apply to himself, and the results are then analyzed and compared to findings on more indirect personality tests.

A second procedure is to interpret personality inventory responses on such tests as the Minnesota Multiphasic (MMPI) in terms of self-conceptualization. Loevinger (1959) has made a thorough study of this approach and believes that the ability to "assume distance" from one's self and form a self-concept is an important personality trait. She finds that the individual progresses from an almost total lack of self-concept during infancy and early childhood to a stereotyped, conventional concept developed during adolescence—and as he becomes increasingly mature, he may go on to develop a differentiated, realistic self-concept in which he recognizes his abilities and shortcomings and accepts himself for whatever he is. However, many if not most individuals remain at the stereotype stage—and, interestingly, score higher than differentiated individuals on tests of emotional adjustment.

A third technique is the Q sort, developed by Stephenson (1953). The subject is asked to sort a set of cards or trait names into piles which range from "most characteristic" to "least characteristic" of himself, with a specified number in each pile. The items may be part of a standardized group, but are often selected with the individual case in mind. In making a detailed investigation of an individual, he is usually asked to re-sort the cards in a number of ways—for example, those applying to himself on the job, at home, or in social situations. He may also sort them according to how he believes he is, how he thinks others see him, or

how he would like to be. Q sorts may also be obtained at different stages in psychotherapy as a means of assessing changes. In addition, the technique may be used in determining the individual's concept of other people, such as members of the family, or in discovering a clinician's or interviewer's evaluation of an individual.

SENILE PSYCHOSIS (Senile Brain Disease, Senile Dementia). A state of mental, emotional, and social deterioration resulting primarily from degeneration of the brain in old age; classified by the American Psychiatric Association (1952) as "Chronic Brain Syndrome associated with senile brain disease."

Due to increasing longevity, cases of senile brain disease have multiplied in the past thirty years, and in 1965 accounted for 4.4 per cent of first admissions to public mental hospitals. The average age at first admission is about seventy-five for both sexes, although the disorder may set in as early as sixty. Female patients outnumber male patients by about four to three because of their longer life span.

The onset of senile brain disease (or senile dementia) is usually gradual, although it may be hastened by illness or stress. The first observable symptoms are generally a narrowing of interest, a dislike for change, and a reduction in alertness and adaptability. The patient grows increasingly self-centered and isolated from others; he is preoccupied with his own thoughts and bodily functions and begins to forget recent events. He may also become irritable and easily agitated, unsympathetic or even hostile, restless and insomniac.

As the disorder progresses, the memory impairment increases to the point where the patient not only tells the same story over and over again, but may fabricate events, become confused about the time relationships, and forget the names of children or whether he has ever been married at all. Many patients become extremely untidy and careless about personal habits. They tend to forget where they placed objects and may accuse others of stealing them. Sometimes they wander off and become lost. They may also engage in sexual indecencies, such as exhibiting themselves or molesting children. As time goes on they become disoriented, incoherent, and develop delusions and hallucinations.

Senile psychoses are classified into five clinical types: simple deterioration, paranoid, presbyophrenic, delirious and confused, and depressed and agitated. *See* these topics. There is much overlapping between these types, and the distinctions are often arbitrary.

The symptom picture in senile psychosis is not thought to be due solely to cerebral atrophy, but to an interaction of organic and psychological factors. Evidence for this lies in the fact that brain changes are not proportionate to intellectual changes, and personality changes often seem to be related to "premorbid" attitudes and behavior patterns such as irritability, rigidity, and immaturity. Moreover, preventive measures are primarily psychological rather than physical.

It is generally agreed that senile dementia can be prevented, or at least postponed or reduced in severity, by alleviating conditions that produce stress, anxiety, loneliness, feelings of helplessness and uselessness in aging individuals. Families should therefore help them find satisfying interests, new ways to be of service, and suitable companions to replace others they may have lost. The need for affection and emotional security, a sense of dignity and worth, recognition from others, and a sense of belonging does not diminish with age.

It is usually considered advisable to care for milder forms of senile dementia in the home, where the patient has his emotional roots and does not have to revise his lifetime habits. If serious problems develop from intellectual, ethical, and emotional impairment, he usually has to be institutionalized. Treatment may include mild sedatives to encourage sleep, tranquilizers to combat agitation, restlessness, and confusion, a vitamin-enriched diet to slow down brain atrophy and prevent confused and delirious states, and electroshock therapy in cases of severe depression. A program of social and occupational activity should be maintained as long as possible. In spite of these measures, some patients gradually deteriorate until they become oblivious of their surroundings and sink to a vegetative level. *See* AGING, DETERIORATION, VEGETATIVE STATE.

SENILE PSYCHOSIS (DELIRIOUS AND CONFUSED TYPE). This syndrome occurs in either acute or chronic form and comprises about 10 per cent of senile psychoses.

The acute and usually transient form may be due to hypoglycemia (low blood sugar), urinary infection, overuse of bromides or barbiturates, surgery requiring general anesthesia, trauma such as a broken hip or leg, and, less frequently, vitamin deficiency. In milder cases the patient is bewildered, disoriented, insomniac, and has frequent hallucinations. In severe cases he becomes restless, resistive, combative, incoherent, and completely confused. These reactions usually subside within a few hours or days. In some instances, especially in terminal cases, they may become chronic. *See* DELIRIUM, INFECTIOUS DISORDERS (SYSTEMIC TYPE).

Illustrative Case: SENILE PSYCHOSIS, DELIRIOUS AND CONFUSED TYPE

Mrs. S., aged sixty-eight, had a public-school education, was of average intelligence; married, no children; had no real marital difficulties; and had had no serious illnesses or operations during her life. She had an attack of influenza from which she did not seem to recover. Physically there were no outstanding symptoms, but she became mentally deranged. She became irrational, assaultive, and untidy, so that it was impossible to manage her at home. When brought to the hospital she was resistive and confused, she cried easily, and complained of many delusions concerning her health. She was incoherent, irrelevant, and rambling. She was disoriented as to time, place, and person, and her memory impairment was pronounced.

When asked what was the matter with her, she replied, "Injected you see, that spinal nerve which has to do with—what—hypnotize—I said they started so fact that. I remember my mother, grandmother and grandfather, they keep telling it to you till I find death. Gee, what she gave me that back. You have completely done that. Father had the same thing done to him that I have done to me. Uncle Abe was perfectly healthy, so that proves nothing was hereditary, that proves that, which the sick wards injected into my head, in my thinking head, in the head that does the controlling. Take me out, if you will take me out. I know didn't anybody put me in here. I'm talking about my life and health right now. My Aunt Hattie talked to me most. My mother is a very jealous person."

Her mental confusion gradually cleared up. Emotionally she remained very unstable, having frequent crying spells and complaining about small events or imaginary happenings. After six weeks in the hospital she returned to her home. Six months later her behavior again became such that home care was impossible. She was returned to the hospital, where she died after several months. (Landis and Bolles, 1948)

SENILE PSYCHOSIS (DEPRESSED AND AGITATED TYPES). In these cases, which represent less than 10 per cent of senile psychotic reactions, the patient becomes not only intellectually impoverished, but is subject to persistent depression and agitation. He wrings his hands, bemoans his lot, claims he is a useless burden whom nobody wants. These symptoms are usually accompanied by hypochondriacal delusions which frequently take the form of fear of cancer, syphilis, or other dread diseases. Some patients are afflicted with delusions of poverty, insisting that they are headed for the poorhouse. Other common symptoms are delusions of unpardonable sin and nihilistic delusions— the belief that their blood has ceased to circulate, that they have no pulse or stomach, that they are dead, or that all their relatives have died. Some of these patients develop suicidal impulses, which must be guarded against. See AGITATION, DEPRESSION, HYPOCHONDRIASIS, DELUSION.

SENILE PSYCHOSIS (PARANOID TYPE). This is the most clearly defined type of senile psychosis, characterized by the gradual appearance of delusions with hallucinations, but not accompanied by impairment of intellectual functions in the early stages. The delusions are usually of the persecutory type. The patient may, for example, insist that his relatives have conspired to "put him away." A delusion of this kind may be supported by the hallucination that he has been served poisoned food or that he has been sprayed with poison gas. About 30 per cent of senile psychoses take a paranoid form.

Paranoid patients do not suffer from the marked memory loss, disorientation, or confusion that afflict other senile patients. Their attitudes toward others, however, are deeply affected, and they are typically quarrelsome, complaining, and demanding. These symptoms usually occur in individuals who have shown similar personality traits all their lives. They appear in exaggerated form during senility because the patient has an unconscious need to use them as defensive measures.

The delusions are a more extreme form of defensive action and develop when the elderly person can no longer cope with problems posed by physical deterioration and emotional isolation. It is not surprising, therefore, that the delusions are sometimes grandiose and erotic as well as persecutory. They occur in increasing severity as these patients deteriorate for, as Noyes and Kolb (1963) point out, "As memory defect appears, delusional extension and further defensive emotional reaction may take place in an attempt to repair the additional psychobiological deficit. Similarly, as judgment fails the delusions become more absurd, partly because beliefs are no longer subject to any critical scrutiny, and partly because the damaged personality requires more fantastic beliefs for its support."

Illustrative Case: SENILE PSYCHOSIS, PARANOID TYPE

The patient, a woman of seventy-four, had been referred to a hospital after the death of her husband because she became uncooperative and was convinced that her relatives were trying to steal the insurance money which her husband had left her. In the hospital she complained that the other women had joined together against her and were trying to steal her belongings. She frequently refused to eat, on the grounds that the food tasted funny and had probably been poisoned. She grew increasingly irritable and disoriented for time and person. She avidly scanned magazines in the ward reading room but could not remember anything that she had looked at. The following conversation reveals some of her symptoms:

DR: Do you find that magazine interesting?

PT: Why do you care? Can't you see I'm busy?

DR: Would you mind telling me something about what you are reading?

PT: It's none of your business . . . I am reading about my relatives. They want me to die so that they can steal my money.

DR. Do you have any evidence of this?

PT: Yes, plenty. They poison my food and they have turned the other women against me. They are all out to get my money. They even stole my sweater.

DR: Can you tell me what you had for breakfast?

PT: . . . (pause) I didn't eat breakfast . . . it was poisoned and I refused to eat it. They are all against me. (Coleman, 1964)

SENILE PSYCHOSIS (PRESBYO-PHRENIC TYPE). A senile reaction occurring primarily in women, and characterized by memory impairment, a jovial mood, and confabulation.

Presbyophrenic patients are active, talkative, and appear alert. They engage in meaningless activities, such as collecting useless articles or repeatedly packing and unpacking their clothing, all the while talking in a rambling manner about events in their past. When memory fails, they cheerfully fabricate details or amplify fictional material suggested by others. As the disorder progresses they lose touch with reality and exhaust themselves in talking and aimless activity. These patients sometimes become so debilitated and deteriorated that they sink to a vegetative level and pneumonia or other infections eventually put an end to their lives.

The presbyophrenic type constitutes less than 10 per cent of all senile psychotics. *See* CONFABULATION.

SENILE PSYCHOSIS (SIMPLE DE-TERIORATION TYPE). This is the most common form of senile psychosis, comprising about 50 per cent of the entire group. The symptoms are for the most part an exaggeration of the usual changes that occur with advancing age. These include memory defect for recent and, later, remote events, a narrow range of interest, apathy, intolerance of change, tendency to reminisce, loss of judgment, restlessness and irritability. As the condition progresses, the patient loses contact with his environment, becomes neglectful of personal care and appearance, confused and disoriented, and may develop a mildly stuporous state.

The following case illustrates many of the features of simple senile dementia, but also shows that other types of reaction—in this case, paranoid and presbyophrenic—may be combined with it.

Illustrative Case: SENILE PSYCHOSIS, SIM-
PLE TYPE

H.S. was admitted to a public hospital for mental disorders when seventy-two years of age. When six years old she sustained a fracture of the hip. Four years later an operation was performed in an effort to correct the deformity and disability. It was necessary to strap her to the bed for six months following the operation. The functional results of this operation were disappointing, and the patient was always self-conscious concerning the considerable degree of disability that persisted. She always felt that people did not wish to mingle with her because of this infirmity and did not seem comfortable in the presence of others. It is quite possible that the few paranoid features accompanying the patient's senile dementia may have had their origin in this defensive characteristic.

Five years before the patient's admission her adopted son with whom she resided noted that she was becoming forgetful, especially concerning her usual household duties and recent incidents. She hoarded articles and sometimes said that someone had stolen them. She remembered events of her childhood quite well and at times was somewhat boresome in her accounts of early experiences. Her adopted son noted that she became increasingly neglectful of her personal appearance. For many months prior to her admission she would not bathe unless reminded to do so. Recently she often went to bed without removing either clothing or shoes. At times she put on her clothing "inside out." For four years prior to admission she seemed to find it difficult to prepare meals at accustomed times.

On many occasions she completed the preparation of the midday meal at 8 A.M. and insisted that the family should eat at that time. In preparing coffee she often put sugar instead of coffee in the coffee pot but failed to recognize her error. In a few instances she wished to pay bills she had already paid. She was restless at night but often slept during the day. The patient became increasingly confused in surroundings with which she had formerly been quite familiar. Often, when crossing the street, she paid no attention to approaching automobiles. At times she wandered away from home.

There were periods during which she constantly packed and unpacked her clothing. During recent months she had often failed to recognize friends. She became increasingly suspicious, said that neighbors were talking about her, spoke of them in extremely derogatory terms, maintained that her son had lied to her and had tried to poison her, and that her neighbors had threatened to kill her. She claimed that her son and an elderly woman who had been employed to give her protective care had been secretly married. She complained that everyone was trying to control her activities and threatened to commit suicide if not permitted to do as she wished.

When the patient was brought to the mental hospital, she rose to meet the admitting physician, shook his hand, asked him where he was and if there was anything she could do for him. She knew her name but could not give her address or other identifying data. She claimed that her son, who had really been extremely devoted to her, had ejected her in order to secure possession of her house, which was located "down the hill." At the time of this writing she has been in the hospital for eighteen months. Affectless and placid, she sits in a rocking chair all day, paying little or no heed to her environment. Her existence is now but little above a vegetative level. (Noyes and Kolb, 1963)

SENSATION. An experience produced by stimulation of a receptor and resultant activity of a specific brain center. For example, when sound waves impinge on the eardrum, their energy is transmitted through the ear and auditory nerve and eventually activates a portion of the auditory center in the temporal lobe of the brain.

The study of sensory processes and their underlying physiological mechanisms was a major preoccupation at the start of modern psychology, and laboratory techniques developed by men like Ernst Weber, Gustav Fechner, Hermann Helmholtz, and Wilhelm Wundt did much to launch the scientific study of human behavior. Recent investigations have been focused less on basic research than on the application of our knowledge of sensory processes to problems arising in industry, military service, and space exploration—for example, the ability to detect instructions against a background of noise, to pick up signals on a radar screen, or to read instruments quickly and accurately. *See* ENGINEERING PSYCHOLOGY, EQUIPMENT DESIGN, DETECTION THEORY.

The significance of sensory investigations, both basic and applied, rests upon two crucial facts: everything we know about the world around us, as well as the world inside our own bodies, comes to us through our sense organs— and every act we perform is ultimately dependent on the information we receive through them. Investigations of sensation deal with the special problems posed by each sense, as well as certain general problems that apply to them all. The general problems are: (a) the type of stimulation—thermal, mechanical, chemical—and the range of stimulation to which the various receptors are attuned; (b) the thresholds of sensitivity, in other words, the minimum energy necessary to activate each sensory system (absolute threshold), and to detect a just noticeable difference between stimuli (difference threshold); (c) sensory adaptation, or the increase or decrease in sensitivity that occurs under continuous stimulation (for example, increased sensitivity to light as we remain in a dark room); and (d) the physiological basis for sensation in the receptors, nerve tracts, and brain centers for each of the senses. For discussion of these four aspects *see* VISION, HEARING, TOUCH, TASTE, SMELL, SKIN SENSES, KINESTHETIC SENSE, ORGANIC SENSES, as well as ABSOLUTE THRESHOLD, JUST NOTICEABLE DIFFERENCE, SENSORY ADAPTATION, FECHNER.

It may be useful to round up the special problems posed in the study of each sense in order to present an overall view of the subject of sensation. Far more research has been devoted to the visual and auditory senses than to any others, since they are the major sources of experience, knowledge, and control of behavior in the human being. In addition to the general questions raised above, the visual problems include the question of the dimensions of color (hue, brightness, saturation) and its representation on the color circle and color solid; color mixture; color blindness; night blindness; visual acuity; contrast effects; afterimages; and the theories which attempt to explain all these phenomena.

The auditory sense raises the following problems: the dimensions of tone (pitch, loudness, timbre) and their physiological correlates; complex tones and noises; and the theories devised to explain these characteristics. The sense of smell poses the problem of classification of odors, as well as the problem of the olfactory stimulus (whether it is based on chemical energy, radiant energy, or the shape of molecules). There is more agreement on the classification of the primary qualities of taste (salt, sweet, bitter, sour) than of smell, but special problems are raised by the various mixtures of tastes and their combination with odor to produce flavor.

The questions raised by the four skin senses (warmth, cold, pain, and pressure) are largely physical and physiological—particularly, the nature and location of the various receptors, variations in sensitivity in different parts of the body, and the type and intensity of stimulation necessary to arouse each type of response. There are also special problems such as localization of the source of pain or pressure, the distinction between different sensations, such as itching and tickling, and the unusual or abnormal sensations known as paresthesias which occur in certain disorders—for example, the sensation of insects crawling under the skin. *See* SENSITIVITY DISTURBANCES.

Static sensitivity (the sense of balance or equilibrium) is dependent on special organs in the inner ear, and includes awareness of both the position and motion of the body. Among the questions it raises are how we right ourselves when falling, the effects of movement on vision, and the nature of motion sickness. Kinesthesis is the name given to the sensory system that informs us of the position and movement of parts of the body through receptors embedded in the muscles, tendons, and joints. The study of this sense helps to answer questions about posture, estimation of weight by "hefting" objects, our ability to move about in the dark, the way we learn to walk and speak, and the achievement of automatic control of our muscles in activities such as reaching and manipulation.

Finally, the term organic sensitivity is applied to awareness of changes occurring in the internal organs of our bodies, such as the stomach, kidneys, throat, and legs. Sensations from these organs enable us to experience thirst, hunger, bladder and intestinal tensions, sexual desire and gratification, nausea, and suffocation. Organic sensitivity serves not only as a signal for internal needs, but as a warning when bodily organs are out of order. See the Category Index, under SENSATION and PERCEPTION.

SENSITIVITY DISTURBANCES. A
term used in this book to designate various conditions of reduced, exaggerated, or distorted sensitivity, either organic or functional in origin.

Anesthesia is a total loss of sensitivity to stimuli due to nerve impairment or destruction, narcotic drugs, psychiatric disorder, or hypnotic suggestion. Various kinds of anesthesia—glove, stocking, trunk, girdle, garter, wrist, etc. —occur in cases of hysteria, or conversion reaction. Anesthesias of this type are psychogenic in origin, and can often be shown to serve unconscious purposes and bring secondary gains. They are distinguished from organic anesthesia

due to nerve injury by the fact that the insensitive areas do not correspond to the distribution of nerve fibers. Anesthesias of taste (ageusia) and smell (anosmia) are also occasionally observed. Coleman (1964) cites the case of an elderly mother who lost her sense of smell when her only son came home night after night with the odor of alcohol on his breath. Hysterical skin anesthesias were particularly common in the Middle Ages, and were used as one of the major proofs of witchcraft. See CONVERSION REACTION, DEMONOLOGY, HYPNOSIS.

Hypoesthesia, or hypesthesia, is a partial loss of sensitivity. This reaction is also a common hysterical symptom, as is the opposite extreme, hyperesthesia. In the latter case, the patient may be inordinately sensitive to one or another kind of sensory impression—to sound, light, heat, cold, and particularly to tactile stimuli. Hypersensitivity also occurs in a number of organic conditions, such as alcoholic polyneuritis and menopause.

Three other types of sensitivity disturbance occasionally occur in patients with conversion reaction: analgesia, the loss or impairment of pain sensitivity; hyperalgesia, extreme sensitivity to pain; and paresthesia, which includes various sensitivity distortions such as tingling, tickling, or burning sensations. Paresthesias are also found in a variety of other disorders, including cerebral arteriosclerosis, alcoholic polyneuritis, and hyperventilation syndrome. Formication, the feeling that bugs are crawling on or under the skin, is a form of paresthesia occurring in delirium due to infection, cocaine, or acute alcoholic hallucinosis. See HYPERVENTILATION SYNDROME, FORMICATION, COCAINE HABITUATION, ACUTE ALCOHOLIC HALLUCINOSIS.

Brief mention should also be made of other sensitivity disturbances which may be due either to psychological disorders (particularly, conversion reaction), or to physical conditions associated with disease or neurological defect. Among them are gargalanesthesia, absence of tickle sense (or its opposite, hypergargalesthesia); hyper- (or hypo-) ageusia, excessive or diminished acuteness of the sense of taste; hyper- (or hypo-) kinesthesia, over- or underactivity of the sense of motion or position; hyper- (or hypo-) thermoesthesia, excessive or diminished sensitivity to heat; thermoanesthesia, absence of heat sense; hyper- (or hypo-) baresthesia, over- or underactivity of the pressure or touch sense; pallesthesia, excessive sensitivity to vibrations; palmanesthesia, loss of sensitivity to vibrations; hyper- (or hypo-) algesia, excessive or diminished sensitivity to pain; and hyper- (or hyp-) acusia or -acusis, extreme or reduced sensitivity to sounds. *See* DERMO-OPTICAL PERCEPTION.

SENSORIUM. All senses and perceptual abilities taken together; roughly equivalent to consciousness.

A "clear sensorium" means that our special senses are functioning well, and we know who and where we are and what we are doing. "Clouded sensorium" means that the ability to perceive and understand the environment is impaired. The individual may be confused or disoriented as to time, place, circumstances, and his own identity. The most extreme and dramatic defects in the sensorium occur in such organic disorders as acute alcoholism and toxic psychosis. The patient may hear strange music, smell peculiar odors, see pink elephants, or feel insects crawling over his body. The sensorium is also affected in some schizophrenic and manic-depressive reactions.

The state of the sensorium is always noted during any psychiatric examination, and if there is an indication of clouding of consciousness, questions of this type are asked: Where are we now? Who are you? What are you doing here? Who am I? Vivid sensorial changes are produced by "mind-distorting" and psychotomimetic drugs such as LSD and mescaline. They may also occur in states of meditation and in conditions of sensory deprivation. *See* LYSERGIC ACID, HALLUCINOGEN, SENSORY DEPRIVATION, DELIRIUM, ACUTE ALCOHOLIC HALLUCINOSIS, TOXIC PSYCHOSES, PSYCHIATRIC EXAMINATION.

SENSORY ADAPTATION. Changes in the sensitivity of a sense organ due to the presence or absence of stimulation. In general, an organ becomes less sensitive when under continual stimulation, and more sensitive in the absence of stimulation.

Adaptation is one of our most familiar experiences, and illustrations can readily be found in practically every sense modality: (1) *temperature:* when we first step into a hot bath the water feels almost unbearable, but within a few moments we adjust to it; (2) *taste:* food usually appears more tasty at the beginning of a meal than at the end, especially if we eat large amounts of the same dish; (3) *smell:* we notice the pleasant odor when we first enter a bakery, but within a few minutes it begins to fade; (4) *pressure:* we are acutely aware of a new wristwatch, eye glasses, or shoes when we first put them on, but in time we fail to notice them at all; (5) *motion:* we are all too conscious of the rolling of an ocean liner during the first few hours, but it becomes far less noticeable in a day or two—*if* we stay well; (6) *sound:* people who work in shipyards or live near an airport usually find that in time the sounds appear to diminish in intensity and become less disturbing; (7) *light:* actors find that the stage lights become less and less blinding as the play progresses; (8) *pain:* the acute discomfort of a cut or sprain usually decreases even without medication or other treatment.

These experiences are not merely due to counteradjustments, as in adapting our posture to the rolling of a ship, but to physical changes that take place in the sense organs themselves (Geldard, 1962). The exact mechanism that underlies the changes is largely unknown, but psychological experiments have disclosed a number of principles involved in the process. First, measurements of stimulus intensity have shown that in general the more intense the stimulation, the more rapid the adaptation. We therefore adapt more quickly to a loud sound than to a faint sound, to an intense pressure than to a slight one. Second, "adaptation time" measurements show that in the case of pain the process is neither so quick nor so complete as for other senses. It takes only a few seconds or minutes for our hand to adapt to a new temperature level when we immerse it in water, but a toothache or a headache may be felt for hours. The slower adaptation for the pain sense has survival value in reminding us that something is wrong with the organism. Third, all sense organs show recovery from the effects of adaptation—that is, they become more sensitive when stimulation is removed. If we take off our wristwatch, we may experience an "after sensation" for a moment or two, though in a little while our wrist resumes its normal sensitivity. When we first go into a darkened room we cannot see the luminous hands of a clock, but in a few minutes our eyes become sensitive to low illumination and we are able to read it. See DARK ADAPTATION.

These illustrations show that sensory adaptation can work both for us and against us. It enables us to endure pain, tolerate loud sounds, and adjust to the unpleasant odors of a chemical laboratory or sanitation plant. On the other hand, it makes us lose our capacity to enjoy the odor of perfume and the taste of food. It can also be a hazard in certain occupations, such as mining, where the detection of gas odors can make the difference between life and death.

Finally, a series of experiments performed by Helson has shown that the degree of adaptation is determined by the state of the organism at the time of stimulation. His "adaptation-level" theory states that the level of temperature, sound, or other stimulation to which the organism is currently adapted becomes a norm or frame of reference against which new stimulation is judged. One of the clearest examples is the classic experiment in which the left hand is immersed in hot water and the right hand in cold. Within a few moments the adaptation process establishes a different "psychological zero" for each hand, and, as a result, when both hands are placed in warm water, it will feel cold to the left and hot to the right. Similarly, the first mild day of spring will feel warmer than the first cold day of fall, even though the temperature on the spring day is actually considerably lower than the temperature on the fall day. In a typical experiment, Helson (1948) let one group of subjects judge a series of weights of 200 to 400 grams after holding a weight of 900 grams, while another group judged the same weights after holding only 90 grams. The first group judged the 200–400 gram series to be much lighter than the second.

Adaptation-level theory has been applied to a wide variety of judgments. The same salary will appear high to one person and low to another. The traffic in a small town will seem heavy to a farmer and light to a city dweller; a beatnik's behavior will look "way out" to the ordinary run of people but not to fellow beatniks; Beethoven's music sounded cacophonous to the audiences of his time but seems melodious to us. In a word, stimuli do not impinge on a passive or neutral organism, but on one that has already reached a certain level of adaptation.

SENSORY DEPRIVATION. Reduction of sensory stimulation to a minimum, usually for experimental purposes.

How will human beings react if they are deprived of all normal contact with their environment through sight, hearing, and movement? To answer this question, subjects have been confined to tank-type respirators (the kind used for polio victims), underwater chambers, and tiny cubicles equipped with food and necessary facilities. In some experiments, the subjects wore translucent goggles to break up light patterns, and heavy gauntlets to restrict movement and tactile sensation; in others, they lay quietly on cots for as long as four days inside a lightproof and soundproof "black room" (Vernon, 1963). All subjects were assured that they would be released from confinement as soon as they informed the experimenter or pressed a "panic button" (*Fig. 47*).

The impetus for these experiments came from many sources: the abnormal behavior of animals and children kept in isolation for long periods; the peculiar sensations experienced by truck-drivers, astronauts, and aviators who perform repetitive tasks in a limited environment; the reactions of polio victims and other patients who have been isolated and immobilized; and the behavior of prisoners of war who have been "softened up" and prepared for brainwashing by being subjected to solitary confinement. Beyond all these practical considerations there is the theoretical problem of acquiring new knowledge about perception and the operation of the nervous system.

The experiments have revealed that sensory deprivation can have marked effects on practically every mental process, although these effects have varied from subject to subject, and from condition to condition. The most common emotional effects were restlessness, boredom, and irritability. Some subjects enjoyed the experience during the first few hours, but tended to become apprehensive after two days of isolation. In a few cases anxiety rose to panic proportions: "The quiet was so loud it was like a knife stabbing through my eardrums." The effects on thinking processes also increased as time wore on. At first, the subjects welcomed the opportunity to wrestle with problems without distraction (most of the subjects were graduate students), but in a few hours they found it increasingly hard

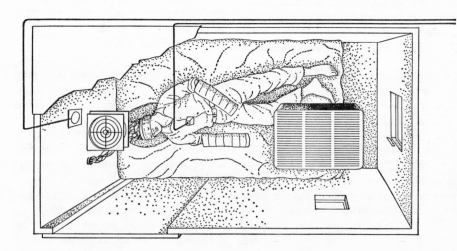

Fig. 47. An experimental setup used in studying the effects of sensory deprivation.

to concentrate and control their thoughts. They finally drifted into daydreaming and incoherent fantasies.

Tests conducted during the isolation period or immediately afterward showed a distinct loss in the ability not only to solve problems but to adjust to novel situations. There was also a general loss of efficiency in motor ability. Co-ordination was poorer and reaction time was longer than usual—a warning to pilots and astronauts.

Two other effects were particularly significant. First, many subjects were given suggestibility tests during isolation and immediately after release. These tests revealed that practically all subjects were more easily swayed by propaganda than were control groups—a fact that helps to explain the use of isolation in brainwashing. Second, gross perceptual changes frequently occurred during sensory deprivation. Some subjects experienced illusions and even hallucinations, similar to those produced by mescaline and other drugs. Although they were in a completely dark and silent environment, they heard strange music and chirping birds or saw door knobs on imaginary walls. One subject described his experiences in these words: "The herd of elephants. That was pretty. That came very spontaneously. It was just sort of elephants in back, with pink and blue and purple."

So far the experiments have indicated beyond much doubt that the human being cannot continue to function in a normal way if he is deprived of sensory impressions from the external world. In the absence of continuous and varied stimulation, all psychological processes tend to become disrupted and disorganized: "The cognitive, perceptual, and emotional changes associated with and consequent to deprivation leave the subject less competent to meet the adaptational demands of his environment" (D. O. Hebb in Solomon, 1961). *See* BRAINWASHING, SOCIAL ISOLATION, HALLUCINOGEN, ANACLITIC THERAPY.

SENTENCE COMPLETION METHOD. A projective technique in which the subject completes a fragmentary sentence.

The Sentence Completion Method is a further development of the Word Association Test, in which a subject is presented with a stimulus word and responds with the first word that comes to mind. The use of incomplete sentences such as "I wish . . ." or "My most unpleasant experience was . . ." is believed to elicit significant material because it encourages freedom of response and makes it difficult for the subject to know what constitutes a "good" or "bad" response. Usually the subject is not asked to give the first response that comes to his mind, as in the Word Association Test, since it is important for him to exert some control over his responses. In this sense the sentence completion technique is more like the Thematic Apperception Test (Rotter, 1951).

The standard procedure is to give the subject a printed list of incomplete sentences selected to fit the situation. The number of items ranges anywhere from fifteen or twenty to as many as 240. When the technique is used for clinical purposes, most psychologists do not use any formal scoring procedure. Instead, they treat the responses as projective material and employ their own knowledge of behavior dynamics and personality in making interpretations. One specialist (Stein, 1947) suggests that the examiner should pay special attention to the following: rare responses, long answers, overprecise answers, items that elicit tension reactions such as tics or restlessness, intense or colorful language, omissions, and erasures. He suggests that the subject be questioned about these items directly after the test.

Others (Rotter and Willerman, 1947) find it useful to rate responses in specific ways—for example, according to the amount of conflict (C) or positive reaction (P) they show. To illustrate this system, the following endings supplied for the incomplete sentence "Other people . . ." are arranged in order from neutral (N) to maximal conflict (C3): "are some good, some bad" (N), "have their worries too" (C1), "should mind their own business" (C2), "laugh at me" (C3). The following responses to the same incomplete sentence are arranged in terms of positive reaction: "are different" (N), "usually like me" (P1), "are interesting" (P2), "are swell" (P3).

The Sentence Completion Method is readily adapted to a variety of situations. It has been used not only in appraising general emotional adjustment, but in eliciting attitudes on sex, integration, the army, and employer-employee relations. One of its first applications was in the investigation of the thought processes of deteriorated senile patients and disorganized schizophrenics. In the latter case such items as "I am in the hospital because . . .", "My body makes a shadow because . . .", and "I am alive because . . ." were presented orally. It was found that the deteriorated senile patients gave more rational answers than the schizophrenic patients even though they were hopelessly disoriented (Cameron, 1938). The technique has also proved useful in OSS assessment procedures, for instance in identifying college men who had superior intelligence but low achievement due to emotional conflicts (Hadley and Kennedy, 1949). Among the other applications have been the study of family relationships (Lehner, 1947), the investigation of racial problems among Negroes (Campbell, 1950), and the exploration of social attitudes of Germans following World War II. In the latter case, the test included such items as "The National Socialists came into power in 1933 because . . ." and "The anti-Semitism of the Nazis was . . ." (Schaffner, 1948).

There is no universal agreement on exactly what aspects of the personality the Sentence Completion Method taps. Some psychologists contend that it penetrates to unconscious trends (Symonds, 1947), but most investigators believe it discloses thought content that is close to the surface rather than deep unconscious dynamics (Hanfmann and Getzels, 1953). Most likely the level is determined by the accessibility of the subject's unconscious and the effectiveness of the items in arousing his inner needs and feelings.

Some of the sentence completion tests in wide use today are the Rotter Incomplete Sentences Blank (high school, college, adult forms), which can be scored objectively according to the technique described above; the Rohde Sentence Completion Test; the Forer Structured Sentence Completion Test (forms for men, women, adolescent boys, adolescent girls); the Forer Vocational Survey, which explores interests and work adjustments of men and women; and the Marriage Adjustment Sentence Completion Survey, used in identifying marital attitudes and problems.

SEPARATION ANXIETY. Feelings of uneasiness and apprehension experienced primarily by children when they are separated from the mother or mother substitute. They show their anxiety by whimpering, crying, and moving about in an agitated manner.

Separation anxiety is especially intense between the sixth and tenth month, when the infant becomes clearly aware that he has been left alone. Babies who have been abandoned by their mothers after a few weeks of life, or who have been put into institutions at an early age, show clear signs of anxiety and may later develop other reactions, such as apathy or despondency.

Separation anxiety ordinarily subsides by the end of the first year, but may recur in acute form when the child is first taken to school. Occasionally older children develop anxiety reactions at camp or school, fearing that "something awful might happen to Mommie." Psychoanalysts relate these reactions to the Oedipus complex.

The reaction may also occur later in life. Overprotected young men who are inducted into the service and leave their mothers for the first time sometimes experience acute anxiety attacks during the basic training period. Older people may have similar reactions when they lose friends or family members on whom they have long been dependent. They may also become anxious if they move to unfamiliar surroundings. See SCHOOL PHOBIA, RANK, MATERNAL DEPRIVATION.

SEPTAL AREA (Septal Region, Septum). A region of the brain lying beneath the forward end of the corpus callosum, the connection between the two hemispheres. It is part of the limbic system.

Experiments have shown that when lesions are made in the septal area, or in fibers running from this region to the hypothalamus, rats and other animals overreact emotionally. They become ferocious and dangerous to handle, and will attack any object thrust at them. In addition, they become more jumpy, easily startled, and will resist capture and handling (Brady and Nauta, 1953; King, 1958). The intensity of these reactions tends to subside in time (Reynolds, 1963), probably because the lesions were not complete enough to destroy the entire function. When conditioning experiments were performed on septal animals, it was found that they learned active avoidance responses more quickly than normal animals—that is, they learned to avoid a shock by shuttling from a shock compartment to a nonshock compartment in an experimental enclosure. This follows from the fact that the destruction of the area made them more emotional.

These results indicate that the intact septum exerts a restraining influence on the hypothalamus. Further experiments in which the septum and the amygdala were removed one after the other showed that the two areas work in opposition to each other, the amygdala exerting an excitatory and the septum an inhibitory effect. See LIMBIC SYSTEM, AMYGDALA, HYPOTHALAMUS.

SET. Readiness to make a particular response to a stimulus situation; there are motor sets, perceptual sets, and mental sets. The term is usually reserved for temporary or recently developed readiness to react, in contrast to habit, which is a long-established, persistent readiness to respond in a definite way.

At any moment we are bombarded by many stimuli, but our set predisposes us to select and respond to one or another of them. It therefore structures and gives meaning to the situations we meet. For example, in reading we set ourselves to deal with the printed page and ignore incidental sounds coming from the street, the pressure of the chair on our body, and a multitude of other stimuli. Sets of this kind are learned from past experience, although practice and training can strengthen them considerably. A sprinter, for instance, can be coached to attend only to the sound of the starter's gun and to establish the muscular set he needs for a fast start. See REACTION TIME.

Readiness to react to the sound of a starting gun or the sight of a traffic light are examples of *motor set*. This type of set involves postural adjustments made during the act of attending to or watching for a certain stimulus. When we start a race we crouch, tense our muscles, and bend forward; when we are listening for a very faint sound, we protrude our head and breathe through our mouth in order to make less noise. Sometimes this readiness to react can be overdone and misfire: the runner may make a false start when he hears a noise from the grandstand, and the patient in a dentist's chair may respond to the drill before he feels any pain.

The second type, *perceptual set,* is a readiness to register and perceive certain stimuli. A doctor may be set to hear the telephone during the night; his wife, to awaken when their baby cries. When we see our favorite comic on the stage, we are usually set to laugh—and we may not laugh nearly so hard at an equally funny comedian we have never seen before. (*See Fig. 20,* p. 465: if you are set to see a vase, you will see it—and the same for two faces. This principle applies also to *Fig. 21,* p. 465.) This type of set may also misfire. If we are waiting for a friend on the street corner, we may react to someone in the distance who only slightly resembles him. If we are hungry, we may mistakenly think the sign "Rest Room" says "Restaurant." This point has been demonstrated by withholding food from groups of subjects for one, four, and sixteen hours, then showing them a dimly lighted screen depicting objects or people in action. The hungrier the subjects were, the more they interpreted the ambiguous stimuli in terms of food or eating (McClelland and Atkinson, 1948).

A *mental set,* on the other hand, is a selective process which determines the way we think or solve problems. If you ask a person to pronounce Mactavish, Macdonald, Macbeth, and Machinery, he will usually say MacHinery for the last one instead of machinery. Similarly, if you ask him to think of four-letter words ending in -any he will probably say many, zany, etc., but if you then ask him to give a four-letter word ending in -eny he will run into trouble. The -any words will prevent him from finding the solution (deny) because he is set for a certain pronunciation. This suggests that rigid mental sets frequently interfere with our thinking processes. Getting away from the problem often helps us break this set and approach it from a new angle. On the other hand, mental sets can be helpful in keeping our minds "on

target." *See* CREATIVE THINKING, PROBLEM SOLVING.

Sets of all three kinds can be influenced by a number of factors. First, definite instructions are usually effective: the quarterback gives certain signals which get the team set for a certain play. Experiments have shown that even general instructions such as, "Get out of the usual rut. Think freely. Try all possibilities," will often facilitate the solution of a problem. Second, arousing motivation or providing incentives will often promote the desired set: for example, showing a succulent roast beef in a window of a restaurant will bring in customers. Third, intense, changing, or contrasting stimuli will enhance our readiness to respond: a large, illuminated sign in red letters going on and off will be more likely to start us thinking about the product than a less arresting sign. *See* ATTENTION.

The concept of set has innumerable applications. It determines the type of reaction we make to both situations and people: the optimist sees obstacles as temporary setbacks, while the pessimist sees them as proof of failure. It helps to account for many of our social attitudes: the prejudiced person is set to judge a whole group by one objectionable individual, while the tolerant person will realize that unpleasant people can be found in all groups. Likewise, a stereotype is actually a form of set—for example, the "miserly Scot," or the "reserved Englishman." Emotionally disturbed people are particularly "set in their ways"; one man will react aggressively in almost every situation, another will be hypersensitive to the slightest rebuff or hint of criticism, and still another will be suspicious of everyone he meets.

Finally, set is deeply involved in our learning and mental processes. Tests have shown that the most efficient way to study is to be "primed" in advance on what to look for and what is important. The student's motivational set can also make a great difference. If he sets himself to learn the material permanently, he will not readily forget it— but if he sets himself to retain it only long enough to pass an examination, it will fail to "sink in" and stay with him. *See* WÜRZBURG SCHOOL.

SEX DIFFERENCES. The study of the distinctive characteristics of the two sexes is one of the major problems of differential psychology. A great deal of attention has been given to intellectual differences, probably because intelligence is so frequently tested and measured; but a few studies have thrown light on other characteristics as well. The major findings will be summarized, with the usual reminder that there are wide variations within each sex and in many cases a total overlap between them. Samuel Johnson was apparently aware of this fact, for when someone asked him which are more intelligent, men or women, his answer was, "Which men, which women?"

Both biological and cultural factors play a role in sex differences, and in most cases it is difficult or impossible to untangle them. As for physical activities—in which biological factors probably count most—males tend to be more proficient in gross bodily movements, while females usually excel in manual dexterity. The muscular reactions of men in sports or in driving a car average about 10 per cent quicker than those of women, but women are generally superior in perceptual speed and accuracy. The over-all scores on intelligence tests show consistent but insignificant differences in favor of males, but there are substantial differences on specific abilities. Boys tend to be superior in arithmetic reasoning, mechanical comprehension, and spatial relations, while girls as a group exceed them in memory, computation, verbal fluency, vocabulary, and other language abilities. As a general rule, girls make better grades in school than boys, although the two sexes are about equal in college.

Studies conducted with the Allport-Vernon-Lindzey scale indicate that females generally have stronger social interests and show greater concern than males for the welfare of others. They are also more deeply influenced by spiritual and esthetic values, while men have stronger theoretical, economic, and political interests (Allport et al., 1951). Males are more overtly aggressive than females from childhood onward; one study of high school boys and girls has shown a difference in frequency of aggressive acts of two and a half to one. This probably accounts for the fact that boys are more often behavior problems than girls (Gilbert, 1957). All these differences are largely determined by cultural influences, although biological differences in strength and energy probably play some part. *See* ALLPORT-VERNON-LINDZEY STUDY OF VALUES.

There is considerable difference in sexual behavior. Males reach their peak of sexual activity at about seventeen years of age, and females about ten years later. Boys and men masturbate considerably more frequently than girls and women, and are also much more likely to engage in mutual masturbation, sodomy, and other deviations. In general, men have a more urgent and frequent sexual desire than women, and are aroused by a wider variety of stimuli, such as pictures, stage shows, and stories (Kinsey, 1953). On the other hand, men and women do not differ in the speed of achieving orgasm, and "from cross-cultural evidence it seems clear that unless specific pressures are brought to bear against such behavior (as in our society) women initiate sexual advances as often as do men" (Ford and Beach, 1951).

The sexes also differ in emotional adjustment, though with the usual overlapping. During the preschool and elementary years over-all adjustment is approximately equal for boys and girls;

but when maladjustments occur, girls tend to express them in milder and more introverted ways (fears, worries, nail biting, thumbsucking), while boys express them in the form of behavior problems. This difference, however, may be largely if not wholly due to differences in sex roles and socially imposed restrictions. Among adolescents, girls as a whole exhibit more neurotic symptoms than boys.

In adulthood the differences become wider and more specific. In general, the incidence of mild emotional upsets and psychoneuroses is greater among women than among men; women are particularly prone to conversion (hysterical), asthenic (neurasthenic), and dissociative reactions. On the other hand, the incidence of psychotic disorders is higher among males than females; figures on the first admissions to mental hospitals show that males outnumber females by a ratio of four to three. However, females outnumber males in several specific categories, particularly manic-depressive, involutional, and senile psychotic reactions—due primarily to the fact that they live about seven years longer than men.

SEX DRIVE. Sex is classified as one of the primary or physiological drives, along with food hunger, thirst, air hunger, elimination, and other physical needs. Yet it does not wholly conform to other primary drives and in many ways appears to be in a class by itself. As Beach (1956) has pointed out, hunger and thirst result in tissue depletion and eventual death if they are not alleviated. The sex drive, on the other hand, is not an inevitable consequence of deprivation, and individual survival does not depend on it (although survival of the species does). Moreover, the human sex drive is more dependent on experience, learning, and external stimulation than are hunger and thirst. For these reasons Beach suggests that sex

appetite would be a more appropriate term than sex drive.

The character of the sex drive—or appetite—can best be summarized by viewing it in the light of evolution. There appear to be at least seven outstanding differences between the sex drive in lower and higher species, and these differences are most striking in the human being: (1) in the higher species the drive becomes less seasonal and less closely tied to the estrous cycle, (2) it is expressed in more varied sexual behavior, (3) it is channeled into an increasing amount of homosexual behavior, (4) it is aroused by a wider variety of stimuli, (5) it persists longer in life, (6) it is less and less dependent on hormones, and (7) it comes increasingly under the control of cortical functions. These characteristics are separated largely for descriptive purposes; they are actually closely related from a physiological point of view, although the precise mechanisms are not yet fully known.

Some of the major experimental evidence for these differences will now be reviewed. The sexual behavior of both male and female birds, reptiles, fish, and amphibians is seasonal; and in somewhat higher species, such as the rat or dog, mating activities are controlled by the estrous cycle of the female. During the period of "heat," estrogen secreted by the ovaries during ovulation is circulated through the bloodstream and increases the animal's receptivity and chances of fertilization. The male responds to the female only during this period. In still higher animals, male sexual behavior becomes much less dependent on the state of the female, and on the human level the male can usually function any time there is a receptive female. In the higher species female receptivity also becomes less and less dependent on the secretion of hormones.

The decrease in importance of hormones has been proved in many ways.

When lower animals are given hormones they often mate out of season; but when hormones are given to impotent *human* males, they usually have no effect. If male and female homosexuals are injected with the appropriate hormones, there is generally an increase in sexual arousal but no change in the object of sexual interest, and they remain homosexuals (Ford and Beach, 1951). There is usually no change in the sexual desire of women who have had their ovaries removed, and menopause frequently increases rather than decreases their sex drive. There is no single pattern for males who have been castrated. Some report total absence of desire, others experience desire but are impotent, and still others retain full ability for as long as thirty years afterward (Ford and Beach, 1951). *See* MENOPAUSE.

These findings do not of course repudiate hormonal influence altogether; they only prove that it is not the sole determinant of the sex drive. In the course of a child's maturation the testes and gonads develop through response to gonadotrophins, hormones secreted by the anterior pituitary gland. As a result of this stimulation, the quiescent gonads secrete their own hormones— testosterone in the male and estrogen and progesterone in the female. These hormones bring about the typical changes that take place during puberty: the production of sperm and egg cells, and the appearance of the secondary sex characteristics in young men and women. It is an interesting fact that some of the components of mature sex behavior actually precede and anticipate the ability to reproduce. Kinsey et al. (1948) have reported a case of genital erection on the day of birth, and orgasms (without ejaculation) have been observed in male infants. A number of investigators have also reported autosexual, heterosexual, and homosexual behavior in many societies prior to puberty. These observations show

that the neuromuscular apparatus necessary for mature sex behavior is in working order before puberty. *See* GONADS.

The effect of the hormones has also been proven experimentally. Administration of gonadal hormones or anterior pituitary extract (which stimulates the gonads to secrete) brings about precocious sexual behavior in lower animals. Pituitary extracts also help to cure cryptorchism (undescended testes) in boys. Excessive hormone secretion accelerates the development of sex organs and secondary sex characteristics, and removal and dysfunction of the pituitary leads to abortive sexual development in both human beings and lower animals (Ford and Beach, 1951).

Hormones, then, play an active role in sexual development; but when maturity is achieved a variety of nonhormonal factors enter into the picture. Experience, habit, emotional reactions, and cultural environment all have a significant effect on this drive among both men and women. First, the brain plays an important part in integrating sexual activity and in devising variations on the sex act. Cortical activity is also proved by the fact that males (more than females) are aroused by erotic stories and pictures. (One experiment showed that men prefer pictures of women with dilated pupils, apparently because this was unconsciously taken as a sign of interest in *them!*) Second, the surroundings have considerable effect on human beings and other higher species. Some animals will only mate in complete privacy, and some will not mate at all in captivity. In our society women usually prefer to mate at night and in the dark, but this does not hold for societies in which they are not taught to be inhibited.

Third, the expression of the sex drive is conditioned by social custom. Stimulation provided by the partner plays an important part, but there are wide variations in the kinds of stimulation used.

There is more kissing, manipulation of the breasts and genitals, and oral stimulation of the genitals, as well as more experimentation and a greater variety of positions on the higher than on the lower socioeconomic levels in the United States. On the other hand, the greatest *amount* of sexual activity occurs among men with some high school education who hold semiskilled jobs, and among women with at least a high school education. In Western countries men take the initiative in sex activities more often than women, but there are societies in which women are as aggressive as men, and sometimes more so.

Every known society has been found to place some restrictions on sexual activity. Incest taboos are probably the most common form of prohibition, since they are practically universal. However, different societies have different types of taboos. There are some in which brother and sister on certain social levels—for instance, early Egyptian royalty—are required to marry and have children. In a study of 158 societies, 70 per cent permitted premarital sexual relations but only five "freely allowed" adultery (Murdock, 1949). In another study, covering sixty societies, 25 per cent allowed intercourse during the ninth month of pregnancy (Ford and Beach, 1951). Many societies have a post-partum taboo on coitus, but the length of time varies widely from culture to culture (Whiting, 1954). *See* INCEST.

Religion is also an important cultural factor in many cases. Devout individuals —especially women—are as a rule less sexually active, more sexually conservative, and begin their sex life later than nonreligious people (Kinsey et al., 1948).

Fourth, emotional factors exert a great influence on the human level. Tensions and interpersonal conflicts have a more negative effect on the female sexual drive than on the male, and because of their upbringing women are more likely to be inhibited by feelings of guilt or shame. The huge number of available sex manuals is testimony, however, that both men and women are deeply concerned not only about "technique" but about the normality of their reactions. Many of them are also concerned about inhibitions or feelings of disgust which originated from their parents' attitudes.

Sexual ability is a significant ingredient of the self-image of most people, and some psychiatrists regard the achievement of orgasm as one criterion of mental health. Sexual difficulties are one of the more common reasons for undertaking psychological treatment, and some investigators claim that psychotherapy tends to increase both the frequency and enjoyment of coitus (Wolpe, 1958).

Fifth, experience and attitude have a considerable effect on the persistence of the sex drive in later life. Women frequently retain their desire and responsiveness long after the change of life, particularly when their marital relationship has been satisfying. Men experience a natural diminution in potency with advancing age: the average frequency of intercourse is about five times a week at twenty and 1.3 times in the sixties. However, interest and even desire do not always show a corresponding decline, since memory, habit, and fantasy continue to have their effect after the hormone flow has decreased. *See* SEX DIFFERENCES, HOMOSEXUALITY, EXHIBITIONISM, VOYEURISM, NYMPHOMANIA, SATYRIASIS, BESTIALITY, RAPE, PEDOPHILIA, FETISHISM, PROMISCUITY, FROTTAGE, HYPOTHALAMUS.

SEX ROLE. Attitudes and behavior patterns adopted as an expression of masculinity or femininity.

Sex differentiation and sex identification are among the most essential aspects of human behavior, and play a particularly important part in the development of the child. The sex role is a major ingredient of the self-concept, and persistent confusion over sex identification is bound to have drastic effects on the individual's attitude toward himself as well as his relationships with others. It not only gives rise to feelings of insecurity and inadequacy but deprives him of a definite place in society. On the other hand, a clear concept of one's sex role is a source of self-acceptance, emotional security, and confidence in dealing with other people.

The child does not start out in life with a fixed sex role. It has to be gradually acquired as a consequence of social expectation, treatment by others, and self-discovery. The first step is an awareness of physical sex differences through comparisons between his own body and the bodies of others. Today genital organs, hair styles, and urination posture play a larger part in this process than clothing since the sexes dress so much alike. Girls usually learn to identify these differences sooner than boys, but by four or five years of age both are reasonably successful, and by eight there are striking differences in their drawings of the human figure (Knopf and Richards, 1952).

Awareness of psychological differences comes later than awareness of physical differences. The school and the parents both teach the growing child that boys and girls are "supposed" to prefer different play activities, books, movies, and television programs, and that among adults as well some activities and interests are typically masculine and others typically feminine. At the same time they gradually discover that people have different attitudes toward male and female and treat the two sexes differently. These attitudes are determined both by the general culture and by the special social level of the child's family. In general, American society encourages the boy to accept an aggressive, "tough masculine" sex role, and to show a special interest in activities that require daring and active leadership, while girls are encouraged to be kind, helpful, and well-mannered. This distinction is especially sharp on the lower economic levels where boys learn to scorn "woman's work" and apply the label "weak sister" to the tenderhearted. On the middle level, the sharp divisions between the sexes are breaking down somewhat, partly because fathers and mothers often share the household chores and care of the children, and partly because aggressive behavior is less necessary for survival in favored neighborhoods. See SEX DIFFERENCES.

Children begin to adopt their appropriate sex roles shortly after they become aware of the physical differences, and before they are fully cognizant of psychological differences. Most girls begin to accept the feminine role by four or five, and most boys a little earlier because they are constantly told to be "manly." Our society is more tolerant toward the girl who has tomboy tendencies than toward the boy who is "sissified." At every age boys have been found to be more clearly aware of their role than girls, and our culture is still so masculine-oriented that girls as well as boys generally regard the male role as superior. At one time or another most girls envy the boys' greater freedom and wish they were boys; boys rarely want to be girls. However, by the age of eleven or twelve the girls have usually developed interests and activities of their own and are ready to accept their feminine role in full, even though their self-concept remains somewhat less favorable than the self-concept of boys. See PENIS ENVY, MASCULINE PROTEST.

The adoption of a satisfactory sex role is a particularly acute problem among hermaphrodites—persons born with anatomical characteristics of both sexes. A wide variety of abnormalities may occur in these individuals, involving five different characteristics singly or in combination: abnormality in chromosomes, hormones, gonads, internal sexual structure, and external sex organs. In true hermaphroditism, an extremely rare condition, the gonads of both sexes are present; in pseudohermaphroditism the individual has gonads of one sex but malformed genital characteristics of both. From a psychological point of view it has been found that both types have the best chance of achieving a stable adjustment if the condition is diagnosed shortly after birth, and the parents encourage a definite sexual orientation from the start of life. Money, Hampson, and Hampson (1957) recommend that the choice of sex be made where possible on the basis of the external organs as well as the possibility of surgical alteration— but once the choice is made, it should be permanent, since attempts to change the child's sex identity almost inevitably result in confusion and psychiatric disturbance. These investigators found that in intersexed individuals, the gender in which a child is reared has a far greater effect than the biological characteristics on his sexual orientation, as the following quotation indicates: "Thus, some patients were predominantly female with respect to the physical variables of sex but, having been reared as boys, had the sexual psychology of a boy, or man—and vice versa for patients reared as girls.

"The clinching piece of evidence concerning the psychological importance of the sex of assignment and rearing is provided when, among persons of identical physical diagnosis, some are reared as boys, some as girls. It is indeed startling to see, for example, two children with female hyperadrenalcorticism in the company of one another in a hospital playroom, one of them entirely feminine in behavior and conduct, the other entirely masculine, each according to upbringing. As a social observer, one gets no suspicion that the two children are chromosomally and gonadally female, for psychologically they are entirely different." See TRANS-SEXUALISM.

SEXUAL DEVIATIONS (GENERAL). There is considerable confusion about the definition of sexual deviation. One approach puts the primary emphasis on social disapproval, and defines it as "sexual behavior at variance with more or less culturally accepted sexual activities." This is the definition given by the American Psychiatric Association, which cites homosexuality, transvestism, sexual sadism, and sexually violent (criminal) acts as examples.

The element of social disapproval cannot be avoided because what is considered deviant in one society may not be considered deviant in another. Polygamy, prostitution, and homosexuality are acceptable in some cultures, but not in ours. There may also be wide differences even within the same society —for example, variations in sexual foreplay and coital position are generally more acceptable on higher than on lower socioeconomic levels in this country; a deviation, therefore, must be defined in terms of the total society and not simply one segment of it. Rosen and Gregory (1965) have proposed the following definition specifically for our culture: "persistent preference for a sexual object or mode other than genital heterosexual behavior with an adult."

Rosen and Gregory's definition applies to such clear-cut deviations as sodomy, fetishism, exhibitionism, and sadism, but does not include all types of socially disapproved sexual behavior, such as promiscuity and prostitution, nor does it embrace such pathological conditions as frigidity, impotence, and nymphomania. Since these are usually included in discussions of sexual deviation, it would probably be useful to specify that sexual deviations include not only culturally unacceptable sex behavior but also sex behavior that is pathological in origin. It is also important to distinguish between sexual *offenses* (which only have to be unacceptable to society) and sexual *deviations,* although the two frequently coincide. Sexual offense is a legal distinction; sexual deviation is a psychiatric distinction with social overtones. Extramarital relations would be considered a legal offense but not ordinarily a psychiatric deviation; impotence would be a psychiatric deviation (or a physical disorder) but not a legal offense.

This book will deal with all sexual deviations that can be viewed as psychological disorders. Their range is extremely wide, but they can be classified under the following categories: (1) deviations in intensity and frequency of sex activity and drive: nymphomania, satyriasis, promiscuity; impotence, frigidity; (2) deviations in the mode of gratification: excessive masturbation, voyeurism, exhibitionism, frottage, orogenital activity (fellatio, cunnilingus), anogenital activity (sodomy), transvestism, sadism, masochism, forceable rape; (3) deviations in the object of the sexual act: homosexuality, fetishism, pedophilia, bestiality, incest, necrophilia; (4) deviations related to a special social context: promiscuity, prostitution.

Because of the private character of most sexual activity, the incidence of these deviations is hard to estimate. Probably more people engage in some form of "perverse" activity at one time or another than is generally recognized. Kinsey et al. (1949) concluded that:

In spite of the many centuries in which our culture has attempted to suppress all but one type of sexual activity, a not inconsiderable portion of all the sexual acts in which the human animal engages still fall into the category which the culture rates as "perverse." The specific data show that two thirds to three quarters of the males in our American culture, and some lesser number of females, engage in at least some "perverse" sexual behavior at some time between adolescence and old age. One half to two thirds of the males engage in such behavior with appreciable frequency during some period of their lives and a fair number engage in such behavior throughout their lives.

Police figures are only partly indicative of the extent of deviation, since a great many sexual offenses are unreported and there is wide variation from state to state both in the laws and in their enforcement—for example, the penalty for sodomy in different jurisdictions ranges from thirty days to life. In Connecticut 25 per cent of the prison population have been sentenced for sexual offenses, as contrasted with 10 per cent in New York. Probably only 15 per cent of reported offenses result in actual conviction, since the reports are often false or the victim withdraws his case to avoid publicity. Also, some offenses are considered minor: a Michigan study showed that 42.5 per cent of sex offenders were voyeurs or exhibitionists who are usually given probation or suspended sentences. Other offenses which most frequently come to the attention of the police are incest, rape and assault, molesting of children, and homosexuality.

About one third of all sex offenders have previous police records, and in the Michigan study, 60 per cent of offenses were directed against children. Few women are convicted of sex offenses, but when they are, it is usually for prostitution or acts against children. The highest incidence of sex crimes is among young unmarried males, and a large percentage of them have been sex delinquents during adolescence. There are, however, a number of false ideas about these offenders. Contrary to popular opinion, (a) less than 10 per cent are repeaters, and most of these commit minor offenses such as peeping; (b) only about 5 per cent inflict physical injury; these offenders are usually psychotic as well as sexually deviant; (c) very few offenders progress from minor to major sex offenses, since they usually adopt and persist in one type of satisfaction; (d) most of them are not oversexed, but rather undersexed, misinformed, inadequate, and even prudish individuals.

Although the origins of specific deviations are discussed under separate topics, certain general causal factors can be outlined at this point. First, personality disturbances of varying degrees of severity afflict the great majority of deviates. A large group consists of inhibited neurotics who either compensate for feelings of inadequacy by engaging in promiscuous behavior, or seek an unthreatening outlet in peeping, exhibitionism, fetishism, or homosexuality. These individuals often show some degree of impotence or frigidity. Second, psychosis affects about 2 per cent of sexual deviants, and another 8 per cent are borderline psychotics. Manic patients may be promiscuous and occasionally sadistic or assaultive. Depressives are usually impotent or frigid, and are sometimes masochistic as a result of guilt feelings. Schizophrenic and paranoid individuals often have no sexual feelings for others and may rely on masturbation as an outlet. Some overt schizophrenics, however, may engage in highly deviant behavior, such as rape, pedophilia, extreme fetishism, and bizarre acts of sadism or masochism.

In addition, there are three other types of disorders, each of which affects about 4 or 5 per cent of deviants. Individuals suffering from organic brain disorders, often associated with senility, commit such offenses as incest, exhibitionism, and acts against children. Mild mental retardation is a factor in some cases of female promiscuity as well as male exhibitionism, and occasionally in cases of sexual assault or intercourse with animals. The antisocial personality, or sociopath, is frequently promiscuous and may resort to force, intimidation, or fraud in his sexual pursuits. Male sociopaths are often attracted to adolescent girls, and are sometimes charged with seduction, sexual assault, or rape.

Sexual deviations, then, are associated with a wide variety of psychological disorders. There are certain kinds of early experiences and personality factors, however, which may give us a clearer idea of the causes. The following are most frequently cited, and studies have shown that they are most likely to lead to sexual deviation when the personality has been weakened by an unhappy home life and faulty development:

(a) Sexual incidents in childhood or youth, such as seduction by an older homosexual;

(b) failure to learn appropriate sex roles: a boy who has been raised as a girl or who has identified with his mother instead of his father may develop homosexual tendencies;

(c) rigid upbringing, isolation from other children, and lack of sex education: this may cause a child to fear the opposite sex; he then shies away from normal relationships and may seek an outlet in voyeurism, exhibitionism, or excessive masturbation;

(d) general immaturity and fear of responsibility: this may lead to avoidance of adult heterosexual relationships and pave the way for homosexuality;

(e) deprivation of normal outlets, as in prison or boarding school; may lead to homosexuality or other deviations;

(f) intense feelings of hostility or resentment against parents and society; may result in a pattern of "acting out" inner tensions in the form of antisocial sex offenses;

(g) arrested psychosexual development—that is, fixation at an infantile level: psychoanalysts maintain this may set the stage for orogenital or anogenital behavior as well as dependence on masturbation, voyeurism, or exhibitionism.

Heredity and other biological factors have also been investigated, but the results have been largely negative. It is true that families of deviates show a higher than normal rate of neurosis, psychopathic behavior, and other deviations—but today the difference is usually attributed to environmental rather than hereditary factors. The physical constitution and endocrine functions of homosexuals are practically always the same as for heterosexuals, and no hereditary basis for homosexuality has yet been proven. As pointed out above, sexual deviates—even nymphomaniacs and satyriasists—are rarely if ever physiologically oversexed. Except in rare cases, deviates do not differ from normal individuals in sex chromosomes or sex hormones.

Treatment procedures vary considerably for the different deviations, but certain general points can be made here. Sexual deviants are frequently prone to either anxiety or depression, and in these cases tranquilizing drugs or antidepressants are likely to be administered. Tranquilizers are also used to reduce the sex drive, particularly in older men who molest children. In some cases female hormones are administered to suppress sex activity in males, and castration is permitted or even mandatory in some localities. However, these physical measures do not alter the structure of the personality or the character of the sex impulse.

Psychotherapy is rarely successful with long-standing deviations, but is sometimes effective with cases of recent onset, or where the patient is basically heterosexual even though his behavior is occasionally homosexual or deviant in some other respect. As to the specific kind of psychotherapy, psychoanalysis is usually more difficult with deviates than with typical neurotics because they derive so much pleasure from their sexual activities that they resist change. More direct techniques often fare better; for example, providing the misinformed deviate with accurate sexual information, or helping the inhibited deviate abandon his prudish attitudes toward normal relations. A therapist can sometimes shift a patient toward more normal behavior by a step-by-step approach: a homosexual male may be encouraged to develop friendships with boyish-looking females as a bridge to relationships with more feminine women. Hypnotic suggestion has also been tried, but the results have usually been disappointing.

One of the most promising techniques is reconditioning therapy. In one experiment, male transvestites were given a nauseating drug, and were then shown photographs of themselves wearing feminine clothing. In most of the cases this brought about a lasting aversion to transvestism. A somewhat similar technique has been used with homosexuals. Desensitization techniques have also been applied in cases of exhibitionism and voyeurism. See BEHAVIOR THERAPY, HOMOSEXUALITY (MALE).

Finally, group therapy has been effectively employed in helping sexual deviates gain insight into their motivations, and in encouraging them to alter basic attitudes and develop more acceptable behavior patterns. Currently, group techniques are being combined with rehabilitation procedures in treating sex offenders in mental hospitals instead of putting them in prison. In a significant experiment in California, Cabeen and Coleman (1962) used a variety of approaches: group discussions led by patients, patient self-government, psychodrama, mental health films, talks by staff members, more formal group psychotherapy, and meetings with legislators, judges, educators, clergymen, physicians, and other members of the community at large. An independent organization of ex-patients was also established. Of 126 offenders, 79 were found to improve enough to return to society, and a follow-up study showed that only three of them were later arrested for sex offenses. Similar approaches have also been tried in prisons, although many psychiatrists do not consider the prison setting conducive to effective psychotherapy.

There is evidence that society is moving in the direction of the procedure outlined by the Committee on Forensic Psychiatry of the Group for the Advancement of Psychiatry, which has recommended that every person convicted of a sexual offense should be given a psychiatric examination, and "If we di-

agnose this sex offender as mentally disordered he should be treated as a mental case in a facility for that purpose
. . . If the offender is curable he can
be eventually released to society; if not,
he should never be released." For discussion of individual deviations, *see*
Category Index, under PERSONALITY
DISORDERS.

SHELTERED WORKSHOP. A work
situation designed for vocational training or rehabilitation of the mentally
retarded, victims of chronic physical
diseases, and convalescing mental patients. The workshop simulates actual
industrial conditions as closely as possible, but is operated under the guidance
of a team of specialists.

An outstanding example is Altro
Workshops in New York City, which
carries on three types of businesses in
the open competitive market: the manufacture of cotton garments for industrial
and institutional use, a clerical service
bureau which contracts for letter-shop
and computational work, and a mechanical division in which machine and
bench operations are performed under
subcontract from industry. Most of the
work is on the semiskilled level, such
as operation of sewing machines or addressing apparatus, and the pay is the
same as business or union rates. The
patients usually work less than full-
time, but spend the entire day in the
factory alternating between work and
rest.

The Altro program is designed to
improve and stabilize the functioning
of posthospitalized persons in a work
environment, at the same time surrounding them with a "ring of protective services" that meet individual
needs for counseling, casework, medical
supervision, and environmental changes.
The patients are referred from tuberculosis treatment centers, cardiac clinics, and psychiatric treatment centers.
Working arrangements are maintained
with the New York City Department

of Welfare, the Division of Vocational
Rehabilitation, and the State Employment Service. The psychiatric program
operates under contract with the New
York City Community Mental Health
Board under the New York State Mental Services Act. The clinical rehabilitation staff consists of a team of physicians, vocational counselors, and clinical
psychologists, with a social worker assigned as co-ordinator of services. Registered nurses (who do not wear uni-
forms) serve as a liaison between the
clinic and the shop.

The Altro program is divided into
four phases: intake and assessment
(clinical and vocational); the workshop
experience, lasting six to twelve months;
an after-care or adjustment period during which psychiatric patients may continue to receive clinical services for up
to a year; and a follow-up period in
which the organization keeps in touch
with graduates in order to prevent relapse.

An evaluative research study has been
conducted by Meyer and Borgatta
(1959), comparing a group of schizophrenic patients served by Altro with
a control group who did not participate
in the workshop. The results indicate
that the workshop experience reduced
the likelihood of rehospitalization "to
a moderate degree," but the study did
not include enough patients to be conclusive. Bertram J. Black, director of
the Altro Health and Rehabilitation
Services, estimates the program's "rehabilitation success" for psychiatric patients at about 60 per cent, despite
the fact that the referred patients had
been rated in the bottom 5 per cent
in rehabilitation potential. It must also
be recognized that they had all been
hospitalized and therefore away from
the everyday world for long periods of
time, and that their work skills as well
as their social relationships had deteriorated.

It is still too early to know what
kinds of work are most effective with

these patients, for "We just don't know what limiting factors of stress, energy output, noise, motion, etc., have significance for the psychiatrically handicapped" (Black, 1959). Nevertheless a few general points can be made. First, the use of psychoactive drugs has increased the need for sheltered workshops as well as other rehabilitation services for mental patients, since drug treatment enables many of them to live outside the hospital even though they are still clinically ill. Second, there is growing evidence that the time to plan for vocational rehabilitation is before discharge from the hospital rather than after. Third, the emphasis, where possible, should be on reviving past jobs rather than developing new skills through training programs. Fourth, money is a powerful incentive in attracting psychotics and keeping them in work programs, especially since it represents success and status. Fifth, there is little relationship between symptoms and job behavior; even patients with active hallucinations or depressive reactions can be productive, provided the tasks are simple and routine. Sixth, observations of patients in the sheltered workshop should be fed back to the clinical staff and can furnish valuable material for planning treatment and preventing relapse. Seventh, postpsychotics with sheltered workshop experience often become employable on the open market—but they are not easy to place since their productivity is apt to be below standard. They are also likely to need special help from the rehabilitation team both in getting and keeping a job. See MENTAL RETARDATION (PREVENTION, CARE AND TREATMENT), REHABILITATION.

SHERRINGTON, CHARLES SCOTT

(1857–1952). Sherrington, to whom we owe much of our knowledge of nerve activity, obtained his medical degree in 1885, then devoted himself to physiological research at Cambridge. His first major experiments dealt with the interaction of spinal reflex patterns, and the results were described in *The Integrative Action of the Nervous System,* published in 1906. According to Boring (1950), this book stimulated more interest in physiological psychology than any previously published work.

Sherrington made significant contributions to the study of reflexes, and was the first to show the importance of proprioceptive reflexes in posture. In the course of his investigations of the nervous system, he introduced the concept of the synapse as the place where neurons interact. He also demonstrated many of the specific functions of the synapse, such as facilitation and inhibition. He showed, for example, that stimuli too weak to produce a response by themselves may add to each other, or "summate," at the synapse, and sometimes gather enough strength to facilitate a response. On the other hand, stimuli which are strong enough to produce a reflex response by themselves may be inhibited at the synapse by impulses from other nerve fibers. *See* SYNAPSE.

Sherrington also demonstrated the effects of drugs and fatigue on the nervous system. He found that nerve tissue which contains synapses is able to conduct for only a brief period of time, while tissue that does not contain synapses is unaffected by fatigue. Similarly, he discovered that certain drugs produce a blockage of impulses in regions where synapses are present, but no such blockage occurs in regions where there are no synapses. He also showed the great importance of the synapse not only in lower sensory and reflex activities, but in the higher mental processes.

Sherrington's discoveries have had widespread application in the fields of neurology and neurosurgery. But they have had an equally great effect on psychology, since they have contributed much to our understanding of the neural basis of behavior. His work was widely recognized during his lifetime, and he served as president of the Royal Society from 1920 to 1925. He was one of the few scientists to receive the Order of Merit, and in 1932 was awarded the Nobel Prize for pioneer work on neural activity, an honor he shared with E. D. Adrian. His last published work, written at the age of eighty-three, was *Man on His Nature,* a book which dealt with the philosophical question of the relationship between mind and matter as seen from the standpoint of a physiologist.

SIBLING RIVALRY. Rivalry between children of the same family.

Some degree of sibling rivalry, mild or bitter, is probably inevitable. In young children it may take many direct and open forms—for example, attempting to harm the baby by dropping him, smothering him, coughing in his face, or giving him a knife to play with. Or it may take the more indirect form of sticking pins into a doll or grinding it underfoot. Later on the older child may tease, hit, punch, or jeer at a younger brother or sister, and the younger child may complain against the older, tattle on him, or make himself a nuisance when his friends come to visit. In general, rivalry between sisters is less intense than rivalry between brothers or between brother and sister.

Sibling rivalry probably originates in competition for the mother's affection and attention. The older child feels that the baby is usurping his position, and the baby remains the primary target for two years or more. After that, the younger child becomes aware of his older brother's or sister's superior strength, skill, and freedom, and develops his own rivalry feelings. These feelings are likely to be particularly acute in children who are possessive and demanding, tendencies which sometimes stem from parental favoritism or indulgence. A typical example of such

favoritism is the preference many mothers show for their sons (Bossard and Boll, 1960; Koch, 1960). *See* JEALOUSY, OEDIPUS COMPLEX, REGRESSION.

A study by MacFarland (1938) has shown that parents who attempt to be fair by adopting a policy of "two of everything" are rarely successful in preventing rivalry, since this is only an external approach to the problem. In fact, this policy may even intensify the rivalry if the younger child is given the same playthings or privileges as the older child. Other parents try to reduce rivalry by preaching kindness and consideration, or by constantly reminding their children of their close relationship. These approaches not only fail to eliminate bitter feelings but tend to drive them underground or cause them to take indirect form. Repressed rivalry often lasts longer than expressed rivalry, and there are cases in which mothers have stored up these feelings for years and treat their own children as potential rivals (Hilgard, 1951).

How, then, can sibling rivalry be reduced? The answer seems to be: by making each of the children feel fully loved and accepted; by encouraging them to develop their own interests, activities, and friends; and by gradually helping them to realize that each member of the family should have his own rights and prerogatives by virtue of age, experience, or special abilities.

SKIN DISORDERS. The general proposition that the skin is responsive to emotional changes meets no challenge, since everyone has observed that people blush with shame and grow pale with fright. Many common expressions also testify to this fact: "He's itching for a fight," "She gets under my skin," "He's a thick-skinned (or thin-skinned) person." The question is how far these skin reactions go: can they produce not only superficial changes, but actual diseases? And if so, do different kinds of emotional situations or internal conflicts produce different kinds of diseases?

The first question can be definitely answered in the affirmative, on the basis of both observation and experimentation. Hundreds of cases have been reported in which the onset or exacerbation of such skin diseases as hives, eczema, or urticaria coincide with situations of acute emotional stress. Similarly, many experiments have revealed that skin reactions can be induced simply by reactivating the conflict or trauma through suggestion during a hypnotic trance or even in a waking state. Today not only psychiatrists but dermatologists recognize the close association between psychological disturbance and skin disease, and some clinics report a significant connection in over 75 per cent of their patients. In light of this connection, many skin conditions are viewed as psychophysiologic disorders, even though the exact physical mechanism is not completely known.

The answer to the second question is more complex and conjectural. The skin may express emotional disturbances in many ways. It is subject to the direct influence of the autonomic nervous system and the indirect effects of glandular changes that occur during psychological stress. It is wide open to self-inflicted injury by individuals who have an urge to punish themselves. It can also be utilized in the symbolic expression of unconscious conflicts. One investigator, Graham (1950), found that an attack of hives could be precipitated in a patient who had suffered repeatedly from the condition simply by having him talk about a painful family situation. The patient reacted to "the things they did to me" with a feeling of being struck on the arm, and significantly his skin broke out in red wheals just as if he had actually been hit with a ruler or stick.

Some forms of neurodermatitis, especially when it is accompanied by pruritus (itching), seem to be exacer-

bated by events that produce feelings of anger mixed with depression and guilt. These patients have frequently been found to be overdependent on the mother, but at the same time resentful of her domination. The itching and scratching are interpreted as a masochistic reaction. By scratching themselves, they are inflicting pain as punishment for their sense of guilt; but in relieving the itching they are also attaining a feeling of pleasure. In other words, these patients are unconsciously expressing their hostility but are at the same time paying a price for it.

Other forms of dermatitis have been at least tentatively related to specific types of situations. Urticaria—a fleeting rash with swelling and itching—is sometimes precipitated by what psychiatrists describe as a "threat to an important dependency relationship"—that is, danger of being rejected or abandoned instead of being cared for. In a case studied by Saul (1941), a young engaged woman experienced numerous frustrations because she had a strong desire for warmth and affection which was not being met by her fiancé, who was rather cool and reserved. If she cried after these experiences, her emotions were released and her skin did not break out; but if she suppressed her desire to cry, the rash appeared. It seemed as if her skin were weeping for her.

Many other types of skin disorder appear to be produced by conflicts and repressions. An exudative or atopic dermatitis sometimes occurs in children who have been rejected by their mothers. Itching rashes in the genital and anal areas may be due to sexual conflicts. Ring-finger dermatitis was at one time attributed to an allergy to metal or to soap or dirt under the ring, but today it is more likely to be regarded in married people as symbolizing irritation over the marriage. Thumb dermatitis, which sometimes occurs in immature women overwhelmed by prob-

1208

lems, may be interpreted as an unconscious defense against a desire to return to the security of the thumbsucking stage. Otitis externa, a skin disorder of the external ear, may represent an attempt to avoid hearing bad news, particularly when such news arouses the patient's conflicts. Finger rashes may be a protective device unconsciously adopted to prevent masturbation or other erotic activities that arouse guilt. Lip rash in teenage girls may be due to conflicts over kissing. Eyelid dermatitis sometimes occurs in women who are "sick of the sight of" their husbands.

The most dramatic of all illustrations of the symbolic character of skin reactions is the phenomenon of stigmatization. In the typical case, a deeply religious woman develops sores on her head, hands, feet, and side which correspond to the location of the wounds received by Jesus during the crucifixion —and these sores bleed profusely on Good Friday. So many cases have occured throughout history, and so many thousands of individuals, including physicians and psychiatrists, have observed and examined these women that there can be no question about the reality of this phenomenon. It can probably be termed a hysterical or conversion reaction, though it is sometimes included in discussions of psychophysiologic disorders. Kisker (1964) comments that "The inner anxiety [aroused by the religious event] appears to be converted into the physical expression of the intense identification with Christ or some other religious figure." He cites the following excerpt from a physician's report on a Canadian woman, a Mrs. McIsaac, published by *Time* magazine, September 25, 1950:

"During the early part of the week she was in very good health despite the marks ... On Friday afternoon the marks on her body began to lose their hardness and toward six o'clock they appeared more like fresh wounds.

It was apparent that she was beginning to feel pain ... She appeared to lapse into a trance ... Her pain seemed to intensify to agony ... Soon a drop of blood began to form at one of the foot wounds ... Gradually the hands and the other wounds began to bleed ... Toward nine o'clock the flow of blood stopped, the pain seemed to go, and she appeared to sleep normally ... On Saturday morning she appeared surprisingly fresh and youthful-looking, and in very good health."

Illustrative Case: SKIN DISORDERS, ECZEMA

Mr. S.L., aged twenty-nine years, had on the back of his hands and his neck eczema which had been present for several years. X-ray therapy as well as soothing and irritative ointments were of no avail.

This man was a lawyer. He had been one of the leading men in his class and had promise of great success. On leaving school, however, he encountered the business depression of 1932, and was unable to establish himself. He finally married the girl he loved, but had to depend in part on her earnings. He was a proud person and could not tolerate the idea of having to depend for his livelihood on the daily work of his wife, whom he wished to see as a homemaker. They could not afford to have children because of his financial state, and he developed tension toward all his difficulties. When confronted by a law problem, he was so in earnest and desirous of carrying it through successfully that he would scratch at his hands and neck till the skin would bleed. If he covered the areas with adhesive tape, he would scratch it off in his sleep. Even when he was able to stop the scratching the intensity of the eczematous process would vary with the emotional intensity of the day. (Kraines, 1948)

SKINNER BOX. A problem box used in the study of animal learning.

Until the 1930s the study of animal learning was limited largely to classical or Pavlovian conditioning, in which a stimulus (for example, food) is paired with another stimulus (for example, the sound of a bell) in order to produce a conditioned response (salivation). At that time the psychologist B. F. Skinner pointed out that most learning behavior does not fit this model. Animals and human beings do not merely respond mechanically to stimuli but learn to make active efforts that will enable them to reach a goal or avoid pain. He named this type of conditioning instrumental, since the organism's behavior is instrumental to gaining a reward.

In 1938 Skinner devised a piece of apparatus for the study of instrumental conditioning. It consisted of a small, soundproof box containing a device such as a string, pushbutton, or lever that could be manipulated as a means of obtaining a measured amount of reward, termed a "reinforcement" since it strengthens the conditioned response. He found that such animals as pigeons and rats made trial and error responses at first, but if they manipulated the device successfully and received a reward of food or water, they seemed to "get the hang of it" and continued to use it with greater vigor and regularity. In its highly developed form, the box permits automatic timing of each response, and regulates the number of responses during any unit of time, the interval between responses, and almost every other aspect of the animal's behavior. It also allows variations in the "schedule of reinforcement," that is, in a lever-pressing situation the reward (say, a food pellet) may be given, automatically, every time the lever is pressed, or every five seconds, or at every tenth displacement, and so on.

The Skinner box can also be adapted to variations in both the stimulus and the response. In one type of experiment, a rat is trained to use a particular lever, then other levers are introduced at a higher or lower level, or to the right or left of the original one. Or, in attempting to see whether a pigeon can differentiate between colors, the animal is given a reward when he pecks at a red-illuminated button but not when other colors are presented. After a time he learns to peck only at the red button since it alone brings the reward.

The Skinner box has been used in many ingenious ways. In recent brain research, electrodes were implanted directly in the septal area of the brain of rats, and it was found that they responded to electrical stimulation by making as many as five thousand lever-pressing responses per hour for several hours (Olds and Milner, 1954). Pigeons trained in a Skinner box have helped to keep guided missiles on target better than the electronic equipment available at the time. They were taught to peck only when a particular target showed on a screen, but not at images of clouds or flak. If the target drifted away from the center of the screen, their pecking communicated this information to the guidance mechanism of the missile which automatically kept it on target. More recently some of the principles developed by Skinner box experiments have been applied to teaching machines. *See* PROGRAMMED LEARNING, CONDITIONING, REINFORCEMENT, LIMBIC SYSTEM.

SKIN SENSES (Cutaneous Sense). The senses of warmth, cold, pain, and touch (pressure) located in the skin.

Skin sensations are the source of relatively simple experiences such as itching and tingling, pain due to injury, and feelings of hot and cold. Though they often play a crucial role in our lives, we depend far less on them than on sight and hearing for our knowledge of the external world. However, one of these senses, the sense of touch, is more closely related to perception than the others, since we can often identify objects by the way they feel. This ability would be greatly increased if we had to rely more completely on this sense mechanism, as is the case with the blind.

The sensations of touch, pain, warmth, and cold are experienced through four distinct kinds of sensitive spots on the skin surface. They are not evenly distributed and therefore a given area of the skin will not respond with every type of sensation when appropriately stimulated. This selective functioning is termed "punctate sensitivity." On most parts of the skin pain spots are most thickly distributed, then touch, cold and warmth spots in that order. For discussion of individual skin senses, see TEMPERATURE SENSE, TOUCH, PAIN SENSE.

SLEEP DRIVE. Psychologists have long studied sleep as a basic need, or "physiological drive." Various investigations have shown that there is relatively little variation from individual to individual in the amount of sleep that is needed. Although constitutional differences do exist, the great majority of adults appear to require about eight hours, and one rarely finds a person in good health who requires less than six hours or more than nine hours. Infants sleep about two thirds of the day and adults reverse that ratio, usually requiring one hour of sleep for every two hours of wakefulness (Kleitman, 1957). A study conducted during the British North Greenland expedition showed that this ratio was maintained even when the men were allowed to sleep as much as they liked and at whatever hours they chose. Although it seemed that they were sleeping excessively, the average was found to be 7.9 hours a day when the actual hours were totaled. Another study conducted in Norway showed that the normal pattern is maintained even when people have to sleep under the midnight sun. Apparently the traditional eight hours of sleep is based on bodily needs.

The need for sleep is dramatically illustrated by experiments in which individuals have remained awake for long periods of time. The loss of one full night's sleep does not usually have a substantial effect on either mental or physical ability as measured on psychological tests, but behavior is increasingly affected after thirty to seventy-two hours of wakefulness. The effects are selective at first: subjects who have kept awake for thirty to sixty hours showed no impairment on novel and challenging tasks, but boring jobs such as keeping watch could not be tolerated (Wilkinson, 1960). If the subjects stayed awake much longer, bizarre reactions set in. Speech became slurred, with many repetitions and mispronunciations; handwriting was reduced to a scrawl; and after six or seven days without sleep many of the symptoms of psychosis began to appear. The subjects became disoriented as to space and time, their body image was disturbed, perception became distorted, and there was an increasing sense of detachment from reality. Paranoid reactions also seemed to be common. In one of the first sleep deprivation experiments (Katz and Landis, 1935) the subject remained awake for seven days punching a time clock every ten minutes. Toward the end of this period he frequently fell asleep during the ten-minute interval; however, he could not be convinced that he had been asleep, and insisted that someone had tampered with the clock. This and other experiments had to be terminated because the extreme loss of sleep induced psychotic reactions.

The course of a normal night's sleep has also been studied extensively (PLATE 16). It does not progress from light to deep sleep and then to gradual wakefulness in any fixed order. In general, our deepest sleep occurs in the first four hours, and physiological measurements indicate that the restorative effects take place primarily during this period. Throughout the night light sleep periods seem to occur approximately every ninety minutes, and are believed to be a vestige of our infantile sleep cycle. Observation of eye movements and EEG records indicate that we do most of our dreaming during these restless periods (Aserinsky and Kleitman, 1955). Other observations indicate that we make a major change in our position every twenty minutes or so, and minor movements every four to five minutes. These changes help us to relax different sets of muscles as well as relieve skin tension and blood congestion. See DREAM-STATE.

We rarely if ever "sleep like a log"; neither are we "dead to the world." Any number of experiments and observations demonstrate that we not only react to stimuli during sleep, but do so selectively. Many people will remain sleeping if others read aloud in the room, but they will usually wake up the moment their own name is even whispered. A mother will sleep through loud traffic noises from the street below, but wake up the moment her baby whimpers. There is further evidence in the fact that somnambulists usually dodge obstacles without awakening. Moreover, dreams are sometimes initiated by external stimuli such as moonlight falling on the face of the sleeper. An experimental study has shown that some subjects will dream about airplanes if a tuning fork is sounded near their ear; and if a cold coin is placed on their forehead at the same time, they may picture the plane flying through a blizzard. However, Dement and Wolpert (1958) have shown that external events such as a ringing bell usually play a minor role in dreaming. The internal motivations count for much more. See DREAM INTERPRETATION (MODERN).

None of these phenomena can be fully explained at this time. The basic physiology of sleep is equally mysterious, although some recent findings have added substantially to our knowledge. Early investigators maintained that it results from an accumulation of waste products or toxic chemicals in the bloodstream, but research has failed to support these theories. Blood transfusions from sleeping dogs fail to put waking dogs to sleep, and Siamese twins do not always sleep at the same time in spite of the fact that they have the same circulatory system.

More recent investigations have focused on brain mechanisms. There is little doubt that a regulatory center exists in the hypothalamus. Patients afflicted with tumors or disease in this area have been found to show an abnormal tendency to sleep, and surgical excision of part of the area has been found to induce continuous sleep in monkeys for four to eight days, followed by months of drowsiness (Ranson, 1939). Later experiments have indicated that there are actually two centers which work counter to each other, a waking and a sleep center. When the sleep center was destroyed in rats, the experimental animals stayed awake and active until they finally fell into a state of exhaustion and coma (Nauta, 1946).

At the present time these two centers appear to be only a small part of the total mechanism. They are probably an extension of the network of cells in the brain stem known as the reticular activating system (RAS). This system connects both to the lower centers that control our internal organs and to the higher cortical centers involved in sensation and thought. Sleep appears to be brought about by a general deactivation of the RAS. This occurs when we reduce stimulation from both the outer and inner world by closing our eyes, relaxing our muscles, and letting our "mental motor" idle. See RETICULAR FORMATION, HYPOTHALAMUS.

SLEEP TREATMENT. The use of prolonged sleep as therapy in certain psychiatric disorders.

Sleep therapy has a long history, going back to the Egyptians and early

Greek physicians, such as Asclepius and Aretaeus, who used "temple sleep" for both mental and physical disorders. In 1700 Hermann Boerhaave recommended sleep in treating melancholia, and during the late 1900s there were a number of reports of recovery from acute excitement when sleep was induced by massive doses of bromides. The technique, however, was not widely accepted until the 1920s, when the Swiss psychiatrist Jacob Klaesi treated schizophrenia by keeping patients asleep for eight to ten days through the use of barbiturates and other drugs, a technique he termed "prolonged narcosis." See ARETAEUS.

Sleep treatment has been applied since then not only to cases of schizophrenia (catatonic excitement states), but to manic-depressive psychosis (depressive phase), and anxiety reactions as well. Though originally used for excited and unmanageable patients, it appears to be more successful with the affective reactions than with schizophrenia. Today tranquilizers are sometimes used in combination with barbiturates or other drugs, and sleep is prolonged for about twenty hours a day for periods of three to sixty days. Pulse, blood pressure, and respiration are checked periodically, the patient's position is frequently changed to avoid the danger of pneumonia, and he is awakened for ten to fifteen minutes at a time for a fluid diet and elimination. The induced sleep usually resembles natural sleep, but sometimes a state of somnolence or "twilight sleep" is maintained. Interviews may be conducted with the patient during the drowsy state between periods of sleep.

Sleep may also be induced by the technique of "electronarcosis," first investigated by Stéphane Leduc in 1902. A standardized method has been developed in which a current is applied to the head for thirty seconds, producing rigidity and loss of consciousness, and then lowered in voltage to produce relaxation and sleep. Russian technologists have developed an instrument termed the "electrosone" which induces deep sleep in a few seconds and maintains this condition as long as the low voltage current is applied to the sleep centers of the brain.

There is little agreement on the theory behind this treatment. Klaesi believed that prolonged sleep broke the vicious cycle of excitement-restlessness-excitement that often occurs in mental disorders. Some authorities emphasize physiological effects, such as the restorative value of sleep, the facilitation of metabolic changes, or the opportunity for cortical cells to recover their normal state. Others suggest psychological explanations, attributing its effect to relief from frustration, arousal of the instinct for self-preservation, or a return to an infantile state during which the patient goes through an emotional rebirth.

Continuous sleep treatment is employed fairly widely in Europe and the Soviet Union, where some hospitals have special sleep wards. In America the technique has few proponents today because of the high relapse rate and the risk of physical complications such as cardiovascular failure. Nevertheless it is occasionally used when other therapies fail.

SMELL (Olfaction). The sense which is activated by stimulation of receptor cells in the nasal cavity.

The cells responsive to the chemical substances we call odors are located in the "olfactory epithelium" high up in the nasal passages leading from the nostrils to the throat. Since they are not in the main route of air as it moves through the nose, our sense of smell is not very keen when we are breathing normally. A vigorous intake of air, a sniff, is usually needed to stir up the air in the nasal passages and bring it into more direct contact with the receptors. Fibers from the olfactory epithelium connect with the olfactory bulb, an extension of the brain, and from there the impulses travel to structures in the ventral (lower) surface of the brain, particularly the prepyriform area and parts of the amygdala. Other parts of the limbic system—the hippocampus, fornix, and septum—appear to play a secondary role in that their activity is influenced by olfactory impulses. *See* LIMBIC SYSTEM.

Most authorities believe that olfaction, like taste, is a chemical sense. But instead of being in solution, as occurs in taste, chemical substances must be in a volatile state before the receptors in the olfactory epithelium can respond. We know it only takes a few molecules of a substance to arouse these receptors, but we know little about the mechanism by which this takes place. Some experts even question whether smell is a chemical sense at all. They suggest that the olfactory receptors radiate a variety of infrared wave lengths (Beck and Miles, 1947). In passing by these receptors a particular kind of molecule absorbs a particular pattern of wave lengths, and heat energy is therefore lost from those receptors. This loss of heat is translated into neural impulses and "interpreted" as an odor by the brain. Recently (1964), Amoore et al. have advanced a stereochemical theory based on the idea that different substances give off molecules with different shapes and different patterns of electrical discharge. The molecules fit into different "sockets" in the olfactory receptors according to these patterns, like a key into a lock. At the present time we are not in a position to choose between the various theories.

Newborn babies have a well-developed sense of smell. This sense may be a factor in the ability of infants to select appropriate foodstuffs in "cafeteria feeding" experiments. People in general, however, vary greatly in their sensitivity to odors. In our society women appear to be particularly affected. In an experiment with hosiery of exactly the same quality, six times

as many women preferred narcissus-scented samples as unscented samples —yet only two of the 250 subjects suspected that any of the stockings had been perfumed (Laird, 1932). Some primitive peoples utilize the sense of smell to a much greater degree than civilized man. The Chukchee, a tribe of Siberia, describe many objects we would differentiate by textures in terms of smells. The customary greeting in this tribe consists of sniffing behind the ear. *See* CAFETERIA FEEDING.

Many animals have a keener sense of smell than man. Odors play a larger part in their lives since they are used in detecting enemies and locating food. It is therefore not surprising that a greater amount of the animal brain is devoted to this sense. In the dog, for example, about one third of the temporal lobe is used for olfactory functions; in man the center for smell occupies only about one twentieth of this area. *See* CEREBRAL CORTEX.

There is an immense difference in the capacity of substances to stimulate the sense of smell. Musk, which is extensively used in the perfume industry, can be detected in a concentration of only four per million parts of air. Our sensitivity to mercaptan is even greater. This chemical is mixed with odorless cooking gas to warn of danger in case of leakage. It is also mixed with wood alcohol to prevent its accidental use as a beverage.

There is little agreement on the fundamental qualities of smell. The inaccessibility of the olfactory receptors makes direct experiments on them next to impossible and no direct correlations have been found between the chemical makeup of substances and the odor qualities they evoke. In the absence of scientific clues to odor analysis, investigators have therefore attempted to classify odors by resemblances and differences. Hans Henning (1924) listed six primary qualities: flowery, fruity, spicy, resinous, foul, and burnt. Industrial chemists, however, list only four basic types: fragrant (as in musk), acid (vinegar), burnt (roast coffee), and caprylic (goaty or sweaty).

The greatest barrier to setting up a system based on personal experience is that people so often fail to agree on the categories—also, an individual may put the same odor in different categories at different times. In one experiment subjects were asked to classify thirty-two different odors. Some individuals required only four categories, but several used twelve or more. (Ross and Harriman, 1949)

The obliteration of unpleasant odors is a major industry. Unpleasant smells can often be absorbed by activated carbon or washed away with water. They can also be masked by strong pleasant odors or reduced by the use of chemical deodorants. In addition, experiments have been made on air deodorizers that temporarily anesthetize the olfactory receptors.

Actually, nature provides a mechanism that helps to neutralize odors. After experiencing any odor, good or bad, for some period of time we "get used to it" and it tends to "fade." This process, called adaptation, is found in most sensory experience. Workers in chocolate factories or perfumeries soon lose their sensitivity to the heavy odors. In wartime, members of burial parties become unaware of the stench and may lose their sense of smell entirely, a condition termed anosmia. In some occupations this adaptation of the sense of smell is not desirable and may actually be dangerous. Miners become immune to the smell of gas and carry mice or canaries underground to warn them of danger. These animals topple over when mine gas is present in harmful quantities, even though the miners themselves cannot sense it. For anosmia as a conversion symptom, *see* SENSITIVITY DISTURBANCES.

The senses of taste and smell combine to give us the flavor of food. They also operate together in arousing past feelings and emotional experiences. Sometimes reactions which are inappropriate to the present situation become reinstated by their association with a smell or taste experienced in the past. Such experiences may occasionally be responsible for the false memories and mysterious feelings of familiarity termed paramnesia. We are usually not aware of these sensory influences on memory. *See* SENSORY ADAPTATION, PARAMNESIA.

SMELL PRISM. A three-dimensional diagram representing six "primary" odors and their mixture.

Scientists have not yet been able to pin down the physical and chemical makeup of substances that cause them to smell different from each other, but they have devised classification schemes based on the direct experience of odors and their mixtures. The most important is the system proposed by Hans Henning, a German research scientist. It is based on the assumption that all odors can be analyzed into six primary qualities: flowery (violet), fruity (lemon), spicy (cloves), resinous (pine), foul (bad fish), and burnt (tar). Henning (1924) held that if these basics are mixed in proper proportions they will produce any odor we can experience. To show this diagrammatically, he drew a prism and placed one of the six primary qualities at each corner. The prism was conceived as hollow, to indicate that odors can be made up of as many as four elementary constituents, but never more. Theoretically, any given odor can be pinpointed on this prism according to its analysis—for example, if it is close to both fruity and spicy it will be largely a combination of these odors.

Henning's system works only moderately well. The odors of many substances that would be placed in the same portion of the prism actually do not resemble each other. Other aspects of odor perception are not included in the classification. It does not take into account the fact that some substances are simultaneously tasted as well as smelled; nor does it recognize the cutaneous component in smell, the fact that substances often sting, feel warm or cool, or have an astringent effect. But the greatest objection to the prism lies in the absence of conclusive evidence that there are only six primary odors.

SMOKING. Smoking is generally described as a habit, but there is evidence that it may also become an addiction resulting from physiological dependence on nicotine. At any rate, most individuals who smoke for a period of months or years tend to acquire a psychological if not a physiological need that in many cases amounts to a compulsion. Moreover, they usually experience withdrawal symptoms such as headaches or nausea if they suddenly give up smoking, and such symptoms are characteristic of addiction. *See* WITHDRAWAL SYMPTOMS.

The factors that induce adolescents to start smoking are primarily social: the urge to appear mature, pressure to conform to the group, assertion of independence from adults who disapprove. Curiosity and the urge to "try anything once" also play a role. Some young people discontinue after the first few attempts, especially if cigarettes produce dizziness or stomach upsets, or if they fail to give them the pleasure they expected. In many cases, however, they continue long enough to establish a habit, and claim that smoking gives them satisfactions which they cannot always put in words. Many of the common reasons given are "Smoking cigarettes gives me something to do with my hands," "It helps to relax me when I'm tense or upset," "It's the sociable thing to do," and "It curbs my appetite and helps to keep my weight down." Perhaps one of the reasons for the prevalence of smoking is that it provides a *variety* of mild satisfactions. Undoubtedly advertising reinforces these satisfactions by suggestion.

Psychoanalysts have attempted to discover deeper reasons for the habit. In Freudian terms, the satisfaction gained from smoking is a residue of the oral phase of psychosexual development, the infantile period in which the mouth is the chief pleasure zone of the body. Moreover, smoking may provide a measure of emotional security as well as physical, erotic pleasure, since it harks back to an earlier stage when the smoker was given constant care and attention. According to this theory, then, a cigarette serves as an oral "pacifier," providing temporary relief from the tensions and stresses of life.

Compulsive smoking has also been attributed—in occasional cases—to a masochistic drive for self-destruction, since the life expectancy of heavy smokers is considerably less than that of non-smokers.

Psychological studies have not revealed any marked effects of smoking on behavior. Experiments on problem-solving yield equivocal results. There seems to be a slight negative effect on fine manual co-ordination, and in some cases on the sense of balance, but no detectable change in gross movement. The physiological effects are more pronounced, especially among heavy smokers. Small amounts of absorbed nicotine have a stimulating effect on the brain and nervous system, but large amounts tend to act as a depressant. In rare cases the optic nerve may be affected and lead to "tobacco amblyopia," dimness of vision, especially for color. Effects on the circulatory system include an elevation of blood pressure, increase in heart and pulse rate, constriction of peripheral arteries, and decrease in skin temperature, especially in the extremities. Gastrointestinal effects include increased gastric acidity, suppression of hunger contractions, and loss of appetite, although the last-named effect is probably due primarily to the fact that smoke dulls the senses of taste and smell. The most obvious effect of heavy smoking on the upper respiratory tract is irritation, as is evident in the common complaint known as "smoker's cough." This condition may be accompanied by wheezing, dyspnea (shortness of breath), chest pains, and frequent respiratory infection.

In view of these effects, it is not surprising that physicians strongly advise against smoking among patients suffering from Raynaud's disease and Buerger's disease, which affect the small blood vessels of the extremities, as well as in cases of stomach ulcer, coronary heart disease, high blood pressure, and bronchitis. Emphysema, a condition in which the patient suffers from shortness of breath due to air pockets in the lung tissue, is believed to be caused or at least aggravated by heavy smoking. Since emotional factors are often suspected in cases of emphysema, this condition is sometimes discussed under the heading "psychophysiologic disorders of the respiratory system." It is an indicative fact that the disorder is frequently associated with peptic ulcer, and many psychiatrists feel that emotional factors related to unconscious conflict may be involved in both of these conditions. In addition, studies have indicated that heavy smoking during pregnancy may lead to premature delivery, although it is possible that a third factor, such as anxiety, may be the actual cause of both the smoking and the premature delivery.

There is constantly increasing evidence of the close relation between excessive smoking and lung cancer as well as coronary artery disease, although some physicians deny that a causal relationship has been established. In a report to Congress made in 1968, the United States Public Health Service stated that "It is concluded that cigarette smoking can contribute to the development of cardiovascular disease and particularly to death from coronary heart disease," due to the fact that smoking reduces the blood's ability to supply oxygen to the heart. The report also stated that smokers in the twenty-five to thirty-five age bracket who consume more than two packs a day can expect an eight-year loss in life expectancy, and those who consume less than half a pack a day can expect a four-year loss. In addition, the report reasserted the widely held view that heavy smoking is the main cause of lung cancer in men, and stated that there is a cause-and-effect relationship between cigarette smoking and lung cancer in women. This connection had previously been denied, since lung cancer is less common in women than in men —but the report showed that the rate among women has risen 400 per cent since 1930.

The growing conviction that cigarette smoking is a hazard to health has led many individuals to seek to break the habit. Simple remedies such as gum-chewing (an "oral satisfaction") rarely work for any length of time. Hypnosis has proved effective with many smokers, although the suggestion usually has to be renewed at intervals. Dr. Daniel Horn, Director of the National Clearing House for Smoking and Health, makes the significant point that an analysis should be made of the reasons why the particular individual smokes, and this analysis should guide any attempts to break the habit. On the basis of a large-scale questionnaire survey, he concluded that about 50 per cent smoke for "positive" reasons such as stimulation (10 per cent), something to do with the hands (8 per cent), and pleasant relaxation (30 to 40 per cent); while 40 to 50 per cent smoke for "negative" reasons—that is, to relieve anxiety and tension. The positive group can usually be persuaded to give up smoking by presenting the facts about its effect on health, and by instituting a plan for overcoming the habit—for instance, by cutting out smoking during a vacation, or by refraining from smoking during certain hours of the day and then gradually extending the abstinence.

For the negative group, who use cigarettes as a tranquilizer, a clinical approach may be needed. A good example is the antismoking clinic headed by Dr. D. T. Frederickson of the New York City Health Department. His procedure begins with a lecture designed to help the smokers understand why they smoke. The participants are then divided into small units resembling Alcoholics Anonymous groups, each under the leadership of a former smoker who relates his own experiences, provides emotional support, and makes specific suggestions for overcoming the habit. Major features of the clinic approach are these: first, the participants study their own smoking pattern by keeping a record of the situations that precipitate smoking as well as their feelings at the time. A housewife found that she smoked whenever she felt even the slightest anxiety, anger, or uncertainty—for example, when one of her children was late for dinner, or even when the telephone rang. Second, they are advised to eliminate the least important cigarettes first—for instance, one businessman chain-smoked at the office and also at parties, but found it easier to give up the social smoking first. Third, they are taught a breathing exercise consisting of inhaling deeply and expelling the air slowly, and are urged to perform this exercise repeatedly whenever they feel the need to smoke. Fourth, they are urged to inhale less deeply when they do smoke, in order to reduce the dependence on nicotine reactions. Fifth, they try simple tricks designed to make them more conscious of their smoking as well as to carry them over periods when the craving is greatest—for example, hiding ashtrays, not carrying matches, or putting cigarettes in a different pocket each day. Finally, they are encouraged to take regular vigorous exercise, since this not only helps them to discharge their emotional tensions but speeds up their system and gives them the kind of "lift" they have been getting through smoking, but in a healthier way.

Most of the participants use these techniques in a gradual "tapering off" process. In some cases, however, addicted smokers are advised to quit smoking all at once, though they usually experience withdrawal symptoms and even a period of "mourning" due to losing the close companionship of the cigarette. Follow-up meetings, which are an integral part of the procedure of the clinic, have shown that two thirds of those who completed eight months of the program quit smoking entirely, while another fifth cut their smoking at least in half.

SOCIAL BREAKDOWN SYNDROME.

A group of symptoms observed primarily in chronic mental patients, consisting of such reactions as withdrawal, disinterest, loss of initiative and hostility, and believed to be due to the restrictions of a hospital environment. Other terms for this syndrome are asylum lunacy (obsolete), institutionalism, institutional neurosis, and chronicity.

The concept of the social breakdown, or social disability, syndrome holds that many of the characteristics long attributed to mental illness itself—particularly schizophrenia—are actually, and ironically, the result of the institutional conditions under which the patients live. As Zusman (1966) points out, "This explanation suggests that the hospitalized mentally ill respond to being crowded into locked, barred, unstimulating rooms by becoming deteriorated and animal-like. Staff attitudes which give little hope for recovery, combined with the patient not being permitted to wear his own clothing, have clocks, calendars or mirrors, and an unchanging daily routine, lead to lack of concern for personal appearance, present activities, or future prospects. The social breakdown syndrome concept assumes a very direct relationship between the surroundings of a mentally ill person and the course of his illness. It explains why so many varied forms of treatment for acute and chronic psychosis—therapeutic community, remotivation, compensated work, open hospital, day care, patient-government, etc.—have had striking successes. All of them involve humane treatment of the patient coupled with social pressure to act in a socially acceptable way. They permit and encourage the patient to make use of the normal social skills which he has and help him to develop new ones. They prepare him during all phases of treatment to return to his life as a functioning member of society."

As Zusman, Gruenberg and others have also pointed out, recognition of the social breakdown syndrome is one of the major forces behind the current drive to develop community mental health centers where patients will be intensively treated within the community instead of being relegated to isolated hospitals where many of them receive little more than custodial care.

The concept has its roots in the past but has only recently been studied systematically. In the early part of the nineteenth century, Philippe Pinel in Paris, and William Tuke and John Conolly in England recognized that many of the disabling symptoms of mental patients were due to the way they were handled in hospitals. As a result, "moral treatment" was introduced in many institutions, and physical restraint and control were replaced with a gentle, humane approach. In consequence, a great many patients made social recoveries and discharge rates rose sharply. Toward the end of the century, however, the policy of confinement and subjugation of patients again became dominant. This resulted in rapid deterioration instead of recovery, and

bolstered the view that mental illness was hopeless and incurable.

Around the turn of the century, Freud insisted that neurotic symptoms have a psychological meaning and are treatable, and Bleuler applied the same idea to psychoses. Bleuler also recognized that patients often manifest "secondary symptoms" which stem from the hospital environment rather than from the disease itself. Other steps in recognition of the social breakdown syndrome were these: Myerson's "total push" method, designed to counteract withdrawal and regression through an activity program; Sullivan's emphasis on interpersonal relationships between patients and staff, and on "social recovery" through improvement of social skills; Maxwell Jones' concept of the hospital as a total therapeutic community; and the development of the open hospital where doors are unlocked and the patients take a large measure of responsibility for themselves. See TOTAL PUSH THERAPY, MILIEU THERAPY, SULLIVAN, MENTAL HOSPITAL.

As these changes took place, a number of investigators developed theories explaining hospital behavior. Russell Barton (1959) applied the term "institutional neurosis" to a syndrome characterized by apathy, loss of initiative and interest, deterioration of personal habits, loss of individuality, resigned acceptance, and a typical drooping posture and shuffling gait. He held that this syndrome developed from lack of contact with the outside world (locked doors, few visits, enforced idleness), bossiness of the staff, loss of friendships and personal possessions, heavy sedation, the ward atmosphere, and having nothing to look forward to outside the institution. D. H. Miller (1961) describes five types of reaction occurring primarily in custodial institutions: a chronic paranoid response consisting of the feeling that the environment is against the patient, a depressive reaction, a catatonic response consisting of withdrawal with bursts of diffuse aggressive activity, a psychopathic response in which the patient tries to obtain gratification by manipulating others, and a passive neurotic response in which he gives in to the demands of the institution by becoming submissive and infantile.

R. Sommer and G. Witney (1961) describe a "chain of chronicity" consisting of a definite sequence which could be interrupted by a constructive approach anywhere along the line. The sequence starts with the patient's manifestation of peculiar behavior and continues as he goes through the admission ward and into the continued treatment ward, where the staff accepts him as a failure and where he himself accepts a passive institutional role. Similarly, D. B. Martin (1955) describes "institutionalization" in terms of "cooperative" surrender to institutional life, with loss of initiative and individuality. E. Goffman (1957) contrasts life in a "total institution," where every part of the day is scheduled and where all activities are carried out with others under a central authority, with ordinary noninstitutional life in which we tend to sleep, play and work with different people in different places and under different authorities. The institution "strips away personal identity," "mortifies the self" by removing personal possessions, replaces occupational and career differences with a single "stigmatized status," and eliminates active communication with the outside world while developing its own customs and lingo. This entire process contributes to the deterioration of the patient.

The Program Area Committee on Mental Health of the American Public Health Association (1962) has applied the term social breakdown syndrome to a pattern consisting of withdrawal manifested in loss of interest in social functions (work, housekeeping, social life), and loss of concern about personal appearance and cleanliness, as well as anger and hostility manifested in resentfulness, quarrelsomeness and occasionally physical violence—all of which tend to destroy personal relationships. The Committee felt that behavior of this kind was produced by depersonalized institutions and is largely responsible for the "noisy violence" and "craziness" associated with mental illness—much of which would disappear if patients were treated as human beings.

Finally, Gruenberg (1963) and Gruenberg and Zusman (1964) have added greatly to our understanding of this syndrome by outlining the following seven steps in its development, and by pointing out that these steps may apply to persons, such as the aged and even housewives, who live outside of institutions: (1) *susceptibility due to deficiency of inner standards*—that is, the syndrome occurs only in persons with weakened self-identity, lack of relationship with a group, poor ego-strength due to a physical handicap, defective or destructive social experiences, or an acute episode of mental turmoil; (2) *dependence on current cues*—that is, since the individual does not have inner standards to fall back on, he becomes dependent on others to tell him how to think and act; (3) *social labeling as incompetent and dangerous*—that is, he is called incompetent or crazy and sent to a mental hospital, which convinces him that he is even more unfit for society than he had thought; (4) *induction into the sick role:* he now becomes a patient instead of a person and, through the admission procedures, loses his identity and becomes a passive, helpless, "sick" individual with little prospect of change; (5) *learning the chronic sick role:* he replaces his previous identity with the role of chronic withdrawal, chronic intermittent hostility or chronic dependence without extreme withdrawal or aggressiveness; (6) *atrophy of work and social skills:* since he has no opportunity to use the skills of everyday living, they atrophy from disuse or become obsolete due to changes in technology as the years go by; (7) *identification with the sick:* a chronic state of sickness is accepted by the patient and he begins to see himself as the same as other sick people, later becoming an "old patient" who is completely converted to institutional life.

The social breakdown concept is a definite advance since it suggests that many of the symptoms associated with mental illness are not the result of the disease process itself but stem from the environment to which the patient is subjected. If this environment is improved, many of the disabling influences which now stand in the way of recovery would undoubtedly be eliminated.

SOCIAL CLASS (Social Stratification). A broad social grouping based upon level of prestige determined by such characteristics as occupation, income, family genealogy, moral standing, residential area, and social relationships.

Class is distinguished from caste by the fact that the boundaries of the class group are less rigid. A caste system, as in India, is based on hereditary distinctions, and the lines cannot be crossed without incurring severe social punishment. A class system, on the other hand, permits a degree of social mobility or crossing of class lines. America is predominantly a class system, though the color line has some features of a caste system, such as discouragement of "mixed" neighborhoods and illegality of intermarriage in certain states.

In the present period rigid class distinctions are slowly breaking down, and social mobility is on the increase. A study by Lipset and Bendix (1959) has indicated that it is particularly high in the occupational sphere, at least among nonfarm workers, both in this country and abroad. Their findings show that from 29 to 45 per cent of the population have been shifting upward from manual to nonmanual work between generations, while 13 to 32 per cent have shifted downward from nonmanual to manual occupations.

The idea that American society has a class structure is often denied; yet it appears to have been demonstrated by a number of sociological investigations —notably Warner and Lunt's study of an old New England city ("Yankee City") in 1941, and Warner, Meeker and Eells' survey of a Midwestern town ("Jonesville") in 1949. These studies were based on interviews in which large numbers of citizens were asked to rate their fellow townsmen on social status. The subjects were free to use their own criteria, which were in general those enumerated in the definition of social class given at the head of this article, with the greatest emphasis on occupation and economic level. An analysis of the results showed that the subjects viewed their fellow townsmen in terms of three major classes, each with a lower and upper level; and the comparison between percentages in New England and Midwestern cities showed, interestingly, that they were remarkably similar: upper-upper, 2 per cent and 3 per cent; lower-upper, 2 per cent and 3 per cent; upper-middle, 10 per cent and 11 per cent; lower-middle, 28 per cent and 31 per cent; upper-lower, 33 per cent and 41 per cent; lower-lower, 25 per cent and 14 per cent.

A number of significant studies have been made of the psychological and social effects of class structure. One important finding is that even where the classes are not rigid and mobility is possible, as in America, there is still a great difference in the prestige of the different classes and in the power, respect, and honors which they command. It has frequently been shown, for example, that even at the grade school level children consider people from the higher social classes more attractive than those from the lower classes (Bonney, 1944). Other investigators have found that members of the higher classes are somewhat freer than members of lower classes to violate group mores and to deviate from group opinions, that they are accorded greater opportunities to speak and voice their opinions in group discussions, and that people are more likely to believe them and follow their lead than to be influenced by individuals from lower social levels.

Another major finding is that social level to a great extent determines the entire environment of the individual, including opportunities for completing high school and going to college, leisure-time activities, general values of life, and type of job. Recent studies have indicated that children brought up in a deprived environment are often grossly handicapped in sensory discrimination, motor skills, vocabulary and problem-solving ability due to lack of opportunity for normal communication, diversified play activities and varied stimulation in their homes. As Davis and Havighurst pointed out in 1946, "The social-class system maintains cultural, economic and social barriers which prevent intimate social intermixture between the slums, the Gold Coast, and the middle class . . . By setting up barriers to social participation, the American social-class system actually prevents the vast majority of the working classes, or the slums, from learning any culture but that of their own group. *Thus the pivotal meaning of social class* to students of human development is that it defines and systematizes the different learning environments for children of different classes."

Psychological investigations have shown that social classes differ not only in status and opportunity but in the attitudes, behavior and personalities of their members. Some of these findings will be briefly summarized. It is a well-recognized fact that the higher the class of the individual, the more likely he is to hold conservative political opinions (although there are many exceptions). In another sphere, Kinsey et al. (1948)

found significant differences in sexual behavior on different levels of society. The semiskilled-labor group engaged in considerably more premarital intercourse and considerably less masturbation than the professional group, with the lower white collar group intermediate between the two. Interestingly, people who ultimately moved from the skilled-labor to the professional class manifested sexual patterns similar to those of the class to which they moved, and the same principle held if they moved downward to the unskilled-labor class.

Studies have also shown that young people from the upper and middle social strata not only show a higher level of achievement-motivation than children from the lower levels (Rosen, 1956), but are also more likely to have personal values and characteristics that make for occupational success. In addition, a number of investigations have been made of class differences in child-rearing practices and their effect upon personality development. *See* DISCIPLINE, OVERPROTECTION.

SOCIAL DEVELOPMENT. The gradual establishment of relationships with other individuals and groups; the acquisition of attitudes and behavior that enable the individual to function as a member of society.

Social development follows a regular sequence even though there may be considerable variation in the timing of each of the steps. Some children make more rapid progress than others because they are more intelligent, better motivated or have superior opportunities for social experiences, but the general pattern tends to be orderly and predictable. This can be demonstrated by tracing the process through three broad stages: infancy, early childhood, and later childhood. The following sequences are summarized from Hurlock, *Child Development* (1964).

For the first few weeks of life, the human infant makes diffuse responses to intense stimuli and can usually be soothed by cuddling, humming and rocking—but there is no evidence that he is responding to the human being or the human voice as such. By the beginning of the third month, however, he shows a need for companionship, since he appears contented in the presence of others and often whimpers or cries when by himself. He now appears to distinguish between people and objects, and makes his first genuinely social responses: turning his head at the sound of a human voice, smiling in response to a smile or clucking sound, kicking and waving his arms in pleasure when he is with other people. During the third month he stops crying when his attention is diverted or when he is talked to. At this time he indicates that he recognizes his mother or other familiar people, and cries when they leave him. He also shows a fear of unfamiliar people by crying or tensing his head in their presence.

In the fourth month the average baby smiles when spoken to, looks in the direction of a person who is leaving him, fixes his attention on faces, and coos and laughs when he is played with or given attention. Between the fifth and sixth month he reacts differently to smiling and scolding, smiles when he recognizes familiar persons, imitates clapping and waving, enjoys peek-a-boo play, reacts to interference, and clearly expresses fear of strangers. The sixth month brings more active responses: grabbing noses and glasses, pulling hair, touching and exploring faces.

By the eighth or ninth month the infant tries to imitate speech sounds, simple actions and gestures; and between the tenth and twelfth months he shows an interest in his own image in the mirror, and sometimes kisses it. In the twelfth month he begins to obey a repeated "No," and exhibits even more intense fear of strangers than before. From the fifteenth month on, the baby shows an increasing desire to be with adults and to imitate their behavior; and by the time he reaches two he can co-operate with them in routine activities such as sweeping the floor with a toy broom, picking up clothes, and putting the silver on the table. In other words, he has developed from a passive to a participating member of a social group.

It takes longer for babies to react to other children than to adults. They begin to smile at each other at four or five months, and touch each other in a friendly way, or try to take things from each other, between six and eight months. About a year later one baby will pull the hair or clothes of another, fight with him over toys, and attempt to imitate his movements or babbling. During the first half of the second year the young child shows a definite interest in his playmates, and fights less over toys; and during the second half of this year he establishes tentative social relationships during games, and then starts to play more or less co-operatively with other children.

Most of the types of behavior required for life with other people begin to develop during the early childhood years from two to six, and by the time he enters school the youngster is usually well enough socialized to participate in group activities. Some, of course, make more rapid strides than others, depending not only on the number but the kind of social contacts they have an opportunity to make. Kindergarten children who have gone through nursery school usually make better adjustments than those who have not had this experience (Bonney and Nicholson, 1958). Follow-up studies show that the attitudes and behavior established in this period tend to be lasting (Ryan, 1949). *See* NURSERY SCHOOL EXPERIENCE.

During the so-called "pre-gang age," the child's interest gradually shifts from adults to peers. The two-year-old depends almost completely on his parents for care and attention, but within a year he usually enters the resistant period and becomes self-assertive and hard to handle. In another year or so he becomes more co-operative. But all through the three to five year period he is bound to be influenced by the social attitudes—friendly or hostile, tolerant or critical—of the adults in his life.

As to his relations with other children, the typical two-year-old engages only in solitary or parallel play, and will recognize the existence of others only by imitating them, watching them or grabbing their toys. Between three and four, children begin to play and talk together, mainly in groups of two or three. They also begin to select their playmates and make more friendly and fewer hostile contacts. In a word, although this early period is self-centered on the whole, there is a gradual shift to more socialized behavior, and by six most children have learned the elements of give and take, sharing with others and conforming to the patterns of their group.

When a child enters school he also enters the "gang age" during which social consciousness and social behavior develop rapidly. Although the family continues to exert an influence, it is gradually supplemented and largely replaced by the peer group, which Havighurst (1953) defines as "An aggregation of people of approximately the same age who *feel* and *act* together." Early in this process the child shifts over from individual games to group games, and from informal to more organized play—and since group activities involve a greater number of children, he widens his circle of friends. These changes do not happen all at once. Rather, the child goes through a "shifting group" stage between the sixth and eighth year, during which he tries one group and then another, and oscillates between group and individual activity. After that the gang takes over more and more.

The typical childhood gang is formed by the children themselves as an effort to create their own society. It exists without support or authorization from adults, and its aims are not dictated by society but by the interests and needs of its members. It is not necessarily at war with authority, but it does offer relief from adult supervision. In contrast to adolescent gangs, the childhood gang is basically a play group primarily devoted to having a good time, including a little mischief-making on occasion. The members are usually chosen by the more active members on the basis of similar interests and ability to enter into the activities which the group as a whole enjoys.

Gangs are practically always made up of children of the same sex, but boy gangs are generally formed earlier and last somewhat longer than girl gangs. Girl gangs tend to be more tightly organized, more secretive and more socially exclusive than boy gangs. However, boy gangs are much more likely to use external symbols of belonging: a gang name, secret signals and pass words, armbands or other insignia, and initiation ceremonies in which skill or physical endurance are tested. They usually meet in out-of-the-way places such as a barn, garage, or vacant lot, while the girls meet at a drugstore, a home, or the school playground, since they are more closely supervised by adults.

The activities of childhood gangs vary from community to community. Among them are sports, games, hikes, movies, building a meeting-place, parties, hobbies, exploring, and reading. Boy gangs are apt to be more noisy, carefree and rowdy than girl gangs, and are also more likely to engage in forbidden activities such as smoking, gambling, drinking, sexual experimentation, annoying people, or stealing. Girl gangs are far less likely to engage in objectionable behavior except for smoking. They spend less time in sports and games, and much more in talking about parents, teachers, classmates and members of rival gangs. They are also more likely to put on plays, cook food, go on picnics, or engage in service or charitable activities.

Childhood gangs contribute to social development in many ways. They give the growing youngster a sense of security in his first important venture into social life. They arouse a sense of loyalty to a group. They provide companionship with peers in an atmosphere of fun and adventure. And they challenge the child to make his own way in society without protection and supervision from adults. *See* ADOLESCENCE, SOCIAL ROLE, SOCIAL NORMS, SOCIAL CLASS, SEX ROLE.

SOCIAL DISTANCE. The degree of sympathy and acceptance existing between groups or members of groups.

Social distance is not a function of social intimacy or social contact. Soldiers may occupy the same barracks for months and yet feel they belong to two different worlds. Office workers may have a great deal of contact with executives in a business firm, yet the social distance between the two groups may be immense. But the same office workers may feel close to workers in their own category in another branch of the company which is located hundreds of miles away.

Feelings of social distance stem primarily from our membership in groups. We identify with a certain race, nationality, religion, occupational group, socioeconomic level, or club, and often without thinking adopt the attitudes of the group toward outsiders. These attitudes can be materially influenced by propaganda designed to widen the gap between, say, labor and management, or between white man and Negro. Fortunately these gaps can be narrowed by efforts aimed at achieving greater collaboration and understanding.

Social distance may also be closely related to our level of aspiration and our desire for prestige and standing. According to Hartley and Hartley (1952), "In our society, social distance estimates seem to be related to power and status. There seems to be a tendency to perceive a relatively greater distance between one's own group and those less powerful and a relatively lesser distance between one's own group and those more powerful." Studies of class identification lend support to this statement, since they show a greater tendency to identify with the class above than with the class below. Desire for "social mobility" seems to be involved in many cases. A person who is eager to raise his status will usually feel closer in social distance to the higher group than the person who is content to maintain his present status. It has also been found that an individual who has already "made the grade" may perceive the distance as less than one who has not yet achieved the higher status. To the man who aspires to be vice-president of his company, the upward step may seem enormous, but once he has "arrived," the distance back looks far shorter.

Social distance is generally measured by attitude scales. These scales are made up of a range of statements expressing degrees of acceptance, spaced at equal appearing intervals from socially near relationships to socially far. One of the first and most widely used scales was created by E. L. Bogardus (1925), who is primarily responsible for the development of the concept of social distance. In this scale the subject is asked if he would accept members of a specific nationality group in the following relationships: (1) close kinship by marriage, (2) in my club as personal chums, (3) on my street as neighbors, (4) in my occupation, (5) as citizen in my country, (6) as visitors only in my country, or (7) would exclude my country. The subject's attitude as registered on this scale is taken to express the highest degree of intimacy he would accept.

The Bogardus Scale has been modified and adapted by other investigators to measure attitudes toward a wide variety of persons and groups. W. G. Binneweis (1926) used a six-point scale to show that people from small cities felt closer to rural groups than those who came from large cities. Horowitz (1936) constructed a pictorial variation of the social distance scale, consisting of twelve photographs of pleasant-looking Negro and white boys, and asked his subjects to select the pictures according to such instructions as the following: "Show me all those you want to sit next to on a street car"; "Show me all those that you would go swimming with"; and "Show me all those that you'd like to have for a cousin." Crespi (1945) designed a Social Rejection Thermometer for the measurement of attitudes toward conscientious objectors during World War II. This scale goes somewhat beyond mere statements of psychological distance, for it ranges from "accepting conscientious objector as any one else, even so far as close kinship by marriage," to "I feel CO's should be imprisoned" and "I feel CO's should be shot as traitors." *See* ATTITUDE SCALES, PREJUDICE.

SOCIAL FACILITATION.

The enhancement of behavior through social stimulation—for example, workers often produce more in a group situation than when working alone; also, it has been found that fish eat more food and ants dig more dirt when in a group than by themselves.

The term was first used by F. H. Allport to explain the results of a series of experiments he performed just after World War I (1920, 1924). In substance, he assigned his subjects a number of tasks to be performed under two different conditions: working alone, and working in the presence of three or four associates. The results showed that on several different tasks a large majority turned out more work (though

often less accurately) in the group situation than in the solitary setup. To make sure that the difference was not due to rivalry, he performed further experiments in which the subjects were assured that their scores would not be compared. When output was again greater in the group situation, he concluded that the improvement could be attributed to the presence of other people, and particularly to the fact that the "sight and sound of others doing the same thing" had a stimulating effect on their performance.

Allport conceived social facilitation solely in terms of the quantity of stimulation that affected the individual's work activities. In his opinion this stimulation released greater energy and therefore led to increased output. In 1930, Dashiell repeated some of his experiments with a few modifications. Using larger groups of subjects and more exacting controls, he found evidence that competitive attitudes almost inevitably entered into the situation and had a greater effect on production than social facilitation in the strict sense in which Allport used it. Other studies have shown, for example, that stenographers usually type faster when many of them work in the same room than when working alone. There is little doubt that this is due not only to the clatter of the machines and the movements of their neighbors, but to feelings of rivalry which often operate beneath the surface.

In discussing the question of social facilitation, Newcomb, Turner and Converse (1965) suggest that "Perhaps the most striking instances .of the energizing effects of the sight and sound of others doing the same thing are to be seen in the 'spiraling' excitement of certain crowds, especially in crisis-like situations. If, as occurs at a fire in a theatre, all members of the crowd have the same motive (to escape), any observable (and, in this case, excited) expressions of the common motive are indeed likely to have energizing effects." *See* MASS BEHAVIOR, MASS HYSTERIA, GROUP DYNAMICS.

SOCIAL ISOLATION. Scientists have often suggested that considerable light could be thrown on human development if infants could be raised completely apart from society. Experiments of this kind might help us to answer a number of intriguing questions. What would be the effect of complete lack of social and cultural experience on their future life? Would they develop human or animal characteristics? How early could human beings survive without human help?

Many short-term isolation studies have been made in sensory deprivation experiments, but needless to say, no experiments on long-term social isolation have been undertaken with human beings. Nevertheless there are a number of fairly well authenticated reports of children who have either lived alone in the wilderness or who have been brought up by animals, and there are other cases in which children have been confined for long periods in attics or dungeons. The effects of social isolation will be best indicated by describing four of the most widely accepted cases on record. *See* SENSORY DEPRIVATION.

The Wild Boy of Aveyron. In 1799 a group of hunters came upon a wild boy roaming the forests in the neighborhood of Aveyron in Southern France. They reported that he walked, ran and climbed more like an animal than a human being, and apparently had kept himself alive by eating nuts, roots and berries. He was later captured and brought to Paris, where he was put in the care of Jean Itard, a physician and director of the Institution for the Deaf and Dumb. There he was examined by Philippe Pinel, the leading French psychiatrist of the day, and pronounced an incurable idiot. Itard's own examination revealed that the boy's vision and hearing were dull, his powers of attention and observation completely undeveloped, and his body wracked with frequent spasms and convulsions. He showed no evidence of social behavior of any kind and made no attempts at communication except an occasional grunt. In the doctor's own words, "His whole life was a completely animal existence."

In spite of these handicaps, Itard undertook to civilize and educate the boy. He spent five solid years in these attempts, using every available technique and developing many procedures of his own. The boy learned to respond to the name given him, Victor, and progressed somewhat in the use of discrimination materials devised by the doctor. He also learned to speak, read and recall three or four simple words, notably the word lait (milk), and was even able to spell it with alphabet blocks.

In time, Victor lost his bestial manners and appearance and developed strong ties of affection toward those who cared for him. However, he did not learn to play or behave like a normal individual even though he survived to an estimated age of forty. Most psychologists have therefore concluded that he was mentally defective, probably on the moderate or severely retarded level, and was originally abandoned for this reason. Some authorities, however, feel that he could not have coped with life in the wilds if he had been defective, and attribute his backwardness to living in a non-human environment during his formative years. It is quite possible that Victor's behavior resulted from both factors, a low mentality and lack of human contact. *See* SEGUIN.

The Wild Boy of Salvador, a more recent case (1932) presents an interesting comparison with Victor. This wild boy was captured by police after a struggle at the age of about five, and was soon put under the care of a psychologist named Jorge Ramirez Chulo. The boy was named Tamasha, meaning village, since this was the only word he could speak when he was found. Apparently he had been lost or abandoned in the jungle, and had lived with animals; for he refused cooked foods, lapped up liquids from a dish and preferred to curl up on the floor instead of sleeping in a bed. The boy had learned to swim, threw stones with amazing accuracy, and soon earned the nickname "Tarzancito" for his ability to swing skillfully through the trees. Under Chulo's tutelage he progressed rapidly and within three years had not only accepted clothes, baths and haircuts, but had acquired a normal vocabulary for a child of his age. When asked about the past, he described eating with animals but could not recall human parents. Apparently this boy had a normal potential and was discovered early enough to enable him to recover fully from the effects of social deprivation.

The Wolf Children of Midnapore. This is the remarkable case of two girls who were apparently brought up by wolves in the Bengal province of India. Many reports of children actually raised by wild animals (wolves, sheep, cattle, bears) can be found throughout literature, as well as in legends of the Romulus and Remus type. Linnaeus applied the term "feral men" to such cases in 1758. However, the wolf children of India are the first to be authenticated by photographs, a day-by-day journal, and careful investigation by a recognized scientist. The following brief account is based on the diary kept by the Reverend J. A. L. Singh and his wife, who trained the children, and the book *Wolf Children and Feral Men* which they wrote with the anthropologist Robert M. Zingg (1942).

Stories of children suckled and raised by wolves have circulated in India for many years, but the Midnapore case is unique in that several people claimed they actually saw small human beings running along on all fours with a family consisting of a mother and father

wolf and two cubs. An Anglican missionary, Reverend Singh, decided to investigate these "man ghosts," as the natives called them, and succeeded in capturing the two "wolf children." Both were girls, and he took them to the orphanage which he directed. Mrs. Singh estimated that the older girl, whom they later called Kamala, was about eight years of age, while the younger one, Amala, was only about a year and a half.

When the children were discovered, their heads were covered with matted hair and their hands and knees were disfigured by sores from walking on all fours. They lapped up food from a pan, bolted meat ravenously, and growled when anyone approached while they were eating. Their teeth were sharp, with long pointed canines, their eyes "glared in the dark like blue lights," their hearing was remarkably acute, and their sense of smell was so highly developed that they could smell meat from a distance of seventy yards. At night they roamed around the compound howling like a wolf. Several months after their capture, Kamala found a dead chicken in the yard, seized it in her jaws, and ran on hands and feet into the bushes to devour it.

The Reverend and Mrs. Singh attempted to raise the children as newly born human beings, but they encountered great difficulties. The girls tore off every bit of clothing, and finally diapers had to be sewn on them. At first the only way to make contact was by offering them biscuits and cakes, but in time they became tame enough to permit Mrs. Singh to massage their bodies and stretch their muscles so that they could walk upright. Neither child learned to run upright, but Kamala eventually managed to walk in a somewhat awkward fashion. Her younger sister, Amala, made better progress because she was not hampered by long-term habits—but unfortunately she died a year after capture. Her sister wept two tears and soon became attached to Mrs. Singh.

In the course of the next eight years, before her death at seventeen, Kamala learned to wear clothes, ceased to bare her teeth in anger, gave up prowling at night, and even developed a wariness of the dark. She learned about fifty words which she used in short sentences, and seemed to enjoy attending the morning religious services. She also developed a sense of responsibility and initiative, frequently running errands and caring for the smaller children in the orphanage. In a word, she was able to throw off her wolf-like habit patterns and develop an essentially human way of life.

Kasper Hauser. This celebrated case of extreme isolation was described by a prominent Bavarian lawyer, Anselm von Feuerbach, in 1832. He reported that a young man of approximately seventeen years of age, later called Kaspar Hauser, had been incarcerated in a dark dungeon since early childhood. The cell was so low and narrow that he could neither stand up nor stretch out his arms, and he was not even allowed to see or communicate with the attendant who brought his food. When discovered, he was only 4 feet 9 inches tall, and although his upper body was well formed, his legs were poorly developed. According to Feuerbach's description, his face had a "brutish appearance," his hand and finger control were very poor, and even after months in the outside world he tottered about uncertainly due to defective balance, weakness, and abnormal knee development. Although his mental age was estimated at approximately three years at the time of his release, he was completely unable to understand human speech. However, he learned rapidly and within a few years had mastered not only German but Latin. He was even able to write a brief memoir on his life in the dungeon. However, this proved to be his undoing, for when

it became known that he was going to publish his story, he was assassinated, probably by the same men who had imprisoned him originally.

The mystery of the young man's identity and the reason for his imprisonment have never been completely solved, but there is some evidence to suggest that he was the legitimate heir to a small German principality and was removed for political reasons. Over a thousand pamphlets, plays, and novels have been written about Hauser, most of them using his life as a symbol of political cruelty. Psychologically speaking, the case well illustrates the phenomenal resilience of the human mind as well as the human body. However, it must be recognized that certain factors operated in his favor. He did not have to unlearn animal-like habits. He may have been incarcerated at an age, say two, when he had already developed human qualities. And he was fed, clothed, and cared for by a human keeper with whom he may have had some contact.

SOCIALIZATION. The gradual development of behavior patterns which are acceptable to society.

Three closely related processes are involved in socialization. First, the child must learn *proper performance behavior*—that is, he must discover what kind of behavior is approved by the social group, and shape his own behavior accordingly. Second, he must learn to play *social roles* according to the expectations of the group—for example, a masculine or feminine role, and roles as brother or sister, student, or member of a team. Third, he must develop *social attitudes* which enable him to establish constructive relationships and engage in activities with different kinds of people.

During the developmental period of life, the child is expected to adopt behavior, roles and attitudes which are acceptable to others. The primary emphasis is therefore on conformity. Nevertheless, this does not have to mean *slavish* conformity or conventionality, for every individual has a right to be himself, and no one can develop to his fullest unless he can express his own individuality. It means, rather, that he must learn to adapt himself to necessary regulations, participate in normal group activities, and feel comfortable in the presence of other people. In contrast, a nonsocial or asocial individual fails to develop the ability to function in groups, and an antisocial individual knows what is expected of him but adopts antagonistic attitudes and behavior toward others.

Man seems to be, as Aristotle put it, a "social animal" almost from the start of life. Few if any human impulses are stronger than the so-called "gregarious drive." Yet social attitudes and behavior do not simply unfold from within; they have to be learned through a long and varied series of experiences. The most crucial part of this process occurs in the early years of life and is vitally dependent on both the quality and number of opportunities for learning to live with other people. The general nature of these opportunities can be most clearly indicated by outlining the influences exerted by the home and the world outside.

Since socialization begins almost at the start of life, the family exerts the primary influence on the child. It is the basic source of social behavior and social attitudes, and has a powerful influence on crucial social roles such as the child's sex role and his role as a contributing member of a group. Studies indicate that children from large families make more rapid strides in social adjustment than children from very small families, but on the whole medium-sized families from favored environments provide the greatest opportunities for good social adjustment both within and outside the home. Only children, and children who are widely separated from their brothers and sisters in age, tend to be somewhat less sociable than others outside the home; and children with siblings of the same sex find it much easier to associate with their own sex than with children of the opposite sex (Boll, 1957; Koch, 1960). *See* FAMILY SIZE, ONLY CHILDREN, BIRTH ORDER.

In spite of these generalizations, parental attitudes and child-rearing practices probably have a greater effect than the size of the family or the relationships between siblings. If the climate of the home is a warm one and if there is a democratic relationship between the parents and the child, he will usually adjust to others without sacrificing his own individuality (Marshall and McCandless, 1957). On the other hand, if he is rejected or treated harshly, he will usually develop aggressive attitudes which interfere with his relationships. If parental discipline is rigid and authoritarian but *not* harsh, he may become so quiet and well-behaved that he simply will not venture into relationships with outgoing children. If he is overindulged, he is likely to be apprehensive, inactive and too spoiled and egocentric to be accepted by his peers. These facts indicate that socialization outside the home is directly related to the behavior patterns established within it.

The child who has favorable experiences with other children early in life will want to repeat and build on them—but if his experiences are unpleasant, he will fall back on his family. The average child will begin to adopt social behavior that is acceptable to his playmates in the preschool years, although his relationships with other children will not have as great an influence as later on, since the young child is not group conscious and the members of his play groups frequently change. The child who goes to nursery school has the benefit of more constant relationships, more varied experiences and the guidance of a knowing adult. From about seven years of age on, there is an increasing dependence on the group, and within a few years the child's social life will be characterized by adherence to the mores of the gang. As he grows older, he spends relatively more time with his peer group in school and on the play field, and peer influence usually becomes greater than teacher influence. It also begins to supersede the influence of the home. See NURSERY SCHOOL EXPERIENCE.

The effect of the social group is determined by many factors. In general, the child who possesses skills which are recognized by other children will center his life more and more on the peer group than on the family. If he also has a strong sense of security and confidence, he will set the pace for others rather than blindly conform to their standards. Insecure children or children who have trouble gaining acceptance from the group will take one of two general courses. Some of them will become hostile to the group or withdraw into social isolation. Others, the majority, have such irrepressible social needs that they will do everything possible to win group favor. These are the children who blindly accept group standards, tag along even when they are not wanted, or kowtow to the leaders. Some of them engage in various kinds of misbehavior if they feel that this will gain them status and recognition. Some will work below their capacity and become underachievers because their gang or clique frowns upon "grinds." But the child who has been raised in a home which has provided practice in constructive social behavior in a warm and secure atmosphere will rarely have to go to such lengths to attain status and recognition in his social group. See SOCIAL DEVELOPMENT, SEX ROLE, SOCIAL ROLE.

SOCIAL MATURITY TEST. A psychological test designed to assess social development in terms of such factors as degree of independence and ability to take responsibility and co-operate with others.

The most widely used instrument is the Vineland Social Maturity Scale, devised by Edgar A. Doll (1953, 1965) for testing individuals from infancy to thirty years of age on various categories of social adjustment. The 117 items in this test are arranged according to age levels, as in the Stanford-Binet Test, with appropriate behavioral criteria for each category. Some examples are *self-help:* reaching for nearby objects (age 0 to 1); *locomotion:* walks about room unattended (age 1 to 2); *occupation:* helps at little household tasks (age 3 to 4); *communication:* makes telephone calls (age 10 to 11); *self-direction:* buys own clothing (age 15 to 18); *socialization:* demands personal attention (age 0 to 1), advances general welfare (age 25 plus). A similar scale has been developed by Maxfield and Buchholz (1957) for blind preschool children.

The test is scored on the basis of information obtained from interviews with the subject, or with persons well acquainted with the subject if he is too young to be interviewed himself. It yields a social age (SA) score as well as a social growth (SG) score obtained by dividing the score made on the test by the subject's chronological age. These scores show varying correlations with the Stanford-Binet, but the originator claims that the content of the two tests is so distinct that they measure different traits. There is evidence for this in the important fact that an individual whose IQ is considerably below normal may have a high enough SA to adjust to life outside an institution. Equally important is the fact that social development usually continues somewhat longer than mental growth. In addition, behavior problems or delinquency are suggested if the mental age is considerably higher than the social age.

The test was originally conceived as an aid in diagnosing mental deficiency, and particularly for distinguishing between retardates who are socially incompetent and those who are capable of making an adequate personal and social adjustment. It is therefore used in making decisions on institutionalization, but it is also widely administered in child and adolescent clinics during interviews with both parents and children. Experience has shown, however, that the instrument must be employed with considerable caution since it has certain weaknesses. The small sample population on which it was standardized represented middle-class mores, and subjects may deviate from its norms because of cultural differences as opposed to differences in social maturity. Moreover, some of the items cannot be applied to institutional subjects because the demands and expectations of the institution may differ materially from those of life in the outside world.

SOCIAL NORM (Group Norms). The standards by which behavior is judged in a given social group; the way the members of a group are expected to think, feel or act.

Social norms determine to a large extent whether we feel that our attitudes are sound and our actions appropriate. An example cited by Secord and Backman (1964) is the set of standards implicitly or explicitly adopted by the more traditional fraternities: making moderately good grades, loyalty to the fraternity, congeniality with fraternity brothers, dating girls from certain sororities and not others, helping on fraternity projects, and believing that one's own fraternity is the best on campus.

Norms are not always ready-made affairs, as they are in this instance. We sometimes establish them in the course of our experience. Sherif (1948) has performed an ingenious experiment which shows how these frames of reference may be set up. He seated three persons in a dark room and told them that in a few moments a point of light would appear, move a short distance and then go out. The subjects were instructed to call out the number of inches they thought the light moved. The light was then turned on repeatedly at intervals, and the subjects' judgments were recorded.

The experiment produced an interesting result. Although the three subjects differed rather widely on their initial judgments, the differences tended to narrow down after a number of trials, eventually coming within an inch or two of each other. But in truth they had no real basis for judging the amount of movement, for the light was completely stationary.

This experiment was based on a well-known peculiarity of perception known as the autokinetic effect. For reasons unknown, a stationary point of light in a dark room will appear to move by itself. On what basis, then, did the subjects alter their judgment? Sherif's answer was that in the absence of clear perceptual cues upon which to base their estimates, the subjects turned to each other for guidance. Many other groups have been studied in the same general situation, and the end result has nearly always been a narrow range of judgment. This agreed-upon range then acts as a social norm.

The Sherif experiment has thrown further light on group norms. When subjects who had established a norm in the group situation were tested alone, they still responded in terms of the norm. On the other hand, when subjects who had formed their norm in an individual situation were later placed in a group, they were found to change these norms gradually until they arrived at a group norm.

Many investigators have sought to define the forces that bring about group norms. One important theory is that pressures toward conformity arise when "reward-cost outcomes" are likely to be adversely affected by nonconformity—that is, we feel that we lose more than we gain if we go against the group. This is especially likely to occur when group goals are involved, for the disadvantage, or cost, of nonconformity is high in such cases and the rewards of conformity are considerable. In committee work, for example, it is important to establish a rule against everyone talking at once; and when military planes are flying in formation, it is essential to have them adhere strictly to carefully defined maneuvers.

The advantages of conformity are obvious in these practical matters, but far less apparent in the case of opinions and attitudes. The explanation of adherence to social norms in the latter case is that in forming our attitudes toward things and people, we rely on two sources of information—our own observations and sense experience; and the interpretations and information we get from others. The latter source, termed "social reality," is often less certain than our observations of physical reality, since the opinions of other people differ so much. At any rate, the relative weight of the two sources varies with different circumstances. In general, we depend more on our senses in cases where we can make a direct perceptual judgment or where our information leads to an obviously correct answer; but we are prone to rely on the judgment of other persons when our sense stimuli are ambiguous or unstructured, as in the autokinetic situation. The influence of other people is particularly great when there is no perceptual reality at all against which to check our judgment and where, in addition, distinct social and emotional "rewards," such as social acceptance, approval, and the satisfaction of belonging operate in favor of conformity. An example is adherence to the dogma of a particular religious faith.

Typically, social norms develop in situations where the attitudes or actions in question would not ordinarily be adopted, for there is no need for group controls where people spontaneously adapt themselves to others. But where the situation is ambiguous or unstructured, or where individuals have a resistance against actions that are necessary to group functioning, normative processes emerge in order to provide direction or to ensure that certain behavior is carried out.

The operations by which norms are communicated and enforced have been termed "norm-sending processes" (Rommetveit, 1955) These processes comprise, first, defining the attitudes or behavior in question; second, monitoring the extent to which individuals conform to the norm; and third, applying sanctions in the form of reward or punishment for conformity or nonconformity. All these processes may be carried out in either direct or subtle ways.

An adequate theory of normative behavior must answer the following questions: What determines the kinds of attitudes or behavior that become the targets for norm-sending? Why is a greater degree of conformity found in some groups than in others? What makes some members of the group more conformist than others? Attempts have been made to answer these questions in terms of four conditions emphasized by "exchange theory." These are: (1) the degree to which group members find the behavior or attitudes of other people rewarding or costly; (2) the distribution of rewards, dependencies and alternatives that determines the power structure of the particular group; (3) the degree to which behavior in accordance with the norm is intrinsically rewarding or costly; and (4) the degree to which behavior is open to surveillance and to the imposition of sanctions.

In general, it can be said that normative controls arise where individuals have become dependent upon the group for satisfaction of their needs. In such cases actions and ideas that satisfy the most powerful persons in the group are most likely to give rise to norms. Where behavior required to achieve group goals is especially costly, no group norms at all may result, or else they may be formed merely to minimize the cost or distribute it evenly throughout the group. Behavior that is hard to monitor is also less likely to be subjected to normative control.

All these points can be illustrated by the single problem of controlling nuclear tests. First, the need for group norms is based on the fact that each nuclear nation is dependent on others for the achievement of peace. Second, the most powerful nations are most deeply involved in creating the necessary agreements. Third, these agreements have been hard to establish because they are costly to the nations involved, for they mean that the usual secrecy and sovereignty cannot be maintained. Fourth, these "costs" can, nevertheless, be minimized if they are shared among the different nations. Fifth, difficulties involved in monitoring nuclear activities, as well as in gaining acceptance for the principle of monitoring, have held up the process of establishing full control over these activities.

SOCIAL PSYCHIATRY. A broad area of psychiatric investigation and practice covering the relation between mental health and the social environment.

The social viewpoint in psychiatry has only recently come into its own, and the field is still in process of development. Perhaps it can be viewed as a reflection of the more general emphasis on social forces which has led to the development of such sciences as sociology, anthropology and social psychology. In psychiatry itself, the social viewpoint has come to the fore as a result of (a) the recognition of social and cultural factors in the etiology of mental illness

by Horney, Fromm, Sullivan and others; (b) the growth of the public health approach to mental disorder; and (c) the development of the field of community psychiatry, which puts this approach in practice.

Strong impetus was given to the field of social psychiatry when the Committee on Research in Psychology and the Social Sciences of the Social Science Research Council delineated its major areas in 1950. The following enumeration of topics and problems is based on the book, *Explorations in Social Psychiatry* (1957), written by three members of that committee, A. H. Leighton, J. A. Clausen, and R. N. Wilson.

1. *Major Concepts:* Normality (Is normality relative to the culture?); symptomatology (Do symptom patterns differ in different cultures?); personality and development (Are they culture-bound?); social pathology (Can an entire society or social movement be pathological?).

2. *Social Environment and Mental Health:* The relation of mental illness to family relationships, role patterns, dominant values, marital attitudes, and environmental stresses in different cultures—for example, the relation between achievement needs and peptic ulcers, the effect of mothering and maternal deprivation on mental health; social patterns in drug use, alcoholism, sexual behavior, etc.; sociocultural factors in the etiology of different disorders.

3. *Cultural and Cross-Cultural Diversity:* Can a middle class therapist understand a slum-bred adolescent, and will the adolescent understand and accept the treatment? Are there different patterns of mental illness on different sociocultural levels of the same society? Should diagnostic and mental tests be adapted to different social levels and cultural groups? Do sexual attitudes and patterns differ on different levels?

4. *Reactions to Mental Illness:* Pre-

vailing attitudes toward mental illness in different segments of society; effect of social attitudes on such issues as employment after mental illness, legal codes relating to mental disorders, support for research projects on mental illness, and standards for public mental hospitals; impact of mental illness on society in terms of such factors as economic loss and effects on the family.

5. *Social Treatment and Prevention:* Group psychotherapy, psychodrama, the therapeutic community; community clinics and mental health centers; industrial psychiatry; mental health education programs. *See* COMMUNITY PSYCHIATRY, SOCIOTHERAPY, MILIEU THERAPY, MENTAL HEALTH AND SOCIAL LEVEL, ATTITUDES TOWARD MENTAL ILLNESS, GROUP PSYCHOTHERAPY, COMMUNITY MENTAL HEALTH CENTERS, MENTAL HEALTH CLINICS, SOCIAL BREAKDOWN SYNDROME, PSYCHODRAMA, OCCUPATIONAL PSYCHIATRY, ECOLOGICAL STUDIES, NORMALITY, MATERNAL DEPRIVATION, ETIOLOGY, SEX DRIVE.

SOCIAL ROLE. The part played or function performed by an individual in a specific group situation, such as the role of a teacher, foreman or squadron leader.

The concept of social role is based on the fact that each individual tends to occupy a functional position in the groups to which he belongs, and other members of each group tend to agree on certain expectations concerning his behavior in their group. In current social psychology the position the individual occupies is termed his "role category" (such as vice president), and the attitudes and behavior associated with that category are termed "role expectations" or "role behaviors." Social role is a general term which includes both of these aspects.

Social role is an extremely important concept for two major reasons. First, any social system can be viewed as a group of related social roles; the eluci-

dation of these roles is an essential factor in describing that system. Each role must be defined by reference to other, related roles, or "counterpositions," and to the rights and obligations which each role possesses in the social system: for example, a foreman has the right to make certain decisions, but an obligation to direct the workers and keep them moving; and the workers have certain rights, such as the right to strike, plus an obligation to accomplish a certain amount of work.

The second important function of social role is in defining the individual's self-image, and in particular his conception of himself as a member of society. This is no simple matter, since every person plays many roles in life, and these roles interlock in many ways. Often, however, one role plays a major part in determining his self-image. In American society this is frequently the occupational role, although there are many instances in which church, community, lodge, or household activities are the dominant factor. One important personality theory, termed role theory, is based upon the roles an individual assumes in society (Newcomb, Turner and Converse, 1965). *See* PERSONALITY THEORIES.

Since the process of acquiring roles is described under the topic SOCIAL DEVELOPMENT, we will merely note some of the major aspects here. In childhood, this form of social learning depends largely on opportunities to observe the activities of the postman, nurse, truck driver, etc., and then to imitate their behavior in play—that is, roles are learned largely through role *playing.* A major stimulus for the adoption of roles and role aspirations is identification with admired individuals. In adulthood, role-learning is usually more conscious and deliberate than in childhood: in medicine an experienced doctor actually shows the young student how to deal with patients and their problems during his internship and residency; in business an older employee inducts a new or newly advanced worker into his role by showing him "the ropes." On an executive level, the employee's wife may also be involved in this process, as Whyte has shown in *The Organization Man* (1956). *See* SOCIALIZATION, SEX ROLE, ADOLESCENCE, SOCIAL NORM, SOCIAL CLASS, ROLE PLAYING.

SOCIOMETRY. A procedure for discovering the interpersonal relationships —attractions, repulsions, indifferences— that exist among members of a group. The relationships are usually depicted in the form of a "sociogram" in which the individuals are indicated by circles and their preferences by arrows pointing from one to another (*Fig. 48*).

The technique is used with groups of people who have been associated long enough to be acquainted with one another, as in a club, team, work group, class, or military unit. In plotting the relationships, each member is asked to choose one or more individuals with whom he would like to eat, work, study, or share some other relevant activity. In some applications a single member is selected for each function; in other cases, a first, second and third choice may be made. The resulting sociogram may therefore be relatively simple or quite complex. The individual who receives the most nominations is called a star, and the one who receives the least or none at all is termed an isolate. In addition, the diagram reveals mutual pairs, triangles, cliques and other patterns of group structure. Tests indicate that sociometry is a highly dependable method of uncovering relationships within a group, probably because the choices are made by a group of peers who are directly involved with each other and who actually determine the relationships. (Lindzey and Borgatta, 1954)

Sociograms have many uses. They indicate in a graphic way (1) whether a group is integrated or fragmented;

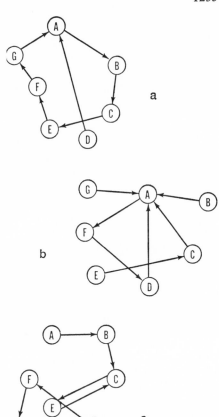

Fig. 48. Three sociograms, depicting group relationships. Group *a* is cohesive but does not have a strong leader; group *b* has a strong leader; group *c* is unstructured, with cliques and isolates.

(2) whether it revolves around a single individual or several individuals; (3) whether a member of a minority group is an "out." They may also be helpful in identifying leaders, in assessing popularity or unpopularity; and, when several choices are made on the basis of different factors, the specific functions for which different individuals receive nominations. This information can then be applied in attempting to improve the cohesiveness of the group, to find ways of involving the isolates,

or to assign individuals to subgroups where they will function most effectively.

J. L. Moreno employs four different forms of the technique in psychodramatic therapy: an "intuitive sociogram" based on relationships the therapist notices during the first session; an "observer's sociogram," consisting of a cotherapist's impressions, for purposes of comparison; an "objective sociogram," based on a sociometric test, as above; and a "perceptual sociogram," in which the group member indicates which other members in his opinion choose or reject him: "He may think of himself as being liked by everyone, but in the objective sociogram he may be shown to be a rejected individual. Such discrepancy between his perceptions and the objective facts may provide important clues to his interpersonal status and a further refinement of his position in the sociogram." (Moreno, 1959)

A standardized and well-validated series of sociometric tests, the Syracuse Scales of Social Relations, has been developed for use in elementary, junior high, and senior high schools. The students are first asked to select five names from all the persons they have ever known to serve as key points on their scale. Then they assign each member of the class to a position on the scale with regard to two questions based on Murray's system of needs. Examples of these questions are: Would he be a possible source of help with a personal problem? (succorance, the need to seek aid and protection); Would he help you to do something well so people will praise you? (achievement-recognition, the need to overcome obstacles and excite commendation); and Would he be someone to look up to as an ideal? (deference, the need to admire and follow). Scale positions are averaged for each individual in order to determine both (a) ratings received (how his classmates regard him); and (b) ratings given (how his classmates as a group satisfy his particular needs). The test has been standardized on a large sample, and percentile norms are provided for each grade. See PERSONOLOGY.

SOCIOPATHIC PERSONALITY DISTURBANCE. A group of personality or character disorders marked primarily by failure to adapt to prevailing ethical and social standards and by lack of social responsibility. The Diagnostic and Statistical Manual of the American Psychiatric Association (1952) applies this category to individuals who are "ill primarily in terms of society and of conformity within the prevailing cultural milieu, and not only in terms of personal discomfort and relations with other individuals. However, sociopathic reactions are very often symptomatic of severe underlying personality disorder, neurosis or psychosis, or occur as the result of organic brain injury or disease."

Four types of disorder are classified under this heading. First, *antisocial reaction*, comprising individuals who are constantly in trouble, do not profit from experience or punishment, tend to have no genuine loyalties, and are usually callous, egocentric, emotionally immature and irresponsible, yet rationalize their behavior so that it appears reasonable and justified. Second, *dyssocial reaction*, comprising individuals who disregard or come into direct conflict with social codes, who—though often capable of strong loyalties—live all their lives in an abnormal moral environment, and who usually adhere to a criminal code, but without showing any other significant personality deviation. Third, *sexual deviation*, comprising persons who exhibit such deviations as homosexuality, transvestism, pedophilia, fetishism, and sexual sadism (rape, sexual assault, mutilation, etc.), when these practices are not symptomatic of more extensive syndromes such as schizophrenic or obsessional reactions. Fourth, *addiction*, including well-established addiction to alcohol or narcotic drugs without a recognized underlying disorder such as organic brain syndrome, psychosis, or psychoneurosis.

These disturbances are grouped together for several reasons. First, they are all forms of social pathology, since the behavior of sociopaths is in basic conflict with the laws, norms, and customs of society. Second, sociopathic individuals have certain general personality characteristics in common; notably, lack of restraint and control over behavior, a weak or distorted conscience (superego), absence of a normal sense of guilt, and disturbed relationships with other people. Third, they are rarely neurotic, since they are not torn by unconscious emotional conflicts and their behavior is not basically a defense against anxiety. Fourth, they seldom become psychotic, since they are in good contact with reality and their personalities are generally well integrated. Fifth, they generally accept their reactions and behavior patterns as a fixed way of life which they see little reason or possibility to change. For this reason they tend to be highly resistant to the usual types of therapy.

The classification and distinctions given above need qualification. The four categories cannot be strictly separated, since many individuals are mixed types, such as antisocial sexual deviants and dyssocial alcoholics. Although many sociopaths adopt one type of unacceptable behavior, others engage in many kinds: rape, theft, drug addiction, etc. Moreover, a sizable minority—particularly certain sexual deviants, alcoholics, and drug addicts—have been found to be neurotic, and some extreme sociopaths are psychotic.

In general, sociopathic individuals constitute a high percentage of our criminal and delinquent population, including confidence men, unscrupulous businessmen, impostors, embezzlers, racketeers, child molesters, prostitutes, burglars, and murderers. A study of ten thousand inmates of Sing Sing indicated that 66 per cent could be classified as antisocial or dyssocial, and many of the remaining 34 per cent were sociopathic alcoholics and sexual deviants (Gaetaniello, 1963). These men were all gross offenders against society.

On the other hand, a great many sociopaths are of a milder type, constituting the huge number of highly self-centered, unreliable, uninhibited, amoral, untruthful individuals who live as they please in careless disregard of the rights of others and their own responsibilities to society. (The four types of sociopaths, as well as various subcategories, are discussed under separate topic headings.)

SOCIOTHERAPY. A supportive psychological approach based on modification of the patient's personal environment.

Sociotherapy is usually carried out by a psychiatric social worker, often with the help of welfare and community service agencies. The worker seeks to improve the patient's adjustment and promote his recovery by making changes in his life situation. This may be done in many ways. He may create a more comfortable and relaxed atmosphere for a stutterer by working with the parents. He may recommend foster-home placement for an emotionally disturbed child when recovery is hampered by an unhealthy family environment. Or he may relieve home tensions by counseling a couple on marital or child-rearing problems. Other typical areas of activity include lending support to an alcoholic's treatment by giving his wife the guidance and understanding she needs in dealing with him, visiting the former employer of a recovered mental patient in order to help him understand the employee's illness and pave the way for his return to work, helping a patient readjust to community life by visiting him periodically and discussing his economic or personal problems, or associating with a delinquent gang in order to exert a salutary influence from within.

In its broadest sense, sociotherapy also includes working with the patient's environment in the hospital or convalescent home itself. Geriatric patients with brain damage often become more alert and independent when their surroundings are made more comfortable and pleasant, or when they have an opportunity to engage in stimulating activities. A remarkable number of retarded children make substantial progress in the friendly, personal atmosphere of a small community-centered unit. These centers are generally preferable to huge state schools, but the latter may help many of the retarded to develop useful skills and even become self-supporting—provided the entire environment is geared to activities that foster growth, including not only self-care and vocational training, but dances, choirs, picnics and sports. Finally, the concept of the mental hospital as a "therapeutic community" is a recognition of the importance of sociotherapy, since the entire milieu is designed with one aim in mind—to encourage patients to participate in the normal processes of living with other people. See MILIEU THERAPY, PSYCHIATRIC SOCIAL WORK, MENTAL HOSPITAL.

SOMATIC COMPLIANCE. The tendency of bodily functions to reflect psychological disturbances.

The theory of somatic compliance has been created to explain why emotional conflicts and tensions are expressed through bodily symptoms, and why one function rather than another breaks down—that is, why a particular conversion neurotic becomes hysterically blind rather than paralyzed, or why a psychosomatic patient is afflicted with a headache instead of a back ache. One hypothesis states that the affected organ has already been weakened by illness or cogenital defect ("organ inferiority"), and is therefore particularly amenable,

or "compliant," to breakdown. When stress occurs at a later date, it is likely to focus on the organs that are already vulnerable.

Some investigators also point out that "temporary compliance" may exist when a particular organ is deeply involved in a disturbing experience, or put under special stress during an emotionally charged emergency. During World War II, a merchant seaman developed a peculiar jerking movement of the left hand. Under hypnosis, this symptom was traced to the fact that a shell had exploded on the deck of his ship and had blown away his machine gun just as he was going to fire it. The peculiar motion of his arm was an unconscious attempt to complete the action which had been interrupted at that crucial moment.

Two other explanations may also apply in certain cases. First, according to psychoanalytic theory, the organ in question may symbolize the individual's unconscious impulses or conflicts—for example, the nose may be affected since it is believed to represent the penis and masculine wishes. Second, the afflicted organ may be associated with unconscious fantasies or drives seeking expression—for instance, an individual with an oral fixation may develop an oral symptom such as stuttering.

The theory of somatic compliance seeks to answer the important question of the "selection of symptoms" in psychiatric disorders. See also SYMPTOM, CONVERSION REACTION, PSYCHOPHYSIOLOGIC DISORDERS (ETIOLOGY AND THERAPY), SYMBOLIZATION, BODY LANGUAGE.

SOMATIZATION REACTION. A pathological change in the structure or function of a bodily organ due to a neurotic disorder.

The term is sometimes used to indicate that some psychosomatic (psychophysiologic) disturbances are manifestations of neurosis rather than separate types of disorder. Lidz (1959) states that "most persons suffering from neuroses, including the transitory neurotic symptoms in most lives, suffer from some physiologic dysfunction that gives rise to somatic complaints."

Some investigators maintain, however, that somatization reaction does not refer to the bodily symptoms that occur in almost every neurosis, but that it constitutes a separate type of neurosis on a par with anxiety reaction, phobic reaction and other categories of neurosis. In this view, the term is applied to every kind of psychophysiologic disorder, such as psychogenic asthma, hypertension, peptic ulcers and migraine —and all these disorders are considered basically neurotic. Most psychoanalysts take this position, but usually prefer the term "organ neurosis" to somatization reaction. *See* ORGAN NEUROSIS.

SOMATOPSYCHIC DISORDERS. A term applied by some psychiatrists to psychological disturbances resulting from bodily disorders.

An example is the post-encephalitic syndrome, in which a reaction pattern consisting of impulsiveness, overactivity and lack of restraint follows epidemic encephalitis. Calling this syndrome somatopsychic emphasizes the fact that the somatic or bodily disorder (an inflammation of the brain) is primary and the psychological changes are secondary. The term is sometimes used in contradistinction to "psychosomatic" or "psychophysiologic," which usually apply to cases in which the emotional maladjustment is the primary factor and the bodily disturbance the result or by-product. The latter terms are often used to cover both types of disorder. *See* SOMATOPSYCHOLOGY.

SOMATOPSYCHOLOGY. An area of research devoted to the psychological effects of physical illness and disability, as contrasted with psychosomatic medicine, which focuses on the physical effects of psychological conditions. The two approaches do not conflict, but supplement each other in a comprehensive study of disorders.

The term somatopsychology was coined by Barker, Wright and their associates (1954) as a result of research in the field of rehabilitation. Their explorations have thrown considerable light on the long-range effects of various disabilities on personality and adjustment. Other investigators have concentrated on the individual's more immediate reaction to physical illness, as well as the possible influence of the patient's attitudes on his recovery.

The long-range studies of disability and defect have identified the areas of adjustment which are most likely to be affected. These include the individual's self-concept (he may lose his feeling of self-esteem, personal worth, and adequacy); social relationships (he may be affected by attitudes of pity, oversolicitousness, avoidance, or rejection shown by others); personality patterns (he may develop tendencies toward withdrawal, dependency, irritability, or aggressiveness); and intellectual development (he may be hampered by sensory or motor deficiencies, inadequate schooling, or limited opportunities for recreational activities). This enumeration should not be taken to imply that these negative effects are inevitable. Most of them can be mitigated, counteracted, or prevented altogether. Moreover, reactions to disability and defeat are extremely varied, as the following discussion will show.

Many categories of disabled patients have been investigated through the use of intensive case studies, questionnaires, interviews, and psychological tests. These studies have shown wide differences in the reactions of different individuals to the same type of disorder, such as deafness, blindness, disfigurement, or amputation. Some individuals are profoundly affected in all areas—emotional, social, and intellectual —while others show remarkably few signs of maladjustment. These variations are due not only to the nature and severity of the handicap, but to differences in basic personality and ability, as well as environmental factors such as the home situation, and opportunities for schooling, special training, useful work, a healthy social life.

In spite of these individual differences, research has not revealed any consistent relationship between specific types of disability and specific personality characteristics. It is not possible to construct a list of traits which clearly distinguish the blind from the orthopedically handicapped or the deaf from the disfigured, nor can we even differentiate the disabled as a whole from people who are physically intact. The only general statement that can be made is that the severely handicapped tend to show some kind of maladjustment—anxiety, depression, withdrawal, etc.—but even this group difference is not very great.

A number of studies have focused on the more immediate reactions to such illnesses as tuberculosis and cancer. Vernier et al. (1961) used rating scales, questionnaires, interviews, psychological tests, and biographical data in determining the hospital adjustment and the later community adjustment of eight hundred veterans afflicted with pulmonary tuberculosis. This disease was chosen for study because it presents especially severe personal problems due to the necessity for isolation and long hospitalization, as well as the threat of lung surgery and permanent disability. The investigators found that patients who were passive and dependent enough to adjust well to the hospital were apt to make poor community adjustment later, and those who resisted the regimentation and inactivity of ward life tended to fare well in the community. Only one type of reaction, anxiety, was found to be detrimental to both hospital and community adjustment.

Another investigation, conducted by Derner (1953), has contradicted the prevalent opinion that tuberculosis patients tend to be optimistic and euphoric, an attitude known as *spes phthisica* ("tubercular hopefulness"). Intensive psychological studies failed to reveal any characteristic personality pattern. The only finding that was at all widespread was a tendency to anxiety, depression, and concern about their physical condition. As in the Vernier study, some patients actively resented the need for dependent living while others adjusted well to hospital life.

In some hospitals psychologists are playing an active part in helping to alleviate the anxiety of cancer patients and their relatives. Cobb (1962) has shown that counseling can be effective even with terminal patients. Many of them are more disturbed by feelings of rejection and abandonment, or by concern over the future of their families, than they are about the imminence of death. Moreover, most patients are eager to discuss not only practical matters but their impending death with a warm and experienced counselor.

The common notion that the patient's attitude can affect his recovery has also been systematically studied. In the investigation cited above, Vernier and his associates found that TB patients who were relatively confident, free from anxiety, and eager to try new approaches tended to respond favorably to treatment. A number of research projects conducted at different hospitals have also suggested that a stable personality, an optimistic attitude, and a "will to live" can enhance the chances for recovery from certain forms of cancer, possibly due to hormonal effects. The evidence here is by no means conclusive, and further research is needed. *See* REHABILITATION, DEAFNESS, BLINDNESS.

SOMNAMBULISM. A dissociative reaction in which repressed impulses, anxieties or conflicts are acted out during sleep.

Somnambulism is more than merely walking in one's sleep, since the sleeper not only leaves his bed, but engages in some more or less complex activity that fulfills a wish or releases tension. Somnambulistic states have been described as fugue states occurring during sleep. They are, usually shorter than fugues, since they last only a few minutes or at most a half hour. Different types of activities may be performed during the episode—for example, the sleeper might re-enact a traumatic event, write a letter revealing hidden feelings, or rummage through the attic to find a photograph of an old flame.

There are a number of fallacies about chronic sleepwalkers. Contrary to popular opinion, they may actually injure themselves. Somnambulists have been known to fall down stairs and step in front of moving cars. Such accidents do not often occur, however, since their eyes are open and they usually respond to warnings. Many people think it is dangerous to awaken a sleepwalker, but this too is false. He may be surprised and bewildered when suddenly awakened, but this does him no particular harm.

Somnambulism occurs primarily in individuals who have a tendency to act out their tensions rather than discharge them in dreams and fantasies alone. The actions they perform may, however, serve other purposes than reduction of tension. The re-enactment of a disturbing experience may be an unconscious attempt to gain control over it, and the peculiar gestures or strange behavior of the sleepwalker may represent an attempt to resolve an emotional conflict. During sleep one young man climbed on a table and waved his arms as if he were addressing an audience. When he was awakened, he revealed that he had dreamt he was standing on a soap box in Hyde Park delivering a speech about freedom for all men. It was later found that he had been rebelling against his parents, who were loathe to give him any independence.

Somnambulism is most common among adolescents, and occurs in males more often than females. They are generally immature, suggestible, dependent individuals who exhibit other neurotic symptoms as well. Short-term therapy is usually effective in eliminating the symptom, but it may be replaced by other neurotic manifestations. In that case, more extended psychotherapy is usually recommended. *See* DISSOCIATIVE REACTION, DISSOCIATION, FUGUE STATE.

Illustrative Case: SOMNAMBULISM

A thirteen-year-old boy would get up in his sleep and walk to his parents' bedroom, open the door, and attempt to get into their bed. If they asked him what he wanted, he would either murmur unintelligibly or walk on toward the front of the house. If they said, "Go back to bed," he would turn round, go to his own room, and sleep until morning.

This boy was strongly attached to his mother. His father, of whom he had always been afraid, was idealistic, but strict and demanding; he never showed the boy any affection. The latter's attitudes toward his father were so strongly repressed that he never became consciously angry at him, although he was frequently severely punished. He was often in a state of severe conflict about masturbation, felt worthless and guilty and feared discovery and disapproval. As a result of this fear, he became markedly fatigued. Unconsciously he longed for his parents' affection and approval and at the same time felt strong hostility, particularly toward his father. One by-product of this situation was that he became excessively religious.

Walking into his parents' bedroom was an unconscious way of satisfying impulses which were totally repressed in the waking state. (Maslow and Mittelmann, 1951)

SPACE PSYCHIATRY AND PSYCHOLOGY. Though a number of successful space flights have been accomplished, and many tests and case studies have been made of astronauts, the field of space psychiatry and psychology must still be regarded as in its infancy. At present it is possible only to outline problems and suggest a few solutions on the basis of limited experience, for the full psychiatric implications of space travel will not be ascertained until interplanetary landings are attempted. This article will summarize some of the findings, to date, based largely on an article by G. E. Ruff (1966). It will also indicate a few of the problems that will have to be faced in the future.

Psychiatrists and psychologists have been involved chiefly in five aspects of the space program: identification of sources of stress, study of the artificial environment of the spacecraft, selection and training of the crew, examination of responses to flight, and personality characteristics of astronauts.

Stress. Early in the space program, studies of stressful experiences on earth —for example, observations made during shipwrecks and polar expeditions as well as experiments on sensory deprivation—were used in identifying potential sources of stress during space missions. These studies pinpointed such stresses as long periods of inactivity, confinement, lack of communication, monotony, and reduced stimulation. It is interesting that the suborbital and orbital flights revealed no psychological disruption unique to the space situation —and there is a high probability that none will be experienced in missions, including lunar trips, of less than a few weeks. The ten-orbit trip around the moon by Colonel Frank Borman, Captain James Lovell, and Colonel William Anders at the end of 1968 seems to have borne this out. Important factors in preventing adverse effects appear to be the series of scheduled tasks they had to perform, the fact that the crew was composed of three congenial men, and their frequent communication with the home base in Houston.

The experience of weightlessness (both inside and outside the spacecraft) long remained in the realm of speculation since it was so hard to study on earth, but actual experience with this phenomenon in flight has revealed that it is not particularly stressful over relatively short periods of time, and even when the astronauts float about the spacecraft, as in Apollo 8. The high acceleration, which increases gravitational force on the astronaut's body, has been successfully counteracted by a reclining position, special suits, and training in a human centrifuge. Illusions and spatial disorientation occurring in space flight have also been successfully handled by teaching the astronaut what to expect and training him in the use of instruments and other checks on the stimuli he receives. This is not to say that psychological stress is nonexistent in space flights, only that it has so far been found to be within manageable limits for carefully selected, highly trained astronauts. *See* SENSORY DEPRIVATION.

The Artificial Environment. So far, conditions faced by the crew have been anticipated with remarkable accuracy, and the spacecraft have met the basic needs of the astronauts on relatively short flights. Psychologists, psychiatrists, and other physicians are now studying special problems involved in longer flights, such as the need for varying sensory input, providing sufficient physical activity, and finding substitute gratifications in a limited social and emotional environment. Experiments have amply proved that if these problems are not solved, adverse effects can be anticipated.

Another major problem is the sleeping-wakefulness cycle. It is generally accepted that fixed periods of activity and rest must be adopted, but it has not yet been determined if the cycle used on earth will be optimal for conditions in outer space. Kleitman (1961) has suggested two or three hour periods of duty, but this remains to be fully tested.

Of special importance for long missions is the problem of "small-group dynamics"—that is, relationships that take place between a limited number of men who must remain together in a restricted environment for many months or even years. The space crew will have even less opportunity for privacy and withdrawal than a submarine crew. There is a danger that minor irritations may develop into major threats to mental health and to the teamwork needed on space expeditions. Studies of isolated small groups in real as well as laboratory situations have indicated that hostile and depressive reactions increase, and performance tends to decline noticeably. Research is now in progress on methods of handling prolonged confinement, and on the utilization of principles of group dynamics in the training of crew members. *See* GROUP DYNAMICS.

Selection of Crew. Development of a personnel selection program requires four steps: a detailed study of the precise requirements of the mission; determination of the personal requirements of the men themselves, both mental and physical; selection or construction of tests and other evaluative instruments; and validation of these predictors, so far as possible, by measuring the performance of the crew on actual missions.

At the present time clinical rather than statistical methods are used in evaluating the psychological characteristics of candidates, since actuarial tables cannot be developed from the limited amount of data gathered in the few missions that have so far been undertaken. On the basis of intensive interviews, background information and test scores, the clinician makes an "educated guess" on the ability of the candidate to carry out a mission. Project Mercury, for example, set up thirty hours of psychological tests, psychiatric interviews designed to determine unconscious dynamics, and observation of performance under experimental stress situations. The psychological tests included the Miller Analogies, the Doppelt Mathematical Reasoning Test, the Wechsler Adult Intelligence Scale, various special aptitude tests, and a number of personality tests, including the Minnesota Multiphasic, the Rorschach, the Thematic Apperception Test, and the Draw-A-Person Test. The experimental stress situations were designed to test such characteristics as adaptation to noise, vibration and acceleration, and performance of a frustrating complex task while in complete isolation.

Training Procedures. Psychologists have been active in the design of training devices and simulators which reproduce as completely as possible both the routine and the emergency tasks to be performed in spacecraft. They have also applied the results of research on the design and positioning of controls and displays (dials) as well as experience with man-machine systems.

Training has been largely focused on in-flight functions, though it will soon have to include preparation for living on another planet. The in-flight functions include monitoring the environmental, attitude, electrical and communications systems, as well as assuming manual control in the event of malfunction; programming and monitoring of the sequences involved in launching and re-entry; control of vehicle attitude; navigation; maintenance of communication to receive navigation, fuel and trajectory data, and to keep the ground informed of the progress of the flight; and making research observations and evaluations of systems performance. In addition, the astronaut must be given ample physical training and must be well versed in space physics, astronomy, physiology and communications in order to observe phenomena encountered on the mission, and also to be able to instruct future astronauts. *See* EQUIPMENT DESIGN.

Responses to Flight. Psychiatrists have been particularly involved in testing the astronaut's responses to space flight, and in determining the personality traits required for this work. Ruff cites, as an example, the personality studies carried out in Project Mercury. In the first phase, the following personality aspects were investigated during the selection program and the training period: (a) motivation: why the man volunteered, what personality needs are served by participation in the project; (b) self-concept of the astronaut, and its relation to his concept of the astronaut's role; (c) emotional arousal and control: conditions that arouse pleasurable and unpleasurable emotions, as well as their intensity and somatic aspects; (d) typical defense patterns to threatening situations, and how stress affects these mechanisms; (e) social behavior: relations to family, other astronauts, and management; (f) other personality aspects, including energy level, fatigue level, achievement drives, and activity-passivity tendencies.

The second phase involved administering tests and interviews both before and after stressful training activities, such as simulations of orbital flights in the human centrifuge, and comparing the results of the scores on the same tests given under relaxed conditions. The third phase of psychological evaluation consisted of long interviews given two days prior to actual sub-orbital and orbital flights, tests and brief interviews given immediately before and after the flights, and long interviews given two days after flight, in which the entire flight was reviewed.

In general, all the men on project Mercury showed a high level of performance during both training and actual flight periods. Even though the pre-flight tests were given in the early morning when efficiency is usually low and anxiety at its peak, the scores on performance tests were at their highest level—indicating a "state of facilitative activation." Post-flight performance scores were lower but not out of the normal range. The general mood of the astronauts was positive, with some increase in excitement and tension just before flights, but with little anticipatory anxiety since they felt fully prepared to meet the situation. In general, the men were more occupied with the operational details than with thoughts about what "might happen," and more concerned about the success of the mission than about their own safety.

During the flight the same general pattern emerged. A successful launch and smooth operation produced a feeling of exhilaration, possibly enhanced by the effects of weightlessness. Anxiety was at a low level and remained within the normal range when emergencies developed—even in the face of the possibility of death. After the flight, the astronauts experienced feelings of fatigue mingled with a sense of relief and some elation.

Personality Traits. Ruff groups these under the following headings: (a) *general characteristics:* extensive professional experience, high intelligence, a problem-solving orientation, concrete rather than abstract or speculative thinking, high degree of emotional stability, interest in action rather than introspection or fantasy; (b) *motivation:* showed mastery and achievement needs early in life; such needs often started as a way of reducing doubt or uncertainty, but now constitute an autonomous state associated with the desire to fly; (c) *affective, or emotional, management:* has faced fear in the past and has proved his ability to function efficiently under stress; possesses a stable personality organization and good emotional control; (d) *frustration tolerance:* although high achievement motives carry with them a high potential for disappointment, these men show great resilience in handling frustration. Characteristically, they experience their greatest disappointment when they have not been chosen for a particular mission or when the flight has been delayed.

SPECIFIC ENERGIES. The view that the various kinds of sensory experience, such as touch, taste, and sight, are dependent on the specific nature of the nerve fibers involved.

This doctrine was proposed in 1826 by Johannes Müller, (1801–1858) often called "the father of experimental physiology." It had actually been suggested 15 years earlier by Charles Bell (1774–1842), but Müller gained acceptance for the concept by including it in his *Handbook of Physiology* (1838), the first important compendium ever published in this field. Some of its aspects had also been foreshadowed by Aristotle, Descartes and Locke in their efforts to explain the relation between the mind and the external world.

The specific energy theory is an attempt to give a scientific answer to some basic epistemological questions: How do we know the environment? What actually happens in the process of perceiving? The commonsense answer is that minute replicas of objects are directly presented to the brain. A somewhat more sophisticated explanation is the Greek view that the messages which reach the brain are not identical to the objects but are "simulative representations" of them. In contrast to these ideas, Müller and others developed the view that we are never directly aware of objects, but only of the nerve excitation stimulated by them. Nerves, then, are intermediate between the mind and perceived objects, and impose limitations of their own. As an example, we respond only to a restricted range of wavelengths in sight and hearing, due to the limitations of our sense organs, and are blind to infrared waves and deaf to frequencies which a dog or a porpoise can hear. What we term reality is therefore merely that portion of energy to which our nerves happen to be sensitive.

In elaborating this doctrine, Müller held that each sensory nerve has its own specific quality, and this quality determines the characteristic sensations we experience when it is aroused. This means that receptors will always react in their own specific way to any effective stimulus—for example, the optic nerve responds to light and also to pressure (as it does when we "see stars" after being hit over the head). In other words, the different sense qualities we perceive depend on the nature of the receptor rather than merely on the source of stimulation.

Even if we grant that we are only aware of the activity of our nerves and that different receptor cells yield different sensory qualities, we still have to explain how these qualities are elaborated into our perceptual world. At this point there is a divergence in theory. Müller held that the nerves deliver qualitatively different types of impulses to the brain and that this is sufficient to explain the different kinds of perception and the different properties of objects in the external world. His contemporary, Bell, however, held that the specific nature of sensory experience is not the product of the impulse by itself, but depends on the particular part of the brain to which it is delivered. Subsequent research has proved that Bell was right on this point. Studies have also shown that all nerve impulses are similar, since they are all electrochemical waves moving along the fibers—in fact, if we were able to cross-connect the optical and auditory nerves, we would probably be able to hear light and see sounds. The quality of the sensations we experience is therefore not determined by the impulses but by the specific area of the cortex which they stimulate. In short, we see because our optic nerve carries patterns of excitation to the occipital cortex, where they are decoded and elaborated into visual experience in some as yet unknown way. Likewise, we hear because our auditory nerve carries impulses to the temporal lobe.

Both interpretations had a profound effect on physiological psychology. The idea that different receptors respond to different forms and ranges of energy led to the discovery of specific nerve endings for taste, touch, warmth, cold and pressure, as well as to the identification of structures in the eye and ear that respond to waves of light or air. And the view that the specificity of response can be explained in terms of the brain rather than the nerves spurred research into the localization of sensory functions in the cortex. See CEREBRAL CORTEX.

Recent research, however, suggests that both the stimulation of the nerve fibers and the processes that take place in the brain are far more complex than these early investigators anticipated. We have learned, for example, that the activities of the reticular formation enable us to receive stimuli that are important in ongoing behavior and to shunt aside inputs from less important sources. In other words, much can happen to a nerve impulse on its way to a brain center. Moreover, it is now possible to record the activity of a single nerve fiber, and such recordings have shown that a single taste fiber will fire in response to all types of substances, sweet, salt, bitter and acid. It has therefore been suggested that the combined activity of *many* cells sets up a complex code that is different for each taste we experience (Pfaffman, 1959). Similarly, there is evidence that the same group of neurons connected to the retina may signal different events through differences in the frequency of impulses they deliver to the brain. See RETICULAR FORMATION.

These and other findings have rendered the doctrine of specific fiber types and specific energies obsolete. Nevertheless, these ideas served the important function of focusing attention on physiological investigation as contrasted with philosophic speculation.

SPECIFIC HUNGER. Hunger for specific types of food that fulfill different bodily needs.

Jungle animals do not need a dietitian to prescribe a healthy diet, nor do domestic animals, laboratory rats, human infants or primitive people. Many experiments and observations have shown that if any of these are left to themselves they will practically always choose a balanced diet of protein, fats, carbohydrates, vitamins and minerals. They seem to have a specific hunger for every type of food their bodies require, and if any major type is lacking, they tend to redress the balance whenever possible.

Cafeteria feeding experiments, in which infants were given a free choice of various foods, have shown that they may neglect one important part of diet for a short period, but will make up for this deficiency in the long run. In one experiment, an infant cured his own case of rickets by consuming large amounts of cod liver oil (vitamin D), but stopped taking it when the condition had cleared up. Similar results were obtained when vitamin A and salt were withheld from the diet of rats (Harriman, 1955). Primitive Eskimos show the same inner drive for a balanced diet. Observers wondered why they ate the skin of the white whale until they discovered that it was as rich as orange juice in vitamin C. They also found that the Eskimos supplemented their almost exclusively meat diet by eating the vegetable contents of the stomachs of diving birds. See CAFETERIA FEEDING.

Although a balanced diet is often achieved by self-regulation, this process is by no means infallible. No study on either human beings or lower animals has shown that self-selection works perfectly for all subjects. Moreover, poor eating habits and learned preferences often overrule the body's natural needs. Candies and soft drinks will temporarily arrest the appetite because of their high sugar content, but they do not answer the body's requirements for other food substances. The vitamin deficiency disease beri beri is largely due to a preference for polished rice over whole-grain rice; the polishing process removes the vitamin B. Diabetic patients have to fight against the temptation to eat sweets, because their blood sugar level is already dangerously high. Even rats show detrimental food preferences. In one study, an artificial deficiency of protein was created, and the rats were offered both protein and sucrose. They ignored the protein and chose the sucrose as long as they could get it. Like children, they had a sweet tooth (Young and Chaplin, 1945). *See* BERI BERI.

Specific hunger is often created by temporary conditions. Animals have been known to travel hundreds of miles to get to salt licks. Athletes have an unusual desire for protein foods, apparently to rebuild muscles depleted by physical stress. Pregnant women require a greater amount of fat, protein and certain minerals to meet the demands of the developing fetus. When they send their husbands out for pickles in the middle of the night, they are probably motivated by bodily need rather than whim. Children who eat chalk or plaster off the wall are usually found to have a calcium deficiency.

These examples can be matched by a variety of food *aversions* due to physical conditions. Hormonal imbalance due to heredity or disease can produce an intense distaste for certain types of food. A defect in the parathyroid gland, for example, will lead a person to avoid foods containing phosphate. Animals will reject foods on which they are satiated, but will have an appetite for others for which they have a bodily need. Similarly, we ourselves may not be able to take another bite of steak, but will suddenly have an appetite again when the dessert is offered. There are therefore specific satiations as well as specific hungers.

The mechanics that control specific hungers are still a matter of conjecture. However, taste receptors probably play a part in the process, since rats no longer select a balanced diet when these receptors are removed (Richter, 1943). There is also little doubt that conditioning is involved. If we have found in the past that fresh shrimps or chocolate satisfy certain feelings of hunger, we will have an urge for these specific foods when the same feelings arise again. *See* HUNGER, PICA.

SPEECH DEVELOPMENT. Speech development begins at the start of life, for babies generally announce their presence with a loud wail, and continue to use this means of exercising their lungs and expressing their feelings for many weeks. By the second month, however, it is often possible to differentiate between the infant's cries of distress and of delight. Soon after this he adds babble to his vocal repertory. This not only helps to develop his speech mechanism, but enables him to hear and enjoy sounds of his own making.

By the fourth month, most children react to other people's voices by turning their head, and by the sixth month they can usually distinguish between friendly and angry tones. Analysis of the babblings of two to six months old babies reveals that they can produce all the vowel and practically all the consonant sounds of any language.

In the ninth or tenth month, children begin to imitate the intonations and inflections in the voices of other people. At about this time they also start to associate the words used by others with appropriate objects. During this entire period, the baby uses many grunts and gestures to make known his wants, and by the end of his first year he can usually say at least one clear word. There is, however, a wide normal variation: the first word is spoken anywhere between the eighth and the twenty-fourth month.

The child's first word is practically always a noun, and nouns continue to predominate in early speech. Verbs, adverbs, adjectives and pronouns follow in that order. Words of one syllable, or words shortened to one syllable ("fraid" for afraid) are used about 70 per cent of the time until two years of age. During the child's third year, phrases and sentences come into play, often repetitiously. At eighteen months the average child uses single words to express himself, but by four years of age he can speak in sentences of about four words. Especially bright children may use double that number of words per remark. Another important change is the shift from egocentric to socialized speech—that is, from a predominant use of "I" in the first two or three years to the use of "you" and "we" by four or five. At that time the child is also learning to exchange ideas with other people.

Once language begins, it develops with startling rapidity. Studies have shown that vocabulary increases from about twenty words at fifteen months to 270 at two years, 900 at three, 1500 at four and 2000 at five. By the end of elementary school, the average child understands about 20,000 words. This number rises to almost 80,000 by the time he finishes high school, and if he attends a four-year college, it increases to about 250,000. These figures, however, constitute only the *recognition* vocabulary. The writing vocabulary is perhaps 15 to 20 per cent of the total, and the speech vocabulary is still smaller.

Many factors affect the rate of linguistic development. There is wide variation from child to child and family to family in the physiological maturation that must precede the ability to speak and understand language. The environment exerts important effects. Children from privileged homes and neighborhoods, and children who associate primarily with adults, advance more rapidly than others. On the other hand, the speech development of twins tends to be slower than average, especially before they go to school, since they are often alone, without the stimulation of other children, and are also likely to use gestures and other forms of communication instead of words. Children raised in bilingual homes are apt to be somewhat retarded in learning both languages. One study has shown that they fare better if they hear each language from a different adult (Smith, 1935).

In general, girls progress more rapidly than boys in practically all features of language development: age of first talking, vocabulary, amount of speech, use of sentences, and articulation. Finally, there is a fairly close relationship between intelligence and speech development. Gifted children start talking about four months ahead of average but their progress may be due not only to their intelligence but to the stimulation they receive at home.

SPEECH DISORDERS. Marked deviations in the manner or content of speech. These deviations include speech that is not readily intelligible or audible; definitely unpleasant because of manner of production; deviant in rhythm, pitch or stress; or abnormal in voice, articulation or language. (Eisenson, 1965)

Speech disorders are usually classified into four major groups: (a) impairments of articulation (dysarthria, cleft-palate speech); (b) defects of phonation or voice production (falsetto voice, hoarseness, raspiness, harshness etc.); (c) stuttering; and (d) language dysfunctions (delayed language, childhood and adult aphasia, baby talk, lisping, cluttering).

The American Speech and Hearing

Association has estimated that at least three million children in the United States are in need of remedial attention for defects of speech or impairments of hearing that affect their educational, emotional and social adjustment. This figure represents approximately 5 per cent of the total child population, and breaks down to: articulatory disorders, 3 per cent; stuttering, 1 per cent; voice, cleft-palate and cerebral palsied speech, .1 per cent each; retarded speech development, .2 per cent; and speech problems due to impaired hearing, .5 per cent. The incidence among boys is consistently higher than among girls, with some estimates running as high as three to one. Although many highly intelligent people lisp, stutter, or show other speech disorders, the over-all incidence is highest on the lower intellectual levels. At least 60 per cent of retarded children are afflicted with speech defects. There is also a higher than average incidence among children with reading difficulties, since training in reading is hampered by indistinct articulation and poor discrimination of speech sounds. Studies also show that, with important exceptions, students with defective speech tend to be somewhat retarded at all academic levels, especially those who have physical handicaps such as poor hearing. No definitive studies of the incidence of speech disorders among adults have been made.

The causes of speech disorders may be either organic or functional. Among the organic conditions are: (1) severe hearing impairment, especially when it is congenital or acquired early in life; (2) cleft-palate, sometimes including cleft-lip; (3) paralysis of the speech or vocal mechanisms; (4) cerebral palsy when it involves speech mechanisms; (5) aphasias and dysarthrias resulting from neural lesions. The first four of these conditions affect both voice and articulation; dysarthria is an articulatory dysfunction; and aphasia is a loss of understanding of language due to brain damage.

The functional conditions are of two general types. First, deviant patterns of speech may be acquired through imitation of the defective speech of other people. These patterns frequently improve spontaneously as the child identifies with new models in the course of his development. Second, several studies have shown that defective speech is often associated with faulty psychological patterns in the home. Among the factors most frequently emphasized are: poor adjustment on the part of the mother; maternal tendencies toward overprotectiveness, rigidity, restrictiveness and domination through excessively high standards and adverse criticism; and a home environment characterized by disorganization and tension. (Wood, 1946, Peckarsky, 1952, Moncur, 1952)

Discussion of individual speech disorders is found under the following topics: STUTTERING, CLUTTERING, DYSLALIA, DYSARTHRIA, APHASIA, JARGON-APHASIA, VOICE DISORDERS. For other disturbances involving speech see CIRCUMSTANTIALITY, MUTISM, NEOLOGISM, ECHOLALIA, PARAPHASIA, VERBIGERATION, LOGORRHEA, WORD SALAD.

SPINAL CORD. The cord-like nervous system encased in the backbone, serving as a pathway for impulses to and from the brain (PLATE 1), and as a connection center for reflexes.

The spinal cord has a uniform structure throughout its entire length. Its H-shaped interior consists of gray matter composed of cell bodies and their interconnections; its exterior contains columns of white matter made up of ascending and descending fibers. In general, the dorsal columns (toward the back) conduct sensory or afferent impulses up to the brain, and the ventral columns (toward the front) carry motor or efferent impulses down to the rest of the body. The lateral columns, at the two sides, are mixed. *See* SPINAL NERVES.

The two functions of the cord, as a path for conduction of impulses and as a relatively independent center for reflex activities, have been relatively fixed throughout evolution. However, changes of two kinds have taken place in its relation to the higher centers of the brain. First, typical spinal nerves are found in the lowest fishes, but a separate autonomic system is found only in higher fishes and mammals. Second, in fishes and amphibia connections between the spinal cord and the higher centers of the brain are usually relayed by way of the medulla; in man and other mammals only a few are so relayed, since the most important connections are made directly between the brain and spinal cord. These connections enable the cerebral cortex to regulate many sensory and motor activities which are the exclusive province of lower centers in more primitive species.

Physiological psychologists have investigated five areas of behavior in which the spinal cord is involved: the somatic senses (somesthesis), motor functions (especially reflexes), sexual behavior, conditioning, and emotion. The nerve tracts for the somesthetic system have been rather fully explored. The body is divided into segments, called dermatomes, and the sensory and motor fibers from each segment gather together to form a single bundle. Just before entering the cord the bundle splits into a dorsal root containing the sensory fibers, and a ventral root containing the motor fibers. The dorsal root itself then divides into two bundles, a medial bundle consisting of fibers from pressure receptors in the skin and muscles, and a lateral bundle made up of fibers from pain and temperature receptors in the skin and deeper parts of the body. Some fibers in both groups make immediate connection with motor neurons to enable us to perform simple reflex movements such as drawing our

hand away from a hot object. Others connect with ascending fibers which go to the cerebellum, thalamus and upper parts of the brain. This enables us to feel the changes in the receptors that respond to muscular tension, touch and pressure, pain and temperature throughout the body. *See* ORGANIC SENSES, KINESTHETIC SENSE, TEMPERATURE SENSE, PAIN SENSE, TOUCH.

All motor functions of the organism except those occurring in the head region are served by spinal nerves. The motor fibers, like the sensory fibers, enter the cord at various segments and either ascend to the cerebellum, thalamus and cortical areas for the control of posture and co-ordination, or make connections within the cord itself for reflex activities. Reflex mechanisms are of two types: first, segmental arcs; these usually consist of sensory neurons, interneurons, and motor neurons, although some are direct connections without interneurons. Examples of the segmental arcs are the simple flexion of an arm or leg in response to pain and pressure stimuli, and the stretch reflexes that enable us to maintain our posture, run or play tennis (*Fig. 45*). The second type of reflex mechanism is the intersegmental arc, in which the sensory fibers connect with fibers that travel up or down the spine before connecting to the motor neurons. These arcs make possible more complicated activities since different body segments and spinal levels are involved. Examples are the scratch reflex, which consists of repeated rhythmic movements, and the pattern of reflex activities employed in walking. *See* REFLEXES.

Although the hypothalamus plays a central role in sexual behavior, the spinal cord mediates certain elementary responses. When the connections between the cord and upper levels of the nervous system are destroyed, male animals and male human beings are still capable of erection and even ejaculation as a result of mechanical stimulation. However, human patients, and presumably the animals as well, are not aware of *sensations* arising from the genitals. Experiments with castrated animals have shown that these reactions occur even in the absence of sex hormones, although the hormones have an added effect if they are present. *See* SEX DRIVE.

Animal experiments have indicated that conditioning—particularly of the classical type—can take place even after practically any region of the brain has been damaged. This suggests that the brain may not be necessary for conditioning, and that this simple form of learning might be mediated entirely by the spinal cord. Experiments designed to test this hypothesis have been contradictory. Shurrager and Culler (1940) stripped out flexor muscles from the thighs of over 200 dogs, eliminating brain connections but retaining spinal connections. They were then able to condition about *half* of them to a shock applied to the tail instead of the foot pad, which is the normal place for stimulation. On the other hand, Kellogg et al. (1947) found *no* evidence of spinal conditioning when they attempted to obtain a conditioned muscle response in the right leg of an operated dog by applying a shock to the left leg instead of the tail. One cannot draw a final conclusion from these experiments, although it does appear that conditioning at the spinal level is not an important type of learning if it takes place at all. As Morgan (1965) remarks, "If it exists, it probably accounts for little or nothing of the learned behavior of adult mammalian organisms."

Most of the autonomic responses involved in emotional behavior—increased heart rate, muscular tension, etc.—occur in spinal animals, that is, animals deprived of connections between the spinal cord and the brain by a transsection (cut) below the medulla. An even more complete response is obtained if the transsection is made above the medulla because of its importance in respiration and circulation. These responses are, however, only one aspect of the total emotional response. *See also* EMOTION (GENERAL), EMOTION (THEORIES), AUTONOMIC NERVOUS SYSTEM.

SPINAL NERVES. The thirty-one pairs of nerves of the somatic nervous system, which enter and leave the spinal cord between the spinal vertebrae. They are classified into five groups according to the part of the cord with which they are associated: (1) the eight cervical nerves are in the neck area, (2) the twelve thoracic nerves are in the chest area, (3) the five lumbar nerves are in the loin, (4) the five sacral nerves are near the base of the spinal column, and (5) the one coccygeal nerve is at the bottom end of the column.

Just before entering the vertebral column, the spinal nerves divide into a dorsal root which is sensory in function and a ventral root which is usually motor. The sensory portions of the nerves come from tactile, pain and thermal receptors in the skin; receptors in the blood vessels; pressure and pain receptors in the muscles, tendons and joints; and from certain internal receptors in the body cavities and digestive tract. Each sensory nerve represents a relatively small body area called a dermatome. In lower animals these areas are sharply defined segments, but in man they are less regular and overlap considerably. The motor portions of the nerves control all the striated muscles of the arms, legs, and the rest of the body below the neck. The face, neck and head regions are not served by the spinal nerves, but by the cranial nerves. *See* CRANIAL NERVES, NERVOUS SYSTEM.

STANFORD-BINET TEST. An individual intelligence test designed primarily for children in the school years.

The Stanford-Binet is a revision of

the first intelligence test, which was created by the French psychologist, Alfred Binet, in collaboration with a physician, Théophile Simon. In 1904 Binet was commissioned by the French government to develop a test that would (a) identify children who were too dull to profit from ordinary schooling, and (b) locate children who were potentially able to make normal progress but were not making the effort. The authorities felt that these choices could not be left to teachers, since they often favored children for personality reasons and did not have the psychological knowledge to make the necessary distinctions. *See* BINET.

Binet was faced with unexplored territory, since no one had adequately measured intelligence before. He started with the assumption that dull children resemble normal children in every way except that they are retarded in mental growth. This suggested that they would perform like normal children of a younger age, and that intelligence could be scaled as a change that ordinarily occurs with increasing age. A child of five would normally be brighter than a child of three, because he had more experience and more time to learn. To test this hypothesis, Binet set up a number of problems and tried them on children of various ages. He then grouped together problems which a majority of average children (about 60 per cent) of each age could pass—for example, five-year-olds were able to copy a square and count four pennies, while most eight-year-olds could count from 20 down to 0 and give the day and date. Finally, he constructed a test which presented a variety of problems at each age level, and determined the child's mental age on the basis of the number he could pass at each of these levels. If an eight-year-old passed all items at the eight-year level but none at the nine, his mental age was eight; and if a twelve-year-old could pass only the eight-year items, he too would have a mental age of eight. The concept of

IQ, which related the mental age to the chronological age, was not introduced until the test came to the United States.

The first Binet-Simon scale appeared in 1908, and soon after it was brought over to Stanford University. There psychologists under the direction of L. M. Terman revised and extended the original scale. The first revision, which became known as the Stanford-Binet or Stanford Revision was published in 1911, and others followed in 1937 and 1960. These revisions (1) strengthened the extremes of the scale, making it possible to test two-year-olds and superior adults; (2) added alternative forms for re-testing; (3) improved the instructions and illustrations; (4) included items appropriate to an American population; and (5) introduced the IQ, which made possible comparisons between the relative abilities of individuals at all ages. The IQ is the ratio of the mental age to the chronological age—that is, MA $\div$ CA $\times$ 100 (to eliminate decimal points). As an example, the eight-year-old mentioned above would have an IQ of 100, the midpoint of the average range, while the twelve-year-old would rate only 67, well in the subnormal range.

The Stanford-Binet consists of six tests and one alternative for each half year between the ages of two and five, six items per year of mental age between six and fourteen, and a larger spacing above that year. A subject is not given the entire set of tests, but usually starts one year behind his chronological age and continues until he fails to answer all questions for an entire age level. The highest level at which he answers all questions correctly is called his basal mental age, but he gets two months credit for each question answered beyond that level—for example, if an eight-year-old answers three of the six questions at the nine-year level, two at the ten, one at the eleven and 0 at the twelve, his mental age will be eight years and twelve months, or nine years. The test includes scoring guides which give specimens of acceptable and unacceptable answers, to make the scoring as objective as possible.

The test calls for different abilities at different ages. At the lower age levels it stresses information about objects, parts of the body and pictorial material. At the higher ages it presents reasoning problems that involve numbers and words. Vocabulary, memory span and use of words are tested at all levels, since they represent general aspects of intelligence. The test is administered individually and requires a good deal of skill on the part of the examiner. With younger children it is extremely important to establish rapport in order to elicit sustained attention and reduce tension. A child who feels anxious or insecure in a testing situation may score far below his potential—in fact, studies have shown that such children may refuse even to *try* certain items on one day but be willing to try them at another time; and this alone may make a difference of as much as fifteen IQ points in their scores (Rust, 1931). The importance of the child's reactions to the test situation is so great that no child should be labelled dull or subnormal on the basis of a single test. In addition, factors such as school performance and emotional stability must be taken into account before making even a tentative estimate of intellectual ability. Follow-up tests are also advisable, especially in doubtful cases.

The Stanford-Binet is basically used for prediction of school performance and ability to adjust to everyday demands. It is also effective in choosing children for adoption, determining seriousness of mental retardation, and locating the gifted. Although it was not designed for clinical use, it provides an excellent opportunity for observing the child at work. A perceptive examiner can obtain considerable insight about his approach to problems, his emotional attitudes, and possible thinking disturbances. Impulsive and inhibited children attack the items in quite different ways, and disturbed children do not give the same type of responses to vocabulary items as normal children; for example, they tend to give descriptions, explanations and illustrations rather than synonyms.

The test has its limitations. It puts a heavy emphasis on verbal ability, since the directions and most of the answers require the use of language. This means that it cannot do justice to subjects who are having difficulty with English for one reason or another. Although there is a technique for adapting the test to older adolescents and adults, it is still considered inadequate for the upper age levels. Finally, it yields only a single score indicating over-all mental development, and therefore fails to lend itself sufficiently to the assessment of an individual's strengths, weaknesses and special abilities. In spite of these limitations, the Stanford-Binet remains one of the most widely accepted intelligence tests in use today. *See* INTELLIGENCE TESTS.

STARTLE REACTION (Startle Pattern). An extremely rapid response to a sudden, unexpected stimulus, such as a pistol shot or a face looming up in the darkness.

Analysis of the startle reaction through high speed photography (Landis and Hunt, 1939) has shown that it is a highly complex pattern which passes like a wave over the entire body. The eyes suddenly close, the mouth widens, the chin tilts upward, and the muscles of the neck are tensed. The wave response rapidly descends, and the shoulders hunch, the midsection contracts, and the knees bend. At the same time heart beat and respiration are abruptly increased as if to put the organism in a state of emergency. This entire reaction is so rapid that a person can go through it and return to his normal posture in less than one second.

The startle response is found in all normal people from infancy to adulthood, and in all mammals that have been tested. The pattern is so uniform from individual to individual that it appears to be inborn. It is probably the most primitive of all emotional reactions, and appears to be an instinctive self-preservation mechanism in which the organism prepares itself to repel attack.

Unlike other emotional responses, the startle reaction is highly resistant to modification by learning and experience. It can, however, be reduced in intensity if it is frequently repeated or partially anticipated. Children who make a game of frightening others find their sudden "boos" have less and less effect, and adults find they can soften reaction by warning a person to "prepare for a shock" when they have upsetting news to tell him. Other conditions increase the intensity of the reaction. It is likely to be particularly violent when we are overfatigued or under an emotional strain. One of the most common afflictions of combat veterans is an intense startle reaction to sudden loud noises such as the backfiring of a car. This reaction has been known to persist for months after a serviceman has returned to civilian life. *See* COMBAT REACTIONS.

STARVATION REACTIONS. The effects of starvation and semistarvation have been studied extensively through both observation and experimentation.

The scientist has little trouble finding examples of undernourishment in a world where about 25 per cent of all human beings exist on a marginal level, and where famine almost inevitably follows wars and long periods of drought. The most common physical effects are general weakness, or asthenia, sluggishness, hunger pangs and susceptibility to disease. These effects are accompanied by a generalized psychological debility which includes a slowing down of thought, difficulty in concentrating and solving problems, irritability, apathy, and daydreaming. Psychotic reactions seldom occur except when undernourishment is complicated by infection or extreme stress. Observations made in German prisoner of war camps have confirmed both the physical and the mental asthenic symptoms, but additional reactions were also noted: loss of pride in appearance, reduced sexual desire, disinterest in cleanliness, and a general moral deterioration.

In an experiment on semistarvation conducted during World War II a group of conscientious objectors volunteered to live for six months on a diet typical of the famine areas. The physical effects were pronounced: a 25 per cent loss in body weight, a 40 per cent decrease in basal metabolism, and a 30 per cent reduction in strength. These effects were accompanied by emaciation, fainting attacks, easy fatigability, and loss of sexual and affectional interest. Psychological effects were so marked that the experimenters coined the term "semistarvation neurosis" to describe them:

"The outstanding characteristic of the 'neurosis' was apathy; humor disappeared, a depressing air of gloom and dejection appearing in its place. There was also a marked decrease in sociability. The men became nervous and irritable, tended to be boorish and tactless when invited to parties, sometimes went unshaven and dressed sloppily, lost their cooperative spirit, and were inclined to 'blow up' at each other. Self-confidence was replaced by feelings of inferiority and depression.

"Tests of intellectual capacity administered at different times throughout the study failed to reveal any marked changes." . . . But "because of their constant preoccupation with thoughts of food and their inability to concentrate on other things, the subjects worried considerably about declining in intelligence and believed that they were really suffering such a loss . . . Food, either directly or indirectly, dominated their conversation, reading, leisure activities, and daydreams. Over half of the men devoted their spare moments to reading cookbooks and collecting recipes. Others became intensely interested in such subjects as dietetics, agriculture, and frozen food lockers. Some subjects even gave serious consideration to the idea of changing their occupations and becoming cooks." (Keys et al., 1950)

STATUS. The standing or position of an individual or group of individuals in a social system.

Society tends to be organized into a series of hierarchies or status systems, with some individuals or groups occupying high and others intermediate or low positions. A person whose standing is high is said to enjoy high prestige, or recognition of superiority. Since society is made up of many different status systems, based on different dimensions such as wealth or birth or learning, the same individual may be accorded high status in one system and low in another. The following criteria have been proposed by Benoit-Smullyan (1944): the person of high status, or prestige, is an object of admiration, an object of deference, an object of imitation, a center of attention, and a source of prestige suggestion (for example, associating him with a product suggests superiority).

There are two principal ways of acquiring a position in a social group—through some fortuitous factor, such as race, sex, birth, complexion or age; and through special accomplishments and contributions. In some cases the two types of factors may both be present. The specific bases of status, however, vary from society to society, and from social group to social group. In America there is a wide variety of determinants, including family, wealth, power, education and skill, but many studies have

shown that the two most pervasive criteria are income and occupation, both of which tend to be basically economic. The emphasis on material values is one of the major themes of *Middletown* (1929, 1937), by R. and H. Lynd, who found, as one example, that maintaining a car in proper style was of greater importance than providing an adequate diet for the family—undoubtedly because the car is a more public and visible symbol of income than food. Similar illustrations can be found in Warner's *Yankee City* (1941), Dollard's *Caste and Class in a Southern Town* (1937), and West's *Plainsville, U.S.A.* (1945).

Individuals often measure themselves by the same criteria that society uses in judging them. One of the problems involved in raising the social level of certain racial, nationality or occupational groups is that they accept the low status accorded them by society and in so doing develop an inferior self-image. On the other hand, Hyman (1942) has shown that an individual's evaluation of his own status may in many cases be based on his position in a small group of intimate associates rather than on his position in society as a whole. Many people also have a tendency to rate themselves above their actual position in the social hierarchy —for example, by placing themselves in the social class to which they aspire.

As Davis, Gardner and Gardner (1941) have shown, an individual's conception of his class membership has an effect on his estimate not only of his own status but also the status of others. Members of the upper-upper class, for instance, were found to apply their own special labels to all classes. Instead of the usual designations, they used "old aristocracy" (for themselves), "aristocracy but not old," "nice respectable people," "good people but nobody," and "poor whites." As this classification indicates, they employed several differentiating terms for **groups** close to themselves in the social hierarchy, and tended to lump together all those who were socially distant. People who are low on the scale also tend to make more distinctions among groups close to themselves, and usually find that there is a social level below the one they occupy.

An important aspect of status is the use of outward and visible signs of one's place in the social hierarchy. These signs, or status symbols, are most in evidence on the upper social level and among those who wish to identify themselves with a higher level. Obvious examples are a good address, a "name" car, a private school for one's child, an Ivy League college, a mink coat, a high-sounding title. (In some companies there is a profusion of vice-presidents, some of higher and some of lower grade, primarily for carrying on business with the outside world on the theory that "a vice-president will only talk to a vice-president.") An interesting example of status in reverse is the tendency of wealthy individuals to wear old clothes and drive a dilapidated or antique car, perhaps to indicate that they are so secure in their status that no external props are needed. On the other hand, people of lower rank in society frequently spend disproportionate amounts of money on status symbols, such as luxurious but rarely used living-room furniture. Installment plans encourage such "conspicuous consumption," but overbuying tends to boomerang since the entire façade is likely to collapse during an emergency. *See* SOCIAL ROLE, SOCIAL CLASS.

STEREOTYPE. A relatively fixed, oversimplified and usually biased concept, generally of a person or social group. The term derives from the metal stereotype used in printing, which cannot easily be changed once it is cast. Some common examples are: "Teenagers are unstable," "Geniuses are queer," "Bankers are hard-hearted," "Redheads are hot-tempered."

Psychologists have shown an interest in stereotypes since the mid-1920s. In one of the early studies, Rice (1926) asked a group of students to match photographs of nine persons with a list of occupations and ethnic groups. He found their judgments substantially correct, and even where they were wrong they tended to agree in their choices. As a result, he concluded that "there exist common stereotypes concerning the appearance of various classes of persons."

Since the Rice study there have been a number of fruitful investigations of stereotypes. In general, three basic characteristics of this process have been emphasized, as Secord and Backman (1964) point out. First, a stereotype is a special form of categorization in which certain attributes are selected and used to identify a group, while other characteristics tend to be ignored. Membership in a given category may be based on a distinctive behavior pattern or simply on affiliation with a particular nationality, race, religion or organization, but in any case it "is sufficient to evoke the judgment that the person possesses all the attributes belonging to that category."

Second, there is a consensus on the traits attributed to the group—that is, a substantial number of people agree on the group's identifying characteristics. They may, for example, share the common image or "picture in the mind" that all elderly people are old-fashioned, cantankerous and conservative, or that all professors are absent-minded, impractical, idealistic, and eccentric.

To test this tendency, Katz and Braly (1933) conducted a classic study in which they presented college students with a list of ten ethnic groups, together with a list of words describing various personal attitudes, asking them to select the five traits which they thought most characteristic of each group. The results showed a striking consensus for certain ethnic groups— for example, Germans were characterized as scientifically minded by 78 per cent and industrious by 65 per cent, while Negroes were described as superstitious by 84 per cent and lazy by 75 per cent. There was much less agreement, however, on the Irish, Chinese and Turks, indicating that some stereotypes are more clear-cut than others.

This led to an interesting finding. When the students were asked to rank the ten groups according to preference, their choices showed substantial agreement. At the top of the list were Americans, English and Germans; at the bottom were Negroes and Turks. Yet the stereotypes of these groups varied greatly in clarity, indicating that the definiteness of the stereotyped picture of an ethnic group is not related to the degree of preference. The subjects, for example, were most negative toward the Turks, yet their picture of this group was the vaguest of all.

Another significant finding in the Katz and Braly study was the fact that small numbers of subjects often selected attributes included in the check list but not believed to belong to the stereotype of the particular ethnic group. This suggests that there may be two kinds of stereotypes; personal stereotypes, reflecting highly individual opinions; and social stereotypes, representing the consensus of the majority of a given group of judges. The term is most often used in the latter sense.

It is interesting that when the Katz and Braly study was repeated about twenty years later in the same Eastern college, the stereotypes were found to be much less definite than at the time of the original investigation (Gilbert, 1951).

A third characteristic is a discrepancy between attributed traits and actual traits. Stereotypes are almost always at least partly false, either because they are an oversimplification or because they have little basis in fact. One reason for their inaccuracy is the assumption that everyone who belongs to a given class possesses the traits assigned to that class, an assumption that makes us overlook individual variations. In other words, we fail to distinguish between statements about a class of persons in the abstract and actual perception of individuals whom we meet face-to-face. This is especially likely to occur when we are provided only with ethnic identification and no other information, since we are thereby induced to ignore individual differences and respond to the group only as a class. This tendency has been demonstrated by Hartley (1946) in a study in which he invented three fictitious national groups and asked subjects to rate them along with many known national groups. He found that a large number of subjects not only rated the fictitious groups but usually assigned them unfavorable traits.

Other experiments have shown that when subjects are encouraged to recognize subgroups within an ethnic group, instead of lumping all the members together, they are less likely to employ stereotypes. When Bayton, McAlister, and Hammer (1956) asked a group of subjects to characterize "upper class Negroes" and "lower class Negroes," they discovered that only the lower class Negroes were stereotyped. One way of attacking stereotypes would therefore be to insist on a more precise definition of the group itself. This would have the effect of challenging the stereotype and inducing a more critical attitude toward making generalizations.

It is important to recognize that stereotypes can be positive as well as negative. We tend to have excessively favorable attitudes toward our own group or groups to which we aspire. One way of making these ideas less rigid and extreme is to show that even when they are predominantly favorable, they may contain unfavorable elements. The opposite also tends to be true. In a study sponsored by UNESCO (Buchanan, 1951) it was found that even though more favorable traits are attributed to a country when people are more friendly toward it, they also tend to assign *some* favorable traits to countries toward which they are extremely negative. This suggests that it may be possible to reduce the rigidity and bias of some stereotypes by accentuating the positive rather than the negative components. *See* PREJUDICE, HALO EFFECT, SOCIAL CLASS.

STEREOTYPY. A persistent pathological repetition of the same words, phrases, or movements.

Normal children derive considerable satisfaction and security from repeating the same acts in play, or from hearing the same stories over and over. Adults have the same tendency, though to a lesser degree. This is not generally classed as stereotypy, however, since the term is usually reserved for repetition of *inappropriate* behavior that stems from an unconscious effort to allay anxiety and gain a feeling of security.

Stereotypy, or "stereotyped behavior," is most frequently found in compulsive reactions and schizophrenia, but is also observed in autistic children. In obsessive-compulsive neurosis it may take the form of a definite ritual, such as saying the same prayer or repeating the same gesture a certain number of times. The elaborate rituals which some anxious children go through are also examples of stereotypy. These actions usually serve the unconscious purpose of appeasement or alleviation of guilt feeling, but their significance in individual cases can only be fathomed by a study of the patient's special experiences and reactions.

In schizophrenic cases the meaning of the behavior is usually obscure and deeply buried; to the outside observer it usually appears totally senseless. There are two major types of psychotic stereo-

typy: *mannerisms,* which include facial grimaces, peculiarities of posture and gait, bizarre gestures and series of movements; and *verbigeration,* endless reiteration of the same incoherent word, phrase, or sentence. These verbalizations may originally have had some meaning for the patient, but they have probably lost whatever significance they once had and have become purely mechanical.

Although obsessive-compulsive reaction and schizophrenia provide the most conspicuous and extreme examples of stereotypy, many authorities have pointed out that there is an essential element of stereotypy in the behavior of all neurotics. They persist in using rigid patterns which are unsuited to the situations they meet: extreme submissiveness or assertiveness, insistence on perfection, refusal to face facts, blaming others for their failures. These faulty patterns are believed to originate in childhood as reactions to disturbing experiences and difficult situations, such as constant criticism from parents or insistence on "perfect" behavior. Since they served fairly well during their early years, individuals with neurotic tendencies automatically repeat them instead of learning new patterns that are more appropriate to adult situations: "A neurosis may be defined as a series of such stereotyped reactions to problems that the patient has never solved in the past and is still unable to solve in the present" (Alexander and French, 1946). *See* OBSESSIVE-COMPULSIVE REACTION, SCHIZOPHRENIC REACTIONS (GENERAL), RITUAL, VERBIGERATION, REPETITION-COMPULSION, SCHIZOPHRENIA (CHILD-HOOD TYPE), EARLY INFANTILE AUTISM, TIC.

Illustrative Case: STEREOTYPY

A Polish woman who had been in a state psychiatric hospital for two years did little all day but sit humped over a stool repeating the sound "Boligo!" and making a peculiar downward swoop with her right hand, followed by a waving, pushing motion of her palm. Her left arm, which was held motionless, showed a marked atrophy of disuse, whereas the musculature of her right shoulder and arm was hypertrophied from her apparently tireless exercise. The patient would struggle against any interference with her stereotyped motions; if they were forcibly restrained, she would go into a state of mute, semi-catatonic passivity, only to resume her chant and gestures upon release. One day a matronly attendant of Polish origin was assigned to duty in the ward, and because of their ethnic kinship, began to take particular interest in the patient. The latter responded slowly and suspiciously, but after several weeks began to converse hesitantly in Polish with the newcomer. Through this relationship some history was obtained, in the light of which the patient's behavior could in part be interpreted. Briefly, the patient had emigrated from Poland at seventeen and had been given no opportunity to attend school or even learn more than a few words of English. Instead, she had been almost immediately apprenticed by her family to a middle-aged tailor, whom she was forced to marry two years later. He had mistreated her from the start and soon after marriage added beatings and various sexual abuses to their relationship. The patient appealed to her family, but their cultural attitude and religious convictions made correction of the situation impossible. The patient's repressed hostilities to her husband and children took various forms, among them an obsessive fear that her cooking might poison them; later this changed to a delusional conviction that she had poisoned them and was therefore excommunicated from the Church. Unfortunately, she was committed to a state hospital where no one spoke her language or gave her any but the barest custodial care; under these circumstances, her habit patterns deteriorated rapidly into the peculiar stereotypes previously described. Symbolically, these consisted of a common Polish word of her childhood: "boli," meaning "pain," combined with the English word "go." This wishful combination "pain, go!" was accompanied endlessly by the sweeping motion of a tailor working his needle (symbolically, her husband), terminated with the palm-outward, pushing gesture of avoidance and dismissal. (Masserman, 1961)

STIMULUS (literally "goad"). In general terms, any event that initiates be-

havior; or more specifically, any energy change that activates a sense organ.

The idea of energy change needs clarification. When we put our hand on a hot radiator, the sudden change in energy level stimulates the nerve endings for warmth and pain embedded in our skin. However, if the temperature of the radiator were the same as the room, it would not stimulate these sense organs, although it might stimulate the touch endings. Stimulation, then, depends on a *change* in energy level; if the change ceases, the stimulation will also cease. As an example, when we first come into a room, we may notice the ticking of a clock due to the sudden rise in the sound level; but we soon become unaware of the ticking because this level remains so constant. This process of adaptation occurs in all sense modalities. Broadcasters sometimes try to overcome its effect by turning up the volume during commercials. This is an attempt to capture attention by increasing the stimulus level. *See* SENSORY ADAPTATION.

Psychologists make a distinction between two major types of stimuli. The physical energy which excites the sense organs is termed the distal stimulus, and the activity of the sense organ itself is termed the proximal stimulus. The light energy reflected by the print you are now reading is a distal stimulus, but the chemical changes taking place in your retina constitute a proximal stimulus. This means that we do not actually experience the properties of the distal stimulus, but only its effects on the receptors. Yet, surprisingly, the two can appear the same even when they are different—for example, if a person stands five feet from you he produces a larger proximal stimulus than when he is 75 feet away, yet you do not see him as a full grown man in the first case and as a midget in the second. Instead, you see him as a grown man at different distances from you. *See* PERCEPTUAL CONSTANCY.

We are responsive to only a limited number of stimuli because our receptors are sensitive only to a small range of energy changes. In hearing, this range is 20 to 20,000 cycles per second, although we can respond in other ways than hearing to frequencies that are both below and above that range—for example, earthquake tremors and ultrasonic waves. In vision, our eyes are sensitive to only a small range of electromagnetic waves known as the visible spectrum. We would be living in quite a different world if we could see ultraviolet and radar waves, or hear the sound made by insects, bats, and a gently swaying tree. And our world would be still different if we could taste as well as the lowly worm, respond to changes in water pressure as well as fish, and smell as well as a hunting dog.

Our receptors are also limited to six different *types* of stimuli. Our eyes are sensitive to photic energy, our ears to acoustic energy, and receptors in our nostrils and tongue to chemical energy. Some receptors in our skin are sensitive to thermal changes (heat and cold), while others are responsive to mechanical energy (pressure or touch), or to destruction of tissue (pain). Electrical energy has the unique ability of exciting all sense channels, since the nerve impulse is electrical in nature. These six types of stimuli are not so fixed as they sound, since one type of energy may affect the operation of an organ that is primarily geared to another type —for instance, heating the skin makes it more sensitive to mechanical pressure, and a blow to the eye can make us "see stars."

Most stimuli come from the external world, but we are sensitive to internal energy changes as well. Much of our behavior is guided by stimuli which activate receptors embedded in our muscles, joints, and internal organs. If we did not receive them we would not be aware of our need for food or water, or know that our stomach is upset. We could not even tie our shoelaces or type a letter, since these activities consist of a behavioral chain in which each new response produces a feedback effect that becomes the stimulus for the next response.

Stimuli play an indispensable part in all psychological experimentation. The standard laboratory technique is to vary a stimulus systematically and observe how this affects a response. If we want to find out whether a two-year-old child can distinguish between square and circular blocks, we might keep hiding a piece of candy under the square one, and interchange the position of the square and circle to determine whether he will respond to the shape alone. If our problem is to determine how internal stimuli affect behavior, we might see whether a rat will learn a maze more quickly when he is hungry than when he is satiated. We might also systematically vary the stimulus by depriving the rat of food for a longer or shorter time to see whether his learning ability changes proportionately.

These experiments bring up a final point about stimuli. If the child discriminates correctly between a square and circle, and if the rat's learning ability changes as his hunger changes, exactly what are they responding *to?* Is the child responding to the whole cube or only to a part of it—and in the rat experiment, what is the specific stimulus that is actually controlling his behavior? Attempts are often made to pinpoint these "effective stimuli," as they are called, but in most cases, including the two just given, it is extremely hard to devise experiments that will provide a definitive answer. For an interesting attempt, *see* VISUAL CLIFF. *See also* STIMULUS-RESPONSE ASSOCIATION, STIMU-LUS-STIMULUS ASSOCIATION.

STIMULUS-RESPONSE ASSOCIA-TION (S-R Association). The tendency of a particular stimulus to produce a particular response.

One of the most characteristic features of human and animal behavior is that the organism is constantly responding to stimuli. The light flashes red, and we put our foot on the brake; a friend calls to us, and we look in his direction; the novel we are reading describes an exciting scene, and our pulse quickens. In each of these cases there is a connection, or association, between a stimulus and a response. Some psychologists, especially in America, view such S-R associations as the fundamental units of behavior. They hold that everything we do or think or feel is based on these "building blocks"—from the wailing of an infant to the fantasy of a poet and the theories of an Einstein.

Among the S-R theorists, however, there is a basic cleavage as to the conditions which produce the bond between stimulus and response. One group contends that an association is established only when the response is followed and "reinforced" by a reward of some kind (the "law of effect"): we eat because we have found that food reduces hunger, and we respond to the red light because it assures us safety or keeps us from getting a ticket. The other group holds that the only thing needed to form an association is contiguity, that is, the stimulus must be closely followed by the response. According to this theory we depress the brake when we see the red light merely because the two events have occurred in close temporal order in the past. Many psychologists favor the reward view for certain types of learning, such as operant conditioning, and the contiguity view for other types of learning such as classical conditioning. *See* CONDITIONING, LAW OF CONTIGUITY, THORNDIKE, DRIVE REDUCTION THEORY, REINFORCEMENT.

The S-R concept has been applied not only to learning but to personality formation. In particular, Dollard and Miller (1950) have employed it in great detail to describe the way children form habit patterns and basic attitudes during the first six years of life. They have shown that these reactions are the result of early learning based on personal experiences—in other words, they are associations established through repeated responses to specific stimuli. These investigators have also performed experiments to show that personality formation is the result of a learning process, and in so doing have offered compelling evidence for some important psychoanalytic concepts.

A typical example is the study of the mechanism of displacement. In this case, a psychologist informally sounded out the attitudes of a group of summer campers about Mexicans and Japanese. At a later time, they were given a questionnaire that dealt with their attitudes toward these nationalities, but in order to answer the questions they had to miss an exciting social event. The results indicated that their attitudes were significantly more negative toward these groups after this frustration than before. They had apparently transferred, or "displaced," their resentment to the subject of the questionnaire (Miller and Bugelski, 1948). *See* PERSONALITY THEORIES.

Miller also proved that the same type of reaction can be elicited from animals. He first conditioned two white rats to rise up on their hind legs and strike each other in order to cut off a painful electric shock. Then he placed one of the rats in a cage with a white doll about the size of a rat, and again administered the shock. The rat responded by striking the doll, (Miller, 1948). *See* DISPLACEMENT.

The stimulus-response theory has been criticized on several counts. First, it does not adequately define either stimulus or response. Human beings are constantly responding to highly complex situations, and it is practically impossible to identify the precise stimulus to which they are reacting. The same argument holds for the response; it is rarely as simple as blinking the eyes or even reacting to a traffic light—and even these responses may vary from situation to situation. The fact that we are usually engaged in making complex responses to complex stimuli and cannot analyze our behavior into such small units makes it difficult to accept the S-R association as the basic psychological molecule. For this reason Miller has called the S-R concept a "hyphen theory" since it is clearer about the connection between stimuli and responses than in describing either of these components separately.

Probably the most telling criticism of the theory is that in attempting to describe behavior in observable terms, it does not do justice to the richness and complexity of experience. It sounds extremely scientific to describe stimuli in terms of the wavelength of a red traffic signal, the energy that reaches the motorist's eyes, and the speed and strength of his reaction in putting his foot on the brake. But what of the driver's inner motives, anxieties and feelings, and the many unconscious events that influence behavior? S-R theorists tend to ignore these factors because they are too subjective to be "scientific." And even when they recognize that internal processes intervene between stimulus and response, they usually put much less emphasis on them than on the measurables in the situation.

STIMULUS-STIMULUS ASSOCIATION (S-S Association, Sensory-Sensory Association). A learned association between two stimuli.

S-S associations are commonly formed when we learn to use one stimulus as a cue to another. For example, when we construct a mental map of a given neighborhood, we note that a right turn at a certain corner will lead to the drugstore but a left turn will take us to the post office. The S-S associations will therefore be right turn—drugstore,

left turn—post office. Such learning comes about by exploring the area, and during this process the corner acquires a new quality: it becomes a sign or signal that a new stimulus (drugstore or post office) can be reached by making the appropriate turn. Once we learn these associations, we find it easy to get our bearings and arrive at the destination we want.

S-S associations are found throughout our experience. We establish them when we learn to associate a face with a name, a theory with its originator, or one word with another in a familiar quotation. The general idea was first proposed by the associationist philosophers John Locke and David Hume in the eighteenth century. They described these associations in terms of ideas or images in the mind—for instance, turning to the right gives rise to the *idea* of drugstore—and they formulated many principles which govern the formation of these associations.

Many of these principles, such as the law of contiguity (events close together tend to be associated) remain in use today, but more recent investigators of learning do not put so much emphasis on ideas and images, since they are hard to define and cannot be tested in the laboratory. For these reasons E. C. Tolman conceived associations in terms of stimuli, and applied the term "expectancy theory" to his concept of learning. This term fittingly describes the experience: we expect to see the drugstore if we turn to the right, and we expect to see a certain man if we hear his name called. *See* ASSOCIATIONISM, LOCKE.

STREPHOSYMBOLIA (literally, "twisted symbols"). A term coined by the neurologist S. T. Orton in 1928, to denote the tendency of some children to reverse letters while learning to read or write. Examples are was for saw, no for on, gril for girl.

Orton ascribed the error to inconsistent dominance of one hemisphere of the brain over the other. He knew that in the right-handed person, the left hemisphere is dominant while in the left-handed person the right is dominant, but he believed that in some children there is no set dominance. He also believed that a conflict of dominance may occur if a child is forced to use his right hand when the left is naturally favored.

This raised the question, what does inconsistent and conflicting dominance have to do with reversing letters? Orton's answer was that the two hemispheres are mirror images of each other, and in cases where dominance shifts from one hemisphere to the other, the child actually *sees* the words from left to right at one time and from right to left at the other.

Orton's theory was widely accepted for many years as one of the major explanations of reading disability. Today it carries far less weight for two reasons. First, its neurological basis is considered questionable: there is no concrete evidence for the mirror images, and "the left cerebral hemisphere is usually dominant for speech regardless of the handedness of the individual, with the exclusion of those who have cerebral injuries early in life" (Penfield and Roberts, 1959). Second, many other causes of reading disability have been discovered in recent years. *See* READING DISABILITY, DIRECTIONAL CONFUSION, HANDEDNESS.

STRESS. A condition or situation, internal or environmental, that imposes demands for adjustment on the organism. Any form of stress tends to evoke extra effort and new adaptive activities, but prolonged or excessive stress is apt to overtax the individual's resources and may lead to decompensation, that is, a breakdown of organized functioning. *See* GENERAL ADAPTATION SYNDROME, TRANSIENT SITUATIONAL PERSONALITY DISORDERS.

Stresses may be biological or psychological, or mixtures of the two. Biological stresses call primarily upon the physical defenses of the organism, and include both acute and chronic diseases, all types of handicaps and defects, and special conditions such as malnutrition, starvation, excessive noise, extreme heat or cold, hallucinogens, and poisons. Psychological stresses evoke the individual's ego defenses (sense of security, confidence, willpower, and defense mechanisms), and include any events that produce feelings of grief, panic, guilt, failure, tension or disappointment. Some situations, such as combat, natural catastrophes and extended illness put a strain on both our psychological and physical resources. *See* COMBAT REACTIONS, CIVILIAN CATASTROPHE REACTIONS, PANIC, GRIEF, PRISONER OF WAR REACTIONS, BRAINWASHING, STARVATION REACTIONS.

The situations that produce stress may be divided into the following four types: deprivations, frustrations, conflicts, and pressures. Each of these may arise from either internal or external sources, as indicated in the following brief descriptions:

Deprivation. Examples of psychological deprivation are maternal deprivation (lack of mothering), social deprivation (isolation), oral deprivation (limited sucking opportunity for infants), and sensory deprivation. Physical deprivations include such conditions as anoxia, loss of sleep, vitamin deficiency, and glandular insufficiency.

Frustration. Deprivations and frustrations frequently overlap, but the emphasis in frustration is on obstacles that thwart our drives or impede our progress toward a goal. Major sources of external frustration include physical events such as accidents, storms, earthquakes; and social situations, such as racial or religious discrimination, economic depression, war, and social rules and regulations. Internal frustrations also stem from a wide variety of conditions: disfigurement, lack of social grace, awkwardness, insufficient skill or ability, excessive inhibition, fatigue, and disease.

Conflict. Conflicting needs and goals also put us under a special strain. We frequently find it difficult to make decisions and choices, especially when we have to forego one desirable alternative for another, or when we are called upon to make an important decision for which we feel ill-prepared.

Psychologists classify conflicts into three major types: (1) *approach-avoidance* conflicts, involving strong attractions and strong repulsions toward the same goal—for example, when a job brings substantial rewards but involves heavy responsibility or long separation from one's family; (2) *double-approach* conflicts, in which two or more goals are almost equally desirable—for example, the child who is torn between separated parents, or the young man who is torn between patriotism and pacifism in time of war; and (3) *double-avoidance* conflicts, in which the alternatives are equally objectionable—for example, the woman who has "missed the boat" and must choose between a loveless marriage and a possible lifetime of waiting. *See* GRADIENT, VALENCE.

The examples just given represent conflicts of the internal type in which the individual is engaged in a tug-of-war with himself. Another major source of stress is the environmental type of conflict arising out of such external situations as economic competition, union-management difficulties, and racial problems.

Pressure. Pressures may also stem from inner and outer sources. Some representative internal pressures are unrealistic aspirations, rigid moral standards, excessive conscientiousness. These attitudes, whatever their source, make us drive ourselves too hard, take on the responsibilities of other people, and seek goals that cannot be achieved. They are one of the chief sources of feelings of failure and frustration and disappointment in ourselves—all of which serve to increase our internal stress even further.

Outer pressures arise from the demands of other people and external situations. In our society parental expectations are one of the major sources of pressure, and frequently account for the unrealistic goals people often set for themselves. Examples of other environmental pressures are the business executive's responsibility for his organization, the necessity to make "decisions, decisions, decisions" in any managerial position, the demands of children (both healthy and handicapped) on the mother's time and energy, the added burden of undertaking community responsibilities, and the overall pressure of a society that is constantly becoming more complex and competitive.

Deprivations, frustrations, conflicts and pressures exert varying amounts of stress on our adjustive capacities. Acute but transient stresses impose a strain on our defenses all at once; milder but more persistent stresses tend to corrode them over a period of time. The nature of the stress situation is just as important as its degree. What appears to be minor for one person may be "the last straw" for another. Stresses that touch one individual to the quick roll completely off another. Attitudes and "ego-involvement" are often the determining factors: one person may accept the loss of his job as an inevitable event, another sees it as a basic threat to his inner security. It is also important to recognize that stresses can have positive as well as negative effects. They not only tend to wear us down, put us under excessive strain and exploit our weaknesses, but they may also key us up, intensify our efforts, and challenge us to utilize our maximum resources. Without stress we might have more peace of mind, but our lives would remain at a dead level. *See* EGO INVOLVEMENT.

There are two general types of reaction to stress. One is technically termed "ego defense oriented" and occurs when we resort to escape mechanisms that enable us to avoid threatening situations, or at least soften their impact. We may revert to infantile behavior in order to shift responsibility to others, seek substitute satisfaction in daydreams, deceive ourselves with such phrases as "everything happens for the best," or insulate ourselves from reality by adopting a cynical or "don't care" attitude. On the other hand, with a more positive reaction to stress, we can devote ourselves to meeting the situation and surmounting the difficulties as best we can. This approach is termed "task-oriented."

A task-oriented approach requires us to make an objective appraisal of the situation and choose the most constructive and rational way of handling it. In some cases this may involve attacking the problem head-on; in others, it may be advisable to withdraw by refusing to compete against overwhelming odds, to readjust our goals, or limit ourselves to aspects of the situation with which we can deal; in still others, it may be best to work out a compromise that enables us to accept substitute goals or take half a loaf instead of none at all. In any case, the most difficult step is not in analyzing the problem and considering alternative solutions, but in making a decision one way or another. We usually find that the process of deciding in itself helps to relieve our stress and pave the way toward effective action.

Finally, one of the basic necessities of life is to develop a capacity to withstand stresses. Stress tolerance, or frustration tolerance as it is more often called, is considered one of the major foundations for mental health. How can it be achieved? The process must be started early in life and encompasses at least three steps, with the responsibility resting largely with the parents. It involves, first, establishing a sense of security, self-esteem, and confidence through liberal expressions of approval, encouragement, and affection; second, the cultivation of skills and abilities through a graduated series of physical and social activities, so that the child will be well equipped to meet the demands of life; and third, practice in meeting actual stresses by allowing the child to face situations that involve frustration, deprivation and pressure in manageable doses—especially by avoiding overindulgence and overprotection, and by providing the child with positive opportunities for independence, for taking responsibility, and for finding solutions to his own problems.

STUPOR. A mental state in which the individual is totally, or almost totally, unresponsive and immobile.

The condition occurs in a wide range of mental illnesses, including both organic and functional syndromes. However, it takes different forms in these two types of disorder, and the similarity is probably more apparent than real. In the organic cases, which include toxic states, brain disease, and epilepsy, the stuporous state is accompanied by a complete suspension of conscious thought processes for brief or longer periods. The patient is in a daze, wears a blank look, and is completely unaware of his surroundings.

In the psychogenic cases, on the other hand, the patient is mute and motionless, but there is no loss of consciousness or sensation, and mental activity may be intense. This is particularly true of catatonic and depressive stupors. These patients may become so utterly indifferent to their surroundings that they have to be tube-fed, yet at the same time their minds may be occupied with the most vivid hallucinations and delusions. In some cases, however, they shift suddenly from immobility to extreme or impulsive activity. Psychogenic stupor may also occur in combat exhaustion and severe panic reactions. Patients who suffer from these conditions usually report that their thinking processes were almost completely blocked and that their minds were "frozen" during the period of acute stress. *See* BLOCKING, MUTISM, PANIC.

When a psychogenic stupor is associated with a disorder, such as manic-depressive reaction, from which recovery is the rule, it is termed benign. When it is a symptom of disorders from which there is little or no chance of recovery, as in some cases of catatonic schizophrenia, it is often described as malignant.

STUTTERING. A speech disorder characterized by spasmodic blocking and repetition of initial sounds of words.

In its milder form, stuttering involves only a few important words that require the greatest effort for articulation, particularly those beginning with b, d, s, and t. In its more severe forms the blocking occurs on almost any sound, and the struggle to speak is accompanied by grimacing, head jerking, and body contortions.

Stuttering is most likely to appear in situations that arouse tension and anxiety. It rarely occurs when the stutterer is alone, when he whispers or sings, or when he is talking to an individual who is much younger than himself, or whom he considers inferior. When the attack does occur, it is usually momentary and is followed by a period of smooth and fluent speech.

Stuttering has been reported throughout recorded history and among both primitive and advanced societies in all parts of the world. A great many renowned persons have been afflicted, among them Moses, Aristotle, Demosthenes, Charles Lamb, Winston Churchill, and Somerset Maugham. Today there are close to two million stutterers in the United States alone, with males outnumbering females by about four or five to one. The onset of persistent stuttering occurs before the age of six years in 90 per cent of cases, but

should not be confused with the normal difficulties encountered by children in learning to master speech. The disorder is found on all social levels, although the incidence is highest in middle and upper class families.

Stuttering is a puzzling disorder, and a wide variety of theories has been suggested. At one time it was attributed to anatomical defects of the tongue or palate, but this approach has been completely discredited. Forty years ago Coriat (1928) advanced the Freudian theory that the stutterer is fixated, or arrested, at the oral stage of psychosexual development and derives an unconscious satisfaction from the use of his mouth. Greene and Wells (1927) ascribed the disorder to a basic susceptibility to emotional tension and a tendency to excitability and uncontrolled reactions. Froeschels and Jellinek (1941) believed it is due to a disturbance in thought processes which makes it hard for the stutterer to find words and form sentences. They considered this disorder basically physiological but aggravated by psychological stress.

Recent investigations have centered around three types of causes: hereditary predisposition, neurological defect, and psychological factors. The hereditary theory maintains that there is a constitutional disposition to stuttering in situations of stress. At first sight this theory seems to be supported by the recent investigation of Johnson (1961) which revealed nine times as many stutterers in the families of stutterers as in the families of non-stutterers. However, it is generally believed that the tendency to run in families is not due to heredity but to environmental influences. Children tend to imitate other family members who stutter, and as Johnson himself has pointed out, parents who are or have been stutterers focus so much attention on the child's early speech difficulties that they create a tense situation which encourages the development of the disorder.

Even though there may be no heredi-tary basis for stuttering, the theory of constitutional predisposition may still ap-ply. Berry and Eisenson (1956) com-pared the history of five hundred stut-terers with five hundred non-stutterers and found that the stutterers were, as a group, more awkward, less adept at learning motor skills, and distinctly re-tarded in learning to walk and talk. Barbara (1959) believes that they are predisposed to emotional imbalance in general, and to motor and speech dis-organization in particular. He believes the disorder develops when special stress is placed upon this organic instability by overbearing or neglectful parents who keep the child from expressing himself freely.

Neurological theories have not fared well in recent years. Some investigators have pointed out that many children have suffered from severe infectious dis-eases just before the onset of the dis-order, and suggest that there may be residual brain damage in these cases. Yet there is no evidence of brain damage in the vast majority of cases, and stutterers do not differ from non-stutterers in their ability to co-ordinate their speech muscles.

Newer research also questions the view that forcing a naturally left-handed child to use his right hand causes a neurological confusion that results in stuttering. The theory holds that the right hemisphere of the brain controls speech functions in the left-handed per-son, the left hemisphere controls these functions in the right-handed person, and that compelling the child to use the non-preferred hand is bound to disrupt cortical control. Penfield and Roberts (1959) have shown that this theory could not be correct since the left hemisphere controls speech functions for both right- and left-handed persons. Other researchers have also pointed out that only a few stutterers are naturally left-handed, and that most children who are forced to change hands do not develop the stuttering. Where this does happen, it is probably due to parental pressure and the tensions involved in making the change rather than to any neurological factors. *See* STREPHOSYM-BOLIA.

Psychological theories are receiving the bulk of attention today. Barbara maintains that stuttering is a neurotic symptom which can usually be traced to faulty parent-child relationships. Chil-dren who are unwanted or ill-treated become basically anxious and cannot handle tense and threatening situations in an organized way. The speech situa-tion is particularly difficult for them because they have trouble communicat-ing with their parents. He believes the actual onset of the disorder, however, is often precipitated by a traumatic ex-perience which puts the child under special stress: a bad fright, an opera-tion, severe punishment, or in some cases forced conversion from left- to right-handedness. This first stuttering re-action has a special effect on the anx-ious child. Even if it is slight, it makes him self-conscious and tense. His ten-sion increases—and so does his stutter-ing—if his schoolmates ridicule him and his parents become apprehensive and try to force him to stop. As he grows older, he may try to avoid situations in which he is called upon to speak, and usually adopts bodily gestures and contortions to help him over the hurdle of speech. These solutions do not work well, and speaking becomes an ordeal which fills him with a sense of panic and disaster. In extreme cases he may become increasingly frustrated and un-able to enjoy himself, and later in life he may even withdraw from society to live the life of a hermit.

Johnson (1961) believes that the criti-cal period for the development of stut-tering occurs during the third and fourth years when the child is first learning the delicate art of speaking smoothly. If the parents become concerned about his natural mistakes, and constantly correct him, they may communicate their worry and make him hesitant and fearful whenever he tries to express himself. As a result, the normal "primary stuttering" becomes transformed into "secondary" or "actual" stuttering. Sheehan et al. (1962) believe that children who learn to fear speech situations for this or other reasons develop an "approach-avoidance" conflict—that is, they want to avoid speaking but at the same time feel that they must go through with it. They are then pulled in two directions at once and become momentarily blocked—that is, they stutter. This blocking is followed by actually succeeding in saying the word, and a consequent reduction of tension. The "reward" of reduced tension is believed to reinforce the pattern of stuttering. *See* STRESS.

In general, stuttering may be viewed as a disruption of speech patterns precipitated by situations that arouse acute tension. It is widely prevalent because the speech mechanism is so delicately balanced and communication is so important in life. In fact, most of us stutter at times, especially when we are subjected to special stresses that threaten our security, such as speaking in public, introducing important people to each other, or going through traumatic experiences such as near accidents. Such stuttering is only occasional and clears up soon after the stress situation has passed. Persistent stutterers, on the other hand, are afflicted with an intense state of "stage fright" whenever they speak, and the self-consciousness created by the stuttering itself adds to the tension and prolongs the reaction. In other words, a vicious circle sets in and causes the stuttering to become chronic.

How can this vicious circle be broken? Today the approach to therapy is a comprehensive one in which stuttering is viewed as a function of the total personality rather than merely a speech disturbance. The objective is not only to re-educate speech patterns through training procedures, but to eliminate faulty emotional reactions through psychotherapy and other psychological approaches.

It is important to begin treatment as early as possible, before the faulty speech patterns and emotional reactions become fixed. During the early stage of stuttering, between five and ten years of age, the therapist works primarily with the parents in attempting to ease their demands on the child and create a more relaxed home atmosphere. In some cases the parents enter into individual or group therapy themselves; in others, they are given instruction on such questions as helping to prevent "speech consciousness" by refusing to make an issue of stuttering, reducing tension in the child's life as a whole, developing co-ordination through exercises and sports, improving the child's general health, using better methods of discipline, and encouraging a sense of confidence and security in all situations including those involving speech.

Adolescent and older stutterers become acutely self-conscious and develop feelings of inadequacy and even self-hate. They are easily discouraged and constant reassurance is necessary to keep them in therapy. Here, too, it is important to relieve tension in their lives as a whole. They should also be encouraged to express their inner doubts, conflicts and resentments; group discussions are often helpful in this process. Most of the treatment is devoted to developing a feeling of adequacy in speech situations. Many techniques are used, including practice in articulation and phonation, repeated readings of the same material, group discussion of interesting topics, and breathing exercises.

Some therapists find that training patients to stutter voluntarily helps them gain control over the habit; a mirror and tape recorder are often used as adjuncts in this procedure. Faulty speech patterns can also be modified by combining practice in voluntary stuttering with helping stutterers become aware of the speech muscles involved in making difficult sounds. In addition, tranquilizing drugs are sometimes administered to reduce tension and demonstrate that stuttering is not inevitable in social situations. A well-rounded treatment program is usually effective in completely relieving or at least reducing the severity of stuttering. The symptom may, however, reappear temporarily when disturbing experiences occur. *See* BEHAVIOR THERAPY, READING DISABILITY, DIRECTIONAL CONFUSION, HANDEDNESS.

SUBITIZING. Perceiving at a glance how many objects are presented without estimating or counting.

It takes considerable time for children to learn to count. Ordinarily they achieve this ability two or three years after they first begin to speak. It is therefore considered a rather complex and advanced mental process. Studies of counting, however, have shown that there are two other methods of determining the number of objects. We can estimate or guess the number without counting, and we can "subitize." In subitizing, we grasp the number of objects without going through any process of counting or estimating.

Experiments have turned up the interesting fact that certain animals can subitize as well as human beings. Birds and squirrels can be trained to distinguish six or seven irregularly shaped spots when they are presented for a fraction of a second, and human beings cannot do any better. In one experiment (Koehler, 1943), the birds were even able to solve a problem that involved matching *groups* of spots. They were first trained to raise the lid of a box to get a reward of food. After that they were shown a certain number of spots, say five, and were then presented with several boxes which had different numbers of spots printed on their lids. The birds actually picked out the five spot box, apparently by matching the

two groups of spots. Moreover, they could do the same with other combinations, but again the total number of spots could not exceed seven.

Birds can also learn to stop eating seeds when they have reduced the supply to a certain number, such as three or four. To train them, the experimenter repeatedly shoos them away from a small pile when they have eaten all but that particular number. It is even possible to train them to leave the same number of grains shown to them on a piece of cardboard. (Hassmann, 1952)

These experiments might suggest that the talking and counting horses in vaudeville acts may be "subitizing" even if they cannot really count. However, investigators have shown that they do neither. They are actually responding to subtle cues given by their trainer, even though he may not realize he is giving them—an example of a "self-fulfilling prophecy" (Rosenthal, 1968). *See* LEARNING TECHNIQUES.

Research on subitizing has a much more important bearing. It has revealed that there is a stage below that of counting, and it has helped science to draw a sharper line between animal and human learning. Even though humans can subitize no better than animals, they can develop their mathematical ability to a far higher degree by using the more advanced processes of estimating and counting—not to mention all the other procedures involved in mathematics.

SUBJECTIVE TONES. Auditory sensations or hallucinations in which certain notes or melodies are heard in the absence of external stimulation.

A common type of subjective tone is ringing in the ears, or tinnitus. This disorder frequently accompanies acute ear ailments, such as Menière's disease, and disappears when the condition is remedied. It may also occur when no physical disease can be detected, and in this case may be due either to neural damage or to psychological factors. In the psychogenic cases it is usually diagnosed as a conversion, or hysterical, symptom. Various kinds of subjective sounds may also occur during the aura, or premonitory stage, that often precedes an epileptic attack.

Persistent subjective tones can be extremely disturbing, as they were to the composer Robert Schumann, who suffered from aural hallucinations during his last years. He incessantly heard one particular note, an a, which made life almost unbearable for him. *See* OCCUPATIONAL NEUROSIS, AURA, CONVERSION REACTION.

SUBLIMATION. The unconscious process of finding acceptable expression for unacceptable drives; sometimes classified as a defense mechanism.

Ordinarily urges and impulses which conflict with the dictates of conscience or the rules of society are either suppressed or repressed—that is, we either consciously or unconsciously hold them down and deny them direct expression. But these drives are often too powerful to be simply obliterated by such devices. They not only remain in existence, but exert considerable pressure for an outlet of some kind. One way of providing that outlet is to redirect them into new and more acceptable channels.

If the process of redirecting or rechanneling dangerous drives occurs on an unconscious, or primarily unconscious, level, it is called sublimation. Finding constructive outlets for forbidden or guilt-laden drives not only protects us from the anxiety and tension they would otherwise produce, but often gives us additional satisfactions as well. An overpowering sexual drive may be transmuted into romantic poetry that evokes praise and admiration. Aggressive impulses may be converted into successful activity on the football field. Some theorists of the psychoanalytic school go much further and claim that scientific research may be a sublimation

of voyeurism, the drive to watch the sexual act; or that an ambition to become a mortician may be a sublimation of a powerful "death instinct." *See* LIBIDO, DEATH INSTINCT.

The theory of sublimation has met with opposition on two major counts. First, many people find it hard to accept the idea that higher cultural forms, such as art and science, can be "reduced" to more primitive impulses. Second, it is difficult to conceive that the actual energy—for example, sex or hostility—is rechanneled into new outlets. If this occurred, one would expect the original drive to be reduced in intensity or even eliminated entirely. Yet recent investigations, particularly of sexual activities, indicate that the drive usually remains as strong as ever. And even where it might appear to be diminished, this may only be due to the fact that the new activities reduce the feelings of *tension* which the drive builds up instead of reducing the drive itself.

SUBLIMINAL PERCEPTION. Perception of stimuli below the level of awareness; response to stimulation that is too weak or too rapid to be consciously reported.

Subliminal stimulation can best be described through a simple experiment. A subject is asked to look fixedly at a lighted ten watt bulb, and its intensity is gradually reduced by a dimmer until he no longer reports that he sees it. Stimulation which has an intensity below that level, or "threshold," is called subliminal stimulation. Another technique is to flash a picture so rapidly that it is just below the threshold of normal awareness—that is, when asked if he saw it, the subject says he did not.

Two questions have been raised by investigators who have experimented with subliminal stimulation. Can human beings respond to stimulation that is below the threshold of awareness? And if they can respond, how much can they be affected by the stimulation? Some advertisers have claimed that people can not only register subliminal impressions but can actually be motivated to buy specific products. These claims aroused widespread alarm in the late 1950s, since they suggested that consumers might be influenced by advertising of which they were not even aware. Congress was called upon to put a stop to this insidious form of behavior control, and the periodical *Advertising Age* suggested that a ban be put on subliminal advertisements pending full investigation.

The "experiment" that created this furore consisted of presenting the words "Eat Popcorn" and "Drink Coca-Cola" alternately on a motion picture screen every five seconds during the regular presentation of a film in a New Jersey theater. The exposure time was reported to be 1/3000th of a second, far faster than any previously reported subliminal stimulation. The commercial firm that conducted the trial claimed that the sale of popcorn rose more than 57.5 per cent and the sale of Coca-Cola 18.1 per cent as compared to a "previous period." The details of the procedure, however, were never fully revealed.

The experiment raised a number of crucial questions. Assuming that the results were actually achieved, did the advertisements create a need that was not there before, or did they raise a previously felt need above the threshold of action? How many people purchased popcorn for the first time? Were there uncontrolled factors, such as weather conditions, that could account for the results? Could long-established behavior patterns be changed by subliminal stimulation? These and other pertinent questions were left entirely unanswered by the experimenters.

Others, however, did attempt to test the validity of the technique. The Federal Communications Commission reported that a television station in Maine transmitted public service messages at subliminal levels, but with "negative results." During a regularly scheduled telecast, the BBC flashed the message "Pirie Breaks World Record" at subliminal speed. The results were largely negative, and the few viewers who did respond were believed to possess such low visual thresholds that for them the message was not subliminal (Mannes, 1957). In a better controlled experiment, a film of a speech by a presidential candidate was shown to two audiences. During one presentation the word "good" was flashed on the screen one hundred times, and during the other the word "bad" was exposed the same number of times. These words were found to have no influence whatever on the opinions of the audiences.

Two other experiments are particularly noteworthy. Byrne (1959) projected a slide containing a picture of a spoon of rice with the legend "Wonder Rice" for .01 second at 10-second intervals during the showing of an instructional film. The same film was shown to a control group, with a slide containing four lines in meaningless order. When a picture of the spoon of rice was shown to both groups afterward, there was no significant difference in the number who said they had ever seen it in an advertisement, or in the number who chose the name Wonder when asked if they associated the spoonful with either Monarch or Wonder rice. Calvin and Dollemayer (1959) flashed the words "Choose right" and "Choose left" on a tachistoscope, and found that these subliminal commands had no effect on subjects who were asked to guess whether a "right" or a "left" circle was correct. When the words were exposed at .02 and .03 seconds, a few subjects reported that they could actually see them, indicating that some individuals can respond to much more rapid stimulation than others.

In spite of these negative findings, some investigators suggest that a fragment of a so-called subliminal message might rise above the threshold and influence behavior. The fragment might even be added to a tendency to respond and bring it up to threshold level. Or we might ourselves add to it and complete the perception, just as we interpret the slight gestures of other people or imagine that a shadowy figure seen at night is an animal ready to pounce on us. This means, however, that the stimulation would not be wholly subliminal. It would simply be more subtle and marginal than the stimuli to which we normally respond, and perhaps so slight that we cannot report awareness of it. In any case, it is highly doubtful that such "minimal cues" could have a significant effect on our attitudes or behavior. And even if we grant that response to stimulation that is truly below the threshold actually occurs, there is no present evidence, as Berelson and Steiner (1964) point out, that subliminally presented messages would be more effective than normally recognized messages, or that they could force a person into action against his will. It hardly seems likely that weak stimuli would have a greater influence than strong stimuli. *See* DETECTION THEORY.

SUBSTITUTION. Finding or accepting alternative satisfactions when desired goals are blocked or unattainable.

This is a common and often constructive reaction to frustration. Many people resort to substitution when they have an intense drive toward a goal which they cannot or do not want to surrender. If they cannot go to one college, they go to another; if they cannot have a child of their own, they take steps to adopt one; if they cannot find satisfaction in their occupation, they look for an absorbing hobby.

As these examples indicate, substitution can be a conscious and deliberate process. It may also be a defense mechanism operating on an unconscious level. In this case its primary purpose is to reduce inner tension or anxiety.

The girl who is not invited to a dance may find herself raiding the refrigerator; and if her frustration continues, she may develop a compulsive drive to overeat.

There is often a hidden, symbolic significance in the choice of substitutes. In the case just mentioned, eating may be unconsciously associated with acceptance and love, an association established early in life when the girl's mother held her in her arms during feeding, or gave her special approval when she cleaned her plate. When she resorts to eating after being disappointed, she not only gains a physical outlet for tension but revives feelings of love and acceptance which give her reassurance. *See* OBESITY.

The healthy process of substitution can, and often does, become exaggerated or distorted. Many psychiatric symptoms, particularly in obsessional reactions, represent substitutive and symbolic satisfactions. The man who faces failure may dwell on his past accomplishments to such an extent that it becomes an obsession. Similarly, the woman who is inwardly beset by impure thoughts or immoral urges may develop a compulsive drive to keep her house spotlessly clean. *See* OBSESSIVE-COMPULSIVE REACTION, *also* DISPLACEMENT AND SUBLIMATION AS FORMS OF SUBSTITUTION.

SUBVOCAL SPEECH. Talking silently to one's self; an implicit use of language in thinking.

Most children think out loud until they learn that it is customary, and wiser, to keep their thoughts to themselves. They then develop the habit of holding an internal conversation when they have something to think about. Their thoughts, in other words, gradually take the form of "subvocal speech," or implicit manipulation of words. Some phychologists believe that *all* thinking falls into this pattern. Others, however, believe there are exceptions to this rule— for example, they claim we do not use language when we conjure up mental pictures of objects for which we have no names.

There is considerable experimental evidence for the subvocal use of language. Recordings made by means of electrodes attached to the tongue and throat indicate that these organs are highly active when we think. If a subject is instructed to count to three, the recording apparatus shows three distinct bursts of activity. If he is asked to think about "eternity," the records of nerve activity are very similar to those obtained from actually saying the word. The same is true of longer thinking processes, such as solving a mathematical problem. The professor who walks down the street muttering to himself is doing exactly what all the rest of us do, except that he is doing it vocally instead of subvocally.

Studies have also been made of deaf-mutes who communicate through hand gestures. When electrodes are attached to their hands, they pick up indicative nerve impulses while they are solving mental problems, and also while they are dreaming (Max, 1937). These findings are further evidence for the theory of implicit speech, since gestures are a form of language.

The theory of subvocal speech is interwoven with the larger question of the nature and physiology of the thinking process. There are two competing approaches. The *peripheralist* position holds that thinking actually *consists* in the movements involved in talking to ourselves or making gestures. The movements are always responses to stimuli and follow the principles of the conditioned response. The *centralist* position holds that thinking goes on inside the brain and nervous system, with muscular movements serving merely as accompaniments or facilitators of the central process.

The theory of subvocal speech represents the extreme form of the peripheralist position, as advocated by John B. Watson, founder of behaviorism. To him, the thinking process can be described entirely in terms of the implicit language habits noted above—"implicit" because they cannot usually be observed without the aid of instruments. The theory has been somewhat enlarged recently by studies which show that dreaming of events and imagining objects both involve eye movements.

The centralists, on the other hand, insist that movements which accompany thinking do not themselves constitute the thinking process, since our brain and not our muscles governs the decisions we make and the steps we take in solving problems internally. They claim that there is nothing in the physiology of the brain that requires it to be aroused only by stimuli from the sense organs that bring about muscular or glandular responses (the stimulus-response circuit). Instead, they suggest that groups of cells within the brain, or even the brain as a whole, may become spontaneously active. In support of the role of the brain in thinking, they offer such evidence as the following: (a) many brain-injured patients lose their ability to deal with abstractions even though they may still be able to respond to concrete situations; (b) electrical stimulation of certain parts of the sensori-motor area of the cortex leads to spontaneous production of speech sounds and may interrupt speech that is in progress—and surgical removal of tissue in these areas may produce a form of aphasia (Penfield and Roberts, 1959); and (c) a subject injected with a drug (curare) that completely paralyzed every muscle of the body including speech muscles for four hours showed a normal encephalogram, and reported full consciousness and no interference with thinking processes (Smith, Brown, Toman, Goodman, 1947). *See* HYPERMNESIA.

At the moment there is no way of choosing between the theories—rather, it is highly probable that thinking involves both central processes and motor mechanisms and that at times one of these components is more deeply involved than the other. *See* THINKING.

SUCROSURIA. A rare disorder of carbohydrate metabolism characterized by severe mental retardation, hiatus hernia, and sucrose in the urine. It is probably transmitted by a single recessive gene. *See* MENTAL RETARDATION (CAUSES)

SUGGESTION. The process of inducing uncritical acceptance of an idea or course of action.

Since many details concerning suggestion are discussed under separate topics, we will limit ourselves here to the highlights of the subject. Suggestion takes many forms, of which prestige suggestion and social suggestion are two outstanding types. The clearest illustration of prestige suggestion is the advertisement which associates a product with a well-known personality, either through a picture or a testimonial which implies that use of the product is a major factor in success: "She's beautiful. She uses—." Similar appeals are made by politicians and other propagandists who seek to gain acceptance of their ideas through reference to great men of the past.

Asch et al. (1940) have provided experimental proof of prestige effect. They asked groups of students to rank professions according to social usefulness and amount of intelligence required. Some groups were informed of the rankings supposedly made by other students, while others simply gave their own rankings without receiving other information. The results proved that suggestion had a substantial effect on many subjects in the first group—for example, those who were told that the other students had ranked politicians low tended to rank them low, and those who were told they were ranked

high tended to rank them high. When asked what politicians they had in mind, the group who ranked them low said they were thinking of "Tammany Hall politicians" and "the usual neighborhood politicians," while the group who rated them high thought in terms of statesmen such as Roosevelt, Hull, and La Guardia. No such consistent thought patterns were found in the control group.

The second major type, social suggestion, is the appeal to conformity: "More people buy . . . than any other kind." Experiments have shown that people tend to "follow the crowd" when the situation is ambiguous, fraught with emotion, or when they lack confidence in their own judgment. In ambiguous situations, such as election campaigns, many people tend to vote for the man who appears to be "the people's choice" —although we have a number of striking instances, such as the Landon-Roosevelt and Dewey-Truman campaigns, which show that this does not always occur. Pharmaceutical advertisers frequently make the most of our uncertainty and anxiety about matters of health by associating their products with the medical profession in one way or another. The behavior of individuals during a panic or lynching provide striking examples of the influence of emotional factors.

In his experiment on judgment of the length of lines, Asch (1951) has shown that an individual will tend to adopt the opinions of others who appear to be in unanimous agreement, and even those who resist the suggestion seem to feel anxious and doubtful. Berkowitz (1954) has shown that our acceptance or rejection of majority suggestion depends upon our attitude toward the group. He set up worker groups in such a way that members of one group developed a strong liking for each other and members of the other group did not. When individuals in the first group were told that others in their group wanted to set a standard of high productivity (or low productivity), he found that they were more likely to conform to the group norm than were the subjects who did not particularly like their fellow workers. He therefore concluded that we tend to conform most to groups that are attractive to us.

See also AUTOSUGGESTION, HYPNOSIS, HYPNOTHERAPY, SUGGESTION THERAPY, PROPAGANDA, PANIC, SOCIAL NORM, PUBLIC OPINION SURVEYS, ADVERTISING RESEARCH, PERCEPTUAL DISTORTION, ESTHETICS, ASTHMA, CHARCOT.

SUGGESTION THERAPY. A form of psychotherapy employed to alleviate distressing symptoms stemming from recent experiences rather than from a deep-seated personality disorder. Suggestion is usually classed as a supportive measure since it does not attempt to modify the basic personality of the patient.

The more superficial conversion symptoms, as well as anxiety states following accidents and other stress situations, frequently respond to confident, sympathetic reassurance and direct suggestion. The patient is usually told his symptoms are due to problems he has encountered rather than to a serious or lasting defect. The therapist then offers an explanation of how such symptoms arise and assures him they will soon disappear. After this he uses direct suggestion to show that they can be overcome. Some therapists put the patient into a hypnotic trance before giving the suggestions.

Let us say the patient is suffering from a hysterical paralysis of recent origin. After a diagnostic examination, the doctor assures him that he has no organic defect, and reminds him what a nuisance such a symptom can be. He then instructs the patient to move the affected limb slowly and without intense effort. When the patient has proved to himself that this is possible, he is generally asked to tell his story in full, with particular attention to the circumstances under which the disabling condition arose. The therapist then helps him to understand the meaning of the symptom and the purpose it has been serving, such as protection from a painful or threatening situation.

Suggestion is most often used with immature hysterical personalities, as well as with children and persons of limited intelligence. In the latter cases the explanations are kept to a minimum. If the patient suffers repeated relapses or acquires new symptoms, this is taken as a sign of deeper personality disorder. In such cases psychotherapy, or at least some form of emotional re-education, is recommended. *See* RE-EDUCATION, SUPPORTIVE THERAPY, HYPNOTHERAPY, AUTOSUGGESTION.

SUICIDE. Suicide is a psychological and social problem of great magnitude. It ranks tenth as a cause of death in this country, with about 20,000 taking their own lives each year. Over 200,000 people, however, make suicidal attempts, although some of these are believed to be gestures designed to elicit attention, control others, or express hostility.

Despite the discrepancy between attempted and actual suicide, it is often a fatal mistake to assume that people who threaten to commit suicide will not carry out their threat. In a study of 134 suicides, Robins et al. (1959) found that 68 per cent had expressed suicidal ideas and 38 per cent had stated their definite intention of killing themselves. In a similar study, Pokorny (1960) reported that thirty-one out of forty-four actual suicides had previously threatened or tried to do away with themselves. In any case, it is a cardinal principle of psychiatry to take any suicidal threat or attempt seriously. There is always a chance that it may actually be carried out—and if not, it may well be a desperate "cry for help."

Studies show that the largest number of attempts are made during the spring, and in the morning at the beginning of the week. Firearms account for about half of the deaths, and hanging, sleeping pills, gas (including car exhausts), jumping, poisons, drowning, and cutting arteries account for the rest in that order. The incidence is three times as high in men as in women, but women make more unsuccessful attempts. More than half the victims are over forty-five, with the rate among men increasing until old age, and among women increasing through fifty and then declining. The highest rates are among the divorced, the widowed, and the single, in that order; about 25 per cent live alone. Although all occupations are represented, the highest percentages are on the professional level, especially among lawyers, dentists, and physicians.

There are wide sociocultural differences in suicide. The Negro rate is much lower than the white rate: 3.9 versus 11.4 per 100,000. (However, a study by Hendin, 1969, indicates that the Negro rate is rapidly rising in ghetto areas, and in New York City actually exceeds the rate for whites in the twenty to forty-four age group.) The rate is generally higher in urban than rural areas, and in advanced as opposed to primitive societies. The annual rate is highest in Austria and the iron curtain countries and particularly low in "closed" societies such as the Hutterites. The reasons for some of the social variations seem fairly obvious, but others are extremely obscure. It is hard to account for the fact that Denmark and Sweden have a high rate and that another Scandinavian country, Norway, has a low rate; or that the incidence is low in Catholic Ireland and high in Catholic France. It has also been found that the incidence is much higher during economic depressions than during war or natural catastrophes such as earthquakes. The probable reason is that feelings of isolation and guilt are more likely to occur during depressions, and

people are sustained by group activity in war and other disasters.

Recent estimates indicate that about 40 per cent of male suicides and 20 per cent of female suicides occur as a result of ill health. Severe mental illness accounts for about 35 per cent of all cases. Of these, the highest number occur in psychotic depressions; among these the depressive phase of manic-depressive reaction ranks first, reactive psychotic depression second, and involutional psychotic reaction third. In a study of patients with psychotic depressions reported by Arieti (1959), 75 per cent had suicidal ideas and 10 to 15 per cent actually carried them out. A few patients also took members of their family along with them, to save them from the misery of life. Schizophrenic reactions of the schizo-affective type also account for some suicides. Neurotic depressions do not lead to actual suicide nearly so often as psychotic depressions, although many neurotics are afraid they will do away with themselves. Antisocial (sociopathic, psychopathic) personalities rarely make a wholehearted attempt, even though they may threaten to kill themselves as a means of dominating others and getting what they want.

Studies of the dynamics of suicide show that occasional cases are motivated by revenge, spite, or the desire to make others feel guilty. Sometimes these attempts are only half-hearted but succeed by accident, as when a person cuts his wrists and dies before he can be rescued. More frequently the act is motivated by a personal burden which the individual cannot bear: loss of a loved one, physical pain or disability, social or occupational failure, financial reverses, loneliness, or boredom. One of the reasons social, vocational, and financial failures precipitate suicide is that many people cannot endure loss of status and self-esteem.

In mental illness the motivation for suicide is believed to stem from unconscious levels of the personality. Two factors are most deeply implicated, and are frequently found together. First, the patient may become overwhelmed with feelings of guilt out of all relation to reality. These feelings may be a gross exaggeration of a trivial lapse, or take the form of a frank delusion. He may then try to do away with himself because he feels he is unworthy to live. Second, he may develop intense, overpowering feelings of hostility which "turn inward" and lead to self-destruction. *See* MANIC-DEPRESSIVE REACTION, PSYCHOTIC DEPRESSIVE REACTION, INVOLUTIONAL PSYCHOTIC REACTION.

Although the incidence is highest among older people, the number of suicides that occur among children and young people is substantial. About five hundred children and adolescents kill themselves every year. In fact, suicide is now the number two cause of death among college students, and is outranked only by cancer and accidents for the entire fifteen-to-nineteen-year-old age group. Lourie (1965) reports the case of a three-year-old girl who tried to throw herself in front of a car, to join her five-year-old sister who had recently died. He also cites the case of a four-year-old boy who attempted to jump out of a window after his twenty-year-old brother had killed himself in this way. Of forty suicidal children under study, he found that ten were seeking "punishment for guilt because of death wishes or masturbatory activities," while others were seeking to escape from an intolerable situation. He also suggests that in some cases the suicidal tendency originated in the child's early years when he "learned to hurt others by leaving them."

Yolles has shown that suicidal children usually lack close friends and do not participate in extracurricular activities at school (1965). Teicher and Jacobs (1965) studied a large number of cases and found that in 72 per cent of them one or both natural parents were absent from home, and in 20 per cent one parent had committed suicide. He also found that 22 per cent of the girls were pregnant or believed themselves to be pregnant. In another study, Bruhn (1962) found a much higher than average per cent of broken homes in the childhood of adults who committed suicide. In a large number of these cases (66 per cent), a prolonged absence or death had occurred in the family during the year preceding the suicide, indicating that early deprivation (due to the broken home) makes the individual especially vulnerable to later loss.

Studies made at the Suicide Prevention Center in Los Angeles and elsewhere indicate that the great majority of suicides can be prevented (Farberow and Shneidman, 1961). Here are the major reasons. First, most suicidal individuals are actually undecided about living or dying, and can therefore be headed off if their feelings are taken seriously and if they are given treatment outside the home. Second, the great majority give clear warning before they make any attempt ("My family would be better off without me," "I am putting my affairs in order because I won't be around much longer," "How do you leave your body to a medical school?"). These warnings are probably given because of their ambivalence and their desire to have others help them to *live* and not die. Third, most people who show a desire to kill themselves are suicidal for only a limited time; it is untrue that once a person is suicidal, he will always be suicidal. Fourth, the symptoms of acute depression are clear—despair, loss of interest, self-blame, sleeplessness—and this disorder can be more effectively treated than practically any other mental illness; in fact, the percentage of recovery is well over 90 per cent.

All these facts point to the need for emergency facilities throughout the country. The few that are now in existence have amply demonstrated their value. The Los Angeles center receives about five thousand calls every year, and large numbers of cases are being handled by Rescue, Inc., in Boston, the Save-A-Life League in New York City, Emergency Care in Chicago, and the Friends Center in Miami. All these agencies have trained personnel who help the individual over the crisis and offer more extended assistance from psychological, psychiatric, and religious consultants as well as from social agencies. Each of them has a round-the-clock telephone number which can truly serve as a lifeline for people in desperate straits. See EMERGENCY PSYCHO-THERAPY.

SULLIVAN, HARRY STACK (1892–1949). Sullivan is chiefly noted for his "interpersonal theory," an approach to personality and psychotherapy based on the crucial importance of interactions with other people.

Sullivan defines personality as "the relatively enduring pattern of recurrent interpersonal situations which characterize a human life." If we say a man is "an angry person" we are using a shorthand expression for the fact that he has reacted with anger in a large number of dealings with other people. In simpler terms, our relations with people determine what we are. They also determine our emotional security. If these relationships—especially with the "significant others" in our lives—are based on satisfying experiences, we feel secure; if they are based on experiences which have produced anxiety, we feel insecure and have probably developed defensive measures, or "security operations," that distort our relationships with other people and with ourselves as well. In the latter case, Sullivan (1953) proposes a therapeutic approach aimed at understanding and then altering those interpersonal relationships.

Sullivan presents a highly systematic approach which tends to be obscured by his use of special terms. Perhaps the clearest way of presenting his views is to outline his account of the development of the individual, since he contends that the process of becoming a human being is equivalent to the process of socialization, the process in which the values of the culture are gradually absorbed by the child from his parents and others in his environment. Moreover, personality is not "set" at an early age but is considered extremely malleable. The various stages of development—infancy, childhood, pre-adolescence, early adolescence, and late adolescence—are therefore viewed in the light of social patterns and interpersonal relations, not primarily as a sequence of biological, psychosexual drives, as in Freud. Biological needs are not ruled out, however, since both the "pursuit of satisfactions" (the biological needs) as well as the "primitive security operations" (avoidance of anxiety and attainment of "good feeling") are motivating forces at every stage. But the achievement of these satisfactions is always dependent on our relationships with other people and our ability to understand and manipulate our social environment.

In sketching Sullivan's account of personality development, three basic principles must be borne in mind. First, in his view, interpersonal relations include not only interactions with actual individuals and groups but with imaginary people such as fairy-tale figures (Paul Bunyan), idealized figures (a dream girl or childhood sweetheart), or personifications such as the government. If disturbed relationships to actual people or to personifications of illusory ideals dominate the life of the individual, they produce distorted perceptions, or "parataxic distortions" of the self and others; and in some cases these misconceptions become extreme enough to produce mental illness. Second, the unit of personality study is the "dynamism," a habitual reaction, attitude or feeling toward one or more persons. The term not only applies to part-dynamisms such as the way we tend to satisfy a basic drive like lust, but also to the entire emerging self, or self-dynamism which determines the way we utilize our available experience and carry on our relationships at any point in life. Third, the forces behind the evolution of our self-dynamism are the attempt to preserve self-esteem and security, and to ward off anxiety. In this process we ignore experiences that might arouse anxiety or have no value to our growing self ("selective inattention"), and exclude from awareness people and events that threaten our security and therefore arouse anxiety ("dissociation").

The infant's basic drives, or "satisfactions"—the need for sleep, food, etc. —create internal tensions which can only be dispelled by other people, and particularly by "the mothering one." The way these needs are met determines the kind of self-system he develops. If the mother feels tender and meets his needs without arousing anxiety, he will feel "euphoric" and secure. But if she feels threatened and responds to his signals with anxiety, this feeling will spread to the child by "empathy," and he will feel anxious and insecure.

Communication plays a major part in the development of the self. Interpersonal communication by empathy, or "emotional contagion" is termed "prototaxic"; communication by gesture and symbol, which comes next, is called "parataxic"; and the final stage of communication in which "consensual validation" occurs—that is, ideas expressed in commonly accepted language—is termed "syntaxic." All three modes, and especially the last two, come into play in socializing the child, for they enable him to know how his parents appraise him and what they expect of him. Impulses that arouse their disapproval and anxiety are gradually organized into the "bad-me"; those that are acceptable give rise to the "good-me," and others are ignored by the process of selective

inattention. Still other activities may provoke so much anxiety and anger in others that they are dissociated from conscious awareness—but may reveal themselves in dreams and fantasies. All these responses determine the child's "self-system." If, however, the child feels *totally* disapproved and unwanted, the boundaries of the self may be eliminated and a state of "not-me" characterized by overwhelming anxiety may be experienced in nightmares, emotional crises or the onset of schizophrenia.

As the child learns to communicate through speech, he gradually acquires social patterns and becomes a civilized person. Denial of his desires, often accompanied by punishment, is an important factor in teaching him what society demands. If he feels that the enforcement of authority is just and fair he will accept it without bad effects, but if punishment is irrational, arbitrary, and degrading, a "malevolent transformation" may occur, and he will become convinced that he lives among enemies and must trust no one. This, too, may lay the foundation for future mental illness.

When the child reaches grammar school age, he has his first real opportunity to compare the attitudes and behavior of his own family with significant persons in the outside world. He begins to question the infallibility of his family, and not only revises his conception of his parents but of himself as well. He also learns to compete and to compromise through activities with the gang—and if he does not have these opportunities he will invent imaginary playmates. However, if the patterns he has learned at home deviate greatly from the acceptable behavior in the community, or if his parents disparage his companions, he will lose the opportunity for realistic, corrective experience with his peers, and may come to feel that he is thrust into a world that is not right for him. This will tend to weaken rather than strengthen his personality.

In the preadolescent period a powerful need for personal intimacy appears, and the young person develops an exclusive one-to-one relationship with a close friend. This relationship gives him the experience of love uncomplicated by the "lust dynamism," and also enables him to see himself through the eyes of another who is like him and yet does not represent the authorities of society. Through this association he not only learns collaboration, but gradually corrects the "parataxic distortions," or fantastic ideas, about himself which he may have developed. The less intimate but equally potent relationship with a gang or group also teaches cooperation and helps to correct his ideas about himself. If he does not have the opportunity for any of these relationships, he may retreat into loneliness and become schizophrenic.

Adolescence brings with it a great need for security, a shift from a need for intimacy with a member of the same sex to intimacy with the opposite sex, and a need for "lustful satisfaction." If these three needs are satisfied, the personality continues to develop and interpersonal competence increases. But if the individual finds himself rejected or treated with disdain, or if he is fearful of intimacy of any kind, he may turn inward and seek satisfaction through masturbation. And if he does not grow out of his preadolescent attachment to a member of his own sex, he may develop homosexual fantasies, embark on a lifelong search for the "ideal" woman or man, or begin to lead a homosexual way of life.

The adult who has passed through each of these developmental periods successfully will achieve effective interpersonal relationships, and will find little need for security operations and dynamisms—that is, defensive measures aimed at protecting himself from anxiety. On the other hand, if defects have developed along the way he may become extremely dependent on one or another of the following dynamisms: obsessionalism, sublimation, selective inattention, hypochondria, algolagnia (masochism, sadism), paranoid conditions, "emotion" (fear, anger, conceit, envy, etc.), dissociation, and schizophrenic withdrawal.

For Sullivan, the therapeutic process is viewed—like the rest of life—as an interpersonal relationship. The therapist is not a detached observer, as in Freudian analysis, but a *participant* observer who plays an active part in the situation that confronts the patient. He identifies with the patient's anxiety or anger or delusions, and his *own* emotional reactions give him clues to the patient's faulty ideas and security operations. But in the main he tries to discover what went wrong at each period of the patient's life, using his own sensitivity to the presence of anxiety as his guide. He may, for example, note a sudden shift from one line of thought to another, and use this as an indication that the patient is fending off anxiety. He then follows up this lead to discover what the patient is screening out through selective inattention or dissociation. In this way he gradually discovers the patient's entire self-system, and in collaboration with the patient makes a direct attack on the distortions he has developed.

This whole procedure, or "psychiatric interview," divides itself into four stages: first, the "formal inception," in which the therapist quietly observes the patient as he explains why he is seeking help, noting his manner of speech, facial expression, bodily position, etc. He also allays some of the patient's anxieties by telling him what he already knows about him from other sources. Second, the "reconnaissance," in which the therapist collects all the information he can about the patient and his family through intensive interrogation. Third, the "detailed inquiry," in which the therapist examines areas or periods of the patient's life in which anxiety was particularly acute. In this process he tries to discover the characteristic security operations the patient has used in dealing with such situations as difficulty in playing with other children, in forming intimate relationships during adolescence, or in taking initiative in adult life. At the same time the therapist formulates hypotheses regarding the patient's problem, and tests them in two-way communication with him. Finally, he terminates the therapy by restating the difficulties which have brought the patient to treatment, and by summarizing what this collaborative process has revealed about the patient's interpersonal relationships and the probable effect of the patient's altered attitudes on his future relationships. *See* PARATAXIC DISTORTION, DYNAMISM.

SUPEREGO. The psychoanalytic term for the ethical component of the personality, which determines (a) our standards of right and wrong—our conscience; and (b) our aims and aspirations—the idealized image, or ego ideal, toward which we strive. Some theorists equate the term with conscience alone.

In the Freudian theory there are three divisions of the personality: the id, containing unconscious biological impulses; the ego, or conscious self, which controls these impulses and directs our actions; and the superego, which provides the standards by which the ego operates. The superego is the last of the three to be differentiated during development of the personality, and is regarded as a split-off portion of the ego. Its basic organization takes place gradually and unconsciously during the first five years of life, arising out of the demands and prohibitions of our parents as well as the tendency to identify with them and adopt, or "introject," their standards. It does not begin to take final shape as an internal authority, however, until the Oedipal phase at about four or five years of age, and for this reason is often referred to as the "heir to the Oedipus complex." Some interpreters claim that the ego ideal, with its positive aspirations, stems primarily from identification with the loving mother, while the conscience, with its prohibitions, stems primarily from the feared father and anxiety over castration. *See* OEDIPUS COMPLEX, CASTRATION COMPLEX.

The superego is not wholly formed during early childhood, but continues to develop throughout the adolescent and young adult years as we come into contact with admired models of behavior as well as the rules and regulations of society and the customs of our particular cultural group. These influences work largely on an unconscious level, and result in a more or less well-organized censor of our behavior, which supervises and criticizes both the ego and the id and is responsible for the repression of unacceptable impulses. When we violate its commands, we do so at the risk of incurring feelings of anxiety and guilt.

If the superego is too severe and rigid, the individual will usually become inhibited, anxious and unhappy. If it is too permissive and flexible, it generally leads to immature, irresponsible behavior and an egocentric personality. Either extreme renders the individual vulnerable to neurosis. *See* CENSOR, EGO, ID, EGO IDEAL.

SUPPORTIVE THERAPY. A general form of psychological treatment aimed at reinforcing existing defenses and alleviating distress through techniques that operate on a conscious level. It consists of "relieving symptoms by the use of motivation, suppression, ego-strengthening and re-education without the altering of the basic personality structure" (Watkins, 1960). *See* RECONSTRUCTIVE THERAPY.

The most frequently employed supportive measures are reassurance, encouragement and approval of desirable behavior. In some cases a more "repressive" approach is used—that is, the therapist attempts to eliminate symptoms by command, persuasion or hypnotic suggestion. In either case supportive measures are usually classified as a form of surface therapy, since their object is to help the patient handle his overt difficulties without attempting to explore their unconscious sources or bring about profound personality change.

In general, supportive measures of one kind or another are applied (1) to patients who are faced with relatively minor, limited or external problems, and who appear to have sufficient inner strength to meet them; (2) patients who are hospitalized for serious functional disorders, such as schizophrenia, and need emotional and social support to preserve morale, prevent deterioration, and stimulate socialization; (3) patients who are hospitalized for brain disorders, such as senile brain disease or lead poisoning, in order to make them feel more comfortable and minimize the effects of their distressing symptoms; and (4) patients who are engaged in long-term depth therapy, since the creation of a reassuring, accepting atmosphere helps to establish rapport between therapist and patient, to allay the patient's anxieties, and to encourage him to give voice to his innermost feelings.

A comprehensive enumeration of supportive approaches is found in Watkins, *General Psychotherapy* (1960). He lists the following twenty-eight techniques as "primarily supportive," though some may be partially reconstructive, since they may help to modify the personality of the patient: reassurance, suggestion (including autosuggestion), advice, reasoning and persuasion, motivation procedures (rewards, punishments), desensitization, ventilation and verbal catharsis (talking it out, expressive writing), abreaction, counseling (directive and nondirective; educational, vocational, per-

sonal, marital), rest, progressive relaxation, hypnotherapy, re-education (conditioned reflex and aversion therapy), environmental manipulation, social service, chemotherapies (when used as psychotherapy), placebos, physiotherapy (rehabilitation), occupational therapy, food therapy, recreational therapy, dance therapy, music therapy, art therapy, bibliotherapy, group therapy (supportive types), religious therapy (confession, pastoral counseling, participation in church activities), dynamic-supportive approach (helping the patient to become aware of the unconscious significance of various supportive procedures). *See* the Index and Category Index under Treatment Techniques and Facilities.

SUPPRESSION. A conscious effort to put disturbing thoughts and memories out of mind, or to inhibit the expression of unacceptable impulses and feelings.

When used in moderation, suppression is considered to be a healthy and necessary form of self-protection. We have all undergone distasteful experiences, and while it is useful to "get them out of our system," it is also helpful to allow ourselves a cooling-off period during which we refrain from talking about them. Many people become extremely upset and lose their perspective if they allow themselves to dwell too long or too intensely on their misfortunes.

Suppression is also a necessary and salutary means of protecting us against ourselves. At times all of us have desires or impulses which, if carried out, would violate the code of society, or our own personal code. Therefore, in our own interest and in the interests of our relationship with others, we have to exercise control.

Suppression, however, does not obliterate the experiences and desires we wish to put aside. Out of consciousness is not out of mind. Even if we do not allow ourselves to think about it, the disagreeable decision still has to be made and some outlet for our feelings and emotions has to be found. If we persist in our refusal to attend to them, we may find that a technique which began as a healthy form of adjustment may end up as an invitation to maladjustment. Moreover if suppression is overworked and becomes a standard pattern, it almost inevitably leads to a restricted, uninteresting, unimaginative personality. Often, too, the habit of suppressing one's self leads to the habit of suppressing others. In short, in order to be an asset, suppression must be used selectively, with discrimination.

Rigidly suppressed drives and experiences will almost inevitably find some expression of their own—and the more completely they are held down, the more drastic the expression. The person who refuses to think about a harrowing experience will not merely have dreams but nightmares during his sleep. He is also likely to be harassed by intrusive fantasies during waking life. The child who is constantly required to suppress his anger or jealousy will probably have repeated temper tantrums or develop into an extremely rebellious adolescent. The man or woman who has suppressed all sexual expression may later be overwhelmed by sexual urges, or find that they take strange forms.

In more extreme cases, suppression has been found to contribute to outright disorder. The suppression of all aggression and hostility may produce high blood pressure or other psychosomatic symptoms. The somnambulist tends to act out impulses which have been suppressed (or repressed) in waking life. The obsessive neurotic may become preoccupied with persistent thoughts or impulses which represent ideas that have been forced out of consciousness and denied normal expression. For the distinction between suppression and repression, see the latter topic; also INHIBITION.

SURROGATE. A person who takes the place of another; a substitute. In psychiatry the term is applied to a substitute parental figure.

A father-surrogate or mother-surrogate may replace the natural parent in the emotional life of the child. Contrary to the popular notion, it is quite possible for an infant to develop the same love and devotion toward a surrogate parent as toward the real parent, particularly if he has not been in contact at all with his real parent. If a surrogate is introduced after the child has formed an attachment to his original parent, it is usually more difficult to develop the same sense of intimacy. In some cases, however, it may actually be easier, depending on the personality of the surrogate and the needs of the child.

When a child is deprived of one or the other parent, or both, it is considered highly advisable to find parent substitutes with whom he can identify. A surrogate mother, if warm and accepting, will counteract the harmful effects of maternal deprivation in the very young child. A substitute father is necessary for the development of the child's sex role as well as for discipline and, above all, a sense of security. Older children frequently function more or less effectively as parent surrogates; so do teachers, camp counselors, Scout leaders, uncles, aunts and grandparents. The child may not fully recognize that these persons are acting in the role of parents, yet he usually transfers the emotions ordinarily felt toward real parents to these surrogates.

During psychoanalysis, surrogate parental figures such as uncles or teachers are often found to appear in dreams. They are believed to represent the patient's actual parents and to provide him with an opportunity to by-pass the "censor" and release his resentments or other unacceptable feelings. See MOTHERING, MATERNAL DEPRIVATION.

SYDENHAM'S CHOREA (St. Vitus' Dance). An infectious disease of childhood with both mental and physical symptoms. The condition is due to an inflammation of the cerebral cortex and basal ganglia resulting from rheumatic fever or other infectious diseases.

Physically, the effects of the inflammation are involuntary jerky movements, poor muscular co-ordination, and facial grimaces. Psychologically, choreic children are emotionally unstable, irritable, restless, quarrelsome and frequently subject to night terrors. They may find it hard to concentrate and pay attention, and are likely to be hypersensitive and fretful. Many of these children are disobedient and selfish, and some become extreme behavior problems. Their difficult behavior, however, may be largely a reaction to scoldings and punishment administered by parents who fail to understand the source of their tensions and difficulties.

Far more girls than boys are afflicted with chorea. Treatment consists of complete physical and mental rest as soon as possible after onset. Hospitalization is often recommended, particularly if the home environment may be disturbing to the child. Aspirin-like drugs are generally administered, sometimes with sedatives to control restlessness. Fever therapy is occasionally used for adolescents. The disease generally subsides within two to three months; but if neurotic symptoms and hyperactivity persist beyond that time, there may be a possibility of brain damage. *See* GANGLION.

SYMBIOSIS. A state of extreme mutual dependence between two people, most frequently a mother and young child; literally, "living together."

The term originated in biology, where it is used to describe the relationship between two organisms, such as certain plants and fungi, that live together and benefit each other. A symbiotic attachment between two human beings may be so close and exclusive that it inhibits the full development of one or the other partner. In extreme cases it may give rise to severe emotional disturbance, as in symbiotic psychosis, or lead to the transfer of an emotional disorder from one individual to another, as in *folie à deux*. *See* THESE TOPICS.

SYMBIOTIC PSYCHOSIS. The full name for this condition is "Symbiotic Infantile Psychotic Syndrome." It is one of two major mental illnesses found in early childhood, and occurs between the ages of two and five, with a peak at four. The other psychotic disorder is autism, or "early infantile autism."

In the second and third years of life the child's physical and emotional development ordinarily move rapidly forward, but in symbiotic children emotional development lags far behind. In sharp contrast to autistic children who are emotionally isolated, they remain in the stage of complete emotional dependence on the mother and cannot cope with the demands of walking, talking and social relationships which other children meet as a matter of course. *See* SYMBIOSIS.

A prolonged symbiotic relationship of mutual dependence may develop if a mother is completely "wrapped up" in her child, excluding all other relationships. This is particularly apt to occur if the father is totally disinterested in the child or absent from the home during his first years. As a result of this exclusive relationship, the child becomes so closely identified with the mother that he does not develop a definite ego of his own, and may not even see himself as a separate being at all. For this reason he becomes utterly bewildered and panicky when the mother is not with him.

Symbiotic children grow at an uneven pace and react in extreme ways to the slightest failure or frustration: one fall will make them give up trying to walk for months. Abrupt separation from the mother due to entering nursery school, hospitalization of the mother, or birth of a brother or sister, may precipitate a severe break with reality, and a full-blown psychosis may set in. They then become highly agitated, have violent temper tantrums, and may suffer from hallucinations in which they see themselves reunited with the mother. This stage often gives way to a complete withdrawal into themselves (autism), which they find more bearable than continuous panic. But this is no solution since it divorces them still further from reality.

It is interesting that symbiotic psychosis may lead to the state of withdrawal and unresponsiveness which characterizes early infantile autism, even though the two disorders appear to stem from opposite sources—one from a close, dependent relationship and the other from a cold, distant relationship to the mother. In both cases, however, the child fails to develop his own identity, does not adequately distinguish between himself and the outside world, and feels threatened by contacts with other people. And in both cases he defends himself against anxiety by retreating from reality and restricting his activities and relationships. See EARLY INFANTILE AUTISM.

In treating this severe disturbance, the therapist becomes a substitute mother and encourages the child to relive the early phases of his life, so that he can go through experiences which he missed because of the exclusive relationship to his mother. The objective is to help him develop a firm concept of his own identity—a satisfactory ego—and clear boundaries between the self and rest of the world. Treatment consists largely of giving the child an opportunity to explore many kinds of objects, and to release his feelings through dramatic play with dolls and puppets. In all his activities he needs constant help and encouragement until he is able to achieve greater self-awareness and an ability to function as an independent person. See PLAY THERAPY, PLAY.

Margaret S. Mahler, who discovered and named this disorder, cites the following case:

Illustrative Case: SYMBIOTIC PSYCHOSIS

George's father left for the Navy immediately after his birth. For two years the boy and his mother saw practically no one but each other. They rarely spoke, since speech was not needed, and George was given no opportunity to overcome the usual childhood uneasiness with strangers. Therefore, a "hello" from an unfamiliar person would be taken as a threat, and a pat on the shoulder would throw him into a fit of terror.

George's father returned just before his third year, but was morose and disinterested. Soon after this, the boy began to speak, but only in panic-stricken language which his mother termed "talking tantrums": "Whenever frustrated, but also without apparent cause, he would pace around the room, talking angrily to himself about something which seemed entirely unintelligible and irrelevant to his environment."

When his mother became pregnant, George began to have night terrors. At the same time he developed an absorbing and compulsive interest in exploring things by touch—particularly beer barrels at a neighboring brewery, pipes (his father was a plumber), and electrical appliances. This "reality testing" behavior took place because he was having difficulty discriminating between living and non-living things—as evidenced by the fact that he became frightened by electrical apparatus and fearful of the holes in a picket fence.

After the baby came, George wanted to wear her clothes. He repeatedly asked his mother why he should not be a girl, and was confused about differences in anatomy. When he entered kindergarten at six and a half, he was terrified by other children and kept saying, "I have a cat at home. I like my cat. I am a girl cat." His confusion about his own identity, and his bizarre behavior made it necessary to send him to a hospital. There he developed an acute fear of killing his mother and hallucinations in which he saw a fire destroying his little sister. The boy pleaded with the doctor to help him over-

come "these bad feelings in my head."
(Mahler, 1958, condensed)

SYMBOLIZATION. In psychiatry, symbolization is an unconscious mental process in which images or objects come to represent repressed thoughts, feelings, or impulses. The particular symbol is chosen because it is associated in some way with the repressed material, and can therefore stand for it.

The purpose served by this mechanism is to enable emotionally charged material to obtain expression without arousing excessive anxiety. To take a simple example, a woman who cannot admit to herself that she wants to be chased by a man may dream that she is being chased by a bear. In her dream she invests the bear with some of the emotions she feels for men and therefore gains an indirect, disguised outlet for her secret desire—without the dangerous consequences involved in expressing it openly. *See* CENSOR.

Symbolization has often been called "the language of the unconscious"; and by analyzing and interpreting symbolic gestures, acts and fantasies it is frequently possible to discover hidden conflicts, unacknowledged wishes, threatening impulses and disturbing memories. This can only be accomplished by highly trained and experienced practitioners since the symbols must be related to the individual's unique experience and unconscious tendencies. Even the more common symbols, such as the bear, may have different meanings in different contexts. Instead of sexual desire, the bear may signify sexual fear or the demands of an "overbearing" father (note the unconscious pun). Or it may echo back to a childhood experience when the dreamer actually encountered a bear-like dog.

Symbolization may operate on either a normal or pathological level. Here is a somewhat more complex example on the normal level: a student dreamed night after night that he was driving on a country road, but unaccountably found himself crossing and recrossing the same bridge a dozen times without ever arriving at his destination. Troubled by the dream, he went to see the college psychologist. While exploring the dream, the explanation suddenly occurred to him: he had been devoting evening after evening to playing *bridge* instead of studying, and had not allowed himself to become outwardly concerned about his future.

The following example, cited by Noyes and Kolb (1963), shows symbolization in operation on a pathological level: "A recently married woman was admitted to a hospital for treatment because of her unusual behavior. She stood on her head, was mute, and would communicate by using ballpoint pens which wrote in red ink. Later she explained her behavior as a means of expressing her anger at her husband for taking her money. She was in love with him so could not speak of her rage, yet the red ink symbolized it. Standing on her head represented both a defiant gesture and a wish for help by being found ill." *See* ART THERAPY.

The symbolization mechanism is a major feature of many psychological disorders. In phobic reactions, the patient develops intense, morbid fears of specific objects or situations that represent his underlying anxieties: germs, knives, elevators, crossing the street. In obsessive-compulsive neurosis, the patient experiences an indomitable urge to perform rituals, repeat certain phrases, picture certain scenes, steal certain objects—all of which have special unconscious significance for him. In conversion reaction, emotional conflicts are expressed symbolically through "body language"—that is, through specific functional ailments such as a lump in the throat (globus hystericus), a paralyzed limb, or double vision (diplopia). In schizophrenia, the patient may abandon communication through words and express himself through gestures, grimaces, and posturing. These symbolic acts are particularly hard to fathom since the schizophrenic's mental processes are often distorted beyond recognition; a recovered patient, however, may reveal that his oustretched arms represented an attempt to put a stop to all evil by blessing the world at large. *See* SOMATIC COMPLIANCE, RITUAL, STEREOTYPY, GLOBUS HYSTERICUS, BODY LANGUAGE, PYROMANIA, KLEPTOMANIA, DREAM INTERPRETATION (MODERN), PHOBIC REACTION, CONVERSION REACTION, OBSESSIVE-COMPULSIVE REACTION.

Illustrative Case: SYMBOLIZATION (SYMBOLIC OBJECT)

"A schizophrenic girl invariaby fought as though in panic if any attempt were made to remove a piece of dirty white cloth she habitually wore in her hair. One day while under amytal hypnosis she explained circuitously that this cloth represented a nun's cap and thereby symbolized 'renunciation of mortal sin' and a life of asceticism and depersonalized atonement." (Masserman, 1961)

Illustrative Case: SYMBOLIZATION (SYMBOLIC GESTURES)

"Mr. E.G., aged twenty-three years, was observed standing about the ward at 3:00 A.M., moving in the most peculiar manner. He would bow, and then step high and twist and turn. He would move his arms in a peculiar manner, and make sudden and quick motions, after standing still for a while manipulating his fingers.

These actions were labeled just peculiar mannerisms. They seemed irrelevant, absurd and without reason. Yet, they were a reaction pattern which later the patient explained. 'You see, there was this woman down the street who was trying to tie me up. All night long she wove these radio wires, and I could feel them tightening up on my legs and body. I got up and tried to untangle myself, and the more I tried, the quicker she spun. She got tired of it finally, but I still got the electric shocks.'" (Kraines, 1948)

SYMPATHISM. The defense mechanism of seeking emotional support through arousing sympathy. "Sympathy

seeking" is more commonly used than sympathism.

The individual dwells endlessly on his misfortunes and usually insists that they are bad breaks due to an unkind fate or the faults of others. To elicit concern, he may also exaggerate minor physical ailments or even declare that his mind is too muddled to handle his difficulties. If others respond with expressions of sympathy or outright help, he will probably make little or no effort to solve his own problems.

The individual may be totally unaware that he is striving to arouse sympathy; in that case, this behavior pattern can be clearly classed as a defense mechanism. Frequently, however, it may be a partially conscious process; and in some instances, of course, it may be completely deliberate and calculated.

Sympathism can be quite effective as a means of reducing anxiety, particularly when it is coupled with other mechanisms such as rationalization or projection. Parents who show extreme concern for their children's slightest failures or illnesses run the risk of establishing an unconscious pattern of sympathy-seeking which will be utilized in later life.

SYMPATHY. A feeling of compassion for a person or group experiencing distress.

Sympathy is a fairly complex emotion, since it presupposes an ability to perceive and understand the misfortunes of others, to bring one's feelings into play, and to express and communicate them to others. The first signs of concern about other people usually appear in the second or third year when children stare anxiously or cry when other children hurt themselves. Their crying is probably due in part to identifying with the sufferer, and in part to confusion about what to do. By four or five, they may actively comfort, help, defend or put an arm around the distressed playmate. Some children, however, are too frightened, insecure or absorbed in their own needs to express sympathy at these early ages. (Murphy, 1957)

Children as well as adults vary widely in their sensitivity to others. This is probably due less to constitutional factors than to upbringing. Probably the greatest single contributor to the development of sympathetic feelings is the emotional climate of the home. If the parents are considerate of other people's feelings and readily express concern for their misfortunes, the children are likely to adopt these attitudes. Yet even in homes where consideration is the rule, children rarely show complete sympathy to everyone. Instead, they are quite selective in their expressions. Studies have shown that a child will defend and sympathize with a brother or sister who is attacked by another child, but will not be sympathetic with the attacker if he gets the worst of it. Moreover, if a child's attempt to be sympathetic is rebuffed, his attitude may suddenly switch to anger and hostility.

Children sometimes tease or ridicule others who have some infirmity or lack of skill; but if a friendly teacher or other adult points out that it is not their fault, antipathy will almost surely be replaced by sympathy. In other words, responsive children usually have a capacity for both positive and negative emotions. In fact, L. B. Murphy and others have observed that the most friendly and sympathetic youngsters are usually the most aggressive and quarrelsome. Perhaps the common denominator is that these children have strong feelings and a capacity to react to others, as well as sufficient security to express themselves both aggressively and compassionately. See EMOTIONAL DEVELOPMENT.

SYMPTOM. Any deviation from normal functioning which is considered indicative of physical or mental disorder.

In general, symptoms may be viewed as distress signals which show that some form of medical or psychological help is needed. In psychiatry, as in physical medicine, the range and diversity of symptoms are so wide that no complete catalogue can be offered. They can, however, be grouped into a number of broad categories. The following classification is given by Noyes and Kolb in *Modern Clinical Psychiatry* (1963):

Disorders of Motor Behavior: hyperactivity, retarded activity, repetitious behavior, automatism, negativism, compulsions.

Disorders of Perception: illusions; hallucinations of hearing, sight, taste, smell, touch and body image.

Disorders of Thinking: flight of ideas, retardation, incoherence, blocking, perseveration, dereistic thinking, autistic thinking, delusions, suicidal thoughts, hypochondria, obsessions, phobias.

Disturbances of Affect: elation, exaltation, depression, anxiety, inadequate affect, inappropriate affect, ambivalence, depersonalization.

Disturbances of Consciousness: confusion, clouding of consciousness, delirium, dream and fugue states, stupor.

Disorders of Orientation: confusion as to time, place and personal identity.

Disorders of Memory: hypermnesia, amnesia, paramnesia, déjà vu.

Dementia: mental deterioration.

To these might be added disorders of speech (such as verbigeration, circumstantiality, word salad, paraphasia) and extreme behavior patterns (such as extreme overconfidence, aggressiveness, shyness); psychosomatic symptoms (such as hypertension, peptic ulcer, migraine); and conversion symptoms (such as hysterical blindness, paralysis, hoarseness).

The psychiatrist or clinical psychologist is rarely interested in isolated symptoms. He is concerned about the way they group together to form an identifiable illness, known as a syndrome or symptom-complex. But he is even more concerned with the conditions that have produced this disturbance. Before he can determine what kind of treatment should be applied, he must discover whether the symptoms were primarily produced by a traumatic event, a toxic condition, a stress situation, a long-standing character distortion, or repressed emotional conflicts. Symptoms, then, are always viewed as end-results of other events. See OVERDETERMINATION.

The problem of symptom choice—why the patient develops a phobia rather than an obsession, or becomes hysterically blind rather than paralyzed—is one of the most baffling in all of psychiatry. White (1964) discusses this question fully, noting first that in almost any case "one can easily think of various neurotic devices that seem to fit the circumstances well enough," and that the expression symptom choice is an unhappy one, since "the production of neurotic symptoms is of course not in the least a conscious process." What, then, are the determining factors? He suggests the following three approaches, although the examples are not necessarily his.

First, *constitutional differences* may predispose an individual to use one type of defensive measure or one way of handling his problems rather than another. An extraverted person may tend to repress and forget his failures, and perhaps develop dissociative symptoms such as amnesia; an introverted person may become inwardly resentful or depressed, or may develop anxiety attacks. We might add that constitutional differences or "organ inferiority," to use Adler's term, may also contribute to the choice of one type of psychophysiologic symptom rather than another—hypertension rather than ulcers, for example—although acquired weaknesses due to disease or injury may also establish a predisposition, or "locus minoris resistentiae" (place of least resistance).

Second, *reaction patterns reinforced by family attitudes*—for example, rigid, overconscientious parents may encourage attitudes that lead to an obsessive-compulsive pattern, and oversolicitous parents who are constantly concerned with illness in general, or specific types of illness, may foster hypochondriacal tendencies which come into full force during periods of stress. Suggestion, sympathy, and attention may have much to do with the selection of symptoms. See SECONDARY GAIN.

Third, *time and content of the nuclear neurotic problem*. This is the Freudian theory that emotional growth may be arrested, or "fixated," at one or another stage of emotional development due to disturbing experiences or faulty relationships. As a result, the individual tends to regress and adopt behavior characteristics of that stage when he is placed under stress. Obsessional symptoms, for example, are believed to express primitive ideas of power, hostility, and right and wrong, such as the idea that thinking a certain thought or performing a certain action may do or undo real harm. (The problem of symptom choice is also discussed in articles dealing with specific types of disorders. See especially CONVERSION REACTION AND PSYCHOPHYSIOLOGICAL DISORDERS; *also* IATROGENIC ILLNESS, FOLIE À DEUX, FIXATION, SOMATIC COMPLIANCE, BODY LANGUAGE, SYMBOLIZATION.

SYMPTOMATIC TREATMENT. Treatment aimed at relief of distressing symptoms, or outward manifestations of disturbance, as opposed to treatment focused on causes and underlying conditions. An example is the prescription of drugs for relief of migraine even when it is known that practically all migraine headache stems from an emotional disturbance. Suggestion therapy, behavior therapy, hypnotherapy, and narcotherapy are among the techniques commonly used for removal of psychiatric symptoms. See these topics and SUPPORTIVE THERAPY.

Symptomatic treatment is frequently applied when a patient is acutely agitated or dangerously depressed and immediate action must be taken. It is generally regarded as a temporary expedient which puts the patient in a more comfortable or manageable state until deeper therapy can be employed. It may, however, be the only feasible approach with patients of low intelligence or people who will not accept psychotherapy.

Many therapists believe that a preoccupation with symptom relief can be a trap which may catch doctor and patient alike. In some cases, particularly hysterical conditions, symptoms can be eliminated with such rapidity and ease that the patient believes he is completely cured, and the doctor may not pursue the matter further. Too often it is found that the same symptom returns, or an equivalent symptom replaces it. Nevertheless this does not always occur, and today there are a number of therapists who consider the relief of symptoms to be the "treatment of choice" for all neurotic conditions. The most extreme spokesman for this point of view is probably the English psychologist, H. J. Eysenck, who has strongly advocated the use of behavior therapy, in which standard learning techniques are used for modifying behavior and eliminating symptoms. He maintains that the entire psychodynamic approach should be dropped, and instead of probing the patient's motivations, psychotherapy should be concerned exclusively with removing symptoms.

SYNAPSE. The junction where nerve impulses are transmitted from one neuron to another (*Fig. 49*).

The nervous system is frequently compared to a telephone exchange, yet the individual "wires," or neurons, of this system are not actually in contact with each other. A single nerve cell may have several hundred of these synaptic connections with other neurons, but even though they sometimes intertwine with each other, they are always sep-

arated by an extremely small space, on the order of one hundred millionth of a meter. This means that the nerve impulse must jump a gap, and this causes a delay in transmission. At any one synapse this delay only amounts to from a half to one thousandth of a second, but during this interval a nerve impulse could travel almost a full meter *within* a nerve fiber. Moreover, many nerve impulses have to pass across dozens or hundreds of synapses before they reach their destination, and the accumulative delays can make an appreciable difference in the speed of our responses. These delays can be increased by the use of sedatives that raise synaptic resistance, but they can also be reduced by stimulants.

Traffic across the synapse is always a one-way affair, from the end-brushes of the axon of one nerve cell to the dendrites, or in some cases the cell body, of another neuron. The synapse therefore serves as a kind of valve that keeps the nerve impulses moving in a definite direction. Recently much of the mystery about how these impulses get across the synapses has been solved. Even though the nerve current itself is electrical, certain chemicals have been found to carry it across the gap. So far, two different chemical transmitters have been found: norepinephrine in the autonomic nervous system, and acetylcholine largely in the central and muscular systems. The electron microscope has located structures called synaptic vesicles at the ends of the axons which secrete these transmitters. The chemicals diffuse across the gap, interact with the membrane of the next nerve cell, and produce a nerve impulse. The time taken by these chemical changes accounts for the delay at the synapse.

Several attempts have been made to use this new information in explaining the physiological changes that occur in learning and memory. One theory is that neurons grow closer together at the synapse as we acquire new learning,

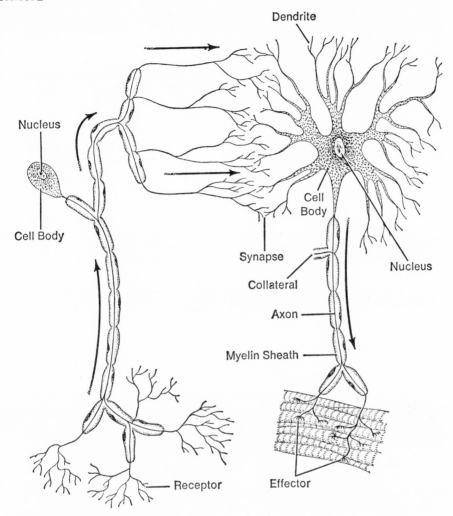

Fig. 49 A typical synapse with its intertwining endings, carrying the nerve impulse from a receptor to an effector.

so that nerve impulses will cross more easily from one neuron to another when the same stimuli are presented again. This is the theory of neurobiotaxis (Hebb, 1949). Another theory assumes that structures containing the synaptic vesicles, known as end-knobs, become sensitized when the neuron is repeatedly fired, and this makes it easier for them to fire in the future. This sensitization theory, as it is called, implies that the secretion of acetylcholine is the basic factor in memory (Milner, 1961), and

probably increases in quantity during the learning process. *See* MEMORY STORAGE, ADRENERGIC REACTION, CHOLINERGIC.

SYNCOPE. Temporary loss of consciousness resulting from a failure of the blood supply in the brain, that is, cerebral anemia.

Syncopal attacks are frequently experienced by patients with cerebral arteriosclerosis, and help to differentiate this condition from senile dementia.

They may also occur in certain psychosomatic disorders of the cardiovascular type, where emotional stress interferes with the circulation of blood to the brain and leads to fainting spells. The precise mechanism involved in this loss of blood circulation is still unknown, but it is possible that the entire organism is so overworked, or "overmobilized," during emotional stress that the brain does not get its share.

Syncope may also be a hysterical or conversion symptom. Here the body responds to the unconscious desire to escape from a distressing situation or to "put on an act" that will gain sympathy and attention. In one case a histrionic young woman fainted during a party, and everyone rushed out of the room at once to get help. When they returned she was lying on the floor in a beautifully arranged position, even though she had originally fallen "in a heap." The fainting was probably real, but the pretense that followed was a clear bid for the "secondary gains" that are usually associated with hysterical reactions.

Kardiner (1941) cites the case of a war veteran who had fainting spells whenever rain fell on him. When asked to describe these spells more fully, he said he first felt an itching in his face, then lost his breath, fainted and awakened with his face swollen and scratched. This reaction was finally traced to a long advance that took place in a heavy rain. During this march the soldier was thrown to the ground by a shell, lay unconscious, and later awoke with his face burned by mustard gas which had leaked through his mask. In this case the rain later reactivated the entire traumatic experience and he relived his physical reactions in complete detail. Here there was no question of unconsciously finding an escape from a difficult situation or of seeking attention, as in conversion reactions. The veteran was, rather, obeying the tendency to repeat disturbing, undigested experiences. See REPETITION-COMPULSION, CONVERSION REACTION, SECONDARY GAIN.

SYNESTHESIA (literally, "feeling together"). An experience in which two senses respond when only one is stimulated; also called crossed perception.

About 5 to 10 per cent of the general population are said to experience this dramatic interaction of the senses. Synesthesia is also experienced by individuals under the influence of hallucinogens such as mescaline and LSD, and occasionally by patients undergoing epileptic seizures. In the most common type, called chromesthesia, sounds, and sometimes tastes, odors and sensations of heat and cold or pain, are experienced as colors. This is not merely a verbal association of colors with sounds or other sensory experiences. Rather, the perception of color actually accompanies these sensations; the individual really sees a definite color when he hears a particular sound. Langfeld (1914) investigated a case of chromesthesia twice within a period of seven years and found highly consistent sound-color relationships: the musical note "c" was always experienced as red, "f" as pink, and "g" as clear blue.

Other investigations have uncovered the following relationships in color hearing: (a) quickening the tempo or raising the pitch increases the brightness of the image; (b) syncopated music produces jagged lines; harmonious music, flowing and graceful lines; (c) different musical instruments produce different colored lights; and (d) increasing the volume of sound increases the size of the images. In most cases the music has to be actually present, but in some instances the act of recalling music can itself produce colored images. (Karwoski and Odbert, 1938)

The mechanism that lies behind these experiences is still unknown. Some investigators, however, have suggested that synesthesia is a vestige of an early stage of development in which the infant or young animal does not distinguish between specific sights, sounds and tactile sensations, but only between such general dimensions as light or dark, bright or dull, smooth or rough. This theory gains some support from common expressions such as "brown taste," "loud colors," and "dark sounds."

SYPHILIS (Cerebral Syphilis). Syphilis, known also as lues and the pox, is a progressive infectious disease caused by a corkscrew-shaped germ called either spirocheta pallida or treponema pallidum.

The disease is transmitted primarily through sexual intercourse, and occasionally through kissing or direct contact with syphilitic sores. The germ gains entrance to the body through minute scratches in the skin, or directly through the membranes of the mouth or genital tract. It may also be transmitted from mother to child in the prenatal period (congenital syphilis). Since the spirochete is one of the few microorganisms which can readily penetrate the blood-brain barrier, the infection is likely to spread to the brain in time. In untreated cases this may lead to widespread cerebral damage resulting in mental deterioration, disabling physical symptoms, and eventual death.

Syphilis is a particularly insidious disease for several reasons. It ordinarily develops slowly, and its early symptoms can easily be overlooked. These symptoms usually disappear for a time, but return in different form. In the interval the patient may believe he has completely recovered. Moreover, the symptoms are so varied that syphilis can readily be mistaken for other more benign diseases. For this reason it has been called "the great imitator."

The attack on the organism takes place in four stages. In Stage One, the spirochetes multiply rapidly and within ten to forty days a sore called a *hard chancre* appears at the point of infec-

tion. The patient may be unaware of its existence, or he may dismiss it as of no importance, since it disappears spontaneously within four to six weeks. After that, Stage Two sets in, and a copper-colored skin rash, of a mild or severe nature, gradually spreads over the entire body. Sometimes this condition is mistaken for measles or smallpox, especially since it is often accompanied by symptoms not usually associated with syphilis: headache, fever, indigestion, spotty loss of hair.

During Stage Three, the so-called "latent period," these symptoms generally disappear, but the germ concentrates on the internal organs, such as the lymph glands, spleen, bone marrow, and especially the blood vessels and their cells. This stage may last for ten to twenty years before the destruction becomes noticeable. Any number of serious symptoms can then develop, including visual disturbances, locomotor ataxia (unco-ordinated gait), mental disorders, and intellectual deterioration.

There are three major mental disorders associated with syphilitic infection of the brain. In *general paresis*, the tissue (parenchyma) of the brain is gradually destroyed and the patient reacts to the physical and mental changes that result in several different ways: he becomes expansive and euphoric, depressed, or apathetic and demented. *Juvenile paresis* results from congenital syphilis and, if untreated, leads to a gradual mental and physical deterioration that reaches marked proportions in the preadolescent period. In *meningovascular syphilis,* the blood vessels and meninges, or coverings, of the brain are attacked, leading to a varied but serious symptom picture. In addition, there are two minor paretic disorders. In *Lissauer's type,* cerebral destruction is localized on one side of the cortex and results in a moth-eaten appearance called status spongiosis. The major symptoms are aphasic speech disorders, deafness, epileptic attacks and paralysis on one side of the body. Patients with *tabo-paresis* not only show the usual mental symptoms of general paresis but those of tabes dorsalis as well—especially locomotor ataxia and shooting pains in the legs. See GENERAL PARESIS, JUVENILE PARESIS, MENINGOVASCULAR SYPHILIS.

Since the diagnostic techniques, treatment procedures and preventive measures are similar for all types of syphilitic disorders, they will be discussed here instead of under separate topics. The Wassermann blood test is a clear indicator of infection in about 80 per cent of cases. Cerebrospinal fluid tests are positive in about 65 per cent, and are particularly effective in differentiating syphilis from neurasthenia, Alzheimer's disease, senile dementia, multiple sclerosis, cerebral tumor and other diseases involving brain damage.

The treatment of choice for all types of syphilis is massive amounts of penicillin, although a combination of penicillin and malaria (fever) therapy may be administered in some cases. If the patient receives the penicillin injections before syphilitic symptoms appear, his chances of complete recovery are 80 to 85 per cent. If treatment is started in the early clinical stages, an average of 60 per cent improve sufficiently to return to work. In cases where brain impairment has already set in, the rate of improvement varies with the severity of the damage and the patient's ability to compensate on both a neurological and psychological level. In hospitals where patients are admitted in all stages of the disease, approximately 20 to 30 per cent show good recovery, 30 to 40 per cent show improvement but may have to be transferred to simpler jobs, 10 to 25 per cent show no improvement, and 10 per cent die during the course of treatment.

Where the disease runs its full course without treatment, death occurs, on the average, between three and five years after the first appearance of symptoms.

It is usually due to other infections, or the breakdown of body functions caused by syphilitic invasion of vital organs.

The number of cases of juvenile paresis has declined substantially, due largely to early detection through the use of the Wassermann test. General paresis, however, has shown a threefold increase in recent years, particularly among teenagers and young adults. About twenty thousand new cases are reported annually, and this number is said to represent only about a third of all actual new cases.

At this time, an estimated 1,200,000 untreated cases have accumulated in the United States alone. The most urgent problem is therefore to locate all untreated cases. To this end, the Surgeon General of the United States Public Health Service has been experimenting with various case-finding methods. In one test, over fifty-four hundred syphilitic patients were interviewed and asked to name their close aquaintances and persons with whom they have had sexual contact. Practically all these patients were willing to give the information, and as a result over forty-five hundred other cases were discovered. Other promising approaches in use today are: free diagnosis and treatment, compulsory examinations before marriage, and extensive public education, particularly in the schools.

Illustrative Case: SYPHILIS

M., aged forty-one, a roofing salesman, was transferred to a state hospital from the jail to which he had been sentenced for violation of the motor vehicle laws. The prodromal symptoms of the patient's oncoming disease were apparently slight. The informant, his sister, who had seen him but infrequently, stated that she had not noticed any change in him except that for a year he had seemed somewhat "worried." While driving his car, he disregarded the collector at a toll bridge and drove across the structure at high speed. When overtaken by a police officer, the patient was found to have no license to drive an automobile, the permit having been revoked several years previously. Three days later, while awaiting trial for his offense, he was again arrested for driving an automobile without a license. He was given a short sentence in jail, where a physician soon recognized the patient's disorder and had him committed to the hospital.

On arrival at the admission office of the hospital, he told the office attendant that he was going to give her a million dollars because she was a "nice lady." As he was being questioned for the usual admission data, he began to boast of his wealth, claiming that he had three automobiles, thousands of dollars in the bank, a "diamond watch," and much other valuable jewelry. His son, he said, was lieutenant governor of the state, was soon to be governor, and later would be President of the United States. After having expressed various absurdly grandiose plans, he added, "I have another plan, too. I'm going to the wardens of the prisons in this state and all the other states and I'm going to buy the prisoners. I'll have an agreement with the warden to take their prisoners and put them to work on farms, and I'll charge each prisoner $300 for doing it and for getting him out of jail. I made $105,000 with prisoners just last week, and when I get going, I'm going to make plenty of money." (Noyes and Kolb, 1963)

SZONDI TEST. A projective test in which the subject examines a set of photographs of people with different types of mental disorder and chooses those he likes and dislikes.

The test consists of forty-eight cards divided into six sets of eight. Each set depicts faces of the following psychiatric patients: homosexual, sadist, epileptic, hysterical, catatonic, paranoid, depressed, and manic. One set is presented at a time and the subject is instructed first to "pick out the two pictures you like best" and then "select the two pictures you dislike most." A different set of photographs is usually presented on six successive days. The test is remarkably easy to administer and verbal responses are not required. It can therefore be applied to individuals who have a language handicap and

to patients who balk at more complicated testing situations.

The test is an outgrowth of a genetic theory of personality originated by its inventor, Lipot Szondi, a Hungarian psychiatrist. According to this theory, which he termed "fate analysis," the life of every individual is governed by a hidden plan determined by latent recessive genes. Our most characteristic drives stem from a hitherto unexplored area termed the "familial unconscious," which contains these genetic tendencies. Through this level of the unconscious, which he contrasted with both the personal unconscious of Freud and the collective unconscious of Jung, our "repressed ancestors" direct our selective behavior, determining our choice of friends and occupation, and even our diseases and form of death. An example given by Szondi is the attraction which two people feel toward each other. This is not a surface attraction but is described as "genotropic," since he believed it stems from the fact that the two individuals have similar or related recessive genes.

On the basis of this theory—which is generally regarded as unproved and highly questionable—Szondi held that in reacting to the pictures on the test, the subject is not responding to superficial likes and dislikes but to deeper drives from his innermost self. His choices are determined by recessive hereditary factors, and therefore reveal his true personality.

The test can be applied without accepting Szondi's genetic theories. In the scoring procedure, the examiner sets up a profile of positive and negative responses to each of the diagnostic categories. The scores are then statistically compared with scores that could be obtained by chance. This is only part of the process, since Szondi claimed that only four dynamic drive-vectors underlie the eight categories. Each of these vectors comprises two of the basic categories—for example, the S-vector, or sexual drive, is expressed in the choice of both sadist and homosexual pictures. A preference for the homosexual picture shows a need to be tender, feminine, motherly, and passive, and may be expressed in such occupations as barber, cosmetician, and dancer. Preference for the sadist represents the sexual drive for masculinity and aggression, and is expressed in such occupations as animal training, prize fighting, and butchering. The other three vectors are the T-vector, made up of the epileptic and hysterical factors; the SCH-vector, comprising the catatonic and paranoid factors; and the C-vector, made up of the depressive and manic factors. The interaction between these four basic vectors is supposed to determine the entire personality of the individual. (Szondi 1952)

The Szondi test has been subjected to both practical and theoretical criticism (Borstelmann and Klopfer, 1953). It seems to be based on long-rejected theories of instinct and physiognomy, and the eight clinical types do not correspond with those used in well-established tests such as the Rorschach or Thematic Apperception Test. Moreover, as Anastasi (1961) points out, "Attempts at empirical validation of its various assumptions have so far yielded overwhelmingly negative results," and when used as a clinical instrument, "it is probably one of the least promising of the currently popular projective techniques." See PHYSIOGNOMY.

T

TALION LAW (Talion Principle). These terms refer to the idea of punishment or retaliation in kind: the "lex talionis." This is the primitive and usually unconscious belief in retribution, as expressed in the early Biblical injunction, "an eye for an eye, a tooth for a tooth."

The talion principle has an important place in psychoanalysis. It includes both the general idea of retribution for defying the superego, and the specific fear that all injury, whether actual or intended, will be punished in kind. Freud applied the "idea of the talion," for example, to the visual disturbances which sometimes afflict peeping Toms (voyeurs). He said it is "as if an accusing voice had uplifted itself within the person concerned, saying 'Because you have chosen to use your organ of sight for every indulgence of the senses, it serves you quite right if you can see nothing at all now.'" (Collected Papers, Volume 2, 1924). In cases of this kind,

he believed that the superego imposes the disability as a punishment for violation of its behests. In similar vein, an unconscious wish for the death of another person may give rise to a neurotic fear of death or a hysterical attack during which the patient feels he is dying.

Psychoanalysts believe that the fear of retribution, or "talion dread," is a significant neurotic symptom. Individuals who harbor unconscious incestuous wishes are particularly likely to develop this fear. They are frequently beset with anxieties that represent the unconscious fear of being punished by castration—for example, a fear of accidents or a phobia for sharp instruments. See CASTRATION COMPLEX.

TALKING IT OUT. The free verbal expression of feelings and emotions.

"Talking it out," in the usual sense of giving vent to what is uppermost on one's mind, is regarded as a relatively superficial process—yet it may afford temporary relief and open the way to deeper therapy. Individuals who are anxious or emotionally upset frequently report that they feel more relaxed and comfortable after an opportunity to "let off steam" and give voice to their problems and worries in the presence of an understanding listener. Many a therapist has had the experience reported by Maslow and Mittelmann (1941): A woman who came in for an interview talked volubly about her problems for fifty minutes straight, then got up to leave, remarking, "Thank you, doctor, you have helped me immensely." The doctor had not uttered a word.

Talking is an essential aspect of the psychiatric interview, but in any of the deeper procedures it involves far more than having the patient unburden himself about his conscious difficulties. In non-directive or client-centered therapy, the patient leads the way and says whatever is on his mind—yet talking is only one aspect of the therapy. The patient's progress and growth are believed to be dependent on rapport with the therapist and on his ability to reflect back the patient's own thoughts and feelings in such a way that he sees himself in a new light, gradually modifies his aims and attitudes, and begins to realize his own inner potential.

In psychoanalysis, too, talking it out is only one part of the process, even though this type of therapy is often characterized as "the talking cure." Although talking is essential, the object is to get the patient to give voice to what is *innermost* in his mind, not what is *uppermost*. Moreover, the process goes far beyond catharsis or simply giving vent to emotions, since its aim is to discover the hidden sources of the patient's distress and help gain insight into his unconscious motivations—for only in this way can a basic change be brought about. To accomplish this, the psychoanalyst employs the special techniques of free association and dream interpretation, which are designed to probe beneath the surface and relate present difficulties to earlier experiences. In so doing, the analyst recognizes that what the patient *cannot* "talk out" is likely to be more crucial than what he *can* talk about. He must therefore use his ingenuity in overcoming the patient's resistances to revealing significant material.

In general, then, it may be said that although talking out frequently makes a patient feel better, it does not in itself effect a cure. Its major value lies in the fact that it often helps to pave the way to genuine treatment. *See* CATHARSIS, PSYCHOANALYSIS (THERAPY).

TASTE (Gustation). The cutaneous sense mediated by receptor cells known as taste buds, located on the surface of the skin. These cells are clustered together in bumps, or "papillae," distributed primarily over most of the surface of the tongue. Others are found in the pharynx and larynx and on the palate and floor of the mouth. The expression "palatable food" indicates this wider distribution.

All our taste buds are present at birth, about 245 per papilla. The newborn baby's sense of taste is well developed; it will make sucking movements to sweet or salty substances and react negatively to things that are sour or bitter. The taste buds remain unchanged until the end of middle age when there is a drastic decline in their sensitivity—which accounts for the complaint of older people that their meals taste flat. The very old are sometimes unable to taste at all, a condition known as ageusia.

Taste is termed a chemical sense because substances must be soluble in saliva in order to activate the taste buds. There are four fundamental taste qualities—sweet, sour, bitter, and salt—but the tongue is not uniformly sensitive to them. The sides respond mainly to sour, the tip to sweet, the base to bitter, and the tip and sides to salty substances. These four qualities, singly and in mixtures, are believed to account for all the tastes we experience.

Science is still in the dark about the chemistry of sweet and bitter substances. Sugar and saccharine taste equally sweet, but there is little or no chemical relation between them. The correlation between chemical composition and sour and salty tastes is better known. Acids always taste sour, and what the chemist terms a base (a mixture of acid and alkali) usually tastes salty. It seems that the taste buds can also be activated by extreme cold. Charles Horvath (1956) has reported that on a polar expedition he could literally taste the "bitter cold" when the temperature reached 60 degrees below zero.

What we call taste is actually the result of many sense experiences. It includes sensations of warm and cold, pressure and, with some types of seasoning, even pain. The flavor of the food we eat is determined by both smell and taste. In fact, smells are often confused with tastes, since the sense of smell is much more sensitive than that of taste. For this reason we can identify many common foods like coffee, steak or orange juice only when we smell as well as taste them. This fact also accounts for the enhancement of flavor brought about by the "aroma" of foods, and for the fact that people with stuffy head colds complain that food seems tasteless.

Smoking, too, has an effect on taste. It temporarily dulls sensitivity to sweet and salty substances and may even reduce the appetite. Some gourmet clubs do not permit smoking during meals because tobacco smoke masks the delicate flavor of the food.

If our sense of taste is continuously stimulated by a particular substance we gradually become less sensitive to it. This process of "adaptation" occurs fairly rapidly, and accounts for the fact that the full flavor of a meal can be appreciated only when we first taste it. By the time we are halfway through we may even wonder why we liked it at all. This is one of the reasons it is usually better to serve small amounts of differently flavored foods than larger quantities of one or two.

Attempts to improve or change the flavor of foods have been made since ancient times. It has recently been found that monosodium glutamate (MSG) improves some flavors since it increases our sensitivity to sour and bitter tastes. Salt and sweet sensitivity, however, remain unchanged. Its effect on bitter sensitivity is particularly lasting, especially if it is added during food preparation. Cigarettes may taste bitter for the rest of the day after exposure to MSG.

Certain tastes tend to neutralize each other. Sweet neutralizes sour: sugar takes away the sourness of lemons. Bitter and sweet are also complementary. Salt and sweet, bitter and sour also tend to neutralize each other, but less completely than the other combinations. Other taste combinations produce "contrast effects"—for example, lemonade tastes sour if we drink it after eating pastry.

There are vast individual differences in taste sensitivity. Some people rate saccharine twice as sweet as sugar; others find it two thousand times as sweet. This difference in sensitivity is especially pronounced for certain complex organic chemicals. A few individuals have been reported to be completely unable to taste certain substances, particularly phenyl-thio-carbamide (PTC). These people have been termed "taste-blind" and compared to the color blind; their "taste-blindness" has been attributed to a recessive gene. However, this division into "tasters" and "non-tasters" on the basis of their reaction to PTC is probably unfounded. When PTC is present in purified form and in very high concentrations, *all* subjects report a flavor. Some people need more of the substance to arouse taste, but they are not "taste-blind." Moreover, the parallel to color-blindness breaks down because color-blind people are insensitive to certain common hues, and the chemical PTC is extremely uncommon.

Symptoms involving taste are found in many psychiatric disorders. Absence or impairment of the sense of taste (ageusia) may be a conversion (hysterical) symptom related to the patient's unconscious conflicts. It is also fairly common in depressions and schizophrenia. Transitory perversions of taste (dysgeusia) sometimes occur in adolescents and hysterical patients who eat such substances as ashes, salt, or vinegar. The disorder known as pica, a craving for earth, starch, hair, and other inedible substances, can result in severe deficiencies. A peculiar taste in the mouth may be one of the symptoms of schizophrenia, and may also be experienced as an aura, or warning signal, preceding an epileptic attack. In addition, some people experience specific taste sensations when they hear certain sounds or see certain colors. See SYN-ESTHESIA, PICA, SENSITIVITY DISTURB-ANCES.

TAY-SACHS DISEASE (Infantile Amaurotic Idiocy, Infantile Cerebral Lipoidosis).
A rare metabolic disorder characterized by an accumulation of lipid (fat) in the nerve cells of the brain, resulting in severe mental retardation. The disease was first described by the English physician, Warren Tay (1843–1927) and the American neurologist Bernard Sachs (1858–1944).

Tay-Sachs is hereditary and transmitted by a single gene. It is found primarily but not exclusively in Jewish families originating in certain areas of eastern Europe. The infant appears normal at birth, but within a year grows increasingly apathetic and weak, and cannot hold his head steady or grasp objects firmly. Later symptoms include

progressive spastic paralysis, seizures, and blindness (amaurosis). Victims of the disease usually fail to survive beyond the third year. Juvenile and adolescent forms of amaurotic idiocy also occur, and in these cases the patient may survive for about ten years after onset. See AMAUROSIS, MENTAL RETARDA-TION (CAUSES).

TELEPATHY IN PSYCHOTHERAPY.
An attempt to utilize extrasensory perception in the therapeutic process.

Today a small number of psychiatrists and psychotherapists believe it is possible to communicate directly with the unconscious of patients and thereby elicit material that will be useful in interpreting and analyzing their behavior. This possibility was suggested by both Wilhelm Stekel and Sigmund Freud. In the 1920s Stekel contended that "thought transference" between doctor and patient does not occur accidentally, but is most apt to take place when the therapist achieves intense emotional rapport with his patient. Freud accepted telepathy as a fact, and held that unconscious material communicated by this means is subject to the same laws as other unconscious material, such as the content of dreams. The most important of these are the principles of distortion and symbolic representation: "He showed that unravelling the distorted derivatives of unconsciously elaborated material by means of psychoanalysis could bring to light latent correspondences which made it possible to unmask telepathic events that would otherwise not be identified as such." (Eisenbud, 1952)

Eisenbud illustrates his own use of telepathy by citing the case of a middle-aged female patient who dreamed that she dropped a red purse while climbing over a picket fence. The patient herself associated "red purse" to "uterus" and suggested that the dream was related to menstruation. On second thought, she felt that it probably had to do with the termination of her treatment (climbing across a fence) and her fear of continued dependence on the therapist ("leaving behind a rather costly erotic attachment"). However, Eisenbud himself suggested a third, and telepathic, interpretation based upon the fact that the day *following* the dream, the patient had received a letter from a surgeon friend to whom she had written about her inability to conceive.

In his letter, the surgeon mentioned that he was treating an unmarried woman who was soon to have a child, hinting that his correspondent might arrange to adopt the baby. Eisenbud suggests that if we assume that the patient was telepathically aware of this letter and its proposal before it arrived, her dream would take on a new meaning: "In the dream she reacts favorably toward the idea of getting a quick baby, without either physiological fuss on her part or the bother of agency red tape and delay. In climbing across a picket fence she is indeed crossing a picket line, indicating that she is quite willing to avail herself of the cheap, scab 'labor' that has been offered. She is also not above circumventing the difficulties of regular agencies (which represents organized 'labor') by utilizing a fence (disposer of illicitly gotten goods). The representation of her uterus as a purse, finally, appears overdetermined by the allusion to the equivalence of the two in relation to securing a baby: she does not have to make excessive demands on her middle-aged uterus when she can buy a baby, produce one out of her purse, so to speak."

Eisenbud believes that this interpretation of the dream throws a new and penetrating light on his patient's inability to conceive. To him it suggests that she actually did not wish to have a child, and that "her real aim is to get out (of the analysis) with the compromise of a quickly and illicitly ac-

quired baby while her continuing unproductiveness remains yet unanalyzed."

Eisenbud claims that the application of the telepathy hypothesis has frequently enabled him to discover significant relationships behind events that would otherwise appear completely unrelated. He has also found that the patients themselves accept interpretations based on telepathy as readily as any other type of interpretation. He points out that we cannot at this time fully evaluate the place of telepathy in human behavior, but appears to be convinced that it is an established fact and can play an important role in psychotherapy. *See* EXTRASENSORY PERCEPTION, PSYCHICAL RESEARCH.

TELEVISION EFFECTS. Studies of the effects of television on behavior have been largely confined to children and adolescents. These effects are not easy to determine because of their complexity, their interaction with other influences, their cumulative character, and the fact that it is often not possible to carry out definite experiments—it would, for example, be unethical to attempt to produce delinquent behavior through television. Nevertheless, there have been extensive surveys in four countries (Schramm et al., in the United States, Himmelweit et al., in England, Maletzke in Germany, and Furu et al., in Japan), and over 160 more specific investigations of a scientific nature have been made. These have all been reviewed in an annotated bibliography and overview prepared by the International Association for Mass Communication Research, and published by UNESCO (Wilbur Schramm, editor, 1964). The following summary of significant findings will be largely based on that publication.

Appeal to children. Television is immensely popular with children not only because it is so accessible, but because it seems to provide both an escape from everyday life and an opportunity to learn about life. The screen also gives them a chance to enjoy passive entertainment and identify with exciting people and live a vicarious fantasy life. In addition, they learn practical details of dress and manners, get some insight into news events as they occur, and satisfy particular needs such as gaining release from emotional tension or finding topics for social conversation.

Leisure time. Estimates from different countries show that the average child spends two to three hours a day watching television, with three-year-olds already averaging forty-five minutes, five- and six-year-olds two hours, twelve- and thirteen-year-olds reaching a peak of about three hours, and high school students declining to two hours. Wherever it is available, television "dominates the leisure time" of young children, tending to reduce the time they spend on other activities that satisfy the same needs, such as radio, movies, and comic books. It has cut into the reading of fiction more than nonfiction, but has had little effect on social life and organized activities such as Boy Scouts and Girl Scouts. In general, the most impressive fact is the total amount of time spent on this one pursuit. For average viewers it comes to almost half the time spent in school, and for avid viewers it nearly equals the total amount, taking into account vacations and holidays.

Program preferences. Preschool children generally prefer programs dealing with animals, puppets, and familiar people doing familiar things. By the age of six, most youngsters begin to lose interest in these presentations and view more adult programs than children's programs—especially Westerns, situation comedies, crime and adventure stories. More boys than girls prefer programs with aggressive heroes, and more girls than boys prefer domestic comedies. The taste patterns of both sexes are relatively fixed by ten or twelve, but there is little agreement about favorite programs—that is, no more than one third agree on any single choice.

Do children have a basic preference for violent programs, or do they come to enjoy them because there are no attractive alternatives available? This question is still unsettled. A study in England showed that children did become interested in programs of a higher cultural level when only those programs were available—however, when the ordinary programs were also available, they usually continued to prefer them.

Educational value. Although many educational activities, such as laboratory work and discussions, cannot be carried on by television, this medium can be used as an effective teaching instrument. Over four hundred experiments have been made in the United States, comparing television classes with regular classes. In most cases no difference was found in the general quality of the final examination—and where there was a difference, it was usually in favor of the TV class. Television can be used most effectively to enrich classroom work, to make maximum use of expert teachers, to strengthen home and extension study, and to provide education for developing countries.

Ordinary home viewing does not as a rule improve children's school work, nor does it lower their grades. It has been found that heavy viewing and poor grades do go together, but both the viewing and the school performance are often due to other causes such as stresses, frustrations, and unsatisfactory relationships. But even though television does not improve schoolwork, does it at least widen the child's horizons and give him helpful information? Some parents and teachers believe it does, but most investigators think it has fallen far short of its potential and often gives the child a distorted view of adult life. Himmelweit, for example, states that it has not made our children more curious, better informed, or more enterprising. A Canadian survey did show that first-graders brought up with television had more advanced vocabulary than children in a town without television, but a follow-up study made a few years later showed that these differences had disappeared and the television children actually knew less about public affairs (but more about entertainment matters) than the children without television. This study and others have shown that after twelve or thirteen the slower children use television more and gain more from it, while the brighter ones depend more and more on the printed word.

Violence and aggression. There is no doubt that television gives children many opportunities to learn how to commit a crime and provides many models for antisocial behavior. Nevertheless, few investigators believe this medium plays a large part in causing delinquency and crime. Most observers point out that the roots of criminal behavior lie within the child's personality and in his family and social experience, not in television itself. At most, the programs may be a contributory cause, triggering already-existing delinquent tendencies or suggesting that problems can be solved by violence, "But in any of these cases television by itself cannot make a normally well-adjusted child into a delinquent. This is the almost unanimous conclusion of research and clinical investigation." (Schramm).

Some observers have claimed that the violence on television has a positive value as a "safety valve" for aggressive tendencies, and one early experiment seemed to support this view. Several recent experiments, however, have led to the opposite conclusion. In these experiments, one group of children was subjected to frustrating experiences and then shown television dramas which depicted highly aggressive behavior, while another group was shown the same program without having undergone the frustrating experiences. When the two groups were given an opportunity to

express aggression either in behavior or in tests, the frustrated group usually showed more aggression, and it was often of the same type as shown in the drama; the non-frustrated group, on the other hand, was no more aggressive than usual. The experiments indicate that violence on television does not reduce aggressive behavior, but, if anything, increases it among children who have recently experienced frustration. Since we know that children with high levels of aggression are especially attracted to violent programs, it is highly probable that these programs will feed their antisocial tendencies even though they may not originate them.

Mental Health. Not enough long-term clinical studies have been made to draw firm conclusions on the effect of television on mental health. There is ample evidence that programs depicting realistic violence and horror frighten some children, particularly when they watch while alone in the dark. However, children often enjoy being frightened, and harmful effects can be avoided if they are raised in a warm, secure atmosphere and if parents limit the amount of violence they view. On the other hand, there is evidence that television can in some cases aggravate emotional disturbances that already exist, although this depends on the child's personality and environment, and not merely on the program content. It is likely that children with schizoid tendencies use television as a further retreat from other people into a realm of fantasy; psychopathic children, already poised to rebel, may find a model for defiance in the action stories, and violent episodes may bring to the surface the hostile and confused impulses which already beset some psychotic children (Freedman, 1961).

There is no proof that ordinary children will become emotionally withdrawn as a result of television, but it does make them more accustomed to passive entertainment. Some writers have claimed that TV improves adjustment within the family, since it keeps children at home and the family often views programs together—but this effect is probably exaggerated. Group viewing does not by itself strengthen relationships, since each viewer reacts individually and viewing more often curbs than stimulates conversation. "The conclusion is that television is not likely either to ruin a healthy home relationship or rescue an unhealthy one." (Schramm)

Physical Health. Television has little if any effect on physical health. Studies conducted in various countries show that it postpones bedtime a few minutes, but that the child generally goes to sleep more quickly. There are cases of fatigue due to late viewing or sleep disturbed by frightening programs, but these are occasional and usually occur in homes that would set poor standards without television. Under proper viewing conditions there is no harmful effect on eyesight; any eyestrain that occurs is probably less than would be produced by reading. Obese children are often avid viewers because they avoid strenuous play, and eating snacks while watching programs may aggravate their problem.

The many studies of television lead to some general conclusions: (a) For too many children, the amount of time spent on television is out of all proportion to the time spent on other activities; (b) there is a danger that repeated exposure to crime, terror and killing will blunt their sensitivities and incite already-inclined children to aggressive behavior; (c) the viewing of more imaginative and informative programs is not sufficiently encouraged, and children therefore become accustomed to watching the more exciting, fast-moving programs that set false standards; (d) the child whose emotional and social needs are not being met in real life is more likely to use television as an escape mechanism or substitute

satisfaction than the more fully satisfied child; (e) the emotionally healthy child is less likely to be adversely affected than the unhealthy or aggressive child; (f) in general, too many parents fail to guide or control their children's use of television.

TEMPERAMENT. A general term for emotional make-up, including characteristic energy level, moods and mood changes, intensity and tempo of reactions to people and situations.

Most psychologists today believe that temperament is basically determined by constitutional factors but can be modified by life experiences. The constitutional aspect is particularly apparent at the very beginning of life, before the child can be deeply influenced by people and events. It is common knowledge that infants react in their own unique way from the moment of birth, and psychologists have described the variations among them in terms of the amount of crying, tempo and intensity of sucking behavior (Balint, 1948), response to frustrations (Jones, 1930), delight in motor play (Shirley, 1931), energy output and motor demeanor (Gesell and Ames, 1937). The origin of these variations is largely a matter of conjecture, but many investigators attribute them primarily to inborn differences in hormonal secretion, sensitivity to sound, or constitutional factors that cannot as yet be isolated.

This interpretation is supported by a number of long-term studies. Gesell followed up a group of children and found that relative ratings on such factors as energy output and emotional expressiveness remained virtually unchanged after an interval of twenty-five years. Neilon (1948) found that personality sketches of children made at the age of two could be matched far above chance with sketches made at the age of seventeen. Even though we may grant that *some* of the reactions of the infant and small child may be due to temporary discomforts or stresses, these studies would seem to argue in favor of a basic, persistent temperament that is largely present at the beginning of life.

Studies of animals show the effects of constitutional differences of temperament with particular clarity. Rats have been selectively bred for excitability (Yeakel and Rhoades, 1941) and for aggressiveness (Frederikson, 1952). It is interesting that the more emotional males were found to have heavier thyroid and adrenal glands, while the more emotional females had heavier thyroids and pituitaries. The commonest examples of constitutional differences, however, are found in dog breeding, which has given us the energetic German shepherd, the lethargic basset hound, and the alert hunting dog that retrieves the prey for his master. Among human beings it is not so easy to prove the existence of constitutional differences because scientists cannot engage in breeding experiments with people. They also have trouble measuring hormonal changes in normal individuals; and even when decided endocrine changes do occur, as in puberty and menopause, the physiological factors interact in complex ways with such nonphysical conditions as cultural expectation, the stresses of life, and acquired psychological tendencies. However, we have clear evidence of the effect of constitutional factors in certain pathological cases—for example, the phlegmatic hypothyroid individual who becomes more alert and active when he is given thyroxin extract, and the agitated patient who becomes bland and undisturbed after undergoing lobotomy. See MENOPAUSE, MENSTRUAL DISORDERS, CRETINISM, PSYCHOSURGERY.

Limited studies have been made of temperamental differences among races and nations. Psychologists are well aware of the common tendency to overgeneralize the traits of social groups, yet it is hard to deny that differences in national temperament do exist. One has only to compare the average Englishman with the average Italian to see that this is the case. Most probably these differences are due to a combination of constitutional and cultural factors. However, it is even harder to assess the biological component for huge groups of people than it is for individuals, for we know too little about the laws of human genetics to pin down the contributions of heredity. For this reason—plus the environmentalist trend in modern American psychology as a whole—the major interest today seems to be in finding non-hereditary explanations. Climate, nutrition, topography, geographical location—all these circumstances and many others have been invoked to account for differences in temperament.

Relatively recently another factor has come into prominence: child-rearing practices. A study by Gorer and Richman (1950) has suggested that the typical impassivity and covert hostility of the Great Russians may be due in part to the way they were swaddled as infants. Another investigation attributes the difference between the Yurok and Sioux Indians to differences in weaning practices. The Yurok wean their young at six months of age, and since they have to fend for themselves from almost the beginning of life, they tend to become hostile, suspicious and stingy. Among the Sioux, on the other hand, weaning does not take place until a much later date because the mother waits until the child himself refuses the breast. In contrast to the Yurok, this tribe is noted not only for its energy in hunting but for its generosity. There is little doubt that child-rearing can have a considerable influence on temperament, but it is equally probable that it is only one among many operative factors, including hereditary tendencies. See CONSTITUTIONAL TYPES, RACE DIFFERENCES, SEX DIFFERENCES.

TEMPERATURE SENSES. Thermal sensitivity; the senses of warmth and cold located in the skin.

There are two distinct kinds of skin receptors for heat and cold receptivity. When the skin is mapped for warmth and cold by applying a heated or cooled metal stylus, separate sets of sensitivity spots are found. It is only at "psychological zero" or skin temperature that no sensation is experienced. This temperature is 90 degrees for most of the body, but ranges from 82 degrees in the exposed ear to 98 degrees in the protected armpit.

The adaptive nature of the temperature sense can be easily demonstrated. If the left hand is put into 80 degree water and the right into 100 degree water, a new psychological zero point is soon reached for both hands, and the receptors are not activated. If the hands are now plunged into 90 degree water, the left hand will feel it as warm, the right as cold. Adaptation follows within a short time, however, and the water is then experienced as tepid.

Cold-sensitive spots are normally receptive below psychological zero, and indifferent to those between this point and 110 degrees. A curious phenomenon occurs, however, when these spots are stimulated by temperatures above 110 degrees: a cool sensation known as "paradoxical cold" occurs. It is due to this paradoxical cold reaction that we sometimes shiver when we step into a hot shower. There is a comparable phenomenon for warmth. When we go out on a frosty day the air may momentarily feel warm, and when we touch a steak in the freezer it may feel hot at first.

The psychological experience of heat and cold is not caused by temperature alone. Two objects in a 90-degree room, one metal and one woolen, feel different in temperature. The metal object seems cooler than the woolen one. Actually the two objects register the same temperature but the metal absorbs body heat. The effective stimulus here is the addition or subtraction of heat from the tissue of the receptors. Since the metal absorbs heat, the receptors become cooler and this sensation is ascribed to the metal. Similarly, when the body is warmer than its surroundings, cold is experienced. Ocean water will feel cooler than the air at the beach even when it is the same temperature, since water, like metal, is a good conductor of heat while air conducts more poorly. The water, however, will quickly become tolerable as the senses adapt to this new environment.

Sensitivity to temperature (thermal sensitivity) varies widely. When one person immerses his hand in icewater, his blood pressure may increase thirty points, but another person may show no change at all. With advancing age we can expect an increase in cold sensitivity and a decrease in the automatic regulation of body temperature. Elderly people complain of drafts because they actually feel them, not because they are cantankerous. *See* SENSORY ADAPTATION, SENSITIVITY DISTURBANCES, HYPOTHALAMUS.

TEMPER TANTRUM. A violent outburst of anger commonly occurring between the ages of two and four, with a peak at three. Recurrent tantrums are classified as habit disturbances of childhood, and are usually accompanied by other symptoms such as enuresis, nail-biting, feeding problems, stuttering, or tics.

The typical tantrum rarely lasts more than four or five minutes. In the outbursts that occur between the ages of two and three the child usually lies on his back, screaming and kicking; in those between three and four he is more likely to direct an attack at other people—hitting, biting, kicking, or spitting at them. At around four the child adds language to his outlets: "I'll kill you dead!" "I'll flush you down!" From that time on words gradually replace action and the tantrums begin to taper off. The decline occurs more quickly in girls than in boys, probably because boys have more energy and are expected to be more aggressive than girls.

Tantrums occur as a reaction to frustration, and the frustration is usually due to being denied something the child desires. They also occur when he fails to accomplish something he wants to do, such as building a high tower out of blocks, or when he is thwarted by inability to express himself and helplessness in coping with the adults who tower over him. The tantrum sets in when these frustrations mount to a point where he is completely overwhelmed. He then regresses to a primitive, uncontrolled expression of rage.

These "spells" of anger are often out of all proportion to the immediate provocation. The reason is that they are usually an expression of accumulated tensions which are triggered by the moment's frustration. The three-year-old has been living through an extremely trying period of his life, when he has been required to learn many kinds of behavior at once—and occasionally "something's got to give." This often happens when it is least expected, and at a time when it is most embarrassing for the parents. It is probably a mistake to think that he deliberately chooses these inopportune moments. In most cases he is simply too tired or too tense to manage his emotions any longer.

When a tantrum occurs, the child needs help, not harshness. At the height of his fury he cannot be reached by reason and his attention cannot be captured long enough for distraction to work. (These measures, however, can sometimes be used to advantage while the storm is gathering.) The best approach is to hold firm, and to sit down quietly—or leave him alone—until his anger burns itself out. Meeting

a tantrum head-on by shouting at the child only reduces the parent to his level and prolongs the agony. We have to give him a chance to cool off, get hold of himself, and realize that it is best to yield to the inevitable. If, on the other hand, we surrender to his demands, these outbursts may become a persistent behavior pattern.

While it is necessary to deal with tantrums as they occur, it is equally important to take preventive steps, such as avoiding overfatigue; providing plenty of interesting activities that will drain off the child's excess energy, as well as "quiet times" when he can learn to relax; reducing family tensions wherever possible; and allowing him more latitude in his behavior. If these measures do not work, and the tantrums are recurrent and uncontrollable, outside help is indicated. The most common treatment technique is play therapy. *See* ANGER, NEGATIVISM, PLAY THERAPY, RELEASE THERAPY.

TENSION. A feeling of physical and psychological strain accompanied by discomfort, uneasiness, and apprehension.

Tension is most typically experienced when we are faced with a threatening situation. It may be a physical situation, such as a sudden emergency while driving a car; or a psychological situation, as in giving a speech before a critical audience. In either type of circumstance, the organism mobilizes its emotional and physiological resources to meet the danger. In acute tension, all or most bodily systems are activated. The muscles are taut, the fingers tremulous, the facial expression is fixed, the heart quickens its pace, and the peristaltic action of the stomach is inhibited. At the same time there is some degree of awareness of the consequences of the danger, and this gives rise to feelings of apprehension.

Threats to our personality, such as concern over the possibility of embarrassment or loss of self-esteem, generally produce more persistent and pervasive feelings of tension than purely physical emergencies. This is particularly true when the threat arouses unconscious impulses and conflicts. In such cases the tension contains a large component of anxiety. See ANXIETY.

Tension is not a static condition but a motivating force. The feelings of strain and discomfort are so great that they generate a demand for relief and release. The person who lives under tension has a restless urge to "do something—anything," and if constructive outlets are not offered, he may discharge his tension through impulsive or even violent behavior. Many accidents are caused by the urgent need for tension reduction, and a good deal of delinquency is due to the "acting-out" behavior of young people who lead tense, frustrated lives. Persistent feelings of tension may also produce certain specific symptoms, such as tension headache, enuresis, tics, and nail-biting. Tension is also frequently a major factor in alcoholism and drug addiction.

In view of these harmful effects, it is not surprising that the constructive release of tension is considered one of the most important contributors to our physical comfort and mental health. Thorpe, Katz and Lewis (1961) offer the following suggestions, all of which are more or less within the power of the average individual. First, learn to accept what cannot be changed, and reconcile yourself to unavoidable circumstances, physical limitations, personality patterns in others, economic conditions in society—even though they may restrict your chances for full achievement and satisfaction. Second, try to work off emotional tensions. Since "emotional tension is energy generated by conflicts and frustrating situations," it seeks an outlet and may often be released and worked off through sports, dancing, working in the garden, taking a long walk: "It is better to 'blow off steam' by some type of physical activity than

to get into hassles with other people, which creates additional problems." Once we have released our tension, we usually find it easier to handle our problems in a calm and objective manner.

Third, learn to relax and reduce muscular tension by putting aside all worries and lying down in a dark and quiet room. If the mind cannot be emptied of all thought, visualize a mountain stream or a sailboat in a setting sun. It also helps to relax muscles one by one, beginning with the face and neck, and progressing downward to the feet. Many people find the Yoga exercises highly effective both mentally and physically. A short period of total relaxation each day not only relieves tension but enables us to deal with problems more vigorously—and it is usually best to tackle one problem or one piece of work at a time without being concerned about the total amount that has to be done. It is also important to recognize that not only adults but hard-driven children need to cultivate the leisurely use of leisure. This can be done in many ways: "There is browsing in books, quietly reading instead of actively studying their contents. There are slow walks and meanderings rather than hikes to 'get places.' There are the wanderings of the mind over 'the wilderness of Being,' to use a phrase of Santayana. And communication with a painting or piece of sculpture, quite apart from its name or date or the 'influences' that produced it. The silent companionship of a dog may be the answer for some, as it was with Emerson. Or fishing that is not done for the sake of catching, sunbathing without competing for a tan, canoeing in which we drift as much as we paddle. And sitting quietly in a house of worship, reading poetry, conversing without 'carrying on a conversation,' or listening to music in the dark. In a word, every one of us needs to escape from 'reality' at times. It renews our energies, corrects our perspective, and 'it restoreth the soul.'" (Hartley and Goldenson, 1963)

Fourth, try to talk out troubles with a sympathetic friend, physician, or clergyman. The talking-out process can be helpful not only in relieving inner tension but in seeing our problems and reactions in a new light. A few discussions with a psychotherapist are frequently sufficient to bring us to terms with more persistent problems. Deep-seated disturbances, however, require more extended treatment. See TALKING IT OUT, RELAXATION THERAPY.

TENSION HEADACHE. A headache produced by acute or prolonged emotional tension.

This is probably the most common type of persistent headache. It consists of a constant but diffuse pain in the forehead, back of the head, shoulders and neck, usually accompanied by insomnia and general irritability. The pain is due to prolonged contracture of the neck muscles resulting from pent-up emotion, and for this reason tension headache is classified as a psychophysiologic reaction of the musculoskeletal system. In contrast, migraine involves changes in circulation and heart action, and is classified as a cardiovascular reaction. See MIGRAINE.

Tension headaches may occur in the same type of personality as migraine (overcontrolled, perfectionistic, resentful), or in individuals who find it difficult to face problems and conflicts. As English and Finch (1964) point out, a tension headache "results from some type of frustration and is the outgrowth of a situation in which the individual is angered and yet at the same time unable to solve his frustrating situation . . . A tension headache may result, for instance, when the boss gives a subordinate criticism and the subordinate is unable to vent his resultant anger."

Tranquilizing drugs and muscle re-

laxants are prescribed for symptomatic relief, but since the headache is a psychosomatic symptom, psychotherapy may be required. This treatment is aimed at helping the patient acquire insight into the stresses or conflicts causing his anxiety and tension, so that he will be able to modify his faulty reaction patterns and meet his problems more realistically and effectively.

TERMAN, LEWIS MADISON (1877–1956). Born in Indiana, Terman studied at Clark University, writing his doctor's dissertation in the field for which he became famous, mental testing. In 1910 he was appointed to a teaching position at Stanford University, where he continued his work on intelligence by experimentally validating and standardizing the Binet scales for use in America. The results of these studies were published in *The Measurement of Intelligence* (1916), which presented the Stanford Revision, or Stanford-Binet Intelligence Scale. The new scale shifted many of the original items to other age levels, added new and alternate items, extended the tests downward to age three and upward to ages sixteen and eighteen, and established a scoring system in terms of both mental age and IQ. Another revision was published in 1937, and a third in 1960, after Terman's death.

Terman was instrumental in developing a number of other psychological tests. He was the leading member of the team that constructed the Army Alpha and Army Beta tests given to inductees during World War I. In 1923, he published one of the first educational achievement tests, the Stanford Achievement Test, collaborating with others in later revisions. He also designed a questionnaire and other instruments for the purpose of discovering relationships between personality and marriage, and published his findings in book form under the title *Psychological Factors in Marital Happiness* (1938).

Terman contributed not only to the construction of tests but to the analysis of results obtained when they are applied to different groups in the population. Since these findings will be discussed under a number of other topics, we will limit ourselves at this point to a brief résumé. He discovered that (1) the IQ is fairly constant from year to year, (2) urban children score six points higher, on the average, than rural children, (3) children with professional fathers average nineteen points above those with fathers in unskilled occupations, (4) sex differences in overall intelligence are slight but differences in special abilities and interest areas tend to be significant, (5) the average individual appears to reach the peak of his mental ability at about fourteen years of age, as indicated by the Army tests. These findings are largely reported in two books, *Measuring Intelligence* (1937), written in collaboration with Maud S. Merrill, and *Sex and Personality* (1936), written with C. C. Miles. In interpreting these and other findings Terman leaned toward hereditary explanations, and many psychologists now believe he failed to recognize the fact that environmental factors play a large part in urban-rural, occupational, and sex differences.

In addition to his extensive studies of the general population, Terman is noted for two special investigations. In 1921 he selected approximately a thousand gifted ten-year-olds from California schools, and then made periodic follow-up studies of their physical, social, and emotional adjustment. The results of these studies were published in a series of reports, including *The Gifted Child Grows Up* (1947), appraising the group at thirty-five years of age, and *The Gifted Group at Midlife* (1959) covering 98 per cent of the original group at an average age of forty-five. This continuing study helped to debunk many common stereotypes about the gifted, for it showed that they were not only intellectually superior but also better than average in physical health, emotional stability and all-around achievement.

Terman's interest in the superior individual was also reflected in the monumental collaborative work *Genetic Studies of Genius,* published in three volumes, the first in 1926 and the last in 1948. In this work the IQ's of three hundred eminent individuals were estimated through a study of their early productions and special achievements. While many of the estimates have been questioned, the work has undeniable value in documenting the early development of individuals who were widely recognized later in their lives. *See* IN-TELLIGENCE TESTS, STANFORD-BINET TEST, GIFTED CHILDREN, GENIUS, SEX DIFFERENCES, DIFFERENTIAL PSYCHOLOGY.

THALAMUS. An area of the forebrain lying beneath the cerebral hemispheres, and serving as a relay center for impulses passing between the cerebral cortex and the lower centers of the brain and spinal cord (PLATE 1).

The thalamus serves many relay functions which are important in the understanding of behavior. One group of cells (the lateroventral nucleus) co-ordinates the activities of the cerebellum and the frontal lobe of the cortex in their control of muscular movement. Another group (the posteroventral nucleus) relays sensory fibers from the skin and muscle senses to the cortex. A third area (the lateral geniculate body) is the station through which impulses from the eyes are relayed to the cortex and other visual centers; and the fourth region (the medial geniculate body) does the same for hearing.

In lower vertebrates, such as fish, the thalamus occupies almost the entire forebrain and is primarily concerned with only one function, vision. Recent experiments have shown that its functions are not only more diversified but more highly developed in man. If the pathways between the posteroventral area and the cortex are damaged, people lose their ability to make fine taste discriminations (Oakley and Pfaffman, 1962). Nerve fibers from pain, temperature, and pressure receptors also connect to the thalamus, but these fibers have not yet been sorted out. There is some reason to believe that this structure is also concerned with emotional reactions, since electrical stimulation of the posteroventral nucleus produces anxiety reactions (Delgado, 1955) and pain-like responses in animals (Roberts, 1962). In addition, stimulation of the dorsal medial nucleus evokes aversion responses (Roberts, 1962), and lesions in this area result in a decrease in fear responses.

A portion of the thalamus called the diffuse thalamic projection system (DTPS) has been found to arouse the organism, probably acting as an accessory to the reticular activating system. Electrical stimulation experiments have also produced eating responses (Robinson and Mishkin, 1962). Still other experiments have implicated the thalamus in conditioned responses, since lesions made in three different areas (the posterior, dorsal, and diffuse thalamic systems) materially affect the ability of animals to learn and retain active avoidance responses (Thompson, 1963). Destruction in these areas also affects the ability of rats to learn a maze.

THEMATIC APPERCEPTION TEST (TAT).

A projective test in which subjects reveal their attitudes, feelings, and personality characteristics by making up stories about a standard series of pictures.

The TAT was developed by the psychologist H. A. Murray and his co-workers in 1938. It is based on the theory that relatively ambiguous and unstructured pictures will be perceived (apperceived) in the light of the individual's prior experience and that the themes of his stories will reflect his basic personality—hence the title "Thematic Apperception." The test consists of thirty black and white pictures (and one blank card), some for male subjects, some for females, but most of them for both. They depict a wide variety of people and scenes which are amenable to many different interpretations (*Fig. 50*). After careful testing,

Fig. 50. A picture of the general type used in the Thematic Apperception Test. The subject tells a story based on the picture—and unconsciously projects his own feelings and fantasies into its characters and plot.

this particular series was selected for its ability to elicit stories that reveal personal and social adjustment, including attitudes toward authority, feelings about sex, basic emotional reactions, defense mechanisms, fantasies, and aspirations.

The examiner introduces the pictures as a test of imagination. The pictures are then shown one at a time and the subject is asked to tell a story based on each of them—but it must be a complete story that shows what led up to the scene, how the characters act and feel, and what the outcome will be. The subject usually becomes deeply absorbed in creating his stories, and through them expresses needs and urges which he cannot easily express in other ways. He generally projects himself into the central role, but may identify with other characters instead. Sometimes the stories are based on actual occurrences, sometimes on pure fantasy, but in any case the plot and outcome are believed to mirror his own inner life.

The stories are recorded, and afterward the subject is usually asked to comment on each of them and indicate how he came to tell it. All this material is later studied and interpreted. Several formal scoring techniques have been developed, based on such aspects as the emotional tone of each story, the use of the picture as a whole or in part, the nature of the major and minor characters, and the type of ending (happy, sad, indifferent, etc.). Most interpreters, however, use a less formal procedure. They examine the first story and set up hypotheses based on plot, style, symbolism, and other characteristics, then check these hypotheses against information supplied by the rest of the stories. A repetition of the same general theme, mood, or type of ending is regarded as significant. Interpretation is not a mechanical procedure. It depends, rather, on the sensitivity of the interpreter, his experience with different personality patterns, and his ability to view the stories on different levels.

Through this procedure, the psychologist may gain new insight into the emotional conflicts, defense mechanisms and general dynamics of the respondent. He usually verifies his findings not only through interviews with the subject, but through a battery of other tests that might include the Rorschach, Sentence Completion, Wechsler-Bellevue or others.

The following two protocols, taken from TAT records of the same ten-year-old boy, illustrate some aspects of this technique. Note that both stories contain the same emotional themes: feelings of inferiority and neglect, the need for success and recognition, and a wish for an easy, magical solution to problems. Note, too, that each story is dominated by an important figure

who arouses fear and respect—the boy's father was a distinguished professional man. The first picture showed a child with a musical instrument:

"This little boy has been practicing the violin. He is really a very good violin player, but nobody seems to realize it, or to care much about how he gets along with his playing. Right now he is thinking about how nobody gives him much encouragement. Pretty soon he goes back to practicing, and when he does, it happens that a very famous concert master comes along and hears him. He takes the little boy and puts him on the stage. Soon, this little boy becomes very famous and known everywhere as a child prodigy."

The second story was prompted by a picture of a marshy landscape:

"This is a swamp in which there are live alligators. Among them is a little alligator that all of the other alligators pick on all the time. He is not very happy. Over in the distance there is another swamp where there lives a very large alligator. This big alligator decides that he is going to be king of all the alligators and he comes over to this swamp to tell them so. But the other alligators don't want him to be their king and decide to pick one of their own. When they look around for a king, they notice that the little alligator is different from the rest, and feel that he must be something special. So they make him king of all the alligators." (Kimble and Garmezy, 1963)

Many studies have been made of the TAT. It has been found especially effective in detecting overt aggressiveness (Mussen and Naylor, 1954), and in reflecting increased feelings of aggression in response to frustration (Bellak, 1954). The test successfully separated dependent, conformist college students from those who were more independent (Mussen and Kagan, 1958). It has also proved sensitive to environmental influences; Mussen (1953) found that stories reflected feelings of hostility of minority groups from depressed areas, indicating that social influences must be taken into account in interpreting TAT records. The test has been used with good effect in studying cultural differences among different groups such as Indian tribes, since the stories show the type of family relationships, sex roles, authority systems, and interpersonal relations in different societies. It has also been found to shed light on mental organization, thinking processes, and general level of intelligence. On the other hand, although the stories reflect fantasy and imagination, tests show that they could not be used to detect creativity in a group of twenty outstanding artists. They also failed to predict success of student pilots.

In general, the chief value of the TAT lies in determining general personality trends and indications of emotional disturbance. In recent years it has been used by an increasing number of clinical psychologists, rivaling the Rorschach as the most important projective technique.

Many variations of the TAT technique have been devised for special purposes. Among them are forms for crippled children and various nationality and ethnic groups; for vocational counseling and executive appraisal; for studying attitudes on labor problems, minority groups, authority, and school; and for the measurement of such drives as sex, aggression, and the need for achievement. Some versions utilize sound films or colored pictures, or present auditory stimuli (dialogue, sound effects) incorporated into a story.

In addition, the Symonds Picture-Story Test presents pictures that are especially appropriate for adolescents. Other variations have been constructed for children of about three to ten years of age. The CAT, published by Leopold Bellak in 1954, uses pictures involving animal characters on the theory that young children will project more readily to animals than to human beings. The

situations are typically human, as in cartoons, and are designed to elicit stories dealing with such problems as sibling rivalry, parent-child relations, aggression, toilet-training, and feeding. Studies, however, have shown that children produce as many or more significant responses with human as with animal pictures. As a consequence, Bellak and Hurvich have developed a human version of the test, the CAT-H, for older children, and have suggested that the age and personality of the child determine which form is more effective in a particular case.

Still another children's test, the Blacky Pictures, developed by C. S. Blum, depicts scenes in the life of a dog, Blacky, and his family. The situations are more psychoanalytic than in the TAT and CAT, since they are based on critical stages in psychosexual development— for example, the cartoon in which Momma is nursing Blacky is meant to evoke oral erotic feelings, and another in which Momma and Poppa are displaying affection for each other is designed to determine "Oedipal intensity." As each cartoon is shown, questions are asked, and after the child has replied to them, he chooses the one he likes best and the one he dislikes most. He is then encouraged to talk about his own family and relate the pictures to them. Blum believes that the test can be used not only to uncover emotional difficulties, such as those involved in stuttering, but to demonstrate the validity of psychoanalytic concepts. Cronbach (1960) believes the Blacky pictures are not sufficiently validated to offer proof of these concepts. He points out, as an example, that even if stutterers show a disturbance in oral eroticism or oral sadism, we are still in the dark as to what these findings mean.

THINKING. Cognitive behavior in which we recall or manipulate images or ideas that stand for objects and events; symbolic behavior.

Thinking takes many forms—conjuring up a mental picture of a past acquaintance (thinking *of* someone), writing a letter, planning a trip, selecting a job, solving a mathematics problem, or daydreaming as we wander along a road. All these forms of thinking are termed symbolic or "implicit" processes since we are not dealing with things themselves but only with their inner representations. It is this character that gives our thought processes their fundamental character and value, for symbolic reference frees us from immediate contact with things and events, and enables us to perform many operations, such as imagining, remembering, and problem-solving, that give us greater understanding of our world and greater control over reality.

The range of thinking can be best appreciated by making a distinction between two types of thought processes: associative thinking and directed thinking. *Associative thinking* is a relatively uncontrolled activity that takes place during reverie, dreaming, or free association on the analyst's couch. Even though this form of thinking is under little or no conscious direction, it may nevertheless be an expression of the individual's inner needs or desires. The popular name for this process is "wishful thinking"; the technical label is autistic thinking, and when it is completely out of touch with reality as in some forms of schizophrenia, it is sometimes described as dereistic thinking. In spite of the fact that associative thinking is not carried out under rational control—and probably *because* it is free and untrammeled —it may be the source of deeper understanding and creative ideas. *See* INSIGHT, DAYDREAMING, AUTISM, DEREISTIC THINKING.

The second general kind of thinking, *directed thinking,* is far more controlled and purposeful than associative thinking, since it is aimed at a definite goal or outcome. One of its forms, critical thinking, includes such mental activities as examining the validity of a scientific principle, interpreting the meaning of a poem, or comparing the effectiveness of different treatments for the same disease. Another form, creative thinking, is directed toward the solution of practical or theoretical problems, the invention of new devices or procedures, and the production of original works of art.

Far more psychological research has been devoted to directed than to associative thinking. The various studies are discussed under separate topics in this book; here we will indicate their scope by enumerating the areas and problems they cover. These include: (1) *the study of meaning:* the difference between verbal and nonverbal symbols, abstract and concrete words, denotative and concrete meanings; the measurement of meaning, for example through the semantic differential technique. *See* LANGUAGE, SYMBOLIZATION, EXPRESSIVE BEHAVIOR, IMAGELESS THOUGHT; (2) *the nature and formation of concepts:* the types of concepts and their formation through the processes of generalization and differentiation; experiments on concept formation in children and animals; the use of concept formation tests in detecting brain damage. *See* CONCEPT FORMATION, MENTAL IMPAIRMENT TESTS, VIGOTSKY TEST, BENDER-GESTALT TEST; (3) *thinking and language:* the functions of language in communication and thought processes; the form and structure of language; how language is acquired; language as a reflection of culture; thinking as implicit speech. *See* LANGUAGE, INFORMATION THEORY, SUBVOCAL SPEECH, SPEECH DEVELOPMENT; (4) *problem-solving:* experiments on habitual vs. flexible approaches, group vs. individual approaches, the brainstorming technique. *See* PROBLEM-SOLVING, MANAGEMENT DEVELOPMENT, ALTERNATION; (5) *creativity:* stages in productive thinking, insight, tests for creativity, esthetic creativity, the background and personality of creative individuals. *See* CREATIVE

THINKING, CREATIVITY TEST, INSIGHT, ESTHETICS, GENIUS.

THIRST DRIVE. The drive arising from a physiological need for water.

Thirst is one of the most potent of all drives in both animals and human beings. In his early study of the relative strength of motives, Warden (1931) compared the number of times rats would cross an electric grid and endure a shock to reach food, water, and a mate. Thirst proved to be stronger than the other two drives, perhaps because the organism can survive longer without food (or sex) than without water. Our vital need for water may also help to explain the fact that thirst produces more acute tension and more excruciating pain than almost any other organic condition. In addition, studies show that lack of water has a far more disrupting effect on mental processes than lack of food, as witness the acute delirium suffered by persons lost in the desert and by patients afflicted with dehydration. *See* DEHYDRATION REACTIONS.

Thirst stems from the need to replenish water that is lost by evaporation and urination. The exact mechanism of the drive is extremely complex and not fully understood. In 1918, W. B. Cannon suggested that the salivary glands are the key to thirst, since the mouth and throat grow dry and uncomfortable when the flow of saliva is insufficient. We then seek water or some other fluid to relieve this discomfort. More recent research has shown that this is not the whole story. Many water animals and birds do not have salivary glands, and removal of these glands in dogs does not alter their water intake (Montgomery, 1931). A man who was born without salivary glands drank only enough water to meet his biological needs, even though his mouth was continually dry. Normal people have also reported that they have dry throats without being thirsty (Wolf, 1958), and tests have shown that gum chewing will not reduce thirst if the individual is in a dehydrated state, even though it produces a heavy flow of saliva (Winsor, 1930). And finally, if the dry throat hypothesis were valid, we would stop drinking after our first swallow of water, since this immediately moistens the mouth and throat.

Physiologists now believe that dryness of the mouth is a *signal* of thirst rather than its cause. The basic condition that determines whether or not we are thirsty is the distribution of fluids in various parts of the organism. When there is insufficient water in the body, the cells give up water and become dehydrated, and this brings on thirst. In the process, the salivary glands must also give up water, and since saliva is 97 to 99 per cent pure water, these glands are an excellent indicator of general body dehydration. Other evidence suggests that the state of the stomach is also involved, for when an animal's stomach is artificially distended, it immediately ceases to drink (Adolph, 1950). Probably the mouth and the stomach act together in "metering" the intake of water, for experiments have shown that when water is put directly into the stomach of animals, they cease to be thirsty after it has had time to be absorbed by the tissue (Bellows, 1939).

These findings suggested that there must be some kind of regulator for the thirst drive, and further experiments have indicated that a control center actually exists in the hypothalamus, a structure situated at the base of the brain. In proof of this fact, a goat which had drunk to the full immediately started to drink again when a salt solution was injected into this structure (Andersson, 1953), and goats and rats also started to drink when it was stimulated electrically. The opposite effect has also been produced. When the hypothalamus was injected with a small amount of water, thirsty cats stopped drinking (Miller, 1958), and a girl who suffered from insatiable thirst became normal when a surgeon removed a cyst that had been pressing on this structure. In addition, experimental studies with cholinergic and anti-cholinergic drugs indicate that various structures in the limbic system are also implicated. There is evidence, then, that the brain itself is involved in the regulation of the thirst drive, but science is still in the dark about the exact relation between the hypothalamus, the limbic system, and the other components—that is, the mouth, the stomach, and the cells throughout the body. *See* HYPOTHALA-MUS.

THORNDIKE, EDWARD LEE (1874–1949). Thorndike, a pioneer in educational psychology, was born in Massachusetts, and received his B.A. degree at Wesleyan, his M.A. at Harvard, and his Ph.D. at Columbia. At Harvard he was greatly influenced by William James, who allowed him to use his house to incubate, hatch and test chicks for use in experiments on animal intelligence. These investigations were continued at Columbia under J. M. Cattell's supervision, and provided the subject matter for his doctoral thesis.

The importance of this experimental work cannot be overestimated, for it offered a quantitative analysis of human learning, as opposed to the anecdotal, descriptive accounts on which previous studies depended. Thorndike set up the classic "puzzle-box" situation in which the animal could open his cage and obtain a reward only by performing an operation or a series of operations such as clawing a rope or moving a latch. His experiments with this device are regarded as the first laboratory study of animal learning. By measuring the time taken in repeated performances, he found that the learning curves of animals were quite similar to those discovered by Hermann Ebbinghaus for human beings.

Thorndike termed this type of learning "trial and error," and showed that

it applied to higher animals (monkeys) as well as lower. The results of these experiments (which were later recorded in book form in *Animal Intelligence,* 1911) helped to combat the widespread notion that animals learn only through observation and imitation. His techniques were criticized by members of the Gestalt school, who argued that the puzzle-box tasks could not, by their nature, show that animals are capable of insight. Nevertheless, he held to his position and at the suggestion of Cattell applied his procedures to the study of thought processes of children and young people. As a result of this work, he developed a learning theory which he called "connectionism," propounding it in *Educational Psychology* (1903), *Elements of Psychology* (1904), and *Mental and Social Measurements* (1904).

In essence, the connectionist theory holds that when we learn we establish connections termed "S-R bonds" between stimuli and responses. Two basic laws apply to this process: (1) the law of *exercise,* which states that the bonds are strengthened by repetition and weakened by disuse; and (2) the *law of effect,* which states that the bonds are strengthened by satisfaction and weakened by punishment or other negative effects. The bonds themselves were conceived in terms of synaptic activity.

Throughout his life, Thorndike kept experimenting on learning and revised some of his views on the process—for example, he came to believe that punishment does not break a bond, though it does affect motivation and tends to discourage the learner from further activity. This view helped to cut down on the use of punishment in correcting deviant behavior; it also focused greater attention on the importance of rewards (both verbal and material) in "stamping in" the connections. Further studies showed that reward—such as having the experimenter say "Right"—tend to "spread" both backwards and forwards, reinforcing the learning that has just occurred as well as the learning that takes place immediately afterward. *See* STIMULUS-RESPONSE ASSOCIATION, REINFORCEMENT.

Thorndike was a remarkably prolific investigator, and a brief biography can only indicate the general scope of his achievements. Practically all of his work was done at Columbia University, where he served as professor of psychology and head of the Institute of Educational Research. In his early period he made a number of outstanding contributions in addition to those noted above. He wrote one of the first layman's books on psychology, *The Human Nature Club;* performed the first controlled study of twins, showing that they were far more similar in their performances on mental tests than ordinary siblings; promoted the use of the Binet-Simon scales in the school system; and carried out pioneer investigations of transfer of training with R. S. Woodworth, proving that a study of mathematics and Latin does not automatically improve learning ability in all subjects. During his next period, starting in 1911, he revised and enlarged his books on educational psychology and mental measurements, showed how statistical procedures could be applied to educational problems, and developed scales for the appraisal of drawing and handwriting. *See* TRANSFER OF TRAINING.

Between 1916 and 1920 Thorndike devoted himself to the war. He wrote on military psychology, helped to devise the Army Alpha and Beta tests, investigated the effects of ventilation and humidity on the work curve, and published eight educational tests. In the 1920s he published *On Adult Learning, Elementary Principles of Education,* and *The Measurement of Intelligence,* all with associates. During the 1930s he wrote on the psychology of learning, with special reference to algebra and arithmetic (*Fundamentals of Learning,* 1932). He then launched his monumental projects in lexicography, including his

Teacher's Workbook, which gives the relative frequency of thirty thousand English words, and his *Thorndike-Century Junior Dictionary,* in which the definitions are given in words frequently used by children. In his later years he turned to the wholly different and wholly new field of studying and measuring the characteristics of cities and states, publishing *Your City* in 1939 and *American Cities and States* in 1942. His final psychological work was *Human Nature and the Social Order* (1940).

Thorndike's impact on educational psychology was, and is, widely felt. His leadership was recognized by his colleagues, who elected him president of the American Psychological Association in 1912 and president of the American Association for the Advancement of Science in 1934. He well earned not only these official titles, but the unofficial title of Dean of American Psychology, bestowed upon him in the publication *American Men of Science.*

THUMBSUCKING. Thumbsucking, as well as finger and fist sucking, is a common though not universal phenomenon in infants and young children. Excessive thumbsucking is classified by the American Psychiatric Association as a habit disturbance of childhood, under transient situational personality disorders.

Sucking the thumb appears to serve two and possibly three purposes. First, it is considered an expression of a basic sucking impulse which yields satisfactions of its own. Some investigators believe that the activity originally becomes pleasurable because of its association with feeding and the alleviation of hunger, and then continues to be pleasurable in its own right. According to this view, "sucking satisfaction" not only takes the form of thumbsucking but of such activities as gnawing at pencils, biting the lips, and sucking at a pipe or cigar.

Other   authorities,   notably   Levy

(1937), believe these activities stem from a biological need to exercise the sucking mechanism and not from an association with feeding satisfactions. This theory is supported by the fact that many children who do not get enough sucking satisfaction at the breast or the bottle avidly suck their thumbs. Levy performed a number of experiments which appear to support this interpretation. When puppies were fed from a bottle with a large aperture, and were therefore given little opportunity to suck, they tended to suck on anything they could put in their mouths. And when calves were not permitted to suckle their mothers, they were found to suck the finger of the experimenter or the ear or tail of other animals.

Second, thumbsucking serves as a "comfort device." It apparently soothes and relaxes the child when he wants to go to sleep or when he is frustrated or upset. It also helps to relieve the irritation of the gums during the teething process. Many children who have had ample sucking satisfaction during infancy resort to thumbsucking for these purposes. Moreover, the comfort theory explains why older children and even adults sometimes revert to the thumb during periods of fatigue or emotional distress.

Third, the Freudian theory holds that thumbsucking and other activities performed with the lips are expressions of the oral stage of psychosexual development. The mouth is viewed as an erotic zone, and adequate stimulation of this zone is considered essential if the child's sexual and character development are to proceed normally. Keeping the thumb in the mouth may also represent a desire not to be separated from the mother, since the child's first feelings of satisfaction and security were gained from sucking at the mother's breast or being held while feeding from a bottle. According to Fenichel (1945), full satisfaction of the oral drive results in self-assurance and optimism, while frustra-

tion of this need leads to a dependent personality, since the individual is still seeking the effortless satisfaction denied him in infancy. Little direct evidence has been offered for these conclusions. *See* PSYCHOSEXUAL DEVELOPMENT, ORAL CHARACTER, INCORPORATION.

Whether or not thumbsucking is interpreted as sexual, there is no doubt that it is an absorbing and satisfying activity for the child. At one time child care specialists tried to curb this habit since they felt it was infantile and might lead to buck teeth. As a result, some parents applied a disagreeable chemical to the thumb, or made their children wear a thumbguard or even an arm splint. Today most psychologists are convinced that these devices are not only inhuman but basically frustrating, since they deprive the child of an important source of comfort and satisfaction.

Observations have shown that in most cases the gums are unaffected, or if they become slightly warped they return to normal when the thumbsucking ceases. There is, however, some chance of malformation if the practice is continued vigorously after the child has his second teeth (Lewis, 1937), or already has a poor bite (Sillman, 1951). In these cases, and in cases where the child sucks his thumb excessively after the preschool period, efforts should be made to provide other interesting activities and emotional satisfactions so that he will not need to take refuge in his thumb. If the habit appears to be symptomatic of emotional disturbance, play therapy may be utilized. *See* PLAY THERAPY, TRANSIENT SITUATIONAL PERSONALITY DISORDERS.

THYROID GLAND. An endocrine gland in the neck, producing the hormone thyroxin which regulates metabolism and influences growth and intelligence.

The gland consists of two lobes located on either side of the windpipe. The production of its principal hormone, thyroxin, is under the control of the thyrotrophic hormone of the anterior pituitary, and the two glands form a feedback loop to maintain a proper balance. Thyroxin regulates the metabolism, or energy expenditure, of the organism by controlling the way the cells utilize carbohydrate and synthesize protein. (Weiss and Sokoloff, 1963)

If the metabolic rate is normal, the individual's energy level is adequate and growth is within normal limits. Oversecretion of thyroxin (hyperthyroidism) releases excessive energy and overstimulates the nervous system. If the excess is extreme and prolonged, it leads to rapid heart action, loss of weight, exophthalmia (protruding eyeballs), tenseness, tremors, insomnia, emotional excitability, and in some cases psychotic reactions (Basedow's or Graves disease). An extreme deficiency of thyroid secretion early in life may result in cretinism, a disorder in which physical and mental development are both impaired. If this condition is not arrested by thyroid treatment, the child's body becomes stunted and dwarflike, and his intelligence remains moderately or severely retarded. A pronounced defect in adulthood (hypothyroidism) leads to myxedema, a condition in which the patient becomes overweight and sluggish in action and thought. The heart rate, circulation and temperature are all below normal, and in some cases brain metabolism is so disturbed that the patient develops symptoms that resemble those in hyperthyroidism, including nervousness, restlessness, anxiety and even delirium. See CRETINISM, MYXEDEMA.

TIC. Persistent periodic twitching of a small group of related muscles, most often in the face.

Tics are extremely varied, including blinking, head-turning, licking the lips, clearing the throat, shrugging the shoulders, repetitious gestures, and any number of facial grimaces. In some instances the individual is aware of the

mannerisms, but in most cases they are completely automatic and unconscious. Tics are most common between the ages of six and fourteen but are also found among adults. Psychogenic tics occurring in childhood are classified as neurotic traits, under transient situational personality disorders. (American Psychiatric Association, 1952)

Some tics have an organic basis; they may, for example, be after-effects of epidemic encephalitis. The great majority, however, are psychological in origin and are of two general types: a small group of hysterical reactions, and a large group of tension-reducing mannerisms. The hysterical tics are symbolic activities which represent an attempt to ward off danger; for instance, blinking the eyes or repeatedly turning the head may represent a desire to escape from an emotional conflict or disturbing situation. Such tics frequently start in the middle period of childhood as a reaction to traumatic experiences that may have occurred much earlier in life. Here is an example from Cramer (1959): "Peter, aged seven . . . blinked, gasped and threw his arm in front of his face, at the same time flexing his thigh and bending at the waist. The entire, painfully bizarre constellation was a habitual, uncontrollable partial re-enactment of a shocked and panicky recoil from the anesthetic applied before a tonsillectomy at age three during which a circumcision, which he had not been told about, was also performed. Following the double operation he was symptom-free for a year until the birth of a younger brother, when his severe tic appeared."

Most tics cannot be traced to specific past experiences, but appear to be unconscious attempts to reduce tension. An embarrassed child will jerk his head or blow through his nostrils, a self-conscious speaker will repeatedly cough or twitch his mouth. If other people comment on these mannerisms, the "ticqueur" will feel more tense and uncomfortable than ever and the movements are likely to become more exaggerated and persistent: the greater the tension, the greater the effort to relieve it. Some recent writers apply the theory of reinforcement to these mannerisms. They claim that if the effort at reduction of tension is even partially successful, the response will be rewarded each time it is performed, and this reward will reinforce the tic.

The treatment of choice for psychogenic tics is psychotherapy, although tranquilizing drugs are sometimes used as a therapeutic aid in reducing the general tension level. When tics are due primarily to current stress, briefer therapy may be sufficient to increase the patient's sense of security and ability to handle himself. Where the reaction is due to a specific traumatic experience, hypnosis or sodium amytal interviews may get to the root of the problem fairly quickly. Hypnosis is sometimes used in eliminating tics by suggestion, but they may return or take a different form if the individual remains tense. Behavior therapy can also be employed on a symptomatic basis. More extended psychotherapy is usually required where they are symptomatic of long-standing hysterical (conversion) reactions. *See* BEHAVIOR THERAPY, CONVERSION REACTION, GILLES DE LA TOURETTE SYNDROME.

TIME-MOTION STUDY. Analysis of the behavior of production workers in terms of movement and time, with the purpose of increasing productivity and bringing about other changes, such as reducing fatigue and lowering the accident rate.

In 1881, Frederic W. Taylor, a mechanical engineer, made the first attempts to analyze industrial operations into their component parts and to note the time required to perform each of them. His aim was, as he put it, to eliminate useless movements and find the best way to perform each of the remaining movements. This approach was radically different from the practices of his time, but he successfully demonstrated that the productivity of steelworkers and others could be greatly increased by focusing attention on the worker instead of the machine. (Taylor, 1911).

Taylor's methods were later refined and utilized by another engineer, Frank B. Gilbreth, with the assistance of his wife, Lillian, a psychologist (Gilbreth and Gilbreth, 1917). Through the use of photographs, motion pictures, wire models and stereoscopic slides, he dissected the movements of the worker into much smaller components than Taylor had done. In order to describe and record industrial operations in standard terms, he devised a set of 17 units called therbligs (his own name spelled backward), together with a special abbreviation, symbol and color code for each unit—for example, "assembly" is abbreviated A, is designated by the symbol ⚭, and coded by a deep violet color. By examining the films and charts of a particular operation, Gilbreth determined the exact movements of each hand and the time spent in each of them, then eliminated unnecessary movements and rearranged the remainder into an improved pattern. In his most celebrated study, he succeeded in reducing the number of separate movements required for bricklaying from 18 to 5, and increased the average productivity from 120 to 150 bricks per hour without any apparent increase in fatigue.

Gilbreth also suggested a number of principles to guide work performance, and more recent investigators have amplified them considerably. Here are the rules for "motion economy" cited by Barnes (1963): (1) the two hands should begin and end their motions at the same time; (2) the two hands should not be idle at the same time except during rest pauses; (3) motions of the two arms should be made simultaneously and in opposite and symmetrical directions.

(When these three principles, which were first formulated by the Gilbreths, were applied to the assembly of a bolt and three washers, production increased 53 per cent; (4) with some exceptions, hand and body motions should be confined to the lowest classification possible for satisfactory performance—the fingers being classified lowest, then the wrist, forearm, upper arm and shoulders in that order; (5) momentum should be employed to assist the worker wherever possible, but it should be reduced to a minimum if it must be overcome by muscular effort; (6) smooth continuous curved motions of the hands are preferable to straight-line motions involving sudden and sharp changes of direction; (7) ballistic (throwing) movements are faster, easier and more accurate than restricted or "controlled" movements; (8) work should be arranged to permit an easy and natural rhythm wherever possible—that is, there should be a regular sequence of uniform or accented motion; (9) eye fixations should be as few and as close together as possible.

Time and motion study has been criticized from a number of points of view. The major weaknesses have been summarized by Anastasi (1964): the atomistic approach overlooks the fact that the speed of movements is influenced by movements that occur before and after. Movement patterns that look geometrically simple may actually be awkward and fatiguing; behavior does not always conform to geometry. The approach also ignores individual differences and assumes that there is one best way of performing each job—yet this is by no means the case in every situation, since workers differ in skill, experience, age and other relevant characteristics. The single criterion of efficiency is emphasized so much that little attention is given to errors, accidents, fatigue and the attitude of the worker. When motion studies are made in a plant, especially by outsiders, they frequently arouse the suspicion of the employees, who are afraid that the company is planning to introduce a speed-up system that would cut pay and lay off workers. And finally, some of the principles themselves have been questioned even though they appear to be based on common sense. It has been found, for example, that it is not always efficient to involve both hands, for single-handed methods have proved superior in certain operations, such as picking up screws from a bin and even in brick laying. Additional research is therefore needed.

Time-motion studies are still widely used, but the technique has been modified in a number of ways. First, in many plants the workers themselves take part in the process, since they frequently offer valuable suggestions for the improvement of work methods. Their participation is also a reminder of the need for flexibility and for allowing for individual differences. Second, the time-motion approach is now integrated with others methods, such as making improvements in equipment design, work layout, lighting and ventilation, and the grouping of workers into a team.

Third, the inventory of worker behavior has been widened from Gilbreth's therbligs to include other factors such as reaction time, manual dexterity, finger dexterity, arm-hand steadiness; and basic research is being carried out on psychomotor performance. One study of load-carrying, for example, used pulse rate and oxygen consumption as measures of energy cost, and led to extremely helpful findings. The optimal weight for a load appears to be about 35 per cent of the carrier's body weight, and the optimal rate of walking speed is 85 to 95 yards per minute, with the load carried in such a way that it interferes as little as possible with normal balance and center of gravity. Another example is the study of blind positioning movements. Such movements are involved in reaching for a control lever in an airplane or car without looking at it.

Experiments have shown that individuals reach most accurately when the lever is in front of them and least accurately when it is in an extreme side position. Also, positions below the level of vision seem to be best, while positions above the head are hardest to manage. Experiments of this kind show the need for refining the old time-motion techniques and for adapting them to new situations. *See* EQUIPMENT DESIGN.

TIME SENSE. Direct experience of the passage of time.

The variability in our sense of time is so apparent that it hardly needs to be documented. During a boring play time appears to "last forever"; at an entertaining party it seems to "fly." An absorbing two-hour movie may seem to be over before we know it, but the fifteen minutes we had to wait for our friend outside the movie house seemed to take an eternity.

The experience of time also depends on our attitude toward a task. If we throw ourselves enthusiastically into what we are doing, we usually feel it passes rapidly; if we resent it and have to plod along, time appears to slow down almost to a halt. The professor deeply interested in his topic will feel that his lecture has speeded by, while the student waiting to attend football practice will say it dragged. In such cases the difference between our feeling of the passage of time and the actual interval may be great enough to be termed an illusion.

In general, then, time which is filled with interesting, engrossing activity seems to pass much more quickly than periods of little interest or relative inaction.

Several general factors help us to become aware of the passing of time. Among them are events occurring in sequence, each taking a certain amount of time; our memory of the past and orientation toward the future; and our direct feeling of how long it has been since a specific event occurred. Experiments suggest that our estimation of short periods of time is in some way related to the speed of certain metabolic processes. It has been found, for example, that when body temperature is elevated, metabolism increases and time appears to go faster. Hoagland (1932) showed that time estimation is directly related to the amount of fever. When his subject's temperature was 97.4°, she estimated an actual minute to last 52 seconds, but at 103° her estimate was only 34–40 seconds. Drugs that speed up metabolism, such as benzedrine and dexamyl, have the same effect as fever. Barbiturates and certain tranquilizers seem to have the opposite effect. Marijuana appears to slow down the passage of time, and mescaline may eliminate it altogether. Hypnotic suggestion can effectively speed up or slow down the passage of time. Under the latter directive, some subjects are able to memorize material up to four times more quickly than usual, since they have—apparently —more time at their disposal.

In general, intervals of up to five or six seconds are judged most accurately. We have trouble estimating longer periods because we have to depend on cues as to how much has happened or how much has been accomplished in the interval.

Some people can set themselves to wake up at a specific hour, regardless of how tired they are or how soon after going to bed they must awake. This ability is probably based on the fact that many physiological processes are correlated with time. Hunger occurs at regular periods; bladder tension increases as time passes. When people set themselves to awaken at a particular hour, they probably become more aware of these changes, and the extra stimulation wakes them up. They also become more responsive to external cues, and gear their awakening to the milkman's arrival, the ignition of a neighbor's car, the sound of birds, odors from a nearby restaurant, or various other sensory stimuli that occur at approximately the same time every day. It is possible that they are awakened by several of these cues, but forget all but the last of them. They are also likely to forget the occasions when their "mental clock" fails to work as well as they claim it does.

There is considerable evidence that some lower animals have an internally regulated "time sense." In one experiment, bees were trained in Paris to feed only between certain hours. When they had established this pattern they were transported to New York, which has a five hour difference in time. The bees continued to feed on Paris time, apparently guided by internal cues rather than the changed external environment (Renner, 1959). Human beings who fly the same route usually feel out of kilter for some time since they must suddenly change not only their feeding but their sleeping schedules from Paris to New York time. In fact, recent studies have shown that many businessmen, pilots, journalists, diplomats, and others who repeatedly fly across time zones suffer a number of ill effects for several days, including exhaustion, slowed reaction time, and nausea. The reason is that they have violated the circadian ("about a day") time cycle which appears to govern the body, and as a consequence normal physiological rhythms are interrupted and thrown out of phase with each other. Research has shown that the excessive stress can be minimized through careful planning to allow an extra day of rest. This will restore the usual cycle and help the body get into phase with local time.

The human being requires a great deal of experience before he can adequately deal with the concept of time. Even children of high to superior intelligence are unable to utilize the past, present, and future tenses until they reach four years of age, and they usually cannot name the day of the month until

they are eight (Ames, 1946). The slow development of the time sense is attested by the fact that between the ages of ten and sixteen children reduce their error in estimating a five-minute period by only 79 seconds, and still make a 91-second error at sixteen.

There is evidence that television is helping to hasten the development of time perception among children. The desire to watch a particular program at a specific hour stimulates an interest in time. Moreover, most children's shows last fifteen minutes or half an hour, and most commercials are of a standard length. These factors accelerate the normal improvement in accuracy that takes place during the school years.

Most of us are such slaves to the clock that we tend to forget that the intervals we use, such as seconds and hours, are arbitrary divisions created by man and not by nature. It is well to remember that some primitive tribes measure time in terms of social events rather than units of duration. The language of the Trobriand Islanders of New Guinea is completely without both past and future tenses; all events are viewed as occurring in a mystical present. In our culture, on the other hand, time is so important that temporal disorientation is one of the surest signs of severe mental disturbance. *See* DISORIENTATION, HALLUCINOGEN.

TITCHENER, EDWARD BRADFORD

(1867–1927). Titchener, the chief exponent of structuralism in American psychology, was born in Chichester, England. After attending Oxford, where he specialized in philosophy and physiology, he studied for his Ph.D. under Wilhelm Wundt in Leipzig. In 1892 he accepted a position at Cornell University, where he was appointed professor of psychology in 1895 and professor in the graduate school in 1909, at which post he remained until his death. In the course of his activities, he published over two hundred articles, eight books of his own, and translations of eleven German textbooks by Wundt, Külpe, and others. In addition, he served as editor of the *American Journal of Psychology* from 1894 to 1920, and in 1904 founded the Society of Experimental Psychology to further his own point of view.

When Titchener arrived at Cornell he was deeply imbued with the structuralist approach of Wundt. Although this viewpoint was outside the mainstream of American psychology, he did not alter his approach even when newer developments made it appear outdated. In contrast to the prevailing emphasis on individual differences and the later development of behaviorism, he focused his attention exclusively on the normal, generalized adult mind, which he investigated through the method of introspection. His object was to uncover the elements of experience and determine the laws and principles by which these elements are combined. This approach was modelled after the physical sciences and, in his opinion, excluded any consideration of animal, child, applied or abnormal psychology, since introspection could not be used or could not be trusted in these fields.

Titchener became the unofficial head of the "old guard" in psychology and occupied the important position of critic of newer developments in the field. The clash of views served the positive purpose of sharpening the issues and putting the adversaries on their mettle. He described his own position as structural psychology, and placed it in direct opposition to what he termed the functional psychology of James and Dewey. This juxtaposition had the effect of attracting more adherents to the functionalist point of view than to his own.

Titchener directed the laboratory work at Cornell strictly along structuralist lines. He trained his students in the difficult art of introspection, which required them to report the immediate content of experience rather than to describe the events that pro-

duced the experience. To give one example, he pointed out that "I am tired" is an interpretation, and therefore to be avoided, but a description of the various somesthetic and visceral sensations involved in the feeling would fulfill the requirements of the introspective method. He first reported his findings in *Outlines in Psychology* (1896), which was supplanted by *Textbook of Psychology* in 1910. Another early work was *Primer of Psychology* (1898), which later appeared in a revised form under the title *Beginner's Psychology* (1915). His most important book was his four-volume *Experimental Psychology: A Manual of Laboratory Practice* (1901–5), a work of encyclopedic scope which Boring (1950) believes is possibly the most erudite treatise on the subject of psychology in the English language. This book served as a guide for the operation of experimental laboratories not only in this country but throughout the world, and did much to establish psychology as an independent science.

Titchener's next two books presented his views on the controversial subjects of thought, attention and feeling: *Psychology of Feeling and Attention* (1908) and *Experimental Psychology of Thought Processes* (1909). In opposition to the Würzburg School, he held that thought was thoroughly sensory in nature, and that the idea of "imageless thought" resulted from inadequate introspective analysis. And in response to the claim of the Würzburg School that meaning comes into consciousness more quickly than images, he insisted that the only basic elements were sensations, images and feelings, and we therefore do not apprehend meaning directly. In his view, all feelings could be described along a one-dimensional scale, that of pleasantness and unpleasantness (in contrast to Wundt's three-dimensional theory). Attention was considered an attribute of sensation, for when we attend to something we increase the clearness or "attensity" of the sensory proc-

ess. *See* INTROSPECTION, WÜRZBURG
SCHOOL, IMAGELESS THOUGHT.

In spite of his insistence on a laboratory approach, Titchener's conservative
views prevented him from being integrated into American psychology. The
following estimate of his work is contained in an obituary written by C. S.
Myers and published in the *British Journal of Psychology:* "He took little
interest in individual mental differences,
in Behaviourism, the 'Gestalt Psychologie,' mental testing, or in applied psychology. His single aim was the study
of the human mind 'in general,' and to
express all mental processes in terms
of a fixed number of hypothetical elements and attributes. Although such
atomistic procedure has been largely
superseded now as a psychological ideal,
Titchener's views were useful in their
day in provoking much experimental
research."

TOILET TRAINING. The process of
acquiring control over elimination. The
term "training" is, or should be, a
misnomer since the child should be allowed to learn for himself instead of
being actively trained.

Bowel and bladder control ordinarily
take months and even years to develop
since they require both physiological and
psychological "readiness." During the
first year or two of life, the child's
neural and muscular mechanisms are
too immature for self-regulation, and
he cannot fully understand what is required of him. As Spock has pointed
out (1957), "The most that the mother
needs is to watch her child—to see what
stage of readiness he is in—and give
him some positive encouragement." If,
on the other hand, she exerts severe
pressure, the chances are he will become
stubborn and rebellious. He may also
lose confidence in himself and develop
behavior problems such as enuresis, nail
biting, stuttering or excessive concern
about neatness and cleanliness (Mac-
Farlane et al., 1954).

There are wide variations from child
to child, but on the average the beginnings of bowel control occur at about
six months of age and of bladder control
at fifteen or sixteen months. The reason
for the difference is that bowel movements are more regular, less frequent,
and more readily anticipated than urination, and this facilitates the learning
process. Fairly complete bowel control
is generally achieved by the time the
child is two. Daytime bladder control
is acquired between two and two and
a half years, and nighttime control
about a year later. Temporary lapses
are to be expected for another two or
three years, especially when the child is
fatigued, ill, upset, or absorbed in interesting activities. He may also revert
to bedwetting when a new baby arrives. In any case, he should be reassured and not criticized when slips occur.

Progress in achieving control is subject to many conditions. Scolding, sham-
ing, ridiculing, or making unfavorable
comparisons with other children will
do more harm than good. So will approaching the "problem" with a grim,
determined air, or forcing the child to
stay in the bathroom until he "performs." On the other hand, a patient,
understanding attitude, with occasional
gentle reminders when he shows signs
of a "need" will help him learn to take
care of himself. If the home is reasonably relaxed, and the child is accepted and loved for himself and not
because he is dry or clean, the control
of elimination will rarely become a
problem. This is especially the case
where the parents take the attitude that it
doesn't matter in the long run whether
it takes a few months more or a few
months less.

**TOMKINS-HORN   PICTURE   AR-
RANGEMENT TEST (PAT).** A projective technique based on the arrangement of pictures in story sequence.
The subject is presented with twenty-

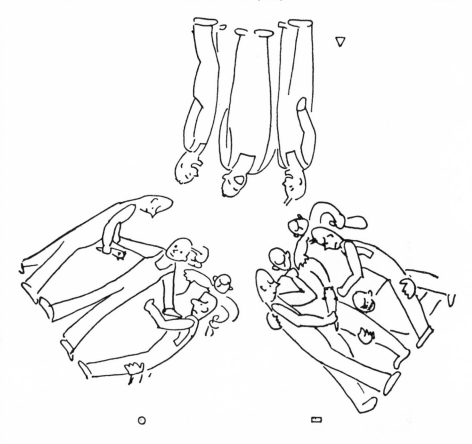

Fig. 51. A sample item from the Tomkins-Horn Picture Arrangement Test. The subject indicates the sequence of pictures that makes the best sense, then writes a sentence about each of them.

five plates, each containing three sketches pertaining to a single situation. He is asked to examine each set and to indicate the sequence "which makes the best sense," then write one sentence that tells the story depicted. All the items deal with personal relationships, and are designed to sample three aspects of behavior: social orientation, optimism-pessimism, and level of function (*Fig. 51*).

The test was originally designed for use in the selection and guidance of industrial personnel, and therefore about half the scenes are work situations. As an example, one of them shows: (a)

three men talking, (b) a group of men arguing and fighting with clubs, and (c) a man mediating between two opponents. The three pictures are arranged in round-robin fashion so that the subject will not be influenced by position.

The test is easily administered to individuals or large groups. Norms for different ages, IQs and educational levels have been obtained from large, representative samples of the country as a whole as well as from clinics and hospitals. The authors have worked out 655 scoring patterns adapted to machine-scoring. The interpreter puts special emphasis on uncommon responses which have proved diagnostic. Though the test provides better norms than most projective techniques, and is useful as an adjunct to the interview process, it has not yet been sufficiently validated to be widely applied in clinical programs (Anastasi, 1961; Freeman, 1962). *See* PROJECTIVE TESTS.

TOTAL PUSH THERAPY. A supportive approach originated by Abraham Myerson for the treatment of chronic schizophrenics and other patients confined to mental institutions.

To maintain morale and prevent deterioration among these patients, Myerson (1939) proposed to surround them with a highly stimulating environment and to involve them in constant activities. He felt that this would prevent them from lapsing into apathy and retreating from reality. The activities included daily walks, classes in bowling and other sports, showers and massages, and close attention to attractive clothing and neat appearance.

As the patients improved, music, dance, crafts, and occupational therapy were used to rechannel feelings of hostility and promote social relationships and a sense of personal worth. Praise and reward as well as criticism and punishment were liberally used as motivations. All these procedures were combined to counteract the patient's feeling that he had been rejected by a hostile world, and to replace the chronic frustrations usually experienced in a drab hospital environment with basic emotional satisfactions.

The total push approach has had considerable effect on the improvement of the institutional conditions, including the introduction of music rooms, beauty parlors, and gymnasiums, as well as the wider use of psychiatric aides and volunteers who serve as a bridge to normal life. It is also closely related to the concepts of milieu therapy and the therapeutic community. *See* MILIEU THERAPY, MUSIC THERAPY, DANCE THER-APY, RECREATION THERAPY, OCCUPATIONAL THERAPY, VOLUNTEER WORKERS, MENTAL HOSPITAL, SUPPORTIVE THERAPY, SOCIAL BREAKDOWN SYNDROME.

TOUCH (Pressure Sense). A sensation produced by an object which contacts or presses upon the surface of the skin. Pressure and touch are actually distinguishable, since pressure involves depression of the skin surface and touch does not. But since both experiences utilize the same nerve endings, they are usually considered together.

When the skin is stimulated by a pencil point, the sensation of pressure is experienced. This sense also enables us to determine, at least roughly, the location and area of an object such as a coin placed on the palm. There are wide differences in sensitivity to pressure over the body's surface. The ball of the thumb, the tip of the tongue, the lips and the hands are the most sensitive areas. The arms and legs are less sensitive, and the trunk, back and calloused body areas are the least sensitive of all. The back is so devoid of pressure spots that it has been called the "human desert."

The relative density of pressure points can be demonstrated by a simple experiment. On all surfaces of the skin two stimulated points must be separated by a certain distance if they are to be felt as two points rather than one. If you open an ordinary compass to about four inches and gently place the steel tip and pencil on a subject's back, he will probably report that he feels two points. When this difference is reduced to about two and a half inches, he will probably feel it as a single point. The same experiment performed on the much more sensitive finger tip will reveal a "two-point threshold" of only .08 inch.

The phenomenon of adaptation applies to touch as it does to vision and other senses. If gentle pressure is constantly maintained for a period of time, as in wearing a ring or wrist watch, we soon become unaware of it.

The sense of touch can become highly developed through use. Engravers at the Bureau of Engraving and Printing use their hands to regulate the amount of ink applied to engraving plates, and are said to detect a film of ink with a thickness of only one layer of molecules. Blind persons utilize this sense to read Braille—and a sightless boy whose arms and legs had been amputated as a result of a war injury learned to read Braille with his lips and nose. Russian investigators claim to have found a woman who can read ordinary print by touch. Though sighted herself, there were several blind persons in her family, and she had developed her sense of touch by reading Braille. *See* DERMAL-OPTICAL PERCEPTION, SENSORY ADAPTATION.

TOXIC PSYCHOSIS. Acute or chronic brain disorders resulting from infectious diseases, drugs, poisons, or exhaustion. *See* BRAIN DISORDERS.

The most common type of toxic psychosis is delirium resulting from an infectious disease, such as pneumonia, diphtheria, typhoid fever, and to a lesser extent influenza, scarlet fever, malaria, rheumatic fever, uremia, pernicious anemia, meningitis, epidemic encephalitis, and Sydenham's chorea. Toxic deliria and other mental disturbances may also be associated with ingestion of drugs (bromides, barbiturates, ACTH, cortisone, isoniazid, amphetamines, sulfonamides, thiocyanates, etc.) and metals (lead, mercury, manganese); inhalation of gases and sprays (carbon monoxide, carbon disulphide etc.); or postoperative disturbances and exhaustion. The onset of these disorders can frequently be traced to one or another of the following: self-medication with drugs, dangerous industrial processes, improperly supervised medical treatment, or suicidal attempts.

Toxic reactions vary in nature and severity, but the most common disturbance is some degree of delirium. Since the details are given under that topic, we will only give a brief summary here. Early manifestations of delirium are restlessness, apprehensiveness, increased sensitivity to noise and light, and frightening dreams. These reactions may be followed by clouding of consciousness, disorientation, inability to concentrate and attend, and in some cases by hallucinations, unsystematized delusions, agitation and coma. Well-integrated individuals can often withstand a high fever; poorly adjusted persons may become acutely delirious during a mild fever. If the toxic condition is only temporary, the delirium usually clears up rapidly; if it persists, permanent brain damage may result. In some cases the stress of an acute toxic condition may exploit underlying weaknesses and precipitate a lasting psychosis. *See* DELIRIUM, INFECTIOUS DISORDERS, LEAD POISONING, CARBON MONOXIDE POISONING, MERCURY POISONING, MANGANESE POISONING, POSTOPERATIVE DISORDERS, EXHAUSTION DELIRIUM, AMPHETAMINES, BARBITURATE INTOXICATION, BROMIDE INTOXICATION, SYDENHAM'S CHOREA, EPIDEMIC ENCEPHALITIS.

TOXOPLASMOSIS. An infectious condition caused by the protozoan parasite, toxoplasma gondii.

The parasite is usually transmitted from mother to fetus but may also be acquired in infancy, probably from animals. At birth or shortly afterwards the infected infant may in some cases develop convulsions, spasticity, eye inflammations, blindness, deafness, and wasting. These symptoms are usually accompanied by hydrocephaly or microcephaly with severe mental retardation. The parasite is thought to attack the infant's brain directly. The mother herself may show only slight evidence of the disorder or none at all. *See* HYDROCEPHALY, MICROCEPHALY.

Recent reports indicate that the toxoplasmosis parasite may be more common than had been thought, for tests have shown that at least 20 per cent of all Americans and a high percentage of Central Americans have developed antibodies against it. This indicates that they have been infected at least once. Unfortunately, however, the disease is frequently misdiagnosed due to the varied nature of its symptoms and the fact that they are not limited to this disorder.

A diagnostic test for toxoplasmosis in newborn babies has recently been developed by J. S. Remington of the Stanford University School of Medicine, based on the discovery made only a few years ago, that the human fetus can itself produce at least one major type of antibody material (Remington et al., 1968). The test utilizes a sample of the baby's blood serum, a specimen of the parasite's substance, and animal antibody known to react with the kind of antibody material found in newborn infants. The latter material is treated to make it fluorescent, and if antibodies against toxoplasmosis are present in the baby's blood, the three ingredients will clump together and be detected by the fluorescence. It is hoped that this test will lead to effective prevention and improved treatment for the disease. *See* MENTAL RETARDATION (CAUSES).

TRANQUILIZER. The term tranquilizer applies to a number of drugs used to calm disturbed and excited mental patients without affecting consciousness or intellectual functions.

Tranquilizers, or "ataraxics," are distinguished from drugs, such as hypnotics and narcotics, which have a sedative effect but interfere with mental processes. At present there are three groups of tranquilizers: phenothiazine derivatives (chlorpromazine and others), rauwolfia derivatives (Reserpine, Serpasil and others), and the milder tranquilizers (Librium, and the meprobamates, Miltown or Equanil).

Chlorpromazine (trade name Thora-zine) is a synthetic drug developed in France and brought here for testing in 1952. Doses are individualized to the patient, and are often given intramuscularly at first, then orally. It is most effective with acute forms of schizophrenia; excited, restless, and agitated patients usually calm down within forty-eight hours, and within two weeks hallucinations and delusions are eliminated or reduced to a point where they are not upsetting to the patient. Chronically disturbed patients respond more slowly, and several months of treatment may be required before results can be fully assessed. In both types of patients a wide variety of symptoms are brought under control, particularly excitement, destructiveness, resistiveness, and aggressiveness. Large-scale studies have reported an average improvement of over 80 per cent, with best results for patients who have been ill for less than six months. About 30 per cent of the long-term hospitalized patients are not materially improved, but the rest either improve sufficiently to leave the hospital or become more manageable and cooperative. In most cases assaultive patients no longer have to be put in seclusion, withdrawn patients become merely quietly indifferent, and regressed patients no longer soil or discard their clothing.

Chlorpromazine is also useful for other disorders than schizophrenia. Although it is not a substitute for electroshock therapy in manic-depressive psychosis, it quiets patients in the early manic phase and relieves the agitated type of depression. Under the drug disturbed, disruptive children become calmer and more cooperative, and restless, agitated senile dementia patients often become manageable enough to be cared for at home. It is effective in controlling the motor excitement and delirium of acute alcoholics, and in counteracting withdrawal symptoms such as nausea and vomiting. Hyperactive, aggressive reactions occasionally experienced by epileptics can also be controlled in most cases. Although the drug is less frequently used in treating neurotic than psychotic reactions, it has been found effective with severe cases of anxiety.

Chlorpromazine is a relatively safe medication, but must be carefully administered to prevent an extended period of somnolence, lowered blood pressure, unsteady gait, or fainting. It is sometimes accompanied by undesirabie side effects such as jaundice, dermatitis, dryness of the mouth, nasal congestion, and sensitivity to sunlight—but these symptoms usually disappear with regulation of the dosage or discontinuation of the treatment. In acute cases the drug is usually discontinued after the reactions of the patient have been normal for two weeks, but chronic schizophrenic patients are often kept on maintenance doses indefinitely.

A number of chemical analogues of chlorpromazine have been developed. Some of these phenothiazines have specific applications and differ somewhat in side effects. Promazine (Sparine) is used particularly for delirium tremens, as well as senile and arteriosclerotic brain disorders, since it lowers blood pressure less than chlorpromazine. Triflupromazine (Vesprin, Vespral) has the advantage of being administered intravenously, and is therefore useful for catatonic or senile patients who have trouble swallowing pills. Perphenazine (Trilafon) has few side effects and is helpful with tension headaches and painful neurodermatitis as well as psychotic states. Prochlorperazine (Compazine) is often recommended for relief of neurotic anxiety as well as for psychosomatic conditions. Trifluoperazine (Stelazine) is frequently more effective than chlorpromazine with the chronically apathetic, withdrawn or depressed schizophrenic. Fluphenazine (Prolixin, Permitil) has been found to have an especially prolonged action. Thioridazine (Mellaril) has fewer side effects than the above phenothia-zines, but is equally effective in the treatment of psychoses, and also relieves symptoms of insomnia, fatigue, tension headaches, and anxiety associated with psychosomatic reactions. Some phenothiazines produce tremors and ataxia (impaired co-ordination) and some are apt to induce a form of restlessness known as acathisia. *See* this topic.

The second major tranquilizer, reserpine (Serpasil) is derived from the snake root plant, rauwolfia serpentina, which has long been used in India for treating mental and other disorders. A report on its use in the treatment of schizophrenia made by an Indian doctor, R. A. Hakim, in 1953, prompted Nathan S. Kline to experiment with it in this country (Kline, 1954). He found it effective in 86 per cent of chronically disturbed schizophrenic patients, and later studies showed that it was often successful in cases where electroshock and insulin shock therapy had failed.

Although reserpine and chlorpromazine are totally different chemicals, they have strikingly similar effects. Like chlorpromazine, reserpine is most effective in calming restless, excited, or combative patients—including disturbed schizophrenics, manic-depressives in the manic state, hyperactive brain-injured children, and irritable, hostile senile patients. It also eliminates delusions and hallucinations, and can be used for regressed patients whose basic habits have deteriorated to a point where they have been isolated. As with chlorpromazine, reserpine can help to reduce anxiety and tension in neurotic patients, but on the whole it is not as effective with neurotic as it is with psychotic disorders. There may be unpleasant side effects, such as weakness, ulcers, and nasal congestion. Serious reduction in blood pressure and suicidal depression occur more often than with chlorpromazine. It is sometimes found that a combination of the two drugs is more effective with chronically disturbed patients than either drug alone. Recent studies, however, have indicated that when used singly, reserpine is somewhat less efficacious than chlorpromazine, and its use is therefore declining.

Another type of drug, lithium carbonate, has recently been found to have a calming effect on manic patients, and there is evidence that it also dampens and shortens depressive episodes in manic-depressive psychosis.

In addition to these more powerful tranquilizers, which are primarily used for psychotic patients, two milder drugs, chlordiazepoxide (Librium) and meprobamate (Miltown, Equanil), are in wide use for reducing tension and anxiety, and in promoting sleep in normal as well as neurotic individuals. Meprobamate is also helpful in phobias, tension headaches, psychosomatic disorders, insomnia, premenstrual tension, and neurodermatitis. Large doses sometimes produce skin reactions, and prolonged use may lead to habituation and possibly to addiction. If the drug has been taken for some time and is suddenly stopped, the patient may react with such withdrawal symptoms as insomnia, tremors, hallucinations, and convulsions. Librium is particularly useful in allaying apprehension, alleviating anxiety attacks and in treating alcoholism. It also has side effects in some individuals, particularly drowsiness and impaired concentration, and prolonged use may lead to habituation.

Other relatively mild tranquilizers in use today include diazepam (Valium), which is somewhat stronger than Librium, benactyzine (Suavatil), hydroxyzine (Atarax, Vistaril), phenaglycodol (Ultran), chlormezanone (Trancopal), mephanoxalone (Trepidone), and emylcamate (Striatan). Benactyzine promotes relaxation but occasionally with thought-blocking and depersonalization. It is sometimes used in combination with meprobamate (Deprol) for the relief of tension and neurotic depression.

Antidepressants are frequently used in combination with tranquilizers for the relief of states of anxiety or tension accompanied by depression. The energizers Tofranil or Elavil may be combined with such tranquilizers as Librium, Valium, Mellaril, or Thorazine. Triavil, containing perphenazine and amitriptyline, is an example of a drug combining the two types in a single tablet.

TRANSACTIONAL ANALYSIS. A form of group psychotherapy originated by Eric Berne, which focuses attention on characteristic interactions between individuals and the "games" they play in social situations.

Berne holds that group therapy, if it is to be effective, must develop methods of its own and not simply adopt procedures used in individual therapy. The logical starting point, he believes, is the multitude of transactions which take place in the group situation, since they reveal the internal "ego states" which lie behind these social responses. These ego states can be classified into (1) exteropsychic, that is, borrowed from external reality and labeled "Parent"; (2) neopsychic, oriented to current reality and labeled "Adult"; and (3) archaeopsychic, consisting of relics from the past, and labeled "Child." A structural analysis of the individual will show how these three systems interact intrapsychically— that is, "their mutual isolation, conflict, contamination, invasion, predominance, or cooperation within the personality."

According to this theory, all transactions between individuals, whether constructive or destructive, reflect these inner relationships. Transactional analysis is therefore concerned with (a) the diagnosis of the specific ego states involved when a person interacts and communicates with others, and (b) the way these states can lead to understanding or misunderstanding by the people involved in the transaction.

Berne reports that patients can readily recognize the Parent, Adult, and Child components when clinical material is brought to their attention. For example, he is able to show them that they assume different postures, gestures and tones of voice when one or another of these states is in control. Moreover, he believes that each of these states is complete in the sense that it is formed of id, ego, and superego components—that is, egocentric impulses, conscious goals, and the precepts and norms of society. Diagrams are presented to illustrate the way the three states are involved in different transactions and to show how misunderstandings take place. As an example, a statement made by one patient in an adult ego state may be encoded by another patient on an adult level—a transaction that makes for smooth communication and full understanding. On the other hand, a so-called "crossed transaction" may take place, in which patient two makes a response which he intends to be adult, but patient one misperceives it and sees it as the product of the Parent and not the Adult ego state of patient two. He then reacts to it as a child would react to a critical parent. Berne maintains that misperceptions of this kind are the most prevalent cause of misunderstandings in marriage, social life and work situations.

The object of transactional group therapy is to make each participant aware of the Parent, Adult and Child components of his attitudes, feelings and behavior, so that he can learn to function in a more integrated manner. This involves analyzing the conflicts among the systems and working toward control by the Adult state. Berne stresses, however, that integration does not mean destruction of the Child component— for when the confusions which originated earlier in life are rectified, the Child ego state can contribute to the individual and his relationships exactly what an actual happy child can contribute to family life. (Berne, 1958)

In his original article, Berne used the term "game" to denote the habitual, and often deceitful, transactions which

people adopt in dealing with others. In his own language, a game is "a recurring series of transactions, often repetitive, superficial rationally with a concealed motivation." He held that each of these games is by itself merely a segment of a "script" which a person uses in "performing" throughout life. When this script is analyzed, it is found to be an unconscious plan based on fantasies derived from early experience, and a major force in shaping the individual's entire life. Transactional analysis has therefore been described by Berne as the analysis of scripts.

In a recent book he has attempted to describe the most common *Games People Play* (1964). To dramatize these games, and to demonstrate their relevance to everyday life, he gives each type a colloquial label and exposes its true purpose as a "con," a "gimmick" or a "payoff"—that is, a deceptive trick, an ulterior motive, or a reward of some kind. In the "Yes, but" game, for example, a woman courts a compliment but tries to show that it was undeserved. In this way she attempts to demonstrate her superiority by making the complimenter feel stupid. This, then, is the "pay-off" which he has been "conned" into making. Other game titles are "Rapo," "Let's You and Him Fight," and "Ain't It Awful."

The aim of this popular presentation is to make people more aware of their social interactions, although its net effect might be to make them self-conscious and overconcerned about social manipulations of a relatively trivial nature. The crucial question is whether this type of interaction actually plays an important part in the emotional disturbances that afflict human beings.

Berne has applied his transactional approach not only in private group therapy sessions but with patients in prisons and hospitals who are not usually handled by psychoanalytic methods. He also holds seminars, publishes a journal, and has organized the

International Transactional Analysis Association.

TRANSFERENCE. In psychoanalysis, the projection or displacement upon the analyst of unconscious feelings, thoughts and wishes which the patient originally directed toward important individuals in his childhood.

In the course of psychoanalytic therapy the patient forms a complex emotional relationship with the therapist. One of its major features is the tendency to identify the therapist with his father (or other significant person) and to "transfer" to him the emotional reactions felt toward this important person during his early years—emotions which are still affecting him on an unconscious level. As Nunberg (1955) points out, "During psychoanalytic treatment, the repressed, unconscious material is revived, and since this material contains many infantile elements, the infantile strivings are reactivated and seek gratification in the transference. As the most important relationship of the child is with his parents, the relationship between patient and analyst established in the transference becomes analogous to, or at times, even similar to the patient's relationship with his parents in childhood. The patient endows the analyst with the same magic powers of omniscience which, in childhood, he attributed to his parents. The traits of submissiveness and rebellion, in transference, likewise reflect the attitude of the child to his parents. The patient behaves irrationally in a psychoanalytic situation; it often takes a long time to make him see the irrationality of his behavior, which is deeply rooted in his unconscious, infantile life."

The feelings directed toward the analyst may be either positive or negative in nature. The positive transference consists of emotional attachment, idealization, or in the case of a female patient and a male analyst, it may take the form of viewing the therapist as an "ideal husband and lover." The negative transference takes the form of hostility expressed in criticism, anger and resentment. These patterns are rarely simple, since the patient has usually had ambivalent feelings toward his parents; he may therefore show admiration for the therapist or seek his love, but at the same time distrust him or feel hostility toward him as a symbol of authority.

The transference process serves two general purposes. First, it brings unconscious feelings into the open where they can be studied, understood and "worked through." As Noyes and Kolb (1963) state, "By encouraging the patient to retrace his memories to early childhood, he may find the source of these feelings and make it possible to eliminate them or lessen their influence. The secret of the patient's illness may often be found in these transferred feelings." Second, it enables the therapist to provide experiences the patient needs—for example, the chance to release impulses which have been inhibited or frustrated by the parents; or the opportunity to feel accepted and esteemed, to counterbalance rejection or neglect experienced early in life.

Although most psychotherapists recognize and utilize the transference relationship, only the psychoanalysts have built a body of theory around the process and regard it as the essential therapeutic tool. Moreover, other theorists differ from Freud in their interpretation of the process. Jung, for example, places less emphasis on the reactivation of childhood relationships and more on the use of transference as a means of developing more satisfactory attitudes. He refers to it as "psychological rapport," "an intensified tie to the physician which is a compensation symptom for the defective relationship to present reality . . . The phenomenon of transference is inevitable in every fundamental analysis. The patient must find a relationship to an object in the living present, for without it he can never adequately fulfill the demands that adaptation makes upon him" (1928). *See* PSYCHOANALYSIS (THERAPY).

TRANSFER OF TRAINING. The influence of old learning on new. When prior learning furthers new learning, the process is termed positive transfer; when it hinders new learning, it is termed negative transfer.

The problems we meet are seldom wholly new; they usually bear some resemblance to situations we have already encountered. When present tasks involve either *components* or *principles* that are similar to those found in tasks which have already been mastered, some degree of positive transfer usually occurs. Learning to drive one make of car enables us to drive many others, since the same types of behavior are generally required in handling different makes. Similarly, the study of Latin helps us master French, Italian and Spanish, since Latin roots are found in all these languages. Educational psychologists have also found that the basic techniques of study can be readily transferred from one school subject to another, and that teachers should emphasize principles rather than rote learning, since the principles can be applied to a multitude of problems in the field. For this reason it is better to learn the general principles of mathematics than to memorize the solution to individual problems.

Responses learned by one part of the body often transfer to another part. In "bilateral transfer," we learn to do something with one hand or foot, and the other gains from the experience. This helps to account for the fact that the famous tennis player, Tilden, was able to transfer his racquet to his left hand with little extra practice when he injured his right hand. A Viennese surgeon used to require his right-handed students to practice surgical skills with their left hand, not only because the left hand could then be called upon in awkward situations, but because the training automatically transferred to the right and reinforced the normal learning process. *See* CORPUS CALLOSUM.

The feeling of familiarity we sometimes experience in a new situation is still another example of positive transfer. This experience, called déjà vu (already seen), usually occurs because the present situation has some outstanding feature or general characteristic in common with a situation already experienced. *See* PARAMNESIA.

Prior experience does not always advance our performance on new tasks; it may sometimes hamper us. When the responses we have previously learned are opposite, antagonistic or unsuitable to those required in a new situation, such "negative transfer" takes place. Americans driving in England find it hard to drive on the left side of the road because of interference with established behavior patterns. Airplane accidents have been caused by switching from one type of instrument panel or set of controls to another; during an emergency the pilot tends to revert to his former habits. In studying a new science, we may be hampered by assuming that the terms mean the same as in ordinary speech. In physics, for example, force, work, energy and mass all have technical meanings that are quite different from colloquial usage.

Experiments indicate that negative transfer occurs much less often than might be expected. Our initial attempts to master a novel situation usually override any negative effects of past learning, since we are likely to pay close attention and bring all our mental processes to bear on it. Moreover, once we get the "feel" of what is required in the novel situation, we fall into new patterns of thinking or acting, and automatically cut out anything that conflicts with these patterns.

The theory of transfer has undergone a radical change in modern educational psychology. In the last century educators believed that only a limited number of "mental faculties" had to be trained, and once trained they would enable a student to master every type of subject-matter. In particular, the study of Greek, Latin and Mathematics was believed to be basic in the educational process, since these subjects were supposed to cultivate such faculties as reasoning, memory, and systematic thinking better than any others. This theory, known as "formal discipline," also held that all mental faculties could be progressively strengthened through practice, in the same way that we strengthen our muscles through exercise. See FACULTY PSYCHOLOGY.

The mental faculty theory has been disproved. In a classic investigation, Thorndike and Woodworth (1901) showed that no single high school subject trained the intellect better than any other. They also found that positive transfer from one subject to another was less than had been claimed—in fact, they concluded that the principal thing that could be transferred is efficient methods of study. In a word, the essential objective is to "learn how to learn." See THORNDIKE.

Today, educational psychologists have not by any means abandoned the idea of utilizing the ability to transfer both components and principles. Rather, they emphasize the fact that this can best be done if the entire curriculum is well-integrated, and if all subjects are made as interesting and meaningful as possible. Positive transfer is promoted by relating everything that is learned to real and understandable situations, as well as to ideas the student has encountered in the past. In this way new learning becomes attached to the student's already established associations, and at the same time ties up with his ongoing experience. If, for example, one of the purposes of studying Latin is to increase English vocabulary, special attention is given to the Latin derivation of English words the pupil is likely to come across. Likewise, modern arithmetic books cast the problems into a form that touches the real life experience of the pupil.

TRANSIENT SITUATIONAL PERSONALITY DISORDERS. Acute re-actions experienced by basically stable individuals in response to situations of overwhelming stress.

These reactions may occur at any period of life. An infant may experience feeding or sleep difficulties if his mother is taken to the hospital. A nursery school child may develop enuresis if there is too much tension in his life. A school child may acquire a tic or have repeated nightmares after being terrified by a large dog. An older child may commit vandalism or play truant if he is made to feel socially rejected at school. An adolescent may become painfully self-conscious and sensitive as a result of problems in his social or sexual life. Adults may become panic-stricken as a result of combat stress or civilian catastrophes, such as hurricanes or earthquakes. They may also respond to severe stresses, such as marital conflict and unemployment, by resorting to alcohol or by joining a "hate" group. Older people may become irritable, hypochondriac or apathetic as a consequence of forced retirement from work, the death of a loved one, or being forced to move to a home for the aged.

The same outward situation may have widely different effects on different people. It is not merely the intensity of the event but its meaning to the individual that counts. Moreover, past experiences and special vulnerabilities have a great deal to do with these reactions. The resulting symptoms may therefore be extremely varied, running practically the entire gamut of typically neurotic to frankly psychotic reactions. Some of the more common symptoms are insomnia, loss of appetite, irritability, tremors, temporary stuttering, tics, and anxiety attacks. Less common are amnesic episodes, startle reaction, hysterical paralysis, guilt feelings, and mental confusion. Milder symptoms often clear up by themselves in time, but more severe reactions may require short-term psychotherapy. If the condition does not improve, it is usually taken as evidence of pervasive personality maladjustment that requires more extensive treatment.

Transient situational personality disorders is one of the newer categories adopted by the American Psychiatric Association. It replaces the older term "traumatic neurosis," since the term neurosis implies a persistent disorder deeply embedded in the personality as opposed to a temporary situational reaction. The APA *Diagnostic Manual* (1952) describes these disorders as "reactions which are more or less transient in character and which appear to be an acute symptom response to a situation without apparent underlying personality disturbance. The symptoms are the immediate means used by the individual in his struggle to adjust to an overwhelming situation. In the presence of good adaptive capacity, recession of symptoms generally occurs when the situational stress diminishes."

The *Manual* lists these situational disorders under six subheadings. First, gross stress reactions, which expose the individual to severe physical demands and extreme emotion stresses, comprising combat reaction and civilian catastrophe reaction (for example, to fire, earthquake or explosion). Second, adult situational reaction, such as marital discord, pregnancy, premature birth, spontaneous abortion, menopause, job difficulties, financial insecurity, acute illness, and surgery. Third, adjustment reaction of infancy, associated with the birth experience, feeding problems, sleeping difficulties, maternal rejection, and overprotection. Fourth, adjustment reaction of childhood, subclassified into habit disturbance (including nail biting, thumbsucking, enuresis, masturbation, temper tantrums, feeding problems), conduct disturbances (including truancy, stealing, destructiveness, sexual offenses, fire-setting, vandalism, cruelty, use of alcohol, and running away from home), and neurotic traits (such as tics, somnambulism, stuttering, overactivity, phobias). Fifth, adjustment reaction of adolescence, associated with "emancipatory strivings" and

inability to control impulses and emotions (including truancy, vandalism, sexual acting out, running away, stealing, defiance of school rules). Sixth, adjustment reactions of later life, stemming from involutional physiological changes, retirement from work, loss of family members and friends, illness, decline in attractiveness, financial insecurity, dependency upon relatives, and the prospect of death. *See* COMBAT REACTION, CIVILIAN CATASTROPHE REACTION, PANIC, BRAINWASHING, PRISONER OF WAR REACTIONS, SPACE PSYCHIATRY, MARRIAGE COUNSELING, MENOPAUSE, POSTOPERATIVE DISORDERS, CHILD PSYCHIATRY, BIRTH ADJUSTMENTS, MATERNAL DEPRIVATION, OVERPROTECTION, ENURESIS, NAIL BITING, THUMBSUCKING, MASTURBATION, TEMPER TANTRUM, PYROMANIA, KLEPTOMANIA, TIC, SOMNAMBULISM, STUTTERING, ADOLESCENCE, AGING.

Illustrative Case: TRANSIENT SITUATIONAL PERSONALITY DISORDER

This patient was a twenty-year-old senior student nurse referred for psychiatric consultation by an internist whom she had consulted. Her history revealed that she had been born in a small town, the third child in a family of four. Both her parents were school teachers. Her family, from the history, seemed well adjusted in every respect. She had always been an above-average student. She had been active in sports and popular with both boys and girls. She had decided to become a nurse while still in junior high school. She had worked part-time in order to save money for her tuition in nursing school. Her social life was normal as far as could be determined and she had become engaged to a boy from her own home town. She had intentions of being married after the completion of her training. During her two-and-a-half years of training she was regarded as a "Class A" nurse both from practical and academic points of view. She had been popular with all of her roommates, as well as with most of the other nurses in her class.

All had gone well until she was placed in a particular job which had previously been filled by a skilled graduate nurse. She averaged fourteen hours of work each day and, in addition to this, had been on call four nights during the week. The tension in this position was particularly high and the pressure from her supervisors became greater as the shortage of nurses increased. She was constantly being checked, corrected, and criticized, until she began to feel that she was failing in a job for the first time in her life. Symptoms of nervousness, tensions, fatigue, insomnia, lack of ambition, nightmares, and poor school work began to occur. Finally one night, after twelve hours of assiduous work, the patient went home and had a severe attack of vomiting and diarrhea which required hospitalization.

The internist whom she consulted realized quite soon that her entire problem was an emotional one and referred her for psychiatric consultation. She was seen for two visits. During these visits her life history and nursing situation were reviewed with her. As she talked she revealed a remarkably good ability to see the tension and undue stress to which she was subjected and also her great concern lest she not measure up. She began to realize that more responsibility had been placed upon her than she was able to carry because of her student status and began to see more clearly how she had been striving for an impossible goal. The psychiatrist assisted in obtaining her transfer to another section of the hospital where her duties were commensurate with her stage of training. This resulted in immediate improvement and she was able to return to work within a period of twenty-four hours.

A follow-up revealed that she continued to adjust very well. She was quite happy and efficient and was subsequently elected to an executive position in the student body. She led a satisfactory social life and was getting along so well that, to her at least, the above experience seemed like a nightmare of the forgotten past. (English and Finch, 1964)

TRANS-SEXUALISM. The conscious desire for an anatomical change of sex.

Trans-sexualism may occur in either men or women, and in many cases is believed to arise out of intense homosexual drives. The desire for sex change may in some instances result from early upbringing in which the individual has been dressed and treated as a member of the opposite sex. In a minority of cases it appears to be a symptom of mental illness, usually a paranoid reaction in which the body image is distorted. In such cases the patient suffers from a delusion that he is actually a member of the opposite sex in spite of outward appearances. (Randell, 1959)

The most celebrated case of transsexualism in recent times is that of George Jorgensen, a former private in the Army, who shocked the world in 1952 by going to Denmark for castration surgery. In changing his gender, he changed his name to Christine, and is now living as a female in a Long Island community. He has remained unmarried and has made many nightclub appearances as a singer.

This highly publicized case led many male homosexuals to request surgical removal of their genital organs. Five of these men were thoroughly studied by Worden and Marsh in 1955. They all declared that they were actually meant to be women but were given male bodies by mistake, and they felt that society was obligated to treat them as women. The investigators, however, found that they had an "extremely shallow, immature, and grossly disturbed concept of what a woman is like socially, sexually, anatomically, and emotionally." Moreover, they discovered that sexual behavior of any kind aroused intense conflicts in these men. They therefore concluded that the desire for surgery was actually an attempt to escape from sexual impulses rather than a genuine desire for a feminine social and sexual life. See TRANSVESTISM.

Until recently requests for a surgical change of sex have been refused in this country for a variety of reasons, ethical, medical, and legal. In 1966, however, the Gender Identity Clinic was established at Johns Hopkins to make a thorough study of the problem and to perform surgery on carefully selected and examined individuals who could not be cured psychiatrically. In the words of its director, J. E. Hoopes, a plastic surgeon, "If their minds cannot be changed to fit the body, then perhaps we should consider changing the body to fit the mind." He has also stated that the desire to assume the complete role of the opposite sex is so great among trans-sexuals that an estimated three in every ten commit suicide, and many others mutilate their sexual organs when they cannot obtain surgical help.

Hundreds of applicants have applied to the clinic, nine out of ten of whom are males who wish to become females. Male operations include not only full castration but construction of an artificial vagina and artificial enlargement of the breasts through plastic injection. Surgery on females includes a hysterectomy, removal of the breasts, and in some cases construction of an artificial penis from the abdomen. Both receive doses of the appropriate sex hormones to encourage development of the secondary characteristics of the opposite sex. Many of the patients marry, although none can have children. They will be followed up for many years to see how well they adjust and to determine whether surgery is the most effective method of handling the problem.

Although many women desire a change of sex—and "penis envy" is a pillar of psychoanalysis—comparatively few, as noted above, demand an anatomical change. In the following case, however, the request was actually made:

Illustrative Case: TRANS-SEXUALISM

A thirty-one-year-old woman came to a physician complaining that her "sexes are all mixed up," and asked him to alter her sexuality by removing her breasts and uterus and constructing artificial male genitals. She dressed and acted like a man, spoke in a somewhat masculine voice, and had legally adopted a male name. Medical examination revealed that the woman was anatomically female in every way, including breast development, genital organs, and sex hormone secretion. However, her general physique was that of a strong, muscular male, and psychological tests indicated a completely masculine pattern of interests and attitudes.

This young woman had been raised on a farm, where she identified with the male role early in life. Her parents had accepted this identification and encouraged it by giving her every kind of heavy work, exploiting her unmercifully. She had never worn a dress, began shaving (unnecessarily) during adolescence, and developed her muscular skills and endurance to a point where she could compete with any male in basketball and football as well as farm work.

Early in her twenties she fell deeply in love with a woman four years younger than herself. The two women lived together, without sexual relations, for eight years and finally her "fiancée" suggested the surgery so that they could get married. The patient's family was entirely in favor of the operation, and the woman herself pleaded to have it done, saying that she was "banking everything" on it, especially since she would soon have to go out into the world on her own and hire out as a man in order to support her "wife." The surgery, of course, had to be denied and the couple separated, since they had only wanted to remain together if they could conform to the social norm of marriage. The patient became somewhat depressed, but refused psychotherapy. (Condensed from Rosen and Gregory, 1965)

TRANSVESTISM (or **TRANSVESTITISM,** literally "cross-dressing"). A sexual deviation in which the individual dresses in the clothes of the opposite sex, usually for the purpose of achieving greater sexual gratification.

The male transvestite not only wears women's clothing but usually uses a wig, make-up, nail polish, adopts a feminine gait and mannerisms, and takes great delight in his choice of colors and jewelry. The female transvestite dresses as a man, cuts her hair, lowers her voice, and behaves in a generally masculine manner.

Transvestism has been recorded among both men and women throughout human history. Investigations of this deviation have been largely confined to males. In one intensive study (Hirschfeld, 1944) 35 per cent were found to be homosexual, 35 per cent heterosexual, 15 per cent bisexual, and

15 per cent either autoerotic or asexual. Feminine transvestites show a similar diversity.

This diversity is probably due to the fact that transvestism serves a variety of purposes. First, in a homosexual or bisexual individual it may be adopted to attract other members of the same sex and to increase sexual excitement and gratification. Also, these individuals may be so strongly identified with the opposite sex that they feel happier and more comfortable wearing the appropriate clothes. It is a mistake, however, to think that the majority of homosexuals are transvestites. Recent studies show that most homosexuals dress and look like members of their own sex. *See* HOMOSEXUALITY (MALE), HOMOSEXUALITY (FEMALE), SEX ROLE.

Second, transvestism may be a form of fetishism in a predominantly heterosexual individual, particularly when there is some latent homosexuality. The clothes symbolize the opposite sex and arouse sexual feeling. Here is a case in point:

"A young civil engineer, a man of athletic build and mild appearance, astonishes and horrifies his wife by bringing home lacy lingerie, silk nightgowns, and satin negligees—and wearing them about his home in the evening. He is distressed by his wife's attitude, but undeterred. He says he loves women's clothes and has always wanted to wear dainty undergarments." (Menninger, 1945).

Third, transvestism may express a conscious desire to change anatomically from one sex to the other, a condition that is known as trans-sexualism (See this topic). Most of these individuals are homosexuals; a few are paranoid psychotics afflicted with the delusion that they are basically members of the opposite sex. In some of the homosexual cases the deviant behavior pattern can be traced to early upbringing. Here is an illustration:

Illustrative Case: TRANSVESTISM

"Mr. K.T., aged thirty-six years, liked to dress in women's clothes, and he came to the clinic with the request that he be operated on and have his genitalia removed and a vaginal-like orifice substituted. He was not psychotic, had a responsible position, and apparently adjusted well, except for his concern with the above-mentioned problem. His mother was very eager to have a girl child, but had four boys, the last one being the patient. The mother, feeling disappointed, kept the patient away from boys and dressed him like a girl. She gave him dolls to play with and taught him all the arts taught to a girl. This farce was kept up to the point that when he was six, he was sent to a girls' school dressed as a girl. When he was seven, "I had the greatest disappointment of my life. My father took me to a barber and had my beautiful hair cut off. When I got home, both my mother and I cried. The next day I was sent to a boys' school, and I did not like to be dressed as a boy. My pants were rough, and the blouse was coarse, and I delighted in going home, taking off these clothes, and putting on my bloomers and dress, with its bows and ribbons." (Kraines, 1948)

Illustrative Case: TRANSVESTISM

Sonny B. is a seventeen-year-old boy who was sent to the Psychiatric Clinic after he used improper language on the telephone to the mother of a young girl he had called. The mother, who answered the phone, referred to him as "half-boy, half-girl." Sonny became enraged, and used obscene language in denouncing her.

When seen at the clinic, Sonny was a rather small, slenderly built man with very marked effeminate features and mannerisms. He spoke in a rather high and feminine voice, and his hands fluttered about in an effeminate way as he talked. He admitted to a history of transvestite behavior for a period of years, often appearing on the street dressed as a young woman. He has appeared at private parties as a female impersonator, and has engaged in striptease acts. Sonny said the performances are somewhat disgusting to him, since he dislikes exposing his body publicly to other males. He takes part in the shows only because he is paid for his act. He commented that while everyone tells him he looks and acts like a woman, he does not think he looks like one. He admitted, however, that he feels deep inside as a woman. He would really like to be a woman, and when he dresses in feminine clothing he feels as if he is a completely different person.

Sonny has three sisters, one of whom he described as being bisexual and having emotional attachments both to men and women. He volunteered that his second sister is a prostitute, but that his third sister is "O.K." His earliest and fondest memories are those of living in his grandmother's home where he was treated as a girl. He was permitted to play only with girls until he was thirteen, and his most cherished toys were dolls. (Kisker, 1964)

TRAUMA. A wound or injury, either physical or psychological.

Psychological traumas are deeply disturbing experiences which produce overt or repressed emotional reactions and render the individual vulnerable to later stresses. There are no universal traumatic events, since each person's reactions depend on his personality and prior experience. Therefore what appears to be an insignificant event may have an intense effect, and what appears catastrophic may be accepted with relative equanimity and leave little or no mark. Nevertheless, certain experiences are far more likely to be traumatic than others —particularly events that involve loss of self-esteem and feelings of guilt and insecurity, or stresses that extend the individual to the limit of his capacities.

Some common traumatic experiences of childhood are: parental rejection, divorce of parents, death of a beloved person, school failure, and social rejection. Early traumas of this type can have an especially far-reaching effect. Although they may occasionally help to immunize a child to later difficulties, they are usually too overwhelming for the immature personality to absorb, and often have an adverse effect on his entire future development. A number of analytically oriented writers, particularly Fenichel and Horney, hold that early emotional traumas produce "weak spots" in the psychological armor which may later become the nucleus for neurotic reactions. They may also lay a

basis for other types of disorder—for example, Wahl (1956) found that a substantial percentage of schizophrenics had suffered traumatic experiences in childhood, and Clarke (1961) found that delinquent acts were frequently preceded by highly traumatic events, such as the death of a parent or the child's discovery that he was adopted.

Examples of traumas occurring in adulthood are: jilting or rejection for marriage, demotion or loss of a job affecting self-respect, experiences of racial or religious discrimination, accidents involving serious injury, and extreme stress situations such as a flood or earthquake. Reactions to such events are sometimes classified as traumatic neuroses, and a distinction is made between cases in which the traumatic event triggers pre-existing neurotic tendencies, and cases where it temporarily overwhelms a relatively stable individual. The American Psychiatric Association has abandoned the category of traumatic neurosis. The chronic reactions are included in the standard categories of neurosis according to their outstanding symptomatology (anxiety, phobia, etc.), and the acute reactions to stress are subsumed under the heading "Transient Situational Personality Disorders." The major types of acute disorders are reactions to combat and reactions to civilian catastrophes. See COMBAT REACTION, CIVILIAN CATASTROPHE REACTION, PANIC, EMERGENCY PSYCHOTHERAPY, TRANSIENT SITUATIONAL PERSONALITY DISORDERS.

In psychiatry, the major physical traumas are blows to the head that produce either acute or chronic brain disorder. Acute traumatic disorders may be mild or severe, and include cerebral concussion, cerebral contusion, and cerebral laceration. Although many people make good recoveries from brain injuries, a few victims are afflicted with chronic, residual symptoms. Moderate injury produces such symptoms as chronic headaches, dizziness and fatigability; more severe injuries may result in the loss of intellectual capacity and one or another form of aphasia. A small number of patients suffer from post-traumatic personality changes or traumatic epilepsy. *See* HEAD INJURY (ACUTE TRAUMATIC DISORDERS), HEAD INJURY (CHRONIC TRAUMATIC DISORDERS), COMPENSATION NEUROSIS, OCCUPATIONAL NEUROSIS, APHASIA, PRIMAL SCENE, BIRTH TRAUMA.

Illustrative Case: TRAUMA

An air gunner, aged thirty-three, who had previously flown without symptoms, occupying the rear turret of a bomber for the first time, was seized with acute panic on a practice flight. When he was released from the turret his breathing was observed to be deep and noisy. It was remarked by his medical officer that on the ground he had shown no symptoms at all. His history revealed that at the age of fourteen he had a particularly disturbing experience when he found himself one Saturday afternoon shut in the vaults of the office in which he worked; moreover, soon after he found the exit closed against him, the lights went out and the watchman went off for the weekend. He became increasingly uneasy, and the intensity of his anxiety can be gauged from the fact that it was only after many hours that he noticed in the darkness a little red bulb which had the word PULL printed on it. This set off the burglar alarm throughout the building, which after nearly twenty-four hours' incarceration brought people to his rescue. The air had become increasingly hot and dry, or so it seemed to him, and his prevailing fear during his imprisonment was that of being suffocated. The door was opened and he ran out in a state of extreme tension. He was off work and in bed for the two days following. For nearly two years afterwards he had nightmares in which usually he was in a tunnel which caved in on him. He remarked, apropos of the episode in the rear turret, that his breathing when he left the turret was very much the same as he recollected it when he got out of the vault. His pilot remarked that he "sounded like a steam engine." He was a man of stable character and temperament, and in the intervening years he was apparently well; but closer investigation showed that he had had mild claustrophobic symptoms all

the time since the original trauma. When he drove a car it was always with the windows open, and he chose to drive a tourer rather than a saloon (sedan). On the first occasion in which he traveled in a tube train he had the thought that it was a risky business, but he was reassured by the lights and the open platform. For some time after his original experience he refused to take the elevator to his place of work, which was on the fourth floor—he walked up the stairs. This phobia he ultimately surmounted. (Henderson, Gillespie, and Batchelor, 1962)

TRIGEMINAL ANGIOMATOSIS (Sturge-Weber-Dimitri's disease). A congenital disorder characterized by a "port-wine" facial stain (in the region of the trigeminal nerve) with calcification of the occipital cortex on the same side. The brain defect may lead to mental retardation as well as epilepsy and weakness of one side of the body (hemiparesis). Familial cases have been reported, suggesting the possibility that the disorder may be irregularly inherited through a dominant gene. The defect is one of the rarer causes of mental retardation. *See* MENTAL RETARDATION (CAUSES).

TUBEROUS SCLEROSIS (Epiloia). A congenital disorder characterized by severe mental defect, grand mal epilepsy, and a butterfly-shaped rash usually extending over the nose and cheeks.

Epiloia is transmitted by a dominant gene with "reduced penetrance"—that is, although the condition runs in families, it is not found in as many individuals as would be theoretically expected. The brain shows diffuse disturbances, such as calcification, overgrown or "monster" nerve and glial (supportive tissue) cells, and tumors. Tumors may also appear in the kidney, heart, and lungs, and in some cases may be malignant.

Epiloia is often difficult to diagnose, since there are many incomplete forms (formes frustes) of the disease, some without skin lesions and some without epilepsy. There is no specific treatment and life expectancy may be considerably shortened by the occurrence of malignant tumors. The incidence of the disorder among institutionalized mental retardates is about .5 per cent. *See* MENTAL RETARDATION (CAUSES).

TUKE, WILLIAM (1732–1822). Tuke, one of the great pioneers in humane treatment of the mentally ill, was an English coffee and tea merchant who devoted much of his time to philanthropic work. At the age of 60 he became interested in the problem of mental illness as a result of the unexplained death of a Quaker woman at the York Asylum for the Insane, a mystery that was compounded by the fact that her relatives had not been allowed to visit her. Tuke visited the asylum and was so appalled by the conditions encountered there that he devoted the remaining thirty years of his life to improving the care of the mentally ill.

Tuke was himself a Quaker and proposed that the Society of Friends build its own institution, which he would supervise. Four years later, in 1796, the York Retreat opened its doors and inaugurated a new era of humane treatment of the mentally ill. At a time when the "insane" were kept in strait jackets during the day and strapped to their beds at night, Tuke introduced a policy of complete nonrestraint except for unusual cases. He took the position that mental patients were not criminals or demons but were more like children in need of encouragement and teaching. His regimen therefore included a wide range of activities to arouse their interest and keep them occupied, outdoor exercise to make them healthy, and "personalized attention" to give them a sense of worth.

Tuke claimed that his "moral approach" worked well, but he met bitter and widespread opposition. Some attacked him for running an asylum like a "rural farm," others characterized the retreat as "the wild scheme of a philanthropic visionary." He was criticized by superintendents for abandoning restraint and by physicians for ignoring the usual remedies of bleeding, suppuration and emetics. Many members of the Society itself objected to his revolutionary ideas, and even his wife declared: "William, thou hast had many children of thy brain, but this will prove an idiot."

Tuke was not the only member of his family to be involved in asylum reform. His son Henry worked with him until his death in 1814, and his grandson Samuel wrote *A Description of the Retreat* in 1813 and took over when William died. Daniel Hack Tuke, Samuel's son, became a physician and continued the tradition. His *Manual of Psychological Medicine,* written with J. C. Buckmill, became a standard work on the subject of mental illness.

The Retreat itself became a showplace for many observers from America and the continent. This recognition, plus Samuel's account of the origin of the institution, had an unexpected outcome. The York Asylum, in which the Quaker woman had died, took offense and demanded redress. As a result, the government ordered an investigation of the asylum itself—but before it could be held, the wing of the building which contained the most revolting conditions was set afire and at least four of the inmates lost their lives. This incident and others aroused the House of Commons, and in 1815 it ordered a general inspection of asylums. William Tuke, then eighty-three, was a tireless participant in these investigations, and many examples of inhuman treatment came to light. The revelations brought some improvement in conditions, but it was not until about 1850 that Tuke's pioneering work resulted in far-reaching reform. *See* MENTAL HOSPITAL, ASYLUM.

TURNER'S SYNDROME. A rare female disorder associated with abnormal sex chromosomes. Afflicted individuals have only one X chromosome instead of two, lack gonads, and fail to develop secondary sexual characteristics, such as breasts and pubic hair. In addition to sexual infantilism, there usually are other congenital abnormalities, including short stature, webbed neck, and deafness. All victims of Turner's syndrome are sterile and severely retarded in mental development. *See* MENTAL RETARDATION (CAUSES).

TWILIGHT STATE (Dream State). A mental disturbance characterized by a dream-like clouding of consciousness accompanied by visual and auditory hallucinations.

The individual usually appears confused and unaware of his surroundings. In response to his hallucinations, he may perform irrational acts, such as taking off his clothes in public, running away, or committing violence. The disturbance may last from several minutes to several days. On regaining normal consciousness, the patient usually reports that he felt as if he were dreaming, but he has little or no recollection of anything that happened during the dream state.

Twilight states occur primarily in dissociative reactions (amnesia), alcoholism, and psychomotor epilepsy. In the dissociative reaction, the dream state is considered an expression of the patient's wish to escape from a distasteful situation, and his irrational acts are viewed as a means of gratifying inner urges. In alcoholic intoxication, "sudden excitations or twilight states (may occur) ... usually with a mistaking of the situation, often also with illusions and hallucinations, and excessive affects, mostly of anxiety and rage" (Bleuler, 1930). In some cases of epilepsy, the motivation seems to be of a similar type, but in other cases no psychological explanation can be found, and the symptom appears to be due solely to transitory disturbances in brain rhythms (cere-

bral dysrhythmia). *See* FUROR, AUTOMATISM, FUGUE, EPILEPSY (SYMPTOMS AND TYPES).

TWINS. Many psychological studies of twins have been made, not only to compare them with each other and with ordinary siblings, but to throw light on the question of heredity versus environment with respect to intelligence, personality and mental disorder. The latter question is dealt with under such topics as INTELLIGENCE, MANIC-DEPRESSIVE REACTIONS (ETIOLOGY) and SCHIZOPHRENIC REACTIONS (ETIOLOGY). This article will report the results of investigations into the physical, intellectual, social and personality characteristics of twins.

As expected, research shows that the closer twins are from a hereditary viewpoint, the more they resemble each other and the more they differ from other siblings. Identical (uniovular, monozygotic) twins are assumed to have the same heredity, since they come from the same fertilized egg cell, are always of the same sex, and have the same prenatal environment, usually sharing the same placenta and fetal sac. Fraternal (nonidentical, biovular, dizygotic) twins are the product of two ova fertilized simultaneously by different sperms. They may be of like or unlike sex, have two distinct placenta, and each has its own assortment of hereditary traits. Twins occur, on the average, once in eighty-seven births, and about three quarters of them are of the fraternal type.

Physically, twins are more prone to miscarriage, prematurity and birth injuries than singletons, and in the early years they tend to be slightly frailer and slower in developing. Fraternal twins sometimes resemble each other in appearance, but are often no more alike than ordinary siblings. Identicals are strikingly alike in appearance, and frequently indistinguishable. As they grow, their marked resemblance usually continues in spite of differences in environment, and in old age it has been found that there is great similarity in graying of hair, wrinkles, and tooth defects (Kallmann and Sander, 1949). Physical similarity has important psychological effects, since it makes it difficult for identical twins to develop individuality and independence of each other.

As a whole, twins score slightly below the average level of siblings in intelligence tests, possibly because these tests depend so much on verbal ability, and twins tend to fall behind in all phases of language development. This is particularly true of identical twins, who think so much alike and have so many common experiences that they often use gestures instead of words, and may even develop a private language of their own. Identical twins reared together differ, on the average, by only about five IQ points; but when they have been reared apart the difference varies from about three to twenty-one points, depending on the differences in their environments (Newman, Freeman and Holzinger, 1937). The average difference between fraternal twins is eight points, while that between ordinary siblings is fifteen points.

Identical twins are also remarkably similar in social development, according to both general observation and social maturity tests. They show about the same degree of competence in dealing with others, usually have similar interest patterns, and enjoy similar reputations among their peers. They also have similar attitudes and feelings, and have a strong tendency to form a self-sufficient and exclusive "club" of their own. Fraternal twins differ from each other in social development to almost the same degree as ordinary siblings, especially if they are of different sex. The attitude of parents, however, can have a marked effect on the similarities and differences. If twins are encouraged to develop individual interests and find different companions, their social development will often take quite different forms. This applies to both types of twins, but more completely to the fraternal type.

The same general findings apply to personality development. When parents and teachers encourage identical twins to become extremely close and mutually dependent, they tend to develop very similar personalities—but if they are encouraged to go their separate ways, and to have individual experiences, they become almost as different as nonidentical twins (Jones, 1955). An interesting thing occurs in the relationship of identical twins who spend a great deal of time together: one twin sometimes becomes dominant and therefore develops more leadership or aggressive traits than the other. In some cases, however, leadership shifts periodically from one to the other.

The Kallmann and Sander study referred to above throws additional light on the characteristics of twins. Their life histories show that many more identical twins lead celibate lives than fraternal twins, and if they marry they have fewer children. There is also a high proportion of marital conflict due to their twin relationship. In senility they tend to develop the same psychoses, and their life spans differ on the average by only three years as opposed to six years among fraternal twins.

U

UNCONSCIOUS. As an adjective, unconscious is a broad and often loosely used term for lack of awareness or incapacity for awareness. We frequently speak of an unconscious wish or prejudice, describe defense mechanisms as largely unconscious, or speak of a person in a coma or deep sleep as unconscious. In "depth" psychology the term is used to characterize impulses and thoughts that cannot be brought to awareness by the ordinary processes of memory or imagination, but which may be elicited by such techniques as hypnosis, narcosis or free association. "Unconscious motivation" is a frequently used term for wishes, fears and other drives of which we are not aware, but which nevertheless influence our behavior. *See* MOTIVATION.

The term is also used as a noun, particularly by the psychoanalytic school, to denote the portion of the mind or mental functioning which contains the memories, wishes and impulses that are not directly accessible to awareness, but which have dynamic effects on thought and action. Freud maintained that there are two types of mental contents stored in the unconscious: certain infantile, or "primordial," wishes and impulses that have never become conscious, but which appear or are represented in dreams, fantasies, magical thinking and gestures; and material, such as memories and drives, that has become conscious for a time but has been expelled from awareness. The mental process that screens out the first type of data is sometimes called primary repression, and the process that eliminates the second type is called secondary repression or simply repression. *See* REPRESSION.

Many mental activities and contents exist partly or wholly below conscious awareness, and much of our behavior is determined by them. Physiological drives, such as the diabetic's desire for food containing sugar or the ordinary individual's urge to change his position, often operate unconsciously. Psychological conflicts, tensions and anxieties stem in large part from unconscious sources. So, too, do our goals and decisions, as well as our impulsive and frequently unexplained reactions to people and events. Dreams, sudden flashes of insight or "intuition," the "incubation" process in thinking, "purposive" accidents, and slips of the tongue are further manifestations of unconscious processes. Many psychological symptoms, such as amnesia, are attributed to conflicts between conscious and unconscious forces in the personality. Personality disorders and neuroses are explained in these terms by many authorities.

The principal methods for investigating the unconscious—or, better, unconscious mental activities—are free association, dream analysis, hypnosis, narcotic interviews, projective techniques, and experimental production of neurosis.

UNDERACHIEVER. A student whose academic performance is considerably below his ability; more specifically, his score on achievement tests is 30 or more per cent below his score on intelligence tests.

There are different types of underachievers. The long-term type works below his capacity over a period of time; and the situational, temporary type functions below his level because of a disturbing experience, such as transfer to a new school, a death in the family, or other emotional crisis. "General underachievers" work below their tested ability in all subjects, and "special underachievers" only in particular subjects. Most of the research has been focused on the more persistent and general type.

Recent studies show that many more children work below their capacities than was formerly recognized, and for reasons that were rarely suggested in the past. Earlier investigations put the emphasis on lack of interest, laziness, and unstimulating classes; the newer research emphasizes causes that lie within the child's personality and stem from his environment and relationships. There are more overachievers in the middle economic level, but more underachievers in the lower and upper levels. Lower level parents tend to value education less highly than middle-class parents and show less interest in the child's academic achievements; also, the children often receive less encouragement from teachers. Upper-class parents do not stress achievement in school as a primary means of attaining vocational or social success as much as middle-class parents, and are sometimes satisfied with "gentlemen's grades" (Davis, 1951). However, middle-class parents who *over*stress school achievement may also contribute to underachievement, for their children may feel rebellious and resentful toward the excessive standards set for them, and refuse to work near to capacity.

Underachieving can begin at any time, but most frequently has its start in elementary school. The child ceases to do his work either because the parents show an indifferent attitude toward his grades or because they demand so much that he becomes discouraged. The child himself is usually unaware that he is working below capacity, and gives many excuses when this is pointed out to him. He claims that the teacher is unfair, the subjects are uninteresting, or other children do better because they cheat. By high school the pattern of under-achievement often becomes so habitual that it is difficult to change (Shaw and Grubb, 1958). More boys than girls are underachievers, and the tendency is most common among very bright children.

The single factor most frequently emphasized in the studies is a hostile attitude toward school. This attitude seldom begins at school; it starts for the most part at home, although it may be aggravated in school if the curriculum is above (or below) the child's level, if the teacher is antagonistic, or if the child's friends label good students "grinds" or "sissies." What kind of home leads to underachievement? One group came from "upward striving" homes in which the parents constantly prod and pressure their children to get good marks and get into a "good" college.

The girls frequently react by becoming overachievers, but the boys are more likely to protest and rebel by hating school and working far below their capacities. Moreover, when boys and girls fail to live up to their parents' standards, and are subjected to constant criticism, they often feel anxious and inadequate. These feelings either make them hostile toward school or give them a sense of futility which discourages them from making a full effort. In addition, many of these parents expect them to do equally well in all subjects, and they therefore come to dislike subjects in which they have little aptitude. These are usually the "special" underachievers mentioned above.

Another group of underachievers have been so overprotected at home that they cannot cope with the competitive situation in the average school. These children lower their sights, and often show a great dislike for school. A third group develop hostile or indifferent attitudes toward school because their parents set low standards and show little or no interest in their education. A fourth group are brought up in homes which are disturbed by conflicts between the parents or broken by divorce, separation, or death. These children are frequently neglected or rejected, and become so emotionally upset that they cannot concentrate on school work and do not have the self-confidence and optimism necessary for normal achievement.

Underachievement has important effects on both the child and the school environment. Studies show that under-achievers lower the morale of the school, influence other children to imitate them, and are responsible for most of the behavior problems that beset the teacher. But the effect on the children themselves is even more disruptive. Many of them feel guilty and ashamed, and as a result isolate themselves from competition and even from the social group. Often, too, the underachiever adopts defensive reactions; he may "simulate in-difference or bravado, he might fight blindly and hopelessly, dig in his heels stubbornly, or withdraw into daydreams or unreachable passivity" (Walsh, 1956). Attitudes of this kind can do permanent damage to the personality. *See* OVER-ACHIEVER.

UNDOING. The unconscious defense mechanism of counteracting guilty im-pulses or behavior by acts of atonement.

The healthy individual uses a variety of means to relieve his sense of guilt and restore good relationships. As a child he has learned to say "I'm sorry," and to make amends for bad behavior by being especially good. When he is older he continues to make apologies and find ways of making restitution when he thinks it is advisable. An erring husband may bring his wife a gift after spending an evening on the town. If the situation becomes serious, and he has had a religious upbringing, he may seek to relieve his sense of guilt through penance and repentance. These behavior patterns are technically termed undoing.

The device of undoing can lead to distorted behavior. Unethical individuals sometimes give large sums to charity not only to display their generosity, but to pay an easy price for their misdeeds. Some people seek to "undo" thoughts or actions that violate their conscience by confessing to crimes they did not commit. Others become so guilt-ridden that they resort to extreme self-denial or the supreme atonement of suicide.

Undoing takes still another form in obsessive-compulsive neurosis. Here the individual unconsciously seeks to cancel out wishes or behavior that cause anx-iety by engaging in symbolic activities. If he has overwhelming feelings of hos-tility toward people he is expected to love, he may find himself counting from one to ten all day long, an unconscious revival of his parent's admonition to do this every time he gets angry. Or he may react to unconscious feelings of guilt by saying the same prayer or wash-ing his hands every fifteen minutes. Other forms of symbolic undoing of an even more exaggerated and irrational nature can be found in the psychotic behavior of schizophrenics and depressives. The catatonic schizophrenic may seek to eradicate the sins of all mankind by holding his arms in a gesture of blessing for days or weeks on end. A depressive patient may seek to expiate a feeling of personal guilt by refusing food until he has to be tube-fed. *See* OBSESSIVE-COMPULSIVE REACTION, RITUAL.

V

VALENCE. The capacity of a goal or object to attract or repel; anything we seek to attain has a positive valence, anything we seek to avoid has a nega-tive valence for us.

The psychological usage of this term was first proposed by the social psychol-ogist Kurt Lewin (1935), who repre-sented our reactions in diagrammatic form in his "vector psychology." He pictured human behavior in terms of goals, barriers, and conflicts, and marked the goals we wish to attain with a plus sign, and those we try to avoid with a minus sign. Obstacles were indicated by a heavy bar, and conflicts were graphi-cally represented by different combina-tions of valences, such as plus plus, plus minus, or minus minus. For example, a man might want to make a certain investment, but hesitates for fear of losing his money (plus minus). Or a young man might be torn between two girls who are attractive to him (plus plus). If these valences are equal he may vacillate so long that they will both be taken by other men before he makes up his mind.

The concept of valence is closely related to that of value. The value of an object is, in general, a function of our past experience and our future goals. The particular value determines whether the valence will be positive or negative, strong or weak. It is important to recognize that the valence does not depend on the object itself, but on the person who is reacting to it. The same object will be positively valenced, or valued, by one person and negatively by another: "One man's meat is another's poison." We could go far toward describing an individual if we knew the kind of valences he attached to the various goals in life, such as education, relaxation and success. We could go even further if we knew the types of conflicts and barriers to attainment he was facing, and the interaction between all these factors or "vectors." In other words, the concept of valence can be extremely helpful in personality description. See STRESS, GRADIENT, FIELD THEORY.

VEGETATIVE NERVOUS SYSTEM. An obsolescent term for the autonomic nervous system, based on the fact that this system automatically controls the internal functions of the body, such as heart, lungs, and digestion, which keep the organism alive but do not govern movement, sensation, or thought. These functions parallel the internal mechanisms of a vegetable, which is alive but immobile and insensitive. The term has been all but replaced by autonomic nervous system. See this topic.

VEGETATIVE STATE. A passive, "dilapidated," vegetable-like existence observed in some chronically withdrawn or deteriorated mental patients.

The condition is found in some schizophrenic patients who have been out of touch with their environment for a long period. It also occurs in severe, chronic brain syndromes such as advanced senile brain disease and cerebral arteriosclerosis. Vegetative state should be distinguished from vegetative *retreat*, the tendency of some neurotic individuals to develop visceral symptoms such as diarrhea when faced with a threatening situation. Reactions of this kind are considered regressions, since stomach upsets elicited special care and solicitude from the mother during childhood.

The patient in a vegetative state moves little if at all, rarely responds to questioning, shows only slight reaction to stimulation of any kind, has little or no interest in food, and fails to care for his appearance or basic bodily needs. He may eventually lie in bed with a blank look in his eyes. It is usually necessary to feed him intravenously and take care of his eliminative processes. Patients who have reached the vegetative state rarely make a lasting recovery, although there may be intermittent improvement. Some authors believe that among schizophrenic patients this state represents a final phase in a *natural* process of deterioration that gradually sets in when the disease has not been successfully treated; others ascribe it to "hospitalism," an *artificial* process of deterioration which occurs when chronic patients gradually adjust themselves to the restricted, protected environment of the hospital. See SOCIAL BREAKDOWN SYNDROME, DETERIORATION, WITHDRAWAL.

VENTILATION CONDITIONS. Atmospheric conditions—primarily temperature, humidity, and air flow—constitute an important problem in industrial psychology and human engineering, since they have considerable influence on productivity, accident rate, and morale. They also affect our comfort at home and in the open air.

In general, workers are most comfortable, have the fewest accidents, and are most productive when the temperature is around 70°. However, the optimum range is largely determined by air movement, type of work, and humidity. High humidity is extremely uncomfortable because it prevents the body from using its major mechanism for maintaining heat equilibrium, that is, evaporation of perspiration. Studies show that a temperature of 90° with a humidity of 10 per cent is as comfortable as 80° with 60 per cent humidity or 75° with 100 per cent humidity. We also feel more comfortable at high temperatures if the air is flowing than if it is stationary.

Heavy work can be carried on at lower temperatures than light work because our metabolic rate is greater and more body heat is produced. The hand skin temperature is the most critical factor; it should be no lower than 55° to 60°. The optimum general temperature for light sedentary work in winter is 68° to 73° and in summer 75° to 80°; for moderate hard work it is 65° and for strenuous physical work, it is 60° throughout the year (Baetger, 1944). It is an interesting fact that individual differences are quite small. Nine out of ten workers in different parts of the country and during different seasons of the year have reported that they feel comfortable within a 66° to 77° range when engaged in office and light physical work (Ryan, 1947). This makes the job of the ventilation engineer easier.

Some investigators have found that high temperature has less effect on mental than on physical activity. In an experiment conducted during World War II, Mackworth (1946) found that the number of errors made by telegraph operators was about the same at 79°, 85°, and 88°, but that the error rate rose slightly at 92° and precipitously at 97°. Another investigator, Davis (1957), has shown that optimum ventilation does not always solve the problem of comfort. Workers in an aircraft plant in Texas complained bitterly of stuffiness, humidity, and heat even though the air-conditioning equipment was working and the atmospheric conditions were perfect. The reason for the complaint was traced to the fact that the plant had no windows and the air vents were high above the floor; as a result the workers, who came from rural areas, felt "cooped up" because they were used to being in the open air where they felt a breeze. The managers of the plant conceived the idea of tying streamers to the vents so they could see that the air was moving —and the complaints quickly died down.

VERBIGERATION (Cataphasia). Monotonous repetition of words, phrases, or sentences, usually without apparent meaning.

This is one of the many verbal disturbances found in schizophrenic reactions, particularly the catatonic and hebephrenic types. It is believed that the stereotyped expressions have a definite psychological significance determined by the patient's unconscious needs and motives; but when they are constantly repeated, their original meaning tends to become lost. Moreover, the more they are reiterated, the more distorted and incoherent they are apt to become. Two examples are the catatonic patient who kept repeating "muscle, muscle, muscle" in answer to every question (Hinsie and Campbell, 1960), and the agitated patient who endlessly reiterated the sound "boligo." *See* STEREOTYPY for the latter case; *also,* WORD SALAD.

VERTIGO. Dizziness due to organic disease, psychological stress, or temporary physical condition. Where psychological factors play a large causative role, vertigo is classified as either a psychophysiologic or neurotic symptom.

Everyone has experienced transient vertigo when the labyrinthine, or vestibular, mechanism in the inner ear is temporarily thrown out of gear. This mechanism controls the sense of balance and position. Dizziness of this kind occurs most frequently in vehicles that make rapid, unexpected turns, such as airplanes, cars, or roller coasters. Some individuals are far more susceptible than others, for reasons unknown. Airplane pilots and astronauts are given special tests to determine whether they can adjust to whirling motions. They also undergo training in devices such as the Link Trainer and the complex procedures trainers used to simulate space flight. *See* EQUILIBRIUM, SPACE PSYCHIATRY AND PSYCHOLOGY.

More severe types of vertigo are frequently found in patients who suffer from diseases of the inner ear, transient circulatory disorders caused by acute infections, and a number of brain disorders. A fairly common disorder of the inner ear is Menière's disease, characterized by vertigo, tinnitus (ringing in the ears), and progressive deafness. This disease and other forms of vertigo are aggravated by psychological stress. When the condition is due to disturbance in the inner ear, the whirling movement is more clearly defined than when it is due to brain disorder. Vertigo due to brain pathology occurs most commonly in psychosis with cerebral arteriosclerosis, but is also found in presenile psychosis, Alzheimer's and Pick's diseases, and in brain tumor. "Vertiginous seizures" are one of the rarer forms of epileptic attack; the patient feels unsteady or has the sensation that he or the surrounding world is rotating.

Vertigo is a fairly common psychophysiologic reaction to internal stress and conflict: "I have so many problems that my head is going round and round." The dizziness is usually mild in the more normal, everyday cases. In neurotic disorders, particularly anxiety reaction and conversion reaction, it is apt to be more severe and persistent. In the anxiety cases it appears to be due to severe conflicts which pull the patient in different directions and "make his head whirl." In the conversion cases it serves the same type of unconscious purposes as other somatic symptoms, such as hysterical paralysis or blindness—that is, it is usually a defense against unacceptable impulses or a means of escaping from a threatening situation. It might also have the advantage, or "secondary gain," of eliciting attention and sympathy from others. *See* ANXIETY REACTION, CONVERSION REACTION.

Illustrative Case: VERTIGO

This forty-three-year-old married man had many complaints stemming from a chronic anxiety reaction. One of the most bothersome to him was that of "dizzy spells." Upon inquiry the patient said that at such times he felt shaky and unsteady and in danger of losing his equilibrium. This particular symptom became most evident when he quarreled with his wife, had business difficulties, or had problems with his large family of sisters, brother, and mother. In short, his symptoms became worse when anything occurred to threaten his security and increase his anxiety. As he learned to know his own need for approval and also as he learned to deal more maturely and adequately with his problems, his tension diminished and his giddiness disappeared. (English and Finch, 1964)

VIGOTSKY TEST. A test of conceptual thinking in which the subject classifies blocks according to different characteristics; developed by the Soviet psychologist L. Vigotsky and introduced in the United States by J. Kasanin.

This instrument was devised to study the *process* of thinking and concept formation, as contrasted with intelligence tests, which are primarily concerned with the *products* of thinking. On the Vigotsky the question is not so much whether the subject gets the correct answer to a problem, but how he arrived at his answer and how well he used his powers of abstraction. The information gained from the test is used not only in investigating the thinking process in general, but in detecting thought disturbances that do not appear in ordinary conversation.

The test material consists of twenty-two blocks of different colors, shapes and sizes, each with a nonsense syllable printed on the under side. The subject is shown a block and its name (say, BIK), and asked to find all other blocks that belong with it. If the block marked BIK is red and triangular, he may select other red blocks or other triangular blocks. The examiner turns up these blocks and shows that they do not belong in the same category. The subject then continues to try different categories, and the examiner asks him to state each of his hypotheses aloud so that everything the subject says and does can be recorded. The correct categories require grouping according to combinations of characteristics that are not immediately apparent, such as flat-small, colored-tall, or green-flat-circular.

The test is not usually scored quantitatively. The examiner studies the written record to determine the subject's degree of flexibility (his willingness to give up incorrect hypotheses), resourcefulness (the number of alternative categories tried), and planfulness (the tendency to try different concepts in an organized way), as well as his general level of conceptualization. These observations are highly useful in diagnosis. It has been found that most people take a long time and make many errors before reaching the solution, but they can clearly state the reasons for each attempt. Moreover, when once they find the correct principle, they can apply it quickly and easily. Emotionally disturbed individuals on the other hand, show various peculiarities, such as sorting according to some obscure symbolism, or making patterns out of the blocks.

Impairment in the ability to think abstractiy is even more clearly indicated on this test. Schizophrenic patients and individuals with brain damage often point out the concrete differences of shape, color, and size but fail completely to see the more complex combinations. They are also unable to repeat a solution once it is found, and cannot adequately state the principle involved. If schizophrenics succeed in trying different solutions, they usually give bizarre reasons for their moves instead of clear hypotheses. See MENTAL IMPAIRMENT TESTS and PLATE 28 for the Hanfmann-Kasanin modification of the Vigotsky Test.

VIRILISM. Masculinization of the female, usually due to hypersecretion of the adrenal cortex.

This rare glandular disorder is one form of the "adrenogenital syndrome," and may be either a congenital condition or the result of an adrenal tumor. Overactivity of the adrenal cortex, involving excessive secretion of the male hormone, androgen, results in a pronounced development of masculine secondary sex characteristics. If the disorder occurs before puberty, the breasts fail to develop, and if symptoms appear after puberty, they include deepening of the voice, shrinking of the breasts, absence of menstruation and enlargement of the clitoris.

The effects of virilism on girls and women may be severe, and sometimes reach psychotic proportions. Among the more common reactions are self-consciousness and preoccupation with their masculinized appearance, anxiety over their gender and sex role, absence or reduction of sexual desire, depression, and social withdrawal. They may also be obsessed with thoughts of homosexuality or guilt over masturbation. The condition can be arrested early in life by the administration of small doses of cortisone, and in most cases sexual development will be normal. Surgical removal of part or all of the adrenal gland is usually required in adult cases. When the disorder is caused by a tumor, the physical and psychological symptoms recede after a successful operation. *See* ADRENAL GLAND, CUSHING'S SYNDROME.

VISIBILITY CURVE (Luminosity Curve). A graph representing the sensitivity of the eye to different wavelengths of light. Two types of curves are usually constructed, one for daylight vision and the other for night vision. They are sometimes said to measure "spectral sensitivity," since they cover the range of wavelengths which make up the visible spectrum. *See* VISIBLE SPECTRUM.

Our eyes are not equally sensitive to all types of light. During daylight we register all the colors in a variegated garden, with the yellows and reds appearing particularly bright. As twilight comes on, these colors darken and the greens and blues begin to stand out. The leaves of a rose bush look bright long after the roses have turned to black, and by nightfall no colors at all are visible. This shift in the relative brightness of colors in low illumination is called the Purkinje effect, named after the Bohemian physiologist who first studied it.

The Purkinje effect occurs because the retina contains different cells for color (cone cells) and for brightness (rod cells), and in decreasing illumination the eye shifts from cone to rod functioning. The daylight visibility curve therefore represents cone vision and the night visibility curve represents rod vision. One method of obtaining these curves is to expose the eyes to test patches of various wavelengths, and in each case to increase the intensity of the patch from zero until the subject indicates that he sees it. This point is called the absolute threshold, and the curve shows these thresholds for all visible wavelengths.

The curve for cone vision is obtained by exposing the light patch so that it falls on the fovea of the eye, a small area of the retina that contains only cones and no rods. The resulting curve, called a photopic (daylight) visibility curve, shows that the retina is most sensitive to greenish-yellow light, which has a wavelength of approximately 555 millimicrons. The curve for rod vision is obtained by making the test patch of light fall on the periphery of the retina, which contains all rods and no cones. The resulting curve, known as the scotopic or darkness vision curve, shows maximal sensitivity at 510 millimicrons, a portion of the spectrum that corresponds to bluish-green, even though the colors themselves are visible only as shades of gray. This explains why blues and greens appear especially bright in twilight.

Studies of retinal sensitivity also help to explain dark adaptation. The eye is actually more rather than less sensitive in darkness than in light, since less light is required to activate the rods than the cones. There is usually enough light energy at night to enable us to see the shapes of the flowers in the garden even though we cannot see the colors. These shapes come to us in various shades of gray, according to the visibility curve of the rods for different wavelengths.

Visibility curves can be used in diagnosing certain visual defects. People with hemeralopia (night blindness) show no rod curve at all; only the cones are operative. In day blindness, or total color blindness, the cones do not function and therefore there is only a curve for rod vision. In this rare condition the individual sees only shades of gray. *See* COLOR BLINDNESS, DARK ADAPTATION.

VISIBLE SPECTRUM. The range of electromagnetic waves visible to the human eye.

Our sense of vision is activated by radiant energy emitted or reflected from objects. This energy consists of electromagnetic charges traveling in waves at the rate of 186,300 miles per second. Electromagnetic radiation ranges from cosmic waves only ten trillionths of an inch in length to radio waves of many miles—but the human eye is sensitive only to an area about midway between these extremes. This area, constituting the visible spectrum, comprises waves measuring from sixteen to thirty-two millionths of an inch (380 to 760 millimicrons) in length.

Wavelengths within this range activate the cells of the retina of the eye, and produce electrical impulses which are carried through the optic nerve to the brain. These impulses are sorted out, or "encoded," in the occipital (rear) lobe of the brain, but the exact nature of this process is still unknown. We do know, however, that the retina contains two kinds of cells, one cone-shaped and the other rod-shaped. The cones, concentrated in the center, are responsive to wavelengths that produce color sensations; and the rods, distributed throughout the retina, are sensitive only to black and white. This indicates that some of the sorting out process occurs in the retina itself.

For a long time scientists thought of the visible spectrum only in terms of the solar spectrum. Isaac Newton had discovered that sunlight can be broken up into its component wavelengths if it is passed through a prism, and it was assumed that the human eye was limited to this range. However, experiments have shown that the eye actually registers some colors that are not in the solar spectrum, especially at the red end where longer wavelengths are found. More recently, physiological psychologists have discovered that the eye can also discriminate more colors than had previously been expected. The average individual can discriminate about 350,000 different colors, but this ability, remarkable as it is, can be vastly improved through practice. Experimenters have found that when subjects are trained to notice differences of saturation and brightness as well as hue, some of them become capable of discriminating an estimated seven to ten million separate surface colors. See COLOR CIRCLE, COLOR SOLID.

VISION (GENERAL). The sense of sight; response of the eye and brain to light stimuli.

The stimulus for sight is visible radiant energy, or light waves, occurring in the middle range of the electromagnetic spectrum. The visible spectrum consists of waves from approximately 380 to 760 millimicrons in length (between 16 and 32 millionths of an inch) which move through space at the rate of 186,300 miles per second. Visible light waves are far longer than cosmic rays, which are as short as ten trillionths of an inch, and far shorter than radio waves, which are many miles in length. In barest outline, vision occurs when: (1) visible electromagnetic energy emitted or reflected from objects strikes specialized receptors in the retina (rods and cones), initiating changes in the light-sensitive chemicals of these cells; (2) these changes produce electrical charges, or "generator potentials," which trigger a barrage of impulses carried by the optic nerve to the occipital, or rear lobe of the brain; and (3) portions of this lobe are activated.

The eye is an organ of great complexity, but its general structure can be readily described and illustrated (*Fig. 52*). It is roughly spherical in shape, with walls consisting of three separate layers: the outer, or sclera, layer is made up of tough fibrous tissue which protects the eyeball and maintains its shape. The extraocular muscles which turn the eyeball are attached to this layer. Light is admitted through the transparent bulge in front, the cornea, and travels through the lens. The middle, or choroid, layer is opaque and serves the purpose of absorbing stray light in the eyeball and preventing light

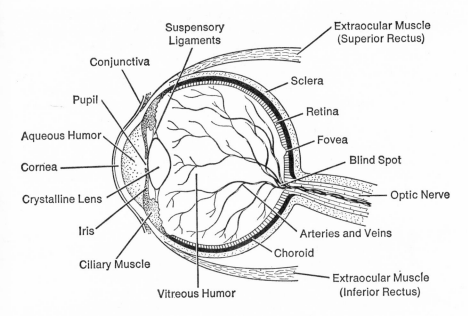

Fig. 52. The human eye, which converts patterns of light energy into electrical impulses carried by the optic nerve to the brain.

from entering the eye except through the cornea. The innermost layer, the retina, contains the sensitive cells that respond to light. Within the eye are two chambers, both of which contain gelatinous fluids, or humors: the anterior chamber is found between the cornea and the lens, and the posterior between the lens and the retina.

The eye is frequently compared to a camera, but the differences are as instructive as the likenesses. Both consist of dark chambers which admit light through a small opening, with a lens to focus it on a sensitive surface. In both, the images falling on this surface are inverted, right for left and top for bottom, and in both it is possible to control the amount of light by adjusting the size of the opening. In the newer cameras this adjustment is automatic; in the eye, the size of the pupil, which admits the light, is controlled by the iris, the colored part of the eye, through a reflex mechanism.

There are three basic differences be-tween the eye and the camera. First, in the camera we see the image which falls on the light-sensitive film; in the eye, we do not see the images that fall on the retina, for vision occurs only through activation of the nervous system. This is a highly complex affair involving many steps between the retina and the brain. The retina itself, unlike photographic film, which contains one major chemical (silver nitrate), consists of many layers, with two general types of cells containing a number of different chemicals. The cylindrical cones, numbering between 6,300,000 and 6,500,000 are primarily sensitive to color and daylight, and are most heavily concentrated in the fovea, which contains an estimated 50,000. Since this is the most sensitive point in the eye, we turn our head and eyes to focus directly on it. The rods, numbering between 110 and 125 million, mediate achromatic and nighttime vision, and are widely distributed but most numerous about 20 degrees away from the fovea. In the "blind spot"—again not found in photographic film—vision does not occur, since it is the point where the cell fibers leave the retina to join the optic nerve, and does not contain any rods or cones. The connections between the rods and cones and the optic nerve are not, however, direct since several layers of cells (horizontal cells, bipolar cells, ganglion cells) intervene.

The second major difference between the eye and the camera is that the eye has a double lens system: most of the refraction, or bending, of light is done by the cornea, with the lens serving primarily to bring near objects into focus on the retina. The focusing of the lens is not accomplished by moving it back and forth, as in most cameras, but by changing its shape, a process called accommodation. In focusing on far objects, the ciliary muscle contracts, making the lens flat, and in focusing on near objects it relaxes. *See* VISUAL DEFECTS, VISUAL ACUITY.

The third difference is that the camera takes a clear picture only when it is at rest, while the eye is continually in motion. Slight tremors of the eye muscles produce small, continual movements of the eyeball known as "physiological nystagmus." Experiments with special devices that prevent excitation from spreading over the retina have demonstrated that we cannot see objects without these movements (Riggs et al., 1953). One theory holds that the spread of excitation prevents fatigue of the receptor components.

The process by which the electromagnetic energy of light is transformed into nerve impulses appears to fall into three stages. First, the rods and cones contain photosensitive pigments which initiate a chain of chemical changes. The major pigment in the rods is rhodopsin, or visual purple, which breaks into orange intermediates and then into retinene, or visual yellow, and opsin when subjected to light. Retinene and opsin change back spontaneously to rhodopsin at a rate that is dependent on the intensity of the illumination. Under dim conditions, the change is rapid, but under intense illumination some of the retinene is first converted into vitamin A, then back into retinene when the illumination becomes less intense, and finally into rhodopsin again. The composition of the cones is still more complex, since one cluster of cones seems to respond to blue (477 millimicrons), another to green (540 millimicrons), and a third to yellow (577 millimicrons), and also to wavelengths in the red range. (MacNichol, 1964)

The second stage is the production of electrical potentials in the retina. The mechanism by which this occurs is still a mystery, but it is probably related to chemical changes occurring in the pigments when light strikes the eye. At any rate, it is known that the generator potential depolarizes the nerve fibers and sets off nerve impulses. The size of these impulses depends on the intensity of the stimulus. Currently, these slow potentials are believed to be generated in the large glial, or supporting cells of the retina. Another type of potential, known as the electroretinogram (ERG) has also been discovered, but its relationship to nerve impulses responsible for visual reception is still unclear.

It does appear, however, that nerve impulses—the third stage—arise in the ganglion cells when the retina receives a light stimulus. Experiments have shown that each ganglion cell can be activated by an area of the retina, called a receptive field, rather than by a pinpoint. This, too, is a complex affair, for the cells fire differently when different parts of the receptive field are stimulated. As Morgan and King (1966) point out, "The message transmitted to the brain from the ganglion cells is not a simple one—it is already highly organized at the ganglion level . . . How bright an object appears is probably related in some way to the density of the neural barrage reaching the brain; the color of an object is probably related to the pattern of firing reaching the brain from the three types of cone pigments; but the details are not known, and the situation is certainly not this simple." *See* COLOR VISION THEORIES.

Although the physiological mechanism of vision is still obscure, we have considerable knowledge of the characteristics and physical basis of visual experience. Color, as we perceive it, has three dimensions: hue (red, greenish blue, etc.), saturation (relative purity), and brightness (intensity). Hue depends primarily on the wavelength of the light, and when several wavelengths are mixed, as they usually are, on the dominant wavelength. Other factors also affect our experience of hue: the eye is not equally sensitive to all wavelengths, its sensitivity changes with the intensity of the light, and adjacent color areas in the visual field induce changes in each other, a phenomenon called "contrast effect." *See* this topic; *also* COLOR PLATE 2.

The second dimension of color, saturation or purity, depends on the degree to which a hue is diluted by grayness or whiteness. A pure or highly saturated color has little if any white in it, and appears strong or deep. A weak or pastel color is relatively unsaturated; an artist or painter produces such colors by mixing a small amount of pigment with a large amount of white. The third dimension, brightness, is primarily determined by the intensity of the physical stimulus, and extends from black, the lowest degree of brightness, to white, the highest degree, through various shades of gray. In painting, the brightness of a given color is varied by mixing it with different amounts of white or black. We must add, however, that the brightness of objects is also determined by the sensitivity of the retina itself. When we are in the dark, our eyes gradually become more sensitive and colors gradually become brighter; when we emerge into a bright light, our eyes lose some of their sensitivity. These phenomena,

termed dark adaptation and light adaptation, are discussed under separate topics. For other aspects of vision, *see* COLOR CIRCLE, COLOR SOLID, MUNSELL SYSTEM, VISIBLE SPECTRUM, VISIBILITY CURVE, AFTERIMAGES.

VISUAL ACUITY. Sharpness of vision; the ability to discriminate details.

Visual acuity is a critical factor in such activities as watch-repairing, hunting, airplane spotting, and reading X-rays. Measurement of this sensory ability is important in placing workers on jobs, in diagnosing reading difficulty, and in determining whether corrective lenses are needed.

The most commonly used testing device is the Snellen chart. It presents letters of different sizes representing what the normal person sees at different distances—that is, the largest letter can barely be read at two hundred feet, the next largest at one hundred feet, etc. The subject is usually tested at twenty feet. If at this distance he can read the same row of letters as a person without eye defects, he is said to have 20/20, or normal vision. If he can read only the letters the normal eye can see at one hundred feet, he has 20/100 vision for the eye tested. 20/10 vision is more acute than normal, since it means that the individual can read letters at twenty feet that the normal person must be ten feet away to identify. In a variation of this test, single letters are presented and the person walks toward them until he can read them.

Other methods are employed in special situations. In the Landolt Ring test, circles with small gaps in them are presented and subjects are required to locate the gaps. Young children are given a model circle with a gap and instructed to turn it to match the gap appearing on the chart. Parallel bars are also used. The subject merely reports whether he sees two bars or one as they are shown progressively closer together. These methods are considered superior to the Snellen chart since letters vary widely in readability and the order can be memorized. They can also be used with people who cannot read.

Two new devices are now widely used in industry and the Armed Forces. The Sight Screener tests depth perception, muscle balance and simultaneous binocular vision, as well as visual acuity. The Ortho-Rater (PLATE 17) consists of a series of slides on which a black and white checkerboard pattern is presented in one of four positions. Smaller and smaller pictures are shown until the subject cannot identify the pattern. This technique is particularly applicable to large groups when individual tests by oculists are impractical.

The visual acuity of infants can be determined with fair accuracy. The test is based on the fact that in a dark room a baby will look toward a light that does not glare. Wires of various diameters are moved across a frosted-glass window lighted from behind. The smallest diameter wire the infant follows is an index of acuity. Test results show that the normal child has 20/400 vision at six months, 20/200 at one year, and 20/50 at three years. Toys for small children must be simple and crude due to their low visual acuity as well as their inability to control the finer muscles. Lack of visual discrimination is also one of the reasons children cannot be taught to read below the age of four or five—and when they do start to read, their books must contain large print and bold pictures. See APTITUDE TESTS (SPECIAL), PERSONNEL TESTS.

VISUAL CLIFF. An apparatus designed to test depth perception in human and animal infants.

The visual cliff apparatus was developed by E. G. Gibson and R. D. Walk (1960) to answer a specific question: Does the human infant have to *learn* to avoid falling off an elevated structure, such as a bed or table, or is this part of his natural endowment? The

experimenters constructed a low table with a top consisting of a large sheet of heavy glass. A wide board was placed across the middle of the table. On one side of the board a patterned piece of cloth was fastened below the glass, and the same type of cloth was placed on the floor beneath the glass on the other side (PLATE 21). The effect of this arrangement (which arose out of a visit to the Grand Canyon) was to make one —a "canyon"—while the other side appeared to be only a shallow drop— though actually there was a glass surface underneath in both instances.

In the original experiment thirty-six infants from six to fourteen months of age were placed on the center board, one at a time, and their mothers were instructed to call to them first from the cliff side and then from the shallow side. Twenty-seven responded, and of these, twenty-four crawled toward the shallow side but balked at crawling toward the deep side. Only three went to their mothers on both sides of the glass, and no baby responded to its mother only on the deep side. The investigators noted that this behavior was clearly dependent on vision. The infants would often peer over the cliff side and then back away. They even backed away if they patted the glass and found it solid. Several children, however, moved awkwardly on the board and actually put their weight on the cliff side without meaning to crawl on it. This indicates that their perception of depth had developed more rapidly than their locomotor co-ordination—and it also underscores the common precaution that very young children should not be left alone close to a brink.

This experiment did not prove that depth perception is innate, since it was possible that the infants acquired the ability from prior experience. Experiments with infant animals, including rats, dogs, kittens and day-old chicks, on the other hand, clearly indicated that they were born with this ability. They were tested as soon as they were able to move around, and almost invariably hopped off the board on the shallow side. It is interesting that aquatic turtles, which have little fear of falling in water, did not choose the shallow side as often as land animals. This shows that depth perception is most highly developed where it has the greatest survival value.

What cues does the human infant use in this situation? In the first place, the experimenters found that visual stimuli predominated. Even the children who patted the glass did not descend on the cliff side, because it did not *look* safe to them. Second, the cloth underneath the glass was patterned, and the pattern under the cliff side was bound to look different from the pattern under the shallow side because it was farther away. To eliminate this difference, the two patterns were altered in such a way that they would look the same on both sides—and the infants still avoided the cliff side.

How, then, did they know the difference between the cliff and the shallow side? Further experiments on animals seemed to give the answer. The experimenters found that they were probably responding to "motion parallax," the fact that in moving the head, nearby objects appear to move more quickly than objects at a distance. They concluded that this cue to depth is innate with animals that depend largely on vision, and probably with human beings as well. On the other hand, cues from shape, pattern and other features of the environment are probably not innate. *See* DEPTH PERCEPTION.

VISUAL DEFECTS. Common visual defects so often affect behavior and adjustment that they are usually included in the field of psychology. Most of them are due to a faulty optical mechanism, although some difficulties may be purely functional and emotionally produced.

In *myopia,* or nearsightedness, the eyeball is too long and the image focuses in front of the retina. Objects at ordinary distances appear fuzzy and paper work must be held close to the eye to improve focus. In *hyperopia,* or farsightedness, the image falls behind the retina since the eyeball is too short for close vision. In this case distant objects are seen distinctly but nearer ones are blurred. Contrary to common opinion, farsighted people do not see any better or farther than others; they see as well as normals at a distance, but less well when objects are close.

Myopia and hyperopia can both be corrected by glasses. Slight cases, however, often go uncorrected and can have subtle effects on interests and activities. Since vision is such an important information sense, a child's comprehension of the world may be seriously hampered by these conditions. He may have trouble learning to read, and will not get enough practice because the task is so difficult, unpleasant and frustrating. He may also have difficulty with sports, may fail to develop self-confidence, and may later choose a vocation that is far below his intelligence level. Because of the importance of good vision, periodic eye examinations are recommended at all ages.

Presbyopia, or oldsightedness, can develop from either far- or nearsightedness. With advancing age, the lens becomes hardened, loses elasticity and grows flat and weak. It becomes increasingly difficult to focus on close objects, and the blur point—the point at which print becomes illegible—is more and more distant. The normal blur point distances for type of about the size of the print on this page is 3 inches at age 10, 4 at 20, 5.5 at 30, 8.5 at 40, 15.25 at 50, and 39 or more at 60. Presbyopia is correctible with glasses.

Astigmatism is a defect caused by irregularities in the cornea or lens. As a result, vision is clear in one dimension and unfocused in another. Slight astigmatism often goes unnoticed, but may cause visual fatigue after an extensive period of reading. It can be corrected by glasses.

Diplopia, or double vision, is most often due to an inherent weakness of the eye muscles. The eye does not receive light from an object on corresponding parts of the two retinas, and two different images are transmitted to the brain. The effect is somewhat like watching a 3-D movie without special glasses. *Strabismus,* or squint, is a form of diplopia, and is also due to a defect in the eye muscles. If not corrected before age five or six severe emotional difficulties may result. Perception is so blurred and unpleasant that the child may keep one eye continually closed until the condition known as amblyopia develops (dimness or loss of vision not due to discoverable lesions in the eye or optic nerve). Children suffering from strabismus are often taunted by names like "squinty" or "cross-eyes," and the ridicule affects their social adjustment. Surgical correction can remove this social stigma even when it is too late to restore normal functioning to the unused eye.

Double vision may also be caused by disease, various poisons or temporarily by alcohol. Emotional conflict is believed to be responsible in some cases. *See* CONVERSION REACTION.

The excessive use of alcohol or tobacco or overexposure to light may produce amblyopia or a temporary or permanent blind spot, a *scotoma.* Scotomas are also found in cases of tumor and migraine headache, and may be caused by retinal injury or disease, optic nerve damage, or brain defect. *See* AMAUROSIS, BLINDNESS, COLOR BLINDNESS.

VOCATIONAL COUNSELING. Professional guidance on preparation for a working life and for choice of a suitable occupation.

Historically, vocational guidance was the first type of counseling developed by psychologists. It continues to maintain a central position since occupational decisions are a crucial factor in the total adjustment of the individual and are intimately related to his abilities, interests, level of maturity, personality characteristics, opportunities and life situation. It has frequently been remarked that choosing an occupation is choosing a way of life; this is largely true, since one's identity, status, place and style of living, and social contacts are deeply involved in this decision. It follows that vocational counseling must be conducted on a highly individual basis, taking into consideration the entire range of the client's interests, goals, needs, and capacities.

Few if any young people are equipped to make a vocational choice without help from others, and most of them would profit from the knowledge and understanding which experienced counselors have at their disposal. The object of the counseling process is not to offer a ready-made solution, and certainly not to choose an occupation for the client, but to help him establish an effective basis for making his own decision. Another aim is to reduce the likelihood that he will be overinfluenced by such factors as parental pressure, romantic notions about certain vocations, unrealistic ideas about his own abilities, or a faulty assessment of employment opportunities.

It is important to recognize that vocational counseling is not a matter of making a single choice, once and for all, for vocational planning involves many decisions extending over a period of years—decisions that are conditioned by changes in the individual's aims, wants, and abilities as well as changes in familiar jobs and the emergence of new fields of work. On the high school or pre-high school level counseling is, of course, concerned with making immediate choices of schools, courses or trial jobs, but it must also help the client gain knowledge about himself and the world of work which he can use at a later date

—and, as Anastasi (1964) points out, it must also offer the client an opportunity to learn more effective procedures for decision-making itself.

It follows from all that has been said that professional vocational counseling is a highly complex affair requiring many skills and a high degree of specialized knowledge. It is not a matter of "throwing a few tests" at the client and discussing the results in a single superficial interview. Tests are an essential part of the process, but it is important that they reveal, so far as possible, all relevant aspects of the individual's life: his interests, his general intellectual ability, his personality characteristics, and his special abilities. This means that the counselor must become well enough acquainted with his client, through the interview process, to select a battery of tests that will adequately measure all four of these characteristics. But, more important, he must be able to interpret the results of these tests in the light of the individual client's situation and needs. To do this, he must be fully informed about the interest patterns and (so far as present knowledge extends), personality characteristics, average and range of IQ scores, and special aptitudes required for different occupations. *See* PERSONNEL TESTS, INTEREST TESTS.

The other essential component of the guidance process is the interview. The client should be interviewed both before and after the tests are given. The initial interview serves the purpose of providing information that will help both in the selection of tests and in the later guidance process. The information should include early interests, hobbies, work experience, and course preferences at school. In the final interview, the counselor sounds out the client's attitudes, characteristics, values, goals, and needs as thoroughly as possible. This discussion frequently takes on the dimension of a "depth interview," requiring considerable insight on the part of the counselor as well as the development

of rapport with his client. Through this process he may discover, for example, that one client has a strong need for status, another a distrust for authority, and a third a deep-rooted feeling of insecurity. Such characteristics do not usually come to light in the initial interview or in the testing process, yet they may be of crucial importance in helping the client assess the results of the tests and make his selection of a suitable occupation.

The counselor of today should be thoroughly versed in occupational information as well as recent research on the psychology of vocational choice. Occupational information includes data on the changes in basic requirements for different fields of work, the development of new occupations including the skills and educational background they require, and specific employment opportunities that must be taken into consideration in making an immediate decision.

It is also important for the counselor to be acquainted with the newer attempts to classify occupations in terms of psychologically meaningful dimensions, as contrasted with the older categories which simply divide occupations into professional and managerial, clerical and sales, service, skilled and unskilled. One of these newer classifications is that of Super (1957) who distinguishes between level (general educational requirements, social status, responsibility, etc.), field of work (type of activity such as brick-layer, electrician, physiologist), and enterprise (the setting or industry, such as agriculture, transportation, laboratory work, manufacturing). Various combinations of the three dimensions have been worked out in terms of actual jobs such as "civil engineer employed in conservation work with the National Park Service," and these descriptions can then be matched with the client's own interests and abilities.

A second type of classification is based on trait patterns demanded by different jobs. The Minnesota Occupational Rating Scales (MORS) rate 432 occupations in terms of seven abilities: academic ability, mechanical ability, social intelligence, clerical ability, musical talent, artistic ability, and physical agility. Various occupations are listed according to patterns of these abilities. Occupational ability patterns have also been established on the basis of General Aptitude Test Battery (GATB) scores, and research is now in progress aimed at incorporating interests, needs, and educational preparation into these patterns. See APTITUDE TESTS (MULTIPLE).

It may be that the classifications of the future will also be based on personality patterns, for the research literature on personality differences among occupational groups is steadily growing. Questionnaires, interviews, personality inventories, projective tests and biographical histories are being applied in an effort to ascertain particular patterns for different occupations. In one investigation, high scores for specific occupational categories on the Strong Vocational Interest Blank were found to be positively correlated with personality descriptions of subjects tested by clinical psychologists—for example, high scorers on the "mathematician" key were described as self-abasing, concerned with philosophical problems, introspective, lacking in social poise, not an effective leader, reacts poorly to stress. High scorers on the "real estate salesman" key tended to be self-indulgent, opportunistic, aggressive, persuasive, ostentatious, not sympathetic. In a study of eminent scientists, Roe (1951) found certain characteristics particularly prominent: strong inner drive, sustained effort, importance of prestige motivation, and absorption in work to the exclusion of other interests.

Research on personality patterns, however, is still considered in its infancy, for it leaves many unanswered questions—for example, does the personality pattern of the eminent scientist distinguish him from a successful busi-

ness executive, artist or statesman? And how far do the characteristics of the real estate man represent original and basic traits rather than a response to the demands of the job itself?

VOICE DISORDERS. Disturbances of the voice are usually divided into aphonia—a partial or complete loss of voice—and dysphonia, a distortion of the voice. Dysphonias include any deviations from the normal and more or less pleasing state of "euphonia": hoarseness, raspiness, harshness, falsetto, or the weak and breathy voice condition known as phonasthenia.

The vocal mechanism is a particularly sensitive area of the organism, and is responsive to both emotional disturbances and structural changes. In a psychiatric examination, particular note is taken of the pitch and timbre of the voice, its relation to posture and gesture, as well as any hesitations, blockings, repetitions, excessive speed, or confusion in speech. Many types of specialists may be involved in the diagnosis, treatment, and rehabilitation of voice disorders—including the neurologist, otolaryngologist, psychiatrist, internist, clinical psychologist, and speech correctionist.

Voice disturbances are common symptoms of conversion reaction (conversion hysteria), and are also observed in a number of other psychiatric disorders arising from both psychogenic and physical causes. The voice quality in depression—an example of a functional disorder—is highly distinctive: in the retarded type, the voice is heavy, hesitant, monotonous, with a narrow range of pitch; in the agitated type, it is often rasping, low-pitched, tense, rapid and with a considerable range of pitch. In the chronic condition following encephalitis lethargica—an example of an organic disorder—the voice tends to be nasal, monotonous, somewhat singsong, often trailing off into nothingness, and is frequently accompanied by "palilalia," a needless repetition of words and phrases. The following are some specific voice disorders:

Aphonia. This is a loss or severe impairment of voice; the patient can comprehend speech and articulate normally, but cannot talk above a whisper. The condition may be due to a disease of the larynx or a disorder of the nervous system that paralyzes the vocal cords. In such cases the patient cannot phonate; that is, he cannot make sounds with the vocal cords either when he tries to talk or when he coughs. Treatment procedures consist of retraining the speech muscles and showing the patient how to place his tongue and lips in order to produce sound.

Aphonia is even more commonly a symptom of hysteria or conversion reaction. Anxiety appears to be the governing force in these cases. The patient cannot speak normally because he is in the grip of emotional conflicts which inhibit expression. He may have an unconscious fear that he will say the wrong thing, or may be protecting himself from situations that arouse apprehension. These cases require brief or extended psychotherapy. Behavior therapy has also been used as a symptom removal technique. *See* BEHAVIOR THERAPY.

In making a differential diagnosis the therapist usually finds that the neurotic patient, in contrast to the organic case, can phonate while coughing even though he cannot phonate while speaking. Sometimes the condition arises from a severe emotional shock or catastrophe, but in such cases the aphonia usually subsides without treatment. *See* CONVERSION REACTION.

Falsetto Voice. This is not merely a high-pitched voice, but "an unnatural, tense, shrill and piping voice with very limited range and monotonous inflection" (Franklin, 1957). Although there are occasional organic cases of falsetto voice, this condition is considered fundamentally psychogenic, and is the most common vocal anomaly originating during the period of puberty. Without re-medial treatment it can persist throughout life. The tone itself is due to an unconscious habit of overstretching the vocal cords during phonation, accompanied by tense and shortened respiration.

One of the tests used to differentiate functional from organic cases is to have the patient cough or clear his throat. In functional cases this will always reveal the normal voice. Though falsetto patients are generally normal in physical growth and all other sexual characteristics, their maleness is often questioned by others, and they are frequently humiliated by this undeserved stigma. A true castrate or endocrinological eunuchoid does not speak in the typical falsetto voice, but simply in a clear, high, childish tone without the false quality.

Generally speaking, falsetto voice stems from the problems and conflicts that occur in the period of puberty: "to an emotionally immature and hypersensitive half-child, this transitional period can be an overwhelming experience" (Franklin). Typically, these boys are frightened at the thought of growing up and assuming responsibilities expected of an adult male. Many of them have had difficulty in identifying with the masculine role, often because of overprotection and overanxiety on the part of the mother or a demand for excessively masculine behavior on the part of the father. Most of them have passively identified with the mother. In short, falsetto voice represents "a basically hysterical conversion symptom which is unconsciously adopted as an attempt to escape facing the reality of growing into adult life" (Franklin).

The symptom does not solve the young person's emotional problems but aggravates them by provoking ridicule and embarrassment and by limiting employment opportunities. Though some patients cling tenaciously to the symptom, the majority are amenable to therapy, and relatively simple treatment brings dramatic results. The approach varies somewhat with individual patients and individual therapists, but usually involves recording and playing back the voice to show that it is false and unnatural; mild manipulation and massage to lower the larynx and relax tensions, at the same time having the patient cough or clear the throat to show that he is capable of producing a normal sound; drillwork consisting of reading or repeating numbers and syllables with increasing intensity; re-education of the breathing mechanism for more generous respiration; and psychological therapy on a counseling level, aimed at increasing confidence and general adjustment. Intensive, prolonged psychotherapy is usually unnecessary, since the voice changes in a short time. Interestingly, the patient tends to forget completely what his falsetto voice sounded like.

Hoarseness. This condition is not considered a disease in itself, but rather a symptom of either a functional or organic change in the vocal cords. Organic conditions causing hoarseness, raspiness, and other forms of dysphonia include: acute, transitory infection of the upper respiratory passages, as in the common cold; a malignant growth; a thickening or other change in the cords due to inflammation, polyps, nodes, etc.; injuries to the larynx or laryngeal nerves. Among the functional causes of hoarseness are: abuse of the vocal cords, as in professional speaking (this may also produce phonasthenia); tensing of the vocal cords due to emotional stress; and an aggressive personality which expresses itself in a harsh tone of voice. The following is a fairly typical case of psychogenic hoarseness:

Illustrative Case: VOICE DISORDERS, HOARSENESS

"A woman in younger middle life talked to the psychiatrist with a hoarse voice. The laryngologist who had referred her for psychotherapy found no evidence of nodes or polyps, but only some slight redness and a mild swelling of her vocal cords. He had reassured her that she did not have cancer of the throat or the larynx . . . She related that her childhood memories were composed chiefly of episodes of belittlement and rejection by a harsh and critical mother. The latter had always favored the patient's elder brother who had been given a college education. She had always dreamed of graduating from college and making both a career and a name for herself. . . . Her father, who didn't like girl children, insisted that she obtain a job as soon as she finished high school. He refused to send her to business college; she worked for several years in a 5-and-10-cent store before she contrived to escape from home by means of an impulsive marriage.

She married a man who was twenty-three years older than herself. Now, at the age of forty-four, she found that married life with a sixty-seven-year-old crotchety husband had become more than she could tolerate. The psychiatrist drew from her reluctant recital of the facts of her life that she regretted her marriage from the day she was wed. She had refused to consider annulment, separation or divorce because of fear of her parents' criticisms: they had disapproved loudly of her choice of a husband. In the course of psychotherapy, it was not long before she perceived the neurotic basis for her marriage: it symbolized a bid for freedom from a rejecting, unloving father through the substitution of a father-image in the person of a much older man who, in quick courtship, seemed to accept her totally, uncritically, and lovingly.

Actually, as the years passed, she was unable to have children. This made her feel that her maternal instinct and fulfillment as a complete woman were doomed to bitter disappointment; inwardly, she blamed her husband for her barrenness. She found that his demands upon her, and, indeed, the basis of his interest in her, amounted to those ordinarily assumed by a hired housekeeper, and not by a wife. He met with a series of business reverses following which he became morose, irritable, and was no longer interested in listening to her talk. During the past several years, after he came home from work and quickly ate his dinner, he watched television all evening and would silence his wife's attempts to engage in conversation. At one point, she felt she must live apart from him. Since her brother had become well-to-do, she asked him to contribute to her support until she found work. He refused flatly and told her she was ridiculous to consider such a thing.

It was coincident with this rejection by her brother and the sustained preference of her husband for TV entertainment to her conversation that she first developed hoarseness . . . If her husband went out of town on business trips, or when she did not see friends for a while, her normal voice returned. At the time of her first interview with the psychiatrist, she gradually relaxed and sat back in the chair; the doctor noticed also that her voice gradually lost its semihoarseness. He asked her how she felt at that moment. He wasn't surprised by her reply. She said that she had gotten a great deal off her chest that she had been trying for months to talk about—her feelings of resentment and anger and hostility toward her husband and her parents. Her husband would never listen to her; he wasn't ever interested in what she had to say. The psychiatrist suggested that this was the same attitude her parents had had toward her during her childhood and adolescence. The patient agreed and added that this formerly made her yell and shout at them and that they shouted back. The family quarrels were loud and long. With her husband, it was different: even when she yelled and screamed at him, he wouldn't reply in kind. Instead, he changed the channel on the televison set, or turned up the volume to drown her out. After a while, it got so she just cried angry tears and felt completely miserable. Her throat felt tightened up in the same way she felt all over and she was hoarse when she tried to talk.

This case illustrates a primitive type of rage reaction, successfully suppressed on a cortical level of expression, being manifested physically and symptomatically by intermittent hoarseness . . . Thus, the symptom of hoarseness served as an audible distress signal that her life-long search for love and approval and recognition was empty of these rewards. Eventually, in therapy, she learned that her angry outbursts at her husband were like the wailings of an infant who demands that it be fed. It required many sessions with the psychiatrist before she felt she could abandon her role of childhood dependency for approval upon elder figures for adult, socially acceptable aggressive actions and attitudes directed in more productive and satisfying substitute channels." (Heaver, 1957)

VOLUNTEER WORKERS.

In recent years mental health clinics and mental hospitals have been using more and more volunteers, not only because of the shortage of personnel but because of the unique services they can provide. Today's volunteers not only keep patients occupied and give them extra care, but serve the vital function of keeping them in touch with the world. They also keep the community in touch with the hospital and increase public understanding of mental illness.

The development of volunteer programs has been greatly advanced by the National Association for Mental Health. As the Association points out, if a program is to be fully effective, it must be carefully planned and organized by a well-qualified volunteer director who is responsible to the medical staff. His major duties are to survey the requirements of the institution, then recruit and screen volunteers, plan orientation sessions and in-service training, prepare schedules and assignments, and supervise their activities. A recruitment drive for volunteers is usually conducted through local community groups and news media. It has been found that the most successful volunteers have not only warm, outgoing personalities, but special skills, and regard their work as a regular job rather than casual philanthropy.

Mental health volunteers are considered an effective adjunct to therapy and an integral part of the rehabilitation process. Their activities cover a wide range. They teach crafts, feed withdrawn or handicapped patients, assist the librarian, conduct hobby groups and athletic events, manage the hospital beauty parlor, assist in psychodrama, edit the hospital newspaper, and give clerical assistance to the staff. When patients are preparing for discharge, volunteers may take them on tours of local industry and help them locate a place to live if they have nowhere to go.

There are two new trends in volunteer work. Many men are now participating on a regular basis, and are particularly active in sports and occupational therapy, as well as discussion groups on work opportunities. And in a number of hospitals, college students are now serving as volunteers, and high school students may come in for special duties such as decorating the recreation hall. Practical experiences of this type not only give these young people personal insight into the problem of mental health, but help to prepare them for possible work in the field. *See* NATIONAL ASSOCIATION FOR MENTAL HEALTH.

VOYEURISM (Scotophilia, Scoptophilia, Inspectionalism). A sexual deviation in which gratification is obtained from observing the bodies or sexual activities of other people.

Voyeurs are generally young men— "peeping Toms"—who secretly watch girls or women undress, or observe couples engaged in sexual relations. An occasional voyeur is primarily interested in watching homosexual behavior or other deviant sexual activity, such as sadistic acts.

Practically all males derive sexual pleasure and stimulation from looking at female nudity. They are also curious about the mystery of sexual activity. The voyeur, however, deviates from the normal in persistently searching for opportunities to spy on others, and in deriving most or all of his sexual satisfaction from observing them. He generally achieves orgasm while looking, either spontaneously or through masturbation. Sexual response is heightened by the suspense, excitement, and danger of being caught, and it is therefore not surprising that most voyeurs do not react sexually when observation is permitted, as in watching a burlesque show. Some houses of prostitution seek to exploit

the voyeur impulse by presenting elaborate performances of deviant sexual activity.

The voyeur is typically an isolated, shy individual who fears women and doubts his sexual adequacy. The peeping gives him satisfaction without risk of rejection or failure. It also reassures him of his potency. In addition, it probably serves as an outlet for aggressive, hostile drives, since peeping is a stealthy act and probably makes the voyeur feel superior to the people he is watching. Older men, sometimes married, may engage in peeping as a result of sexual frustration. In some cases the voyeur identifies with one or the other partner in sexual relations as a result of homosexual impulses. A parallel deviate is the écouteur, who obtains inordinate gratification from listening to accounts of sexual experiences.

When voyeurism is the result of emotional immaturity, it can often be corrected through short-term psychotherapy; but where it is a persistent pattern and an expression of an inadequate personality, as it frequently is, treatment may be difficult or unsuccessful. Contrary to rumor, the typical peeper is not criminally inclined and seldom attacks women. In rare instances, however, voyeurs have been known to develop into rapists or arsonists. Such cases stem from deeper disturbances and are even more resistant to therapy. *See* SEXUAL DEVIATIONS (GENERAL), BEHAVIOR THERAPY.

Illustrative Case: VOYEURISM

S.C.E., male, age twenty-eight, single. Patient employed as mechanic by large aircraft company in Southern California. Lives with mother and younger brother, age ten.

Chief Complaint: S. apprehended for "peeping" by police officer in exclusive residential district of city. Since it was second offense of this type within three months, he was sentenced to six days in county jail and ordered to see psychologist or psychiatrist for treatment.

Family History: Patient's father died

when S. was about eight. Mother placed S. with friends, with whom he stayed for eleven years. Mother remarried when patient was about fifteen. At that time S. went to live with mother and stepfather. Stepfather delighted in "picking on" S. He was prohibited from going with girls until twenty-one. Has stepbrother, ten, with whom he has very little to do.

Personal History: Patient always seclusive, shy, retiring; never had more than one or two friends, and these were never very close. Relationships with other sex limited to social visiting during school hours and later during working hours.

S. better than average student in school. Always got along well with teachers and classmates. Also very compatible with mother. Real father never cared for children and was not very friendly with S. Stepfather developed marked dislike for him and did not hesitate to show it, always finding fault with S.

At thirteen S. began to masturbate. Developed deep feelings of guilt as a result. Shortly after graduating from high school, at eighteen, was encouraged by friend to visit a prostitute. Result very unsatisfactory, was unable to attain erection and was belittled by the woman. Since that time has made no overt advances of a sexual nature to any woman.

Five years ago S., walking home from theater one evening, happened to pass bathroom window. Stopped and looked in to observe a young woman undressing to take a bath. Seeing her in the nude caused him to become sexually aroused and in a few moments he was sexually satisfied. From that time on he made it a point to pass bathroom and bedroom windows at night in hope of seeing a woman undress. Had to see genitalia of woman before he would be sexually gratified. S. states he has no desire for heterosexual relationships and is quite satisfied with present means of sexual gratification.

Physical Examination: Thorough medical examinations showed practically no defects, only difficulty chronic sinus condition. Basal metabolism test made, findings negative.

Treatment: Interview therapy (confidential counseling sessions) instituted. S. came for conferences twice a week for five months. During that time achieved considerable insight into condition. Development of tendencies exhaustively studied and evaluated. Began to develop new attitudes about himself and his capabilities. Was encouraged to participate in social functions. Started to take dancing lessons at dancing school; joined church and attended youth meetings every Sunday evening; became member of his plant's social committee. During fourth month of interview therapy S. met a young woman at a church social, three weeks later became engaged to her. They were married six months later. Has been married for over a year and a half; when last interviewed stated that scoptophiliac tendencies had been overcome. (Thorpe, Katz, and Lewis, 1961)

W

WARMING UP (Warm-Up Effect). An adjustment process taking place at or before the start of an activity. In industrial psychology, warming up is indicated by a rise in the work curve during the initial part of a work period.

Everyone is familiar with warming-up activities of athletes: throwing the ball around, shadow-boxing, going through limbering-up exercises. We sometimes overlook the fact that these activities have a twofold purpose: to prepare the muscles for action, and to prepare the mind for maximum effort. Both sides of the process are essential, since the body has to be primed for extra stress and the mind has to be set to make split-second decisions. The player who is thoroughly warmed up in both ways quickly gets into the swing of the game and has a great advantage over a slow-starting opponent.

Warming-up applies not only to athletics but to all types of tasks, both mental and physical. Some people take longer to warm up than others and some jobs require a longer warm-up period than others. However, the general features of the period do not vary a great deal. In business activities it takes time to set out our work, decide how to start, and clear our mind for action. Then it takes a little more time to gear ourselves to the actual work, to "warm up to the task." In some cases this process is telescoped, in others it is stretched out until it is more of a delaying action than a warm-up period. This happens with an individual who resents his work or is too indolent to get down to business.

One of the reasons for constructing work curves in industry is to find out whether the warm-up period is of normal length for a particular employee or group of employees. If the production rate starts very slowly and increases for several hours, it is undoubtedly too long. On the other hand, a worker may start with a "beginning spurt" and completely cancel out the warm-up effect. This is the kind of worker who starts "like a house afire"—but too often he trails off when he realizes that the particular task will continue for a long period of time. In such a case the work curve is the opposite of the normal curve since it starts high and decreases, instead of starting low and steadily increasing. The more normal curve is usually considered more desirable in the long run. See WORK CURVE.

WECHSLER INTELLIGENCE SCALES. These include the Wechsler Adult Intelligence Scale (WAIS), an individual test designed to measure the intelligence of persons above the age of sixteen; the Wechsler Intelligence Scale for Children (WISC), designed for children between the ages of five and fifteen; and the Wechsler Preschool and Primary Scale of Intelligence.

The first form of the adult scale, known as the Wechsler-Bellevue Scale I, was developed in 1939 by David Wechsler at Bellevue Hospital, in New York City, to establish the mental level of people who might be feebleminded, psychotic, or illiterate, and to refer them to the most appropriate treatment. It was put to effective use in hospitals during World War II, and became one of the major clinical tools after the war. In 1955 Wechsler replaced this test with the Wechsler Adult Intelligence Scale, which has proven to be better constructed and more valid.

This scale, which takes about one hour to administer, is divided into two parts, one measuring verbal and the other performance ability. The verbal part consists of the following six sub-tests: (1) *Information,* containing items like "What is the population of the United States?" "Where does rubber come from?"; (2) *Comprehension:* "What does the saying, 'Shallow brooks are noisy' mean?" "Why should we stay away from bad company?"; (3) *Arithmetic:* "How many yards are there in 36 feet?" (with a time limit for each problem); (4) *Similarities:* "In what way are the following alike: an orange and a grape, a statue and a poem?"; (5) *Digit Span:* reciting back a series of numbers in order, and another series in reverse order; (6) *Vocabulary:* "Define or explain fabric, conceal, tirade etc." The items on these tests become progressively more difficult, and the subject must stop after making a certain number of errors.

The performance part of the test consists of five sub-tests, all of which require the subject to manipulate or arrange different materials without the use of words: (1) *Picture Arrangement:* arranging a series of cartoons to make an orderly story; (2) *Picture Completion:* what is missing from these pictures?; (3) *Block Assembly:* copying a design with blocks; (4) *Object Assembly:* putting together a jigsaw picture of a human face, manikin, hand, and elephant; (5) *Digit Symbol:* inserting the appropriate symbol for a list of numbers by referring to a given sample (*Fig. 53*). Each of these subtests is timed, and bonuses are given for rapid performance.

Each subtest on both parts of the scale can be independently scored. This enables the examiner to compare the subject's relative abilities and note his strengths and weaknesses. In addition, the scoring manual shows how to compute an over-all verbal and an over-all performance score. These scores can be compared with average scores obtained by 1700 people between the ages sixteen and sixty who comprised the group on which the test was originally standardized. Scores on the two parts of the test can be translated into a verbal IQ and a performance IQ. Finally, an over-all IQ can be computed from tables provided by the author.

An IQ obtained on the WAIS is not necessarily the same as that obtained on other instruments; on the average it is about seven points below the Stanford-Binet score. The general distribution in the population, however, is similar, although the Wechsler scale does not have sufficient range to include very high and very low abilities: above 130 (very superior): 2.2 per cent; 120–129 (superior): 6.7 per cent; 110–119 (bright normal): 16.1 per cent; 90–109 (average): 50.0; 80–89 (dull normal): 16.1 per cent; 70–79 (borderline): 6.7 per cent; below 70 (defective): 2.2 per cent.

The WAIS is frequently administered in making a clinical evaluation of a subject, as part of a battery of tests that includes the Rorschach, Thematic Apperception Test, and others. Many clinics also use the test by itself as a projective tool. They note the way the subject attacks the problems and any comments he makes as he goes along. Undue caution, erratic planning or performance, and emotional blocking may be important leads to areas of emotional difficulty. These sometimes show up more clearly on the performance than on the verbal items, since they require a longer period of concentrated effort. Certain types of brain injury and mental illness also manifest themselves on this portion of the WAIS. In addition, it is particularly useful in estimating the IQ of subjects with a foreign background, poorly educated people, or individuals with language difficulties. *See* MENTAL IMPAIRMENT TESTS.

The Wechsler Intelligence Scale for Children (WISC), 1949, contains the same group of subtests as the adult scale (WAIS), except that Digit Symbol is replaced by the less difficult problem of coding a simple message. The Digit Span is optional, as is a Maze Test in which the child is asked to trace the shortest path to a goal.

The WISC is scored and interpreted in the same general way as the WAIS. Unlike the Stanford-Binet, which shows how fast a child's abilities are growing in relation to his chronological age, the WISC sets up an average value for each age with which the subject's score is compared. Moreover, there are separate scores for the verbal and performance items in addition to an over-all score. These scores, as well as the scores on individual items such as Comprehension, Vocabulary, etc., are

0	1	2	3	4	5	6	7	8	9
V	Γ	III	⊔	⌐	⊢	O	=	⊃	X

Fig. 53. A code-substitution test similar to the one used on the Wechsler-Bellevue Scales. The subject writes the proper symbol under a given list of numbers as quickly as possible.

valuable in determining the special strengths and weaknesses of the child. When the over-all results are used, it is important to recognize that they average about seven points less than the Stanford-Binet IQ scores for children and young adults.

For the recently developed Wechsler Preschool and Primary Scale of Intelligence, see INFANT AND PRESCHOOL TESTS.

WERNICKE'S SYNDROME (Wernicke-Korsakoff's Syndrome). A brain disorder caused by a deficiency of vitamins, particularly thiamine and niacin; first described in 1881 by the German neurologist Carl Wernicke (1848–1905).

The principal symptoms are memory loss, confabulation, clouding of consciousness, ophthalmoplegia (paralysis of eye muscles with ptosis, or drooping of eyelids; Argyll-Robertson pupil, a failure of the pupil to respond to light changes), and ataxia, an unsteady gait resulting from damage to nerves in the brain stem. The brain stem damage is due primarily to petechial mid-brain hemorrhages brought on by the vitamin deficiencies. The onset of the disease may be acute, with nausea, vomiting, and clouded consciousness; or it may develop more slowly out of a dreamy, confused delirium and distortion of memory. The patient tends to remain apathetic, moody, irritable, and easily fatigued. In some cases the symptoms of lassitude and general weakness are the same as in beri beri. See BERI BERI, PELLAGRINOUS PSYCHOSIS.

Korsakoff's syndrome is now generally considered to be the behavioral aspect of Wernicke's disease. The disorder is most frequently seen in chronic, "skid-row" alcoholics, but also occurs in cases of pernicious anemia, gastric cancer, and in vitamin-starved prisoners of war. It is seldom found in the general population today, now that the enrichment of bread and flour has been widely adopted. In most cases the psychological disturbances rapidly disappear when large doses of thiamine are administered. The neurological symptoms may take longer to overcome, and in some instances there may be permanent defects. See KORSAKOFF'S SYNDROME, CONFABULATION.

Illustrative Case: WERNICKE'S SYNDROME

H.B., aged sixty-two, a chronic alcoholic who had been arrested many times for drunkenness, was taken to a general hospital October 1, 1951, because of confusion and difficulty in walking. There was a history that following a long alcoholic debauch he had been taken into custody by the Salvation Army. For several days the supervision of this organization made it impossible for him to secure alcohol. He then remained at its hotel for several days more, performing light duties until his physical disabilities made employment impossible. Soon after entering the general hospital he became confused, restless, demanding, and was noisy at night. He was then transferred to a psychiatric hospital where the confusion soon subsided. On neurological examination, he showed marked bilateral ptosis, his pupils reacted very slightly to light, and he was totally unable to follow a light in any direction. His speech was thick and slurred; there was a great defect in coordination of his extremities; all tendon reflexes, except the biceps, were absent. The calves of both legs were tender, and he was unable to walk unaided. A diagnosis of Wernicke's syndrome plus peripheral neuritis was made. He was at once placed on large doses of thiamine. He soon began to improve, but the evidence of ophthalmoplegia did not completely disappear for seven months. (Noyes and Kolb, 1963)

WERTHEIMER, MAX (1880–1943). Wertheimer, originator of the Gestalt theory, was born in Prague, studied law at the university, then became interested in psychology and philosophy. He obtained his Ph.D. at Würzburg (1904) and during the following five years worked and studied at Prague, Vienna and Berlin. In 1909 he was appointed professor at Frankfurt, holding that position until 1933, when he accepted a post at the New School for Social Research in New York.

Wertheimer is regarded as the founder of the Gestalt school of psychology, a movement which started as a protest against the structuralist attempt to explain complex experiences entirely in terms of elementary constituents. In contrast to this "atomistic" approach, the Gestalt theory holds that many of our perceptions and other experiences are unique wholes which cannot be reduced to their parts without destroying them, and cannot be predicted from a knowledge of the parts—just as the properties of water cannot be predicted from the properties of the two gases that combine to produce it.

The origin of this movement can be traced to a specific event. In 1910 Wertheimer began to experiment on the perception of motion. Using a toy stroboscope as an instrument, he showed that when two objects are illuminated in rapid succession, the individual perceives a movement of one toward the other instead of two discrete objects. He reported this finding in 1912, and this date is usually regarded as the beginning of the movement. His demonstration of one type of apparent movement, the phi phenomenon as it was later called, is considered one of the crucial experiments in psychology, for it dramatically pointed up the inadequacy of the elementaristic view of experience, and showed that it actually analyzed movement out of existence. *See* GESTALT PSYCHOLOGY, APPARENT MOVEMENT.

During the next few years, Wertheimer and two associates, Wolfgang Köhler and Kurt Koffka, attacked two other postulates of structuralism—the view that sensations are the elements of experience, and that their combination can be completely understood through the laws of association. Wertheimer characterized the latter view as a "bundle hypothesis," and argued that perception is an integration which derives its character not merely from individual sensations but from the relationships between them. He attempted to explain the physical basis for perception by advancing an "isomorphic" theory of brain activity, stating that perceptual organization takes place in the brain, and formulated a number of Gestalt principles to explain the dynamics of perceptual patterning, such as closure and grouping of similar items. He believed these principles demonstrated that immediate experience is basically an orderly affair—that is, we do not have to create order, since it is already there.

Wertheimer's point of view was developed and disseminated by Köhler and Koffka. Köhler is best known for his study of insight, and his comparative studies of the thinking processes of men and apes carried out between 1917 and 1922. Koffka introduced the theory to America in 1922, and applied the Gestalt principles on thinking in the field of education. These principles were most fully presented in a posthumously published book of Wertheimer's, *Productive Thinking* (1945). In it he showed that the educational systems of the time closely followed the association theory, and as a result the child was taught by rote memory rather than by gaining insight into principles. He demonstrated, for example, that children who were taught to find the area of a parallelogram by rote could not solve the same problem if the figure was rotated 90 degrees. On the other hand, if the teacher helped them understand the reasons behind the solution, and if they were given practice in seeing problems as a whole, their thinking became more flexible and productive. Children taught in this new way developed an ability to "re-center their thinking"—that is, to see the problem in a fresh light and discover new relationships that usually suggested a solution. *See* INSIGHT, KOFFKA.

WEYER, JOHANN (1515–1588). The man who has been called "the father of modern psychiatry" was born in Grave on the Meuse, and is regarded by some as a Netherlander and by others as a Rhenish German. At seventeen he became a pupil of the great physician Agrippa, and three years later went to Paris to obtain his medical degree. After completing his preparation, he was appointed court physician to Duke William of Cleves, a position which gave him the security to continue his studies, and later provided some protection against the enemies he made when his revolutionary views became known.

Weyer made a number of original contributions to physical medicine, including observations on scurvy and menstrual problems, but his major interest was the study of mental illness. He was living at the time when witchcraft was rampant and the devil was blamed for all types of abnormal behavior. The accepted authority was *Malleus Maleficarum* (*The Witches' Hammer*), a book written by two theologians, Heinrich Kraemer and Johann Sprenger, which not only argued for the existence of witches, but showed how to identify them by discovering anesthetic areas of their bodies. It also gave detailed instructions for trying them and condemning them to burn at the stake. Working in this inflammatory atmosphere, Weyer relentlessly attacked these cruel superstitions, pointing out that the so-called witches were not possessed by supernatural forces but were mentally sick people who should be treated rather than punished. He even suggested that the theologians who tortured and executed them were the guilty parties and should be brought before the courts instead of the witches.

These courageous ideas were expressed in Weyer's most important work, *De Praestigiis Demonum* (*On the Delusions about Demons*), published in 1673. The book was in essence a plea for the establishment of psychiatry, for he proposed to replace the dogmatic approach of philosophy, theology, and jurisprudence with a medical approach to mental illness. One by one he demolished the "silly and often godless absurdities" of the "Malleus" by citing facts, observations, and statements from Scripture itself. He argued that the confessions of witches were unreliable and had no legal value since they were manifestations of mental illness, and he insisted that people with diseased minds should be treated rather than punished. He pointed out that the correct translation of the Hebrew word "khasph," which was rendered as witch or sorcerer, was actually closer to the Greek word "pharmakos," meaning "a person who uses medicaments or poisons unwisely or with criminal intent," and he suggested that the witches might be under the influence of known drugs that produce delirium or stupor. He supported this idea with descriptions of visual hallucinations experienced under the influence of hashish; and there is evidence that he performed experiments with other drugs as well.

In his attempts to combat demonology, Weyer was following the lead of his first teacher, Agrippa. But he also developed a remarkably advanced approach of his own. He proposed to eliminate all superstition and concentrate instead on the naturalistic observation of mental life in all its forms. He described schizophrenic delusions and fantasies in great detail, and was the first to suggest that paranoia and auditory hallucinations were related to homosexuality. He described the epidemics of mental illness which occurred at the time, and suggested that they were due to mass suggestion. He also pointed out that some individuals are temporarily more suggestible than others, and therefore more susceptible to group contagion. He recognized that abnormal fantasies are capable of distorting reality to fit the character of the underlying pathology, and he even suggested that these fantasies are waking expressions of what normally occurs only in dreams. As Zilboorg and Henry (1941) point out, these insights could actually have provided the foundations for a clinical approach to psychopathology, even though they remained unrecognized until late in the nineteenth century.

Typical of Weyer's approach was his handling of the case of ten-year-old Barbara Kremers, a girl who was reputed to live without eating or eliminating. Instead of accepting this story as a miracle, he went to see the mother, and with her permission took the girl and her twelve-year-old sister into his own home. In this simple but effective way he was able to prove that the older girl had been secretly bringing food to Barbara. It was probably the first time a doctor and his family cooperated in exposing a case of malingering.

Unfortunately Weyer's common sense yet scientific approach made little headway at the time. One of his leading opponents, Jean Bodin, labeled him "a very ignorant or a wicked man," and joined others in accusing him of sorcery, just as they had previously accused his teacher Agrippa. When Duke William was stricken with a cerebral hemorrhage and became mentally disturbed, these enemies cited his condition as proof of Weyer's sorcery, and even succeeded in placing his book on the Index, where it remained until the beginning of this century. But the important fact is that with Weyer "a new man, a new type of individual had entered upon the scene of medicine and medical philosophy" (Zilboorg and Henry, 1941)—even though it took over three hundred years for psychiatry to heed his call to arms: "Love man, kill errors, go into combat for truth without cruelty."

WHITE, WILLIAM ALANSON (1870–1937).

White, a leading figure in the development of American psychiatry, was born in New York City and re-ceived his medical degree at Long Island College. He was then appointed to the staff of the Binghamton State Hospital. While serving there he became vitally interested in brain pathology, and also collaborated with a psychologist, Boris Sidis, on an investigation of the concept of the unconscious. In 1903 he became superintendent of the Government Hospital for the Insane in Washington (later named St. Elizabeth's Hospital), a position he held for the rest of his life. There he instituted new approaches and sweeping reforms that helped to establish the hospital as a "scientific community," a phrase that fully applies to this day.

White became head of the Government Hospital at a time when practically no research was being conducted at such institutions, since their function was almost entirely custodial. To reverse this tradition, he developed a pathology laboratory which had been started by his predecessors, and organized one of the first psychology laboratories to be located in a mental hospital. He also turned the attention of the hospital toward active treatment of patients by developing a full department of internal medicine. It became the first in the Western Hemisphere to administer malarial therapy for general paresis, and the first in a public mental hospital to be accredited for the training of interns. Under his direction the hospital also recognized the psychological needs of mental patients by installing such services as a circulating library, a beauty parlor, and a cafeteria.

White was convinced that students of psychiatry should receive training in a mental hospital setting, and as a result of his efforts, St. Elizabeth's became a leading center for psychiatric training and was used to train medical officers of the Veterans Administration after World War I. White himself taught both in Army and Navy medical schools, as well as in the Georgetown University and George Washington University

Schools of Medicine. In addition to these activities, he played a leading role in forensic psychiatry, not only rendering expert testimony in the courts, but writing many articles and two books on the subject (*Insanity and the Criminal Law*, 1923, and *Crimes and Criminals*, 1933). He was also largely instrumental in creating a "pact" which resulted in greater co-operation between the American Bar Association and the American Psychiatric Association.

White's early interest in the unconscious came to full fruition when he came into direct contact with the works of Freud. He and Smith Ely Jelliffe became second only to A. A. Brill in disseminating the psychoanalytic doctrine in the United States. Together, these two men founded and edited the *Psychoanalytic Review* in 1913. His defense of psychoanalysis at meetings of the American Psychiatric Association is believed to represent a turning-point in the history of the movement in this country. He later became president of the American Psychiatric Association, the American Psychoanalytic Association, and the American Psychopathological Association. He was also an early supporter of the National Committee for Mental Hygiene and presided over the first Congress of Mental Hygiene in 1930.

His many duties and responsibilities did not prevent White from becoming one of the most voluminous psychiatric authors of his time. In addition to numerous articles and monographs, he wrote seventeen books, including the widely used text *Outlines of Psychiatry* (1907), *Diseases of the Nervous System* (with Jelliffe, 1915), *Principles of Mental Hygiene* (1919), *Foundations of Psychiatry* (1921), *Essays on Psychopathology* (1925), and *The Meaning of Disease* (1926). While he was still alive his admirers established the William Alanson White Foundation, an organization which has exerted an important influence on the development of psychiatry in this country. The William Alanson White Institute was founded in 1943 by Harry Stock Sullivan, Clara Thompson, Erich Fromm, David Rioch, Janet Rioch, and others, "for the training of resourceful psychoanalysts sensitive to man's changing role in modern society." Among its other activities today are research on mental illness, psycholinguistics, emotional disturbance in preschool children, and special projects on high school and college dropouts and the emotional well-being of blue-collar workers. For the latter, *see* MENTAL HEALTH AND ECONOMIC LEVEL.

WITHDRAWAL. A defensive reaction consisting of retreat from threatening situations and, in its pathological form, retreat from reality as a whole.

There are many types and degrees of withdrawal. The most primitive is probably the tendency to withdraw the hand or foot from a painful physical stimulus. Physical withdrawal and flight constitute one of the basic responses to stress and frustration, paralleling the tendency to attack and to find substitute satisfactions or compromises. These reactions are shared with animals, but the human being also develops psychological forms of withdrawal of many kinds. He may refuse to become "involved." He may become apathetic or resigned. He may lower his level of aspiration, or simplify his life to avoid problems. He may react to defeat or failure by curtailing his efforts or by inhibiting his impulses and desires as much as possible.

Withdrawal is an attempt to escape dangerous and frustrating situations through retreat or surrender. It is usually carried out at considerable psychological expense, since the individual is likely to become more fearful and frustrated than ever. In addition, he may become prey to feelings of guilt for having given up, or be consumed with hostility toward others as a reaction to frustration.

Withdrawal is often classed among the defense mechanisms, and as such is considered a basically normal type of reaction. However, it may take exaggerated and morbid form. One type of pathological reaction is withdrawal or "flight" into illness, the tendency to take to one's bed and develop hypochondriacal complaints. Another and more malignant type is the schizophrenic's tendency to withdraw from the whole of reality. This reaction generally begins with a loss of interest in people and events accompanied by detachment, apathy, uncommunicativeness, and disinterest in school or work. (PLATE 8) If this tendency is not arrested it may progress to a full retreat into an autistic world of fantasy and, in some cases, to infantile behavior, a vegetative state, or even stupor or coma. See SCHIZO-PHRENIC REACTIONS (GENERAL), AUTISM, DAYDREAMING, EMOTIONAL INSULATION, INHIBITION, REGRESSION, VEGETATIVE STATE.

WITHDRAWAL SYMPTOMS. Mental and physical symptoms experienced when drugs are unavailable to individuals who have become addicted or habituated to them.

These symptoms may be relatively mild, moderate, or extremely intense, depending on the existence and degree of physiological dependence on the drug. Milder effects include vague uneasiness, headaches and slight depression. Typical moderate effects are insomnia, nausea, and restlessness. Severe symptoms are mental confusion, excruciating abdominal pain, convulsions, and delirium.

In cases of physical dependence, as in heroin addiction, the symptoms generally follow a regular sequence in which they develop, reach maximum intensity, and decline at fairly specific times. This sequence is sometimes termed "abstinence syndrome." The severity of heroin withdrawal symptoms can be reduced by administration of tranquilizers and the synthetic narcotic, metha-

done. For specific withdrawal symptoms, see DRUG ADDICTION, BARBITURATE ADDICTION, ALCOHOLIC ADDICTION, SMOKING.

WORD ASSOCIATION TEST. A projective test of emotional reactions in which the subject responds to a stimulus word with the first word that comes to mind; sometimes called a free association test.

The most common procedure is to set up a free association situation with the subject seated comfortably or reclining, sometimes in a darkened room. The examiner reads from a prepared list and records the subject's replies, the time taken to respond to each word ("latency of reply"), and any speech or behavioral mannerisms he observes. Some examiners also repeat the test shortly after it is completed, instructing the subject to respond with the same words previously given. The object is to see whether responses to certain key words are changed.

The word association test was invented by Francis Galton in 1879 as a means of exploring individual differences. Emil Kraepelin was apparently the first to apply it to the study of abnormality, in 1892. When psychoanalysis came into prominence, Carl Jung began to use the technique as a clinical tool. His original list of one hundred words was designed to uncover complexes by presenting emotion-provoking words scattered among neutral words. See JUNG.

The most widely used form of the test is the one devised by Kent and Rosanoff in 1910. Their list consists of one hundred neutral, familiar nouns and adjectives (table, fruit, cold, eagle, bite) which, unlike Jung's list, are not selected to tap possible areas of conflict. These words were presented to a group of a thousand normal subjects, and a frequency tally for each word was made —for example, "needle" led to 160 responses of "thread," and 158 of "pin," but only one each of blood, broken, camel, and weapon. On the basis of such investigations tables of common and uncommon responses have been constructed.

In scoring the Kent-Rosanoff Free Association Test, the table is used to determine the number of "individual reactions" (zero frequency), and the median frequency value for the total set of responses. Special tables have also been constructed for children and normal people of different ages and races. Other scores are computed for failure to react, doubtful reactions, nonspecific reactions (general words such as "good" or "useful" given to every stimulus word). When the test is used for detection of complexes, some of the indications cited by Jung may be applied: long reaction time, very short reaction time, repetition of stimulus word before responding, extremely personal responses, clang responses, behavioral signs of excitement or embarrassment, whispered or shouted responses, stammering, laughing, inability to recall the response on the post-test. Hull and Lugoff (1921) showed that these measures correlate fairly highly with each other and are important clues to the unconscious dynamics of the subject. Once a complex is isolated, the therapist explores the sensitive area through interviews.

The word association technique is sometimes administered, along with other procedures, in diagnosing mental illness. Rapaport, Gill, and Schafer (1946) have devised a special list of sixty words for this purpose. It includes a number of familial, anal, oral, aggressive, and sexual terms. According to Schafer, there is some indication that obsessive-compulsive patients give ostentatious reactions such as dance–terpsichore, house–domicile, and often have delayed responses when several possibilities come to mind at once; hysteric patients are apt to hesitate over words with sexual connotations and often give infantile reactions or use evaluative words

such as snake–slimy, or cockroach–hate. Common reactions among schizophrenic patients are: blocking, highly unique responses, clang associations (bite–light), phrase completions (taxidermist), personal association (masturbation–loss). (In the latter example the subject was disturbed by the loss of semen.) On other applications of the test, schizophrenics were found to give twenty-five to thirty individual reactions, while normal adults with elementary school education gave 5.2 and the college educated 9.3 individual reactions.

A number of variations on the basic method have been tried. Thurstone 1952) used words that could be interpreted in different ways—a technique called "homographic free association" —to tap social attitudes; for example, "revolution" could evoke either "social upheaval" or "turning around." Goodenough (1942, 1946) developed a similar test for masculinity-femininity; for example, the response to "bow" could be either "hair ribbon" or "arrow." Others have used lists of words that sound alike (homophones), such as "sell" and "cell"; Foley and MacMillan (1943) found that on this form of the test many people gave responses in line with their vocational interests. A forced-option, multiple-choice technique has been applied to testing such dimensions as masculinity-femininity and normality-abnormality, but this variant is of doubtful value since it limits freedom of expression. See FORCED CHOICE.

The Word Association technique has been used for other purposes than personality study and psychodiagnosis. As early as 1907 Münsterberg applied it to guilt detection. The usual method here is to scatter "giveaway" words among neutral words and to compare the reaction time of the subject to each of these types. However, studies by Marston (1938) and others have shown that the technique is not conclusive, since there is no regular relation between guilt and reaction time, and sophisticated subjects can often control their responses. The test is therefore highly questionable when used alone, but has some value when applied in conjunction with physiological measurements.

In addition, the test is sometimes used in market research to discover reactions to company names or brand names; in social psychology as a means of uncovering prejudices or other social attitudes; and in police investigations as a means of identifying drug addicts, homosexuals, and criminals, since these individuals tend to respond to stimulus words with their own special argot.

WORD BLINDNESS (Congenital Word Blindness). Inability to read due to brain lesions.

These terms were in common use about forty years ago but are now obsolete. They were based on the theory that many if not most children who cannot learn to read were born with a fundamental but unspecified brain defect. It is still recognized that a significant percentage of children (some estimate 15 per cent) are afflicted with neurological defects that make it impossible or extremely difficult for them to learn to read. Some of these defects are congenital while others appear to be acquired.

The term "congenital word blindness" has been discarded for two reasons. First, it seems to ignore the many cases in which reading disability may be due to psychological causes; and second, it seems to imply that the condition is incurable—but this is seldom the case when systematic, individualized efforts are made to overcome the child's specific difficulty. *See* READING DISABILITY, ALEXIA, MINIMAL BRAIN DYSFUNCTION, APHASIA.

WORD SALAD (Word Hash). A jumbled, unintelligible mixture of words, usually containing both real words or phrases and neologisms.

This disturbance in verbal communication is most frequently found in advanced schizophrenic reactions. It may also occur in other severely disoriented patients, particularly during delirium or manic states. The following excerpts, cited by Kisker (1964), are typical of this symptom.

From an interview with a female schizophrenic patient:

"I am here from a foreign university . . . and you have to have a 'plausity' or all acts of amendment to go through for the children's code . . . and it is no mental disturbance or 'puterience' . . . it is an 'amorition' law . . . there is nothing to disturb me . . . it is like their 'privatilinia' . . . and the children have to have this 'accentuative' law so they don't go into the 'mortite' law of the church."

Delusional utterances of a paranoid patient:

"Why nylons, autos, men, city people more cancer—because more polluted meat and drinks not one single connection with cigs—never jitters from narcotics or disorganization of nervous system—'I-am-ity' megalomania—why Napoleon had to conquer world—Hitler and Mussolini and Me Too so now that I have conquered all mystery diseases (asthma and rheumatism too/experiment any dementia case) I am going to conquer the Russians/It is just a mathematical problem/New York, Cleveland, St. Louis, Detroit, California, Miami/ they have control of now pulling in Cincinnati so I won't die of cancer, or the apparent heart attack/but a couple of bullets—so KEEP my name out." *See* VERBIGERATION, NEOLOGISM.

Illustrative Case: WORD SALAD

This creation in which we live began with a Dominant Nature as an Identification Body of a completed evolutionary Strong Material creation in a Major Body Resistance Force. And is fulfilling the Nature Identification in a like Weaker Material Identification creation in which Two Major Bodies have already fulfilled radio body balances, and embodying a Third Material Identification Embodiment of both; which is now in the evolutionary process of fulfillment but fulfills without the Two Parents' Identification Resistances, therefore shall draw the resistances and perpetuate the motion interchanging of the whole relationship; thus completing this Creation in an interchanging Four in Three Bodies in One functioning self contained, self-controlled and self-restrained comprising the Dominant Moral Nature and consummating a ratio balanced Major Body of maximum resistance, in a separated second like Weaker Material Major Body Functioning Counter Resistance Force to the Strong Material Major Body Resistance Force, the beginning of this creation; and the dual Force Resistances then as a Major Body and Major Body Functioning completes a Universe in material balance functioning the preservation of all things. (White, 1964)

WORK CURVE. A graph representing the amount or efficiency of work done over a given interval of time.

Work curves are constructed to present a bird's-eye view of the performance of an individual or group throughout a given period, such as a day, week, or month. They are based on the fact that workers of all kinds—mental or manual, skilled or unskilled—do not maintain the same pace or the same efficiency over a substantial period of time. The curves reveal what to expect in a given job and how well individual workers are performing. They are also useful in studying the effects of new work conditions such as improved ventilation, music, or coffee breaks, and in identifying portions of the work period that need greater attention, such as the start of the day or the late afternoon sag.

Work curves are a composite of four different components, each representing an important factor in performance:

1. *Warm-up.* A steady upward trend showing an increase in production and efficiency as the worker gets organized and warms up to the task.

2. *Beginning Spurt.* A high point at the start indicating peak production resulting from initial vigor and enthusiasm. This spurt does not always occur, but if it does, it may cancel out the warm-up period entirely. It is usually followed by a gradual downward trend over the long run.

3. *End Spurt.* A sudden rise in the curve at the end of the work period indicative of increased production when the end is in sight.

4. *Over-all Downward Trend.* This trend reflects declining efficiency and effort due primarily to fatigue, and secondarily to loss of motivation because of the increasing effect of such factors as monotony, distraction, and discomfort.

Work curves, then, represent the effects of a number of basic factors. Individual curves vary considerably, since these factors operate differently from task to task and from individual to individual. The curves for industrial work do not necessarily apply to office work or academic study. In heavy handwork, for example, production over an eight-hour day typically shows a sharp increase up to the second hour, then a steady decrease, with a sharper drop just before lunchtime. After lunch, performance starts at a slightly higher level than where it left off, and drops for the rest of the afternoon, with an especially steep drop in the last hour. The general level of morning production is higher than the level for the afternoon. *See* WARMING UP, END SPURT, FATIGUE.

WORK HOURS. Industrial psychologists have made a limited number of studies of the effects of long versus short work hours and day versus night work. Probably the most influential investigation is a survey made by Kossoris and Köhler (1947) in thirty-four plants in which there had been a change of hours of work during and after the war, but no other major changes. Although the data showed considerable variation among individuals, depending on such factors as method of pay (hourly or incentive), machine pacing and heavy versus light work, the over-all results indicated that the eight-hour day and forty-hour week were more effective than longer hours in terms of productivity per hour, absenteeism and safety. Even though longer hours resulted in greater output, the *rate* fell in almost every case. For light work, a three-hour increase produced only two additional hours of output, and for heavy work it took a two-hour increase to produce one hour of additional output. The number of injuries was found to increase as the hours were lengthened.

Some studies have shown that when an extremely long week is shortened the total output may actually increase. The most noteworthy example here is a series of studies conducted by the Industrial Fatigue Research Board of Great Britain during World War I. They revealed, for example, that in one large munitions plant shortening the work week from 66 to 47.5 hours increased the weekly output by 13 per cent (Vernon, 1920). This finding is partly explained by the fact that during a longer week the actual number of hours of work is proportionately less than during the shorter week since more time is lost through absenteeism, tardiness, and unauthorized rest pauses. Moreover, the work rate is slower since the employees adjust their efforts to the length of the period. On the other hand, shortening the work period beyond a certain point (which differs for different types of work) yields diminishing returns, since too great a proportion of the working time is devoted to nonproductive activities such as obtaining supplies, adjusting equipment, warming up, and returning materials at the end of the day.

Laboratory studies involving mental multiplication indicate that efficiency of mental work shows a consistent over-all drop during a twelve-hour period. Other observations lend support to this conclusion. The amount of the drop, however, has been found to vary from about 30 per cent to 60 per cent in different studies (Ray, Martin and Alluisi, 1961). In a controlled experiment on driving performance conducted by Herbert (1963) and Herbert and Jaynes (1964), groups of men drove continuously for different periods (one, three, seven, and nine hours) and were given a series of driving tests immediately after their stint. The results showed an over-all decline from good to medium for the three-hour group, and from good to poor for the seven- and nine-hour groups. The implications for long-distance trucking as well as ordinary driving are significant.

The problem of night versus day work is a particularly important one today, since the demand for shift workers is constantly increasing due to the rapid expansion in our economy and the need for amortizing the high cost of automated equipment. An early study conducted in the munitions industry showed that continuous night workers averaged 8 per cent less output than continuous day workers (Vernon, 1921). More recent research emphasizes the difficulties encountered by shift workers and the effects of frequent changes on personal well-being and work performance. The most common problem is inability to sleep during the daytime because of noise, light, and heat; but workers also complain of interference with social life, living habits, and relationships with their families. The effects are especially severe among workers on rotating shifts; research has revealed that they are subject to a high error rate, a high accident rate, disturbances in eating and sleeping, and reduced general health. One survey has shown that gastric ulcers occurred eight times as often among shift workers as among day workers. For these reasons Bloom (1961) recommends fixed shifts over rotating shifts, and suggests that if rotation is unavoidable the workers should have several days off between changes.

WORKING THROUGH. In psychoanalysis and other forms of psychotherapy, working through is the process of actively exploring feelings, impulses, and conflicts in attempting to solve emotional problems and reach improved adjustment.

In the process of working through, the patient faces his deeper feelings and attitudes over and over again under the therapist's supervision until new reaction patterns are firmly established and he can meet and manage his difficulties in everyday life. It is therefore conceived as a growth experience in the direction of greater maturity and better adaptation.

According to psychoanalytic theory, this process operates largely on an unconscious level, since it involves recapturing repressed feelings and experiences, and converting them into conscious thoughts, wishes, and impulses. One of the major problems is to overcome resistance to the disclosure of the unconscious material: "One must allow the patient time to know this resistance of which he is ignorant, to 'work through' it, to overcome it by continuing to work according to the analytic rule of defiance of it" (Freud, 1924–25). As the unconscious material is disclosed and worked through, the patient modifies his reactions and redirects his energies into more constructive channels. *See* PSYCHOANALYSIS (THERAPY), RESISTANCE.

WUNDT, WILHELM MAX, (1832–1920). Wundt, the founder of experimental psychology, was born near Mannheim, the son of a Lutheran minister. After years of tutoring by his father's assistant, he attended the Gymnasium at Heidelberg and entered the University in 1852. Although he was a medical student, his major interest was physiology, and therefore after receiving his degree, he went to Berlin to study this field under the great Johannes Müller. He then returned to Heidelberg to serve as Privat Dozent in physiology and assistant to Hermann Helmholtz.

Between 1857 and 1864 Wundt published several papers and three books— one on the movements of the muscles, a second on the senses, and a third on the psyche of men and animals. The book on the senses, *Beiträge zur Theorie des Sinnes-Wahrnehmung,* contains an outline of his endeavors for the rest of his life, and makes a plea for the application of experimental methods to psychology. The book on the psyche introduced many topics which experimental psychology dealt with for years after, including psychophysical methods, the "personal equation" in its relation to reaction time experiments, and perceptual problems.

In 1864 Wundt was appointed assistant professor of physiology at Heidelberg, and during the next ten years published a textbook on physiology and a handbook on medical physics. When Helmholtz left in 1871, Wundt appeared to be in line for his position, but was passed over. Nevertheless, he continued teaching and experimenting in physiological psychology, and in 1873–74 published a monumental two volume work, *Grundzüge der Physiologischen Psychologie,* which Boring (1950) calls "The most important book in the history of modern psychology." In it he not only brought together every known fact on psychology, but presented his own system. It has been described as a "Declaration of Independence" calling for the establishment of experimental psychology as a separate science.

In 1875 Wundt transferred his activities to Leipzig, where he answered his own call for experimental psychology by establishing the first "official" psychological laboratory in 1879. He also founded the first journal devoted to reporting the findings of this new discipline, *Philosophische Studien*. Among his students in the laboratory were many who later became eminent in their fields: Kraepelin, Cattell, Külpe, Angell, Titchener, and James, to name only a few.

Wundt generally determined the problems to be studied. They covered a wide range of subjects, including analysis of word associations; development and elaboration of psychophysical methods; problems of attention, judgment, and emotions; psychophysiology of the senses; and studies of reaction time. The investigations were carried out primarily through the method of introspection, and were limited to an exploration of the generalized human adult mind. No experimentation was done on children or animals, nor did he concern himself with individual differences, which he regarded as a bothersome interference with his main purpose. Some of his students, however, later focused attention on these neglected fields—for example, J. M. Cattell developed the study of individual differences. *See* CATTELL.

Wundt, a man of encyclopedic mentality, produced a number of works on philosophy as well as psychology. The most notable were *Logik* (1880), *Ethik* (1886), and *Systeme der Philosophie* (1889), the latter presenting a system of scientific metaphysics. In addition to continuing his work as director of the laboratory, he accepted the position of Rector of the University in 1889. Not long after, he added to his amazing output—which totaled 53,735 pages—by publishing *Grundriss der Psychologie*, in which he introduced his theory that feelings vary along the three dimensions of pleasantness-unpleasantness, excite-ment-quiescence, and strain-relaxation, a theory which led to a great deal of productive research.

In the last twenty years of his life, from 1900 to 1920, this indefatigable investigator turned his attention to the psychological interpretation of the data of history and anthropology. His findings were published in a monumental ten-volume work, *Völker Psychologie*, which contributed heavily to our knowledge of the higher psychological processes, especially in the field of language, which he believed to be an accurate index of the mental make-up of any society.

Although much of Wundt's work has been superseded, and psychology has broken the rigid bounds which he put upon it, many authorities would agree with Boring's statement that "He is the first man who without reservation is properly called a psychologist." *See* TITCHENER.

WÜRZBURG SCHOOL. A school of psychology which held that our judgments, thoughts, and meanings are determined by intangible mental activities, and not merely by sensations and images.

The Würzburg School, stemming from the German town of that name, developed primarily as a reaction to the structuralist doctrine which dominated psychological thought in the latter part of the nineteenth century. Structuralism attempted to follow the lead of the physical sciences by reducing experience to its basic elements (sensations, images, feelings), and by formulating the laws by which these elements are synthesized. At the very beginning of this century (1901–7), Oswald Külpe, director of the psychological laboratory at Würzburg, sought to show the shortcomings of this approach by performing experiments on thinking, a topic shunned by the structuralist school.

In a typical experiment, subjects were asked to judge which of two weights was the heavier, and were further required to describe what went on in their minds before and during the act of judging. Külpe discovered that, contrary to the structuralist claim, no images or sensations were involved in the act of judging, and, as a matter of fact, there was no conscious weighing activity at all. This suggested that we do not make our decisions according to the laws of syllogistic reasoning—at least not in a way that could be pinpointed by the introspective method. He therefore came to the conclusion that a new type of mental content, different from the sensations and images of the structuralists, was involved in judging and other thought processes.

This type of content was termed "conscious attitude" (Bewusstseinslage), and characterized as unanalyzable, indescribable, obscure, and intangible. As many psychologists have pointed out, these attitudes bore a close resemblance to the concept of "imageless thought." They were regarded as important components of mental activities, which the structuralists had failed to recognize because of their preoccupation with the more tangible contents of consciousness. *See* IMAGELESS THOUGHT.

In their attempts to find out more about these newly-discovered mental processes, the members of the school performed a huge number of introspective investigations. One of the most fruitful was the word-association experiment, in which they studied thought processes that occurred between the presentation of the word and the subject's response to it. In one case, the subject was told that he would be given the concept of a whole object, such as a house, and must respond with a word for some part of it—for example, window or door. The experimenters discovered that most of the subject's mental activity seemed to run off by itself the moment the stimulus word was pre-sented, and not in the period when the response word was actively sought. It is as if he set himself to react in a certain way *prior* to the presentation of a specific stimulus. In other words, once the "whole-part" task, or "Aufgabe," was set, the major mental activity had been accomplished, and the actual response to the given stimulus word became a more or less automatic affair.

The Aufgabe was renamed "determining tendency" by Narziss Ach, a member of the school. The modern term "mental set" is a direct descendant of this concept. It is actually a preparation or predisposition which unconsciously determines the way we handle a situation. If we are given the problem

$$5$$
$$2$$

and the task, or Aufgabe, of adding, we get 7; but if we are prepared for subtraction, the answer will be 3. *See* SET.

The concept of determining tendency brought the Würzburg School close to a number of important ideas in modern psychology. It took a long step toward a psychology of meaning, since it could be shown that individuals with different determining tendencies will interpret the same external situation in totally different ways. This idea, in turn, suggests the importance of attitudes in our mental and emotional life, for it shows that the *way* we see things is more important than *what* we see. Man is therefore not simply a passive recipient of stimulation, but is active in the sense that processes taking place within him determine the way he responds to his world. But these processes are not themselves directly open to him—that is, our conscious mental life represents only a small fraction of the mental activity that is actually going on. It was not a far cry from these ideas to the dynamic psychology of today.

Y

YERKES, ROBERT MEARNS (1876–1956). During his years as a graduate student at Harvard, Yerkes shifted from an early interest in medicine to research on the evolution of behavior from the lowest organisms to man. His first work was done in the laboratory of comparative zoology, and soon after publishing a book entitled *The Dancing Mouse* (1907), he was appointed to the comparative psychology staff. The book was followed by many papers on a wide range of organisms and, in 1909, by a review in which he and S. Margulis introduced Pavlov's work to American psychologists. In 1911 he published his *Introduction to Psychology,* which stressed the importance of a comparative approach to behavior.

Yerkes left Harvard to accept an appointment as full professor at the University of Minnesota in 1917, and in the following year became president of the American Psychological Association. When America entered the war he was put in charge of the psychologists who developed the Army intelligence tests, and helped to devise a point scale to be used in testing recruits. He also served as chief of the psychological division of the Surgeon-General's Office and chairman of the Information Service of the National Research Council, later becoming chairman of its Committee on Research in Problems of Sex. In 1924 he accepted the post of research professor at Yale's Institute of Human Behavior, and established the Yale Laboratories of Primate Biology at Orange Park, Florida. This center fulfilled a dream he had as a graduate student, that of breeding and experimenting on chimpanzees un-der ideal conditions. His work at the laboratories made him the world's leading authority on higher primates, and a year after his retirement in 1942, the name was changed to the Yerkes Laboratories in his honor.

Yerkes is responsible for a wealth of new information on the mental processes of monkeys and apes. He discovered that chimpanzees will imitate each other and also imitate human beings when they are in situations that capture their interest. He anticipated Köhler in showing that an orang-utan will stack several boxes and stand on them to reach for food, provided he first sees how it is done. He also found that once the problem is learned, the animal can repeat it and transfer the solution to a similar problem.

Yerkes combatted the widespread use of instinctual explanations by proving that mouse-killing in kittens is not innate but depends on learning experiences. He developed a "multiple choice" method for testing the mental ability of lower animals by lining up a series of boxes and placing food in one of them. The subject was then tested to see if it could remember that a box placed in a certain position contained food. He also collaborated in formulating the Yerkes-Dodson Law which states that strong motivation usually interferes with learning a difficult discrimination task, but has a positive effect on the learning of easier tasks. As an example, excitement might prevent us from threading a needle but help us with the easier task of picking out a friend in a crowd. *See* INSTINCT.

Yerkes' most important books are *The Great Apes,* (with his wife), *The*

Mental Life of Monkeys and Apes (1916), *Almost Human* (1925), *The Mind of a Gorilla* (1927), and *Chimpanzees: A Laboratory Colony* (1943). He also published numerous scientific articles and monographs, and served on the editorial staff of several journals. His contributions earned him recognition as America's leading comparative psychologist.

Z

ZEIGARNIK EFFECT. The tendency to recall uncompleted tasks better than completed tasks.

In the course of a day we finish many activities but leave many unfinished. Which of these are we more likely to remember? To answer this question, Bluma Zeigarnik, a Russian psychologist, gave 138 children a number of tasks (puzzles, mental arithmetic, clay modeling, etc.), one half of which were interrupted and one half carried through to completion. When they were asked to name the tasks an hour later, 110 remembered more interrupted tasks, seventeen more completed tasks, and eleven the same number of each (Zeigarnik, 1927). These results suggested that completed tasks tend to be forgotten because the motivation to perform them is satisfied, while the drive persists and enhances memory when they are left uncompleted.

Other investigations have refined and qualified this finding. Marrow (1938) found that subjects who were told they were working successfully tended to forget their tasks even though they were interrupted. Although this result seemed to conflict with that of Zeigarnik, it actually supported her finding since it meant that the subjects' drive was being satisfied. In this case, then, interruption was the equivalent of completion, since it gave the subject a feeling of success.

Rosenzweig shed additional light on this question in experiments performed in 1943. The same problems were presented to two groups of people. Group 1 was told the problems were not a test of ability, and that they might not even be given a chance to complete them because it did not matter how well they did. Group 2 was told they were an intelligence test, and that they might be stopped if they were not doing them quickly enough. Group 2 therefore felt threatened and worked under stress, while group 1 felt relaxed. Later on, when both groups were asked to name all the problems they worked on, the non-stress group exhibited the typical Zeigarnik effect, recalling more uncompleted than completed tasks, while the stress group showed the opposite result, recalling more completed than uncompleted tasks. The implication seemed to be that when self-esteem is directly involved, people tend to remember their successes and forget their failures. This ties up with the common experience of dwelling on our triumphs and dismissing our defeats, since the triumphs are gratifying and flattering while the defeats are painful and threatening to the ego.

ZEN BUDDHISM. The Zen approach has aroused considerable interest among Western psychologists and psychiatrists (including Jung, Horney, Fromm, and the existentialists) who believe that (1) psychotherapy should be concerned with the meaning of life rather than merely with the elimination of symptoms or the improvement of social adjustment, and (2) this meaning is a unique, personal affair which the individual can achieve only through direct, intuitive experience and not by a scientific, intellectual approach. The goal is therefore not to learn but to become, not to know but to attain insight.

The Zen form of Buddhism began to take shape in China during the sixth century. According to Watts (1957) it was designed to make Buddhism a way of life for ordinary people, with the objective of "seeing into our own nature, and not of practicing dhyana (meditation) or obtaining liberation." Seeing into our own nature involves immediate, intense, and sudden illumination which can be attained only through long and arduous dedication. The process is best illustrated by the devotion to the solution of a baffling question, the Koan, to which there is no logical or intellectual solution—for example: What is the sound of one hand clapping? or What original features did you have even prior to birth?

Such questions cannot be answered through reasoning or learning. The solution must come from the individual's own life: "Penetrating insight is born of the inner depth of consciousness, as the source of a new life has to be tapped, and with it the Koan yields up its secrets" (Suzuki, 1956). Illumination, or "satori," is experienced as a sudden relief of tension, an explosion in which a new world is revealed and a new spiritual unity achieved. After this experience the individual feels that his entire life has been transformed.

Zen has caught the imagination of psychoanalysts and other psychotherapists because these approaches have much in common. Like depth psychology, Zen puts the emphasis on feeling, insight, and understanding rather than on logic, knowledge, or intellectual formulations. Solutions must stem from personal experience, not from the teacher, and the solution for one individual may not apply to another. The Zen master and his disciple, like the analyst and his patient, must share this insight and experience. This sharing, however, seems to go beyond the usual processes of rapport and empathy.

Suzuki has emphasized three factors which make for success in the study of Zen: "Great faith, great resolution, and great spirit of inquiry"—and there is little doubt that all three of these qualities are needed to make psychotherapy most effective. And finally, many therapists now believe that therapy is more than an attempt to overcome pathology, since it is an effort to grapple with the nature of man. This effort requires the patient—and the therapist as well—to contemplate his own existence. As Ben-Avi (1959) has put it, "If psychotherapy or psychoanalysis is to look toward dealing with the essential human problem rather than what might be the person's unique way of contending with the problem, that is, his pathology, there is a need to become expert in living rather than expert in the problems of living."

These similarities do not, of course, eliminate the differences between the two general approaches. Psychotherapists do not aim to bring about a single climactic experience in which intellect and logic are abolished and subject and object, thought and substance become fused into one—although they may recognize that we have transitory experiences, as in love and art, in which this occurs in a limited way. Nor do they attempt to put their patients in touch with ultimate reality. Nevertheless, Zen Buddhism is a healthy and important reminder that a purely intellectual approach does not do justice to man's full nature, and that change and growth must be rooted in the experience and insight of the individual. *See* EXISTENTIALISM.

REFERENCES

Abramson, H. A. (ed.). THE USE OF LSD IN PSYCHOTHERAPY. New York: Josiah Macy, 1960.

Abt, L. E. and L. Bellak. PROJECTIVE PSYCHOLOGY. New York: Alfred A. Knopf, 1950.

Ackerman, N. W. "Toward an Integrative Therapy of the Family," *American Journal of Psychiatry*, 114 (1958), 727–33.

———. "Family Therapy," AMERICAN HANDBOOK OF PSYCHIATRY, S. Arieti (ed.). New York: Basic Books, 1966. Volume 3, Chapter 14.

Adams, C. and V. Packard. HOW TO PICK A MATE. New York: Dutton, 1946.

Adams, T. "Hypothalamic Temperature in the Cat During Feeding and Sleep," *Science*, 139 (1963), 609–10.

Adamson, R. E. "Functional Fixedness as Related to Problem Solving: A Repetition of Three Experiments," *Journal of Experimental Psychology*, 44 (1952), 288–91.

Ader, R. and M. L. Belfer. "Prenatal Maternal Anxiety and Offspring Emotionality in the Rat," *Psychological Reports*, 10 (1962), 711–18.

Adler, A. THE PRACTICE AND THEORY OF INDIVIDUAL PSYCHOLOGY. New York: Harcourt, 1924.

———. THE EDUCATION OF CHILDREN. New York: Greenberg, 1930.

Adolph, E. F. "Thirst and Its Inhibition in the Stomach," *American Journal of Physiology*, 161 (1950), 374–86.

Adorno, T. W., E. Frenkel-Brunswik, D. J. Levinson and R. N. Sanford. THE AUTHORITARIAN PERSONALITY. New York: Harper, 1950.

Ainsworth, M. D. "The Effects of Maternal Deprivation: A Review of Findings and Controversy in the Context of Research Strategy," DEPRIVATION OF MATERNAL CARE: A REASSESSMENT OF ITS EFFECTS. Geneva: World Health Organization, 1962. 97–165.

Albert, K. and C. Warden. "The Level of Performance in the White Rat," *Science*, 100 (1944), 476.

Aldrich, C. K. AN INTRODUCTION TO DYNAMIC PSYCHIATRY. New York: McGraw-Hill, 1966.

Alexander, F. "Neurotic Character," *International Journal of Psycho-Analysis*, 11 (1930), 292–311.

———. "The Indications for Psychoanalytic Therapy," *Bulletin of the New York Academy of Medicine*, 20 (1944), 319–44.

———. PSYCHOSOMATIC MEDICINE. New York: Norton, 1952.

——— and T. M. French. PSYCHOANALYTIC THERAPY. New York: Ronald, 1946.

Alexander, F. and L. J. Saul. "Respiration and Personality, A Preliminary Report," *Psychosomatic Medicine*, 2 (1940), 110.

Alexander, I. E. and A. M. Adlerstein. "Affective Responses to the Concept of Death in a Population of Children and Early Adolescents," *Journal of Genetic Psychology*, 93 (1958), 167–77.

Allee, W. C., N. E. Collins and C. Z. Lutherman. "Modification of the Social Order in Flocks of Hens by the Injection of Testosterone Propionate," *Physiological Zoology*, 12 (1939), 412–40.

Allen, F. H. PSYCOTHERAPY WITH CHILDREN. New York: Norton, 1942.

Allport, F. H. "The Influence of the Group upon Association and Thought," *Journal of Experimental Psychology*, 3 (1920), 159–82.

———. SOCIAL PSYCHOLOGY. Boston: Houghton-Mifflin, 1924.

Allport, G. W. "Attitudes," HANDBOOK OF SOCIAL PSYCHOLOGY, C. Murchison (ed.). Worcester, Massachusetts: Clark University Press, 1935. 798–844.

———. THE NATURE OF PREJUDICE. Cambridge, Massachusetts: Addison Wesley, 1954.

———. PERSONALITY: A PSYCHOLOGICAL INTERPRETATION. New York: Holt, 1937.

———. "The Psychologist's Frame of Reference," *Psychological Bulletin*, 37 (1940), 1–28.

——— and H. S. Odbert. "Trait-Names: A Psycho-Lexical Study," *Psychological Monographs*, 47 (1936), Number 211.

Allport, G. W. and T. F. Pettigrew. "Cultural Influence on the Perception of Movement: The Trapezoidal Illusion Among Zulus," *Journal of Abnormal and Social Psychology*, 55 (1957), 104–13.

Allport, G. W. and L. Postman. "The Basic Psychology of Rumor," *New York Academy of Science Series II,* 8 (1945), 61–81.

———. THE PSYCHOLOGY OF RUMOR. New York: Holt, 1947.

Allport, G. W. and P. E. Vernon. STUDIES IN EXPRESSIVE MOVEMENT. New York: Macmillan, 1933.

——— and G. Lindzey. STUDY OF VALUES: MANUAL OF DIRECTIONS. Boston: Houghton Mifflin, 1951.

Alper, T. G. "Task-Orientation vs Ego-Orientation in Learning and Retention," *American Journal of Psychology,* 59 (1946), 236–48.

Alt, H. RESIDENTIAL TREATMENT FOR THE DISTURBED CHILD. New York: International Universities Press, 1960.

Altman, A. and H. Baumann. "Finding Jobs for the Blind," *Employment Sec. Review,* 22 (1955) 9–12.

American Institute for Research. "Situational Tests for Evaluating Supervisory Skills," *AIR Research Notes,* Number 14, 1957.

American Medical Association. STANDARD NOMENCLATURE OF DISEASES AND OPERATIONS. New York: McGraw-Hill, 1961.

American Psychiatric Association. DIAGNOSTIC AND STATISTICAL MANUAL, MENTAL DISORDERS. Washington, 1952.

American Public Health Association. MENTAL DISORDERS: A GUIDE TO CONTROL METHODS, by Program Area Committee on Mental Health, Ernest M. Gruenberg, Chairman. 1962.

Ames, A. "Binocular Vision as Affected by Relations Between Uniocular Stimulus-Patterns in Commonplace Environments," *American Journal of Psychology,* 59 (1946), 333–57.

———. "Visual Perception and the Rotating Trapezoidal Window," *Psychological Monographs,* Number 324, 1951.

Ames, L. B. "The Development of the Sense of Time in the Young Child," *Journal of Genetic Psychology,* 68 (1946), 97–125.

——— and J. Learned. "Imaginary Companions and Related Phenomena," *Journal of Genetic Psychology,* 69 (1946), 147–67.

Ammons, R. B. "Reactions in a Projective Doll-Play Interview of White Males Two to Six Years of Age to Differences in Skin Color and Facial Features," *Journal of Genetic Psychology,* 76 (1950), 323–41.

Amoore, J. E., J. W. Johnston, Jr., and M. Rubin. "The Stereochemical Theory of Odor," *Scientific American,* 210 (1964), 42–49.

Anand, B. K. and J. R. Brobeck. "Hypothalamic Control of Food Intake in Rats and Cats," *Yale Journal of Biological Medicine,* 24 (1951), 123–40.

Anastasi, A. DIFFERENTIAL PSYCHOLOGY. New York: Macmillan, 1958.

———. PSYCHOLOGICAL TESTING. New York: Macmillan, 1961, 1968.

———. FIELDS OF APPLIED PSYCHOLOGY. New York: McGraw-Hill, 1964.

——— and R. F. Levee. "Intellectual Defect and Musical Talent: A Case Report," *American Journal of Mental Deficiency,* 64 (1960), 695–703.

Anastasi, A., N. Cohen and D. Spatz. "A Study of Fear and Anger in College Students Through the Controlled Diary Method," *Journal of Genetic Psychology,* 73 (1948), 243–49.

Anders, P. "Über den individuellen Eigenrhythmus beim menschlichen Gang und seine Beziehungen zum Rhythmus der Herz- und Atemtätigkeit," *Pflüg. Arch.,* 220 (1928), 287–99.

Anderson, H. H. "Test of a Model for Opinion Change," *Journal of Abnormal and Social Psychology,* 59 (1959), 371–81.

——— and G. L. Anderson (eds.). AN INTRODUCTION TO PROJECTIVE TECHNIQUES. Englewood Cliffs, New Jersey: Prentice-Hall, 1951.

Andersson, B. "The Effect of Injections of Hypertonic NaCl Solution into Different Parts of the Hypothalamus of Goats," *Acta Physiologia Scandinavia,* 28 (1953), 188–201.

———. P. A. Jewell and S. Larsson. "An Appraisal of the Effects of Diencephalic Stimulation of Conscious Animals in Terms of Normal Behavior," NEUROLOGICAL BASIS OF BEHAVIOR, G. E. Wolstenholme and V. M. O'Connor (eds.). London: Churchill, 1958. 76–89.

Angers, W. P. "Psychotherapy with the Epileptic," TOTAL REHABILITATION OF EPILEPTICS, G. N. Wright et al. (eds.). Washington, D.C.: United States Department of Health, Education and Welfare, January 1962.

Arbitman, H. D. "The Present Status of Glutamic Acid Therapy for Mental Deficiency," *Training School Bulletin,* 48 (1952), 187–99.

Ardrey, R. THE TERRITORIAL IMPERATIVE: A PERSONAL INQUIRY INTO THE ANIMAL ORIGINS OF PROPERTY AND NATIONS. New York: Atheneum, 1966.

Arieti, S. "Manic-Depressive Psychosis," AMERICAN HANDBOOK OF PSYCHIATRY, S. Arieti (ed.). New York: Basic Books, 1959. Volume 1, Chapter 2.

——. "Schizophrenia," AMERICAN HANDBOOK OF PSYCHIATRY, S. Arieti (ed.). New York: Basic Books, 1959. Volume 1, Chapter 24.

——. "A Re-Examination of the Phobic Symptoms and of Symbolism in Psychopathology," *American Journal of Psychiatry*, 118 (1961), 106–10.

—— and J. M. Meth. "Rare, Unclassifiable, Collective and Exotic Psychotic Syndromes," AMERICAN HANDBOOK OF PSYCHIATRY, S. Arieti (ed.). New York: Basic Books, 1959. Volume 1, Chapter 27.

Arnheim, R. "Experimentelle-psychologische Untersuchungen zum Ausdrucksproblem," *Psychologie Forschung*, 11 (1928), 1–132.

——. PICASSO'S GUERNICA: THE GENESIS OF A PAINTING. Berkeley: University of California Press, 1962.

Arnold, G. E. "Analysis and Management of Voice Disorders," VOICE DISORDERS. New York: National Hospital for Speech Disorders, 1957.

——. "Studies in Tachyphemia: III. Signs and Symptoms," *Logos*, 3 (1960), 82–95.

Arnold, M. EMOTION AND PERSONALITY. New York: Columbia University Press, 1960.

Aronson, E. and J. Mills. "The Effects of Severity of Initiation on Liking for a Group," *Journal of Abnormal and Social Psychology*, 59 (1959), 177–81.

Asch, S. E. "Effects of Group Pressure upon the Modification and Distortion of Judgments," GROUPS, LEADERSHIP AND MEN, H. Guetzkow (ed.). Pittsburgh: Carnegie Press, 1951. 177–90.

——. H. Block and M. Hertzman. "Studies in the Principles of Judgments and Attitudes. II. Determination of Judgments by Group and by Ego Standards," *Journal of Social Psychology*, 12 (1940), 433–65.

Aserinsky, E. and N. Kleitman. "Regularly Occurring Periods of Eye Motility and Concomitant Phenomena During Sleep," *Science*, 118 (1953), 273.

——. "A Motility Cycle in Sleeping Infants as Manifested by Ocular and Gross Bodily Activity," *Journal of Applied Physiology*, 8 (1955), 11–18.

Ashby, W. A. DESIGN FOR A BRAIN. New York: Wiley, 1952.

Astin, A. W. and S. Ross. "Glutamic Acid and Human Intelligence," *Psychological Bulletin*, 57 (1960), 429–34.

Atkinson, J. W. AN INTRODUCTION TO MOTIVATION. Princeton, New Jersey: Van Nostrand, 1964.

Atkinson, R. C. and D. N. Hansen. "Computer-Assisted Instruction in Initial Reading: The Stanford Project," *Reading Research Quarterly*, 2 (1966), 5–25.

Ausubel, D. P. "Relationship Between Shame and Guilt in the Socialization Process," *Psychological Review*, 62 (1955), 378–79.

Axline, V. M. PLAY THERAPY. Boston: Houghton Mifflin, 1947.

Ayllon, T. and E. Haughton. "Control of the Behavior of Schizophrenic Patients by Food," *Journal of the Experimental Analysis of Behavior*, 5 (1962), 343–52.

Azima, H., R. Vispot and F. J. Azima. "Observations on Anaclitic Therapy During Sensory Deprivation," Sensory Deprivation, Solomon et al. (eds.). Cambridge: Harvard University Press, 1961.

Baber, R. E. MARRIAGE AND THE FAMILY. New York: McGraw-Hill, 1953.

Babich, F. R., A. L. Jacobson, S. Bubash and A. Jacobson. "Transfer of a Response to Naive Rats by Injection of Ribonucleic Acid Extracted from Trained Rats," *Science*, 149 (1965), 656–57.

Babinski, J. "My Conception of Hysteria and Hypnotism (Pithiatism)," *Alienist and Neurologist*, 1 (1908), 1–29.

Bachrach, A. J., W. J. Erwin and J. P. Mohr. "The Control of Eating Behavior in Anorexia by Operant Conditioning Techniques," in CASE STUDIES IN BEHAVIOR MODIFICATION, L. P. Ullman and L. Krasner (eds.), New York: Holt, Rinehart and Winston, 1965, 153–63.

Baetjer, A. M. "Light, Temperature, Humidity," *Industrial Medicine*, 13 (1944), 111–12.

Bagby, E. THE PSYCHOLOGY OF PERSONALITY. New York: Holt, 1928.

Bahn, A. K., V. B. Norman, C. L. McCarty and M. A. Rippy. "Gains in Out-Patient Psychiatric Clinic Services, 1961," *Mental Hygiene*, 47 (1963), 177–88.

Bailey, P. and E. W. Davis. "The Syndrome of Obstinate Progress in the Cat," *Proceedings of the Society for Experimental Biology*, 51 (1942), 307.

Bakwin, H. "Loneliness in Infants," *American Journal of Diseases of Children*, 63 (1942), 30–40.

——. "Emotional Deprivation in Infants," *Journal of Pediatrics*, 35 (1949), 512–21.

Bales, R. F. "How People Interact in Conferences," *Scientific American*, 192 (1955), 31–35.

———. "Task Roles and Social Roles in Problem-Solving Groups," READINGS IN SOCIAL PSYCHOLOGY, E. Maccoby, T. M. Newcomb and and E. L. Hartley (eds.). New York: Holt, Rinehart & Winston, 1958.

Balint, M. "Individual Differences of Behavior in Early Infancy, and an Objective Method of Recording Them," *Journal of Genetic Psychology,* 73 (1948), 57–117.

Balken, E. and J. H. Masserman. "The Language of Fantasy: III. The Language of the Fantasies of Patients with Convulsion Hysteria, Anxiety State, and Obsessive-Compulsive Neuroses," *Journal of Psychology,* 10 (1940), 75–86.

Banay, R. S. "Criminal Genesis and the Degrees of Responsibility in Epilepsies," *American Journal of Psychiatry,* 117 (1961), 875–76.

Bandura, A., D. Ross and S. A. Ross. "Imitation of Film-Mediated Aggressive Models," *Journal of Abnormal and Social Psychology,* 66 (1963), 3–11.

Barbara, D. A. "Stuttering," AMERICAN HANDBOOK OF PSYCHIATRY, S. Arieti (ed.). New York: Basic Books, 1959. Volume 1, Chapter 47.

Barbero, G. J., M. G. Morris and M. T. Reford. "Malidentification of Mother-Baby-Father Relationships Expressed in Infant Failure to Thrive," in pamphlet, "The Neglected-Battered Child Syndrome," Child Welfare League of America, July 1963, 18–22.

Bard, P. "A Diencephalic Mechanism for the Expression of Rage with Special Reference to the Sympathetic Nervous System," *American Journal of Physiology,* 84 (1928), 490–515.

——— and V. B. Mountcastle. "Some Forebrain Mechanisms Involved in the Expression of Rage with Special Reference to Suppression of Angry Behavior," *Research Publications of the Association for Research on Nervous and Mental Diseases,* 27 (1947), 362–404.

Barker, G. H. and W. R. Adams. "Comparison of the Delinquencies of Boys and Girls," *Journal of Criminal Law,* 53 (1962), 470–75.

Barker, R. G. and B. A. Wright. "Disablement: The Somatopsychological Problems," RECENT DEVELOPMENTS IN PSYCHOSOMATIC MEDICINE, E. Wittkower and R. Cleghorn (eds.). Philadelphia: Lippincott, 1954. 419–35.

Barker, R. G., T. Dembo and K. Lewin. "Frustration and Regression: An Experiment with Young Children," *University of Iowa Studies in Child Welfare,* 18, Number 1, (1941), 1–314.

Barker, R. G. et al. "Adjustment to Physical Handicap and Illness: A Survey of The Social Psychology of Physique and Disability," *Social Science Research Council Bulletin,* Number 55, 1953.

Barlow, F. MENTAL PRODIGIES. New York: Philosophical Library, 1952.

Barnes, R. M. MOTION AND TIME STUDY. New York: Wiley, 1963.

Barron, F. "Genius," THE ENCYCLOPEDIA OF MENTAL HEALTH, A. Deutsch (ed.). New York: Franklin Watts, 1963.

——— and G. S. Welsh. "Artistic Perception as a Possible Factor in Personality Style: Its Measurement by a Figure Preference Test," *Journal of Psychology,* 33 (1952), 199–203.

Bartlett, F. C. REMEMBERING: AN EXPERIMENTAL AND SOCIAL STUDY. London: Cambridge University Press, 1932.

Barton, Russell. INSTITUTIONAL NEUROSIS. Bristol: John Wright & Sons, 1959.

Bash, K. W. "Contribution to a Theory of the Hunger Drive," *Journal of Comparative Psychology,* 28 (1939), 137–60.

Bateson, G. "Minimal Requirements for a Theory of Schizophrenia," *Archives of General Psychiatry,* 2 (1960), 477–91.

Bayer, E. "Beiträge zur Zweikomponenten-theorie des Hungers," *Zeitschrift für Psychologie,* 112 (1929), 1–54.

Bayley, N. "Mental Growth During the First Three Years," *Genetic Psychological Monographs,* 14 (1933), 1–92.

———. "Consistency and Variability in the Growth of Intelligence from Birth to Eighteen," *Journal of Genetic Psychology,* 75 (1949), 165–96.

Bayton, J. A., L. B. McAlister and J. Hammer. "Race-Class Stereotypes," *Journal of Negro Education,* Winter 1956, 75–78.

Beach, F. A. "Characteristics of Masculine Sex Drive," NEBRASKA SYMPOSIUM ON MOTIVATION, M. R. Jones (ed.). Lincoln, Nebraska: University of Nebraska Press, 1956. 1–32.

Beck, L. H. and W. R. Miles. "Some Theoretical and Experimental Relationships Between Infra-Red Absorption and Olfaction," *Science,* November 28, 1947, 511.

Becker, S. W. and J. Carroll. "Ordinal Position and Conformity," *Journal of Abnormal and Social Psychology,* 65 (1962), 129–31.

Beckett, P. G. S., C. E. Frohman, R. Senf, G. Tourney and J. S. Gottlieb. "Energy Transfer Systems and the Clinical Manifestations of Schizophrenia," SCIENTIFIC PAPERS AND DISCUSSIONS, J. S. Gottlieb and G. Tourney (eds.). Washington, D.C.: American Psychiatric Association, District Branches Publication Number 1 (1960). 278–96.

———. R. Senf. C. E. Frohman and J. S. Gottlieb. "Energy Production and Premorbid History in Schizophrenia," *American Medical Association Archives of General Psychiatry*, 8 (1963), 155–62.

Beecher, H. K. "The Powerful Placebo," *Journal of the American Medical Association*, 159 (1955), 1602.

Beers, C. W. A MIND THAT FOUND ITSELF. New York: Longmans, 1908.

Békésy, G. V. EXPERIMENTS IN HEARING. New York: McGraw-Hill, 1960.

Bekhterev, V. M. GENERAL PRINCIPLES OF HUMAN REFLEXOLOGY. New York: International, 1932.

Bell, C. ESSAYS ON THE ANATOMY OF EXPRESSION IN PAINTING. London: Longmans, Green, 1806, 1844.

Bellak, L. "A Study of Limitations and 'Failures': Toward an Ego Psychology of Projective Techniques," *Journal of Projective Techniques*, 18 (1954), 279–93.

Bellows, R. T. "Time Factors in Water Drinking in Dogs," *American Journal of Physiology*, 125 (1939), 87–97.

Belson, W. and J. A. Duncan. "A Comparison of the Check-List and Open Response Question System," *Applied Statistics*, 2 (Number 2, June 1962), 120–32.

Ben-Avi, Avrum. "Zen Buddhism," AMERICAN HANDBOOK OF PSYCHIATRY, S. Arieti (ed.). New York: Basic Books, 1959. Volume 2, Chapter 90B.

Bender, L. "Childhood Schizophrenia: Clinical Study of 100 Schizophrenic Children," *American Journal of Orthopsychiatry*, 17 (1947), 40–56.

———. "Childhood Schizophrenia," *Psychiatric Quarterly*, 27 (1953), 663–81.

———. "Twenty Years of Clinical Research on Schizophrenic Children, with Special Reference to Those Under 6 Years of Age," EMOTIONAL PROBLEMS OF EARLY CHILDHOOD, G. Caplan (ed.). New York: Basic Books, 1955. 503–15.

———. "The Brain and Child Behavior," *Archives of General Psychiatry*, 4 (1961), 531.

——— and S. Paster. "Homosexual Trends in Children," *American Journal of Orthopsychiatry*, 11 (1941), 730–44.

Bender, L. and F. Vogel. "Imaginary Companions of Children," *American Journal of Orthopsychiatry*, 11 (1941), 56–66.

Benedek, T. F. "Sexual Functions in Women and their Disturbance," AMERICAN HANDBOOK OF PSYCHIATRY, S. Arieti (ed.). New York: Basic Books, 1959. Volume 1, Chapter 37.

Benedict, R. PATTERNS OF CULTURE. Boston: Houghton-Mifflin, 1934.

Benedict, P. K. and I. Jacks. "Mental Illness in Primitive Societies," *Psychiatry*, 17 (1954), 377–89.

Benoit-Smullyan, E. "Status, Status-Types and Status Interrelations," *American Sociological Review*, 9 (1944), 151–61.

Berdie, R., P. Dressel and P. Kelso. "Relative Validity of the Q and L Scores of the ACE Psychological Examinations," *Educational and Psychological Measurement*, 11 (1951), 803–12.

Berelson, B. and G. A. Steiner. HUMAN BEHAVIOR: AN INVENTORY OF SCIENTIFIC FINDINGS. New York: Harcourt, Brace, 1964.

Beres, D. and S. J. Obers. "The Effects of Extreme Deprivation in Infancy on Psychic Structure in Adolescence: A Study in Ego Development," THE PSYCHOANALYTIC STUDY OF THE CHILD, *Eissler* et al. (eds.). New York: International University Press, 1950. 212–35.

Berg, I. A. "Development of Behavior: The Micturition Pattern in Dogs," *Journal of Experimental Psychology*, 34 (1944), 343–68.

Berger, F. M. "Classification of Psychoactive Drugs According to their Chemical Structures and Sites of Action," DRUGS AND BEHAVIOR, L. Uhr and J. G. Miller (eds.). New York: Wiley-Interscience, 1960.

Berkowitz, L. "Group Standards, Cohesiveness and Productivity," *Human Relations*, 7 (1954), 509–19.

Berlyne, D. E. "The Influence of Complexity and Novelty in Visual Figures on Orienting Responses," *Journal of Experimental Psychology*, 55 (1958), 289–96.

———. CONFLICT, AROUSAL AND CURIOSITY. New York: McGraw-Hill, 1960.

———. "Measures of Aesthetic Preference," *Sciences de l'Art*, 1966.

Berne, E. "Transactional Analysis: A New and Effective Method of Group Therapy," *American Journal of Psychotherapy*, 12 (1958), 735–43.

———. GAMES PEOPLE PLAY. New York: Grove, 1964.

Bernstein, A. "The Psychoanalytic Technique," HANDBOOK OF CLINICAL PSYCHOLOGY, B. B. Wolman (ed.). New York: McGraw-Hill, 1965. Chapter 41.

Berry, M. F. and J. Eisenson. SPEECH DISORDERS: PRINCIPLES AND PRACTICES OF THERAPY. New York: Appleton-Century-Crofts, 1956.

Bettelheim, B. "Individual and Mass Behavior in Extreme Situations," *Journal of Abnormal and Social Psychology,* 38 (1943), 417–52.

———— and M. Janowitz. DYNAMICS OF PREJUDICE: A PSYCHOLOGICAL AND SOCIOLOGICAL STUDY OF VETERANS. New York: Harper & Row, 1950.

Bevan, W. and M. A. Grotsky. "Hoarding in Hamsters with Systematically Controlled Pretest Experience," *Journal of Comparative Psychology,* 51 (1958), 342–45.

Bieber, I. et al. HOMOSEXUALITY: A PSYCHOANALYTIC STUDY. New York: Basic Books, 1962.

Billings, M. L. "The Duration of Attention," *Psychological Review,* 21 (1914), 121–35.

Bills, A. G. THE PSYCHOLOGY OF EFFICIENCY. New York: Harper & Bros., 1943.

Bindra, D. "Hoarding Behavior of Rats: Nutritional and Psychological Factors." Unpublished Ph.D. thesis, Harvard University, 1947.

Binneweis, W. G. "A Method of Studying Rural Social Distance," *Journal of Applied Sociology,* 10 (1925-26), 239–42.

Binswanger, H. "Klinische und charakterologische Untersuchungen an pathologisch Berauschten." *Z. f. ges. Neurol. Psychiat.,* 152 (1935), 703–37.

Birch, H. G. "Sources of Order in the Maternal Behavior of Animals," *American Journal of Orthopsychiatry,* 26 (1956), 279–84.

Birren, F. COLOR PSYCHOLOGY AND COLOR THERAPY. New Hyde Park, New York: University Books, 1961.

Bisch, L. E. CLINICAL PSYCHOLOGY. Baltimore, Maryland: Williams & Wilkins, 1925.

Black, B. J. "The Protected Workshop," REHABILITATION OF THE MENTALLY ILL. Washington: American Association for the Advancement of Science, 1959.

Blackwell, H. R. "Development and Use of a Quantitative Method for Specification of Interior Illumination Levels," *Illuminating Engineering,* 54, Number 6 (June 1959), 317–53.

Bleuler, E. TEXTBOOK OF PSYCHIATRY. Trans. by A. A. Brill, New York: Macmillan, 1930.

————. DEMENTIA PRAECOX, OR THE GROUP OF SCHIZOPHRENIAS. New York: International Universities Press, 1950. Original, 1911.

Block, J., V. Patterson, J. Block and D. D. Jackson. "A Study of the Parents of Schizophrenic and Neurotic Children," *Psychiatry,* 21 (1958), 387–97.

Bloom, W. "Shift Work and the Sleep-Wakefulness Cycle," *Personnel,* 38 (1961), 24–31.

Bogardus, E. S. "Measuring Social Distance," *Journal of Applied Sociology,* 9 (1925), 299–308.

————. FUNDAMENTALS OF SOCIAL PSYCHOLOGY. New York: D. Appleton-Century, 1942.

Boll, E. S. "The Role of Pre-School Playmates: A Situational Approach," *Child Development,* 28 (1957), 327–42.

Bonney, M. E. "Relationships Between Social Success, Family Size, Socio-Economic Home Background, and Intelligence Among School Children in Grades III and IV," *Sociometry,* 7 (1944), 26–39.

———— and E. L. Nicholson. "Comparative School Adjustments of Elementary School Pupils with and without Preschool Training," *Child Development,* 29 (1958), 125–33.

Boring, E. G. A HISTORY OF EXPERIMENTAL PSYCHOLOGY. New York: Appleton-Century-Crofts, 1929, 1950.

———— and E. B. Titchener. "A Model for the Demonstration of Facial Expression," *American Journal of Psychology,* 34 (1923), 471–86.

Borstelmann, L. J. and W. G. Klopfer. "The Szondi Test: A Review and Critical Evaluation," *Psychological Bulletin,* 50 (1953), 112–32.

Bossard, J. H. S. and E. S. Boll. THE SOCIOLOGY OF CHILD DEVELOPMENT. New York: Harper & Row, 1960.

Bousfield, W. A. and H. Barry. "The Visual Imagery of a Lightning Calculator," *American Journal of Psychology,* 45 (1933), 353–58.

Bowlby, J. "Maternal Care and Mental Health," *WHO Monograph Series Number 2.* Geneva: World Health Organization, 1951.

Bowman, H. A., quoted in C. R. Adams, PREPARING FOR MARRIAGE: A GUIDE TO MARITAL AND SEXUAL ADJUSTMENT. New York: Dutton, 1951.

Braceland, F. J. "Rehabilitation," AMERICAN HANDBOOK OF PSYCHIATRY, S. Arieti (ed.). New York: Basic Books, 1966. Volume 3, Chapter 40.

Brady, J. V. and W. J. Nauta. "Subcortical Mechanisms in Emotional Behavior: Affective Changes Following Septal Forebrain Lesions in the Albino Rat," *Journal of Comparative and Physiological Psychology,* 46 (1953), 339–46.

————. "Ulcers in 'Executive Monkeys,'" *Scientific American,* 199 (4) (1958), 95–98, 100.

Brady, M. E. "The Strange Case of Wilhelm Reich," *New Republic,* May 26, 1947, 20–23.

Brain, W. R. DISEASES OF THE NERVOUS SYSTEM. New York: Oxford University Press, 1951.

Brehm, J. and A. Cohen. EXPLORATIONS IN COGNITIVE DISSONANCE. New York: Wiley, 1962.

Brenman, M. and M. M. Gill. HYPNOTHERAPY. New York: Wiley, 1947.

Breuer, J. and S. Freud, STUDIES IN HYSTERIA. New York: Basic Books, 1957. Original, 1895.

Bridges, K. M. B. "Emotional Development in Early Infancy," *Child Development*, 3 (1932), 324–41.

Brim, O. G., Jr. "American Attitudes Toward Intelligence Tests," *American Psychologist*, 20, (1965), 125–30.

Broadbent, D. E. PERCEPTION AND COMMUNICATION. New York: Pergamon Press, 1958.

——— and E. A. J. Little. "Effects of Noise Reduction in a Work Situation," *Occupational Psychology*, 34 (1960), 133–40.

Brobeck, J. R. "Neural Control of Hunger, Appetite and Satiety," *Yale Journal of Biological Medicine*, 29 (1957), 565–74.

Brody, L. "Accidents and 'Attitudes,' " THE PSYCHOLOGY OF SAFETY. New York: Center for Safety Education, Division of General Education, New York University, 1959.

Bromberg, W. THE MIND OF MAN: THE STORY OF MAN'S CONQUEST OF MENTAL ILLNESS. New York: Harper & Bros., 1937, 1959.

Broussard, I. G. et al. "The Influence of Noise on the Visual Contrast Threshold," *Army Medical Research Laboratory Report*, 101 (November 6, 1953).

Brown, G. L. "On the Constancy of the I.Q.," *Journal of Educational Research*, 44 (1950), 151–53.

Brown, J. F. "Genius," THE ENCYCLOPEDIA OF PSYCHOLOGY, P. L. Harriman (ed.). New York: Philosophical Library, 1946.

———. "A Modification of the Rosenzweig Picture-Frustration Test to Study Hostile Interracial Attitudes," *Journal of Psychology*, 24 (1947), 247–72.

Brown, R. SOCIAL PSYCHOLOGY. New York: The Free Press, 1965.

——— and D. C. Hildum. "Expectancy and the Identification of Syllables," *Language*, 32 (1956), 411–19.

Brown, R. L. "Wrapper Influence on the Perception of Freshness in Bread," *Journal of Applied Psychology*, 42 (1958), 257–60.

Brown, R. W. "Mass Phenomena," HANDBOOK OF SOCIAL PSYCHOLOGY, G. Lindzey (ed.). Cambridge, Massachusetts: Addison-Wesley, 1954. Volume II, Chapter 23.

——— and E. H. Lenneberg. "A Study in Language and Cognition," *Journal of Abnormal and Social Psychology*, 49 (1954), 454–62.

Brown, R. W. and D. McNeill. "The 'Tip-of-the-Tongue' Phenomenon," *Journal of Verbal Learning and Verbal Behavior*, 5 (1966), 325–37.

Brown, R. W., R. A. Leiter and D. C. Hildum. "Metaphors from Music Criticism," *Journal of Abnormal and Social Psychology*, 54 (1957), 347–52.

Bruch, H. "Psychological Aspects of Obesity in Adolescence," *American Journal of Public Health*, 48 (1958), 1349–53.

Bruck, C. EXPERIMENTELLE TELEPATHIE. Berlin, 1923.

Brugmans, H. I. F. W. "Une Communication sur des Expériences Télépathiques au Laboratoire de Psychologie à Groninque Faites par M. Heymans, Docteur Weinberg et Docteur H. I. F. W. Brugmans," Compte Rendu du Premier Congrès International des Recherches Psychiques, Copenhagen, 1922, 396–408.

Bruhn, J. G. "Broken Homes Among Attempted Suicides and Psychiatric Out-Patients: A Comparative Study," *Journal of Mental Science*, 108 (1962), 772–79.

Bruner, J. S. and C. Goodman. "Value and Need as Organizing Factors in Perception," *Journal of Abnormal and Social Psychology*, 42 (1947), 33–44.

Bruner, J. S., L. J. Postman and J. Rodrigues. "Expectation and the Perception of Color," *American Journal of Psychology*, 64 (1951), 216–27.

Buchanan, W. "Stereotypes and Tensions as Revealed by the UNESCO International Poll," *International Social Science Journal*, 3 (1951), 515–28.

Buck, J. N. "The H-T-P Test," *Journal of Clinical Psychology*, 4 (1948), 151–58.

Burchard, E. M. L. "Physique and Psychosis: An Analysis of the Postulated Relationship Between Bodily Constitution and Mental Disease Syndrome," *Comparative Psychology Monographs*, 13 (1936), Number 1.

Burgess, E. W. and L. S. Cottrell. PREDICTING SUCCESS OR FAILURE IN MARRIAGE. New York: Prentice-Hall, 1939.

Burgess, E. W. and P. Wallin. "Predicting Adjustment in Marriage from Adjustment in Engagement," *American Journal of Sociology*, 49 (1944), 324–30.

Burns, B. D. "Some Properties of Isolated Cerebral Cortex in the Unanesthetized Cat," *Journal of Physiology*, 112 (1951), 156–75.

Buros, O. K. (ed.). THE FOURTH MENTAL MEASUREMENTS YEARBOOK. Highland Park, New York: Gryphon Press, 1953.

Burt, C. "The General Aesthetic Factor. III," *British Journal of Psychology, Statistics Section,* 13 (1960), 90–92.

Burtt, H. E. "An Experimental Study of Early Childhood Memory," *Journal of Genetic Psychology,* 58 (1941), 435–39.

Buswell, G. T. HOW PEOPLE LOOK AT PICTURES. Chicago: University of Chicago Press, 1935.

Butler, R. A. "Discrimination Learning by Rhesus Monkeys to Visual-Exploration Motivation," *Journal of Comparative and Physiological Psychology,* 46 (1953), 95–98.

———. "Discrimination Learning by Rhesus Monkeys to Auditory Incentives," *Journal of Comparative and Physiological Psychology,* 50 (1957), 239–41.

——— and H. M. Alexander. "Daily Patterns of Visual Exploratory Behavior in the Monkey," *Journal of Comparative and Physiological Psychology,* 48 (1955), 247–49.

Buzby, D. E. "The Interpretation of Facial Expressions," *American Journal of Psychology,* 35 (1924), 602–4.

Byrne, D. "The Effect of a Subliminal Food Stimulus on Verbal Responses," *Journal of Applied Psychology,* 43 (1959), 249–52.

Cabeen, C. W. and J. C. Coleman. "The Selection of Sex-Offender Patients for Group Psychotherapy," *International Journal of Group Psychotherapy,* 12 (1962), 326–34.

Caldwell, B. M. "Is the Critical Period Hypothesis Useful?" *American Psychologist,* 16 (1961), 377.

Calvin, A. D. and K. S. Dollemayer. "Subliminal Perception: Some Negative Findings," *Journal of Applied Psychology,* 43 (1959), 187–88.

Cameron, N. "Reasoning, Regression and Communication in Schizophrenia," *Psychological Monographs,* 50 (1938), 1–34.

———. THE PSYCHOLOGY OF BEHAVIOR DISORDERS. Boston: Houghton Mifflin, 1947.

——— and A. Magaret. BEHAVIOR PATHOLOGY. Boston: Houghton Mifflin, 1951.

Campbell, A. A. "Personality Adjustment of Only and Intermediate Children," *Journal of Genetic Psychology,* 43 (1933), 197–205.

Campbell, D. G. "General Semantics: Implications of Linguistic Revision for Theoretical and Clinical Neuro-Psychiatry," *American Journal of Psychiatry,* 93 (1937), 789–807.

Campbell, D. T. "The Indirect Assessment of Social Attitudes," *Psychological Bulletin,* 47 (1950), 15–38.

Canfield, A. A., A. L. Comrey and R. C. Wilson. "A Study of Reaction Time to Light and Sound as Related to Increased Positive Radial Acceleration," *Journal of Aviation Medicine,* 20 (1949), 350–55.

Cannicott, S. M. "Technique of Unilateral Electro-Convulsive Therapy," *American Journal of Psychiatry,* 120 (1963), 477–80.

Cannon, W. B. "The Physiological Basis of Thirst," *Proceedings of The Royal Society,* London, B. 90 (1918), 283–301.

———. "The James-Lange Theory of Emotions: A Critical Examination and an Alternative Theory," *American Journal of Psychology,* 39 (1927), 106–24.

———. THE WISDOM OF THE BODY. New York: Norton, 1932.

——— and A. L. Washburn. "An Explanation of Hunger," *American Journal of Physiology,* 29 (1912), 441–54.

Cantril, H. THE INVASION FROM MARS. Princeton: Princeton University Press, 1940.

Carlson, L. D. "Gas Exchange and Transportation," MEDICAL PHYSIOLOGY AND BIOPHYSICS, T. C. Ruch and J. F. Fulton (eds.). Philadelphia: Saunders, 1960.

Carothers, J. C. THE AFRICAN MIND IN HEALTH AND DISEASE: A STUDY IN ETHNOPSYCHIATRY. Geneva: World Health Organization, 1953. Number 17.

Carp, B. A STUDY OF THE INFLUENCE OF CERTAIN PERSONAL FACTORS ON A SPEECH JUDGMENT. New Rochelle, New York: The Little Print, 1945.

Carroll, J. B. LANGUAGE AND THOUGHT. Englewood Cliffs, New Jersey: Prentice-Hall, 1964.

Carterette, E. C. and M. Cole. "Comparison of the Receiver-Operating Characteristics for Messages Received by Ear and by Eye," *Journal of the Acoustical Society of America,* 34 (1962), 172–78.

Cason, H. "Common Annoyances: A Psychological Study of Everyday Aversions and Irritations," *Psychological Monographs,* Number 182, 1930.

Cattell, J. McK. "Ueber die Zeit der Erkennung und Benennung von Schriftzeichen, Bildern und Farben," *Philos. Studien,* 2 (1885), 13–25.

Cattell, P. THE MEASUREMENT OF INTELLIGENCE OF INFANTS AND YOUNG CHILDREN. New York: Psychological Corporation, 1947.

Cattell, R. B. DESCRIPTION AND MEASUREMENT OF PERSONALITY. Yonkers, New York: World, 1946.

Cavanaugh, M. C. et al. "Predictions from the Cattell Infant Intelligence Scale," *Journal of Consulting Psychology,* 21 (1957), 33–37.

Chadbourne, J. H. LYNCHING AND THE LAW. Chapel Hill, North Carolina: University of North Carolina Press, 1933.

Chapanis, A., W. R. Garner and C. T. Morgan. APPLIED EXPERIMENTAL PSYCHOLOGY: HUMAN FACTORS IN ENGINEERING DESIGN. New York: Wiley, 1949.

Cherry, E. C. "Some Experiments on the Recognition of Speech, with One and with Two Ears," *Journal of the Acoustical Society of America,* 25 (1953), 975–79.

Child, I. L. "Personal Preferences as an Expression of Aesthetic Sensitivity," *Journal of Personality,* 30 (1962), 496–512.

————. "Personality Correlates of Esthetic Judgment in College Students," *Journal of Personality,* 33 (1965), 476–511.

————. "Esthetics," draft of a chapter for the Revised Edition of HANDBOOK OF SOCIAL PSYCHOLOGY, G. Lindzey and E. Aronson (eds.). Reading, Massachusetts: Addison-Wesley.

———— and L. Siroto. "Bakwele and American Esthetic Evaluations Compared," *Ethnology,* 4 (1965), 349–60.

Chocholle, R. "Variation des Temps de Réaction Auditifs en Fonction de l'Intensité à Diverses Fréquences," *Année Psychologie,* 41–42 (1945), 65–124.

Church, R. M. "Effects of a Competitive Situation on the Speed of Response," *Journal of Comparative and Physiological Psychology,* 54 (1961), 162–66.

Clark, R. A. "The Projective Measurement of Experimentally Induced Levels of Sexual Motivation," *Journal of Experimental Psychology,* 44 (1952), 391–99.

Clarke, J. "The Precipitation of Juvenile Delinquency," *Journal of Mental Science,* 107 (1961), 1033–34.

Cleckley, H. M. "Psychopathic States," AMERICAN HANDBOOK OF PSYCHIATRY, S. Arieti (ed.). New York: Basic Books, 1959. Volume 1, Chapter 28.

Clements, S. D. "Minimal Brain Dysfunction in Children," National Institute of Neurological Diseases and Blindness, Monograph Number 3, U. S. Dept. of Health, Education and Welfare, 1966.

Cobb, B. "Cancer," PSYCHOLOGICAL PRACTICES WITH THE PHYSICALLY DISABLED, J. F. Garrett and E. S. Levine (eds.). New York: Columbia University Press, 1962. 231–60.

Coch, L. and J. R. P. French, Jr. "Overcoming Resistance to Change," *Human Relations,* 1 (1948), 512–32.

Cofer, C. N. "Verbal Behavior in Relation to Reasoning and Values," GROUPS, LEADERSHIP AND MEN, H. Guetzkow (ed.). Pittsburgh: Carnegie Press, 1951. 206–17.

———— and M. H. Appley. MOTIVATION: THEORY AND RESEARCH. New York: Wiley, 1965.

Coffin, T. E., J. B. Landis and M. W. Baiman. STRANGERS INTO CUSTOMERS. New York: National Broadcasting Company, 1955.

Coleman, J. C. PERSONALITY DYNAMICS AND EFFECTIVE BEHAVIOR. Fair Lawn, New Jersey: Scott, Foresman, 1960.

————. THE ADOLESCENT SOCIETY. New York: The Free Press, 1961.

————. ABNORMAL PSYCHOLOGY AND MODERN LIFE. Fair Lawn, New Jersey: Scott, Foresman, 1964.

Coleman, L. L. "Children Need Preparation for Tonsillectomy," *Child Study,* Spring 1952, 18.

Committee on Child Psychiatry. PSYCHO-PATHOLOGICAL DISORDERS IN CHILDHOOD: THEORETICAL CONSIDERATIONS AND A PROPOSED CLASSIFICATION. New York: Group for the Advancement of Psychiatry, 1966.

Conn, J. H. "Psychogenesis and Psychotherapy of Insomnia," *Journal of Clinical Psychopathology,* 11 (1950), 85–91.

Cooke, D. THE LANGUAGE OF MUSIC. New York: Oxford University Press, 1959.

Cooper, L. F. and D. W. Rodgin. "Time Distortion in Hypnosis and Nonmotor Learning," *Science,* 115 (1952), 500–2.

Cooper, M. PICA. Springfield, Illinois: Charles C. Thomas, 1957.

Coriat, I. H. "Stammering: A Psychoanalytic Interpretation," *Nervous and Mental Disease Monographs,* Number 47, 1928.

Corsini, R. J. and B. Rosenberg. "Mechanisms of Group Psychotherapy: Processes and Dynamics," *Journal of Abnormal and Social Psychology,* 15 (1955), 406–11.

Cotzin, M. and K. M. Dallenbach. " 'Facial Vision': The Role of Pitch and Loudness in the Perception of Obstacles by the Blind," *American Journal of Psychology,* 63 (1950), 485–515.

Coué, E. SELF-MASTERY THROUGH CONSCIOUS AUTOSUGGESTION. London: Allen & Unwin, 1922.

Cox, C. M. THE EARLY MENTAL TRAITS OF THREE HUNDRED GENIUSES. Stanford, California: Stanford University Press, 1926.

Crafts, L. W., T. C. Schneirla, E. E. Robinson and R. W. Gilbert. RECENT EXPERIMENTS IN PSYCHOLOGY. New York: McGraw-Hill, 1938.

Cramer, J. B. "Common Neuroses of Childhood," AMERICAN HANDBOOK OF PSYCHIATRY, S. Arieti (ed.). New York: Basic Books, 1959. Volume 1, Chapter 40.

Crawford, M. P. "The Cooperative Solving of Problems by Young Chimpanzees," *Comparative Psychology Monographs*, 14 (1937), Number 68, 1–88.

———. "Cooperative Solution by Chimpanzees of a Problem Requiring Serial Responses to Color Cues," *Journal of Social Psychology*, 13 (1941), 259–80.

Crespi, L. P. "Public Opinion Toward Conscientious Objectors: III. Intensity of Social Rejection in Stereotype and Attitude," *Journal of Psychology*, 19 (1945), 251–76.

Crichton, R. THE GREAT IMPOSTOR. New York: Random House, 1959.

Cronbach, L. J. ESSENTIALS OF PSYCHOLOGICAL TESTING. New York: Harper & Bros., 1960.

Dahlberg, C. C. "Pharmacologic Facilitation of Psychoanalytic Therapy," CURRENT PSYCHIATRIC THERAPIES, J. Masserman (ed.). New York: Grune & Stratton, 1963. 91–97.

Dahle, T. L. "Transmitting Information to Employees: A Study of Five Methods," *Personnel*, 31 (1954), 243–46.

Dahlke, H. O. "Race and Minority Riots—A Study in the Typology of Violence," *Social Forces*, 30 (1952), 419–25.

Danielsson, B. "Some Attraction and Repulsion Patterns Among Jibaro Indians," *Sociometry*, 12 (1949), 83–105.

Darwin, C. THE EXPRESSION OF THE EMOTIONS IN MAN AND ANIMALS. Chicago: University of Chicago Press, 1965. Original, 1872.

Dashiell, J. F. "An Experimental Analysis of Some Group Effects," *Journal of Abnormal and Social Psychology*, 25 (1930), 190–99.

———. "Experimental Studies of the Influence of Social Situations on the Behavior of Individual Human Adults," HANDBOOK OF SOCIAL PSYCHOLOGY, C. C. Murchison (ed.). Worcester, Massachusetts: Clark University Press, 1935. 1097–1158.

Davidson, G. M. "The Syndrome of Capgras," *Psychiatric Quarterly*, 15 (1941), 513.

Davis, A. "Socio-Economic Influences upon Children's Learning," *Understanding the Child*, 20 (1951), 10–16.

——— and J. Dollard. CHILDREN OF BONDAGE. Washington, D.C.: American Council of Education, 1940.

Davis, A. and R. J. Havighurst. "Social Class and Color Differences in Child-Rearing," *American Sociological Review*, 11 (1946), 698–710.

Davis, A., B. B. Gardner and M. R. Gardner. DEEP SOUTH: A SOCIAL ANTHROPOLOGICAL STUDY OF CASTE AND CLASS. Chicago: University of Chicago Press, 1941.

Davis, C. M. "Self-Selection of Diet by Newly Weaned Infants," *American Journal of the Diseases of Children*, 36 (1928), 651–79.

Davis, E. A. "The Mental and Linguistic Superiority of Only Girls," *Child Development*, 8 (1931), 139–43.

———. "The Form and Function of Children's Questions," *Child Development*, 3 (1932), 57–74.

Davis, J. D. PHRENOLOGY: FAD AND SCIENCE. New Haven: Yale University Press, 1955.

Davis, K. HUMAN RELATIONS IN BUSINESS. New York: McGraw-Hill, 1957.

Davis, P. A. "Electroencephalograms of Manic-Depressive Patients," *American Journal of Psychiatry*, 98 (1941), 430–33.

Davis, W. A. and R. J. Havighurst. "The Measurement of Mental Systems (Can Intelligence be Measured?)," *Science Mon.*, 66 (1948), 301–16.

Dean, D. A. "The Relation of Ordinal Position to Personality in Young Children." Unpublished master's thesis, State University of Iowa, 1947.

Dearborn, W. F. and J. Rothney. PREDICTING THE CHILD'S DEVELOPMENT. Cambridge, Massachusetts: Sci-Art, 1941.

De Francis, V. CHILD ABUSE—A PREVIEW OF A NATIONWIDE SURVEY. Denver, Colorado: The American Humane Association, 1963.

Delgado, M. M. R. "Study of Some Cerebral Structures Related to Transmission and Elaboration of Noxious Stimulation," *Journal of Neurophysiology*, 18 (1955), 261–75.

Dember, W. N. THE PSYCHOLOGY OF PERCEPTION. New York: Holt, Rinehart & Winston, 1960.

Dement, W. "Effect of Dream Deprivation," *Science*, 131 (1960), 1705–7.

———. "Experimental Dream Studies," in SCIENCE AND PSYCHOANALYSIS, New York: Grune & Stratton, 1963. Volume 7, 129–84.

——— and N. Kleitman. "Cyclic Variations in EEG During Sleep and Their Relation to Eye Movements, Body Motility and Dreaming," *EEG Clin. Neurophysiology*, 9 (1957), 673–90.

Dement, W. and E. Wolpert. "Relation of Eye Movements, Bodily Motility and External Stimuli to Dream Content," *Journal of Experimental Psychology,* 55 (1958), 543–53.

De Molina, F. A. and R. W. Hunsperger. "Central Representation of Affective Reactions in Forebrain and Brain Stem, Electrical Stimulation of Amygdala, Stria Terminalis, and Adjacent Structures," *Journal of Physiology,* 145 (1959), 251–65.

Dennis, W. "Are Hopi Children Noncompetitive?" *Journal of Abnormal and Social Psychology,* 50 (1955), 99–100.

—— and M. G. Dennis. "The Effect of Cradling Practices upon the Onset of Walking in Hopi Children," *Journal of Genetic Psychology,* 56 (1940), 77–86.

Derner, G. F. ASPECTS OF THE PSYCHOLOGY OF THE TUBERCULOUS. New York: Hoeber-Harper, 1953.

De Robertis, E., L. Salganicoff, L. M. Zieher and G. Rodriguez De Lores Arnaiz. "Acetylcholine and Cholinacetylase Content of Synaptic Vesicles," *Science,* 140 (1963), 300–1.

Despert, J. L. "Emotional Factors in some Young Children's Colds," *Mental Clinics of North America,* 29 (1944), 603.

Deutsch, F. APPLIED PSYCHOANALYSIS: SELECTED OBJECTIVES OF PSYCHOTHERAPY. New York: Grune & Stratton, 1949.

Deutsch, J. A. and D. Deutsch. "Attention: Some Theoretical Considerations," *Psychological Review,* 70 (1963), 51–61.

Deutsch, M. "The Effects of Cooperation and Competition upon Group Process: An Experimental Study," *American Psychologist,* 4 (1949), 263–64.

Dewey, J. "The Reflex Concept in Psychology," *Psychological Review,* 3 (1896), 357–70.

——. HOW WE THINK. Boston: Heath, 1910.

DiVesta, F. J. and J. C. Merwin. "The Effects of Need-Oriented Communications on Attitude Change," *Journal of Abnormal and Social Psychology,* 60 (1960), 80–85.

Dole, V. P. and M. E. Nyswander. "Rehabilitation of Heroin Addicts after Blockade with Methadone," *New York State Journal of Medicine,* 66, Number 15 (1966), 2011–17.

—— and M. J. Kreek. "Narcotic Blockade," *Archives of Internal Medicine,* 118 (1966), 304–9.

Doll, E. A. THE MEASUREMENT OF SOCIAL COMPETENCE. Minneapolis, Minnesota: Educational Testing Bureau, 1953.

——. VINELAND SOCIAL MATURITY SCALES: MANUAL DIRECTIONS (Rev. ed.). Minneapolis: American Guidance Service, 1965.

Dollard J. and N. E. Miller. PERSONALITY AND PSYCHOTHERAPY: AN ANALYSIS IN TERMS OF LEARNING, THINKING AND CULTURE. New York: McGraw-Hill, 1950.

——, L. W. Doob, O. H. Mowrer and R. R. Sears. FRUSTRATION AND AGGRESSION. New Haven: Yale University Press, 1939.

Dorcus, R. M. and G. W. Shaffer. TEXTBOOK OF ABNORMAL PSYCHOLOGY. Baltimore, Maryland: Williams & Wilkins, 1945.

Doust, J. W. L. "Dysplastic Growth Differentials in Patients with Psychiatric Disorders," *British Journal of Social Medicine,* 6 (1952a), 169–77.

——. "Psychiatric Aspects of Somatic Immunity," *British Journal of Social Medicine,* 6 (1952b), 49–67.

Drake, R. M. Review, FIFTH MENTAL MEASUREMENTS YEARBOOK, O. K. Buros (ed.). Highland Park, New Jersey: Gryphon, 1959.

Dudycha, G. J. and M. M. Dudycha. "Childhood Memories: A Review of the Literature," *Psychological Bulletin,* 38 (1941), 668–81.

Duffy, E. "Level of Muscular Tension as an Aspect of Personality," *Journal of General Psychology,* 35 (1940), 161–71.

Dunbar, F. PSYCHOSOMATIC DIAGNOSIS. New York: Harper & Bros., 1943.

——. EMOTIONS AND BODILY CHANGES. New York: Columbia University Press, 1954.

Dunlap, J. M. "The Education of Children with High Mental Ability," EDUCATION OF EXCEPTIONAL CHILDREN and YOUTH, W. M. Cruickshank and G. O. Johnson (eds.). Englewood Cliffs, New Jersey: Prentice-Hall, 1958.

Dunston, B. N. "Pica, Hemoglobin, and Prematurity and Perinatal Mortality." Unpublished dissertation, New York University School of Education, 1961.

Dyer, D. T. "Are Only Children Different?" *Journal of Educational Psychology,* 36 (1945), 297–302.

Ebbinghaus, H. ÜBER DAS GEDÄCHTNIS ("Memory"). Leipzig: Duncker, 1885; New York: Teachers College, 1913.

Edwards, A. L. "Retention of Affective Experiences: A Criticism and Restatement of the Problem," *Psychological Review,* 49 (1942), 43–53.

Eells, K., A. Davis, R. J. Havighurst, V. E. Herrick and R. W. Tyler. INTELLIGENCE AND CULTURAL DIFFERENCES. Chicago: University of Chicago Press, 1951.

Efron, D. and J. P. Foley, Jr. "Gestural Behavior and Social Setting," Zeitschrift für Sozialforschung, 6 (1937), 151–59.

Eisenberg, L. "The Fathers of Autistic Children," American Journal of Orthopsychiatry, 27 (1957), 715–24.

Eisenbud, J. "The Use of Telepathy Hypothesis in Psychotherapy," SPECIALIZED TECHNIQUES IN PSYCHOTHERAPY, G. Bychowski and J. L. Despert (eds.). New York: Basic Books, 1952.

Eisenson, J. "Speech Disorders," HANDBOOK OF CLINICAL PSYCHOLOGY, B. B. Wolman (ed.). New York: McGraw-Hill, 1965. Chapter 28.

Elkind, H. B. and C. G. Doering. "Epidemiology of Mental Disease; Further Studies. I. Variation in Diagnosis," STATISTICAL STUDIES FROM THE BOSTON PSYCHOPATHIC HOSPITAL, Reprint Number 5 on Schizophrenia, 1928.

Elkins, D. "Some Factors Related to the Choice-Status of Ninety Eighth Grade Children in a School Society," Genetic Psychology Monographs, 58 (1958), 207–72.

Ellis, A. "Rational Psychotherapy," Journal of General Psychology, 59 (1958), 35–49.

Emmons, W. H. and C. W. Simon. "The Non-Recall of Material During Sleep," American Journal of Psychology, 69 (1956), 76–81.

English, H. B. and A. C. English. A COMPREHENSIVE DICTIONARY OF PSYCHOLOGICAL AND PSYCHOANALYTICAL TERMS: A GUIDE TO USAGE. New York: Longmans, Green, 1958.

English, O. S. and S. M. Finch. INTRODUCTION TO PSYCHIATRY. New York: Norton, 1964.

Enke, W. "Die Psychomotorik der Konstitutionstypen," Zeitschrift für ang. Psychologie, 36 (1930), 237–87.

Epps, H. O., G. B. McCammon and Q. D. Simmons. TEACHING DEVICES FOR CHILDREN WITH IMPAIRED LEARNING (pamphlet). Columbus, Ohio: Parents' Volunteer Association, Columbus State School.

Erdmann, B. and R. Dodge. PSYCHOLOGISCHE UNTERSUCHUNGEN ÜBER DAS LESEN. Halle: Niemeyer, 1898.

Erickson, M. H. "Experimental Demonstrations of the Psychopathology of Everyday Life," Psychoanalytic Quarterly, 8 (1939), 338–53.

————. "An Experimental Investigation of the Possible Anti-Social Use of Hypnosis," Psychiatry, 2 (1939), 391–414.

———— and L. S. Kubie. "Use of Automatic Drawing in Interpretation and Relief of a State of Acute Obsessional Depression," Psychoanalytic Quarterly, 7 (1938), 443–53.

————. "The Permanent Relief of an Obsessional Phobia by Means of Communications with an Unsuspected Dual Personality," Psychoanalytic Quarterly, 8 (1939), 471–509.

Eriksen, C. W. "Psychological Defenses and 'Ego Strength' in the Recall of Completed and Incompleted Tasks," Journal of Abnormal and Social Psychology, 49 (1954), 45–50.

Erikson, E. H. CHILDHOOD AND SOCIETY. New York: Norton, 1950.

————. "Identity and the Life Cycle," Psychological Issues, 1, Number 1., 1959.

Escalona, S. "Some Considerations Regarding Psychotherapy with Psychotic Children," Bulletin, Menninger Clinic, 12 (1948), 127–34.

————. "The Use of Infant Tests for Predictive Purposes," Bulletin, Menninger Clinic, 14 (1950), 117–28.

Esmarch, F. and W. Jessen. "Syphilis und Geistesstörung," Allg. Ztschr. f. Psychiat., 14 (1857), 20.

Estabrooks, G. H. "A Contribution to Experimental Telepathy," Boston Society of Psychic Research, Bulletin, 5 (1927), 1–30.

Estvan, F. J. and E. W. Estvan. THE CHILD'S WORLD: HIS SOCIAL PERCEPTION. New York: Putnam, 1959.

Ewalt, J., E. A. Strecker and F. G. Ebaugh. PRACTICAL CLINICAL PSYCHIATRY. New York: McGraw-Hill, 1957.

Eysenck, H. J. DIMENSIONS OF PERSONALITY. London: Routledge & Kegan Paul, 1947.

————. THE STRUCTURE OF HUMAN PERSONALITY. New York: Wiley, 1953.

———— (ed.). BEHAVIOR THERAPY AND THE NEUROSES. London: Pergamon Press, 1960.

————. "The Development of Moral Values in Children. VII. The Contribution of Learning Theory," British Journal of Educational Psychology, 30 (1960), 11–21.

————. "Classification and the Problems of Diagnosis," HANDBOOK OF ABNORMAL PSYCHOLOGY, H. J. Eysenck (ed.). New York: Basic Books, 1961. 1–31.

Fairweather, G. W. et al. "Relative Effectiveness of Psychotherapeutic Programs: A Multicriteria

Comparison of Four Programs for Different Patient Groups," *Psychological Monographs*, 74 (1960), Number 5.

Fantz, R. L. "The Origin of Form Perception," *Scientific American*, 204 (1961), 66–72.

Farber, I. E., H. F. Harlow and L. J. West. "Brainwashing, Conditioning and DDD (Debility, Dependency and Dread)," *Sociometry*, 20 (1957), 271–85.

Farberow, N. L. and E. S. Shneidman. THE CRY FOR HELP. New York: McGraw-Hill, 1961.

Faris, R. E. L. "Sociological Causes of Genius," *American Sociological Review*, 5 (1940), 689–99.

Farnsworth, P. R. and H. Beaumont. "Suggestion in Pictures," *Journal of General Psychology*, 2 (1929), 362–66.

Fechner, G. T. ELEMENTE DER PSYCHOPHYSIK. Leipzig: Breitkopf and Härtel, 1860.

Federn, P. EGO PSYCHOLOGY AND THE PSYCHOSES. New York: Basic Books, 1952.

Fenichel, O. THE PSYCHOANALYTIC THEORY OF NEUROSIS. New York: Norton, 1945.

Fenton, N. "The Only Child," *Journal of Genetic Psychology*, 35 (1928), 546–56.

Ferenczi, S. "The Psychoanalysis of Sexual Habits," *International Journal of Psycho-Analysis*, 6 (1925), 372–404.

————. FURTHER CONTRIBUTIONS TO THE THEORY AND TECHNIQUES OF PSYCHOANALYSIS. London: Hogarth Press, 1926.

Fernberger, W. S. "False Suggestion and the Piderit Model," *American Journal of Psychology*, 40 (1928), 562–68.

Ferraro, A. "Presenile Psychoses," AMERICAN HANDBOOK OF PSYCHIATRY, S. Arieti (ed.). New York: Basic Books, 1959. Volume 2, Chapter 52.

————. "Senile Psychoses," in AMERICAN HANDBOOK OF PSYCHIATRY, S. Arieti (ed.). New York: Basic Books, 1959. Volume 2, 1042.

Ferrio, C. LA PSICHE E I NERVI. Turin: Utet, 1948.

Festinger, L. "Wish, Expectation and Group Performance as Factors Influencing Level of Aspiration," *Journal of Abnormal and Social Psychology*, 37 (1942), 184–200.

————. "A Theory of Social Comparison Process," *Human Relations*, 7 (1954), 117–40.

————. A THEORY OF COGNITIVE DISSONANCE. New York: Row, Peterson, 1957.

———— and J. M. Carlsmith. "Cognitive Dissonance of Forced Compliance," *Journal of Abnormal and Social Psychology*, 59 (1959), 209–14.

Festinger, L., H. W. Riecken and S. Schachter. WHEN PROPHECY FAILS. Minneapolis: University of Minnesota Press, 1956.

Fink, D. RELEASE FROM NERVOUS TENSION. New York: Simon & Schuster, 1943.

Fisher, A. E. and J. N. Coury. "Cholinergic Tracing of a Central Neural Circuit Underlying the Thirst Drive," *Science*, 136 (1962), 691–93.

Fisher, C. and W. Dement. "Studies on Psychopathology of Sleep and Dreams," *American Journal of Psychiatry*, 119 (1963), 1160–68.

Fjerdingstad, E. J., T. Nissen and H. H. Rigaard-Petersen. "Effect of Ribonucleic Acid (RNA) Extracted from the Brain of Trained Animals on Learning in Rats," *Scandinavian Journal of Psychology*, 6 (1965), 1–6.

Flanagen, B., I. Goldiamond and N. Azrin. "Operant Stuttering: The Control of Stuttering Behavior Through Response-Contingent Consequences," *Journal of the Experimental Analysis of Behavior*, 1 (1958), 173–78.

Fleishman, E. A. "An Experimental Consumer Panel Technique," *Journal of Applied Psychology*, 35 (1951), 133–35.

Flesch, R. "A New Readability Yardstick," *Journal of Applied Psychology*, 32 (1948), 221–33.

————. THE ART OF READABLE WRITING. New York: Harper & Bros., 1949.

Flugel, J. C. Obituary Notice: Professor William McDougall (1871–1938), *British Journal of Psychology*, 29 (1939), 321–26.

Flynn, P. and S. Hirsch. "Antidepressants and Electroshock," *American Journal of Psychiatry*, 119 (1962), 576–77.

Foley, J. P. Jr. "An Experimental Investigation of the Effect of Prolonged Inversion of the Visual Field in the Rhesus Monkey," *Journal of Genetic Psychology*, 56 (1940), 21–51.

————. "The Use of the Free Association Technique in the Investigation of the Stimulus Value of Trade Names," *Journal of Applied Psychology*, 28 (1944), 431–35.

———— and Z. L. MacMillan. "Mediated Generalization and the Interpretation of Verbal Behavior V. 'Free Association' as Related to Differences in Professional Training," *Journal of Experimental Psychology*, 33 (1943), 299–310.

Ford, C. S. and F. A. Beach. PATTERNS OF SEXUAL BEHAVIOR. New York: Harper & Bros., 1951.

Foreman, P. B. "Pain Theory," *Sociology and Social Research*, 37 (1953), 295–304.

Forgays, D. G. "The Importance of Experience at Specific Times in the Development of an Organism." Address: Eastern Psychological Association, 1962.

Foulds, G. A. and P. Dixon. "The Nature of Intellectual Deficit in Schizophrenia. I. A Comparison of Schizophrenics and Neurotics," *British Journal of Social and Clinical Psychology*, 1 (1962), 7–19.

Francès, R. "Limites et Nature des Effets de Prestige. II. Notoriété de l'Auteur et Jugement de l'Oeuvre," *Journal of Psychol. Norm. Pathol.*, 60 (1963), 437–56.

——— and Voillaume, H. "Une Composante du Jugement Pictural: La Fidélité de la Représentation," *Psychol. Franc.*, 9 (1964), 241–56.

Franck, K. and E. Rosen. "A Projective Test of Masculinity and Femininity," *Journal of Consulting Psychology*, 13 (1949), 247–56.

Frank, J. D. GROUP METHODS IN THERAPY. New York: Public Affairs Pamphlet Number 284, 1959.

Frank, L. K. "Projective Methods for the Study of Personality," *Journal of Psychology*, 48 (1939), 389–413.

Frank, M. H. (ed.). VOLUNTEERS IN MENTAL HOSPITALS. New York: National Association for Mental Health.

Frankl, V. E. THE DOCTOR AND THE SOUL: AN INTRODUCTION TO LOGOTHERAPY. New York: Alfred A. Knopf, 1955.

———. MAN'S SEARCH FOR MEANING: AN INTRODUCTION TO LOGOTHERAPY. Boston: Beacon Press, 1963.

Franklin, R. W. "The Falsetto Voice," VOICE DISORDERS. New York: National Hospital for Speech Disorders, 1957.

Frederikson, E. "Aggressiveness in Female Rats," *Journal of Comparative and Physiological Psychology*, 45 (1952), 254–57.

Freedman, L. A. "Daydream in a Vacuum Tube: A Psychiatrist's Comment on the Effects of Television," TELEVISION IN THE LIFE OF OUR CHILDREN, W. Schramm, J. Lyle and E. B. Parker (eds.). Stanford, California: Stanford University Press, 1961, 189–94.

Freedman, L. Z. and A. B. Hollingshead. "Neurosis and Social Class. I. Social Interaction," *American Journal of Psychiatry*, 113 (1957), 769–75.

Freeman, F. N. EXPERIMENTAL EDUCATION. Boston: Houghton Mifflin, 1916.

Freeman, F. S. THEORY AND PRACTICE OF PSYCHOLOGICAL TESTING. New York: Holt, Rinehart & Winston, 1962.

Freeman, H. E. and O. G. Simmons. THE MENTAL PATIENT COMES HOME. New York: Wiley, 1963.

Freeman, W. and J. Watts. PSYCHOSURGERY. Springfield, Illinois: Charles C. Thomas, 1942, 1950.

French, E. G. and F. H. Thomas. "The Relation of Achievement Motivation to Problem-Solving Effectiveness," *Journal of Abnormal and Social Psychology*, 56 (1958), 45–48.

French, J. R. P. Jr. "Group Productivity," GROUPS, LEADERSHIP AND MEN, H. Guetzkow (ed.). Pittsburgh: Carnegie Press, 1951.

French, J. W. "Validation of New Item Types Against Four-Year Academic Criteria," *Journal of Educational Psychology*, 49 (1958), 67–76.

French, T. M. and E. Fromm. DREAM INTERPRETATION: A NEW APPROACH. New York: Basic Books, 1964.

Freud, A. "An Introduction to the Technique of Child Analysis," *Nervous and Mental Disease Monographs*, Number 48 (1928).

———. THE EGO AND THE MECHANISMS OF DEFENCE. London: Hogarth, 1937.

Freud, S. PSYCHOPATHOLOGY OF EVERYDAY LIFE. New York: Macmillan, 1914. Original, 1904.

———. "The Future Prospects of Psychoanalytic Therapy," COLLECTED PAPERS. London: Hogarth Press, 1924. Volume 2, 285–96.

———. COLLECTED PAPERS. London: The Institute of Psycho-Analysis, 1924–25. Volume 1.

———. COLLECTED PAPERS. London: Hogarth, 1925. 145.

———. THREE CONTRIBUTIONS TO THE THEORY OF SEX, tr. by A. A. Brill. New York: Nervous and Mental Disease Publishing Co., 1930. Original, 1905.

———. THE INTERPRETATION OF DREAMS. New York: Macmillan, 1933. Original, 1900.

———. AN OUTLINE OF PSYCHOANALYSIS. New York: Norton, 1949.

———. "The Origin and Development of Psychoanalysis," in AN OUTLINE OF PSYCHOANALYSIS, J. Van Teslaar (ed.). New York: Modern Library, 1924, 30–31.

———. BEYOND THE PLEASURE PRINCIPLE. New York: Liveright, 1950. Original, 1920.

———. A GENERAL INTRODUCTION TO PSYCHO-ANALYSIS. New York: Permabooks, 1953. Original English translation, 1920.

———. COLLECTED PAPERS. New York: Basic Books, 1959. Volume 2.

——. "The Ego and the Id" (1923), THE STANDARD EDITION OF THE COMPLETE WORKS OF SIGMUND FREUD. London: Hogarth Press and the Institute of Psycho-Analysis, 1962. Volume 19, 12–66.

——. "Group Psychology and the Analysis of the Ego" (1921), THE STANDARD EDITION OF THE COMPLETE WORKS OF SIGMUND FREUD. London: Hogarth Press and the Institute of Psycho-Analysis, 1962. Volume 18, 69–143.

——. "Inhibitions, Symptoms and Anxiety" (1926), THE STANDARD EDITION OF THE COMPLETE WORKS OF SIGMUND FREUD. London: Hogarth Press and the Institute of Psycho-Analysis, 1962. Volume 20, 87–174.

——. "The Neuro-Psychoses of Defense" (1894), THE STANDARD EDITION OF THE COMPLETE WORKS OF SIGMUND FREUD. London: Hogarth Press and the Institute of Psycho-Analysis, 1962. Volume 2, 45–61.

——. WIT AND ITS RELATION TO THE UNCONSCIOUS. Tr. by A. A. Brill. New York: Moffatt, 1916. Original, 1905.

Freund, K. "Some Problems in the Treatment of Homosexuality," BEHAVIOR THERAPY AND THE NEUROSES, H. J. Eysenck (ed.). London: Pergamon Press, 1960. 312–26.

Friedman, P. and L. Linn. "Some Psychiatric Notes on the Andrea Doria Disaster," *American Journal of Psychiatry,* 114 (1957), 426–32.

Fritz, C. E. "Disasters Compared in Six American Communities," *Human Organization,* 16 (2) (1957), 6–9.

Froeschels, E. and A. Jellinek. THE PRACTICE OF VOICE AND SPEECH THERAPY. Boston: Expression Co., 1941.

Fromm, E. MAN FOR HIMSELF. New York: Holt, 1947.

——. THE FORGOTTEN LANGUAGE: AN INTRODUCTION TO THE UNDERSTANDING OF DREAMS, FAIRY TALES AND MYTHS. New York: Rinehart, 1951.

——. THE ART OF LOVING. New York: Harper & Bros., 1956.

Frostig, M. "Developmental Evaluation and the Institution of Remedial Programs for Children with Learning Difficulties," The Marianne Frostig Center of Educational Therapy (mimeographed), 1965.

Fulkerson, S. C. and J. R. Barry. "Methodology and Research on the Prognostic Use of Psychological Tests," *Psychological Bulletin,* 58 (1961), 177–204.

Fulton, J. F. and C. E. Jacobsen. "The Function of the Frontal Lobes, A Comparative Study in Monkeys, Chimpanzees and Man," London: Abstracts of the Second International Neurological Congress, 1935.

Funkenstein, D. H., M. Greenblatt and H. C. Solomon. "Autonomic Changes Paralleling Psychologic Changes in Mentally Ill Patients," *Journal of Nervous and Mental Disease,* 114 (1951), 1–18.

——. "An Autonomic Nervous System Test of Prognostic Significance in Relation to Electro-Shock Treatment," *Psychosomatic Medicine,* 14 (1952), 347–62.

Gaetaniello, J. Reported in ABNORMAL PSYCHOLOGY AND MODERN LIFE, J. C. Coleman (ed.). Fair Lawn, New Jersey: Scott, Foresman, 1964.

Galambos, R. "A Glia-Neural Cell Theory of Brain Function," *Proceedings of the National Academy of Science,* 47 (1961), 129–36.

Galanter, E. H. "Recent Developments in Automated Instruction," in PSYCHOLOGY AND LIFE, F. L. Ruch. Fair Lawn, New Jersey: Scott, Foresman, 1963. 584–89.

Gallagher, J. J. and T. Crowder. "The Adjustment of Gifted Children in the Regular Classroom," *Exceptional Child,* 23 (1957), 306–12.

Gallup, G. "How Voters React on Health Issues," Los Angeles *Times,* August 24, 1956, 4.

Garmezy, N. and E. H. Rodnick. "Premorbid Adjustment and Performance in Schizophrenia: Implications for Interpreting Heterogeneity in Schizophrenia," *Journal of Nervous and Mental Disease,* 129 (1959), 450–66.

Garth, T. R. "A Study of the Foster Indian Child in the White Home," Unpublished paper read at 43rd Annual Meeting of the American Psychological Association, Ann Arbor, Michigan, September 1935. Abstract in *Psychological Bulletin,* 32 (1935), 708–9.

Garvey, C. R. "Comparative Body Build of Manic-Depressive and Schizophrenic Patients," *Psychological Bulletin,* 30 (1933), 567–68, 739.

Gates, G. S. "An Observational Study of Anger," *Journal of Experimental Psychology,* 9 (1926), 325–36.

Gazzaniga, M. S. "The Split Brain in Man," *Scientific American,* 217, August 1967, 24–29.

—— and J. E. Bogen and R. W. Sperry. "Observations on Visual Perception After Disconnexion of the Cerebral Hemispheres in Man," *Brain,* 88 (1965), 221–36.

Geisel, G. B. "Discipline Viewed as a Developmental Need of the Child," *Nervous Child,* 9 (1951), 115–21.

Geldard, F. A. "The Measurement of Retinal Fatigue to Achromatic Stimulation. I, II." *Journal of General Psychology,* 1 (1928), 123–35, 578–90.

———. THE HUMAN SENSES. New York: Wiley, 1953.

———. FUNDAMENTALS OF PSYCHOLOGY. New York: Wiley, 1962.

Gellhorn, E. "Prolegomena to a Theory of Emotions," *Perspectives in Biology and Medicine.* Chicago: University of Chicago Press, 1961. Volume 4, Number 4, 403–36.

——— and G. N. Loofbourrow. EMOTIONS AND EMOTIONAL DISORDERS: A NEUROPHYSIOLOGICAL STUDY. New York: Harper & Row, 1963.

Gentry, J. T., E. Parkhurst and G. V. Bulin, Jr. "An Epidemiological Study of Congenital Malformations in New York City. A Reprint, Including Material Not Previously Published," *American Journal of Public Health,* 49 (4) (1959).

Gerard, R. W. "What Is Memory?" *Scientific American,* 190 (1953), 118–26.

———. "Brains and Behavior," *Human Biology,* 31 (1959), 14–20.

Gerbrands, A. A. ART AS AN ELEMENT OF CULTURE, ESPECIALLY IN NEGRO-AFRICA. Leyden: E. J. Brill, 1957.

Gesell, A. and L. B. Ames. "Early Evidences of Individuality in the Human Infant," *Journal of Genetic Psychology,* 47 (1937), 339–61.

Gesell, A. and F. L. Ilg. FEEDING BEHAVIOR OF INFANTS. Philadelphia: Lippincott, 1937.

Gesell, A. and H. Thompson. "Learning and Growth in Identical Infant Twins: An Experimental Study by the Method of Co-Twin Control," *Genetic Psychology Monographs,* 6 (1929), 1–124.

Gesell, A., F. L. Ilg and L. B. Ames. YOUTH: THE YEARS FROM TEN TO SIXTEEN. New York: Harper & Bros., 1956.

Getzels, J. W. and P. W. Jackson. CREATIVITY AND INTELLIGENCE: EXPLORATIONS WITH GIFTED STUDENTS. New York: Wiley, 1962.

Gibb, G. A. "Leadership," HANDBOOK OF SOCIAL PSYCHOLOGY, G. Lindzey (ed.). Reading, Massachusetts: Addison-Wesley, 1954. 877–920.

Gibson, E. G. and R. D. Walk. "The 'Visual Cliff,'" *Scientific American,* 202 (1960), 64–71.

Gibson, J. J. "Adaptation, After-Effect and Contrast in the Perception of Curved Lines," *Journal of Experimental Psychology,* 16 (1933), 1–31.

———. "Motion Picture Testing and Research." Washington, D.C.: Government Printing Office, AAF Aviation Psychology Program Research Report Number 7, 1947.

Gil, D. G. "A Nationwide Epidemiologic Study of Child Abuse." Paper presented at the National Conference of Social Welfare, Chicago, Illinois, June 1, 1966.

Gilbert, G. M. "Stereotype Persistence and Change Among College Students," *Journal of Abnormal and Social Psychology,* 46 (1951), 245–54.

———. "A Survey of 'Referral Problems' in Metropolitan Child Guidance Centers," *Journal of Clinical Psychology,* 13 (1957), 37–42.

Gilbreth, F. B. FATIGUE STUDY. New York: Sturgis and Walton, 1916.

——— and L. M. Gilbreth. APPLIED MOTION STUDY. New York: Sturgis and Walton, 1917.

Gilford, R. B. and D. A. Worcester. "A Comparative Study of the Only and Non-Only Child," *Journal of Genetic Psychology,* 38 (1930), 411–26.

Ginott, H. GROUP PSYCHOTHERAPY WITH CHILDREN. New York: McGraw-Hill, 1961.

Ginzberg, E., J. W. Ginzberg, S. Axelrod and J. C. Herma. OCCUPATIONAL CHOICE. New York: Columbia, 1951.

Glasser, William. REALITY THERAPY. New York: Harper & Row, 1965.

———. "The Research Frontier: Reality Therapy," *Saturday Review,* March 6, 1965, 54–56.

Glixman, A. F. "Recall of Completed and Incompleted Activities Under Varying Degrees of Stress," *Journal of Experimental Psychology,* 39 (1949), 281–95.

Glorig, A. and D. E. Wheeler. "An Introduction to the Industrial Noise Problem," *Illinois Medical Journal,* 107 (Number 1, January 1955).

Gloyne, H. F. "Tarantism: Mass Hysterical Reaction to Spider Bite in the Middle Ages," *American Imago,* 7 (1950), 29–42.

Glueck, S. and E. Glueck. UNRAVELING JUVENILE DELINQUENCY. Cambridge: Harvard University Press, The Commonwealth Fund, 1950.

———. PHYSIQUE AND DELINQUENCY. New York: Harper & Bros., 1956.

Godfrey, K. "LSD—A Baffling Drug," *The Menninger Quarterly,* 21, Number 2 (1967), 1–9.

Goffman, Erving. "Characteristics of Total Institutions," in Walter Reed Army Institute of Research, Symposium on Preventive and Social Psychiatry, April 15–17, 1957, Washington, D.C.

Gold, L. H. "Psychiatric Profile of the Firesetter," *Journal of Science,* 7 (1962), 404.

Goldberg, I. M. "K voprosy ob vprazhnyaenosti taktilnoi chuvstvitelnosti" (On the Question About Practice of Tactual Sensitivity), *Voprosy Psikhologil,* 9 (1963), 35–40.

Goldenson, R. M. "Step into the World of the Insane," *Look,* September 21, 1954, 30.

———. HELPING YOUR CHILD TO READ BETTER. New York: Crowell, 1957.

Goldfarb, A. I. "Contributions of Psychiatry to the Institutional Care of Aged and Chronically Ill Persons," *Journal of Chronic Disease,* 6 (1957), 483–96.

Goldfarb, W. "Infant Rearing and Problem Behavior," *American Journal of Orthopsychiatry,* 13 (1943), 249–66.

———. "Psychological Privation in Infancy and Subsequent Adjustment," *American Journal of Orthopsychiatry,* 15 (1945), 247–55.

———. CHILDHOOD SCHIZOPHRENIA. Cambridge: Harvard University Press, 1961.

———. "Families of Schizophrenic Children," *Research Publications of the Association for Research on Nervous and Mental Diseases,* 39 (1962), 256–69.

Goldman, A. E. "A Comparative-Developmental Approach to Schizophrenia," *Psychological Bulletin,* 59 (1962), 57–69.

Goldstein, K. THE ORGANISM. New York: American Book Company, 1939.

———. "Some Experimental Observations Concerning the Influence of Colors on the Function of the Organism," *Occupational Therapy,* 21 (1942), 147–51.

Goldstein, M. J. "The Relationship Between Coping and Avoiding Behavior and Response to Fear-Arousing Propaganda," *Journal of Abnormal and Social Psychology,* 58 (1959), 247–52.

———. "The Social Desirability Variable in Attitude Research," *Journal of Social Psychology,* 58 (1960), 103–8.

Goodenough, D. R., A. Shapiro, M. Holden and L. Steinschriber. "Comparison of 'Dreamers' and 'Nondreamers': Eye Movements, Electroencephalograms, and Recall of Dreams," *Journal of Abnormal and Social Psychology,* 59 (1959), 295–302.

Goodenough, F. L. "The Use of Free Association in the Objective Measurement of Personality," STUDIES IN PERSONALITY, Q. McNemar and M. A. Merrill (eds.). New York: McGraw-Hill, 1942.

———. "Semantic Choice and Personality Structure," *Science,* 104 (1946), 451–56.

———. "Edward Lee Thorndike: 1874–1949," *American Journal of Psychology,* 63 (1950), 291–301.

Gordon, D. A. "Individual Differences in the Evaluation of Art and the Nature of Art Standards," *Journal of Educational Research,* 50 (1956), 17–30.

Gordon, K. "A Study of Esthetic Judgments," *Journal of Experimental Psychology,* 6 (1923), 36–43.

Gorer, G. and J. Richman. THE PEOPLE OF GREAT RUSSIA. New York: Chanticleer Press, 1950.

Gottschalk, L. A. "Bibliotherapy as an Adjunct in Psychotherapy," *American Journal of Psychiatry,* 104 (1948), 632–35.

Gottsegen, M. G. and G. B. Gottsegen (eds.). PROFESSIONAL SCHOOL PSYCHOLOGY. New York: Grune & Stratton, 1960 (Volume 1) and 1963 (Volume 2).

Gough, H. G. THE ADJECTIVE CHECK LIST. Berkeley: University of California Press, 1952.

———. CALIFORNIA PSYCHOLOGICAL INVENTORY. Palo Alto, California: Consulting Psychologists Press, 1957.

Graham, D. T. "The Pathogenesis of Hives: Experimental Studies of Life Situations, Emotions and Cutaneous Vascular Reactions," *Research Publications of the Association for Research on Nervous and Mental Diseases,* 29 (1950), 987–1009.

Gralnick, A. "Folie à Deux—The Psychosis of Association: A Review of 103 Cases and the Entire English Literature with Case Presentations," *Psychiatric Quarterly,* 14 (1942), 230–63.

Granit, R. "Neural Activity in the Retina," HANDBOOK OF PHYSIOLOGY, H. W. Magoun and V. E. Hall (eds.). Washington, D.C.: American Physiological Society, 1959. Volume I.

Grant, V. M. "A Case Study of Fetishism," *Journal of Abnormal and Social Psychology,* 48 (1953), 142–49.

Gray, J. A. B. "Initiation of Impulses at Receptors," HANDBOOK OF PHYSIOLOGY, H. W. Magoun and V. E. Hall (eds.). Washington, D.C.: American Physiological Society, 1959. Volume I.

Green, B. F. and L. K. Anderson. "The Tactual Identification of Shapes for Coding Switch Handles," *Journal of Applied Psychology,* 39 (1955), 219–26.

Greenacre, P. "Conscience in the Psychopath," *American Journal of Orthopsychiatry,* 15 (1945), 495–509.

Greenblatt, M. THE PATIENT IN THE MENTAL HOSPITAL. New York: The Free Press, 1957.

——— and D. J. Levinson. "Mental Hospitals," HANDBOOK OF CLINICAL PSYCHOLOGY, B. B. Wolman (ed.). New York: McGraw-Hill, 1965. Chapter 49.

Greene, J. R. and R. L. Sisson. DYNAMIC MANAGEMENT DECISION GAMES. New York: Wiley, 1959.

Greene, J. S. and E. J. Wells. THE CAUSE AND CURE OF SPEECH DISORDERS. New York: Macmillan, 1927.

Greenson, R. R. "The Classic Psychoanalytic Approach," AMERICAN HANDBOOK OF PSYCHIATRY, S. Arieti (ed.). New York: Basic Books, 1959. Volume 2.

Griffin, D. R. and R. Galambos. "The Sensory Basis of Obstacle Avoidance by Flying Bats," *Journal of Experimental Zoology*, 86 (1941), 481–506.

Griffith, R. M., B. W. Estes and S. A. Zerof. "Intellectual Impairment in Schizophrenia," *Journal of Consulting Psychology*, 26 (1962), 336–39.

Grinker, R. R. and J. P. Spiegel. MEN UNDER STRESS. New York: McGraw-Hill, 1945.

Grossman, S. P. "Eating or Drinking Elicited by Direct Adrenergic or Cholinergic Stimulation of Hypothalamus," *Science*, 132 (1960), 301–32.

Gruenberg, Ernest M. "Discussion of Critical Reviews of Pueblo, Western and Denver Tri-County Division," In Stone, Bernard (ed.), A Critical Review of Treatment Progress in a State Hospital Reorganized Toward the Communities Served," Pueblo Association for Mental Health, May 1963 (mimeographed).

——— and Jack Zusman. "The Natural History of Schizophrenia," *International Psychiatry Clinics*, 1 (1964), 699.

Gruenberg, S. M. et al. (eds.). THE ENCYCLOPEDIA OF CHILD CARE AND GUIDANCE. Garden City, New York: Doubleday & Company, 1959.

Guetzkow, H. and P. H. Bowman. MEN AND HUNGER. Elgin, Illinois: Brethren Publishing House, 1946.

Guetzkow, H. and H. A. Simon. "The Impact of Certain Communication Nets upon Organization and Performance in Task-Oriented Groups." *Management Science*, 1 (1955), 223–50.

Guilford, J. P. "A Study in Psychodynamics," *Psychometrika*, 4 (1939), 1–23.

———. "A Factor Analytic Study Across the Domains of Reasoning, Creativity, and Evaluation, I: Hypotheses and Description of Tests," *Reports from the Psychological Laboratory*, Los Angeles: University of Southern California, 1954.

———. PERSONALITY. New York: McGraw-Hill, 1959.

Gundlach, R. H. "A Quantitative Analysis of Indian Music," *American Journal of Psychology*, 44 (1932), 133–45.

Gurney, E., F. W. H. Myers and F. Podmore. PHANTASMS OF THE LIVING. London: Trübner, 1886. Two volumes.

Gutheil, E. A. THE HANDBOOK OF DREAM ANALYSIS. New York: Liveright, 1951.

———. "Sexual Dysfunctions in Men," AMERICAN HANDBOOK OF PSYCHIATRY, S. Arieti (ed.). New York: Basic Books, 1959. 715.

Guttmacher, M. S. THE MIND OF THE MURDERER. New York: Farrar, Straus, 1960.

Hadley, J. M. and V. E. Kennedy. "A Comparison Between Performance on a Sentence Completion Test and Academic Success," *Educ. Psychol. Measurement*, 9 (1949), 649–70.

Haire, M. "Projective Techniques in Market Research," *Journal of Marketing*, 14 (1950), 649–56.

Hall, C. S. THE MEANING OF DREAMS. New York: Harper, 1953.

——— and G. Lindzey. THEORIES OF PERSONALITY. New York: Wiley, 1957.

Hallgren, B. "Enuresis," *Acta Psychiat. Neuro. Scandinavia*, 31 (1956), 379–436.

Halpert, H. P. PUBLIC OPINIONS AND ATTITUDES ABOUT MENTAL HEALTH. Washington, D.C.: United States Department of Health, Education and Welfare, Research Utilization Series, 1963.

Hanfmann, E. and J. W. Getzels. "Studies of the Sentence Completion Test," *Journal of Projective Techniques*, 17 (1953), 280–94.

Hardy, J. D., H. T. Hammel and T. Nakayama. "Observations on the Physiological Thermostat in Homoiotherms," *Science*, 136 (1962), 326.

Harlow, H. F. "The Heterosexual Affectional System in Monkeys," *American Psychologist*, 17 (1962), 1–9.

———, M. K. Harlow and D. R. Meyers. "Learning Motivated by a Manipulative Drive," *Journal of Experimental Psychology*, 40 (1950), 228–34.

Harlow, H. F. and R. R. Zimmerman. "Affectional Responses in the Infant Monkey," *Science*, 130 (1959), 421–32.

Harper, R. A. PSYCHOANALYSIS AND PSYCHOTHERAPY. Englewood Cliffs, New Jersey: Prentice-Hall, 1959.

Harriman, A. E. "Provitamin A Selection by Vitamin A Depleted Rats," *Journal of Genetic Psychology*, 86 (1955), 45–50.

Harris, A. J. HARRIS TESTS OF LATERAL DOMINANCE. Boston: Houghton Mifflin, 1958.

———. HOW TO INCREASE READING ABILITY. New York: David McKay Company, 1961.

Harris, D. "Factors Affecting College Grades: A Review of the Literature," *Psychological Bulletin*, 37 (1940), 125–66.

Harris, D. "Predicting Consumer Reaction to Product Design," *Journal of Advertising Research*, 4 (1964), 34–37.

Harris, D. "Social Status and the Moral Development of the Child," *British Journal of Educational Psychology*, 1 (1934), 75–95.

Harrower, M. "Projective Counseling—A Psychotherapeutic Technique," *American Journal of Psychotherapy*, 10 (1956), 74–86.

Hartley, E. L. PROBLEMS IN PREJUDICE. New York: King's Crown Press, 1946.

Hartley, R. E. and R. M. Goldenson. THE COMPLETE BOOK OF CHILDREN'S PLAY. New York: Crowell, 1963.

Hartley, R. E. and E. L. Hartley. FUNDAMENTALS OF SOCIAL PSYCHOLOGY. New York: Alfred A. Knopf, 1952.

Hartley, R. E., L. K. Frank and R. M. Goldenson. UNDERSTANDING CHILDREN'S PLAY. New York: Columbia University Press, 1952.

Hartmann, E. L. "The Dream-State: A Review and Discussion of Studies on the Physiologic State Concomitant with Dreaming," *International Journal of Psychiatry*, 2 (1966).

Hartmann, H. and E. Kris. "The Genetic Approach in Psychoanalysis," THE PSYCHOANALYTIC STUDY OF THE CHILD. New York: International Universities Press, 1945. Volume I, 11–29.

Hartshorne, H. and M. A. May. STUDIES IN DECEIT. New York: Macmillan, 1928.

Haskins, J. B. "Validation of the Abstract Index as a Tool for Content-Effects Analysis and Content Analysis," *Journal of Applied Psychology*, 44 (1960), 102–6.

Haslerud, G. M. and S. Myers. "The Transfer Value of Given and Individually Derived Principles," *Journal of Educational Psychology*, 49 (1958), 293–98.

Hassmann, M. "Vom Erlernen unbenannter Anzahlen bei Eichhornchen," *Z. Tierpsychologie*, 9 (1952), 294–321.

Hathaway, S. R. and J. C. McKinley. "A Multiphasic Personality Schedule (Minnesota): III. The Measurement of Symptomatic Depression," *Journal of Psychology*, 14 (1942), 73–84.

Hathaway, S. R. and P. E. Meehl. AN ATLAS FOR THE CLINICAL USE OF THE MMPI. Minneapolis: University of Minnesota Press, 1951.

Hathaway, S. R. and E. D. Monachesi (eds.). ANALYZING AND PREDICTING JUVENILE DELINQUENCY WITH THE MMPI. Minneapolis: University of Minnesota Press, 1953.

———. ADOLESCENT PERSONALITY AND BEHAVIOR: MMPI PATTERNS OF NORMAL, DELINQUENT, DROP-OUT AND OTHER OUTCOMES. Minneapolis: University of Minnesota Press, 1963.

Havighurst, R. J. DEVELOPMENTAL TASKS AND EDUCATION. New York: Longmans, Green, 1951.

———. HUMAN DEVELOPMENT AND EDUCATION. New York: Longmans, Green, 1953.

Hayakawa, S. I. "How Words Change Our Lives," ADVENTURES OF THE MIND, R. Thruelsen and J. Kobler (eds.). New York: Alfred A. Knopf, 1959.

Healy, W., A. F. Bronner and A. M. Bowers. THE STRUCTURE AND MEANING OF PSYCHOANALYSIS. New York: Alfred A. Knopf, 1930.

Heath, R. G. "Schizophrenia: Biochemical and Physiologic Aberrations," *International Journal of Neuropsychiatry*, 2, Number 6 (1966), 597–610.

Heath, R. G. and I. M. Krupp. "Schizophrenia as an Immunologic Disorder," *Archives of General Psychiatry*, 16 (1967), 1–33.

———. "Catatonia Induced in Monkeys by Antibrain Antibody," *American Journal of Psychiatry*, 123 (1967), 1499–1504.

Heath, R. G., S. Martens, B. E. Leach, M. Cohen and C. Angel. "Effect on Behavior in Humans with the Administration of Taraxein," *American Journal of Psychiatry*, 114 (1957), 14–24.

Heaton-Ward, W. A. "Psychopathic Disorder," *Lancet*, 1 (1963), 121–23.

Heaver, W. L. "A Study of Forty Male Psychopathic Personalities Before, During and After Hospitalization," *American Journal of Psychiatry*, 100 (1943), 342–46.

———. "A Psychiatrist Listens to Dysphonia Syndromes," VOICE DISORDERS. New York: National Hospital for Speech Disorders, 1957.

Hebb, D. O. THE ORGANIZATION OF BEHAVIOR. New York: Wiley, 1949.

———. "Drives and the CNS (Conceptual Nervous System)," *Psychological Review*, 62 (1955), 243–54.

———. A TEXTBOOK OF PSYCHOLOGY. Philadelphia: Saunders, 1958.

——. Introduction, "Cognition and Physiological Effects of Perceptual Isolation" by W. Heron, SENSORY DEPRIVATION, P. Solomon et al. (eds.). A Symposium at the Harvard Medical School. Cambridge: Harvard University Press, 1961. 6–33.

—— and W. R. Thompson. "The Social Significance of Animal Studies," HANDBOOK OF SOCIAL PSYCHOLOGY, G. Lindzey, (ed.). Cambridge, Massachusetts: Addison-Wesley, 1954.

Hecht, S. and J. Mandelbaum. "Rod-Cone Dark Adaptation and Vitamin A," Science, 88 (1938), 219–21.

Heil, L. M., M. Powell and I. Feifer. CHARACTERISTICS OF TEACHER BEHAVIOR RELATED TO THE ACHIEVEMENT OF CHILDREN IN SEVERAL ELEMENTARY GRADES. Brooklyn, New York: Brooklyn College Bookstore, 1960.

Heinrich, H. W. INDUSTRIAL ACCIDENT PREVENTION. New York: McGraw-Hill, 1959.

Helson, H. "Adaptation-Level as a Basis for a Quantitative Theory of Frames of Reference," Psychological Review, 55 (1948), 297–313.

—— and T. Lansford. "The Role of Spectral Energy of Source and Background Color on the Pleasantness of Object Colors," Illumination Engineering, 1966.

Henderson, D. and R. D. Gillespie. TEXTBOOK OF PSYCHIATRY. Fifth edition, 1940. Ninth edition revised by D. Henderson and I. R. C. Batchelor. London: Oxford University Press, 1962.

Hendin, H. BLACK SUICIDE. New York: Basic Books, 1969.

Hendrick, I. FACTS AND THEORIES OF PSYCHOANALYSIS. New York: Dell, 1963.

Henning, H. DER GERUCH. Leipzig: Barth, 1924.

Henninger, J. M. "Exhibitionism," Journal of Criminal Psychopathology, 2 (1941), 357–66.

Henry, J. "Permissiveness and Morality," Mental Hygiene, New York, 45 (1961), 282–87.

Hepner, H. W. MODERN ADVERTISING: PRACTICES AND PRINCIPLES. New York: McGraw-Hill, 1956.

Herbert, M. J. "Analysis of a Complex Skill: Vehicle Driving," Human Factors, 5 (1963), 363–72.

—— and W. E. Jaynes. "Performance Decrement in Vehicle Driving," Journal of Engineering Psychology, 3 (1964), 1–8.

Hernañdez-Peón, R., H. Sherrer and M. Jouvet. "Modification of Electrical Activity in Cochlear Nucleus During 'Attention' in Unanesthetized Cats," Science, 123 (1956), 331–32.

Heron, W., B. K. Doane and T. H. Scott. "Visual Disturbance After Prolonged Perceptual Isolation," Canadian Journal of Psychology, 10 (1956), 13–16.

Herzberg, A. ACTIVE PSYCHOTHERAPY. New York: Grune & Stratton, 1945.

Herzberg, F., B. Mausner and B. B. Snyderman. THE MOTIVATION TO WORK. New York: Wiley, 1959.

Herzog, H. Reported in PSYCHOLOGY AND LIFE, F. L. Ruch. Fair Lawn, New Jersey: Scott, Foresman, 1963.

Hess, E. H. "Imprinting," Science, 130 (1959), 133–41.

Hettinger, J. THE ULTRA-PERCEPTIVE FACULTY. London: Rider, 1940.

Hevner, K. "An Experimental Study of the Affective Value of Sounds in Poetry," American Journal of Psychology, 49 (1937), 419–34.

Hild, W., J. J. Chang and I. Tasaki. "Electrical Responses of Astrocytic Glia from the Mammalian Central Nervous System Cultivated in Vitro," Experientia, 14 (1958), 211–20.

Hilgard, E. R. INTRODUCTION TO PSYCHOLOGY. New York: Harcourt, Brace, 1962.

—— and R. C. Atkinson. INTRODUCTION TO PSYCHOLOGY. New York: Harcourt, Brace, 1967.

Hilgard, J. R. "Sibling Rivalry and Social Heredity," Psychiatry, 14 (1951), 375–85.

Hill, D. and D. Watterson. "Electroencephalographic Studies of the Psychopathic Personality," Journal of Neurology and Psychiatry, 5 (1942), 47–65.

Hinsie, L. E. and R. J. Campbell. PSYCHIATRIC DICTIONARY. New York: Oxford University Press, 1960.

Hirschberg, G. and A. R. Gilliland. "Parent-Child Relationships in Attitudes," Journal of Abnormal and Social Psychology, 37 (1942), 125–30.

Hirschfeld, M. SEXUAL ANOMALIES AND PERVERSIONS. London: Francis Adlor, 1944.

Hoagland, H. "The Physiological Control of Judgments of Duration: Evidence for a Chemical Clock," Journal of General Psychology, 9 (1932), 267–87.

Hoch, P. H. and P. Polatin. "Pseudoneurotic Forms of Schizophrenia," Psychiatric Quarterly, 23 (1949), 248–76.

Hoeven, J. A. van der. "Psychiatrisch-neurologische Beobachtungen bei Papuas in Neu Guinea," Archives of Psychiatry, 194 (1956), 415.

Hoffet, H. TYPOLOGISCHE GLIEDERUNG DEPRESSIVER SYNDROME. Basel: S. Karger, 1962.

Holland, J. G. "The Influence of Previous Experience and Residual Effects of Deprivation on Hoarding in the Rat," Journal of Comparative and Physiological Psychology, 47 (1954), 244–47.

Hollender, M. H. "Prostitution, the Body, and Human Relatedness," *International Journal of Psycho-Analysis*, 42 (1961), 404–13.

Hollingworth, H. L. "The Influence of Caffein on Mental and Motor Efficiency," *Archives of Psychology*, Number 22, 1912.

———. JUDGING HUMAN CHARACTER. New York: Appleton-Century-Crofts, 1922.

———. ABNORMAL PSYCHOLOGY. New York: Ronald, 1930.

Hollingworth, L. S. SPECIAL TALENTS AND DEFECTS. New York: Macmillan, 1923.

———. CHILDREN ABOVE 180 I.Q. Yonkers-on-Hudson, New York: World Book Company, 1942.

Holmes, T. H., T. F. Treuting and H. G. Wolff. "Life Situations, Emotions and Nasal Diseases," *Psychosomatic Medicine*, 13 (1951), 71.

Hood, A. "A Study of the Relationship Between Physique and Personality Variables Measured by the MMPI," *Journal of Personality*, 31 (1963), 97–107.

Hooker, E. "The Homosexual Community." In *Proceedings of the XIV International Congress of Applied Psychology, Personality Research*. Copenhagen: Munksgaard Press, 2 (1962), 11–12.

Horney, K. THE NEUROTIC PERSONALITY OF OUR TIME. New York: Norton, 1937.

———. NEW WAYS IN PSYCHOANALYSIS. New York: Norton, 1939.

Horowitz, E. L. "Development of Attitude Toward the Negro," *Archives of Psychology*, Number 194, 1936.

——— and R. E. Horowitz. "Development of Social Attitudes in Children," *Sociometry*, 1 (1938), 301–38.

Horrocks, J. E. THE PSYCHOLOGY OF ADOLESCENCE. Boston: Houghton Mifflin, 1962.

Horsley, J. S. "Narcoanalysis," *Lancet*, 1 (1936), 55.

Horvath, C. Reported in Los Angeles *Times*, April 5, 1956.

Hovland, C. I. and H. A. Pritzker. "Extent of Opinion Change as a Function of Amount of Change Advocated," *Journal of Abnormal and Social Psychology*, 54 (1957), 257–61.

Hovland, C. I. and R. R. Sears. "Minor Studies of Aggression: VI. Correlation of Lynchings with Economic Indices," *Journal of Psychology*, 9 (1940), 301–10.

Hovland, C. I., A. A. Lumsdaine and F. Sheffield. EXPERIMENTS ON MASS COMMUNICATION. Princeton: Princeton University Press, 1949.

Howard, J. "Research Described in Write, Rather than Fight," *Science News Letter*, 72 (1957), 169.

Hoyt, W. G. "The Effect on Learning of Auditory Material Presented During Sleep." Unpublished master's thesis, George Washington University, Washington, D.C., 1953.

Hull, C. L. APTITUDE TESTING. Yonkers, New York: World Book Company, 1928.

———. PRINCIPLES OF BEHAVIOR. New York: Appleton-Century-Crofts, 1943.

——— and L. S. Lugoff. "Complex Signs in Diagnostic Free Association," *Journal of Experimental Psychology*, 4 (1921), 111–36.

Hull, C. L. and R. P. Montgomery. "Experimental Investigation of Certain Alleged Relations Between Character and Handwriting," *Psychological Review*, 26 (1919), 63–74.

Hume, P. B. "General Principles of Community Psychiatry," AMERICAN HANDBOOK OF PSYCHIATRY, S. Arieti (ed.). New York: Basic Books, 1966. Volume 3, Chapter 31.

Humphrey, E. M. and L. O. Zangwill. "Dysphasia in Left-Handed Patients with Unilateral Brain Lesions," *Journal of Neurology, Neurosurgery and Psychiatry*, 15 (1952), 184–93.

Hunt, E. P. and P. Smith. "Vocational Psychology and Choice of Employment," *Occupational Psychology*, 19 (1945), 109–16.

Hunt, J. McV. "Experience and the Development of Motivation: Some Reinterpretations," *Child Development*, 31 (1960), 489–504.

Hunter, W. S. "Delayed Reaction in a Child," *Psychological Review*, 24 (1917), 74–87.

———. "A Kinesthetically Controlled Maze Habit in the Rat," *Science*, 91 (1940), 267–69.

——— and S. C. Bartlett. "Double Alternation in Young Children," *Journal of Experimental Psychology*, 38 (1948), 558–67.

Hurlock, E. B. "The Use of Group Rivalry as an Incentive," *Journal of Abnormal and Social Psychology*, 22 (1927), 278–90.

———. CHILD DEVELOPMENT. New York: McGraw-Hill, 1964.

——— and M. Burnstein. "The Imaginary Playmate: A Questionnaire Study," *Journal of Genetic Psychology*, 41 (1932), 380–92.

Husband, R. W. "Television versus Classroom for Learning General Psychology," *American Psychologist*, 9 (1954), 181–83.

Hydén, H. "Biochemical Changes in Glial Cells and Nerve Cells at Varying Activity," BIOCHEMISTRY OF THE CENTRAL NERVOUS SYSTEM. Proceedings of the Fourth International Congress of Biochemistry. London: Pergamon Press, 1959. Volume 3.

—— and E. Egyhazi. "Glial RNA Changes During a Learning Experiment in Rats," Proceedings, National Academy of Science, U.S., 49 (1963), 618–24.

Hyman, H. H. "The Psychology of Status," *Archives of Psychology*, Number 269, 1942.

——. POLITICAL SOCIALIZATION: *A Study in the Psychology of Political Behavior.* New York: The Free Press, 1959.

Hymes, D. H. "Phonological Aspects of Style: Some English Sonnets," STYLE IN LANGUAGE, T. A. Sebeok (ed.). New York: Wiley, 1960. 109–31.

Isaacson, R. L. and W. O. Wickelgren. "Hippocampal Ablation and Passive Avoidance," *Science*, 138 (1962), 1104–6.

Ivanov, A. "Soviet Experiments in 'Eye-Less' Vision," *International Journal of Parapsychology*, 6 (1964), 1–23.

Iverson, M. A. and M. E. Reuder. "Ego Involvement as an Experimental Variable," *Psychological Reports*, 2 (1956), 147–81.

Jackson, C. R. THE LOST WEEKEND. New York: Farrar, Straus, 1944.

Jaco, E. G. THE SOCIAL EPIDEMIOLOGY OF MENTAL DISORDERS. New York: Russell Sage Foundation, 1960.

Jacobson, A. H. "Conflict of Attitudes Toward the Roles of Husband and Wife in Marriage," *American Sociological Review*, 17 (1952), 146–50.

Jacobson, E. YOU MUST RELAX. New York: McGraw-Hill, 1942.

Jacobson, J. Z., B. J. Frost and W. L. King. "A Case of Dermo-Optical Perception," *Perceptual and Motor Skills*, 22 (1966), 515–20.

James, W. PRINCIPLES OF PSYCHOLOGY. New York: Holt, Rinehart & Winston, 1890. Two volumes.

Janet, P. L'AUTOMATISME PSYCHOLOGIQUE. Paris: Felix Alcan, 1889.

——. PSYCHOLOGICAL HEALING. New York: Macmillan, 1925.

Janis, I. L. AIR WAR AND EMOTIONAL STRESS. New York: McGraw-Hill, 1951.

—— and S. Feshbach. "Effects of Fear-Arousing Communications," *Journal of Abnormal and Social Psychology*, 48 (1953), 78–92.

Jellinek, E. M. "Phases of Alcohol Addiction," *Quarterly Journal of the Study of Alcohol*, 13 (1952), 673–78.

Jerison, H. J. "Effects of Noise on Human Performance," *Journal of Applied Psychology*, 43 (1959), 96–101.

Jersild, A. T. CHILD PSYCHOLOGY. Englewood Cliffs, New Jersey: Prentice-Hall, 1960.

—— and R. J. Tasch. "Children's Interests." New York: Teachers College, Columbia University, 1949.

Jersild, A. T., F. V. Markey and C. L. Jersild. "Children's Fears, Dreams, Wishes, Daydreams, Likes, Dislikes, Pleasant and Unpleasant Memories," *Child Development Monographs*, Number 12. New York: Teachers College, Columbia University, 1933.

Johannesson, I. "Effects of Praise and Blame upon Achievement and Attitudes of Schoolchildren," CHILD AND EDUCATION, Å. G. Skard and T. Husén (eds.). Copenhagen: Munksgaard, 1962. 184–97.

Johnson, A. M. "Juvenile Delinquency," AMERICAN HANDBOOK OF PSYCHIATRY, S. Arieti (ed.). New York: Basic Books, 1959. Volume 1, Chapter 42.

Johnson, D. M. "The Phantom Anesthetist of Mattoon: A Field Study of Mass Hysteria," *Journal of Abnormal and Social Psychology*, 40 (1945), 175–86.

Johnson, H. M. THE ART OF BLOCK BUILDING. New York: John Day, 1933.

Johnson, R. C. and G. R. Medinnus. CHILD PSYCHOLOGY: BEHAVIOR AND DEVELOPMENT. New York: Wiley, 1965.

Johnson, W. PEOPLE IN QUANDARIES. New York: Harper & Bros., 1946.

——. STUTTERING AND WHAT YOU CAN DO ABOUT IT. Minneapolis: University of Minnesota Press, 1961.

Joint Commission on Mental Illness and Health. "Action for Mental Health: Final Report of the Joint Commission on Mental Illness and Health." New York: National Rehabilitation Association, 1962.

Jones E. PAPERS ON PSYCHO-ANALYSIS. Baltimore: Wood, 1938.

——. "How to Tell Your Friends from Geniuses," *Saturday Review of Literature*, 40 (1957), 9–11, 39–40.

Jones, H. E. "The Galvanic Skin Reflex in Infancy," *Child Development*, 1 (1930), 106–10.

——. "Perceived Differences Among Twins," *Eugenic Quarterly*, 2 (1955), 98–102.

—— and H. S. Conrad. "The Growth and Decline of Intelligence; A Study of a Homogeneous Group Between the Ages of Ten and Sixty," *Genetic Psychology Monographs*, 17 (1933), 235–308.

Jones, M. THE THERAPEUTIC COMMUNITY—A NEW TREATMENT METHOD IN PSYCHIATRY. New York: Basic Books, 1953.

Jones, T. D. "The Development of Certain Motor Skills and Play Activities in Young Children," *Child Development Monographs*, Number 26. New York: Teachers College, Columbia University, 1939.

Jones, V. "Character Development in Children: An Objective Approach," MANUAL OF CHILD PSYCHOLOGY, L. Carmichael (ed.). New York: Wiley, 1954. 781–832.

Jouvet, M. and J. L. Valatx. "Étude Polygraphique du Sommeil chez l'Agneau," *Comptes Rendus des Séances de la Société de Biologie et de ses Filiales*, 156 (1962), 1411–14.

Jouvet, M., F. Michel and D. Mounier. "Analyse Électroencéphalographique Comparée du Sommeil Physiologique chez le Chat et chez l'Homme," *Revue Neurologique*, 103 (1960), 189–205.

Jouvet, M., B. Pellin and D. Mounier. "Étude Polygraphic des Différentes Phases du Sommeil au Cours des Troubles de Conscience Chroniques (Comas Prolonges)," *Revue Neurologique*, 105 (1961), 181.

Juda, A. "The Relationship Between Highest Mental Capacity and Psychic Abnormalities," *American Journal of Psychiatry*, 106 (1949), 296–307.

Jung, C. G. CONTRIBUTIONS TO ANALYTICAL PSYCHOLOGY. London: Kegan Paul, Trench, Truebner, 1928.

Kalinowsky, L. B. "Appraisal of the 'Tranquilizers' and Their Influence on Other Somatic Treatments in Psychiatry," *American Journal of Psychiatry*, 115 (1958), 294–98.

———. "Electric Convulsive Therapy After Ten Years of Pharmacotherapy," *American Journal of Psychiatry*, 120 (1964), 944–49.

——— and P. H. Hoch. SHOCK TREATMENTS, PSYCHOSURGERY and OTHER SOMATIC PROCEDURES IN PSYCHIATRY. New York: Grune & Stratton, 1952.

———. SOMATIC TREATMENTS IN PSYCHIATRY. New York: Grune & Stratton, 1961.

Kallmann, F. J. "Genetic Aspects of Psychoses," THE BIOLOGY OF MENTAL HEALTH AND DISEASE. New York: Harper & Bros., 1952.

———. HEREDITY IN HEALTH AND MENTAL DISORDER. New York: Norton, 1953.

———. "The Use of Genetics in Psychiatry," *Journal of Mental Science*, 104 (1958), 542–49.

——— and B. Roth. "Genetic Aspects of Pre-Adolescent Schizophrenia," *American Journal of Psychiatry*, 112 (1956), 599–606.

Kallmann, F. J. and G. Sander. "Twin Studies in Senescence," *American Journal of Psychiatry*, 106 (1949), 29–36.

Kanner, L. "Judging Emotions from Facial Expressions," *Psychological Monographs*, Number 186, 1931.

———. CHILD PSYCHIATRY. Springfield, Illinois: Charles C. Thomas, 1935, 1948, 1957.

———. "Early Infantile Autism," *Journal of Pediatrics*, 25 (1944), 211–17.

Kardiner, A. "The Neuroses of War," *War Medicine*, 1 (1941), 219–26.

Karnosh, L. J. and E. M. Zucker. HANDBOOK OF PSYCHIATRY. St. Louis: C. V. Mosby Co., 1945.

Karpman, B. "Objective Psychotherapy: Principles, Method and Results," *Journal of Clinical Psychology*, 5 (1949), 189–342.

Karwoski, T. F. and H. S. Odbert. "Color Music," *Psychological Monographs*, 50 (1938), Number 222.

——— and C. E. Osgood. "Studies in Synesthetic Thinking: II. The Role of Form in Visual Responses to Music," *Journal of General Psychology*, 26 (1942), 199–222.

Katz, B. and G. Lehner. MENTAL HYGIENE IN MODERN LIVING. New York: Ronald, 1953.

Katz, D. and K. W. Braly. "Racial Prejudice and Racial Stereotypes," *Journal of Abnormal and Social Psychology*, 30 (1933), 175–93.

Katz, S. "My Twelve Hours as a Madman," *Maclean's Magazine*, Toronto, October 1, 1953.

Katz, S. E. and C. Landis. "Psychologic and Physiologic Phenomena During a Prolonged Vigil," *Archives of Neurology and Psychiatry*, 34 (1935), 307–16.

Kaufman, I., T. Frank, L. Heims, J. Herrick, D. Reiser and L. Willer. "Treatment Implications of a New Classification of Parents of Schizophrenic Children," *American Journal of Psychiatry*, 116 (1960), 920–24.

Kawi, A. A. and B. Pasamanick. "Prenatal and Paranatal Factors in the Development of Childhood Reading Disorders," *Monographs of the Society for Research in Child Development*, 24 (1959), 1–80.

Keller, F. S. "Studies in International Morse Code. I. A New Method of Teaching Code Reception," *Journal of Applied Psychology*, 27 (1943), 407–15.

Kellogg, W. N., J. Deese, N. H. Pronko and M. Feinberg. "An Attempt to Condition the Chronic Spinal Dog," *Journal of Experimental Psychology*, 37 (1947), 99–117.

Kelly, E. L. "Concerning the Validity of Terman's Weights for Predicting Marital Happiness," *Psychological Bulletin*, 36 (1939), 202–3.

———. "Marital Compatibility as Related to Personality Traits of Husbands and Wives as Rated by Self and Spouse," *Journal of Social Psychology*, 13 (1941), 193–98.

Kelly, J. G., J. E. Ferson and W. H. Holtzman. "The Measurement of Attitudes Toward the Negro in the South," *Journal of Social Psychology*, 48 (1958), 305–17.

Kelman, H. C. and C. I. Hovland, "'Reinstatement' of the Communicator in Delayed Measurement of Opinion Change," *Journal of Abnormal and Social Psychology*, 48 (1953), 327–35.

Kerry, R. J. "Phobia of Outer Space," *Journal of Mental Science*, 106 (1960), 1383.

Keys, A., J. Brŏzek, A. Henschel, O. Mickelson and H. Taylor. THE BIOLOGY OF HUMAN STARVATION. Two volumes. Minneapolis: University of Minnesota Press, 1950.

Kibbee, J. M., C. I. Craft and B. Nanus. MANAGEMENT GAMES: A NEW TECHNIQUE FOR EXECUTIVE DEVELOPMENT. New York: Reinhold Publishing Corp., 1961.

Kiersch, T. A. "Amnesia: A Clinical Study of Ninety-Eight Cases," *American Journal of Psychiatry*, 68 (1962), 51–60.

Kim, C. "Sexual Activity of Male Rats Following Ablation of Hippocampus," *Journal of Comparative and Physiological Psychology*, 53 (1960), 553–57.

Kimble, G. A. and N. Garmezy. PRINCIPLES OF GENERAL PSYCHOLOGY. New York: Ronald, 1963.

Kimble, G. A. and J. W. Kendall, Jr. "A Comparison of Two Methods of Producing Experimental Extinction," *Journal of Experimental Psychology*, 45 (1953), 87–90.

Kinder, E. F. "A Study of the Nest-Building Activity of the Albino Rat," *Journal of Experimental Zoology*, 47 (1927), 117–61.

King, F. A. "Effects of Septal and Amygdaloid Lesions on Emotional Behavior and Conditioned Avoidance Responses in the Rat," *Journal of Nervous and Mental Disease*, 126 (1958), 57–63.

Kinsey, A. C., Pomeroy, W. B. and C. E. Martin. SEXUAL BEHAVIOR IN THE HUMAN MALE. Philadelphia: Saunders, 1948.

——— and P. H. Gebhard, "Concepts of Normality and Abnormality in Sexual Behavior," PSYCHOSEXUAL DEVELOPMENT IN HEALTH AND DISEASE, P. H. Hoch and J. Zubin (eds.). New York: Grune & Stratton, 1949.

Kinsey, A. C. et al. SEXUAL BEHAVIOR IN THE HUMAN FEMALE. Philadelphia: Saunders, 1953.

Kisker, G. W. THE DISORGANIZED PERSONALITY. New York: McGraw-Hill, 1964.

Klaf, F. S. and C. A. Davis. "Homosexuality and Paranoid Schizophrenia: A Survey of 150 Cases and Controls," *American Journal of Psychiatry*, 116 (1960), 1070–75.

Klatskin, E. H. "Shifts in Child-Care Practices in Three Social Classes Under an Infant Care Program of Flexible Methodology," *American Journal of Orthopsychiatry*, 22 (1952), 52–61.

Klein, M. PSYCHOANALYSIS OF CHILDREN. London: Hogarth, 1932.

Kleitman, N. "Sleep, Wakefulness and Consciousness," *Psychological Bulletin*, 54 (1957), 354–59.

———. "Physiological Cycling," PSYCHOPHYSIOLOGICAL ASPECTS OF SPACE, B. E. Flaherty (ed.). New York: Columbia University Press, 1961. 158–65.

Kline, M. V. "Hypnotherapy," HANDBOOK OF CLINICAL PSYCHOLOGY, B. B. Wolman (ed.). New York: McGraw-Hill, 1965. Chapter 46.

Kline, N. S. "Use of *Rauwolfia Serpentina* in Neuropsychiatric Conditions," *Annals of the New York Academy of Sciences*, 54 (1954), 107–32.

Klineberg, O. NEGRO INTELLIGENCE AND SELECTIVE MIGRATION. New York: Columbia University Press, 1935.

———. SOCIAL PSYCHOLOGY. New York: Holt, 1940.

———. "Racial Psychology," AMERICAN MINORITIES, M. L. Barron (ed.). New York: Alfred A. Knopf, 1957.

———, S. E. Asch and H. Block. "An Experimental Study of Constitutional Types," *Genetic Psychology Monographs*, 16 (1934), 140–221.

Klineberg, O., H. A. Fjeld and J. P. Foley, Jr. "An Experimental Study of Personality Difference Among Constitutional, 'Racial,' and Cultural Groups." Unpublished project report, 1936.

Kling, A. "Amygdalectomy in the Kitten," *Science*, 137 (1962), 429–30.

Kluckhohn, C., H. A. Murray and D. M. Schneider. PERSONALITY IN NATURE, SOCIETY AND CULTURE. New York: Alfred A. Knopf, 1953.

Knapp, P. H. and S. J. Nemetz. "Acute Bronchial Asthma," *Psychosomatic Medicine*, 22 (1960), 42–55.

Knapp, R. H. "An Experimental Study of a Triadic Hypothesis Concerning the Sources of Esthetic Imagery," *Journal of Projective Techniques and Personality Assessment*, 28 (1964), 49–54.

Knopf, I. J. and T. W. Richards. "The Child's Differentiation in Sex as Reflected in Drawings of the Human Figure," *Journal of Genetic Psychology*, 81 (1952), 99–112.

Knorr, N. J., M. T. Edgerton and J. E. Hoopes. "The 'Insatiable' Cosmetic Surgery Patient," *Plastic and Reconstructive Surgery* 40, Number 3 (1967), 285–89.

Kobayashi, T. and M. Matsui. "On the Conditions of Reaction Time," *Report of the 6th Congress of the Japanese Psychological Association* (1938), 90–94.

Koch, H. L. "The Relation of Certain Formal Attributes of Siblings to Attitudes Held Toward Each Other and Toward Their Parents," *Monograph of the Society for Research in Child Development*, 25 (1960), Number 4.

Koehler, O. "Zahl-Versuche an einem Kolkraben und Vergleichsversuche an Menschen," Z. *Tierpsychologie*, 5 (1943), 575–712.

Kohler, I. "Experiments with Goggles," *Scientific American*, 206 (May 1962), 62–72.

Köhler, W. THE MENTALITY OF APES. New York: Harcourt, Brace & World, 1925.

———. DYNAMICS IN PSYCHOLOGY. New York: Liveright, 1929.

Kohn, M. L. and E. E. Carroll. "Social Class and the Allocation of Parental Responsibility," *Sociometry*, 23 (1960), 372–92.

Koller, G. "Der Nestbau der weissen Maus und seine hormonale Auslösung," *Verlag deutsche zoologische Gesellschaft*, Freiburg (1952), 160–68.

———. "Hormonale und psychische Steuerung beim Nestbau weiser Mäuse," *Zoologischer Anzeiger* (supplement), 19 (1956), 123–32.

Koponen, A. MOCK READERSHIP SURVEY. New York: J. Walter Thompson Co., 1956.

Kopp, S. B. "The Character Structure of Sex Offenders," *American Journal of Psychotherapy*, 16 (1962), 66.

Koppitz, E. M. "Relationships Between Some Background Factors and Children's Interpersonal Attitudes," *Journal of Genetic Psychology*, 91 (1957), 119–29.

Korzybski, A. SCIENCE AND SANITY. Lancaster, Pennsylvania: Science Press, 1941.

Kossoris, M. D. and R. F. Kohler. "Hours of Work and Output," *United States Bureau of Labor Statistics Bulletin*, Number 917, 1947.

Kraepelin, E. DEMENTIA PRAECOX AND PARAPHRENIA. Edinburgh: Livingstone, 1919.

———. TEXTBOOK OF PSYCHIATRY. Leipzig: Barth, 1927.

Kraft, A. M. "The Therapeutic Community," AMERICAN HANDBOOK OF PSYCHIATRY, S. Arieti (ed.). New York: Basic Books, 1966. Volume 3, Chapter 32.

Kraines, S. H. THE THERAPY OF THE NEUROSES AND PSYCHOSES. Philadelphia: Lea & Febiger, 1948.

———. MENTAL DEPRESSIONS AND THEIR TREATMENT. New York: Macmillan, 1957.

Krech, D. and R. S. Crutchfield. ELEMENTS OF PSYCHOLOGY. New York: Alfred A. Knopf, 1958.

——— and E. L. Ballachey. INDIVIDUAL IN SOCIETY. New York: McGraw-Hill, 1962.

Kretschmer, E. PHYSIQUE AND CHARACTER. New York: Harcourt, Brace & World, 1925.

Krueger, W. C. F. "The Effect of Overlearning on Retention," *Journal of Experimental Psychology*, 12 (1929), 71–78.

Kryter, K. D. "Effects of Noise on Man," *Journal of Speech and Hearing Disorders*, Supplement Number 1 (1950), 18.

Kubie, L. S. "Use of Induced Hypnagogic Reveries in the Recovery of Repressed Amnesic Data," *Bulletin of the Menninger Clinic*, 7 (1943), 172.

Kubis, J. F. "Studies in Lie Detection: Computer Feasibility Considerations," U. S. Air Forces RADC-TR (1962), 62–205.

Kuo, Z. Y. "The Genesis of the Cat's Response to the Rat," *Journal of Comparative Psychology*, 11 (1930), 1–36.

———. "Ontogeny of Embryonic Behavior in Aves. IV. The Influence of Embryonic Movements upon the Behavior After Hatching," *Journal of Comparative Psychology*, 13 (1932), 245–72.

Kushner, M. "Desensitization of a Post-Traumatic Phobia," CASE STUDIES IN BEHAVIOR MODIFICATION, L. P. Ullman and L. Krasner (eds.). New York: Holt, Rinehart & Winston, 1965. 193–96.

Lacey, J. I., D. E. Bateman and R. Van Lehn. "Autonomic Response Specificity and Rorschach Color Responses," *Psychosomatic Medicine*, 14 (1952), 256–60.

Ladd-Franklin, C. COLOUR AND COLOUR THEORIES. New York: Harcourt, Brace, 1929.

Laird, D. A. "How the Consumer Estimates Quality by Subconscious Sensory Impression," *Journal of Applied Psychology*, 16 (1932), 241–46.

Land, E. H. "Experiments in Color Vision," *Scientific American* (May 1959), 84–99.

Landis, C. "Studies of Emotional Reaction: II. General Behavior and Facial Expression," *Journal of Comparative Psychology*, 4 (1924), 447–509.

——— and M. M. Bolles. TEXTBOOK OF ABNORMAL PSYCHIATRY. New York: Macmillan, 1948.

Landis, C. and W. A. Hunt. THE STARTLE PATTERN. New York: Farrar, 1939.

Landis, C. and F. A. Mettler. VARIETIES OF PSYCHOPATHOLOGICAL EXPERIENCE. New York: Holt, Rinehart & Winston, 1964.

Landis, J. T. "Length of Time Required to Achieve Adjustment in Marriage," *American Sociological Review*, 11 (1946), 668.

———— and M. G. Landis. BUILDING A SUCCESSFUL MARRIAGE. Englewood Cliffs, New Jersey: Prentice-Hall, 1963.

Langdon, G. and I. W. Stout. THE DISCIPLINE OF WELL-ADJUSTED CHILDREN. New York: John Day, 1952.

Langfield, H. S. "A Case of Chromesthesia Investigated in 1905 and Again in 1912," *Psychological Bulletin*, 11 (1914), 113–14.

————. "The Judgment of Emotion by Facial Expression," *Journal of Abnormal and Social Psychology*, 13 (1918), 172–84.

Langworthy, O. R. and B. J. Betz. "Narcolepsy as a Type of Response to Emotional Conflict," *Psychosomatic Medicine*, 6 (1944), 222–26.

La Pière, R. T. COLLECTIVE BEHAVIOR. New York: McGraw-Hill, 1938.

Lashley, K. S. "The Behavioristic Interpretation of Consciousness," *Psychological Review*, 30 (1923), 237–72, 329–53.

————, K. L. Chow and J. Semmes. "An Examination of the Electrical Field Theory of Cerebral Integration," *Psychological Review*, 58 (1951), 123–36.

Lasko, J. K. "Parent Behavior Toward First and Second Children," *Genetic Psychology Monographs*, 49 (1954), 97–137.

Lauer, J. and D. G. Paterson. "Readability of Union Contracts," *Personnel*, 28 (1951), 36–40.

Laycock, F. and J. S. Caylor. "Physiques of Gifted Children and their Less Gifted Siblings," *Child Development*, 35 (1964), 63–74.

Lazarus, A. A. "The Elimination of Children's Phobias by Deconditioning," BEHAVIOUR AND THE NEUROSES, H. J. Eysenck (ed.). London: Pergamon, 1960. 114–22.

Lazell, E. W. "The Group Treatment of Dementia Praecox," *Psychoanalytic Review*, 8 (1921), 168–79.

Leavitt, H. J. and R. A. H. Mueller. "Some Effects of Feedback on Communication," *Human Relations*, 4 (1951), 401–10.

Le Bon, G. THE CROWD. London: Unwin, 1917.

Lee, E. S. "Negro Intelligence and Selective Migration: A Philadelphia Test of the Klineberg Hypothesis," *American Sociological Review*, 16 (1951), 227–33.

Leeper, R. "The Role of Motivation in Learning: A Study of the Phenomenon of Differential Motivation Control of the Utilization of Habits," *Journal of Genetic Psychology*, 46 (1935), 3–40.

Legros, L. A. and H. C. Weston. "On the Design of Machinery in Relation to the Operator," *Industrial Fatigue Research Board, Report No. 36*, 1926.

Lehfeldt, H. THE ENCYCLOPEDIA OF SEXUAL BEHAVIOR. A. Ellis and A. Abarbanel (eds.). New York: Hawthorne, 1961. Volume 2.

Lehner, G. "Projections of Men and Women to Items Referring to the Same and Opposite Sex on a Sentence Completion Test," *American Psychologist*, 2 (1947), 407.

Lehrman, D. S. "A Critique of Konrad Lorenz's Theory of Instinctive Behavior," *Quarterly Review of Biology*, 28 (1953), 337–63.

————. "Hormonal Regulation of Parental Behavior in Birds and Infrahuman Mammals," SEX AND INTERNAL SECRETION, W. C. Young (ed.). Baltimore: Williams & Wilkins, 1961.

Leighton, A. H., J. A. Clausen and R. N. Wilson. EXPLORATIONS IN SOCIAL PSYCHIATRY. New York: Basic Books, 1957.

Lemkau, P. V. "Mental Hygiene," AMERICAN HANDBOOK OF PSYCHIATRY, S. Arieti (ed.). New York: Basic Books, 1959. Volume 2, Chapter 99.

Lenneberg, E. H. and J. M. Roberts. *Indiana University Publications in Anthropology and Linguistics*, Memoir 13, 1956.

Lennox, W. G. "Psychiatry, Psychology and Seizures," *American Journal of Orthopsychiatry*, 19 (1949), 432–46.

Lerner, A. B. "Hormones and Skin Color," *Scientific American*, 205 (July 1961), 98–108.

Leuba, C. J. "An Experimental Study of Rivalry Among Young Children," *Journal of Comparative Psychology*, 16 (1933), 367–78.

———— and D. Bateman. "Learning During Sleep," *American Journal of Psychology*, 65 (1952), 301–2.

Levine, J. "Humor and Mental Health," ENCYCLOPEDIA OF MENTAL HEALTH, A. Deutsch (ed.). New York: Franklin Watts, 1963.

Levine, J. M. and J. Butler. "Lecture vs. Group Discussion in Changing Behavior," *Journal of Applied Psychology*, 36 (1952), 29–33.

Levine, S., M. Alpert and G. W. Lewis. "Infantile Experience and the Maturation of the Pituitary Adrenal Axis," *Science*, 126 (1957), 1347.

Levy, D. M. "Thumb or Finger Sucking from the Psychiatric Angle," *Child Development*, 8 (1937), 99–101.

———. "Maternal Overprotection," *Psychiatry*, 1 (1938), 578–79.

———. "Release Therapy," *American Journal of Orthopsychiatry*, 9 (1939), 713–36.

———. "Psychic Trauma of Operations in Children," *American Journal of Diseases of Children*, 69 (1945), 7–25.

———. "Primary Affect Hunger," *American Journal of Psychiatry*, 94 (1947), 644–45.

Levy, S. "Figure Drawing as a Projective Test," PROJECTIVE PSYCHOLOGY, L. E. Abt and L. Bellak (eds.). New York: Alfred A. Knopf, 1950.

Lewin, K. PRINCIPLES OF TOPOLOGICAL PSYCHOLOGY. New York: McGraw-Hill, 1936.

———. A DYNAMIC THEORY OF PERSONALITY. New York: McGraw-Hill, 1935.

———. RESOLVING SOCIAL ISSUES. New York: Harper & Bros., 1948.

———. FIELD THEORY IN SOCIAL SCIENCE. New York: Harper & Bros., 1951.

———, R. Lippitt and R. K. White. "Patterns of Aggressive Behavior in Experimentally Created Social Climates," *Journal of Social Psychology*, 10 (1939), 271–99.

Lewin, K., T. Dembo, L. Festinger and P. S. Sears. "Level of Aspiration," PERSONALITY AND THE BEHAVIOR DISORDERS, J. McV. Hunt (ed.). New York: Ronald, 1944.

Lewinson, T. S. and J. Zubin. HANDWRITING ANALYSIS. New York: King's Crown Press, 1942.

Lewis, H. B. "An Experimental Study of the Role of the Ego in Work. I. The Role of the Ego in Cooperative Work," *Journal of Experimental Psychology*, 34 (1944), 113–26.

Lewis, S. J. "The Effect of Thumb and Finger Sucking on the Primary Teeth and Dental Arches," *Child Development*, 8 (1937), 93–98.

Licht, M. "The Measurement of One Aspect of Personality," *Journal of Psychology*, 24 (1947), 83–87.

Liddell, H. S. "Experimental Induction of Psychoneuroses by Conditioned Reflex with Stress," THE BIOLOGY OF MENTAL HEALTH AND DISEASE, Milbank Memorial Fund. New York: Hoeber-Harper, 1952.

———. "Sheep and Goats: The Psychological Effects of Laboratory Experiences of Deprivation and Stress upon Certain Experimental Animals," BEYOND THE GERM THEORY, I. Galdston (ed.). New York: New York Academy of Medicine, Health Education Council, 1954.

———. "Experimental Neuroses in Animals," STRESS AND PSYCHIATRIC DISORDERS, J. M. Tanner (ed.). Oxford: Blackwell Scientific Publication, 1960.

Lidz, T. "General Concepts of Psychosomatic Medicine," AMERICAN HANDBOOK OF PSYCHIATRY, S. Arieti (ed.). New York: Basic Books, 1959. Chapter 32.

———, A. R. Cornelison, S. Fleck and D. Terry. "Intrafamilial Environment of the Schizophrenic Patient. I. The Father," *Psychiatry*, 20 (1957), 329–42.

Lidz, T., S. Fleck, Y. O. Alanen and A. R. Cornelison. "Schizophrenic Patients and Their Siblings," *Psychiatry*, 26 (1963), 1–18.

Lief, A. (ed.). THE COMMONSENSE PSYCHIATRY OF DR. ADOLPH MEYER. New York: McGraw-Hill, 1948.

Likert, R. NEW PATTERNS OF MANAGEMENT. New York: McGraw-Hill, 1961.

Lindahl, L. G. "Movement Analysis as an Industrial Training Method," *Journal of Applied Psychology*, 29 (1945), 420–36.

Lindner, R. M. "Psychopathic Personality and the Concept of Homeostasis," *Journal of Clinical Psychopathology and Psychotherapy*, 6 (1945), 517–21.

———. "Hypnoanalysis," ENCYCLOPEDIA OF PSYCHOLOGY, P. L. Harriman (ed.). New York: The Philosophical Library, 1946. 245–48.

Lindskog, C. W. "Helmholtz," COLLIER'S ENCYCLOPEDIA. New York: Crowell-Collier and Macmillan, 1966. Volume 12.

Lindsley, D. B. "Emotion," HANDBOOK OF EXPERIMENTAL PSYCHOLOGY, S. S. Stevens (ed.). New York: Wiley-Interscience, 1951.

Lindzey, G. "On the Classification of Projective Techniques," *Psychological Bulletin*, 56 (1959), 158–68.

——— and E. F. Borgatta. "Sociometric Measurement," HANDBOOK OF SOCIAL PSYCHOLOGY, G. Lindzey (ed.). Reading, Massachusetts: Addison-Wesley, 1954. Volume I, Chapter 11.

Linn, L. "Hospital Psychiatry," AMERICAN HANDBOOK OF PSYCHIATRY, S. Arieti (ed.). New York: Basic Books, 1959. Volume 2, Chapter 91.

Lipset, S. M. and R. Bendix. SOCIAL MOBILITY IN INDUSTRIAL SOCIETY. Berkeley: University of California Press, 1959.

Lipton, S. "Dissociated Personality: A Case Report," *Psychiatric Quarterly*, 17 (1943), 35–56.

Little, K. B. and E. S. Shneidmann. "Congruencies Among Interpretations of Psychological Test and Anamnestic Data," *Psychological Monographs*, 73 (1959), Number 6.

Littman, R. A. and H. M. Manning. "A Methodological Study of Cigarette Brand Discrimination," *Journal of Applied Psychology*, 38 (1954), 185–90.

Locke, H. J. PREDICTING ADJUSTMENT IN MARRIAGE: A COMPARISON OF A DIVORCED AND A HAPPILY MARRIED GROUP. New York: Holt, 1951.

Loevinger, J. "A Theory of Test Response," *Proceedings, 1958 Invitation Conference on Test Problems, Educational Testing Service* (1959), 36–47.

Lomax, A. "Song Structure and Social Structure," *Ethnology*, 1 (1962), 425–51.

Longstaff, H. P. and G. P. Laybourn. "What Do Readership Studies Really Prove?" *Journal of Applied Psychology*, 33 (1949), 585–93.

Loomis, C. P. and J. A. Beegle. RURAL SOCIAL SYSTEMS: A TEXTBOOK IN RURAL SOCIOLOGY AND ANTHROPOLOGY. New York: Prentice-Hall, 1950.

Loomis, E. A. Jr. "Pastoral Counseling," ENCYCLOPEDIA OF MENTAL HEALTH, A. Deutsch (ed.). New York: Franklin Watts, 1963. 1449–57.

Loranger, A. W., C. T. Prout and M. A. White. "The Placebo Effect in Psychiatric Drug Research," *Journal of the American Medical Association*, 176 (1961), 920–25.

Lorenz, K. "The Companion in the Bird's World," *Auk*, 54 (1937), 245–73.

———. ON AGGRESSION. New York: Harcourt, Brace, 1966.

Lorr, M. "Measurement of the Major Psychotic Syndromes," *Annals of the New York Academy of Sciences*, 93 (1962), 851–56.

Louria, D. B. "Cool Talk About Hot Drugs," *The New York Times Magazine*, August 6, 1967, 12.

Lourie, R. S. "Attempted Suicide in Children and Adolescents." Unpublished paper delivered at George Washington University School of Medicine Symposium on Suicide, October 14, 1965.

Low, A. A. MENTAL HEALTH THROUGH WILL-TRAINING. Boston: Christopher, 1950.

Lowe, C. R. "Effect of Mothers' Smoking Habits on Birth Weight of Their Children," *British Medical Journal*, Number 5153 (October 10, 1959), 673–76.

Lowen, A. THE ENCYCLOPEDIA OF SEXUAL BEHAVIOR, A. Ellis and A. Abarbanel (eds.). New York: Hawthorne, 1961. Volume 2.

Lubin, A., C. F. Giesekling and H. L. Williams. "Direct Measurement of Cognitive Deficit in Schizophrenia," *Journal of Consulting Psychology*, 26 (1962), 139–43.

Lucas, D. B. and S. H. Britt. MEASURING ADVERTISING EFFECTIVENESS. New York: McGraw-Hill, 1963.

Luchins, A. S. "Mechanization in Problem Solving: The Effect of Einstellung," *Psychological Monographs*, 54 (1942), Number 248.

Luria, A. R. "Neuropsychological Analysis of Focal Brain Lesions," HANDBOOK OF CLINICAL PSYCHOLOGY, B. B. Wolman (ed.). New York: McGraw-Hill, 1965. Chapter 26.

Lykken, D. T. "The Validity of the Guilty Knowledge Technique: The Effects of Faking," *Journal of Applied Psychology*, 44 (1960), 258–62.

Macalpine, I. and R. Hunter. "Porphyria and King George III," *Scientific American*, 221, Number 1 (1969), 38–46.

McCary, J. L. and D. E. Sheer. SIX APPROACHES TO PSYCHOTHERAPY. New York: Dryden, 1955.

McCleary, R. A. "Response Specificity in the Behavioral Effects of Limbic System Lesions in the Cat," *Journal of Comparative and Physiological Psychology*, 54 (1961), 605–13.

——— and C. T. Morgan. "Food Hoarding in Rats as a Function of Environmental Temperature," *Journal of Comparative and Physiological Psychology*, 39 (1946), 371–78.

McClelland, D. C. PERSONALITY. New York: William Sloane Associates, 1951.

———. "The Use of Measures of Human Motivation in the Study of Society," MOTIVES IN FANTASY, ACTION AND SOCIETY, J. W. Atkinson (ed.). Princeton, New Jersey: Van Nostrand, 1958.

———. THE ACHIEVING SOCIETY. Princeton, New Jersey: Van Nostrand, 1961.

——— and J. W. Atkinson. "The Projective Expression of Needs. 1. The Effect of Different Intensities of the Hunger Drive on Perception," *Journal of Psychology*, 25 (1948), 205–22.

McClelland, D. C. and A. M. Liberman. "The Effect of Need for Achievement on Recognition of Need-Related Words," *Journal of Personality*, 18 (1949), 236–51.

McClelland, D. C., J. W. Atkinson and R. A. Clark. "The Projective Expression of Needs. III. The Effect of Ego-Involvement, Success, and Failure on Perception," *Journal of Psychology*, 27 (1949), 311–30.

——— and E. L. Lowell. THE ACHIEVEMENT MOTIVE. New York: Appleton-Century-Crofts, 1953.

McConnell, J. V. "Comparative Physiology: Learning in Invertebrates," *Annual Review of Physiology*, 28 (1966), 107–36.

McCurdy, H. G. "The Childhood Pattern of Genius," *Journal, Elisha Mitchell Scientific Society*, 73 (1957), 448–62.

McDougall, W. OUTLINE OF ABNORMAL PSYCHOLOGY. New York: Scribner, 1926.

McFadden, E. R., Jr., T. Luparello, H. A. Lyons, and E. Bleeker. "The Mechanism of Action of Suggestion in the Induction of Acute Asthma Attacks," *Psychosomatic Medicine,* March–April 1969.

MacFarland, M. B. "Relationships Between Young Sisters as Revealed in their Overt Responses," *Child Development Monographs,* Number 23, 1938.

McFarland, R. A. "Psychological Effects of Oxygen Deprivation (Anoxemia) on Human Behavior," *Archives of Psychology,* 145 (1932).

———. "Psycho-Physiological Studies at High Altitudes in the Andes. II. Sensory and Motor Responses During Acclimation." *Journal of Comparative Psychology,* 24 (1937).

———. "Anoxia: Its Effects on the Physiology and Biochemistry of the Brain and on Behavior," THE BIOLOGY OF MENTAL HEALTH AND DISEASE. New York: Hoeber-Harper, 1952.

MacFarlane, J., L. Allen and M. P. Honzik. A DEVELOPMENTAL STUDY OF THE BEHAVIOR PROBLEMS OF NORMAL CHILDREN BETWEEN TWENTY-ONE MONTHS AND FOURTEEN YEARS. Berkeley: University of California Press, 1954.

McGehee, W. and J. E. Gardner. "Music in a Complex Industrial Job," *Personnel Psychology,* 2 (1949), 405–17.

McGinnis, T. THE FIRST YEAR OF MARRIAGE. Garden City, New York: Doubleday & Company, 1967.

McGraw, R. B. and J. F. Oliven. "Miscellaneous Therapies," AMERICAN HANDBOOK OF PSYCHIATRY, S. Arieti (ed.). New York: Basic Books, 1959. Volume 2, Chapter 78.

McGraw-Hill Research Laboratory of Advertising Performance. "How Repeat Advertisements Affect Readership," *Data Sheet,* 3040 (1962).

McGuire, W. J. "Cognitive Consistency and Attitude Change," *Journal of Abnormal and Social Psychology,* 60 (1960), 345–53.

Machover, K. "Drawing of the Human Figure: A Method of Personality Investigation," AN INTRODUCTION TO PROJECTIVE TECHNIQUES, H. H. Anderson and G. L. Anderson (eds.). New York: Prentice-Hall, 1951. Chapter 12.

MacKenzie, N. DREAMS AND DREAMING. New York: Vanguard Press, 1965.

McKinley, J. C. and S. R. Hathaway. "The Identification and Measurement of the Psychoneuroses in Medical Practice: The MMPI," *Journal of the American Medical Association,* 122 (1943), 161–67.

MacKinnon, D. W. (ed.). THE CREATIVE PERSONALITY. Berkeley: University of California General Extension, 1962.

———. "The Nature and Nurture of Creative Talent," *American Psychologist,* 17 (1962), 484–95.

———. "Personality and the Realization of Creative Potential," *American Psychologist,* 20 (1965), 273–81.

McKinnon, K. M. "A Clinical Evaluation of the Method of Direct Analysis in the Treatment of Psychosis," *Journal of Clinical Psychology,* 15 (1959), 80–96.

Mackworth, N. H. "Effects of Heat on Wireless Operators' Hearing and Recording Morse Code Messages," *British Journal of Industrial Medicine,* 3 (1946), 143–58.

———. "Researches in the Measurement of Human Performance," *Medical Research Council Special Report Series,* London: H. M. Stationery Office, 1950. Number 268.

Maclay, H. and E. E. Ware. "Cross-Cultural Use of the Semantic Differential," *Behavioral Science,* 6 (1961), 185–90.

MacLean, P. D. "Psychosomatic Disease and the 'Visceral Brain,'" *Psychosomatic Medicine,* 11 (1949), 338–53.

———. "The Limbic System with Respect to the Self-Preservation of the Species," *Journal of Nervous and Mental Disease,* 127 (1958), 1–11.

MacLean, J. R., D. C. MacDonald, U. P. Byrne and A. M. Hubbard. "The Use of LSD-25 in the Treatment of Alcoholism and other Psychiatric Problems," *Quarterly Journal of Studies in Alcoholism,* 22 (1961), 34–45.

MacLeod, J. S. PREDICTING THE RESPONSES TO ADVERTISING THEMES FROM SENTENCE COMPLETIONS TO DIRECT ATTITUDE QUESTIONS ABOUT AN ADVERTISED PRODUCT. New York: Advertising Research Foundation, 1958.

McMurry, R. N. "Validating the Patterned Interview," *Personnel,* 23 (1947), 263–72.

McNemar, Q. THE REVISION OF THE STANFORD-BINET SCALE. Boston: Houghton Mifflin, 1942.

MacNichol, E. F., Jr. "Three Pigment Color Vision," *Scientific American,* December (1964), 48–56.

Madden, R. "The School Status of the Hard-of-Hearing Child," *Teachers College Contribution to Education,* Number 499, 1931.

Mager, A. "Die Enge des Bewusstseins," *Studien Ps. Philos.* (Münhener), 1920, Number 5.

Mahler, M. S. "Autism and Symbiosis: Two Extreme Disturbances of Identity," *International Journal of Psycho-Analysis,* 39 (1958), 77.

———. M. Furer, C. F. Settlage. "Severe Emotional Disturbances in Childhood: Psychosis," AMERICAN HANDBOOK OF PSYCHIATRY, S. Arieti (ed.). New York: Basic Books, 1959. Volume 1, Chapter 41.

Mahler, W. R. and W. H. Monroe. "How Industry Determines the Need for and Effectiveness of Training," *Personnel Research Section, Department of the Army,* PRS Report Number 929, March 15, 1952.

Mannes, M. "Ain't Nobody Here but Us Commercials," *Reporter,* 17 (1957), Number 6.

Marks, P. A. "An Assessment of the Diagnostic Process in a Child Guidance Setting," *Psychological Monographs,* 75 (1961), Number 507.

Marmor, J. and E. Pumpian-Mindlin. "Toward an Integrative Concept of Mental Disorder," *Journal of Nervous and Mental Disease,* 111 (1950), 19–29.

Marple, C. H. "The Comparative Susceptibility of Three Age Levels to Suggestion of Group versus Expert Opinion," *Journal of Social Psychology,* 4 (1933), 176–86.

Marrow, A. J. "Goal Tensions and Recall," *Journal of Genetic Psychology,* 19 (1938), 3–35, 37–64.

———. BEHIND THE EXECUTIVE MASK. New York: American Management Association, 1964.

Marsh, L. C. "Group Therapy and the Psychiatric Clinic," *Journal of Nervous and Mental Disease,* 82 (1935), 381–92.

Marshall, H. R. and B. R. McCandless. "Relationship Between Dependence on Adults and Social Acceptance by Peers," *Child Development,* 28 (1957), 413–19.

Marston, W. M. THE LIE DETECTOR TEST. New York: R. E. Smith, 1938.

Martin, D. V. "Institutionalisation," *Lancet,* 2 (1955), 1188–90.

Marx, M. H. "A Stimulus-Response Analysis of the Hoarding Habit in the Rat," *Psychological Review,* 57 (1950), 80–93.

Maslow, A. H. MOTIVATION AND PERSONALITY. New York: Harper & Bros., 1954.

——— and B. Mittelmann. PRINCIPLES OF ABNORMAL PSYCHOLOGY: THE DYNAMICS OF PSYCHIC ILLNESS. New York: Harper & Bros., 1941, 1951.

Masserman, J. H. BEHAVIOR AND NEUROSIS. Chicago: University of Chicago Press, 1943.

———. THE PRACTICE OF DYNAMIC PSYCHIATRY. Philadelphia: Saunders, 1955.

———. PRINCIPLES OF DYNAMIC PSYCHIATRY. Philadelphia: Saunders, 1961.

Max, L. W. "Experimental Study of the Motor Theory of Consciousness. IV. Action-Current Responses of the Deaf During Awaking, Kinesthetic Imagery and Abstract Thinking," *Journal of Comparative Psychology,* 24 (1937), 301–44.

Maxfield, K. B. and S. Buchholz. A SOCIAL MATURITY SCALE FOR BLIND PRESCHOOL CHILDREN: A GUIDE TO ITS USE. New York: American Foundation for the Blind, 1957.

May, M. A. et al. "Do 'Motivation' and 'Participation' Questions Increase Learning?" *Educational Screen,* 26 (1947), 256–59, 274, 283.

Mayer, J. "Regulation of Energy Intake and the Body Weight: The Glucostatic Theory and the Lipostatic Hypothesis," *Annals of the New York Academy of Sciences,* 63 (1955), Article 1, 15–43.

Mayo. E. THE HUMAN PROBLEMS OF AN INDUSTRIAL CIVILIZATION. New York: Macmillan, 1933.

Mead, M. MALE AND FEMALE. New York: William Morrow, 1949.

Meares, A. THE DOOR OF SERENITY. Springfield, Illinois: Charles C. Thomas, 1958.

Medinnus, G. R. "Objective Responsibility in Children: A Comparison with Piaget Data," *Journal of Genetic Psychology,* 101 (1962), 127–33.

Meerloo, J. A. "Emergency Psychotherapy and Mental First Aid," *Journal of Nervous and Mental Disease,* 124 (1956), 535–45.

Meltzer, H. "Students' Adjustments in Anger," *Journal of Social Psychology,* 4 (1933), 285–309.

Melzack, R. and T. H. Scott. "The Effects of Early Experience on the Response to Pain," *Journal of Comparative and Physiological Psychology,* 50 (1957), 155–61.

Menninger, K. A. MAN AGAINST HIMSELF. New York: Harcourt, Brace, 1938.

———. THE HUMAN MIND. New York: Alfred A. Knopf, 1945.

———. "Totemic Aspects of Contemporary Attitudes Toward Animals," PSYCHOANALYSIS AND CULTURE: ESSAYS IN HONOR OF GÉZA RÓHEIM. New York: International Universities Press, 1951.

Menninger, W. PSYCHIATRY IN A TROUBLED WORLD. New York: Macmillan, 1948.

Meyer, A. "The Psychobiological Point of View," COLLECTED WORKS, E. E. Winters **(ed.).** Baltimore: Johns Hopkins Press, 1951.

Meyer, L. B. EMOTIONS AND MEANING IN MUSIC. Chicago: University of Chicago Press, 1956.

Meyer, H. J. and E. F. Borgatta. AN EXPERIMENT IN MENTAL PATIENT REHABILITATION: Evaluating a Social Agency Program. New York: Russell Sage Foundation, 1959.

Michael, J. "Behavioral Approaches to Rehabilitation," Unpublished paper presented at Stanford Medical School, 1963.

Michael, W. B., B. G. Rosenthal and M. A. DeCamp. "An Experimental Investigation of Prestige-Suggestion for Two Types of Literary Material," *Journal of Psychology*, 28 (1949), 303–23.

Midelfort C. F. THE FAMILY IN PSYCHOTHERAPHY. New York: McGraw-Hill 1957.

Miles, C. and H. Ramsden. "Experiments in Thought-Transference," *Proceedings of the Society for Psychical Research*, 21 (1907), 60–93.

———. "Experiments in Thought-Transference," *Proceedings of the Society for Psychical Research*, 27 (1915), 279–317.

Miles, W. R. "Psychological Aspects of Ageing," PROBLEMS OF AGEING, E. V. Crowdry (ed.). Baltimore: Williams & Wilkins, 1942.

Milici, P. "Graphocatharsis in Schizophrenia," *Psychiatric Quarterly*, 11 (1937), 44–73.

Miller, C. R. THE PROCESS OF PERSUASION. New York: Crown, 1946.

Miller, D. H. "Psycho-Social Factors in the Aetiology of Disturbed Behaviour," *British Journal of Medical Psychology*, 34 (1961), 43–52.

Miller, D. R. and G. E. Swanson. INNER CONFLICTS AND DEFENSE. New York: Holt-Dryden, 1960.

Miller, G. A. "The Magic Number Seven, Plus or Minus Two: Some Limits on Our Capacity for Processing Information," *Psychological Review*, 63 (1956), 81–97.

———, J. Bruner and L. Postman. Cited in LANGUAGE AND COMMUNICATION, G. A. Miller (ed.). New York: McGraw-Hill, 1951.

Miller, G. A., E. Galanter and K. H. Pribram. PLANS AND THE STRUCTURE OF BEHAVIOR. New York: Holt, 1960.

Miller, N. E. "The Perception of Children. A Genetic Study Employing the Delayed Reaction," *Journal of Genetic Psychology*, 44 (1934), 321–39.

———. "The Frustration-Aggression Hypothesis," *Psychological Review*, 38 (1941), 337–42.

———. "Theory and Experiment Relating Psychoanalytic Displacement to Stimulus-Response Generalization," *Journal of Abnormal and Social Psychology*, 43 (1948), 155–78.

———. "Central Stimulation and Other New Approaches to Motivation and Reward," *American Psychologist*, 13 (1958), 100–8.

———. "Liberalization of Basic S-R Concepts: Extensions to Conflict Behavior, Motivation and Social Learning," PSYCHOLOGY: A STUDY OF A SCIENCE, S. Koch (ed.). New York: McGraw-Hill, 1959. Volume 2.

——— and R. Bugelski. "Minor Studies of Aggression. II. The Influence of Frustrations Imposed by the In-Group on Attitudes Expressed Toward Out-Groups," *Journal of Psychology*, 25 (1948), 437–42.

Milner, B. "Psychological Defects Produced by Temporal Lobe Excision," THE BRAIN AND HUMAN BEHAVIOR. Research Publication, Association of Nervous and Mental Diseases, (1958), 244–57.

Milner, P. M. "The Application of Physiology to Learning Theory," CURRENT TRENDS IN PSYCHOLOGICAL THEORY, R. A. Patton (ed.). Pittsburgh: University of Pittsburgh Press, 1961.

Mintz, A. "A Re-examination of Correlations Between Lynchings and Economic Indices," *Journal of Abnormal and Social Psychology*, 41 (1946), 154–60.

———. "Non-Adaptive Group Behavior" *Journal of Abnormal and Social Psychology*, 46 (1951), 150–59.

Mitchell, S. W. "Remarks on the Effects of Anhelonium Lewinii (The Mescal Button)," *British Medical Association*, 2:1625 (1896).

Mittelmann, B. and H. G. Wolff. "Affective States and Skin Temperature: Experimental Study of Subjects with 'Cold Hands' and Raynaud's Syndrome," *Psychosomatic Medicine*, 1 (1939), 271–92.

———. "Emotions and Gastroduodenal Function: Experimental Studies on Patients with Gastritis, Duodenitis and Peptic Ulcer," *Psychosomatic Medicine*, 4 (1942), 5–61.

Modern Packaging. "A Robot Redesigns Vicks," Number 7 (March 1961), 90–91.

Moncur, J. P. "Parental Domination in Stuttering," *Journal of Speech and Hearing Disorders*, 17 (1952), 155–64.

Money, J., J. G. Hampson and J. L. Hampson. "Imprinting and the Establishment of Gender Role," *A.M.A. Archives of Neurology and Psychiatry*, 77 (1957), 333–36.

Montgomery, K. C. "The Role of the Exploratory Drive in Learning," *Journal of Comparative and Physiological Psychology*, 47 (1954), 60–64.

Montgomery, M. F. "The Role of the Salivary Glands in the Thirst Mechanism," *American Journal of Physiology*, 96 (1931), 221–27.

Moore, R. A. and M. L. Selzer. "Male Homosexuality, Paranoia and the Schizophrenias," *American Journal of Psychiatry*, 119 (1963), 743–47.

Moravec, M. "Letters to the Editor," *Saturday Review*, May 1, 1965, 64.

Moreno, J. L. PSYCHODRAMA. New York: Beacon House, 1946.

——. THE THEATER OF SPONTANEITY: AN INTRODUCTION TO PSYCHODRAMA. New York: Beacon House, 1947.

——. "Psychodrama," AMERICAN HANDBOOK OF PSYCHIATRY, S. Arieti (ed.). New York: Basic Books, 1959. Volume 2, Chapter 68.

Morgan, C. T. PHYSIOLOGICAL PSYCHOLOGY. New York: McGraw-Hill, 1943, 1965.

——. "The Hoarding Instinct," *Psychological Review*, 54 (1947), 335–41.

——. INTRODUCTION TO PSYCHOLOGY. New York: McGraw-Hill, 1961.

—— and R. A. King. INTRODUCTION TO PSYCHOLOGY. New York: McGraw-Hill, 1966.

Morgan, C. T. and J. T. Morgan. "Studies in Hunger. II. The Relation of Gastric Denervation and Dietary Sugar to the Effect of Insulin upon Food-Intake in the Rat," *Journal of Genetic Psychology*, 57 (1940), 153–63.

Morgan, C. T., E. Stellar and O. Johnson. "Food Deprivation and Hoarding in Rats," *Journal of Comparative Psychology*, 35 (1943), 275–95.

Morgan, H. H. "An Analysis of Certain Structured and Unstructured Test Results of Achieving and Non-Achieving High Ability College Students." Unpublished Ph.D. dissertation, University of Michigan, 1951.

Morgan, J. J. B. "The Overcoming of Distraction and Other Resistances," *Archives of Psychology*, Number 35, 1916.

Moss, C. S. "Therapeutic Suggestion and Autosuggestion," *Journal of Clinical and Experimental Hypnosis*, 6 (1958), 109–115.

Mowrer, O. H. and W. M. Mowrer. "Enuresis—A Method for Its Study and Treatment," *American Journal of Orthopsychiatry*, 8 (1938), 436–57.

Muellner, S. R. "Development of Urinary Control in Children: Some Aspects of the Cause and Treatment of Primary Enuresis," *Journal of the American Medical Association*, 172 (1960), 1256–61.

Mühl, A. M. "Automatic Writing as an Indicator of the Fundamental Factors Underlying the Personality," *Journal of Abnormal Psychology*, 17 (1922), 162–83.

Mullahy, P. "Non-Freudian Analytic Theories," HANDBOOK OF CLINICAL PSYCHOLOGY, B. B. Wolman (ed.). New York: McGraw-Hill, 1965. Chapter 15.

Mullan, H. and M. Rosenbaum. GROUP PSYCHOTHERAPY. New York: The Free Press, 1962.

Mullan, H. and I. Sangiuliano. "Multiple Psychotherapeutic Practice: Preliminary Report," *American Journal of Psychotherapy* 14 (1960), 550–65.

Müller, J. ELEMENTS OF PHYSIOLOGY. Trans. by W. Bailey, of HANDBUCH DER PHYSIOLOGIE DES MENSCHEN (1838). Philadelphia: Lea and Blanchard, 1843.

Muncie, W. PSYCHOBIOLOGY AND PSYCHIATRY. St. Louis: C. V. Mosby, 1939.

Munn, N. L. PSYCHOLOGY. Boston: Houghton Mifflin, 1966.

Munsinger, H. and W. Kessen. "Uncertainty, Structure and Preference," *Psychological Monographs*, 78 (1964), Number 9.

Murdock, G. P. SOCIAL STRUCTURE. New York: Macmillan, 1949.

Murio, J., H. Roffwarg and E. Kaufman. "Alternations in Young Adult Human Sleep, EEG Configuration Resulting from d-LSD-25," Report to the Association for Psychophysiological Study of Sleep, Palo Alto, California, March 27–29, 1964.

Murphy, D. P. "Ovarian Irradiation: Its Effect on the Health of Subsequent Children," *Surgery, Gynecology, Obstetrics*, 47 (1928), 201–15.

Murphy, G. "Parapsychology," ENCYCLOPEDIA OF PSYCHOLOGY, P. L. Harriman (ed.). New York: Philosophical Library, 1946.

——. PERSONALITY: A BIOSOCIAL APPROACH TO ORIGINS AND STRUCTURE. New York: Basic Books, 1946.

——. HISTORICAL INTRODUCTION TO MODERN PSYCHOLOGY. New York: Harcourt, Brace, 1949.

—— and L. Dale. "Parapsychology or Psychical Research" COLLIERS ENCYCLOPEDIA. New York: Crowell-Collier and Macmillan, 1966.

Murphy, L. B. PERSONALITY IN YOUNG CHILDREN. New York: Basic Books, 1957.

Murray, H. A. et al. EXPLORATIONS IN PERSONALITY. New York: Oxford University Press, 1938.

Mussen, P. H. "Differences Between the TAT Responses of Negro and White Boys," *Journal of Consulting Psychology*, 17 (1953), 373–76.

——— and J. Kagan. "Group Conformity and Perceptions of Parents," *Child Development*, 29 (1958), 57–60.

Mussen, P. H. and H. K. Naylor. "The Relationships Between Overt and Fantasy Aggression," *Journal of Abnormal and Social Psychology*, 49 (1954), 235–40.

Muuss, R. E. THEORIES OF ADOLESCENCE. New York: Random House, 1962.

Myers, C. S. "Edward Bradford Titchener," *British Journal of Psychology*, 18 (1928), 460–63.

Myerson, A. "Theory and Principles of 'Total Push' Method in the Treatment of Chronic Schizophrenia," *American Journal of Psychiatry*, 95 (1939), 1197–1204.

Nafe, J. P. "An Experimental Study of the Affective Qualities," *American Journal of Psychology*, 35 (1924), 507–44.

Nagy, M. H. "The Child's Theories Concerning Death," *Journal of Genetic Psychology*, 73 (1948), 3–27.

Nakamura, C. Y. "Conformity and Problem Solving," *Journal of Abnormal and Social Psychology*, 56 (1958), 315–20.

Nardini, J. E. "Psychiatric Concepts of Prisoners of War Confinement," *Military Medicine*, 127 (1962), 299–307.

National Committee Against Mental Illness. "What Are the Facts About Mental Illness in the United States?", pamphlet. Washington, D.C., 1966.

National Institute of Mental Health. "A Manual on Record-keeping and Statistical Reporting for Mental Health Clinics," Washington, D.C.: U. S. Government Printing Office, 1957.

Nauta, W. J. H. "Hypothalamic Regulation of Sleep in Rats; An Experimental Study," *Journal of Neurophysiology*, 9 (1946), 285–316.

Neazles, J. N. and G. Winokur. "The Hot-Rod Driver," *Bulletin of the Menninger Clinic*, 21 (1957), 28–35.

Neilon, P. "Shirley's Babies After 15 Years," *Journal of Genetic Psychology*, 73 (1948), 175–86.

Nelson, H. E. and A. W. Vandermeer, "The Relative Effectiveness of Several Different Sound Tracks Used on an Animated Film on Elementary Meteorology," *Speech Monographs*, 20 (1953), 261–67.

Nemiah, J. C. FOUNDATIONS OF PSYCHOPATHOLOGY. New York: Oxford University Press, 1961.

Newcomb, T. M. PERSONALITY AND SOCIAL CHANGE. New York: Dryden, 1943.

———, R. H. Turner and P. E. Converse. SOCIAL PSYCHOLOGY. New York: Holt, Rinehart & Winston, 1965.

Newell, H. W. "Play Therapy in Child Psychiatry," *American Journal of Orthopsychiatry*, 11 (1941), 245–51.

Newman, H. H., F. N. Freeman and K. H. Holzinger. TWINS: A STUDY OF HEREDITY AND ENVIRONMENT. Chicago: University of Chicago Press, 1937.

Nissen, H. W. "A Field Study of the Chimpanzee," *Comparative Psychology Monographs*, 8 (1931), 1–122.

———. "Social Behavior in Primates," COMPARATIVE PSYCHOLOGY, C. P. Stone (ed.). New York: Prentice-Hall, 1951.

Norris, V. "Mental Illness in London," *Maudsley Monograph Number 6, Institute of Psychiatry*. London: Chapman & Hall, 1959.

Noyes, A. P. and L. C. Kolb. MODERN CLINICAL PSYCHIATRY. Philadelphia: Saunders, 1963.

Nunberg H. PRINCIPLES OF PSYCHOANALYSIS. New York: International Universities Press, 1955.

Oakley, B. and C. Pfaffman. "Electrophysiologically Monitored Lesions in the Gustatory Thalamic Relay of the Albino Rat," *Journal of Comparative and Physiological Psychology*, 55 (1962), 155–60.

Oberly, H. S. "The Range for Visual Attention, Cognition and Apprehension," *American Journal of Psychology*, 35 (1924), 332–52.

Offenkrantz, K. and A. Rechtschaffen. "Clinical Studies of Sequential Dreams," *Archives of General Psychiatry*, 8 (1963), 497–508.

Office of Strategic Services Assessment Staff. *Assessment of Men*. New York: Rinehart, 1948.

Olds, J. "Physiological Mechanisms of Reward," NEBRASKA SYMPOSIUM ON MOTIVATION, M. Jones (ed.). Lincoln, Nebraska: Nebraska Press, 1955. Volume III, 73–139.

———. "Self-Stimulation of the Brain," *Science*, 127 (1958), 315–24.

———. and P. Milner. "Positive Reinforcement Produced by Electrical Stimulation of Septal Area and Other Regions," *Journal of Comparative and Physiological Psychology*, 47 (1954), 419–27.

Olin, C. H. PHRENOLOGY. Philadelphia: Penn, 1910.

O'Neal, P., L. N. Robins, L. J. King and J. Shaefer. "Parental Deviance and the Genesis of Sociopathic Personality," *American Journal of Psychiatry*, 118 (1962), 1114–24.

Osborn, A. F. APPLIED IMAGINATION: PRINCIPLES AND PROCEDURES OF CREATIVE THINKING. New York: Scribner, 1953.

Osgood, C. E. "The Nature and Measurement of Meaning," *Psychological Bulletin*, 49 (1952), 197–237.

————. METHOD AND THEORY IN EXPERIMENTAL PSYCHOLOGY. New York: Oxford University Press, 1953.

————, G. J. Suci and P. H. Tannenbaum. THE MEASUREMENT OF MEANING. Urbana: University of Illinois Press, 1957.

Osmond, H. and J. Smythies, "Schizophrenia: A New Approach," *Journal of Mental Science*, 98 (1952), 309–15.

Ostow, M. "The Death Instincts," *International Journal of Psycho-Analysis*, 39 (1958).

Pace, R. W. "Oral Communication and Sales Effectiveness," *Journal of Applied Psychology*, 46 (1962), 321–24.

Papez, J. W. "A Proposed Mechanism of Emotion," *Archives of Neurology and Psychiatry*, Chicago, 38 (1937), 725–43.

Pasamanick, B. "A Comparative Study of the Behavioral Development of Negro Infants," *Journal of Genetic Psychology*, 69 (1946), 3–44.

————. "Prevalence and Distribution of Psychosomatic Conditions in an Urban Population According to Social Class," *Psychosomatic Medicine*, 24 (1962), 352–56.

————. "Some Misconceptions Concerning Differences in the Racial Prevalence of Mental Disease," *American Journal of Orthopsychiatry*, 23 (1963), 72–86.

————, P. Lemkau, D. W. Roberts and D. E. Krueger. "A Survey of Mental Disease in an Urban Population: III. Prevalence and Demographic Distribution of Some 'Psychosomatic' Disorders," SCIENTIFIC PAPERS AND DISCUSSION, J. S. Gottlieb and G. Tourney (eds.). Chicago: American Psychiatric Association, 1960. 245–53.

Paterson, D. G. PHYSIQUE AND INTELLECT. New York: Century, 1930.

Patterson, G. R. "A Learning Theory Approach to the Treatment of a School Phobic Child," CASE STUDIES IN BEHAVIOR MODIFICATION, L. P. Ullman and L. Krasner (eds.). New York: Holt, Rinehart & Winston, 1965.

Paulhan, F. "La Simultanéité des Actes Psychiques," *Revue Scientifique*, 39 (1887), 684–89.

Pauli, R. "Der Umfang und die Enge des Bewusstseins," *Zeitschrift Biologische*, 81 (1924), 93–112.

Pavlov, I. P. CONDITIONED REFLEXES. Oxford: Clarendon Press, 1927.

Peckarsky, A. "Maternal Attitude Towards Children with Psychogenically Delayed Speech." Unpublished Ph.D. dissertation, New York University, 1952.

Peel, E. A. "On Identifying Aesthetic Types," *British Journal of Psychology*, 35 (1944), 61–69.

Peller, L. E. "Daydreams and Children's Favorite Books," *Psychoanalytic Study of the Child*, 14 (1959), 414–33.

Pelz, D. C. "Influence: A Key to Effective Leadership in the First-Line Supervisor," *Personnel*, 29 (1952), 209–17.

Penfield, W. "Some Observations on the Functional Organization of the Human Brain," *Proceedings, American Philosophical Society*, 98 (1954), Number 5.

————. THE EXCITABLE CORTEX IN CONSCIOUS MAN. Liverpool: Liverpool University Press, 1958.

————. "The Interpretive Cortex," *Science*, 129 (1959), 1719–25.

———— and T. Rasmussen. THE CEREBRAL CORTEX OF MAN. New York: Macmillan, 1950.

———— and L. Roberts. SPEECH AND BRAIN-MECHANISMS. Princeton: Princeton University Press, 1959.

Perls, Frederick, R. Hefferline and P. Goodman. GESTALT THERAPY. New York: Julian Press, 1951.

Perry, R. B. THE THOUGHT AND CHARACTER OF WILLIAM JAMES. Two Volumes. New York: Little, Brown, 1935.

Peterson, C. H. and F. L. Spano. "Breast Feeding, Maternal Rejection and Child Personality," *Character and Personality*, 10 (1941), 62–66.

Pfaffman, C. "The Sense of Taste," HANDBOOK OF PHYSIOLOGY, J. Field, H. W. Magoun and V. E. Hall (eds.). Washington: American Physiological Society, 1959. Volume 1, 111–16.

Phillips, E. L. PSYCHOTHERAPY: A MODERN THEORY AND PRACTICE. New York: Prentice-Hall, 1956.

Piaget, J. LA NAISSANCE DE L'INTELLIGENCE CHEZ L'ENFANT. Paris: Delachaux et Niestlé, 1936.

————. PLAY, DREAMS AND IMITATION IN CHILDHOOD. New York: Norton, 1952.

————. SIX PSYCHOLOGICAL STUDIES. D. Elkind (ed.). New York: Random House, 1968.

Pickford, R. W. " 'Aesthetic' and 'Technical' Factors in Artistic Appreciation," *British Journal of Psychology*, 38 (1948), 135–41.

Piderit, T. MIMIK UND PHYSIOGNOMIK. Detmold, Germany: Meyers, 1925. Original, 1872.

Pigors, P. and F. Pigors. MANUAL FOR GROUP MEMBERS: THE INCIDENT PROCESS, PRACTICAL SUPER-
VISION PROBLEMS, SERIES I. Washington, D.C.: The Bureau of National Affairs, 1955.

Pilgrim, F. and R. A. Patton. "Patterns of Self-Selection of Purified Dietary Components by
the Rat," *Journal of Comparative and Physiological Psychology*, 40 (1947), 343–48.

Podolsky, E. (ed.). ENCYCLOPEDIA OF ABERRATIONS. New York: Philosophical Library, 1953.

Poffenberger, A. T. and B. E. Barrows. "The Feeling Value of Lines," *Journal of Applied
Psychology*, 8 (1924), 187–205.

Pokorny, A. D. "Characteristics of 44 Patients Who Subsequently Committed Suicide," *American Medical Association Archives of General Psychiatry*, 2 (1960), 314–23.

Polatin, P. "What Is Psychiatry?", in THE WHY REPORT, L. Freeman and N. Theodores (eds.).
Purchase, New York: Arthur Bernhard, 1964.

Politz, A. Media Studies: THE ROCHESTER STUDY. Philadelphia: Curtis, 1960.

Popenoe, P. MARRIAGE IS WHAT YOU MAKE IT. New York: Macmillan, 1950.

Porteus, S. D. "The Validity of the Porteus Maze," *Journal of Educational Psychology*, 30 (1939),
172–78.

Postman, L., J. S. Bruner and E. McGinnis. "Personal Values as Selective Factors in Perception,"
Journal of Abnormal and Social Psychology, 43 (1948), 142–54.

Postman, L. and B. H. Schneider. "Personal Values, Visual Recognition and Recall," *Psychological
Review*, 58 (1951), 271–84.

Powers, E. GRAPHIC FACTORS IN RELATION TO PERSONALITY. Hanover, New Hampshire: Dartmouth
College Library, 1930.

Powles, W. E. and W. D. Ross. "Industrial and Occupational Psychiatry," AMERICAN HANDBOOK OF
PSYCHIATRY, S. Arieti (ed.). New York: Basic Books, 1966. Volume 3, Chapter 36.

Pratt, C. C. "The Design of Music," *Journal of Aesthetics and Art Criticism*," 12 (1954), 289–
300.

Prescott, D. A. THE CHILD IN THE EDUCATIVE PROCESS. New York: McGraw-Hill, 1957.

President's Panel on Mental Retardation. *A Proposed Program for National Action to Combat
Mental Retardation*. 1962. Washington, D.C.: United States Government Printing Office, 1963.

Pribram, K. H. "Neocortical Function in Behavior," BIOLOGICAL AND BIOCHEMICAL BASES OF BE-
HAVIOR, H. F. Harlow and C. N. Woolsey (eds.). Madison: University of Wisconsin Press,
1958. 151–72.

——. "A Review of Theory in Physiological Psychology," *Annual Review of Psychology*, 11
(1960), 1–40.

—— and L. Weiskrantz. "A Comparison of the Effects of Medial and Lateral Cerebral Re-
sections on Conditioned Avoidance Behavior of Monkeys," *Journal of Comparative and
Physiological Psychology*, 50 (1957), 74–80.

Prichard, J. C. TREATISE ON INSANITY. London: Sherwood Gilbert and Piper, 1835.

Primac, D. W., A. F. Mirsky and H. E. Rosvold. "Effects of Centrally Acting Drugs on Two
Tests of Brain Damage," *American Medical Association Archives of Neurology and Psychiatry*, 77 (1957), 328–32.

Pronko, N. H. TEXTBOOK OF ABNORMAL PSYCHOLOGY. Baltimore: Williams & Wilkins, 1963.

Provence, S. and R. C. Lipton. INFANTS IN INSTITUTIONS. New York: International Universities
Press, 1962.

Prugh, P. G. and R. G. Harlow. " 'Masked Deprivation' in Infants and Young Children," DEP-
RIVATION OF MATERNAL CARE: A REASSESSMENT OF ITS EFFECTS. Geneva: World Health Organization, 1962. 9–29.

Pulver, M. SYMBOLIK DER HANDSCHRIFT. Leipzig: Voss, 1919.

Radke, M. J., H. G. Trager and H. Davis. "Social Perceptions and Attitudes of Children," *Genetic
Psychology Monographs*, 40 (1949), 327–47.

Raker, J. W., A. F. C. Wallace and J. F. Raymer. *Emergency Medical Care in Disasters: A Summary of Recorded Experiences*. Disaster Study Number 6, National Academy of Sciences,
National Research Council, Publication Number 457, Washington, D.C., 1956.

Randell, J. B. "Transvestitism and Trans-sexualism," *British Medical Journal*, 2 (1959), 1448–52.

Rank, O. TRAUMA OF BIRTH. New York: Harcourt, Brace, 1929 (trans.). Original, 1924.

——. WILL THERAPY AND TRUTH AND REALITY. New York: Alfred A. Knopf, 1945.

Ranson, S. W. "Somnolence Caused by Hypothalamic Lesions in the Monkey," *Archives of
Neurology and Psychiatry*, Chicago, 41 (1939), 1–23.

Rapaport, D., M. Gill and R. Schafer. DIAGNOSTIC PSYCHOLOGICAL TESTING. Two Volumes. Chicago:
Year Book Publishers, 1946.

Rarick, G. L. and R. McKee. "A Study of Twenty Third-Grade Children Exhibiting Extreme
Levels of Achievement on Tests of Motor Proficiency," *Research Quarterly of the American
Association of Health, Physical Education and Recreation*, 20 (1949), 142–52.

Ray, J. T., O. E. Martin, Jr., and E. A. Alluisi. *Human Performance as a Function of the Work-Rest Cycle,*" National Academy of Sciences, National Research Council, Publication 882, 1961.

Rechtschaffen, A. "Psychotherapy with Geriatric Patients: A Review of the Literature," *Journal of Gerontology,* 14 (1959), 73–88.

—— and L. Maron. "Effect of Amphetamine on Sleep Cycle," *Electroencephalography and and Clinical Neurophysiology,* 16 (1964), 438–45.

Rechtschaffen, A., P. Verdone and J. Wheaton. "Reports of Mental Activity During Sleep," *Canadian Psychiatric Association Journal,* 8 (1963), 409–16.

Redlich, F. C. and D. X. Freedman. THE THEORY AND PRACTICE OF PSYCHIATRY. New York: Basic Books, 1966.

Reevy, W. R. "Premarital Petting Behavior and Marital Happiness Prediction," *Marriage and Family Living,* 21 (1959), 349–55.

Reich, W. THE DISCOVERY OF THE ORGONE. Volume I. THE FUNCTION OF THE ORGASM: SEX-ECONOMIC PROBLEMS OF BIOLOGICAL ENERGY. New York: Orgone Institute Press, 1942.

Reiff, R., and F. Riessman. "The Indigenous Nonprofessional: A Strategy of Change in Community Action and Community Mental Health Programs. Report No. 3." New York: National Institute of Labor Education, 1964.

Reiff, R. and M. Scheerer. MEMORY AND HYPNOTIC AGE REGRESSION. New York: International Universities Press, 1959.

Reik, T. "Psychoanalysis of the Unconscious Sense of Guilt," *International Journal of Psycho-Analysis,* 5 (1924), 439–50.

Remington, J. S., M. J. Miller and I. Brownlee. "IgM Antibodies in Acute Toxoplasmosis: 1. Diagnostic Significance in Congenital Cases and a Method for their Rapid Demonstration." *Pediatrics,* 41, No. 6, June 1968, 1082–91.

Renner, M. "The Clock of Bees," *Natural History,* 68 (1959), 434–40.

Rennie, T. A. C. and L. Srole. "Social Class Prevalence and Distribution of Psychosomatic Conditions in an Urban Population," *Psychosomatic Medicine,* 18 (1956), 449–56.

——, M. K. Opler and T. S. Langner. "Urban Life and Mental Health," *American Journal of Psychiatry,* 113 (1957), 831–37.

Renshaw, S. "The Visual Perception and Reproduction of Forms by Tachistoscopic Methods," *Journal of Psychology,* 20 (1945), 217–32.

Restle, F. and J. Davis. "Success and Speed of Problem Solving by Individuals and Groups," *Psychological Review,* 69 (1962) 520–36.

Révész, G. INTRODUCTION TO THE PSYCHOLOGY OF MUSIC. Norman: University of Oklahoma Press, 1954.

Reynolds, R. W. "Ventromedial Hypothalamic Lesions Without Hyperphagia," *American Journal of Physiology,* 204 (1963), 60–62.

Ribble, M. A. "Infantile Experience in Relation to Personality Development," PERSONALITY AND THE BEHAVIOR DISORDERS, J. McV. Hunt (ed.). New York: Ronald, 1944. Volume 2, 621–51.

——. "Anxiety in Infants and Its Disorganizing Effects," MODERN TRENDS IN CHILD PSYCHIATRY, N. D. C. Lewis and B. L. Pacella (eds.). New York: International Universities Press, 1945.

Ribot, T. A. DISEASES OF MEMORY: AN ESSAY IN THE POSITIVE PSYCHOLOGY. New York: D. Appleton and Co., 1882 (trans.).

Ricciuti, H. N. and D. G. Schultz. LEVEL OF ASPIRATION MEASURES AND SELF-ESTIMATES OF PERSONALITY IN RELATION TO ACHIEVEMENT MOTIVATION. Princeton, New Jersey: Educational Testing Service, Contract NONR-694, NR 151–113, 1958.

Rice, S. A. "Stereotypes: A Source of Error in Judging Human Character," *Journal of Personnel Research,* 5 (1926–27), 267–76.

Richardson, H. M. "The Adaptive Behavior of Infants in the Utilization of the Lever as a Tool: A Developmental and Experimental Study," *Journal of Genetic Psychology,* 44 (1934), 352–77.

Richter, C. P. "Total Self-Regulatory Functions in Animals and Human Beings," *Harvey Lectures,* 38 (1942–43), 63–103.

Richter, H. G. "Emotional Disturbances Following Respiratory Infections in Children," *American Journal of Psychiatry,* 100 (1943), 387–96.

Riesen, H. S. "Arrested Vision," *Scientific American,* 183, 1950, 16–19.

——. "Stimulation as a Requirement for Growth and Function in Behavioral Development." In Fiske, D. W. and S. R. Maddi (eds.). FUNCTIONS OF VARIED EXPERIENCE. Homewood, Illinois: Dorsey Press, 1961, 57–80.

Riess, B. F. "The Isolation of Factors of Learning and Native Behavior in Field and Laboratory Studies," *Annals of the New York Academy of Sciences,* 51 (1950), 1093–1103.

Riessman, F. NEW APPROACHES TO MENTAL HEALTH TREATMENT FOR LABOR AND LOW INCOME GROUPS. New York: National Institute of Labor Education, Mental Health Program, 1964.

Riggs, L. A., F. Ratliff, J. C. Cornsweet and T. N. Cornsweet, "The Disappearance of Steadily Fixated Visual Test Objects," *Journal of the Optical Society of America*, 43 (1953), 495–501.

Rimland, B. INFANTILE AUTISM. New York: Appleton-Century-Crofts, 1964.

Rimoldi, H. J. A. "Problem Solving as a Process," *Educational and Psychological Measurements*, 20 (1960), 449–60.

Rinkel, M., R. W. Hyde, H. C. Solomon and H. Hoagland. "Experimental Psychiatry II. Clinical and Physio-Chemical Observations in Experimental Psychosis," *American Journal of Psychiatry*, 101 (1955), 881–95.

Rivers, W. H. R. CONFLICT AND DREAM. New York: Harcourt, Brace, 1923.

Roback, A. A. A HISTORY OF PSYCHOLOGY AND PSYCHIATRY. New York: Philosophical Library, 1961.

Roberts, C. L., M. H. Marx and G. Collier. "Light Onset and Light Offset as Reinforcers for the Albino Rat," *Journal of Comparative and Physiological Psychology*, 51 (1958), 575–79.

Roberts, W. W. "Fear-Like Behavior Elicited from Dorsomedial Thalamus of Cat," *Journal of Comparative and Physiological Psychology*, 55 (1962), 191–97.

Robins, E. et al. "Some Clinical Considerations in the Prevention of Suicide Based on a Study of 134 Successful Suicides," *American Journal of Public Health*, 49 (1959), 888–98.

Robinson, B. W. and M. Mishkin. "Alimentary Responses Evoked from Forebrain Regions in Macaca Mulatta," *Science*, 136 (1962), 260–61.

Roe, A. A. "A Psychological Study of Physical Scientists," *Genetic Psychology Monographs*, 43 (1951), 121–235.

Roethlisberger, F. J. and W. J. Dickson. MANAGEMENT AND THE WORKER. Cambridge: Harvard University Press, 1939.

Roffwarg, H., W. Dement and C. Fisher. "Preliminary Observations of Sleep Dream Patterns in Neonates, Infants, Children and Adults," PROBLEMS OF SLEEP AND DREAM IN CHILDREN, E. Harms (ed.). New York: Pergamon Press, 1964.

Rogers, C. COUNSELING AND PSYCHOTHERAPY. New York: Grune & Stratton, 1942.

———. CLIENT-CENTERED THERAPY. Boston: Houghton Mifflin, 1951.

Romanes, G. J. ANIMAL INTELLIGENCE. New York: D. Appleton & Co., 1881.

Rommetveit, R. SOCIAL NORMS AND ROLES: EXPLORATIONS IN THE PSYCHOLOGY OF ENDURING SOCIAL PRESSURES. Minneapolis: The University of Minnesota Press, 1955.

Rorschach, H. PSYCHODIAGNOSTICS: A DIAGNOSTIC TEST BASED ON PERCEPTION. Berne: Huber, 1942. Original, 1921.

Rosanoff, A. J. MANUAL FOR PSYCHIATRY AND MENTAL HYGIENE. New York: Wiley, 1938.

Rosen, B. "The Achievement Syndrome: A Psychocultural Dimension of Social Stratification," *American Sociological Review*, 21 (1956), 203–11.

Rosen, E. and I. Gregory. ABNORMAL PSYCHOLOGY. Philadelphia and London: Saunders, 1965.

Rosen, H. and H. E. Kiene. "Paranoia and Paranoiac Reaction Types," *Diseases of the Nervous System*, 7 (1946), 330–37.

Rosen, J. DIRECT ANALYSIS. New York: Grune & Stratton, 1953.

Rosenbaum, C. P. "Patient-Family Similarities in Schizophrenia," *Archives of General Psychiatry*, 5 (1961), 120–26.

Rosenbaum, M. "Group Psychotherapy and Psychodrama," HANDBOOK OF CLINICAL PSYCHOLOGY, B. B. Wolman (ed.). New York: McGraw-Hill, 1965. Chapter 45.

Rosenblueth, A., N. Wiener and J. H. Bigelow. "Behavior, Purpose and Teleology," *Philosophy of Science*, 10 (1943), 18–24.

Rosenow, C. "The Incidence of First-Born Among Problem Children," *Journal of Genetic Psychology*, 37 (1930), 145–51.

Rosenthal, B. G. "Hypnotic Recall of Material Learned Under Anxiety and Nonanxiety Producing Conditions," *Journal of Experimental Psychology*, 34 (1944), 369–89.

Rosenthal, H. R. "Psychotherapy for the Aging," *American Journal of Psychotherapy*, 13 (1959), 55–65.

———. "Emergency Psychotherapy: A Crucial Need," *Psychological Review*, 52 (1965), 116–29.

Rosenthal, L. "Group Therapy in a Child Guidance Clinic," *Social Casework*, 32:8 (1951), 337–40.

Rosenthal, M. J. "The Syndrome of the Inconsistent Mother," *American Journal of Orthopsychiatry*, 32 (1962), 637–44.

Rosenthal, R. PYGMALION IN THE CLASSROOM: TEACHER EXPECTATION AND PUPIL'S INTELLECTUAL DEVELOPMENT. New York: Holt, Rinehart and Winston, 1968.

Rosenzweig, S. "An Experimental Study of 'Repression' with Special Reference to Need-Persistive and Ego-Defensive Reactions to Frustration," *Journal of Experimental Psychology*, 32 (1943), 64–74.

————. ROSENZWEIG PICTURE-FRUSTRATION STUDY. St. Louis, Missouri: Author, 1947–49.

Ross, N. and S. Abram. "Fundamentals of Psychoanalytic Theory," HANDBOOK OF CLINICAL PSYCHOLOGY, B. B. Wolman (ed.). New York: McGraw-Hill, 1965. Chapter 14.

Ross, S. and A. E. Harriman. "A Preliminary Study of the Crocker-Henderson Odor-Classification System," *American Journal of Psychology*, 62 (1949), 399–404.

Rosvold, H. E., A. F. Mirsky and K. H. Pribram. "Influence of Amygdalectomy on Social Behavior in Monkeys," *Journal of Comparative and Physiological Psychology*, 47 (1954), 173–78.

Rothney, J. W. M. GUIDANCE PRACTICE AND RESULTS. New York: Harper & Bros., 1958.

Rotter, J. B. "Word Association and Sentence Completion Methods," AN INTRODUCTION TO PROJECTIVE TECHNIQUES, H. H. Anderson and G. L. Anderson (eds.). Englewood Cliffs, New Jersey: Prentice-Hall, 1951.

———— and B. Willerman. "The Incomplete Sentences Test as a Method of Studying Personality," *Journal of Consulting Psychology*, 11 (1947), 43–48.

Rowland, L. W. "Will Hypnotized Persons Try to Harm Themselves or Others?" *Journal of Abnormal and Social Psychology*, 34 (1939), 114–17.

Rubin, E. SYNSOPLEVEDE FIGURER. Copenhagen: Gyldendalska, 1915.

Rudman, H. C. "The Information Needs and Reading Interests of Children in Grades IV Through VIII," *Elementary School Journal*, 55 (1955), 505–12.

Rudolph, J. H. ATTENTION AND INTEREST FACTORS IN ADVERTISING. New York: Funk & Wagnalls (in association with Printers' Ink Publishing Co.), 1947.

Ruesch, J. "General Theory of Communication in Psychiatry," AMERICAN HANDBOOK OF PSYCHIATRY, S. Arieti (ed.). New York: Basic Books, 1959. Volume 1, 895–908.

———— et al. "Chronic Disease and Psychosomatic Invalidism," *Psychosomatic Medicine Monographs*, New York: Hoeber-Harper, 1946.

Ruff, G. E. "Space Psychiatry," AMERICAN HANDBOOK OF PSYCHIATRY, S. Arieti (ed.). New York: Basic Books, 1966. Volume 3, Chapter 25.

Rusk, H. A. "Severe Brain Damage," *New York Times*. June 9, 1968.

Russell, G. W. (Æ). THE CANDLE OF VISION. London: Collier-Macmillan, 1920.

Rust, M. M. "The Effect of Resistance on Intelligence Test Scores of Young Children," *Child Development Monographs*, Number 6, New York: Teachers College, Columbia University, 1931.

Ryan, M. E. "Social Adjustment of Kindergarten Children Ten Years Later," *Smith College Studies in Social Work*, 19 (1949), 138–39.

Ryan, T. A. WORK AND EFFORT: THE PSYCHOLOGY OF PRODUCTION. New York: Ronald, 1947.

Ryans, D. G. CHARACTERISTICS OF TEACHERS. THEIR DESCRIPTION, COMPARISON AND APPRAISAL. Washington, D.C.: American Council on Education, 1960.

Rychoff, E., J. Day and L. C. Wynne. "Maintenance of Stereotyped Roles in the Families of Schizophrenics," *American Medical Association Archives of General Psychiatry*, 1 (1959), 93–98.

Saenger, G. "The Adjustment of Severely Retarded Adults in the Community." Albany: *New York State Interdepartmental Resources Board*, 1957.

Sager, C. J. "The Treatment of Married Couples," AMERICAN HANDBOOK OF PSYCHIATRY, S. Arieti (ed.). New York: Basic Books, 1966. Volume 3, Chapter 15.

Saint-Exupéry, A. de. WIND, SAND AND STARS. New York: Harcourt, Brace, 1939.

Sak, H. G., A. A. Smith and J. Dancis. "Psychometric Evaluation of Children with Familial Dysautonomia," *American Journal of Psychiatry*, 124:5 (1967), 682–87.

Salter, Andrew. CONDITIONED REFLEX THERAPY. New York: Creative Age Press, 1949.

Samuels, I. "Reticular Mechanisms and Behavior," *Psychological Bulletin*, 56 (1959), 1–25.

Sanford, F. H. PSYCHOLOGY, A SCIENTIFIC STUDY OF MAN. Belmont, California: Wadsworth Publishing Company, 1965.

Sanford, R. N. "The Effects of Abstinence from Food upon Imaginal Processes: A Preliminary Experiment," *Journal of Psychology*, 2 (1936), 129–36.

Sarason, S. B. et al. ANXIETY IN ELEMENTARY SCHOOL CHILDREN. New York: Wiley, 1960.

Sargent, S. S. "Emotional Stereotypes in the *Chicago Tribune*," *Sociometry*, 2 (1939), 69–75.

Sarnoff, I. and P. G. Zimbardo. "Anxiety, Fear and Social Affiliation," *Journal of Abnormal and Social Psychology*, 62 (1961), 356–63.

Saul, L. J. "Some Observations on the Relations of Emotions and Allergy," *Psychosomatic Medicine*, 3 (1941), 66–71.

Saul, L. T., H. Rome and E. Leuser. "Desensitization of Combat Fatigue Patients," *American Journal of Psychiatry*, 102 (1946), 476–78.

Schachter, S. THE PSYCHOLOGY OF AFFILIATION: EXPERIMENTAL STUDIES OF THE SOURCES OF GRE-
GARIOUSNESS. Stanford, California: Stanford University Press, 1959.

———— and J. E. Singer. "Cognitive, Social and Physiological Determinants of Emotional State,"
Psychological Review, 69 (1962), 379–99.

Schachter, S. and L. Wheeler. "Epinephrine, Chlorpromazine and Amusement," *Journal of
Abnormal and Social Psychology,* 65 (1962), 121–28.

Schafer, R., I. Berg and B. McCandless. "Report on Survey of Current Psychological Testing
Practices," *Supplement to Newsletter Division of Clinical and Abnormal Psychology,* American Psychological Association, 4 (1951), Number 5.

Schaffer, H. R. "Objective Observations of Personality Development in Early Infancy," *British
Journal of Medical Psychology,* 31 (1958), 174–83.

Schaffner, B. FATHERLAND: A STUDY OF AUTHORITARIANISM IN THE GERMAN FAMILY. New York:
Columbia University Press, 1948.

Schaie, K. W. "Rigidity-Flexibility and Intelligence: A Cross-Sectional Study of the Adult Life
Span from 20 to 70 Years," *Psychological Monographs,* 72, Number 9 (1958), Whole Number
462.

Scheerer, M. and J. Lyons. "Line Drawings and Matching Responses to Words," *Journal of
Personality,* 25 (1957), 251–73.

Scheinfeld, A. YOUR HEREDITY AND ENVIRONMENT. Philadelphia: Lippincott, 1965.

Schilder, P. "Results and Problems of Group Psychotherapy in Severe Neurosis," *Mental Hygiene,*
23 (1939), 87–98.

————. THE IMAGE AND APPEARANCE OF THE HUMAN BODY. New York: International Universities
Press, 1950.

———— and O. Kauders. "Hypnosis," *Nervous and Mental Disease Monograph Series,* Number
46, 1927.

Schmideberg, M. "The Borderline Patient," AMERICAN HANDBOOK OF PSYCHIATRY, S. Arieti (ed.).
New York: Basic Books, 1959. Volume 1, Chapter 21.

Schneirla, T. C. and J. S. Rosenblatt. "Critical Periods in the Development of Behavior,"
Science, 139 (1963), 1110–14.

Schorn, M. "Experimentelle Untersuchungen über die Mehrfachhandlung," *Zeitschrift Psychologie,* 108 (1928), 195–221.

Schramm, W. (ed.). THE EFFECTS OF TELEVISION ON CHILDREN AND ADOLESCENTS. Amsterdam:
The International Association for Mass Communication Research, UNESCO, 1964.

Schramm, W. L. APPROACHES TO A SCIENCE OF ENGLISH VERSE. Iowa City: University of Iowa
Studies, Series on Aims and Progress of Research, Number 46, 1935.

Schreiner, L. and A. Kling. "Behavioral Changes Following Rhinencephalic Injury in Cat,"
Journal of Neurophysiology, 16 (1953), 643–59.

————. "Effects of Castration on Hypersexual Behavior Induced by Rhinencephalic Injury in Cat,"
Archives of Neurology and Psychiatry, 72 (1954), 180–86.

————. "Rhinencephalon and Behavior," *American Journal of Physiology,* 184 (1956), 486–90.

Schuell, H., J. J. Jenkins and E. Jiménez-Pabòn. APHASIA IN ADULTS: DIAGNOSIS, PROGNOSIS AND
TREATMENT. New York: Hoeber-Harper, 1964.

Scott, J. P. AGGRESSION. Chicago: University of Chicago Press, 1958.

————. "Critical Periods in Behavioral Development," *Science,* 138 (1962), 949–58.

————. "Reply to 'Critical Periods in the Development of Behavior,'" *Science,* 139 (1963), 1114.

Scott, W. D., R. C. Clothier and W. R. Spriegel. PERSONNEL MANAGEMENT. New York: McGraw-
Hill, 1961.

Sears, A. B. "A Comparison of Hypnotic and Waking Learning of the International Morse Code,"
Journal of Clinical and Experimental Hypnosis, 3 (1955), 215–21.

Sears, P. S. "Levels of Aspiration in Academically Successful and Unsuccessful Children," *Journal of Abnormal and Social Psychology,* 35 (1940), 498–536.

————. "Doll Play Aggression in Normal Young Children," *Psychological Monographs,* 65 (1951),
Number 6.

———— and H. Levin. "Levels of Aspiration in School Children," *Child Development,* 28 (1957),
317–26.

Sears, R. R. "Relation of Early Socialization Experiences to Aggression in Middle Childhood,"
Journal of Abnormal and Social Psychology, 63 (1961), 466–92.

————. "The Growth of Conscience." In I. Iscoe and H. Stevenson (eds.). PERSONALITY DEVELOP-
MENT IN CHILDREN. Austin: University of Texas Press, 1960.

————, E. E. Maccoby and H. Levin. PATTERNS OF CHILD REARING. Evanston, Illinois: Row,
Peterson, 1957.

REFERENCES

Sears, R. R., J. W. M. Whiting, V. Nowlis and P. S. Sears. "Some Child-Rearing Antecedents of Aggression and Dependency in Young Children," *Genetic Psychology Monographs*, 47 (1953), 135–234.

Seashore, C. E. IN SEARCH OF BEAUTY IN MUSIC. New York: Ronald, 1947.

Secord, P. F. and C. W. Backman. SOCIAL PSYCHOLOGY. New York: McGraw-Hill, 1964.

Seeman, J. A. "A Study of the Process of Non-Directive Therapy," *Journal of Consulting Psychology*, 13 (1949), 157–68.

Segundo, J. P., R. Arana and J. D. French. "Behavioral Arousal by Stimulation of the Brain in the Monkey," *Journal of Neurosurgery*, 12 (1955), 601–13.

Seidman, D., S. B. Bensen, I. Miller and T. Meeland. "Influence of a Partner on Tolerance for a Self-Administered Electric Shock," *Journal of Abnormal and Social Psychology*, 54 (1957), 210–12.

Selye, H. THE STRESS OF LIFE. New York: McGraw-Hill, 1956.

Semmel, M. I. "Art Education for the Mentally Retarded," *School Arts*, May 1961.

Senden, M. von. RAUM- UND GESTALTAUFFASSUNG BEI OPERIERTEN BLINDGEBORENEN VOR UND NACH OPERATION. Leipzig: Barth, 1932.

Shaffer, L. F. "Fear and Courage in Aerial Combat," *Journal of Consulting Psychology*, 11 (1947), 137–43.

———— and E. J. Shoben, Jr. THE PSYCHOLOGY OF ADJUSTMENT. Boston: Houghton Mifflin, 1956.

Shannon, C. E. and W. Weaver. A MATHEMATICAL THEORY OF COMMUNICATION. Urbana: University of Illinois Press, 1949.

Shaw, C. R. THE JACK-ROLLER. Chicago: University of Chicago Press, 1930.

———— and H. D. McKay. JUVENILE DELINQUENCY AND URBAN AREAS. Chicago: University of Chicago Press, 1942.

Shaw, M. C. and J. Grubb. "Hostility and Able High School Underachievers," *Journal of Counseling Psychology*, 5 (1958), 263–66.

Shaw, M. E. "A Comparison of Individuals and Small Groups in the Rational Solution of Complex Problems," *American Journal of Psychology*, 44 (1932), 491–504.

Shaw, R. "A Mixture of Madness," *Harvard Medical School Alumni Bulletin*, 34 (1958), 38.

Sheehan, J. G. "The Modification of Stuttering Through Non-Reinforcement," *Journal of Abnormal and Social Psychology*, 46 (1951), 51–63.

————, P. A. Cortese and R. G. Hadley, "Guilt, Shame and Tension in Graphic Projections of Stuttering," *Journal of Speech and Hearing Disorders*, 27 (1962), 129–39.

Sheldon, W. H. VARIETIES OF DELINQUENT YOUTH. New York: Harper & Bros., 1949.

———— and S. S. Stevens. THE VARIETIES OF TEMPERAMENT. New York: Harper & Bros., 1942.

Sheldon, W. H. et al. ATLAS OF MEN: A GUIDE FOR SOMATOTYPING THE ADULT MALE AT ALL AGES. New York: Harper & Bros., 1954.

Sherif, M. "An Experimental Study of Stereotypes," *Journal of Abnormal and Social Psychology*, 29 (1935), 371–75.

————. AN OUTLINE OF SOCIAL PSYCHOLOGY. New York: Harper & Bros., 1948.

———— and C. W. Sherif. AN OUTLINE OF SOCIAL PSYCHOLOGY. New York: Harper & Bros., 1956.

Sherif, M., O. J. Harvey, B. J. White, W. R. Hood and C. Sherif. INTERGROUP CONFLICT AND COOPERATION: THE ROBBERS CAVE EXPERIMENT. Norman, Oklahoma: University Book Exchange, 1961.

Sherman, M. MENTAL CONFLICTS AND PERSONALITY. Don Mills, Ontario, Canada: Longmans, Green, 1938.

Shields, J. and E. Slater. "Heredity and Psychological Abnormality," HANDBOOK OF ABNORMAL PSYCHOLOGY, H. J. Eysenck (ed.). London: Pitman Medical Publishing Company, 1960.

Shipley, W. C., J. I. Coffin and K. C. Hadsell. "Affective Distance and Other Factors Determining Reaction Time in Judgments of Color Preference," *Journal of Experimental Psychology*, 35 (1945), 206–15.

Shipley, W. C., E. D. Norris and M. L. Roberts. "The Effect of Changed Polarity of Set on Decision Time of Affective Judgments," *Journal of Experimental Psychology*, 36 (1946), 237–43.

Shirley, H. F. "Encopresis in Children," *Journal of Pediatrics*, 12 (1938), 367–80.

Shirley, M. THE FIRST TWO YEARS. POSTURAL AND LOCOMOTOR DEVELOPMENT. Minneapolis: University of Minnesota Press, 1931. Volume 1.

Shneidman, E. S. "Schizophrenia and the MAPS Test: A Study of Certain Formal Psycho-Social Aspects of Fantasy Production in Schizophrenia as Revealed by Performance on the Make a Picture Story Test (MAPS)," *Genetic Psychology Monographs*, 38 (1948), 145–224.

———— and N. L. Farberow (eds.). CLUES TO SUICIDE. New York: McGraw-Hill, 1957.

Shore, P. A., A. Pletscher, E. G. Tomich, A. Carlsson, R. Kuntzman and B. B. Brodie. "Role of Brain Serotonin in Reserpine Action," *Annals of the New York Academy of Sciences,* 66 (1957), 609–15.

Shuey, A. M. THE TESTING OF NEGRO INTELLIGENCE. Lynchburg, Virginia: J. P. Bell, 1958.

Shurrager, P. S. and E. Culler. "Conditioning in the Spinal Dog," *Journal of Experimental Psychology,* 26 (1940), 133–59.

Siegel, E. HELPING THE BRAIN-DAMAGED CHILD. New York: Association for Brain Injured Children, 1962.

Sigerist, H. E. CIVILIZATION AND DISEASE. Ithaca, New York: Cornell University Press, 1943.

Sillman, J. H. "Thumb-Sucking and the Oral Structure," *Journal of Pediatrics,* 39 (1951), 424–30.

Silverman, D. "The Electroencephalogram of Criminals," *Archives of Neurology and Psychiatry,* 56 (1944), 677–85.

Simmel, E. et al. PSYCHO-ANALYSIS AND THE WAR NEUROSES, E. Jones (ed.). London: Psycho-Analytical Press, 1921.

Simms, V. M. "The Relative Influence of Two Types of Motivation on Improvement," *Journal of Educational Psychology,* 19 (1928), 480–84.

Simpson, G. E. and J. M. Yinger. RACIAL AND CULTURAL MINORITIES. New York: Harper & Bros., 1953.

Singh, J. A. L. and R. M. Zingg. WOLF-CHILDREN AND FERAL MAN. New York: Harper & Bros., 1942.

Singleton, W. T. "Symposium on Training: The Training of Shoe Machinists," *Ergonomics,* 2 (1959), 125–32.

Skeels, H. M., R. Updegraff, B. L. Wellman and H. M. Williams. "A Study of Environmental Stimulation: An Orphanage Pre-School Project," *University of Iowa Studies in Child Welfare,* Number 4, 1938.

Skelly, F. R. "Interviewer-Appearance Stereotypes as a Possible Source of Bias," *Journal of Marketing,* 19 (1954), 74–75.

Skinner, B. F. THE BEHAVIOR OF ORGANISMS: AN EXPERIMENTAL APPROACH. New York: Appleton-Century, 1938.

———. "Are Theories of Learning Necessary?" *Psychological Review,* 57 (1950), 193–216.

———. "The Science of Learning and the Art of Teaching," *Harvard Educational Review,* 24 (1954), 86–97.

———. VERBAL BEHAVIOR. New York: Appleton-Century-Crofts, 1957.

Skodak, M. and H. M. Skeels. "A Final Follow-up of One Hundred Adopted Children," *Journal of Genetic Psychology,* 75 (1949), 3–19.

Slater, E. T. O. "Genetics in Psychiatry," *Journal of Mental Science,* 90 (1944), 17–35.

Slavson, S. R. AN INTRODUCTION TO GROUP THERAPY. New York: Commonwealth Fund, 1943.

———. ANALYTIC GROUP PSYCHOTHERAPY. New York: Columbia University Press, 1950.

———. "The Dynamics of Analytic Group Psychotherapy," *International Journal of Group Psychotherapy,* 1 (1951), 208–17.

Sleight, R. B. "The Effect of Instrument Dial Shape on Legibility," *Journal of Applied Psychology,* 32 (1948), 170–88.

Smith, E. M., H. O. Brown, J. E. P. Toman and L. S. Goodman. "The Lack of Cerebral Effects of d-Tubo-Curarine," *Anesthesiology,* 8 (1947), 1–14.

Smith, H. C. "Music in Relation to Employee Attitudes, Piece Work Production, and Industrial Accidents," *Applied Psychology Monographs,* Number 14, 1947.

———. PSYCHOLOGY OF INDUSTRIAL BEHAVIOR. New York: McGraw-Hill, 1964.

Smith, M. and E. A. Wilson. "A Model of the Auditory Threshold and Its Application to the Problem of the Multiple Observer," *Psychological Monographs,* 67 (1953), Number 359.

Smith, M. E. "A Study of the Speech of Eight Bilingual Children of the Same Family," *Child Development,* 6 (1935), 19–25.

Smith, P. C. "The Curve of Output as a Criterion of Boredom," *Journal of Applied Psychology,* 39 (1953), 69–74.

Smith, W. I. and S. Ross. "The Hoarding Behavior of the Mouse. I. The Role of Previous Feeding Experience," *Journal of Genetic Psychology,* 82 (1953), 279–97.

Smith, W. K. "Non-Olfactory Functions of the Pyriform-Amygdaloid-Hippocampal Complex," *Federation Proceedings,* 9 (1950), 118.

Snyder, W. U. THE PSYCHOTHERAPY RELATIONSHIP. New York: Macmillan, 1961.

Solomon, J. C. "Play Technique as a Differential Therapeutic Medium," *Nervous Child,* 7 (1948), 296–300.

Solomon, P. et al. (eds.). SENSORY DEPRIVATION. Cambridge: Harvard University Press, 1961.

Solomon, R. L. and L. C. Wynne. "Traumatic Avoidance Learning: The Principles of Anxiety Conservation and Partial Irreversibility," *Psychological Review,* 61 (1954), 353–85.

Sommer, R. "The New Look on the Witness Stand," *Canadian Psychologist*, 8 (1959), 94–100.

Sommer, Robert and G. Witney. "The Chain of Chronicity," *American Journal of Psychiatry*, 118, (1961), 111–17.

Sommers, V. S. "The Influence of Parental Attitudes and Social Environment on the Personality of the Adolescent Blind," New York: American Foundation for the Blind, 1949.

Sontag, L. W. "The Significance of Fetal Environmental Differences," *American Journal of Obstetrics*, 42 (1941), 996–1003.

——. "War and Fetal Maternal Relationship," *Marriage and Family Living*, 6 (1944), 1–5.

——. "Some Psychosomatic Aspects of Childhood," *Nervous Child*, 5 (1946), 296–304.

——, C. T. Baker and V. L. Nelson. "Mental Growth and Development: A Longitudinal Study," *Monograph Soc. Res. Child Development*, 23, Serial Number 68 (1958).

Spache, G. D. "Is This a Breakthrough in Reading?" *The Reading Teacher*, January 1962.

Spalding, D. A. "Instinct, with Original Observations on Young Animals," *Macmillan's Magazine*, 27 (1873), 282–93.

Spearman, C. "General Intelligence Objectively Determined and Measured," *American Journal of Psychology*, 15 (1904), 201–93.

Spellman, G. G. "Report of Familial Cases of Parkinsonism," *Journal of American Medical Association*, 179 (1962), 372–74.

Sperry, R. W. "Cerebral Organization and Behavior," *Science*, 133 (1961), 1749–57.

——, N. Miner and R. E. Myers. "Visual Pattern Perception Following Subpial Slicing and Tantalum Wire Implantations in the Visual Cortex," *Journal of Comparative and Physiological Psychology*, 48 (1955), 50–58.

Spiegel, R. "Specific Problems of Communication in Psychiatric Conditions," AMERICAN HANDBOOK OF PSYCHIATRY, S. Arieti (ed.). New York: Basic Books, 1959. Volume 1, 909–49.

Spitz, R. A. "Hospitalism: An Inquiry into the Genesis of Psychiatric Conditions in Early Childhood," PSYCHOANALYTIC STUDY OF THE CHILD. New York: International Universities Press, 1945. 53–74.

——. "Emotional Growth in the First Year," *Child Study*, 24 (1947), 68–70.

——. "The Importance of the Mother-Child Relationship During the First Year of Life: A Symposium of Five Sketches," *Mental Health Today*, 7 (1948).

——. "The Role of Ecological Factors in Emotional Development in Infancy," *Child Development*, 20 (1949), 145–56.

——. NO AND YES: ON THE BEGINNINGS OF HUMAN COMMUNICATION. New York: International Universities Press, 1957.

—— and K. M. Wolf. "Anaclitic Depression: An Enquiry into the Genesis of Psychiatric Conditions in Early Childhood, II," THE PSYCHOANALYTIC STUDY OF THE CHILD, A. Freud et al. (eds.). New York: International Universities Press, 1946. Volume 2.

Spock, B. BABY AND CHILD CARE. New York: Pocket Books, 1957.

Spranger, E. TYPES OF MEN. Halle Saale: Max Niemeyer, 1928.

——. PSYCHOLOGIE DES JUGENDALTERS. Heidelberg: Quelle and Meyer, 1955.

Springbett, B. M. "The Semantic Differential and Meaning in Non-Objective Art," *Perceptual and Motor Skills*, 10 (1960), 231–40.

Squires, P. C. "The Shape of the Normal Work Area," *U.S.N. Med. Res. Lab.* Report Number 275 (1956).

Srole, L., T. S. Langer, S. Michael, M. K. Opler and T. A. C. Rennie. MENTAL HEALTH IN THE METROPOLIS: THE MIDTOWN MANHATTAN STUDY. New York: McGraw-Hill, 1962. Volume 1.

Stamm, J. S. "Effects of Cortical Lesions on Established Hoarding Activity in Rats," *Journal of Comparative and Physiological Psychology*, 46 (1953), 299–304.

Stampfl, T. "The Effect of Frequency of Repetition on the Retention of Auditory Material Presented During Sleep." Unpublished master's thesis, Loyola University, Chicago, 1953.

Stanton, F. N. "A Two-Way Check on the Sales Influence of a Specific Radio Program," *Journal of Applied Psychology*, 24 (1940), 665–72.

Staples, F. R. and R. H. Walters. "Anxiety, Birth Order and Susceptibility to Social Influence," *Journal of Abnormal and Social Psychology*, 62 (1961), 716–19.

Starch, D. "Readership and Size of Advertisement," *Starch Tested Copy*, Number 82, 1957.

——. "Should Outdoor Posters Be Repeated?" *Starch Tested Copy*, Number 89, 1960.

——. "Do Inside Positions Differ in Readership?" *Starch Tested Copy*, Number 95, 1961a.

——. MEASURING PRODUCT SALES MADE BY ADVERTISING. Mamaroneck, New York: Daniel Starch and Staff, 1961.

—— and Staff. "Is Preferred Position Worth It?" *Starch Tested Copy*, Number 74, 1961b.

Startle, C. L. EXECUTIVE PERFORMANCE AND LEADERSHIP. Englewood Cliffs, New Jersey: Prentice-Hall, 1956.

Stiegmann, F. "The Peptic Ulcer Syndrome in Negroes," *American Journal of Diseases of Nutrition*, 3 (1936), 310.

Stein, M. I. "The Use of a Sentence Completion Test for the Diagnosis of Personality," *Journal of Clinical Psychology*, 3 (1947), 46–56.

Steiner, L. R. WHERE DO PEOPLE TAKE THEIR TROUBLES? Boston: Houghton Mifflin, 1945.

Steinzor, B. "The Development and Evaluation of a Measure of Social Interaction," *Human Relations*, 2 (1949), 103–22.

Stekel, W. SADISM AND MASOCHISM. New York: Liveright, 1929. Volume 2.

––––––. THE INTERPRETATION OF DREAMS: NEW DEVELOPMENTS AND TFCHNIQUES. New York: Liveright, 1943 (trans.).

––––––. TECHNIQUE OF ANALYTICAL PSYCHOTHERAPY. New York: Liveright, 1950.

Stellar, E. "The Effect of Epinephrine, Insulin, and Glucose upon Hoarding in Rats," *Journal of Comparative Psychology*, 36 (1943), 21–31.

Stephenson, W. THE STUDY OF BEHAVIOR: Q-TECHNIQUE AND ITS METHODOLOGY. Chicago: University of Chicago Press, 1953.

Stern, E. M. "She Breaks Through Invisible Walls," *Mental Hygiene*, 41 (1957), 361–71.

Stern, M. M. "Free Painting as an Auxiliary Technique in Psychoanalysis," SPECIALIZED TECHNIQUES IN PSYCHOTHERAPY, G. Bychowski and J. L. Despert (eds.). New York: Basic Books, 1952.

Stevenson, G. S. "In Memoriam, Clifford Beers, 1876–1943," *American Journal of Psychiatry*, 100 (1943), 437–38.

Stevenson, I. "Processes of 'Spontaneous' Recovery from the Psychoneuroses," *American Journal of Psychiatry*, 117 (1961), 1057–64.

Stone, L. J. and J. Church. CHILDHOOD AND ADOLESCENCE. New York: Random House, 1957.

Stone, S. "Psychiatry Through the Ages," *Journal of Abnormal and Social Psychology*, 32 (1937), 131–60.

Stott, D. H. "Infantile Illness and Subsequent Mental and Emotional Development," *Journal of Genetic Psychology*, 94 (1959), 233–51.

––––––. "Abnormal Mothering as a Cause of Mental Subnormality. I. A Critique of Some Classic Studies of Maternal Deprivation in the Light of Possible Congenital Factors," *Journal of Child Psychology and Psychiatry*, 3 (1962), 133–48.

––––––. "Evidence for a Congenital Factor in Maladjustment and Delinquency," *American Journal of Psychiatry*, 118 (1962), 781–94.

Strachey, J. "The Nature of the Therapeutic Action of Psycho-Analysis," *International Journal of Psycho-Analysis*, 15 (1934), 127–59.

Stratton, G. M. "Vision Without Inversion of the Retinal Image," *Psychological Review*, 4 (1897), 341–60, 463–81.

Strauss, A. L. "The Literature on Panic," *Journal of Abnormal and Social Psychology*, 37 (1944), 317–28.

Strauss, B. V. "The Dynamics of Ordinal Position Effects," *Quarterly Journal of Child Behavior*, 3 (1951), 133–45.

Strecker, E. A. and E. F. Ebaugh. PRACTICAL CLINICAL PSYCHOLOGY. New York: McGraw-Hill, 1940.

Sullivan, H. S. CONCEPTIONS OF MODERN PSYCHIATRY, H. S. Perry and M. L. Gawel (eds.). New York: Norton, 1953.

––––––. THE INTERPERSONAL THEORY OF PSYCHIATRY. New York: Norton, 1953.

––––––. THE PSYCHIATRIC INTERVIEW, H. S. Perry (ed.). New York: Norton, 1954.

Super, D. E. "Vocational Adjustment in Terms of Role Theory," *Vocational Guidance Quarterly*, 5 (1957), 139–41.

Suppes, P. "The Use of Computers in Education," *Scientific American*, 215 (1966), 206–23.

Suzuki, D. T. ZEN BUDDHISM, W. Barret (ed.). Garden City, New York: Doubleday & Company, 1956.

Svendsen, M. "Children's Imaginary Companions," *Archives of Neurology and Psychiatry*, 32 (1934), 985–99.

Symonds, P. M. "The Sentence Completion Test as a Projective Technique," *Journal of Abnormal and Social Psychology*, 42 (1947), 320–29.

Szasz, T. S. "Language and Pain," AMERICAN HANDBOOK OF PSYCHIATRY, S. Arieti (ed.). New York: Basic Books, 1959. Volume 1, Chapter 49.

Szondi, L. EXPERIMENTAL DIAGNOSTICS OF DRIVES. New York: Grune & Stratton, 1952.

Tannenbaum, R. and F. Massarik. "Leadership: A Frame of Reference," *Management Science*, 4, Number 1 (1957), 1–19.

Tanner, W. P. Jr. and J. A. Swets. "A Decision-Making Theory of Visual Detection," *Psychological Review*, 61 (1954), 401–9.

REFERENCES

Taylor, D. W. and W. L. Faust. "Twenty Questions: Efficiency in Problem Solving as a Function of Size of Group," *Journal of Experimental Psychology*, 44 (1952), 360–68.

Taylor, D. W., P. C. Berry and C. H. Block. "Does Group Participation When Using Brain-Storming Facilitate or Inhibit Creative Thinking?" *Administration Science Quarterly*, 3 (1958), 23–47.

Taylor, F. W. THE PRINCIPLES OF SCIENTIFIC MANAGEMENT. New York: Harper & Bros., 1911.

Teicher, D. and J. Jacobs. "The Suicidal Adolescent." Unpublished paper delivered at Annual Meeting of American Public Health Association, October 1965.

Templeton, R. D. and J. P. Quigley. "The Action of Insulin on the Motility of the Gastro-Intestinal Tract," *American Journal of Physiology*, 91 (1930), 467–74.

Terman, L. M. and C. C. Miles. MANUAL OF INFORMATION AND DIRECTIONS FOR USE OF ATTITUDE-INTEREST ANALYSIS TEST (M-F TEST). New York: McGraw-Hill, 1938.

Terman, L. M. and M. H. Oden. THE GIFTED CHILD GROWS UP. Stanford, California: Stanford University Press, 1947.

———. THE GIFTED GROUP AT MIDLIFE. Stanford, California: Stanford University Press, 1959.

Terman, L. M. and L. E. Tyler. "Psychological Sex Differences," MANUAL OF CHILD PSYCHOLOGY, L. Carmichael (ed.). New York: Wiley, 1954. 1064–1114.

Terman, L. M., P. Buttenwieser, L. W. Ferguson, W. B. Johnson and D. P. Wilson. PSYCHOLOGICAL FACTORS IN MARITAL HAPPINESS. New York: McGraw-Hill, 1938.

Terman, L. M. et al. GENETIC STUDIES OF GENIUS: THE MENTAL AND PHYSICAL TRAITS OF A THOUSAND GIFTED CHILDREN. Stanford, California: Stanford University Press, 1925. Volume 1.

Thomas, G. J. and P. A. Stewart. "The Effect on Visual Perception of Stimulating the Brain with Polarizing Currents," *American Journal of Psychology*, 70 (1957), 528–40.

Thomas, J. F. BEYOND NORMAL COGNITION. Boston: Houghton Mifflin, 1937.

Thomas, W. I. THE UNADJUSTED GIRL. Boston: Little, Brown, 1923.

Thompson, G. G. "The Social and Emotional Development of Preschool Children Under Two Types of Educational Program," *Psychological Monographs*, 56 (1944), Number 5.

Thompson, G. N. "Acute and Chronic Alcoholic Conditions," AMERICAN HANDBOOK OF PSYCHIATRY, S. Arieti (ed.). New York: Basic Books, 1959. Volume 2.

Thompson, R. "Thalamic Structures Critical for Retention of an Avoidance Conditioned Response in Rats," *Journal of Comparative and Physiological Psychology*, 56 (1963), 261–67.

Thompson, W. R. and L. M. Solomon. "Spontaneous Pattern Discrimination in the Rat," *Journal of Comparative and Physiological Psychology*, 47 (1954), 104–7.

Thorndike, E. L. "Animal Intelligence," *Psychological Monographs*, Supp. 2 (1898), Number 8.

———. EDUCATIONAL PSYCHOLOGY. New York: Lemcke & Buechner, 1903.

——— and R. S. Woodworth. "The Influence of Improvement in One Mental Function upon the Efficiency of Other Functions," *Psychological Review*, 8 (1901), 247–61, 384–95, 553–64.

Thorndike, R. L. and E. Hagen. TEN THOUSAND CAREERS. New York: Wiley, 1959.

Thorne, F. "Directive and Eclectic Personality Counseling," SIX APPROACHES TO PSYCHOTHERAPY, J. L. McCary and D. E. Sheer (eds.). New York: Dryden, 1955.

Thorne, F. C. "The Etiology of Sociopathic Reactions," *American Journal of Psychiatry*, 13 (1959), 686–89.

Thorpe, L. P., B. Katz and R. T. Lewis. THE PSYCHOLOGY OF ABNORMAL BEHAVIOR. New York: Ronald, 1961.

Thurstone, L. L. "Primary Mental Abilities," *Psychometric Monographs*, Chicago: University of Chicago Press, Number 1, 1938.

———. WORD ASSOCIATION WITH HOMONYMS. Chicago: University of Chicago Psychometric Laboratory, Number 79, 1952.

——— and R. L. Jenkins. ORDER OF BIRTH, PARENT-AGE AND INTELLIGENCE. Chicago: University of Chicago Press, 1931.

——— and T. G. Thurstone. "Factorial Studies of Intelligence," *Psychometric Monographs*, Number 2, Chicago: University of Chicago Press, 1941.

Tiffin, J. and E. J. McCormick. INDUSTRIAL PSYCHOLOGY. Englewood Cliffs, New Jersey: Prentice-Hall, 1965.

Tiffin, J. and F. X. Walsh. "Readability of Union-Management Agreements," *Personnel Psychology*, 4 (1951), 327–37.

Tinbergen, N. "On War and Peace in Animals and Man," *Science*, 160, June 28, 1968, 1411–18.

Tinker, M. A. "Illumination Standards for Effective and Comfortable Vision," *Journal of Consulting Psychology*, 3 (1939), 11–19.

Tinklepaugh, O. L. "An Experimental Study of Representative Factors in Monkeys," *Journal of Comparative Psychology*, 8 (1928), 197–236.

———. "Social Behavior of Animals," COMPARATIVE PSYCHOLOGY, F. A. Moss (ed.). New York: Prentice-Hall, 1942.

Tolsma, F. J. "Some Considerations on the Phenomenon of Aggression," *Journal of Mental Science*, 99 (1953), 473–82.

Tomkins, S. S. THE TOMKINS-HORN PICTURE ARRANGEMENT TEST. New York: Springer, 1957.

Trencherd, K. I. and W. J. E. Crissy. "Readability of Advertising and Editorial Copy in *Time* and *Newsweek*," *Journal of Applied Psychology*, 36 (1952), 161–63.

Trevarthen, C. B. "Double Visual Learning in Split-Brain Monkeys," *Science*, 136 (1962), 258–59.

Tsai, L. S. "Rivalry and Cooperation in White Rats," *American Psychologist*, 5 (1950), 262.

Tsang, Y. C. "Hunger Motivation in Gastrectomized Rats," *Journal of Comparative and Physiological Psychology*, 26 (1938), 1–17.

Tucker, W. T. and J. J. Painter. "Personality and Product Use," *Journal of Applied Psychology*, 45 (1961), 325–29.

Tuddenham, R. D. "The Influence of a Distorted Group Norm upon Judgments of Adults and Children," *Journal of Psychology*, 52 (1961), 231–39.

Tuke, D. H. A DICTIONARY OF PSYCHOLOGICAL MEDICINE. Philadelphia: Blakiston, 1892.

Turnbull, J. W. "Asthma Conceived as a Learned Response," *Journal of Psychosomatic Research*, 6 (1962), 59–70.

Tyler, L. E. THE WORK OF THE COUNSELOR. New York: Appleton-Century-Crofts, 1961.

Uhrbrock, R. S. "Music on the Job: Its Influence on Worker Morale and Production," *Personnel Psychology*, 14 (1961), 9–38.

Ullman, L. P. and L. Krasner (eds.). CASE STUDIES IN BEHAVIOR MODIFICATION. New York: Holt, Rinehart & Winston, 1965.

Van Alstyne, D. and L. A. Hattwick. "A Follow-Up Study of the Behavior of Nursery School Children," *Child Development*, 10 (1939), 43–72.

Van Riper, C. SPEECH CORRECTION: PRINCIPLES AND METHODS. Englewood Cliffs, New Jersey: Prentice-Hall, 1963.

Van Zelst, R. H. "The Effect of Age and Experience upon Accident Rate," *Journal of Applied Psychology*, 38 (1954), 313–17.

Vedder, C. B. JUVENILE OFFENDERS. Springfield, Illinois: Charles C. Thomas, 1963.

Veltford, H. R. and S. E. Lee. "The Cocoanut Grove Fire: A Study in Scapegoating," *Journal of Abnormal and Social Psychology*, 38 (1943), 138–54.

Vernier, C. M. et al. "Psychosocial Study of the Patient with Pulmonary Tuberculosis: A Co-operative Research Approach," *Psychological Monographs*, 75 (1961), Number 6.

Vernon, H. M. "The Speed of Adaptation of Output to Altered Hours of Work," *Industrial Fatigue Research Board*, Report Number 6 (1920).

———. INDUSTRIAL FATIGUE AND EFFICIENCY. London: Routledge, 1921.

Vernon, J. INSIDE THE BLACK ROOM. New York: C. N. Potter, 1963.

Vincent, E. L. and P. C. Martin. HUMAN PSYCHOLOGICAL DEVELOPMENT. New York: Ronald, 1961.

Von Euler, U. S. "Autonomic Neuroeffector Transmission," HANDBOOK OF PHYSIOLOGY, J. Field, H. W. Magoun and V. E. Hall (eds.). Washington, D.C.: American Physiological Society, 1959. Volume 1.

Voronin, L. G. "Some Results of Comparative Physiological Investigations of Higher Nervous Activity," *Psychological Bulletin*, 59 (1962), 161–95.

Waehner, T. S. "Formal Criteria for the Analysis of Children's Drawings," *American Journal of Orthopsychiatry*, 12 (1942), 95–104.

———. "Interpretation of Spontaneous Drawings and Paintings," *Genetic Psychology Monographs*, 33 (1946), 3–70.

Wahl, C. W. "Some Antecedent Factors in the Family Histories of 568 Male Schizophrenics of the United States Navy," *American Journal of Psychiatry*, 113 (1956), 201–10.

Whaler, H. J. "Letters to the Science Editor," *Saturday Review*, May 1, 1965, 64.

Walker, R. C. and R. H. Guest. THE MAN ON THE ASSEMBLY LINE. Cambridge: Harvard University Press, 1952.

Walker, R. G. "A Comparison of Clinical Manifestations of Hostility with Rorschach and MAPS Test Performance," *Journal of Projective Techniques*, 15 (1951), 444–60.

Wallace, S. R. "Studies in Binocular Interdependence. I. Binocular Relations in Macular Adaptation," *Journal of Comparative and Physiological Psychology*, 17 (1937), 307–22.

Wallach, M. A. and R. C. Gahm. "Personality Functions of Graphic Construction and Expansiveness," *Journal of Personality*, 28 (1960), 73–88.

Wallas, G. THE ART OF THOUGHT. New York: Harcourt, Brace, 1926.

Wallin, P. and R. Riley. "Reactions of Mothers to Pregnancy and Adjustment of Offspring in Infancy," *American Journal of Orthopsychiatry,* 20 (1950), 616–22.

Walls, G. L. "Land! Land!" *Psychological Bulletin,* 57 (1960), 29–48.

Walsh, A. M. SELF-CONCEPTS OF BRIGHT BOYS WITH LEARNING DIFFICULTIES. New York: Teachers College, Columbia University, 1956.

Walsh, M. E. "The Relation of Nursery School Training to the Development of Certain Personality Traits," *Child Development,* 2 (1931), 72–73.

Walter, W. G. THE LIVING BRAIN. New York: Norton, 1953.

Warcollier, R. EXPERIMENTAL TELEPATHY. Boston: Houghton Mifflin, 1938.

Ward, L. B. "Reminiscence and Rote Learning," *Psychological Monographs,* 49, Number 4 (1937), Whole Number 220.

Warden, C. J. ANIMAL MOTIVATION: EXPERIMENTAL STUDIES ON THE ALBINO RAT. New York: Columbia University Press, 1931.

Warner, L. "What the Younger Psychologists Think About ESP," *Journal of Parapsychology,* 19 (1955), 228–35.

Warner, W. L. and P. S. Lunt. THE SOCIAL LIFE OF A MODERN COMMUNITY. New Haven: Yale University Press, 1941.

Warner, W. L., M. Meeker and K. Eells. SOCIAL CLASS IN AMERICA. Chicago: Science Research Associates, 1949.

Watkins, J. G. GENERAL PSYCHOTHERAPY. Springfield, Illinois: Charles C. Thomas, 1960.

Watson, G. B. "Do Groups Think More Efficiently than Individuals?" *Journal of Abnormal and Social Psychology,* 23 (1928), 328–36.

Watson, J. B. and R. Rayner. "Conditioned Emotional Reactions," *Journal of Experimental Psychology,* 3 (1920), 1–14.

Watterberg, W. W. "Church Attendance and Juvenile Misconduct," *Sociological and Social Research,* 34 (1954), 195–202.

Watts, A. W. THE WAY OF ZEN. New York: Pantheon, 1957.

Weber, E. H. DE PULSU, RESORPTIONE, AUDITU ET TACTU. Leipzig: Koehler, 1834.

Wechsler, D. "The I.Q. Is an Intelligent Test," *New York Times Magazine,* June 26, 1966, 12.

Weiner, H. and A. Braiman. "The Ganser Syndrome: A Review and Addition of Some Unusual Cases," *American Journal of Psychiatry,* 111 (1955), 767.

Weinstein, E. A. and R. L. Kahn. "Symbolic Reorganization in Brain Injuries," AMERICAN HANDBOOK OF PSYCHIATRY, S. Arieti (ed.). New York: Basic Books, 1959. Volume 1, Chapter 48.

Weiss, E. "Paul Federn's Scientific Contributions: In Commemoration," *International Journal of Psycho-Analysis,* 32 (1952), 283–90.

—— and O. S. English. PSYCHOSOMATIC MEDICINE. Philadelphia: Saunders, 1943, 1949, 1957.

Weiss, W. "Opinion Congruence with a Negative Source on One Issue as a Factor Influencing Agreement on Another Issue," *Journal of Abnormal and Social Psychology,* 54 (1957), 180–86.

—— and B. J. Fine. "The Effect of Induced Aggressiveness on Opinion Change," READINGS IN SOCIAL PSYCHOLOGY, E. E. Maccoby, F. M. Newcomb and E. L. Hartley (eds.). New York: Holt, Rinehart & Winston, 1958, 149–56.

Weiss, W. P. and L. Sokoloff. "Reversal of Thyroxine-Induced Hypermetabolism by Puromycin," *Science,* 140 (1963), 1324–26.

Weitz, J. "Verbal and Pictorial Questionnaires in Marketing Research," *Journal of Applied Psychology,* 34 (1950), 363–66.

Weitzenhoffer, A. M. HYPNOTISM: AN OBJECTIVE STUDY IN SUGGESTIBILITY. New York: Wiley, 1953.

Weldon, R. J. and G. M. Peterson, "Effect of Design on Accuracy and Speed of Operating Dials," *Journal of Applied Psychology,* 41 (1957), 153–57.

Welker, W. I. "Some Determinants of Play and Exploration in Chimpanzees," *Journal of Comparative and Physiological Psychology,* 49 (1956), 84–89.

——. " 'Free' vs. 'Forced' Exploration of a Novel Situation by Rats," *Psychological Reports,* 3 (1957), 95–108.

Welles, H. H. THE MEASUREMENT OF CERTAIN ASPECTS OF PERSONALITY AMONG HARD OF HEARING ADULTS. New York: Columbia University Press, 1932.

Wells, W. D. "The Influence of Yeasaying Response Style," *Journal of Advertisement Research,* 1 (1961), 1–12.

Wells, W. R. "Experiments in Waking Hypnosis for Instructional Purposes," *Journal of Abnormal and Social Psychology,* 18 (1924), 389–404.

——. "Experiments in the Hypnotic Production of Crime," *Journal of Psychology,* 11 (1941), 63–102.

———. "The Hypnotic Treatment of the Major Symptoms of Hysteria: A Case Study," *Journal of Psychology,* 17 (1944), 269–97.

Wender, L. "The Dynamics of Group Psychotherapy and Its Applications," *Journal of Nervous and Mental Disease,* 84 (1936), 54–60.

Wenger, M. A. and M. Wellington. "The Measurement of Autonomic Balance in Children: Method and Normative Data," *Psychosomatic Medicine,* 5 (1943), 241–53.

Werner, H. "Sprache als Ausdruck," *Kong. Dtsch. ges. Psychol.,* 12 (1932).

———. "Studies on Contour. I. Qualitative Analyses," *American Journal of Psychology,* 47 (1935), 40–64.

Wertham, F. THE SHOW OF VIOLENCE. Garden City, New York: Doubleday & Company, 1949.

Wertheimer, M. "Experimentelle Studien über das Sehen von Bewegung," *Zeitschrift Psychologie,* 61 (1912), 59–131.

Wesselhoeft, C. "Rubella (German Measles)," *New England Journal of Medicine,* 236 (1947), 943–78.

West, S. "Sibling Configurations of Scientists," *American Journal of Sociology,* 66 (1960), 268–74.

Westphal, E. "Über Haupt- und Nebenaufgaben bei Reaktionsversuchen," *Archiven gesamte Psychologie,* 21 (1911), 219–434.

Wetterstrand, O. G. HYPNOTISM AND ITS APPLICATION TO PRACTICAL MEDICINE. New York: Putnam, 1902.

Wever, E. G. THEORY OF HEARING. New York: Wiley, 1949.

Wexner, L. B. "The Degree to Which Colors (Hues) Are Associated with Mood-Tones," *Journal of Applied Psychology,* 38 (1954), 432–35.

Wheeler, L. R. "A Comparative Study of the Intelligence of East Tennessee Mountain Children," *Journal of Educational Psychology,* 33 (1942), 321–34.

Whitaker, C. A. and T. P. Malone. THE ROOTS OF PSYCHOTHERAPY. New York: McGraw-Hill, 1953.

White, A. D. A HISTORY OF THE WARFARE OF SCIENCE WITH THEOLOGY IN CHRISTENDOM. New York: D. Appleton & Co., 1896.

White, C. "The Mathematics of Salesmanship," *Printers' Ink,* 41 (2), 34 (1940), 53–54.

White, J. C. and W. H. Sweet. PAIN: ITS MECHANISM AND NEUROSURGICAL CONTROL. New York: Thomas, 1955.

White, M. A. and M. W. Harris. THE SCHOOL PSYCHOLOGIST. New York: Harper & Row, 1961.

White, R. K. and R. Lippitt. AUTOCRACY AND DEMOCRACY. New York: Harper & Bros., 1960.

White, R. W. THE ABNORMAL PERSONALITY. New York: Ronald, 1964.

Whiting, J. W. M. "The Cross-Cultural Method," HANDBOOK OF SOCIAL PSYCHOLOGY, G. Lindzey (ed.). Reading, Massachusetts: Addison-Wesley, 1954. 523–31.

——— and I. L. Child. CHILD TRAINING AND PERSONALITY: A CROSS-CULTURAL STUDY. New Haven: Yale University Press, 1953.

Whittemore, I. C. "The Influence of Competition on Performance: An Experimental Study," *Journal of Abnormal and Social Psychology,* 19 (1924), 236–53.

Whorf, B. L. LANGUAGE, THOUGHT AND REALITY, J. B. Carroll (ed.). New York: Wiley, 1956.

Whyte, W. H., Jr. THE ORGANIZATION MAN. Garden City, New York: Doubleday & Company, 1956.

Wiener, H. J. "Mental Health Rehabilitation for a Union Population," New York: Sidney Hillman Health Center, June 1, 1966.

Wiesner, B. P. and N. M. Sheard. "Sex Behavior in Hypophysectomized Male Rats," *Nature,* London, 132 (1933), 641.

Wilkinson, R. T. "Effects of Sleep-Deprivation on Performance and Muscle Tension," CIBA FOUNDATION SYMPOSIUM ON THE NATURE OF SLEEP, G. E. Wolstenholme and M. O'Connor (eds.). Boston: Little, Brown, 1960. 329–36.

Willey, F. C., E. Inglis and C. H. Pearce. "Reversal of Auditory Localization," *Journal of Experimental Psychology,* 20 (1937), 114–30.

Williams, E. D. "The General Aesthetic Factor. II. (Reply)," *British Journal of Psychology, Statistics Section,* 13 (1960), 88–90.

Williamson, R. C. "Economic Factors in Marital Adjustment," *Marriage and Family Life,* 14 (1952), 298–301.

Wilner, D. M., R. P. Walkley and S. W. Cook. "Residential Proximity and Intergroup Relations in Public Housing Projects," *Journal of Social Issues,* 8 (1) (1952), 45–69.

Wilson, J. L. "Pediatrics," *Annual Review of Medicine,* W. C. Cutting and H. W. Newman (eds.), 5 (1954), 389–404.

Wilson, W. C. "Extrinsic Religious Values and Prejudice," *Journal of Abnormal and Social Psychology,* 60 (1960), 286–88.

Winch, R. F. "The Theory of Complementary Needs in Mate-Selection: A Test of One Kind of

Complementariness; Final Results on the Test of the General Hypothesis," *American Sociological Review*, 20 (1955), 52–56, 552–55.

Windle, W. F. (ed.). NEUROLOGICAL AND PSYCHOLOGICAL DEFICITS OF ASPHYXIA NEONATURIUM WITH CONSIDERATION OF USE OF PRIMATES FOR EXPERIMENTAL INVESTIGATIONS. Springfield, Illinois: Charles C. Thomas, 1958.

Wing, John K. "Institutionalism in Mental Hospitals," *British Journal of Social and Clinical Psychology*, 1 (1962), 38–51.

Winsor, A. L. "The Effect of Dehydration on Parotid Secretion," *American Journal of Psychology*, 42 (1930), 602–7.

Winterbottom, M. R. "The Source of Achievement Motivation in Mothers' Attitudes Toward Independence Training," THE ACHIEVEMENT MOTIVE, D. C. McClelland, et al. (eds.). New York: Appleton-Century-Crofts, 1953.

Wirt, R. D., P. F. Briggs and J. Golden. "Delinquency-Prone Personalities. III. The Sociopathic Personality: Treatment," *Minnesota Medicine*, 45 (1962), 289–95.

Wittels, F. "In Memoriam: Paul Schilder, 1886–1940," *Psychoanalytic Quarterly*, 10 (1941), 131–34.

Wittenberg, R. "Personality Adjustment Through Social Action," *American Journal of Orthopsychiatry*, 18 (1949), 207–21.

Wittkower, E. D. and K. L. White. "Psychophysiologic Aspects of Respiratory Disorders," AMERICAN HANDBOOK OF PSYCHIATRY, S. Arieti (ed.). New York: Basic Books, 1959. Volume 1, Chapter 35.

Wittman, P., W. H. Sheldon and C. J. Katz. "A Study of the Relationship Between Constitutional Variations and Fundamental Psychotic Behavior Reactions," *Journal of Nervous and Mental Disease*, 108 (1948), 470–76.

Witty, P. A. and R. A. Sizemore. "Reading the Comics: A Summary of Studies and an Evaluation," *Elementary English*, 31 (1954), 501–6.

Witty, P. A. et al. "Studies of Children's Interests: A Brief Summary," *Elementary English*, 37 (1960), 469–75.

Wolberg, L. R. HYPNOANALYSIS. New York: Grune & Stratton, 1945.

———. MEDICAL HYPNOSIS. New York: Grune & Stratton, 1948.

———. THE TECHNIQUE OF PSYCHOTHERAPY. New York: Grune & Stratton, 1954.

———. "Hypnotherapy," AMERICAN HANDBOOK OF PSYCHIATRY, S. Arieti (ed.). New York: Basic Books, 1959. Volume 2, Chapter 73.

Wolf, A. "The Psychoanalysis of Groups," *American Journal of Psychotherapy*, 4 (1949), 16–50.

Wolf, A. and E. K. Schwartz. "Irrational Psychotherapy: An Appeal to Unreason," Part I, *American Journal of Psychotherapy*, 1958, 300–14. Part II, 1959, 508–21.

Wolf, A. V. THIRST: PHYSIOLOGY OF THE URGE TO DRINK AND PROBLEMS OF WATER LACK. Springfield, Illinois: Charles C. Thomas, 1958.

Wolff, H. D. and P. E. Huston. "Schizophrenia Associated with Addison's Disease," *American Journal of Psychiatry*, 116 (1959), 365–68.

Wolff, H. G. "Personality Features and Reactions of Subject with Migraine," *Archives of Neurology and Psychiatry*, 37 (1937), 895–921.

———. HEADACHE AND OTHER HEAD PAIN. New York: Oxford University Press, 1948.

———. "Life Stress and Cardiovascular Disorders," *Research Publication of the Association of Nervous and Mental Disease*, 1 (1950), 187–203.

———. "Life Stress and Bodily Disease," CONTRIBUTIONS TOWARD MEDICAL PSYCHOLOGY, A. Weider (ed.). New York: Ronald, 1953. Volume 1.

Wolff, W. "Über Faktoren charakterologischen Urteilsbildung," *Zeitschrift für ang. Psychologie*, 35 (1930), 385–446.

———. THE EXPRESSION OF PERSONALITY. New York: Harper & Bros., 1943.

———. THE PERSONALITY OF THE PRE-SCHOOL CHILD. New York: Grune & Stratton, 1946.

———. DIAGRAMS OF THE UNCONSCIOUS. New York: Grune & Stratton, 1948.

Wolking, W. D., W. Quast and J. J. Lawton, Jr. "MMPI Profiles of the Parents of Behaviorally Disturbed and Nondisturbed Children." Unpublished paper presented at American Psychological Association Meeting, September 1964.

Wolpe, J. PSYCHOTHERAPY BY RECIPROCAL INHIBITION. Stanford, California: Stanford University Press, 1958.

Wood, K. S. "Parental Maladjustment and Functional Articulatory Defects in Children," *Journal of Speech Disorders*, 2 (1946), 255–75.

Woodworth, R. S. DYNAMICS OF BEHAVIOR. New York: Holt, 1958.

——— and M. R. Sheehan. CONTEMPORARY SCHOOLS OF PSYCHOLOGY. New York: Ronald, 1964.

Wooley, D. W. and E. Shaw. "A Biochemical and Pharmacological Suggestion About Certain Mental Disorders," *Science*, 119 (1954), 587.

Worden, F. G. and J. T. Marsh. "Psychological Factors in Men Seeking Sex Transformation: Preliminary Report," *Journal of the American Medical Association*, 157 (1955), 1292–97.

World Health Organization. "Technical Report Series Numbers 19, 21, 42, 48, 57, 76, 84, 94, 95," 1950–55.

Wortis, J. "Pavlovianism and Clinical Psychiatry," RECENT ADVANCES IN BIOLOGICAL PSYCHIATRY, J. Wortis (ed.). New York: Plenum, 1962. Volume 4, 13–23.

Wright, B. and L. Rainwater. "The Meaning of Color," *Journal of General Psychology*, 67 (1962), 89–99.

Wrightstone, J. W. "Demonstration Guidance Project in New York City," *Harvard Educational Review*, 30 (1960), 237–51.

——— et al. "Demonstration Guidance Project," *Research Report Number 43, Bureau of Educational Research, New York City Board of Education*, 1961.

Wulf, F. "Über die Veränderung von Vorstellungen (Gedächtnis und Gestalt)," *Psychologie Forschung*, 1 (1922), 333–73.

Wurtman, R. J. and J. Axelrod. "The Pineal Gland," *Scientific American*, 213 (July 1965), 50–60.

Wyatt, S., J. A. Fraser and F. G. L. Stock. "The Effects of Monotony in Work," *Industrial Fatigue Research Board Report*, Number 56, 1929.

Wynne, L. C., I. M. Rychoff, J. Day and S. I. Hirsch. "Pseudo-Mutuality in the Family Relations of Schizophrenia," *Psychiatry*, 21 (1958), 205–20.

Wyrwicka, W. and C. Dobrzecka. "Relationship Between Feeding and Satiation Centers of the Hypothalamus," *Science*, 123 (1960), 805–6.

Yablonsky, L. "The Anticriminal Society: Synanon," *Federal Probation*, September 1962.

———. "Where Is Science Taking Us?" *Saturday Review of Literature*, 46(5) (1963), 54–56.

Yasukochi, G. "Emotional Responses Elicited by Electrical Stimulation of the Hypothalamus in Cat," *Folia of Psychiatry and Neurology, Japan*, 14 (1960), 260–67.

Yeakel, E. H. and R. P. Rhoades. "Comparison of Body and Endocrine Gland Weights of Emotional and Non-Emotional Rats," *Endocrinology*, 28 (1941), 337–40.

Yerbury, E. C. and N. Newell. "Genetic and Environmental Factors in Psychoses of Children," *American Journal of Psychiatry*, 100 (1943), 599–605.

Yerkes, R. M. "Social Behavior of Chimpanzees: Dominance Between Mates in Relation to Sexual Status," *Journal of Comparative and Physiological Psychology*, 30 (1940), 147–86.

Yolles, S. F. "The Tragedy of Suicide in the United States." Unpublished paper delivered at George Washington University School of Medicine Symposium on Suicide, October 14, 1965.

Young, P. T. MOTIVATION OF BEHAVIOR: THE FUNDAMENTAL DETERMINANTS OF HUMAN AND ANIMAL ACTIVITY. New York: Wiley, 1936.

——— and J. P. Chaplin. "Studies of Food Preference, Appetite and Dietary Habit. III. Palatability and Appetite in Relation to Bodily Need," *Comparative Psychology Monographs*, 18 (1945), Number 3.

Youtz, R. P. "Aphotic Color Sensing, a Case Under Study," *Psychonomic Society*, August 29, 1963.

———. "Can Fingers See Color?" *Psychology Today*, February 1968, 37–41.

———. "Summary of Aphotic Digital Color Sensing—A Progress Report." Unpublished paper presented at the Eastern Psychological Association Meeting, April 18, 1964.

Zax, M. and G. Stricker. PATTERNS OF PSYCHOPATHOLOGY. New York: Macmillan, 1963.

Zeigarnik, B. "Über das Behalten von erledigten und unerledigten Handlungen," *Psychologie Forschung*, 9 (1927), 1–85.

Zeller, A. F. "An Experimental Analogue of Repression: I. Historical Summary," *Psychological Bulletin*, 47 (1950a), 39–51.

———. "An Experimental Analogue of Repression: II. The Effect of Individual Failure and Success on Memory Measured by Relearning," *Journal of Experimental Psychology*, 40 (1950b), 411–22.

———. "An Experimental Analogue of Repression: III. The Effect of Induced Failure and Success on Memory Measured by Recall," *Journal of Experimental Psychology*, 42 (1951), 32–38.

Zilboorg, G. and G. W. Henry. A HISTORY OF MEDICAL PSYCHOLOGY. New York: Norton, 1941.

Zimmerman, F. T., B. B. Burgemeister and T. J. Putnam. "A Group Study of the Effect of Glutamic Acid upon Mental Functioning in Children and Adolescents," *Psychosomatic Medicine*, 9 (1947), 175–83.

Zubin, J. "DOP: A Cautionary Report," *Science*, 147 (1965), 985.

Zuckerman, J. V. "Commentary Variations in Instructional Films: Their Effect on Learning Perceptual Motor Tasks," *Journal of Communication*, 2 (1952), 53–57.

Zusman, Jack. "Development of the Social Breakdown Syndrome Concept," *The Milbank Memorial Fund Quarterly*, 44, 1, Part 2, January 1966.

INDEX

Page references in bold face indicate Encyclopedia articles. See also Category Index for listing of articles grouped according to subject-matter, and pages 00 to 00 for a listing of illustrative cases. For space considerations, Index contains only names directly associated with theories, therapies, disorders, etc. See References for names in association with published works.

Etiology, 220, **422**, 1054
Etryptamine (Monase), 398
Eunuchoid, 1361
Euphoria, 54, 221, 288, 358, 397, **424**, 498, 728, 734, 1279, 1360
Eurymelalgia, 823
Eutonyl, 398
Evaluation and Adjustment Series, 10
Evolution, 292, 491
Exaltation, 728
Exalted paranoia, 920
Exceptional child, 1177
Exchange theory, 1232
Excitatory impulses, 153
Excitatory-inhibitory processes, 1162
Excitatory personalities, 1067
Excitement, 1079, 1328
Executive development, 718
Exhaustion, 1327
Exhaustion delirium, 304, 307, **424**
Exhaustion method, 530
Exhibitionism, 277, **424**, 563, 1200
Existentialism, **426**, 707, 1081, 1382
Existential neurosis, 707
Exogenous factors, 799
Exophthalmos, 11
Exotic psychoses, **428**
Expansive ideas, 515
Ex-patient organizations (*see* Mental Patient Organizations), 1120, 1170
Expectancy effects, 689
Expectancy theory, 1262
Experiential therapy, **431**
Experimentalism, 327
Experimental neurosis, **433**, 582, 930, 1344
Experimental psychology, 1060, 1378
Experimentation, 1059
Expert witness, 696
Exploratory drive, 284, 354, **434**, 731
Exposure deafness, 296, 542
Expressive aphasia, 93
Expressive behavior, 171, 293, **435**
Expressive work, 749
Extension reflex, 1114
External determinants of attention, 124
External hydrocephaly, 570
Extinction, 152, 1121
Extrapunitive response, 1136
Extrasensory perception (ESP), 177, **438**, 1299
Extraspectral purples, 228
Extraversion (Extroversion), **440**, 654
Extreme behavior patterns, 1288
Extremely gifted children, 509
Eye coordination, 841
Eyelid dermititis, 1208
Eye preference, 677
Eysenck, H. J., 441, 1067, 1068, 1290
Eysenck Personality Inventory, 944

Facial expression of emotion, 437
Facial vision, 167
FACT battery, 274
Factor analysis, 441, 943, 946
Factor theory of personality, 441
Faculty psychology, **442**, 474, 551, 646, 981, 1334
Fads, 750
Fainting spells, 1292
Faking bad, 822, 1057
Faking good, 822, 1057

Falret, Jean Pierre, 568
False conditioning, 1025
False pregnancy (Hysterical pregnancy, Pseudocyesis), 38, 262, **444**, 777
Falsetto voice, 1248, 1361
Familial dysautonomia, 363
Familial unconscious, 1295
Family attitudes, 1289
Family care (Foster-family care), 295, **445**, 1120
Family counseling, 803
Family size, **446**
Family therapy, 208, 237, **447**, 740, 814, 845, 1133
Fanning sign of Babinski, 145
Fantasy, 135, 166, 293, 332, 467, 533, 597, 836, 1002, 1129, 1130, 1148, 1159, 1370
Fantasy-cathexis, 188
Farnsworth Dichotomous Test for Color Blindness, 227
Farnsworth Munsell 100-Hue Test for Color Discrimination, 227
Fascist attitudes, 135
Fate analysis, 1295
Father substitute, 1283
Fatigue, 399, **448**, 669, 687, 827, 847, 1205, 1319, 1329
Fatigue measurement, 449
Faulty assumptions, 116
Fear, 90, **450**, 913, 1310
Fear appeal, 1023
Fear of darkness, 450
Fear of death, 452
Fear of failure, 908, 932
Fear of rejection, 932
Fear of strangers, 451
Fechner, Gustav Theodor, 109, 369, 418, **453**, 964, 982, 1070, 1185
Fechner's equation, 1071
Federn Paul, 377
Feeblemindedness, 512
Feedback, 286, 615, 675, 959
Feeding behavior, 180, **454**
Feeding problems, 1123
Feelings, 387
Feelings of unreality, 39, 313, 341, 724
Feeling tone, 33, 39
Fellatio, 157, 1201
Female transvestite, 1337
Femininity, 1198
Femininity complex, 244
Feminism, 32
Fenestration operation, 296
Fenichel, 386, 700, 1068, 1339
Feral men, 1227
Ferenczi, Sandor, 265, **455**
Festinating gait, 925
Fetishism, 154, **457**, 666, 1201, 1338
Fetus, 999
Fever, 1321
Fever therapy, 1294
Fichte, Johann Gottlieb, 347
Fictional finalism, 19
Field investigation method, 952
Field theory, **459**
Figural aftereffects, **461**
Figure drawing, 972
Figure Drawing Test, **462**, 1016, 1018
Figure-ground perception, **464**, 506, 937
Finger maze, 760

Klaesi, Jacob, 1212
Klein, Melanie, 986
Kleptomania, 457, **665**, 722, 776, 889
Kline, Nathan S., 397
Klinefelter's syndrome, **667**, 799
Knauber Art Ability Test, 112
Knowledge of results, 690, 959, 1014
Koan, 1383
Koffka, Kurt, **667**, 1369
Köhler, Wolfgang, 508, 618, 667, 1369, 1381
Kohnstamm test, 575
Koro, 430
Korsakoff, Sergei, 667
Korsakoff's syndrome (Amnesic-confabulatory syndrome), 54, 157, 307, 332, **667**, 918, 933, 1368
Kraemer, Heinrich, 309, 1370
Kraepelin, Emil, 2, 165, 213, 322, 324, **669**, 727, 786, 822, 880, 901, 922, 924, 1029, 1051, 1055, 1069, 1373, 1379
Krafft-Ebing, Richard von, **670**, 862
Kretschmer, Ernst, 946
Kretschmer's typology, 253
Kuder General Interest Survey, 639
Kuder interest test, 469
Kuder Preference Record, 638, 956
Kuhlmann-Anderson Intelligence Tests, 608, 630, 631
Kuhlmann-Anderson Measure of Academic Potential, 1173
Külpe, Oswald, 17, 1379
Kwakiutl Indians, 242, 343

Laboratory training, 718
Labor pains, 913
Labyrinthine sense, 410
Lactogenic hormone, 979
Ladd, George T., 326
Ladd-Franklin theory, 231
Laissez-faire leader, 522
Lamarck, Jean Baptiste, 292
La Mettrie, Julien, 251
Land color theory, 231
Landolt Ring Test, 104, 1355
Lange, Karl G., 389
Language (Psycholinguistics), **671**, 1313
Language dysfunctions, 1248
Lankton First-Year Algebra Test, 11
La Piere, R. T., 915
Laplace, Pierre Simon, 292
Large family, 446
Lasèque, Ernest Charles, 468
Lashley, Karl Spencer, 475, **675**, 974
Latah, 370, 429, 510, 552
Latency of reply, 1373
Latency stage, 1077
Latent content, 340, 348, 350, 1048
Latent homosexuality, 601, 882, 891, 1145, 1338
Latent learning, 607
Latent schizophrenia, 1155
Lateral dominance (Laterality), **677**
Lateral geniculate body, 1309
Laterality, 677, 819
Lateral sulcus, 192
Lateroventral nucleus, 1309
Laurence-Moon-Biedl syndrome, 481
Lavater, Johann, 973
Lavoisier, Antoine, 808
Law of contiguity, **677**, 1262

Law of effect, 1261, 1315
Law of exercise, 1315
Law of proximity, 507
Law School Admission Test (LSAT), 101
Law of similarity, 507
Lazell, Edward W., 77, 524
Leaderless Group Discussion, 907, 957
Leadership, 234, 396, 522, **678**, 829, 915, 1235
Leadership traits, 678
Lead poisoning, 250, **680**, 799, 1000
Learning aids, **681**, 688
Learning curve, **684**, 687
Learning disorder, 817, 1028
Learning during sleep, **685**
Learning (General), 150, 280, 302, 337, 353, 392, 677, **686**, 759, 913, 1310, 1315, 1333
Learning plateau, **687**
Learning readiness, 373
Learning techniques, **688**
Learning theories of personality, 946
Learning theory therapy, 151, 207, 1065
Learning under hypnosis, **691**
Learning vs. motivation, 505
Leduc, Stéphane, 1212
Left-handedness, 538
Legal capacity, 693
Legal psychiatry (Forensic psychiatry), 417, **691**
Legal psychology (Forensic psychology), 96, **696**, 847
Leg and foot movements, 841
Leiter International Performance Scale, 282, 629, 630
Lens, 1352
Leptosome physique, 254
Lesbian, 550
Letters of application, 951
Letters of recommendation, 952
Leukotome, 1080
Level of aspiration, **699**, 836
Leveling, 471, 1137
Levy, D. M., 986, 1126
Lewerenz Tests in Fundamental Abilities of Visual Art, 112
Lewin, Kurt, 29, 459, 519, 719, 1346
Lex talionis, 1296
L-glutavite, 511
Libidinal development, 1076
Libido, 25, 76, 77, 137, 187, 298, 415, 441, 456, 589, 641, 653, **700**, 886, 904, 990, 1039, 1076, 1147
Librium, 398, 1328, 1330
Liébeault, A. A., 199, 578
Lie detector, 493, **701**
Life fear, 1092
Life instinct, 298, 621, 701, 1041
Life space, 29, 460
Life style, 351
Light adaptation, **703**, 1188, 1355
Lightning calculator, 127, 380, 1010
Likert scales, 131
Lilliputian hallucinations, 175, 534
"L'illusion des sosies," 185
Limbic system, 210, 390, 548, 587, **703**, 988, 989, 1193, 1213, 1315
Limb-kinetic apraxia, 97
Lindsley's activity theory, 390
Linear maze, 759
Linear perspective, 316
Linear programs, 1015
Link trainer, 1349

Post-traumatic disorder, 540
Post-traumatic epilepsy, 540
Post-traumatic personality disorder, 540, 1340
Post-traumatic syndrome, 212
Postural adjustments, 125
Postural reflex, 1114
Poverty of ideas, 1167
Power complex, 244
Pox, 1293
Practice effect, 1057
Practice sessions, 959
Pragmatism, 327
Praise vs. blame, 373
Pratt, J. H., 524
Precipitating causes of mental disorder, 422
Precognition, 438
Preconscious (Foreconscious), 191, 252, **994**
Predisposing causes of mental disorder, 422
Pre-Engineering Ability Test, 102
Prefrontal lobe, 1079
Prefrontal lobotomy, 195, 303, 911
Pre-gang age, 1222
Pregenital, **994**
Pregenital fixations, 1040
Pregnancy, 162, 975
Prejudice, 223, 939, **994**, 1137, 1194, 1375
Prelogical thinking, 917
Premarital counseling, 736, 739
Premarital courses, 789
Premature children, 997
Premature ejaculation, 479, 600
Prematurity, 163, 780, **997**, 1000, 1216, 1342
Premenstrual depression, 773
Premenstrual tension, 776, 1330
Premonitory dreams, 1035
Premorbid personality, 54, 539, 993
Prenatal development, **998**
Prenatal influences, **1000**
Preparation (in creative thinking), 271
Pre-psychotic schizophrenia, 1155
Prepyriform area, 1213
Presbyopia, 1357
Presenile psychosis, 1349
President's Panel on Mental Retardation, 799, 804
Pressey, S. L., 1014
Pressure, 423, 1264, 1310
Pressure of activity, 467, 664, 729, 1063
Pressure of ideas, 728
Pressure sense, 4, 1326
Pressure sense adaptation, 1188
Pressure of speech, 707, 728, 1063
Prestige, 1220, 1255
Prestige effect, 130
Prestige suggestion, 160, 420, 1021, 1274
Prestige symbols, 342
Preventive measures, 789
Preventive psychiatry, 238, 893, 1234
Primal anxiety, 164
Primal repression, 164
Primal scene, **1001**
Primary behavior disorder, 149
Primary drive, 1196
Primary gain, 261, **1002**, 1178
Primary Mental Abilities Test, 627
Primary motives, 833
Primary narcissism, 853
Primary needs, 962
Primary odors, 1214
Primary personality, 843

Primary prevention, 779
Primary process, **1002**, 1039, 1165, 1178
Primary reinforcement, 1122
Primary repression, 1344
Primary and secondary qualities, 707
Primary sociopath, 276
Primary stuttering, 1268
Primidone (Mysoline), 405
Primordial impulses, 1344
Prince, Morton, 479, 580, **1003**
Principle learning, 767
Principle of neuronic inertia, 1039
Principle of Prägnanz, 507
Prisoner of war reactions, 177, **1006**, 1254
Prison psychology, 698
Prison psychosis, **1004**
Privation philosophy, 456
Proactive inhibition, 472, 913
Problem solving, 64, 373, 520, 618, 759, **1007**, 1313
Problem-solving interview technique, 718
Processes of Science Test, 11
Process schizophrenia, 1156, 1160, 1171
Prochlorperazine (Compazine), 1329
Prodigy, 161, 571, **1009**
Prodrome, **1013**
Prodromic dreams, 1013
Product image, 256
Product image studies, 35
Productive orientation, 484
Product testing, 257
"Professional" criminal, 277
Profound mental retardation, 805
Profuse menstruation, 776
Progesterone, 1197
Progestins, 513
Prognosis, 216, 1030
Prognosis for neuroses, 1065
Prognosis for psychoses, 1087
Program analyzer, 38
Programmed instruction, 960, 1014
Programmed learning (Automated teaching, Programmed instruction), 249, 682, **1014**
Progressive Matrices, 954
Progressive relaxation, 620, 1125, 1282
Projection, 300, 640, **1016**, 1017, 1044, 1129, 1332
Projection fibers, 193, 266
Projective methods (*see* Projective techniques), 838, 1016, 1017
Projective psychotherapy, **1016**
Projective techniques (see Projective methods), 160, 217, 515, 716, 956, 1134, 1191, 1295, 1324, 1344
Projective Test, 563
Projective tests (Projective methods or techniques), **1017**, 1136, 1295, 1310
Prolactin, 979
Prolixin, 1329
Prolonged hypnosis, 580
Prolonged narcosis, 1212
Promazine, (Sparine), 1329
Promiscuity, 606, 882, **1018**, 1201
Propaganda, 176, **1020**
Propfschizophrenia, 1156
Proprium, 948
Prostitution, **1024**, 1159, 1201, 1364
Protanopia, 226
Protometer, 104
Prototaxic mode, 1279